Web Sites

- How-to videos help students understand and solve homework problems
- Hundreds of character-building and parenting articles and videos
- Sites for everyone from preschool through parenthood

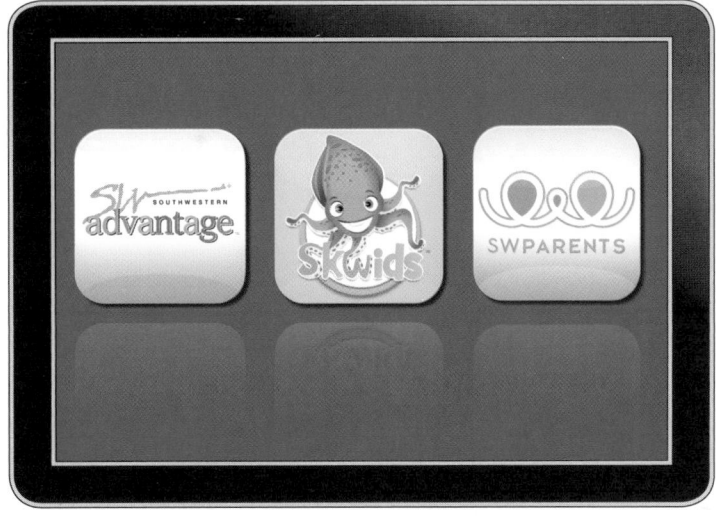

SOUTHWESTERN
advantage
Learning System

Software

- Younger education packages introduce children to computers and give them games to encourage learning
- Older students can use the software to edit and research reports, practice revision techniques, and write practice papers
- The College Prep Pack is specially designed to help college-bound students

Books

- Essential tools to help students excel in school as well as prepare for life
- Easily accessible, yet authoritative for the most important academic subjects
- Designed to teach children through exciting activity-based learning

www.SWadvantage.com

Sharing the Advantage

Southwestern Advantage is an effective learning system and an important key to a better education and achieving success in life. Our mission is to share education and learning skills with every child and every family, regardless of their circumstances, through qualified nonprofit partnerships and local community involvement with organizations focused on helping young people. Southwestern Advantage will also donate one SWadvantage.com membership for each one purchased.

Thank you for helping us Share the Advantage!

MATH II

www.SWadvantage.com

SOUTHWESTERN

Southwestern Advantage

Henry Bedford
Chief Executive Officer, Southwestern/Great American, Inc.

Dan Moore
President, Southwestern

Dave Kempf
President, Southwestern Publishing Group, Inc.

Chris Adams   Robin Mukherjee
Dave Causer   Mark Rau
Lester Crafton   Tim Ritzer
Grant Greder   Chris Samuels
Kevin Johnson   Nate Vogel

Sales Directors

Editorial

Executive Editor and President
Dan Moore

Editorial Director
Mary Cummings

Managing Editor
Judy Jackson

Senior Editor
Barbara J. Reed

Editor
Alison Nash

Section Editors
Julee Hicks
Cathy Ropp
Tanis Westbrook

Design

Senior Art Directors
Steve Newman
Starletta Polster

Senior Designer
Travis Rader

*Composition and
Production Design*
Jessie Anglin
Sara Anglin

Production

Production Manager
Powell Ropp

Production Coordinator
Wanda Sawyer

Preface

Welcome to *Southwestern Advantage Math*. We are pleased to bring you these unique, user-friendly reference books. Designed in such a way that students can spend "more time learning, less time looking," the pages are open and inviting, and critical information is summarized in boxes, lists, and other easily usable and understandable pieces.

Problems are shown worked out step-by-step. Where a problem can be worked by more than one method, those methods are also shown. Additionally, simply by keying in the page number, you can access step-by-step videos of each problem from that page at **SWadvantage.com**.

Got to Know boxes summarize the most essential information; cross-references in the **Need More Help** boxes direct you to pages where you can find additional information or review material. **Try It This Way** suggests alternative ways people with various learning styles can use to more effectively approach, work, or visualize problems and concepts. **Watch Out** boxes alert students to things that might be easily confused or that might give students difficulty.

We hope you will find these books both useful and enjoyable. Every effort has been made to ensure that the information in these books is as accurate as possible. If errors should be found, however, we would appreciate hearing from you. Please send your comments or suggestions to editor@southwestern.com or to Editor, The Southwestern Company, P.O. Box 305142, Nashville, TN 37230.

How to Use Southwestern Advantage

How to Use These Books

Designed in such a way that students can spend "more time learning, less time looking," these books are divided into nine "strands": Foundations of Mathematics; Numbers and Operations; Measurement; Geometry; Trigonometry; Statistics and Probability; Algebra; Advanced Algebra; and Calculus. Each strand is then divided into smaller units.

The first navigational tool is the detailed, color-coded table of contents. Each book contains a detailed listing of its own contents, plus a list of the strands covered in the other book. The contents pages also indicate separately where the special features of the book can be found, such as tables, charts, and glossaries.

FOUNDATIONS OF MATHEMATICS

NUMBERS AND OPERATIONS

MEASUREMENT

GEOMETRY

TRIGONOMETRY

Next, color bars above the heading on the right-hand text pages tell you exactly where you are in the book. The bar that extends all the way to the edge of the page is the unit color; the other bar denotes the strand. The strand color is repeated in a tab at the bottom of the page. When the book is closed, you can tell at a glance where each strand and unit begins and ends.

When the book is open, headings on the pages also help to tell you exactly where you are in the book, for example, the Infinite Limits section of Limits and Continuity in the Calculus strand.

↑

Strand color bar

SEARCH 🔍

To see step-by-step videos of these problems, enter the page number into the SWadvantage.com Search Bar.

Ways to REMEMBER

Think of the weights of items that are familiar to you. For example, a bird weighs a few ounces, flour comes in 1-, 5-, and 10-pound bags, and a truck weighs several tons. This will help you remember when to use the different units of weight.

How to Use Southwestern Advantage Online (www.SWadvantage.com)

An integral part of Southwestern Advantage is the accompanying Web site. Organized by subject areas, it is a comprehensive suite of online study helps, additional in-depth subject matter, tips for parents, and coaching for students on how to get better at life.

STATISTICS AND PROBABILITY

ALGEBRA

ADVANCED ALGEBRA

CALCULUS

SPECIAL ADVANTAGES

Limits and Continuity   **CALCULUS**

Unit within
Calculus

Name of strand
Calculus strand

Unit color bar

Try It
This Way

You can visualize and
then use mental math
to solve Example 4(b).

Add each measure
mentally.

$$3 \text{ yd } 2 \text{ ft}$$
$$+ 5 \text{ yd } 2 \text{ ft}$$
$$\overline{8 \text{ yd } 4 \text{ ft}}$$

Think: 3 ft = 1 yd

Think: 4 ft is 3 ft + 1 ft

8 yd + 4 ft

8 yd + 1 yd + 1 ft

9 yd 1 ft

Bias

Bias can occur in
different stages of the
surveying process. The
identified population,
the sample chosen, or
a survey question is
biased if it in any way
influences the results
of the survey.

Need More
HELP ?

When you write a unit
in a different form, you
rename the unit. The
directions below mean
the same thing.

Rename 5 feet as
inches.

Express 5 feet as inches.

Convert 5 feet to
inches.

Watch Out !

To make a general
statement based on
information from a
sample, the sample
must be *random*.
To learn more, see
Random Sampling on
page 1224.

Strand color tab

Contents

In the Other Book

In This Book

Visit us online at www.SWadvantage.com

Statistics and Probability 1214

Contents

Contents

Advanced Algebra 1750

1211

Contents

Statistics and Probability

Meteorologists use probability models to predict future weather patterns and determine where extreme weather might occur.

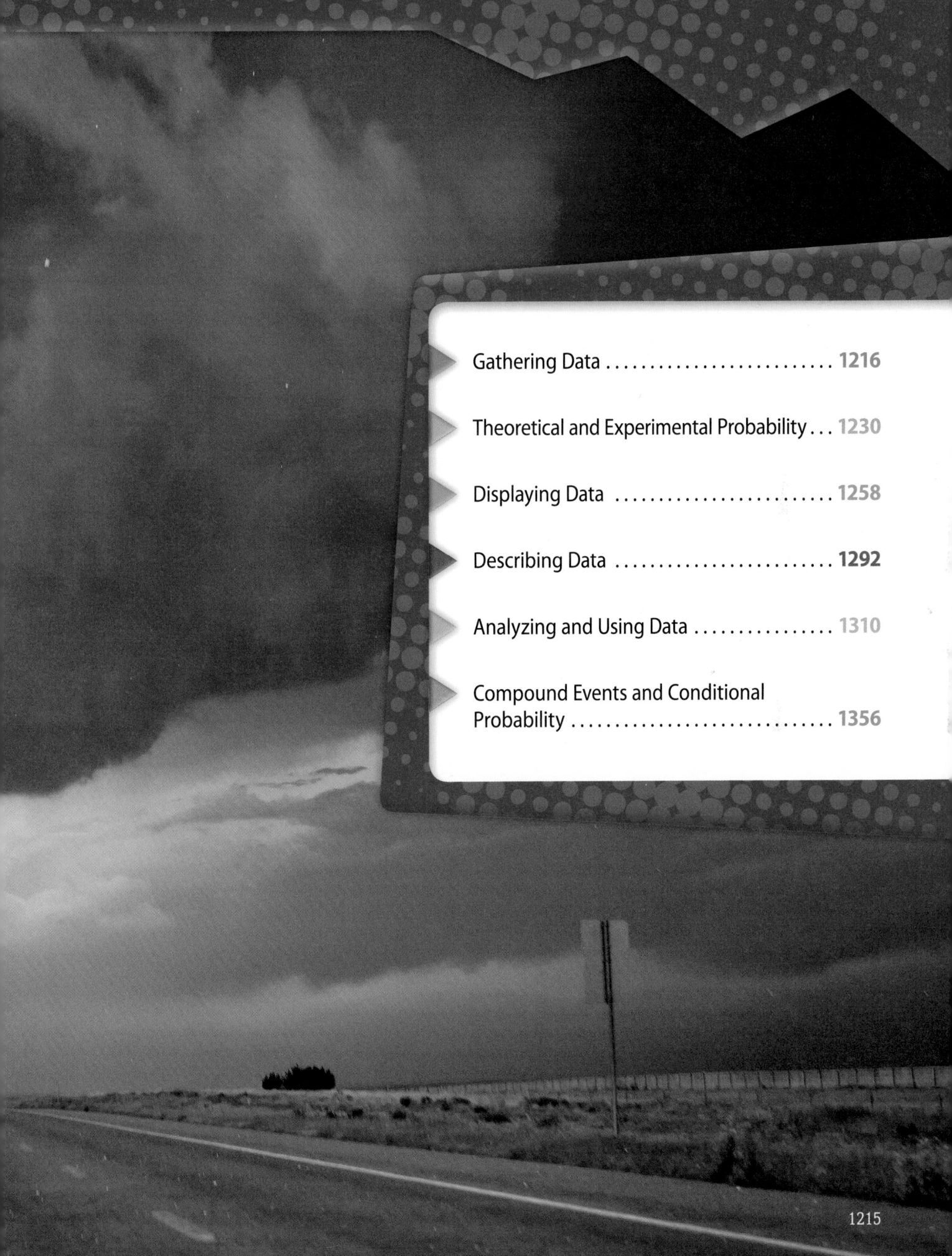

Gathering Data

What Came Before?
- Solving proportions
- Deductive and inductive reasoning

What's This About?
- Methods of drawing a sample from a population
- Recognizing bias
- Random and other methods of sampling

Practical Apps
- Market researchers use well-designed surveys to measure customer satisfaction and preferences.
- Survey designers need to ensure that they choose the right population and surveying method to gather the most useful information for their clients.

Just for FUN!

Q: Why does the survey prefer the warehouse store to the convenience store?

A: It gives out tasty random samples to the general population.

You can find more practice problems online by visiting:
www.SWadvantage.com

Samples and Populations

Data Sets

A set of **data** is a collection of numbers, measures, or other information. For example, a restaurant owner might record whether or not her customers order dessert. The group of individuals who supply the data is called the **population**. In this example, the restaurant customers are the population.

Would you care for dessert?

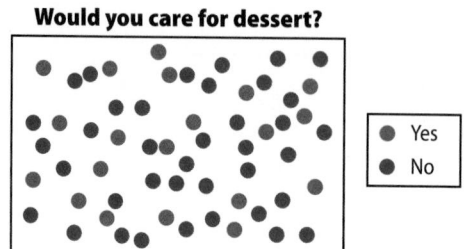

Sometimes it is not possible to collect data for every member of a population. Instead, the restaurant owner might look at every fifth receipt, or the receipts from one day only. The selected receipts are a *subgroup* of a population and are called a **sample**. The process of choosing the subgroup is called *sampling*.

Population

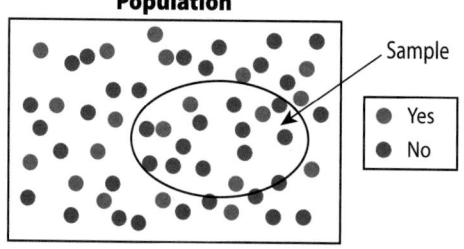

SEARCH

To see step-by-step videos of these problems, enter the page number into the SWadvantage.com Search Bar.

EXAMPLE 1

Identify the sample and population in each situation.

a. A politician asks 50 voters from the registered voter list for their opinions on developing bicycle lanes on city streets.

The population is the voters on the registered voter list.

The sample is the 50 voters who gave their opinions.

b. Radio listeners are invited to log on to a station's website to request songs.

The population is the radio listeners with computer access.

The sample is the listeners who log on to request songs.

Making Predictions

A sample can be used to make predictions about the population or estimates of the size of the population.

Watch Out !

To make a general statement based on information from a sample, the sample must be *random*. To learn more, see *Random Sampling* on page 1224.

EXAMPLE 2

Principal Li wants to know how many of the 1,200 students in her school read the student newspaper. She chooses 90 students at random, and 63 of them say they read the paper. About how many students in the school read the student paper?

Set up a proportion.
$$\frac{\text{newspaper readers in sample}}{\text{students in sample}} = \frac{\text{newspaper readers in population}}{\text{students in population}}$$

Substitute.
$$\frac{63}{90} = \frac{x}{1{,}200}$$

Multiply both sides by 1,200.
$$1{,}200\left(\frac{63}{90}\right) = \left(\frac{x}{1{,}200}\right)1{,}200$$

Simplify.
$$840 = x$$

About 840 students read the student paper.

EXAMPLE 3

At one school, all 476 students participate in a sport. The sports that a random sample of students plays are shown. Estimate how many of the 476 students run track.

Number of Students in Spring Sports	
Ultimate Flying Disc	42
Track	27
Baseball	33

STEP 1 Find the number of students in the sample. $42 + 27 + 33 = 102$

STEP 2 Set up a proportion.
$$\frac{\text{track runners in sample}}{\text{students in sample}} = \frac{\text{track runners in population}}{\text{students in population}}$$

Substitute.
$$\frac{27}{102} = \frac{x}{476}$$

Multiply both sides by 476.
$$476\left(\frac{27}{102}\right) = \left(\frac{x}{476}\right)476$$

Simplify.
$$126 = x$$

About 126 students run track.

Need More HELP ?

For help with proportions, go to *Solving Proportions* in *Numbers and Operations* (Book 1, p. 370).

Capture and Recapture

Scientists use a method called "capture/recapture" to estimate the size of a population. The steps in the method are as follows.

Capture a group from the population. Count and mark the group members.

Return the marked group to the population and wait for it to mix in.

Capture another group. Count how many are marked and unmarked.

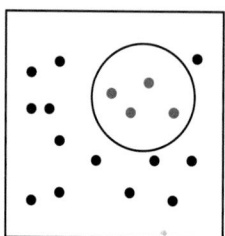
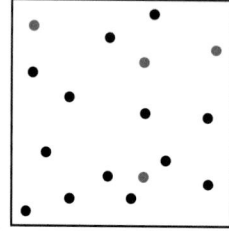
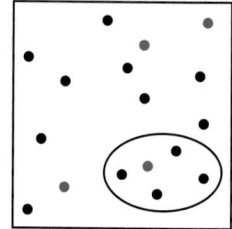

After counting the second group, estimate the size of the population by setting up a proportion.

SEARCH

To see step-by-step videos of these problems, enter the page number into the SWadvantage.com Search Bar.

EXAMPLE 4

A park superintendent wants to estimate how many squirrels are in a city park. Ten squirrels are captured and tagged. Six weeks later, 20 squirrels are captured and 3 of them have tags. Estimate the number of squirrels in the park.

Set up a proportion.

$$\frac{\text{tagged squirrels in population}}{\text{total squirrels in population}} = \frac{\text{tagged squirrels captured}}{\text{total squirrels captured}}$$

Substitute.

$$\frac{10}{x} = \frac{3}{20}$$

Cross multiply.

$$10 \cdot 20 = 3 \cdot x$$
$$200 = 3x$$

Divide both sides by 3.

$$\frac{200}{3} = \frac{3x}{3}$$
$$66.\overline{66} = x$$

Round to the nearest number of squirrels.

$$66.\overline{66} \approx 67$$

There are about 67 squirrels in the park.

Margin of Error

Information about a population that is drawn from a sample is an estimate. A report about a survey or poll may include a *margin of error*. For example, it may read, "The company has a satisfaction rating of 37% with a margin of error of plus or minus 4%."

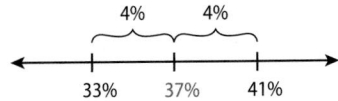

This means it is probable that the percent of satisfied customers is between 33% and 41%. The margin of error is based on the size of the sample and whether or not the sample is a good representation of the population, not on the type of questions asked.

EXAMPLE 5

From a population of 5,000 high school students, a random sample of 850 is selected. The poll shows that 78% are *not* in favor of classes on Saturdays. The margin of error is 3.4%. What is the probable range of students not in favor of Saturday classes?

Need More

HELP

For help with percents, go to *Decimals, Fractions, and Percents* in *Numbers and Operations* (Book 1, p. 272).

METHOD 1

STEP 1 Find 78% of 5,000.	$0.78 \cdot 5{,}000 = 3{,}900$	
STEP 2 Find 3.4% of 5,000.	$0.034 \cdot 5{,}000 = 170$	
STEP 3 Find the range of students.	$3{,}900 - 170 = 3{,}730$	
	$3{,}900 + 170 = 4{,}070$	

There are probably between 3,730 and 4,070 students who do not favor Saturday classes.

METHOD 2

STEP 1 Find the lower percent in the range.	$78\% - 3.4\% = 74.6\%$	
STEP 2 Find the upper percent in the range.	$78\% + 3.4\% = 81.4\%$	
STEP 3 Find the range of students.	$0.746 \cdot 5{,}000 = 3{,}730$	
	$0.814 \cdot 5{,}000 = 4{,}070$	

There are probably between 3,730 and 4,070 students who do not favor Saturday classes.

Terms to Know

Data Collection of numbers, measures, or other information

Population Group of individuals who supply data

Sample Any subgroup of the population

Margin of error An estimate of whether a measure of a sample is a good representative of the measure of the population

Surveys and Bias

Populations

A **survey** is a set of questions designed to gather information about a **population**, or group of people.

> A city parks department plans to improve a run-down park. The park planners want to know whether to add an off-leash play area for dogs, a play structure, or a community garden. They decide to conduct a survey. The first step is to decide what population to survey. The survey could be limited to all the people who currently use the park, to people who walk their dogs in the park, or to some other group.

SEARCH

To see step-by-step videos of these problems, enter the page number into the SWadvantage.com Search Bar.

EXAMPLE 1

Explain why the city park planners might not want to limit the survey to only the following populations.

a. dog owners or parents of small children

These two populations are likely to favor a particular use of the park. Neither group represents all the people who visit the park.

b. people who use the park regularly

This population excludes people who use the park occasionally. For example, adding a play structure could change some occasional users to regular users.

Samples

Once the population is identified, it is usually impossible to survey every member. A small part of the population, a **sample**, is selected to survey. It is important for the sample to represent the larger population so that the sample is not *biased*. A **biased sample** is one that overrepresents or underrepresents some part of the population.

Two ways a sample can be biased are *undercoverage* and *nonresponse*. **Undercoverage** occurs when some portions of the population are left out. **Nonresponse** occurs when some people selected for the sample do not respond to the survey.

Got to KNOW!

Bias

Bias can occur in different stages of the surveying process. The identified population, the sample chosen, or a survey question is biased if it in any way influences the results of the survey.

EXAMPLE 2

Explain what type of bias could occur in each situation.

a. The sample chosen must respond online, using the city's website.

Nonresponse; not everyone has a computer. In this case, nonresponse also results in undercoverage. People who do not have a computer are likely to be undercovered in the survey.

b. The sample is limited to all the registered voters who use the park.

Undercoverage; the sample excludes park users who are not registered to vote.

Survey Questions

The design of the survey questions is very important. It is easier to interpret survey results if the questions are structured so that they provide responses to choose from. It is also important to avoid *leading questions*. A **leading question** is one that makes people likely to answer in a particular way.

For example, in the survey below, the question "Would you prefer that dogs not run loose in the park?" could suggest that having dogs off leash in the park is undesirable. It might also introduce bias into the survey by making people think that dogs do run loose in the park, even if this is untrue. This may cue them to prefer the off-leash play area for dogs when they were considering a different choice.

> **Watch Out !**
> It is not always easy to recognize a leading question. The question "Do you agree that we should go to the movies?" is a leading question. The person asking the question has stated his or her opinion as a question. A less biased question is "Have we agreed on what we are going to do?"

EXAMPLE 3

The city parks department conducted a survey with a sample of 90 people. The results for three of the questions are shown below. The number in parentheses is the number of people who gave a particular response.

1. How many times did you visit this park last month?
   a. 0 times (11)
   b. 1–2 times (19)
   c. 3–5 times (34)
   d. 6–10 times (19)
   e. > 10 times (7)

2. Do you own a dog?
   a. Yes (39)
   b. No (48)

3. Which proposed improvement do you prefer?
   a. A play structure (29)
   b. A community garden (22)
   c. Off-leash play area for dogs (27)
   d. None of the above (12)

a. Look closely at the intervals for the answers to question 1. What do you notice?

The numbers of visits included in the choices vary a lot.
Choice (b) 1–2 means   1 time or 2 times
Choice (c) 3–5 means   3 times, 4 times, or 5 times
Choice (d) 6–10 means   6 times, 7 times, 8 times, 9 times, or 10 times.

The different sizes of intervals make it difficult to compare the responses. Choice (b) has only 2 possible times, but choice (d) has 5 possible times.

b. Only 87 people answered question 2. Give a possible reason for nonresponse.

Some people who rent apartments or homes are not supposed to have pets. A dog owner in this situation might not answer this question.

c. The number of people who prefer an off-leash play area for dogs is less than the number of dog owners. What are some possible reasons for this difference?

Some dog owners do not let their dogs off leash. Some may have children and prefer a play structure. Dog owners who live in apartments may prefer a community garden.

Random Sampling

What Is a Random Sample?

A **random sample** is a sample for which each member of the identified population is equally likely to be selected. For example, a teacher wants to select ten students from the class at random. One method is to write the students' names on identical pieces of paper and place the papers in a container. Mix the papers well and select ten of them without looking. The result is a random sample of ten names.

Selecting a Random Sample

Drawing names from a container is not an effective method when a larger sample is needed. *Examples 1–3 describe three ways to select a random sample for the following situation.*

The student recycling team at Crescent Middle School wants to survey a random sample of 50 seventh graders. The team has a list of the 350 seventh graders in the school. How can they select a random sample?

EXAMPLE 1

A simple method is to use a telephone book as an approximation of a list of random numbers.

5047
6166
4538
3308
2608
1015
8956
8497
6738
5101
1127
2360

STEP 1   Assign a number from 1 to 350 to each seventh grader.

STEP 2   Open the residential listings of a telephone book to any page. Choose a number from any location on the page. Use only the last three digits of the number. For example, as shown at the right, you could choose the seventh number from the bottom in the right-hand column and use the digits 015.

STEP 3   Include in the survey the student whose assigned number corresponds to the number found in Step 2.

STEP 4   Repeat the process in Steps 2 and 3 until you have selected 50 seventh graders. Each time open the telephone book to a different page but go to the same location on the page. Note: If the three-digit number you find is greater than 350 or has already been used, go to another page.

Generating Random Numbers

You can generate random numbers by using a calculator or a computer, by rolling game cubes, by spinning spinners, or by choosing slips of paper from a container without looking. Some mathematics or statistics textbooks contain lists of randomly generated numbers.

Numbers such as street addresses, student identification numbers, and Social Security numbers are NOT random numbers and should not be used for this purpose.

EXAMPLE 2

Use spreadsheet software.

STEP 1 Copy and paste a list of the students into Column A of the spreadsheet.

STEP 2 Fill the next column by using the randomize function. Enter **=RAND()** in the first cell and fill down. This will assign a number between 0 and 1 to each student.

SEARCH

To see step-by-step videos of these problems, enter the page number into the SWadvantage.com Search Bar.

	A	B	C	D
	A1 ▼	= RAND()		
1	Jennifer	0.095145314		
2	Owen	0.578181297		
3	Max	0.057975506		
4	Tizita	0.248711671		
5	Ellie	0.52547009		
6	Taylor	0.46408924		
7	Jaidha	0.058604953		
8	Carmen	0.698276805		
9	Siraj	0.07457809		
10	Miles	0.332110007		

List every person in the population in Column A.

Fill Column B using the randomize function.

STEP 3 Select both columns and choose the Sort function. This will randomly reorder the list of the students' names.

STEP 4 Give the survey to the first 50 seventh graders on the reordered list.

EXAMPLE 3

Use a scientific or graphing calculator that has a RAND function.

STEP 1 Assign a number from 1 to 350 to each seventh grader.

STEP 2 Use the RAND function or key to produce a random number between 0 and 1.

$$0.282336738426238$$

STEP 3 Multiply the number by 351 to get a number between 0 and 351. Discard any number less than 1. Use only the integer part of the number.

$$99.1001951876096$$

STEP 4 Give the survey to the student whose assigned number is this integer. In the example shown, student 99 would be included in the survey.

STEP 5 Repeat this process until you have selected 50 students.

Watch Out !

If you use a calculator to select a sample, multiply the random number by the number that is 1 greater than the number in the population. If you don't, the greatest number in the population will never be chosen. Why?

$n < 1$

$350 \times n < 350$

Other Types of Random Samples

A **simple random sample** (SRS) is one in which every member of a population has an equal possibility of being selected. However, there are other types of random samples including *stratified samples, cluster samples,* and *systematic samples.*

Types of Random Samples	
Stratified sample The population is separated into two or more subgroups. Each subgroup is similar in composition. Then a sample is chosen from each subgroup. If the sample is chosen by SRS, then the sampling method is called *stratified random sampling.*	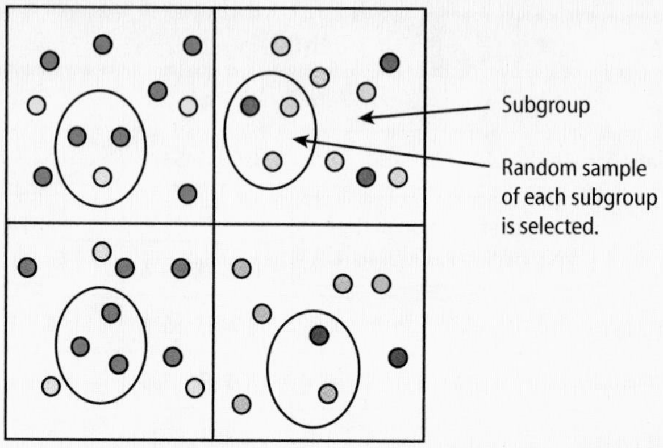 Subgroup — Random sample of each subgroup is selected.
Cluster sample The population is separated into subgroups, which are selected at random. In most cases, every member of the chosen subgroups is included in the sample. (In some sampling situations, not every member of a subgroup is chosen. Instead, members are randomly selected from the selected subgroups.)	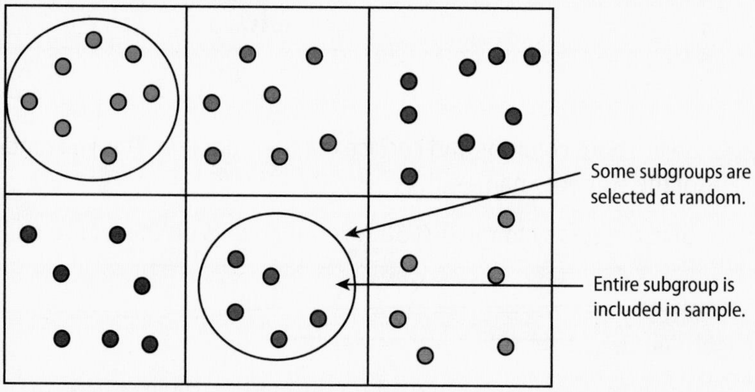 Some subgroups are selected at random. — Entire subgroup is included in sample.
Systematic sample The population is ordered in some way. Then members are chosen at regular intervals throughout the population.	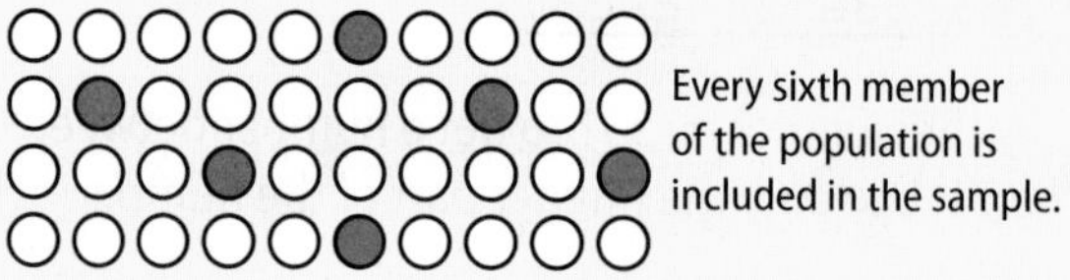 Every sixth member of the population is included in the sample.

Stratified Samples

A stratified sample is a good choice when a population contains subgroups that do not overlap, such as people who live in different ZIP codes. It also ensures that the subgroups in the population are proportionally represented in the sample.

EXAMPLE 1

The state math honors program consists of 132 girls and 108 boys. A math coach wants to choose a representative sample of 12 program members to travel to a tournament out of state. Describe how to use stratified sampling to do this.

STEP 1 The two subgroups are boys and girls. Find the total number of math honors students in the two subgroups: $132 + 108 = 240$

STEP 2 Find the percent of girls and boys in the population.

Girls: $\frac{132}{240} = 55\%$ Boys: $\frac{108}{240} = 45\%$

STEP 3 Find the number of girls in the sample.

$0.55 \cdot 12 = 6.6$ Round 6.6 to 7. Randomly select 7 of the 132 girls.

STEP 4 Find the number of boys in the sample.

$12 - 7 = 5$ Randomly select 5 of the 108 boys.

SEARCH

To see step-by-step videos of these problems, enter the page number into the SWadvantage.com Search Bar.

Systematic Samples

Systematic samples ensure that the population is evenly sampled. They use a fixed interval period and a random starting point, which makes them easy to work with.

EXAMPLE 2

A community health clinic wants to select a sample of 18 patients from the 144 patients who visit the clinic in one day. Describe how to use systematic sampling to choose this sample.

STEP 1 Number the patients from 1 to 144.

STEP 2 Find the interval period, a ratio of the number of people in the population to the number of people in the sample.

$$\text{Interval period} = \frac{\textit{Number of people in the population}}{\textit{Number of people in the sample}} = \frac{144}{18} = 8$$

STEP 3 Choose the starting point, or first patient in the sample, by randomly selecting a number between 1 and the sample size, 8. For example, roll two number cubes and find their sum. Discard any sum greater than 8. Say you roll 2 and 1. Add: $2 + 1 = 3$. Patient 3 is the first patient in the sample.

STEP 4 Start with 3 and count on by 8 to find the other patients in the sample.
$3 + 8 = 11, 11 + 8 = 19, 19 + 8 = 27$, and so on.
The sample will include patients 3, 11, 19, 27, and so on.

Need More HELP?

For help with ratios, go to *Writing and Simplifying Ratios* in *Numbers and Operations* (Book 1, p. 364).

Nonrandom Samples

Suppose you asked a group of your friends, "Who is your favorite author?" You would probably get different answers than if you asked the same question of a random sample of bookstore customers. The sample made up of your friends is called a *convenience sample,* which is one type of nonrandom sample.

Types of Nonrandom Samples	
Convenience sample The members of the population that are easiest to contact or survey are selected for the sample.	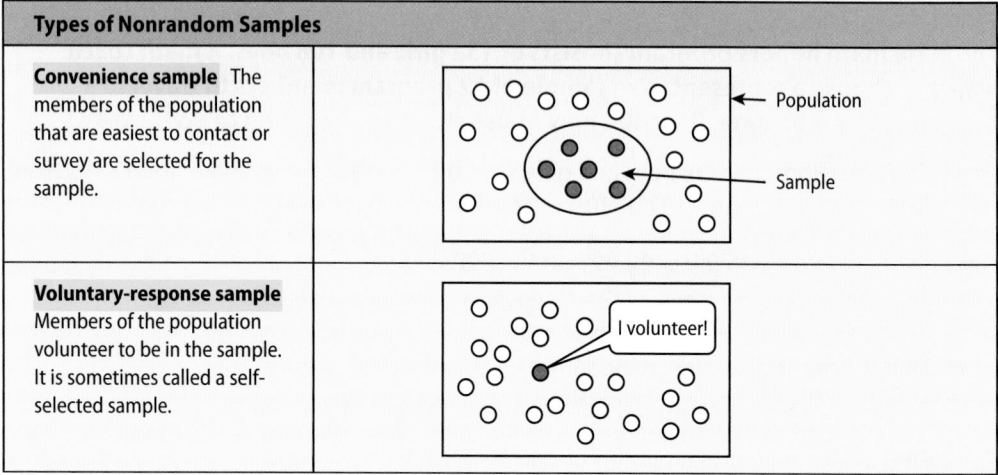
Voluntary-response sample Members of the population volunteer to be in the sample. It is sometimes called a self-selected sample.	

SEARCH

To see step-by-step videos of these problems, enter the page number into the SWadvantage.com Search Bar.

EXAMPLE 3

A nonprofit organization in a state wants to study the recycling programs used in the counties across the state. Researchers randomly select ten counties from all the counties in the state. (This is about one-fourth of the counties.) Then they visit every recycling facility in each of the ten selected counties.

a. **What kind of sample did the organization use? Why is it a good choice for this situation?**

The organization used a cluster sample. Nonprofit organizations usually do not have a lot of money. A cluster sample is a good choice as it reduces the cost of the study. Instead of visiting a few sites in every county across the state, the researchers can visit every site in a few counties.

b. **Using a convenience sample might cost the organization even less. Why might a convenience sample be a poor choice for this study?**

A convenience sample would most likely include only nearby recycling programs. If the state is large, this sample may not represent what is happening across the state. Although it could save money, it is likely to be less accurate.

Identifying Types of Samples

EXAMPLE 4

Identify the type of sample in each situation as *convenience, voluntary-response, stratified, cluster, systematic,* or *random*.

a. **The owner of a store asks every tenth customer for his or her ZIP code.**

This is a systematic sample. Members are chosen at a regular interval.

b. **A teacher has each student roll a number cube. Students who roll an even number present their reports on Monday.**

This is a random sample because all students are equally likely to roll an even number and need to present their reports on Monday.

c. **A student uses a social networking website to ask his friends if they have homework assignments over a holiday weekend.**

This is a convenience sample because it is an easy group to ask. It is also a voluntary-response sample because his friends may choose to respond or not respond.

d. **A principal selects at random 5 students from each grade in the school.**

This is a stratified sample. The different grades are the subgroups. The 5 students from each grade are the random samples of the subgroups.

Need More

HELP ?

Remember that a *sample* is any subgroup of a population. A *random sample* is one in which all members of the population are equally likely to be chosen for the sample.

For help with random samples, go to *Random Sampling* on page 1224.

Advantages and Disadvantages of Different Sampling Methods

Sample Type	Advantage	Disadvantage
Convenience	Easy, quick	Unlikely to represent an entire population.
Voluntary-response	Easy, inexpensive	Likely to be biased. People who have strong opinions or who like to be in surveys are more likely to respond.
Stratified	Subgroups in the population are proportionally represented.	Cannot be used if the population cannot be separated into meaningful subgroups.
Systematic	Simple, ensures that the population will be evenly sampled	Might introduce bias. Suppose a sample is made up of every eighth house on every street. The population has many blocks with only eight houses. The sample might overrepresent corner houses.
Cluster	Less expensive, less time consuming	Less accurate, especially if only a few clusters are selected; may exclude an important subgroup.

Theoretical and Experimental Probability

What Came Before?
- Ratios, proportions, and percent
- Methods of collecting data

What's This About?
- Probability of simple events
- Permutations and combinations
- Odds for and against events

Practical Apps
- Actuaries can analyze probabilities and risk to help set insurance rates.
- Meteorologists use probability models to predict future weather patterns.

just for FUN!

If there is a 50-50 chance that something can go wrong, then 9 times out of 10 it will.

Hmmmm. What is this person missing?

Topics	Vocabulary	Pages
Theoretical Probability	*probability* *theoretical probability* *equally likely* *outcome* *sample space*	1232–1235
Experimental Probability	*experiment* *trial* *experimental probability*	1236–1239
The Counting Principle	*tree diagram*	1240–1243
Permutations	*permutation* *n factorial*	1244–1247
Combinations	*combination* *combinatorial identity*	1248–1253
Odds and Complements	*odds* *complement* *complementary events*	1254–1257

You can find more practice problems online by visiting:
www.SWadvantage.com

Theoretical Probability

What Is Theoretical Probability?

Probability is a way to describe the likelihood that a given event will take place. When probability is calculated by analysis, it is called **theoretical probability**. Theoretical probability tells what you can expect to happen, not what actually happens. Each possible result is an **outcome**. An **event** is any outcome or group of outcomes.

To determine theoretical probability, use the formula below, where *favorable outcomes* are outcomes you want and *total number of outcomes* is the number of all the possible outcomes.

$$P(\text{event}) = \frac{\text{number of favorable outcomes}}{\text{total number of outcomes}}$$

The probability of any event is 0, 1, or a number between 0 and 1.

A probability may be written as a fraction, a decimal, or a percent.

If two outcomes have equal probabilities, the outcomes are **equally likely**.

Identifying Outcomes

- Suppose you perform an experiment in which you roll one of the game cubes shown. The given event is rolling the number cube. There are six possible outcomes for this event—rolling a 1, 2, 3, 4, 5, or 6.

- Suppose the event is tossing a coin. One possible outcome of this experiment is that the coin lands heads up. The other outcome is that the coin lands tails up.

The set of all possible outcomes of an experiment is called the **sample space** for the experiment. The sample space for rolling the game cube is {1, 2, 3, 4, 5, 6}. The sample space for tossing the coin is {heads, tails}.

- The spinner at the left below is divided into four equal sections. The sample space for using this spinner is {1, 2, 3, 4}. Because the sections are of equal size, the outcomes are all *equally likely*. When you measure the likelihood of an outcome, you are finding the *probability* of the outcome.

- The possible outcomes in the sample space are not always equally likely. The sections of the spinner at the right above are not all the same size. If you spin this spinner, the arrow is more likely to land on 3 than on 1 or 2.

Need More
HELP

Read *P*(event) as "the probability of an event." There may be a different term in parentheses. For example, *P*(red) means "the probability of red."

SEARCH

To see step-by-step videos of these problems, enter the page number into the SWadvantage.com Search Bar.

Certain and Impossible Events

A dresser drawer contains 12 T-shirts—3 blue, 5 white, and 4 red. Suppose you select a T-shirt at random and any color is okay. The probability of selecting a blue, white, or red T-shirt is $\frac{12}{12} = 1$. An event with a probability of 1 is called a *certain* event.

Suppose you want to select a gray T-shirt. Since there are no gray T-shirts in the drawer, the probability of selecting a gray T-shirt is $\frac{0}{12} = 0$. An event with a probability of 0 is called an *impossible* event.

EXAMPLE 1

Use the formula for theoretical probability and the definitions of certain and impossible events to find the probability of the following event.

You roll a game cube with sides numbered 1, 2, 3, 4, 5, and 6.

a. Find the probability of rolling a 4.

There are 6 possible outcomes. There is 1 favorable outcome—rolling a 4.

$P(4) = \frac{\text{number of favorable outcomes}}{\text{total number of outcomes}} = \frac{1}{6} \approx 0.17 = 17\%$

b. Find the probability of rolling an odd number.

There are 6 possible outcomes. There are 3 odd numbers—1, 3, and 5.

$P(\text{odd number}) = \frac{3}{6} = 0.5 = 50\%$

c. Find the probability of rolling a number less than 5.

There are 6 possible outcomes. There are 4 numbers less than 5—1, 2, 3, and 4.

$P(\text{number less than 5}) = \frac{4}{6} = \frac{2}{3} \approx 0.67 = 67\%$

d. Find the probability of rolling a number greater than 6.

None of the numbers are greater than 6, so $P(\text{number} > 6) = \frac{0}{6} = 0$.

Need More

HELP

For help converting fractions to decimals and percents, see *Decimals, Fractions, and Percents* in *Numbers and Operations* (Book 1, p. 272).

Got to
KNOW!

Probabilities of 0 and 1

The probability of an event that is *certain* is 1.

The sum of the probabilities of all possible outcomes of an event is 1.

The probability of an event that is *impossible*, and cannot occur, is 0.

Finding Probability

Probability Formula

The formula for finding probability is:

$P(\text{event}) = \dfrac{\text{no. of favorable outcomes}}{\text{total number of outcomes}}$

EXAMPLE 2

Use the spinner to find each probability. The spinner is divided into equal sections.

Spinner sections: 8, 1, 7, 2, 6, 3, 5, 4

a. Find the probability of spinning a 3.

There are 8 possible outcomes. One of them is landing on 3.

$P(3) = \dfrac{1}{8} = 0.125 = 12.5\%$

b. Find the probability of landing on green.

Out of the 8 possible outcomes, 2 of them are landing on green.

$P(\text{green}) = \dfrac{2}{8} = \dfrac{1}{4} = 0.25 = 25\%$

c. Find the probability of spinning a number greater than 2 and less than 7.

Out of the 8 possible outcomes, 4 outcomes are between 2 and 7—3, 4, 5, and 6.

$P(\text{number greater than 2 and less than 7}) = \dfrac{4}{8} = \dfrac{1}{2} = 0.5 = 50\%$

EXAMPLE 3

Need More HELP?

Remember, the sum of all the possible outcomes is equal to 1.

$\dfrac{1}{2} + \dfrac{1}{3} + \dfrac{1}{6} =$

$\dfrac{3}{6} + \dfrac{2}{6} + \dfrac{1}{6} =$

$\dfrac{6}{6} =$

1

A drawer contains 6 black socks, 4 blue socks, and 2 white socks. Suppose you take a sock out of the drawer without looking. Are the probabilities of selecting the three colors equally likely? If not, list the probabilities from least to greatest.

STEP 1 Add to find the total number of possible outcomes: $6 + 4 + 2 = 12$.

STEP 2 Find each probability.

$P(\text{black}) = \dfrac{\text{number of black socks}}{\text{total number of socks}} = \dfrac{6}{12} = \dfrac{1}{2}$

$P(\text{blue}) = \dfrac{\text{number of blue socks}}{\text{total number of socks}} = \dfrac{4}{12} = \dfrac{1}{3}$

$P(\text{white}) = \dfrac{\text{number of white socks}}{\text{total number of socks}} = \dfrac{2}{12} = \dfrac{1}{6}$

STEP 3 Compare the outcomes. $\dfrac{1}{6} < \dfrac{1}{3} < \dfrac{1}{2}$

The outcomes are not equally likely. From least to greatest, the probabilities are white sock, blue sock, black sock.

EXAMPLE 4

In a set of number cards, one number card is selected at random.

SEARCH

To see step-by-step videos of these problems, enter the page number into the SWadvantage.com Search Bar.

a. What is the probability of selecting a card with a number less than 10?

All of the cards have numbers less than 10. This event is certain, so its probability is 1.

b. What is the probability of selecting a card with a number divisible by 5?

No number on the cards is divisible by 5. This event is impossible, so its probability is 0.

c. What is the probability of selecting a card whose number is not 8?

METHOD 1

Count the cards whose numbers are not 8. Set up a probability ratio.

$$P(\text{not } 8) = \frac{\text{number of cards that are not 8}}{\text{total number of cards}} = \frac{6}{8} = \frac{3}{4} = 0.75 = 75\%$$

METHOD 2

Find the probability of selecting a card whose number is 8, and subtract the probability from 1.

$$P(8) = \frac{\text{number of cards that are 8}}{\text{total number of cards}} = \frac{2}{8} = \frac{1}{4}$$

$$P(\text{not } 8) = 1 - \frac{1}{4} = \frac{3}{4} = 0.75 = 75\%$$

Watch Out !

Even though there are four possible numbers one could choose, the total number of cards is eight. Use 8, not 4, as the total number of possible outcomes.

EXAMPLE 5

If a number is chosen at random from the set {3, 6, 9, 12, 15}, what is the probability that the number is a solution of the inequality $6 < x < 15$?

STEP 1 Count the total number of possible outcomes.

There are 5 numbers in the set.

STEP 2 Read the inequality as "x is greater than six and less than fifteen."

STEP 3 There are 2 outcomes that satisfy the inequality.

9 and 12 are both greater than 6 but less than 15.

STEP 4 Write the probability.

$P(\text{number that is solution of the inequality}) = \frac{2}{5}$.

Need More HELP ?

For help with inequalities, see *Graphing an Inequality as an Interval* in *Algebra* (p. 1492).

Experimental Probability

Conducting Trials for an Experiment

Suppose you toss a coin exactly once. It can land either heads up or tails up, so the theoretical probability that it lands heads up is $\frac{1}{2}$. However, for only one toss, you cannot predict the outcome. Heads and tails are equally likely.

If you toss the coin many times, you can compare the frequency of each result with the total number of times the coin is tossed. The act of tossing the coin many times to find outcomes is an **experiment**. Each toss of the coin is called a **trial** of the experiment.

The tally chart below shows the results of tossing a coin 16 times.

Trial No.	1	2	3	4	5	6	7	8	9	10	11	12	13	14	15	16
Heads	✓	✓	✓	✓			✓			✓	✓			✓		✓
Tails					✓	✓		✓	✓			✓	✓		✓	

The **experimental probability** of an event is the ratio of the number of times a favorable outcome occurs to the total number of trials. The coin landed heads up 9 times. In this experiment, the experimental probability of heads is $\frac{9}{16}$.

Look at just the first 2 tosses in the table above. Of these 2 tosses, both landed heads, so $P(\text{heads}) = \frac{2}{2} = 1$.

Now look at just the first 6 tosses—4 heads, 2 tails. For these tosses, $P(\text{heads}) = \frac{4}{6} = \frac{2}{3}$, which is closer to the experimental probability of $\frac{1}{2}$.

In general, as the number of trials of an experiment increases, the experimental probability gets closer and closer to the theoretical probability.

Got to KNOW!

Experimental Probability

$P(\text{event}) = \dfrac{\text{number of times the favorable outcome occurs}}{\text{total number of trials}}$

The experimental probability of an event is also called the *relative frequency* of the event.

Law of Large Numbers

As the number of times an experiment is performed increases, the experimental probability approaches the expected, or theoretical, probability.

EXAMPLE 1

A game cube numbered 1 through 6 is rolled several times. Each number rolled is recorded. The results are shown in the table below.

Result	1	2	3	4	5	6
Number of Occurrences	12	5	8	3	6	6

a. What is the experimental probability of rolling a 1?

Add the total number of occurrences to find the total number of trials:
$12 + 5 + 8 + 3 + 6 + 6 = 40$.
The number of trials with a result of 1 is 12.

$P(1) = \frac{12}{40} = \frac{3}{10} = 0.3 = 30\%$

b. What is the experimental probability of rolling an odd number?

The total number of trials is 40. The number of occurrences of an odd number is:
$12 + 8 + 6 = 26$

$P(\text{odd}) = \frac{26}{40} = \frac{13}{20} = 0.65 = 65\%$

SEARCH

To see step-by-step videos of these problems, enter the page number into the SWadvantage.com Search Bar.

EXAMPLE 2

A bag contains 9 blue marbles, 7 red marbles, and 11 green marbles. A marble is drawn from the bag at random. Its color is recorded, and the marble is put back in the bag. The process is repeated several times. The results are shown in the table below.

Result	Blue	Red	Green
Number of Occurrences	12	7	11

a. What is the experimental probability of selecting a blue marble?

The total number of trials is $12 + 7 + 11 = 30$. A blue marble was drawn 12 times.

Experimental: $P(\text{blue}) = \frac{12}{30} = 40\%$

b. What is the theoretical probability of selecting a blue marble?

The total number of marbles in the bag is $9 + 7 + 11 = 27$. The number of blue marbles in the bag is 9.

Theoretical: $P(\text{blue}) = \frac{9}{27} = \frac{1}{3} \approx 33\%$

c. Was a blue marble chosen more times or fewer times than expected?

More times; 40% is greater than the theoretical probability of 33%.

Need More HELP

For help calculating theoretical probability, go to *Theoretical Probability* on pages 1232–1235.

Observational Results

It is fairly easy to find the theoretical probabilities for an event such as tossing a coin. In other cases, it may be more difficult. In these cases, you can collect information either by performing an experiment or by making observations. Then you can use experimental probability to analyze the results.

EXAMPLE 3

SEARCH

To see step-by-step videos of these problems, enter the page number into the SWadvantage.com Search Bar.

Two game cubes numbered 1 through 6 are rolled several times. The sum of the two numbers rolled—the result—is recorded. The results are shown in the table below.

Result	Number of Occurrences
2	2
3	5
4	3
5	5
6	3
7	12
8	9
9	8
10	0
11	2
12	1

a. Would you expect all the possible outcomes of this experiment to be equally likely? Why or why not?

No. There is only one way to roll a sum of 2 (1 + 1) or a sum of 12 (6 + 6). There are several ways to roll some numbers. For example, you can roll a sum of 7 by rolling 6 and 1, 5 and 2, or 4 and 3.

b. What is the experimental probability of rolling a 3?

Add all numbers of occurrences to find the total number of trials:
2 + 5 + 3 + 5 + 3 + 12 + 9 + 8 + 2 + 1 = 50.
The number of trials with a result of 3 is 5.

$P(3) = \frac{5}{50} = \frac{1}{10} = 0.1 = 10\%$

Try It This Way

Use your calculator to find the total number of occurrences and to calculate probability.

In Example 3(c), enter 32, press ÷, enter 50, and press =. Your calculator will display 0.64.

c. What is the experimental probability of rolling a number greater than 6?

The total number of trials is 50. The number of trials with a result greater than 6 is
12 + 9 + 8 + 2 + 1 = 32.

$P(>6) = \frac{32}{50} = 0.64 = 64\%$

EXAMPLE 4

A coin is tossed onto a checkerboard 20 times. The coin may land entirely on a red square, entirely on a black square, or on both colors at the same time. The results of the experiment are shown in the table below.

Result	Number of Occurrences
Red	4
Black	3
Both	13

What is the experimental probability that the coin lands on both red and black?

$$P(\text{both}) = \frac{\text{number of times coin lands on both}}{\text{total number of trials}} = \frac{13}{20} = 0.65 = 65\%$$

Got to KNOW!

Types of Probability

Experimental probability tells the result of an experiment, or something you actually do.

Theoretical probability predicts an expected result. It is a theory, or idea, which may not always show what really happens.

EXAMPLE 5

On her way to school, Rheana needs to cross two intersections that have traffic lights. For 10 days, she records whether each signal shows Walk or Don't Walk when she reaches it. The results are shown in the table.

Day	1	2	3	4	5	6	7	8	9	10
1st light	Walk	Don't Walk	Walk	Walk	Don't Walk	Walk	Don't Walk	Walk	Walk	Don't Walk
2nd light	Don't Walk	Don't Walk	Don't Walk	Don't Walk	Don't Walk	Walk	Don't Walk	Don't Walk	Walk	Don't Walk

a. What is the experimental probability that both traffic signals show Don't Walk on Rheana's way to school?

Both traffic lights signal Don't Walk on 4 days out of 10. The experimental probability is $P(\text{both Don't Walk}) = \frac{4}{10} = \frac{2}{5} = 40\%$

b. What is the experimental probability that at least one traffic light signal shows Don't Walk on Rheana's way to school?

The only days when Rheana did not record a Don't Walk signal were Day 6 and Day 9. On the other 8 days, at least one light signaled Don't Walk. The experimental probability is $P(\text{at least one Don't Walk}) = \frac{8}{10} = \frac{4}{5} = 80\%$

c. Is it more likely that a light signals Walk or Don't Walk when Rheana reaches it?

In part (b) the probability of at least one Don't Walk is 80%, which is greater than 50%. It is more likely that a light will signal "Don't Walk" when Rheana reaches it.

Try It This Way

You could answer Example 5(c) by counting the results in the chart. Don't Walk occurs 12 times, and Walk occurs 8 times. Since 12 > 8, it is more likely that a light will signal Don't Walk.

The Counting Principle

Tree Diagrams

When counting the number of outcomes of an event, it is important to make sure that every member of the sample space has been counted. For example, if you toss a coin two times, the possible results are:

Heads-Heads   Heads-Tails   Tails-Heads   Tails-Tails

A **tree diagram** shows all the possible outcomes of one or more events in an organized manner. The arrows or lines on a tree diagram are the "branches" of the tree. The tree diagram below shows the possible outcomes of tossing a coin twice.

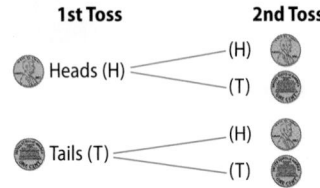

Count the number of branches to find the number of different outcomes. On the first toss, the coin lands heads up or tails up. On the second toss, it lands heads up or tails up. There are four possible outcomes: (H, H), (H, T), (T, H), and (T, T).

EXAMPLE 1

SEARCH

To see step-by-step videos of these problems, enter the page number into the SWadvantage.com Search Bar.

The Bagel Palace sells whole-grain bagels and plain bagels. There are 3 choices of toppings: butter, jam, and cream cheese. Use a tree diagram to find the total number of ways a customer can order a bagel with one topping.

Make a tree diagram. Start with the 2 types of bagels—whole grain and plain. Add branches for the 3 toppings—butter, jam, and cream cheese.

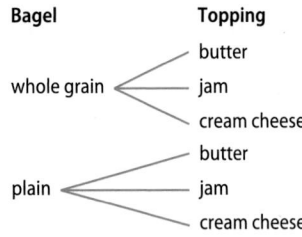

Count the number of branches.

whole grain, butter	whole grain, jam	whole grain, cream cheese
plain, butter	plain, jam	plain, cream cheese

There are 6 different bagel-and-one-topping orders.

EXAMPLE 2

Jim plans to choose one outfit from these choices.

A. 1 shirt
B. 3 pairs of pants
C. 4 pairs of socks
D. 2 pairs of shoes

Use a tree diagram to find the number of possible outfits that Jim can wear.

METHOD 1

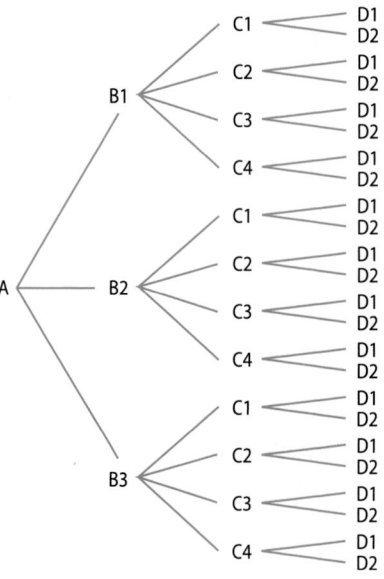

STEP 1 Write A to represent the 1 shirt.

STEP 2 There are 3 choices for pants. Draw 3 branches from A. Label them B1, B2, and B3.

STEP 3 There are 4 choices for socks. Draw 4 branches each from B1, B2, and B3. Label them C1, C2, C3, and C4.

STEP 4 There are 2 choices for shoes. Draw 2 branches each from C1, C2, C3, and C4. Label them D1 and D2.

STEP 5 Count the number of branches on the right side of the tree diagram.

There are 24 branches, so there are 24 possible outfits.

METHOD 2

Multiply the number of possibilities for each choice, or event. This method uses the Fundamental Counting Principle.

The product of the number of choices is equal to the number of outcomes.

1 shirt choice $\times$ 3 pants choices $\times$ 4 socks choices $\times$ 2 shoes choices
$= 1 \times 3 \times 4 \times 2 = 24$ possible outfits

The Fundamental Counting Principle

If one event can occur in m ways and another event can occur in n ways, then there are $m \times n$ ways that both events can occur.

The Fundamental Counting Principle can be extended to any finite number of sets. If there are a outcomes for one event, b outcomes for a second event, c outcomes for a third event, and so on, the number of different ways all these events can occur is $a \times b \times c \times \ldots$.

Using the Fundamental Counting Principle

The Fundamental Counting Principle is a good way to count outcomes of multiple events, especially when the number of choices for each event is very large and it would be difficult to make a tree diagram. To use the Fundamental Counting Principle with a larger number of events, find the product of all the numbers of outcomes for all the events.

SEARCH Q

To see step-by-step videos of these problems, enter the page number into the SWadvantage.com Search Bar.

EXAMPLE 3

At the start of a round in one folk dance, 6 boys and 6 girls stand facing each other in two lines. Each boy must shake the hand of each of the girls. If they dance three rounds, how many handshakes is this?

Use the Fundamental Counting Principle to find the total number of outcomes.

There are 6 boys. Each boy shakes hands with 6 girls. There are 3 rounds.

$6 \times 6 \times 3 = 108$

There are 108 handshakes.

EXAMPLE 4

Traviata Pizza offers a choice of 2 bases (tomato sauce or garlic and olive oil), 4 types of cheese, 5 types of meat, and 8 other toppings. How many different types of pizza can a customer order if he or she chooses only one item from each category?

There are 2 bases, 4 cheeses, 5 meats, and 8 other toppings.

Use the Fundamental Counting Principle to find the total number of possible pizzas.

$2 \times 4 \times 5 \times 8 = 320$

There are 320 different ways to order pizza by choosing only one item from each category.

EXAMPLE 5

State license plate numbers often consist of three letters of the alphabet followed by three digits. How many different license plate numbers can be made?

Use the Fundamental Counting Principle to find the total number of outcomes.

There are 26 letter choices (letters $A–Z$) for *each* of the first three spaces (events) on the plate number.

There are 10 digit choices (digits 0–9) for *each* of the last three spaces (events) on the plate number.

$26 \times 26 \times 26 \times 10 \times 10 \times 10 = 17,576,000$

There are 17,576,000 different license plate numbers.

The Counting Principle and Probability

EXAMPLE 6

A spinner has four equal sections labeled 1–4. The pointer on the spinner is spun twice. What is the probability that the result of the first spin is *less than* the result of the second spin?

Make a tree diagram to organize the information you need to answer the question. You are interested only in outcomes in which the first spin is *less than* the second.

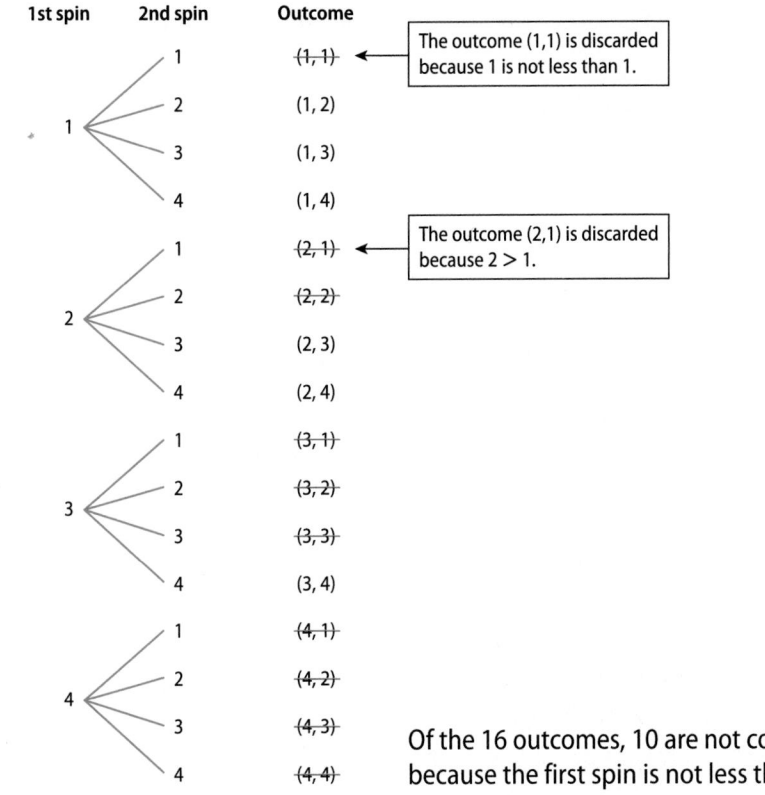

| 1st spin | 2nd spin | Outcome |

The outcome (1,1) is discarded because 1 is not less than 1.

The outcome (2,1) is discarded because 2 > 1.

Of the 16 outcomes, 10 are not counted as favorable because the first spin is not less than the second spin.

6 outcomes show the result of the first spin is less than the result of the second spin.

$P(\text{first spin} < \text{second spin}) = \frac{6}{16} = \frac{3}{8} = 0.375 = 37.5\%$

EXAMPLE 7

Students are invited to make up a three-digit number. Each digit must be greater than 0 and less than 6. If a student's number matches the teacher's number, the student wins a day off from homework. What is the probability of a match?

Use the Fundamental Counting Principle to find the total number of outcomes. There are 5 choices for *each* of the three digits. The number of outcomes is $5 \times 5 \times 5 = 125$.

The probability of winning is $\frac{1}{125} = 0.008 = 0.8\%$.

Watch Out !

In Example 7, when you think of each digit as an event, you will see why you do not multiply 3×5.

1st event: 5 outcomes

2nd event: 5 outcomes

3rd event: 5 outcomes

Multiply the ways in which the three events can occur: $5 \times 5 \times 5$.

Permutations

How Many Different Orders?

You can arrange books on a shelf in alphabetical order or by color or in other ways. You can line people up for a photograph in order of age or height or in some other way. Ordering books on a shelf and lining people up for a photograph in different ways are examples of permutations. A **permutation** is an arrangement of a group, or set, of objects in a particular order.

SEARCH

To see step-by-step videos of these problems, enter the page number into the SWadvantage.com Search Bar.

EXAMPLE 1

A brother, a sister, a father, a mother, and a grandmother are going to be in a family photograph. In how many ways can these 5 people be arranged in a line?

The number of people available to fill a position decreases each time a person is placed. If the sister is placed at the far left in the photograph, she is no longer available for any other position.

Position	First	Second	Third	Fourth	Fifth
Choices available	5	4	3	2	1

There are 5 people available for the first position, only 4 people available for the second position, and so on. Use the Fundamental Counting Principle to find the total number of ways the people can be arranged.

$5 \times 4 \times 3 \times 2 \times 1 = 120$

There are 120 ways the 5 family members can be arranged in a line.

The number of different ways the elements in a set can be arranged does not depend on what the elements are. You can arrange 5 different books on a shelf or arrange 5 different digits to form a number in 120 ways, just as you can arrange 5 people in a line for a photograph in 120 different ways.

In Example 1, notice that to find the number of ways that 5 people can be arranged, 5 is multiplied by all the natural numbers that are less than 5. This rule can be generalized to apply to any natural number n members of a set.

There are $n - 1$ numbers remaining after one place is filled, $n - 2$ numbers remaining after the second place is filled, and so on.

Watch Out !

Remember that a natural number is an integer that is greater than 0.

Permutations of n objects

To find the total number of arrangements of n objects, use this formula.

$n! = n \cdot (n - 1) \cdot (n - 2) \cdot (n - 3) \cdot \ldots \cdot 3 \cdot 2 \cdot 1$

Factorials

The product in which the factors are descending natural numbers is called
n factorial. This product $n \cdot (n-1) \cdot (n-2) \cdot (n-3) \cdot \ldots \cdot 3 \cdot 2 \cdot 1$ can be written
as $n!$ and is read "n factorial." The product in Example 1, $5 \times 4 \times 3 \times 2 \times 1 = 120$,
is $5!$. Factorials become large in value quite quickly, as shown in the table below.

Factorials	
n	$n!$
0	$0! = 1$
1	$1! = 1$
2	$2! = 2 \times 1 = 2$
3	$3! = 3 \times 2 \times 1 = 6$
4	$4! = 4 \times 3 \times 2 \times 1 = 24$
5	$5! = 5 \times 4 \times 3 \times 2 \times 1 = 120$
6	$6! = 6 \times 5 \times 4 \times 3 \times 2 \times 1 = 720$
7	$7! = 7 \times 6 \times 5 \times 4 \times 3 \times 2 \times 1 = 5,040$
8	$8! = 8 \times 7 \times 6 \times 5 \times 4 \times 3 \times 2 \times 1 = 40,320$
9	$9! = 9 \times 8 \times 7 \times 6 \times 5 \times 4 \times 3 \times 2 \times 1 = 362,880$
10	$10! = 10 \times 9 \times 8 \times 7 \times 6 \times 5 \times 4 \times 3 \times 2 \times 1 = 3,628,800$

Try It This Way

Most scientific calculators have a factorial key, labeled $x!$ or $n!$.

Need More HELP?

By definition, $0! = 1$. See *Special Cases of Combinations* on page 1251 to find out why.

EXAMPLE 2

A race has 8 runners competing.

a. In how many orders can the runners finish?

There are 8 possibilities for first place. After one runner finishes in first place, there are
7 runners who might finish in second place, 6 who might finish in third place, and so on.

Use the Fundamental Counting Principle to find the total number of orders in which the
runners can finish the race.

$8! = 8 \times 7 \times 6 \times 5 \times 4 \times 3 \times 2 \times 1 = 40,320$

**b. What is the probability that the runners will finish in the alphabetical order of
their names?**

Of the 40,320 orders in which the runners can finish, only one of them is the alphabetical
order of their names.

$P(\text{alphabetical order}) = \dfrac{1}{40,320} \approx 0.0000248 = 0.00248\%$

0.00248% is about a fourth of 1%.

Finding Permutations

In Example 2, you found the number of different orders in which all 8 runners could finish. Suppose, instead, you want to find the number of different orders in which only the first 3 runners can finish.

SEARCH

To see step-by-step videos of these problems, enter the page number into the SWadvantage.com Search Bar.

EXAMPLE 3

A race has 8 runners. Medals will be given to the first-, second-, and third-place runners. In how many different ways can the three medals be awarded?

There are 8 choices for first place. After the first runner has finished, there are 7 choices for second place. After the second runner has finished, there are 6 choices for third place.

Use the Fundamental Counting Principle to find the number of different ways in which the first three spots can be filled.

$8 \times 7 \times 6 = 336$

There are 336 different ways in which medals for first, second, and third place can be awarded.

You can use this notation to represent the permutations in Example 3.

$$_8P_3$$

number of members in the set   number from the set that are in the permutation

In general, this is written $_nP_r$.

The product in Example 3 is similar to a factorial, but the multiplication stops after the first 3 numbers. The last 5 factors of 8! are canceled.

- Multiply and divide the product $8 \times 7 \times 6$ by the factors that are canceled.

$$8 \times 7 \times 6 \times \cancel{5 \times 4 \times 3 \times 2 \times 1} = \frac{8 \times 7 \times 6 \times 5 \times 4 \times 3 \times 2 \times 1}{5 \times 4 \times 3 \times 2 \times 1}$$

- Write the numerator and denominator as factorials.

$$= \frac{8!}{5!}$$

- Write 5 as the difference of 8 and 3.

$$= \frac{8!}{(8 - 3)!}$$

Got to KNOW!

Factorials

$n! = n \cdot (n - 2) \cdot (n - 3) \cdot \ldots \cdot 3 \cdot 2 \cdot 1$ (Read $n!$ as "n factorial.")

$1! = 1$ and $0! = 1$

Permutations of *n* objects taken *r* at a time

To find the number of permutations of *r* items from a group of *n* items, use $_nP_r = \frac{n!}{(n - r)!}$.

$_nP_r$ may also be written as $P(n, r)$.

Using the formula for $_nP_r$ is much simpler than deriving it. Remember that permutations involve ordering the elements that are chosen from the larger set.

EXAMPLE 4

A class president and a class treasurer will be elected from a group of 12 students. In how many different ways can the two offices be filled?

METHOD 1

Use the permutation formula for 12 items taken 2 at a time. There is a difference between being president and being treasurer, so the order of the items is important.

Substitute 12 for n and 2 for r in the formula. $_{12}P_2 = \dfrac{12!}{(12-2)!}$

Simplify. $= \dfrac{12!}{10!}$

Write 12! as $12 \cdot 11 \cdot 10!$. $= \dfrac{12 \cdot 11 \cdot 10!}{10!}$

Simplify. $= 12 \cdot 11 = 132$

There are 132 different ways the two officers can be elected from the group of 12 students.

METHOD 2

Use the Fundamental Counting Principle. There are 12 different choices for the president. After the president is selected, there are 11 different choices for the treasurer.

The number of possible outcomes is $12 \cdot 11 = 132$.

> **Try It**
> **This Way**
>
> Many scientific and graphing calculators have a permutation function, labeled $_nP_r$. It may be a second function on a scientific calculator. It may also be on the MATH or PRB menu of a graphing calculator.

In some permutation problems, elements of the set may be repeated. This situation is called *permutation with repetition*.

EXAMPLE 5

A locker combination is made up of three numbers from 0 through 99. How many different locker combinations can there be?

Order is important. For example, the combination 53-12-76 is not the same as 12-53-76.

Use the Fundamental Counting Principle. A number may be repeated in the combination. There are 100 choices for the first number, 100 choices for the second number, and 100 choices for the third number.

The number of possible locker combinations is $100 \cdot 100 \cdot 100 = 1,000,000$.

Combinations

How Many Choices?

Choosing people from a group to be on a committee is different from choosing officers of a club or awarding prizes for first, second, and third place in a race. For a committee, the order in which the members are chosen is *not* important. On a committee, the pair "Winton and Alice" is the same as the pair "Alice and Winton."

A selection of items, events, or people from a set without regard to the order is a **combination**. Suppose a group consists of 10 items and 6 of them are chosen and placed in a box. If their order in the box doesn't matter, the set of 6 items is a combination. This is an example of 10 items taken 6 at a time.

SEARCH

To see step-by-step videos of these problems, enter the page number into the SWadvantage.com Search Bar.

EXAMPLE 1

The science department has 8 teachers. Three of the teachers will be chosen to be on a committee. How many different combinations of 3 teachers chosen from the group of 8 teachers are there?

Science Department Teachers			
Ms. Wong	Mr. Riccio	Mrs. Neel	Mr. Costero
Mr. Singh	Ms. Ueda	Mr. Ramirez	Mrs. deVore

If the order of the teachers were important, the number would be $_8P_3$.

$$_8P_3 = \frac{8!}{(8-3)!} = \frac{8!}{5!} = 8 \cdot 7 \cdot 6 = 336$$

However, this number is too high, because it includes groups of teachers that have exactly the same members but in different orders. Since order does <u>not</u> matter in this case, we want to eliminate groups that have the same members as another in a different order.

There are 3!, or 6, ways to arrange 3 teachers in different orders.

To cancel the effect of repeated groups, divide the number of permutations of 8 items taken 3 at a time, 336, by the number of permutations of 3 items, 6.

$$\frac{336}{6} = 56$$

There are 56 different combinations of 8 teachers taken 3 at a time.

Although both combinations and permutations are calculated from a ratio, the result is always a whole number. For example, there cannot be a fractional number of committees formed.

The Combinations Formula

Just as for permutations, there is a formula for combinations. Again, the number of combinations you can choose from a set does not depend on what the elements of the set are. You can choose 3 teachers from a group of 8 in 56 different ways, and you can choose 3 books from a group of 8 in 56 different ways.

You can use this notation to write the combinations in Example 1.

$$_8C_3$$

number of members in the set ⟶   ⟵ number in each combination

In general, this is written $_nC_r$ and is read "n choose r."

As shown in Example 1, the formula for combinations is based on the formula for permutations. Start with the permutation formula, and then divide by r! to eliminate the common permutations:

$$_nC_r = \frac{n!}{r!(n-r)!}$$

Try It
This Way

Many scientific and graphing calculators have a combination function, labeled $_nC_r$. It may be a second function on a scientific calculator or may be on the MATH menu of a graphing calculator.

EXAMPLE 2

There are 4 CDs that Jeremy wants to buy, but he has enough money for only 2 of them. How many different combinations of 2 of the 4 CDs are possible?

Notice that order is not important, since buying CD 1 and CD 2 is the same as buying CD 2 and CD 1.

Use the combinations formula for n items taken r at a time with n = 4 and r = 2.

$$_nC_r = \frac{n!}{r!(n-r)!}$$

Substitute 4 for n and 2 for r. $$_4C_2 = \frac{4!}{2!(4-2)!}$$

Simplify. $$= \frac{4!}{2!2!}$$

$$= \frac{24}{4}$$

$$= 6$$

There are 6 different combinations of 2 of the 4 CDs that Jeremy wants.

Combinations

The formula for n items taken r at a time is $_nC_r = \frac{n!}{r!(n-r)!}$.

$_nC_r$ is read "n choose r."

$_nC_r$ may also be written as $\binom{n}{r}$ or $C(n, r)$.

Using the Combinations Formula

It is not always necessary to find the values of the factorials in the combinations formula. You can rewrite the numerator of the fraction to include one of the factors of the denominator and then use canceling to simplify the calculation.

EXAMPLE 3

A party supply store has 12 colors of balloons. The homecoming committee wants to choose 4 of the colors to decorate the gymnasium. How many ways can they choose 4 different colors?

The committee needs to find how many combinations of 4 colors it can choose from a set of 12 balloon colors. The order is not important. For example, the color group {red, orange, yellow, green} is the same as the group {orange, red, green, yellow}.

Use the formula for $_nC_r$.

$$_nC_r = \frac{n!}{r!(n-r)!}$$

Substitute 12 for n and 4 for r.

$$_{12}C_4 = \frac{12!}{4!(12-4)!}$$

Simplify.

$$= \frac{12!}{4!8!}$$

Factor 8! out of 12!.

$$= \frac{12 \cdot 11 \cdot 10 \cdot 9 \cdot 8!}{4 \cdot 3 \cdot 2 \cdot 1 \cdot 8!}$$

Cancel.

$$= \frac{\cancel{12} \cdot 11 \cdot \cancel{10}^{5} \cdot 9 \cdot \cancel{8!}}{\cancel{4} \cdot \cancel{3} \cdot \cancel{2} \cdot 1 \cdot \cancel{8!}}$$

$$= 11 \cdot 5 \cdot 9$$

$$= 495$$

There are 495 ways to choose 4 colors from a group of 12 colors.

EXAMPLE 4

A cable television company has room for 5 more channels. There are 9 possible channels from which to choose. How many combinations can the cable company consider?

The cable company needs to find how many combinations of 5 channels it can choose from a set of 9 channels. Notice that the order is not important in this case. Find the value of $_9C_5$:

$$_9C_5 = \frac{9!}{5!4!}$$

Factor 5! out of 9!.

$$= \frac{9 \cdot 8 \cdot 7 \cdot 6 \cdot 5!}{5! \cdot 4 \cdot 3 \cdot 2 \cdot 1}$$

Cancel.

$$= \frac{9 \cdot \cancel{8} \cdot 7 \cdot \cancel{6}^{2} \cdot \cancel{5!}}{\cancel{5!} \cdot \cancel{4} \cdot \cancel{3} \cdot \cancel{2} \cdot 1}$$

$$= 9 \cdot 7 \cdot 2$$

$$= 126$$

There are 126 ways in which the cable company can select 5 channels from the 9 choices.

Special Cases of Combinations

It may seem strange that 0! is defined to be 1. There are no natural numbers less than 0 to multiply by 0, and it might seem that any product involving 0 should be 0. However, a special case of combinations can help explain why $0! = 1$.

EXAMPLE 5

There are 3 open seats on a city council, and 3 people are running for city council. In how many different ways can the city council seats be filled?

Since order is not important in this case, there is only one way that the 3 seats can be filled by 3 people. Therefore, the answer must be 1. Check to see what the result of the formula is for $_3C_3$.

$$_3C_3 = \frac{3!}{3!(3-3)!}$$

$$= \frac{3!}{3!0!}$$

This value is equal to 1 if and only if $0! = 1$.

SEARCH

To see step-by-step videos of these problems, enter the page number into the SWadvantage.com Search Bar.

In general, the value of $_nC_n$ is equal to 1. Such a combination is sometimes called a **combinatorial identity**.

Another special feature of combinations is that choosing r items from a group of n gives the same result as choosing $n - r$ items from a group of n.

EXAMPLE 6

Adriana has 6 books. She wants to choose some to take with her on a trip.

a. How many different combinations are there if she chooses 2 books to bring with her?

Find the value of 6 items taken 2 at a time: $_6C_2 = \frac{6!}{2!(6-2)!}$

$$= \frac{6 \cdot 5 \cdot 4!}{2! \cdot 4!}$$

$$= 15$$

b. How many different combinations are there if she chooses 4 books to bring with her?

Find the value of 6 items taken 4 at a time: $_6C_4 = \frac{6!}{4!(6-4)!}$

$$= \frac{6 \cdot 5 \cdot 4!}{4! \cdot 2!}$$

$$= 15$$

Notice that the values found in parts (a) and (b) are the same. This is because when Adriana chooses 2 books, she leaves 4 behind. Since the order of neither group is important, choosing 4 books and leaving behind a group of 2 gives the same result as choosing 2 and leaving behind 4.

Choosing the Combinations or Permutations Formula

Sometimes a problem does not specify whether it involves a combination or a permutation. In that case, part of solving the problem is deciding which formula to use. It is helpful to know the key features of each. The table in Example 7 shows all the choices for both, using equal values for n and r.

SEARCH

To see step-by-step videos of these problems, enter the page number into the SWadvantage.com Search Bar.

EXAMPLE 7

Use the set of 5 letters {A, B, C, D, E}. Compare choosing 2 letters from the set for a combination with choosing 2 letters from the set for a permutation.

List all the elements of $_5C_2$ and $_5P_2$.

$_5C_2$			
AB	BC	CD	DE
AC	BD	CE	
AD	BE		
AE			

$_5P_2$				
AB	BA	CA	DA	EA
AC	BC	CB	DB	EB
AD	BD	CD	DC	EC
AE	BE	CE	DE	ED

In the permutations, the group of 2 letters AB is different from the group BA, because the order is important.

In the combinations, all the repeated groups like this have been eliminated, so there are fewer groups altogether.

The value of $_5C_2$ is 10, and the value of $_5P_2$ is 20.

EXAMPLE 8

The Lee family is planning to take 3 cats home from an animal shelter. There are 11 cats at the shelter. In how many different ways can the Lees choose 3 cats?

STEP 1 Decide whether this situation is a combination or a permutation.

Since the cats will not be in any order once they are chosen, it is a combination.

STEP 2 Use the formula for $_nC_r$ with $n = 11$ and $r = 3$.

$$_{11}C_3 = \frac{11!}{3! \cdot (11 - 3)!}$$
$$= \frac{11 \cdot 10 \cdot 9 \cdot 8!}{3 \cdot 2 \cdot 8!}$$
$$= 165$$

There are 165 different ways in which the Lees can choose 3 cats from the 11 cats at the shelter.

EXAMPLE 9

Eli has been asked to make a list of his top 5 songs, to be played in order at a school graduation party. He has made a list of 14 favorite songs. In how many different ways can he select his top 5 songs from this list?

STEP 1 Decide whether this situation is a combination or a permutation.

Since the order of Eli's top 5 songs is important, this is a permutation.

STEP 2 Use the formula for $_nP_r$ with $n = 14$ and $r = 5$.

$$_nP_r = \frac{n!}{(n-r)!}$$

$$_{14}P_5 = \frac{14!}{(14-5)!}$$

$$= \frac{14!}{9!} = \frac{14 \cdot 13 \cdot 12 \cdot 11 \cdot 10 \cdot 9!}{9!}$$

$$= 240{,}240$$

There are 240,240 different ways in which Eli can list his top 5 songs from a group of 14 favorite songs.

Comparing Combinations and Permutations

Combinations	Permutations
The order of the chosen items is *not* important.	The order of the chosen items is important.
$_nC_r = \dfrac{n!}{r!(n-r)!}$	$_nP_r = \dfrac{n!}{(n-r)!}$
The chosen items are in a group.	The chosen items form a list.
There are fewer possible chosen groups, because the group A, B, for example, is the same as the group B, A.	There are more possible chosen groups, because the list A, B, for example, is different from the list B, A.
The denominator in the formula is greater than the denominator in the formula for $_nP_r$, making the quotient a smaller number.	The denominator in the formula is less than the denominator in the formula for $_nC_r$, making the quotient a larger number.
Symmetric: $_nC_r = {_nC_{n-r}}$	Not symmetric: $_nP_r \neq {_nP_{n-r}}$
$_nC_n = 1$	$_nP_n = n!$
A combination is a permutation with the effect of repeated groups eliminated.	A permutation is an ordered combination.

Odds and Complements

Finding Odds

You might have heard someone say, "What are the odds of that happening?" *Odds* are a way of stating the likelihood of an event. The **odds** of an event are a comparison of the number of favorable outcomes with the number of unfavorable outcomes.

Favorable outcomes	Unfavorable outcomes

← Total number of outcomes →

Odds in favor of an event $= \dfrac{\text{number of favorable outcomes}}{\text{number of unfavorable outcomes}}$

Odds against the event $= \dfrac{\text{number of unfavorable outcomes}}{\text{number of favorable outcomes}}$

The odds may be written as a fraction, a ratio, or as a phrase such as "one to four."

Watch Out !

Because the problem is asking for odds, not probability, the denominator of the fraction is *not* the total number of outcomes.

EXAMPLE 1

A number cube numbered 1 through 6 is rolled. What are the odds in favor of rolling a 3?

There are six possible outcomes. There is 1 favorable outcome, rolling a 3. The other 5 outcomes are unfavorable.

Odds in favor of rolling a 3 $= \dfrac{\text{number of favorable outcomes}}{\text{number of unfavorable outcomes}} = \dfrac{1}{5}$

The odds in favor of rolling a 3 are $\frac{1}{5}$, or 1 : 5.

SEARCH

To see step-by-step videos of these problems, enter the page number into the SWadvantage.com Search Bar.

EXAMPLE 2

Two coins are tossed. What are the odds against both coins landing tails up?

Make a list or a tree diagram to show the possible outcomes.

1st Coin	2nd Coin	Outcome
Heads (H)	(H)	H, H
	(T)	H, T
Tails (T)	(H)	T, H
	(T)	T, T

There are four possible outcomes: 1 favorable and 3 unfavorable.

Odds against both coins landing tails up $= \dfrac{\text{number of unfavorable outcomes}}{\text{number of favorable outcomes}} = \dfrac{3}{1}$

The odds against both coins landing tails up are 3 : 1, or 3 to 1.

Complementary Events

In Example 1, there are 6 possible outcomes of rolling the number cube. They can be divided into two events, rolling a 3 and not rolling a 3. Two events that make up all the possible outcomes of an experiment are called **complementary events**.

Each event is called the **complement** of the other. In general, the sum of the probabilities of two complementary events is 1. You can use this information to find unknown probabilities.

Probability of event	Probability of complement

$\xleftarrow{\hspace{3cm}} 1 \xrightarrow{\hspace{3cm}}$

EXAMPLE 3

The probability of a winning a game is $\frac{2}{5}$. There are no tied games. Find the probability of losing the game.

Winning the game and losing the game are complementary events. The probability of winning and the probability of losing add up to 1.

$$P(\text{winning}) + P(\text{losing}) = 1$$
$$P(\text{losing}) = 1 - P(\text{winning})$$
$$= 1 - \frac{2}{5}$$
$$= \frac{3}{5}$$

The probability of losing the game is $\frac{3}{5}$.

Need More
HELP
For help with finding probability, go to *Theoretical Probability* on pages 1232–1235.

Got to KNOW!

Odds and Complements

Favorable outcomes	Unfavorable outcomes

$\xleftarrow{\hspace{2cm}}$ Total number of outcomes $\xrightarrow{\hspace{2cm}}$

The odds of an event are a ratio of favorable outcomes and unfavorable outcomes. The following formulas apply when the outcomes are equally likely to happen.

$$\text{Odds in favor of an event} = \frac{\text{number of favorable outcomes}}{\text{number of unfavorable outcomes}}$$

$$\text{Odds against an event} = \frac{\text{number of unfavorable outcomes}}{\text{number of favorable outcomes}}$$

$$\text{The probability of an event is} = \frac{\text{number of favorable outcomes}}{\text{total number of outcomes}}.$$

If two events, A and B, are complements, then $P(A) + P(B) = 1$.

Using Complements

Sometimes when you need to find the probability of an event, it is easier to find the probability of the complement of the event. Then subtract the probability of the complement from 1 to find the probability of the event.

EXAMPLE 4

The spinner shown at the right has four equal sections and is spun twice. What is the probability of spinning an even number at least once?

METHOD 1

Find the probability directly.

There are 4 choices for the first spin and 4 choices for the second spin, so there are 16 possible outcomes.

Make a tree diagram to list the outcomes.

Highlight the outcomes that have "at least one even number."

There are 12 favorable outcomes (at least one even number).

P(at least one even number) $= \dfrac{12}{16} = \dfrac{3}{4}$

The probability that at least one spin lands on an even number is $\dfrac{3}{4}$.

First spin	Second spin	Outcome
1	1	(1, 1)
	2	(1, 2)
	3	(1, 3)
	4	(1, 4)
2	1	(2, 1)
	2	(2, 2)
	3	(2, 3)
	4	(2, 4)
3	1	(3, 1)
	2	(3, 2)
	3	(3, 3)
	4	(3, 4)
4	1	(4, 1)
	2	(4, 2)
	3	(4, 3)
	4	(4, 4)

METHOD 2

Find the probability of the complement of the event.

The complement is that both numbers are odd. (You can also think of this as neither number being even.)

List these outcomes without making a tree diagram: (1, 1), (1, 3), (3, 1), and (3, 3).

There are four outcomes, so P(both numbers are odd) $= \dfrac{4}{16} = \dfrac{1}{4}$.

Subtract the complement from 1: P(at least one number is even) $= 1 - \dfrac{1}{4} = \dfrac{3}{4}$.

The probability that at least one spin lands on an even number is $\dfrac{3}{4}$.

Got to KNOW!

Probability of the Complement of an Event

The probability of an event E is equal to the probability of the complement C subtracted from 1.

$P(E) = 1 - P(C)$

EXAMPLE 5

There are 16 boys and 12 girls on the chess team. One-half of the boys and one-half of the girls won their most recent match. If you choose a team member at random, what is the probability that you will choose a girl, a recent match winner, or both?

Find the probability of the complement of the event.

Events: girl—recent match winner—both (girl who is a recent match winner)

Complement: boy who is not a recent match winner

$$P(\text{boy who did not win recently}) = \frac{\text{number of boys who did not with their most recent match}}{\text{total number of chess team members}}$$

$$= \frac{8}{28} = \frac{2}{7}$$

Subtract the complement from 1: $P(\text{girl, recent match winner, or both}) = 1 - \frac{2}{7} = \frac{5}{7}$.

The probability that a chess team member chosen at random is a girl, a recent match winner, or both is $\frac{5}{7}$.

SEARCH

To see step-by-step videos of these problems, enter the page number into the SWadvantage.com Search Bar.

EXAMPLE 6

Find the probability that any two people in a group of six have the same birthday. Use 365 for the number of days in a year. (You may want to use a calculator.)

Find the probability of the complement of the event. The complement of "any two people have the same birthday" is "no two people have the same birthday."

STEP 1 Find the total number of ways that 6 people can have 6 *different* birthdays.

Think of a calendar with all 365 days of the year on it. Each of the six people will write his or her name on a date on the calendar. The first person has 365 choices. The second person does not have the same birthday, and has only 364 choices. The third person has only 363 choices, and so on.
The product of the six choices is $365 \cdot 364 \cdot 363 \cdot 362 \cdot 361 \cdot 360$.

STEP 2 Find the total number of ways that 6 people can have *any six* birthdays.

There are 6 people, and each person has 365 different choices. The total is 365^6.

STEP 3 Find the probability that no two people in six have the same birthday.

$$P(\text{no two with same birthday}) = \frac{\text{number of ways 6 people can have 6 different birthdays}}{\text{total number of ways 6 people can have 6 birthdays}}$$

$$= \frac{365 \cdot 364 \cdot 363 \cdot 362 \cdot 361 \cdot 360}{365 \cdot 365 \cdot 365 \cdot 365 \cdot 365 \cdot 365}$$

$$\approx 0.96$$

The probability that no two people in a group of six have the same birthday is about 96%.

STEP 4 Find the probability that any two people in six have the same birthday.

$P(\text{two people have the same birthday}) \approx 1 - 0.96 = 0.04$, or 4%

The probability that any two people in a group of six have the same birthday is about 4%.

Watch Out !

Remember that 6 is the number of people, and 365 is the number of possible outcomes for each person. The Fundamental Counting Principle tells us to multiply all the numbers of outcomes together, so the product is $365 \cdot 365 \cdot 365 \cdot 365 \cdot 365 \cdot 365 = 365^6$, not $365 \cdot 6$.

Displaying Data

What Came Before?
• Bar graphs, line graphs, circle graphs, and pictographs
• Mean, median, mode, and range of data

What's This About?
• Displaying one or two data sets on graphs, plots, and diagrams
• Reading and interpreting data shown on graphs, plots, and diagrams
• Choosing an appropriate graph for displaying data

Practical Apps
• Elected officials often use data displays to support their positions and recommendations.
• Sound technicians in the music industry rely on data displays to mix sound tracks to achieve the best sound.

Just for FUN!

Q: Why didn't the cat make a bar graph?

A: She preferred a box-and-whisker plot.

Topics	Vocabulary	Pages
Frequency	*frequency* *relative frequency* *cumulative frequency*	1260–1263
Scatter Plots	*scatter plot*	1264–1265
Histograms	*histogram* *frequency polygon*	1266–1269
Choosing an Appropriate Graph	*bar graph* *line graph* *circle graph*	1270–1275
Stem-and-Leaf Plots	*stem-and-leaf plot* *median* *range* *mean* *mode*	1276–1279
Box-and-Whisker Plots	*box-and-whisker plot* *lower extreme* *upper extreme* *lower quartile* *upper quartile* *interquartile range* *outlier*	1280–1283
Displaying Two Data Sets	*double-bar graph* *double-line graph* *trend* *double stem-and-leaf plot*	1284–1287
Venn Diagrams	*Venn diagram* *set theory* *universe* *set* *subset* *intersection* *union* *complement*	1288–1291

You can find more practice problems online by visiting: **www.SWadvantage.com**

Frequency

Frequency Tables

In a data set, **frequency** is the number of times an event, a number, or a range of events occurs. Frequency is often shown on a frequency table like the one below. A **tally** shows the number of times an event occurs. Count the number of tallies to find the frequency.

Where do you get your news?

Source	Tally	Frequency
Internet	|||	3
Print	||	2
Television	ⅢⅠ ||	7
Radio	||||	4

The frequency table above shows that most people represented on the table get their news by watching television. The frequency of television is 7.

EXAMPLE 1

Victor rolled a 0–6 number cube a number of times. He made a tally each time he rolled a number. Use the table to find the frequency of Victor rolling the number 3 in this experiment.

Victor's Experiment

Number	Tally	Frequency
1	ⅢⅠ |	6
2	||	2
3	ⅢⅠ	?
4	|||	3
5	|	1
6	ⅢⅠ ||||	9

STEP 1 Read down the **Number** column to the row for rolling a 3.

STEP 2 Read across to the **Tally** column.

STEP 3 Count the tally marks.

There are five tallies, so the frequency for rolling the number 3 in this experiment is 5.

Try It This Way

Place your fingertip on the word *Number*. Then move your finger down to the 3 row and across to the tally marks. Count the tally marks and write the answer.

EXAMPLE 2

The types of computers preferred by some students in one middle school are shown in the frequency table below. What is the ratio of laptops to desktops?

Which do you prefer?

Computer	Tally	Frequency
Laptop	~~卌~~ ~~卌~~ ~~卌~~ ~~卌~~ l	21
Desktop	~~卌~~ ~~卌~~ ~~卌~~ lll	18
Tablet	~~卌~~ llll	9

STEP 1 Find the number of students who prefer laptops.
The table shows that 21 students prefer laptops.

STEP 2 Find the number of students who prefer desktops.
The table shows that 18 students prefer desktops.

STEP 3 Write the ratio of laptops to desktops.
$\frac{21}{18} = \frac{21 \div 3}{18 \div 3} = \frac{7}{6}$ or 7:6

The ratio of students who prefer laptops to desktops is 7:6.

Need More
HELP

For help with ratios, go to *Writing and Simplifying Ratios* in *Numbers and Operations* (Book 1, p. 364).

EXAMPLE 3

The table shows the range of the number of paintings sold by vendors at the crafts fair. How many more vendors sold at least 16 paintings than vendors who sold at most 15 paintings?

Number of Paintings Sold	Frequency
1–5	1
6–10	2
11–15	10
16–20	18
21–25	3

STEP 1 Find the number of vendors who sold at least 16 paintings. $18 + 3 = 21$

STEP 2 Find the number of vendors who sold at most 15 paintings. $1 + 2 + 10 = 13$

STEP 3 Subtract to find the difference. $21 - 13 = 8$

There were 8 more vendors who sold at least 16 paintings than those who sold at most 15 paintings.

SEARCH

To see step-by-step videos of these problems, enter the page number into the SWadvantage.com Search Bar.

Need More

HELP ?

For help with writing fractions as decimals or percents, go to *Decimals, Fractions, and Percents* in *Numbers and Operations* (Book 1, p. 272).

Relative Frequency

In a data set, the **relative frequency** of an event is a ratio of the number of times the event occurs and the total number of events. The relative frequency can be expressed as a fraction, decimal, or percent.

 **EXAMPLE 4**

Data for a Saturday night at a restaurant is shown. What is the relative frequency of dinner reservations for a table for 5?

Reservation	Frequency
Table for 2	12
Table for 4	9
Table for 5	8
Table for 6	3

STEP 1 Find the frequency for a reservation for a table for 5.   8

STEP 2 Add to find the total number of reservations.
$12 + 9 + 8 + 3 = 32$

STEP 3 Express the frequencies as a ratio in simplest form.

$\dfrac{\text{frequency of a table for 5}}{\text{total number of reservations}} = \dfrac{8}{32}$, which simplifies to $\dfrac{1}{4}$.

The relative frequency of a reservation for a table for 5 is $\dfrac{1}{4}$ of the total reservations.

EXAMPLE 5

Elena is keeping track of the Field Day results. Use the frequency table to find what percent of the games Grade 8 won.

Winner	Frequency
Grade 5	4
Grade 6	6
Grade 7	8
Grade 8	6

STEP 1 Find the number of games won by Grade 8.   6

STEP 2 Add to find the total number of games played.
$4 + 6 + 8 + 6 = 24$

STEP 3 Write a ratio and express it as a percent.
$\dfrac{6}{24} = 0.25$, or 25%

Grade 8 won 25% of the Field Day games.

Got to
KNOW!

Terms to Know

Frequency is the number of times an event, a number, or a range of events occurs.

Relative Frequency is a ratio of the number of times an event occurs to the total number of events in question.

Cumulative Frequency is the sum of the frequencies of the data up to a given level.

Cumulative Frequency

In a data set, the **cumulative frequency** is the sum of the frequencies of the data up to a given level. For example, the table below shows the number of cars washed during a one-week period. The cumulative frequency for Fri–Sat is the sum of the frequency for that interval and the frequency of the intervals that come before it.

Days	Frequency	Cumulative Frequency
Mon–Tue	10	10
Wed–Thu	11	10 + 11 = 21
Fri–Sat	23	**10 + 11 + 23 = 44**
Sun	15	10 + 11 + 23 + 15 = 59

EXAMPLE 6

The table shows the number of volcanic eruptions between Year 1 and Year 8. Find the missing cumulative frequencies to complete the table.

Years	Frequency	Cumulative Frequency
Year 1–Year 2	8	8
Year 3–Year 4	17	8 + 17 = 25
Year 5–Year 6	31	?
Year 7–Year 8	29	?

SEARCH

To see step-by-step videos of these problems, enter the page number into the SWadvantage.com Search Bar.

STEP 1 Add to find the cumulative frequency for Year 1–Year 6.
8 + 17 + 31 = 56

STEP 2 Add to find the cumulative frequency for Year 1–Year 8.
8 + 17 + 31 + 29 = 85

STEP 3 Place the equations in the table.

Years	Frequency	Cumulative Frequency
Year 1–Year 2	8	8
Year 3–Year 4	17	8 + 17 = 25
Year 5–Year 6	31	8 + 17 + 31 = 56
Year 7–Year 8	29	8 + 17 + 31 + 29 = 85

Scatter Plots

What Is a Scatter Plot?

Paired data are sometimes displayed in a data table like the one below. Such data can also be displayed on a *scatter plot*. A **scatter plot** is a graph that shows data points on a coordinate grid. Each data point represents a pair of values.

Need More
HELP ?
Here are other names used for scatter plots.
• scattergram
• scatter diagram
• scatter graph
• scatter chart

EXAMPLE 1

Display the data in the table on a scatter plot.

Total Weight	2 lb	2.5 lb	5 lb	6 lb	6.5 lb	7.5 lb	8 lb
No. of Pears	4	5	6	7	8	9	10

STEP 1 The information in the table tells the total weights of different numbers of pears. The title of the scatter plot could be Pear Weights.

Use the information in the table to label a graph.

STEP 2 Using the paired data, write the coordinates for each data point. (2, 4) (2.5, 5) (5, 6) (6, 7) (6.5, 8) (7.5, 9) (8, 10)

STEP 3 Plot the data points on the scatter plot.

Need More
HELP ?
For help with plotting points, go to *The Coordinate Plane* in *Algebra* (p. 1442).

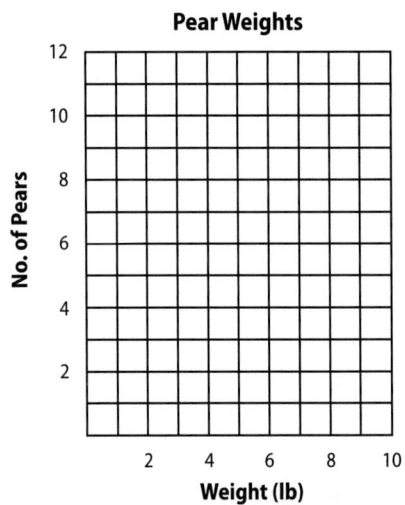

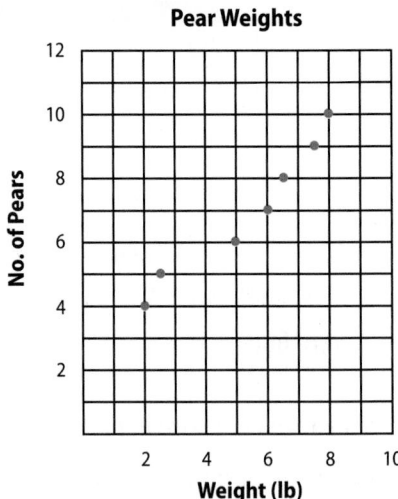

Reading a Scatter Plot

You can record the information on a scatter plot in a data table. Use the labels of the x- and y-axes as the row heads for the data table. Use the coordinates of each point as the data in the table.

EXAMPLE 2

A booth at a street fair has gift items that cost less than $10. The scatter plot shows the prices of the items and the number of items offered at each price. For example, there are ten items that cost $2.

Use the scatter plot to complete the data table below.

The *x*-axis shows the prices of the items. The *y*-axis shows the number of items available at each price. Find the coordinates for each data point, starting with the one on the left.

- The first data point is at (2, 10). There are 10 items that cost $2.00.

- The second data point is at (4.5, 9). There are 9 items that cost $4.50.

- Continue adding coordinates to the table until all the data points on the graph are shown on the table.

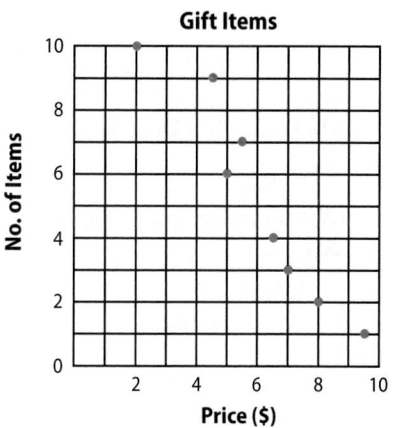

Gift Items

Price	$2.00	$4.50	$5.00	$5.50	$6.50	$7.00	$8.00	$9.50
No. of Items	10	9	6	7	4	3	2	1

Ways to REMEMBER

The first number in an ordered pair represents a data point's position along the horizontal axis, or *x*-axis. The second number represents its position along the vertical axis, or *y*-axis.

To recall this order, remember that *h* comes before *v* in the alphabet. To recall the directions of the axes, think, "*y* points up to the sky."

EXAMPLE 3

Team A played 8 rounds of a game and scored a total of 350 points. The data table shows the total points scored by the end of each round. For example, by the end of round 5, Team A had scored a total of 200 points.

Round	1	2	3	4	5	6	7	8
Total Score	50	75	125	150	200	250	275	350

One of the players on the team displayed the data on a scatter plot but made a mistake. Identify the data point on the scatter plot that is plotted incorrectly.

The table shows that the total score after round 6 is 250. The data point is incorrectly placed at (6, 225) on the scatter plot. The red point shows the correct placement.

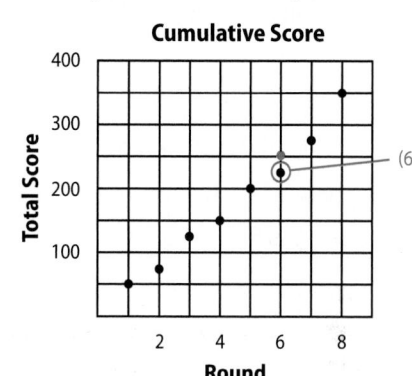

Cumulative Score

(6, 225) should be (6, 250).

SEARCH

To see step-by-step videos of these problems, enter the page number into the SWadvantage.com Search Bar.

Histograms

Reading a Histogram

A **histogram** displays the frequency of a set of data in equal-size intervals, or ranges of data. Because the intervals are equal in size, the bars on a histogram have equal width. There are no spaces between the bars on a histogram because there are no spaces between the intervals.

Need More
HELP

Another name for a histogram is a histograph.

For help with frequency, go to *Frequency* on page 1260.

SEARCH 🔍

To see step-by-step videos of these problems, enter the page number into the SWadvantage.com Search Bar.

EXAMPLE 1

Each week the newspaper lists the 25 top-selling fiction books, known as best sellers. The histogram below shows information about this week's best sellers. Use the labels on the histogram to help you understand the data displayed on it.

The *x*-axis label is "Weeks on List." The *x*-axis numbers are intervals, such as 1 to 5. These intervals are ranges of the numbers of weeks that this week's best sellers have been on the list.

The *y*-axis label is "Number of Titles." The scale is 0 to 14. Use this scale to measure the heights of the bars on the histogram. This will tell you how many book titles have been on the best-seller list for a certain period of time (range of weeks).

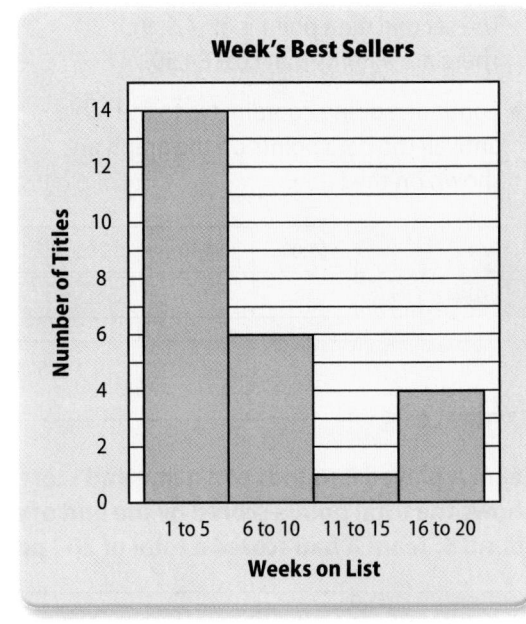

a. **How many of this week's best sellers have been on the list for 5 weeks or less?**

The height of the bar for 1 to 5 "Weeks on List" is 14. Fourteen books have been on the list 5 weeks or less.

b. **What time interval represents the least number of books?**

The shortest bar is for the interval 11 to 15. Its height is 1. This means that only 1 book has been on the list for 11, 12, 13, 14, or 15 weeks.

c. **The sum of the heights of the four bars should be what number? Why?**

The sum of the heights should equal 25 because there are 25 books on the best-seller list.

CHECK Add the heights of the bars.

1 to 5		6 to 10		11 to 15		16 to 20		
14	+	6	+	1	+	4	=	25 ✔

Use a Frequency Table to Make a Histogram

EXAMPLE 2

Twenty-seven students estimated the distance from their houses to school. They displayed the estimates on a frequency table.

Distance *d* (miles)	$0 < d < 2$	$2 \leq d < 4$	$4 \leq d < 6$	$6 \leq d < 8$	$8 \leq d < 10$
Tally	||	||||| ||	||||| ||||	|||||	||||
Frequency	2	7	9	5	4

Display the data on a histogram.

STEP 1 Draw and label the axes of the histogram.

- Let the *x*-axis represent the distance.
- Use the intervals on the table to label the *x*-axis. For example, the first interval shown on the frequency table is $0 < d < 2$.
- Let the *y*-axis represent the number of students.
- The range of the *y*-axis scale should go from zero to the greatest frequency of students, 9.

STEP 2 Add the bars to the histogram.

- Use the information on the frequency table to draw a bar for the frequency of each interval. For example, a frequency of 2 means 2 students.
- Give the histogram a title that describes the data on it. A possible title for this histogram is "Distance from Home to School."

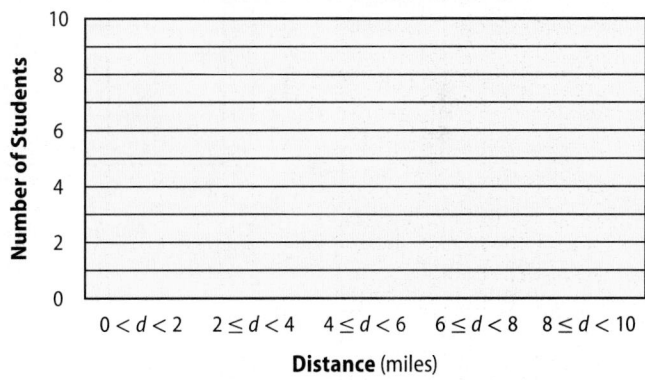

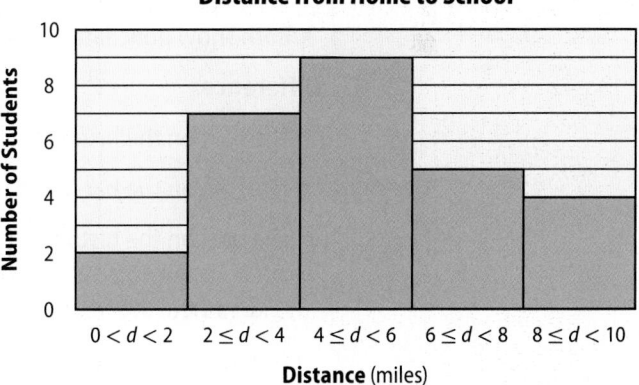

Histograms

The bars on a histogram represent frequency of data in equal-size intervals. Inequality symbols are sometimes used to label the intervals.

Histograms and Bar Graphs

 EXAMPLE 3

SEARCH

To see step-by-step videos of these problems, enter the page number into the SWadvantage.com Search Bar.

Compare and contrast the data displays below. What are three similarities and three differences between the histogram and the bar graph?

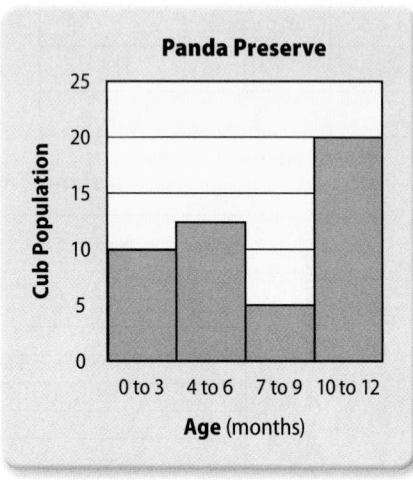

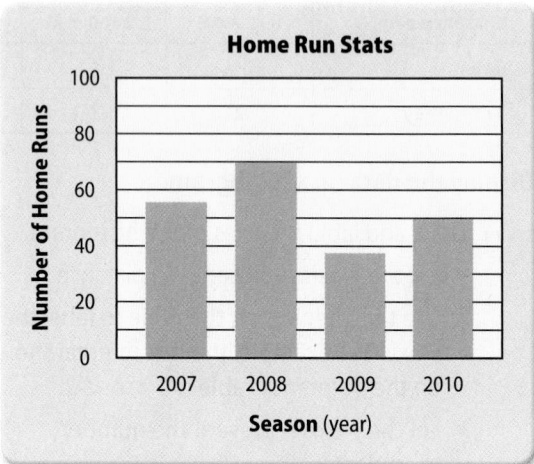

Similarities

- Both have bars, and display the data using the lengths of the bars.

- Both have an *x*-axis and a *y*-axis.

- Both show how data are related or are not related.

Differences

- The bars on the histogram represent frequency within intervals.

- The bars on the bar graph represent specific numbers or quantities.

- The bars on the histogram are connected because there are no gaps between the intervals. All data values are included in the intervals. While the frequency of each interval is identified, the frequency of specific data values is not shown on the graph.

- The bars on a bar graph are not connected because the data are not continuous. For example, you could label the axes of the bar graph above "Favorite Color" and "No. of Students" or "State" and "Population (millions)."

Frequency and Intervals

By convention, in histograms frequency is shown on the *y*-axis, while intervals are shown on the *x*-axis.

Frequency Polygon

A **frequency polygon** is a graph of the data in a frequency table and it shows the midpoints of the intervals, which you can use to estimate the mean.

EXAMPLE 4

Joshua is germinating daisy seedlings for the nature center greenhouse. He records the height of each seedling. Use the information on his frequency table to draw a frequency polygon. Then estimate the mean height of the seedlings.

Height h (cm)	$0 \le h < 2$	$2 \le h < 4$	$4 \le h < 6$	$6 \le h < 8$
Frequency	8	10	12	4

The frequency table shows frequency using the variable h for height. The frequency $0 \le h < 2$ means that the height of a seedling is equal to or greater than zero but less than 2 cm.

STEP 1 Make a histogram of the data. Label the x-axis "Height (cm)" and the y-axis "Frequency." *(See graph below.)*

STEP 2 Find and plot the midpoint of each height interval. Use the ordered pair (height, frequency). Then connect the dots.

- $0 \le h < 2$; 1 cm is the midpoint; the first ordered pair is (1, 8).
- $2 \le h < 4$; 3 cm is the midpoint; the second ordered pair is (3, 10).
- $4 \le h < 6$; 5 cm is the midpoint; the third ordered pair is (5, 12).
- $6 \le h < 8$; 7 cm is the midpoint; the fourth ordered pair is (7, 4).

STEP 3 Estimate the mean (average) height of the seedlings.

$(1 \times 8) + (3 \times 10) + (5 \times 12) + (7 \times 4)$
$= 8 + 30 + 60 + 28$
$= 126$ total height

$8 + 10 + 12 + 4$
$= 34$ seedlings

$126 \div 34$
≈ 3.71

The mean height of the seedlings is about 3.71 cm.

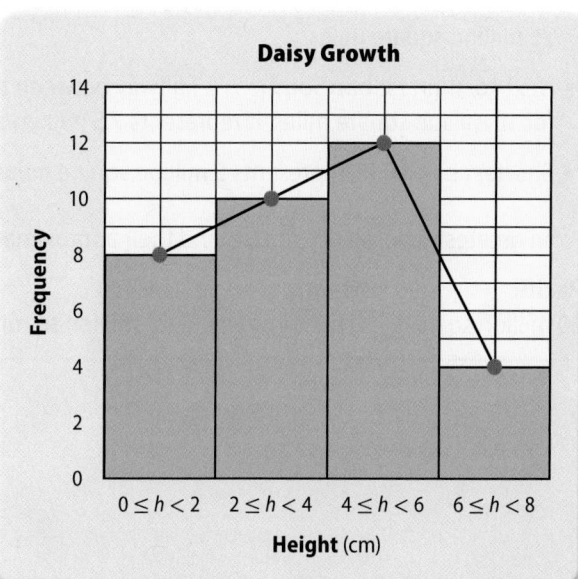

Choosing an Appropriate Graph

Bar Graphs

A **bar graph** uses horizontal or vertical bars to display numerical data that fall into categories. It is a good choice for displaying data you want to be able to compare easily.

EXAMPLE 1

Need More
HELP ?

For more about bar graphs, go to *Bar Graphs* in *Foundations of Mathematics* (Book 1, p. 188).

Use the bar graph to list the names of the world's oceans and their areas from greatest to least.

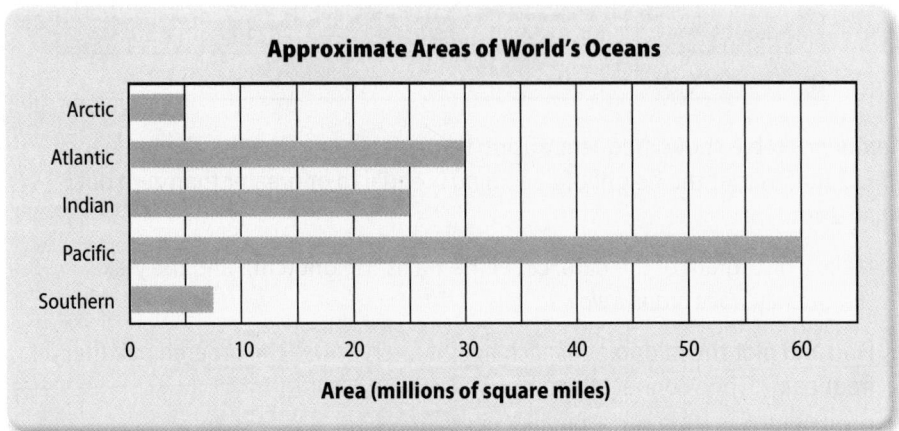

In this bar graph each interval represents 5 million square miles, although only the intervals that are even multiples of 10 million are labeled. Compare the lengths of the bars to order the data.

Watch Out !

When reading a bar graph, pay attention to the scale and the value of each interval.

- Longest bar: Pacific represents the greatest area, 60 million square miles.

- Next-longest bar: Atlantic represents 30 million square miles.

- Third-longest bar: Indian is halfway between 20 and 30 million square miles. It represents 25 million square miles.

- Next-to-shortest bar: Southern is halfway between the unlabeled mark for 5 and the mark for 10 million square miles. It represents 7.5 million square miles.

- Shortest bar: Arctic represents 5 million square miles.

From greatest to least, the oceans and their approximate areas are shown below.

SEARCH

To see step-by-step videos of these problems, enter the page number into the SWadvantage.com Search Bar.

Pacific	**Atlantic**	**Indian**	**Southern**	**Arctic**
60 million sq mi	30 million sq mi	25 million sq mi	7.5 million sq mi	5 million sq mi

Line Graphs

A **line graph** shows how data change over time. The data are plotted on a coordinate grid and connected by line segments. Reading from left to right, use the *y*-axis scale to see how the data change in relationship to the data on the *x*-axis scale.

Depending on the type of data, the ordered pairs in line graphs can be either two numbers or a word and a number—for example (7, 11) or (Sunday, 45).

Need More
HELP
For more about line graphs, go to *Line Graphs* in *Foundations of Mathematics* (Book 1, p. 192).

EXAMPLE 2

The arboretum has a new azalea garden. The landscapers keep track of the amount of rainfall. What is the difference between the amounts of rainfall in May and July?

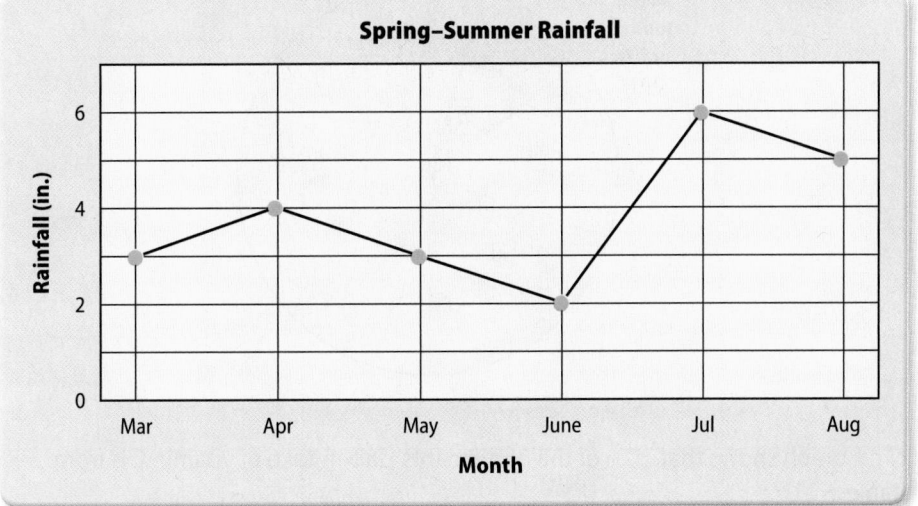

On this line graph, the *x*-axis represents the months from March to August. The *y*-axis represents the amount of rainfall in inches.

STEP 1 Find the point directly above May. Look on the *y*-axis to find the amount of rainfall for May. 3 inches

STEP 2 Find the point directly above July. Look on the *y*-axis to find the amount of rainfall for July. 6 inches

STEP 3 Subtract to find the difference in the amount of rainfall. $6 - 3 = 3$

The difference in the amount of rainfall between May and July is 3 inches.

Try It This Way

To find the value of a point, use a ruler or index card. Align it horizontally just above a point. Look to the left to the *y*-axis scale to find the value of the point.

Look at the graph in Example 2. The lines do not represent data, because there is no "month" between each pair of months on the *x*-axis. The lines simply connect data points. You could display this set of data on a bar graph, but a line graph helps you see the changes in the monthly rainfall more easily.

Circle Graphs

A **circle graph** uses sections of a circle to show how portions of a set of data compare with the whole and with other parts of the data.

One hundred adults participated in a dietary study. The graph below shows their dietary sources of vitamin C. Which two sources together provide the same percentage of daily intake of vitamin C as vegetables provide?

Need More

HELP ?

For more about circle graphs, go to *Circle Graphs* in *Foundations of Mathematics* (Book 1, p. 194).

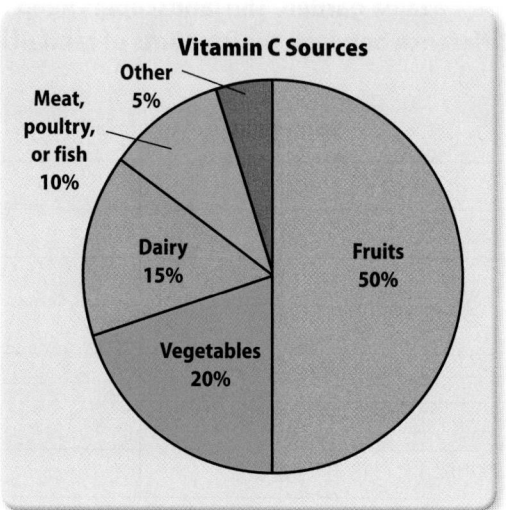

The circle graph shows that 20% of the participants' daily intake of vitamin C is from vegetables.

STEP 1 Make a list of the groups that provide less than 20% of daily intake of vitamin C.
Dairy 15%; Meat, poultry, or fish 10%; Other 5%

STEP 2 Identify the two groups whose sum is 20%.
Dairy + Meat, poultry, or fish = 15 + 10 = 25   too high
Dairy + Other = 15 + 5 = 20   exact
Other + Meat, poultry, or fish = 5 + 10 = 15   too low

The two groups Dairy and Other together provide the same percentage of daily intake of vitamin C as vegetables.

Type of Graphs

• Bar graphs   compare or order the same kind of data
• Line graphs   show how data change over time
• Circle graphs   model the relationship of parts of a data set to the whole

Choose an Appropriate Graph

The type of graph you choose to display data depends on the type of data you want to display.

EXAMPLE 4

The table lists the population of Texas, rounded to the nearest million, at ten-year intervals from 1910 through 1950. Suppose you want to draw a graph to model the change in the population. Which type of graph is most appropriate?

Year	1910	1920	1930	1940	1950
Population (in millions)	2	4	4	5	6

Ask yourself the following questions. Then use your answers to make a decision.

What type of data is on the table? numerical data—year and population

What do you want to show in your graph? change over time

Which is more appropriate, a bar graph or a line graph? line graph

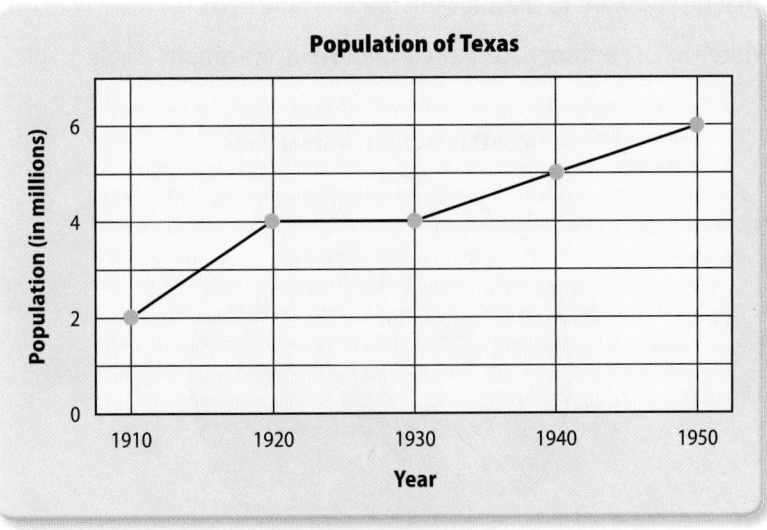

A line graph is most appropriate to display these data because it can show change over time.

You can also use a line graph to make estimates from this type of data, because there are year values between each pair of years on the *x*-axis. For example, you could estimate the population of Texas in 1915. The year 1915 is halfway between 1910 and 1920. Move up from 1915 to the line. Move left to the *y*-axis scale. In 1915, the population of Texas was about 3 million.

You could display the information on a bar graph if you only wanted to compare the population for the five years shown on the table.

Choosing and Drawing an Appropriate Graph

EXAMPLE 5

A company produces steel rods in three grades of steel. The table below shows the total output, or number made, and the output of the three grades of rod for one month.

Steel Grade	Rod Output
A	492
B	861
C	1,107
Total output: 2,460	

a. **The monthly report will display these data on a graph. Which is the better choice for displaying the data, a circle graph or a line graph? Draw a graph.**

STEP 1 What type of data do you have? parts and total data

STEP 2 What do you want to show in your graph? how parts compare with the whole

STEP 3 Which is more appropriate, a circle graph or a line graph? circle graph

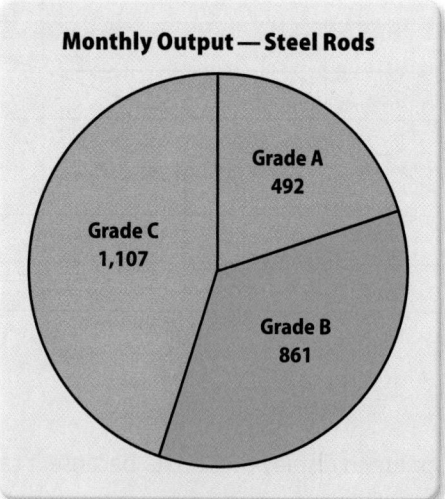

b. **Suppose you want to compare the production of the three types of rod. What type of display would be the best?**

A horizontal or vertical bar graph could be used to compare the production of the types of rod.

c. **Why is a line graph a poor choice for displaying the data on the table?**

A line graph plots data points and is usually used to show change over time. The data on the table are for the same month so it does not make sense to use a line graph.

EXAMPLE 6

Regan reads that there are six species of tigers that live in the wild. He finds this information about three of the six species.

Tigers in the Wild	Number
Malayan tigers	800
Siberian tigers	1,400
Sumatran tigers	500

What type of graph would be best for displaying these data to compare the numbers—a line graph, a circle graph, or a bar graph? Draw the graph.

STEP 1   What type of data do you have?   amounts for some categories of data

STEP 2   What do you want to show in your graph?   how the data compare

STEP 3   Which is most appropriate, a line graph, a circle graph, or a bar graph?   bar graph

STEP 4   Explain the choice.

A line graph is a poor choice because the data do not show change over time, and the three types of tigers can be listed in any order.

A circle graph could be misleading because there are six species of tigers in the wild, but the data include only three of them.

A bar graph is the best choice. You can compare the numbers of the three species shown on the table. Also, a bar graph will not imply that these are the only species of tigers living in the wild.

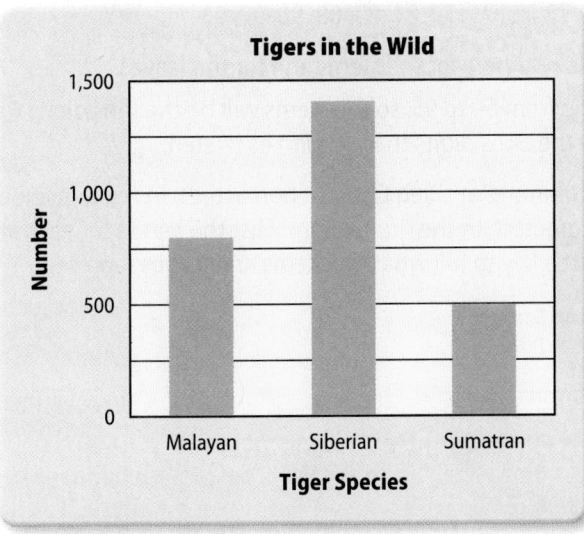

Stem-and-Leaf Plots

Making a Stem-and-Leaf Plot

A **stem-and-leaf plot** is a data display that can be used to show how data are distributed. The data are in numerical order in two columns. The left column contains the *stems*, and the right column contains the *leaves*. The last digit in a number is always a leaf and represents the value of the ones place.

Suppose you have the data values 27, 35, 41, 32, 26, 30, 48, and 27. Group the data in three categories by the values in the tens place—2, 3, and 4. Place each leaf in its corresponding category and put the leaves for each stem in numerical order. Write a key that explains what the digits mean.

Stem	Leaf
2	6 7 7
3	0 2 5
4	1 8

Key: 2 | 6 means 26

Try It This Way

To help you see which digits are stems and which are leaves, try this process.

- List the data in a column.
- Draw a horizontal line under each category that will be a stem.
- Write the stems. Use the last digit of every number in the category as the leaves.

```
64
67   6|478
68            ‚
70
72
75   7|02559
75
79            ‚
81
83   8|138
88            ‚
90
92   9|025
95
```

EXAMPLE 1

Organize the data from the table in a stem-and-leaf plot.

Competition Scores

68	75	75	92	81	88	67
83	72	79	64	70	90	95

STEP 1 Order the data from least to greatest.

64, 67, 68, 70, 72, 75, 75, 79, 81, 83, 88, 90, 92, 95

STEP 2 Determine the numbers for the stems and for the leaves.

The data range from 64 to 95, so the stems will be the tens digits 6, 7, 8, and 9. The leaves will be the ones digits that go with each stem.

STEP 3 Make a two-column plot titled Competition Scores. In the left column, list the stems from least to greatest. In the right column, list the leaves for each stem from least to greatest. Insert a key to tell what the stems and leaves represent.

Competition Scores

Stem	Leaf
6	4 7 8
7	0 2 5 5 9
8	1 3 8
9	0 2 5

Key: 6 | 4 means 64

EXAMPLE 2

a. **The table shows the batting averages for a baseball team. Organize the data in a stem-and-leaf plot.**

Batting Averages

.317	.351	.318	.340	.324	.331	.322	.342	.303
.286	.330	.300	.323	.311	.329	.338	.326	.337

STEP 1 Order the data from least to greatest: .286, .300, .303, .311, .317, .318, .322, .323, .324, .326, .329, .330, .331, .337, .338, .340, .342, .351

STEP 2 Choose the values for the stems. Remember, the leaves are the last digit in each number, so the stems are: .28, .29, .30, .31, .32, .33, .34, and .35.

STEP 3 Write the stems in the left column. Write the leaves for each stem in the right column. Insert a title and a key to explain what the stems and leaves represent.

Batting Averages

Stem	Leaf
.28	6
.29	
.30	0 3
.31	1 7 8
.32	2 3 4 6 9
.33	0 1 7 8
.34	0 2
.35	1

Key: .28 | 6 represents .286

b. **Describe what you can tell about the data by looking at the plot.**

From the graph, you can see these facts.

• No two players have the same batting average.

• No player has a batting average in the .290's.

• The batting average of .286 is an outlier.

• Of the 18 data points, 12 are in the .311-to-.338 range, so the data cluster in that range.

Watch Out !

Even though the data do not include any batting averages in the .290's, you still need to list .29 as a stem with no leaf. You cannot use 0 as a leaf because that would mean that there is a data value of .290.

SEARCH 🔍

To see step-by-step videos of these problems, enter the page number into the SWadvantage.com Search Bar.

Need More

HELP ?

An outlier is a data point that is much less or greater than the rest of the data set. For help with outliers, go to *Outliers* on page 1298.

Median and Range

You can find the median and range of a set of data that is displayed in a stem-and-leaf plot.

Need More HELP ?

For more about median and mean, go to *The "Center" of a Data Set* (p. 1294), and for more about range, go to *Effects of Changing Data Values* (p. 1302).

EXAMPLE 3

A group hiked part of the Appalachian Trail. The stem-and-leaf plot shows the ages of the hikers in the group.

a. What is the median age of the hikers?

Ages of Hikers

Stem	Leaf
1	0 2 5
2	1 3 8
3	0 2 5 9
4	4 7 8
5	2 6

Key: 1 | 0 = 10

The **median** is the middle number in a list. There are 15 numbers, so the eighth leaf represents the median, or middle number, in the data set. Starting at the top of the plot, count to the eighth leaf.

Ages of Hikers

Stem	Leaf
1	1 2 3 0 2 5 →
2	4 5 6 1 3 8 →
3	7 8 0 2 5 9

The median age of the hikers is 32.

b. What is the range of the ages of the hikers?

The **range** is the difference between the greatest number in a list and the least. Subtract to find the range: 56 − 10 = 46.

The range of the ages of the hikers is 46 years.

Try It This Way

To find the median of 15 numbers, write the numbers 1–15. Then cross off numbers two at a time, one from the front and one from the end of the list, as shown here.

1̶, 2̶, 3, 4, 5, 6, 7, 8, 9, 10, 11, 12, 13, 1̶4̶, 1̶5̶

When you have one unpaired number left, it is the median.

Mean and Mode

EXAMPLE 4

The stem-and-leaf plot shows the total number of cars parked at a garage each day for the past 10 days.

Cars Parked
(Past 10 Days)

Stem	Leaf
0	1 2 3 6
1	0 0 3 6
2	0 9

Key: 2|9 = 29

a. What was the mean number of cars parked per day at the garage?

The **mean** is the average of the numbers in a list. List each value on the stem-and-leaf plot. Then find the sum.

$1 + 2 + 3 + 6 + 10 + 10 + 13 + 16 + 20 + 29 = 110$ cars

Divide the sum by the number of days: $110 \div 10 = 11$.

The mean number of cars parked per day at the garage was 11.

b. What is the mode of the data set?

The **mode** is the number or numbers that appear most often in a list.

Look at the data in the plot above. Is there a data value that appears more frequently than others? Yes, the stem 1 has two 0 leaves. The data value 10 appears twice.

The mode is 10.

c. Why is the 0 leaf in the 2 stem not included in the mode count?

As modeled in the key, 2|9 represents 29 cars. So 2|0 represents 20 cars. The mode is 1|0, or 10 cars, which appears twice.

SEARCH

To see step-by-step videos of these problems, enter the page number into the SWadvantage.com Search Bar.

Stem-and-Leaf Plots

The data in a stem-and-leaf plot are displayed by place value. The **stems** may have one or more digits. The **leaves** are always the digits with the least place value in the numbers. The **key** tells how to read the plot.

Key: 13 | 2 = 132

The digits to the left of the bar represent 1 hundred and 3 tens. The digit to the right represents 2 ones. The total value of these digits is 132.

Box-and-Whisker Plots

Making a Box-and-Whisker Plot

A **box-and-whisker plot** is a data display that divides a set of data into four equal parts. It shows how the data are distributed among these parts. The **lower extreme** is the least data point in the set. The **upper extreme** is the greatest data point in the set.

The *median*, or midpoint, of the data divides the data in half. The median of the lower half of the data is the **lower quartile**. The median of the upper half of the data is the **upper quartile**.

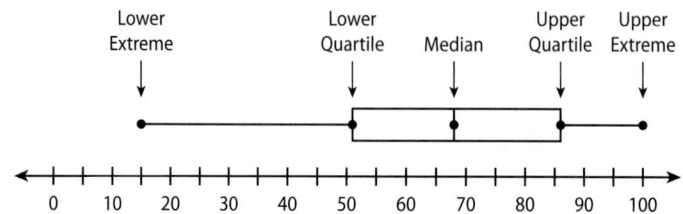

EXAMPLE 1

The list of numbers below shows the lengths of 13 young alligators, in inches. Display the data on a box-and-whisker plot.

$$12 \quad 13 \quad 5 \quad 8 \quad 9 \quad 20 \quad 16 \quad 14 \quad 14 \quad 6 \quad 9 \quad 12 \quad 12$$

STEP 1 Write the data in order, from least to greatest. Then find the median.

Since there are 13 data points, the seventh number is the median.

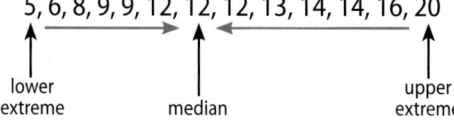

STEP 2 Identify the lower and upper quartiles by finding the medians for the numbers less than and greater than the overall median, 12.

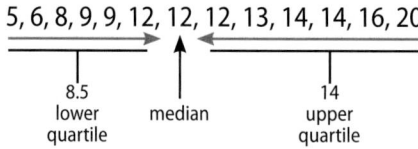

STEP 3 Draw a number line that includes all the numbers in the data set. Above the number line, plot the points for the *lower extreme*, the *lower quartile*, the *median*, the *upper quartile*, and the *upper extreme*.

STEP 4 Draw a rectangular box from the lower quartile to the upper quartile. Add a vertical segment to represent the median.

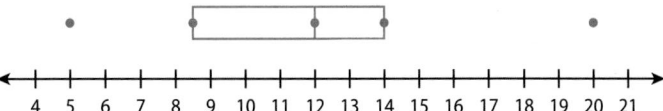

STEP 5 Draw horizontal line segments to connect the lower extreme to the lower quartile and to connect the upper extreme to the upper quartile. These are the whiskers.

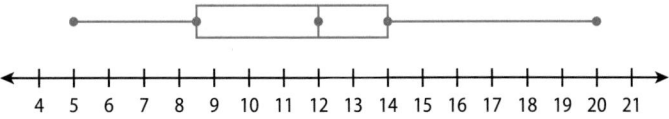

Try It This Way

You can use a graphing calculator to make a box-and-whisker plot or to see whether one you drew by hand is correct.

Look at the completed box-and-whisker plot.

The box contains 50% of the data, and each whisker contains 25% of the data.

- The **interquartile range** (IQR) is the width of the box. You can use it to see how spread out the middle data are. The box is wider from 8.5 to 12, so the data points in this range are more spread out (have a greater range) than the data points from 12 to 14.

- The distance between the upper quartile, 14, and the upper extreme, 20, is longest. This means that the data in this quartile are the most spread out.

- Notice that a box-and-whisker plot does not show the data from which it was made. You cannot tell the number of alligators included or their individual lengths by looking at the box-and-whisker plot shown in Step 5.

Box-and-Whisker Plots

A box-and-whisker plot identifies five points in a set of data and shows how the data are distributed (spread out) across the range of these points.

The *lower extreme* and the *upper extreme* are the least and greatest points in the data set.

The *median* is the midpoint of the data set.

The *lower quartile* is the midpoint of the lower half of the data.

The *upper quartile* is the midpoint of the upper half of the data.

Using a Box-and-Whisker Plot

The box-and-whisker plot below is the same one shown in Example 1, but the quartiles are shaded to make them easier to see.

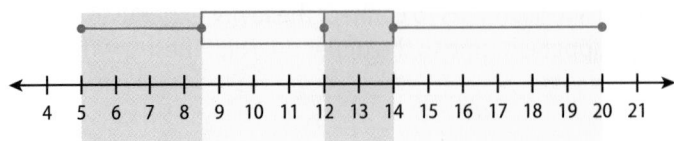

a. **What do the extremes of the data represent?**

the shortest and longest young alligators

b. **What is the median length of the young alligators?**

12 inches

c. **The distance from the median to the upper quartile is the narrowest section. What does that tell you about the data in that section?**

It means that the data in the section are the least spread out. You could also say that the data points in that section are closer in value than the data points in the other sections.

Watch Out !

The width of a section does not reflect the number of data points in it. It reflects the spread of the data.

The box-and-whisker plot shows the ages of children in a playgroup.

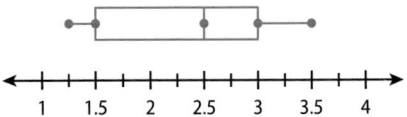

a. **What is the range of ages of the children in the playgroup?**

Subtract the extremes: $3.5 - 1.25 = 2.25$. The range of ages is 2.25 years.

b. **The right "whisker" is longer than the left one. What does this mean?**

The lengths of the whiskers show the spread of the data between the extremes and the quartiles. Both whiskers represent 25% of the data, but the data are more spread out (have a greater range) in the whisker on the right.

c. **Can you tell if there are more children in the age 1.25 to 1.5 section than in the age 3.0 to 3.5 section? Explain.**

No. The box-and-whisker plot does not show the number of children or the ages of the individual children. It shows the range and the spread of the ages.

EXAMPLE 4

The box-and-whisker plot shows the commissions for the realtors who work at one realty company. What is the range of the commissions received?

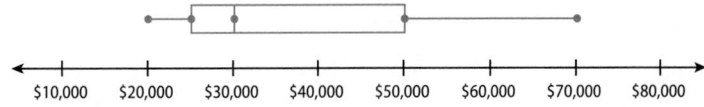

SEARCH 🔍

To see step-by-step videos of these problems, enter the page number into the SWadvantage.com Search Bar.

STEP 1 Find the lowest commission in the data set, the lower extreme. $20,000

STEP 2 Find the highest commission in the data set, the upper extreme. $70,000

STEP 3 Subtract to find the range.
$70,000 − $20,000 = $50,000

Remember that the IQR is the width of the box on the plot. Sometimes a data set contains an **outlier**. An outlier is a data point that lies far from either end of the box. The standard often used to define an outlier is that its distance from *either end of the box* is *more than 1.5 times the IQR*. However, this definition is not always applied when determining outliers.

EXAMPLE 5

Look at the box-and-whisker plot below.

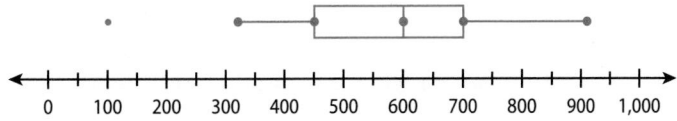

Try It This Way

You can set your graphing calculator to show outliers.

a. What does the smaller point at the left represent?

The point has a value of 100. It represents an outlier, a value that is either much smaller or greater than the other values in the data set.

b. Does this point meet the standard definition of an outlier? Support your answer.

STEP 1 Find the IQR, the width of the box.
700 (upper quartile) − 450 (lower quartile) = 250

STEP 2 Find 1.5 times the IQR: 250 × 1.5 = 375

STEP 3 Find the distance of the outlier to the left side of the box: 450 − 100 = 350

The standard definition states that an outlier must be more than 1.5 times the IQR away from either end of the box.

No, the point does *not* meet the standard definition of an outlier, because 350 < 375.

Displaying Two Data Sets

Double-Bar Graphs

A **double-bar graph** uses side-by-side bars to display related data. A key tells which color of bar represents each set of data.

Need More

HELP

For more about single-bar graphs, go to *Bar Graphs* in *Foundations of Mathematics* (Book 1, p. 188).

EXAMPLE 1

Look at the double-bar graph. The graph compares the after-school sports choices of a group of fifth and sixth graders. You can use the graph to make generalizations about preferences in each grade.

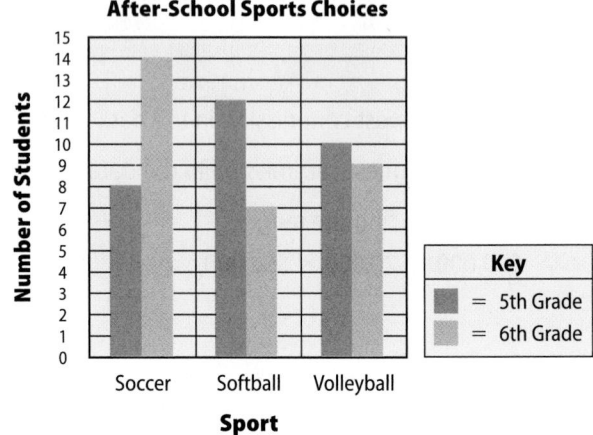

a. How do you know which bar refers to which group of students?

Look at the key. It shows which color represents each group of students.

b. The data represent how many fifth and sixth graders?

Add the lengths of the bars: 8 + 12 + 10 = 30 fifth graders; 14 + 7 + 9 = 30 sixth graders.

c. Which sport is preferred by about the same number of fifth graders as sixth graders? Explain.

Volleyball. The two bars for volleyball are closer in length than the other pairs of bars.

d. Is the following statement true? Explain why or why not.
    Most fifth graders prefer softball.

No. Although 12 fifth graders prefer softball, 18 prefer either soccer or volleyball. So most fifth graders prefer soccer or volleyball to softball. The following sentence is true:
    Softball is the preferred sport of the greatest number of fifth graders.

e. Which sport is the choice of the greatest number of students?

Add the numbers of students who prefer each sport.

soccer: 8 + 14 = 22   softball: 12 + 7 = 19   volleyball: 10 + 9 = 19

Soccer is the choice of the greatest number of students.

Got to KNOW!

Comparing Two Data Sets

Displays that show two sets of related data make it easier to compare the data.

Look at the graph in Example 1. You can see that it would be more difficult to compare these data if they were on two different bar graphs.

Double-Line Graph

A **double-line graph** displays the changes of two related sets of data over time. Line segments are used to connect known data points. A key indicates which color represents each set of data.

Need More

HELP

For more about single-line graphs, go to *Line Graphs* in *Foundations of Mathematics* (Book 1, p. 192).

EXAMPLE 2

The double-line graph below compares sales of cookbooks and travel guides by a major book distributor. A line graph sometimes reveals a trend, or a pattern of change in data over time.

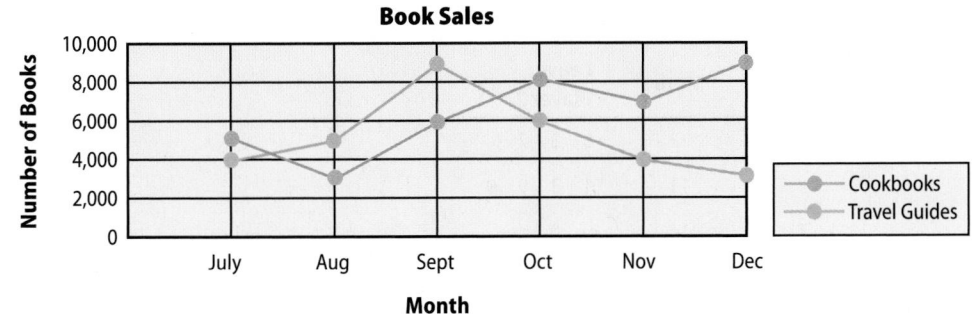

SEARCH

To see step-by-step videos of these problems, enter the page number into the SWadvantage.com Search Bar.

a. What data does this graph show?

The graph shows the numbers of cookbooks and travel guides a distributor sold each month over a period of six months.

b. Why is the key important?

The key shows the color that represents each type of book.

c. For what months did the sales of cookbooks drop below the sales of travel guides?

August and September.

d. For which month are the sales of cookbooks and travel guides the closest? Explain how you know.

July. The dots that represent July sales are closest together.

e. Look at the data for travel guides. How would you describe the trend that starts in September?

From September through December, the sale of travel guides decreases every month.

f. Do the data show any upward trends?

Yes, cookbook sales increase each month from August through October. There is a slight dip in November. However, there is a strong increase in December.

Displaying Two Data Sets

For more about single stem-and-leaf plots, go to *Stem-and-Leaf Plots* on page 1276.

Double Stem-and-Leaf Plot

A **double stem-and-leaf plot** is used to compare two sets of data. Sometimes it is called a *back-to-back* stem-and-leaf plot. The shared stems are in the middle. The leaves are on opposite sides of the stem. The key shows how to read each set of data.

EXAMPLE 3

Service speed is the speed of a tennis ball when a player serves, or hits the ball to start a point. The double stem-and-leaf plot shows service speeds in miles per hour (mph) during a professional tennis match.

Service Speeds

Leaves Player 1	Stem	Leaves Player 2
3	12	0 3 7
3 5	13	1 3 9 9
2 5 7 8	14	0 0
0 4 5	15	0 2

Key:
|12|0 represents 120 miles per hour
3|12| represents 123 miles per hour

To read the data displayed in the stem-and-leaf plot, start with the stems. These digits represent hundreds and tens. For example, 13 means 13_. Use a leaf to fill in the digit in the ones place. For example, 13|9 means 139, and 3|13 means 133.

Read the speeds for Player 1 from the center to the left. Read the speeds for Player 2 from the center to the right.

a. What are the slowest and the fastest serves shown?

The slowest serve is 120 mph for Player 2. The fastest serve is 155 mph for Player 1.

b. How many serve speeds are shown for each player? Explain how you know.

Ten speeds are shown for Player 1 and 11 for Player 2. I counted the leaves.

c. A student looks at the plot and says that Player 2 never served the ball at a speed of 140 mph. Is the student correct? Explain.

The student is not correct. For Player 2, the stem 14 has two 0 leaves. This means that Player 2 served the ball at 140 mph two times.

d. On the whole, which player seems to have the faster serve? Explain your reasoning.

Player 1. The data show that Player 1 has 7 out of 10 serves with a speed of 140 mph or greater. Player 2 has 4 out of 11 serves with a speed of 140 mph or greater.

If you find reading the double plot confusing, use a sheet of paper to cover up the leaf column you are not reading.

You may also want to place two small arrows on the stem column to remind you which direction to read.

Stem

← 12 →

Two Box-and-Whisker Plots

You can stack two or more box-and-whisker plots to compare related data. This stacking is useful when you want to study the spread of different sets of data.

- The box represents 50% of the data set.

- The middle line in the box represents the *median,* or midpoint, of the data set. It divides the data in half.

- The two sides of the box show the median of the lower half of the data (lower quartile) and the median of the upper half of the data (upper quartile).

- The dots at the end of each whisker represent the highest and lowest values in the data set.

- The *interquartile range* (IQR) is the width of the box. You can use it to see how spread out the middle data are.

Need More
HELP ?
For more about box-and-whisker plots, go to page 1280.

EXAMPLE 4

The two box-and-whisker plots display the distribution of math final exam scores for two years.

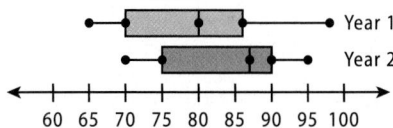

Year 1
Year 2

60 65 70 75 80 85 90 95 100

SEARCH
To see step-by-step videos of these problems, enter the page number into the SWadvantage.com Search Bar.

a. Compare the ranges of the two data sets.

The range for Year 1 is from 65 to about 98, a range of 33 points.
The range for Year 2 is from 70 to 95, a range of 25 points. So Year 1 has a greater range.

b. Compare the medians of the two data sets.

The median for Year 1 is 80. The median for Year 2 is 87.
So the median for Year 2 is greater than the median for Year 1.

c. The medians of the data sets are in different positions in the boxes. What does this difference tell you?

In Year 1, the median is closer to the center of the box, and 25% of the data fall between 80 and 86.
In Year 2, it is closer to the right side of the box; 25% of the data fall between 87 and 90.

Watch Out !
A box-and-whisker plot does not give individual data points. You may know the range of data but not the specific values in the range.

d. For each year, where do the top 50% of the data fall?

In Year 1, the top 50% of the data fall between 80 and 98.
In Year 2, the top 50% of the data fall between 87 and 95.

e. Can you use the plots to compare test scores for a given student?

No, the plots show ranges of scores but not actual data points.

Venn Diagrams

Reading a Venn Diagram

A **Venn diagram** is a graphic display that uses overlapping circles (or squares) to show the relationship between sets and subsets of data. Each circle represents one data group. Data that belong in more than one group are clustered in the overlapping sections of the circles. Data that do not belong to any of the data groups are shown outside the circles.

SEARCH

To see step-by-step videos of these problems, enter the page number into the SWadvantage.com Search Bar.

EXAMPLE 1

The Venn diagram below shows the results of a survey. People were asked, "Do you have a dog or a cat?" Of the people who responded, some have cats, some have dogs, some have both, and some have neither.

Pet Owners

Cat	Dog
10	6	15

Both   Neither: 4

a. How many people were surveyed?

The number of people surveyed is equal to the total number of replies shown on the Venn diagram. The diagram shows these numbers.

only cats: 10   only dogs: 15   both: 6   neither: 4

Add to find the total: $10 + 15 + 6 + 4 = 35$.

A total of 35 people were surveyed.

b. Are there 10 people who own cats, or 16 people? Explain.

According to the diagram, 10 people have only cats at home, and 6 people have both cats and dogs.

The total number of cat owners is $10 + 6 = 16$.

c. How many of the people surveyed have dogs?

Six people have both cats and dogs, and 15 people have only dogs.

The total number of dog owners is $6 + 15 = 21$.

d. Why is the category *Neither* placed outside the circles?

The people in this category are not a part of the other two categories.

Got to KNOW!

Venn Diagrams

Venn diagrams are used to show the relationships among different sets of data. They usually use circles to show where data sets intersect.

Drawing a Venn Diagram

By convention, circles are used in Venn diagrams. However, you may see Venn diagrams that use squares or rectangles.

EXAMPLE 2

June, July, and August are the warmest months in many parts of the world. The table shows the warmest month or months for eight cities.

City	Miami, Florida	Paris, France	Beijing, China	Cairo, Egypt	Edmonton, Canada	Honolulu, Hawaii	Athens, Greece	Tokyo, Japan
Warmest Month(s)	Jul	Jul–Aug	Jun–Jul	Jun	Jul	Aug	Jul	Jul–Aug

a. Draw a Venn diagram to display the data.

STEP 1 Draw three overlapping circles. Label them June, July, and August.

STEP 2 Make a list of the data groups that go in each circle or in the overlaps of circles.
June: Cairo
July: Miami, Edmonton, Athens
August: Honolulu
Overlap of July and August: Paris, Tokyo
Overlap of June and July: Beijing

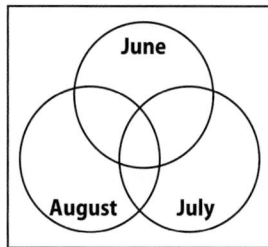

Warmest Months

STEP 3 Add the data to the circles.

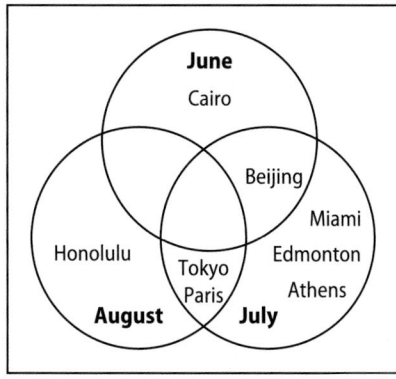

Warmest Months

b. In Riyadh, Saudi Arabia, June, July, and August are equally warm. Where would Riyadh go on the Venn diagram?

Riyadh belongs in all three circles. Write *Riyadh* in the center of the diagram, where all three circles overlap.

Try It This Way

You may find it helpful to shade each overlapping area with a different color. Then write what the area represents. For example, shade the area where June and July overlap light blue, and write in small letters *Ju-Jy*.

Universe, Sets, and Subsets

In mathematics, the study of a collection of items is called **set theory**. A Venn diagram is often used to show the relationships among sets of objects or items.

EXAMPLE 3

Emily, Zelda, and Michael use a Venn diagram to show the relationships among the sets of the letters in their names.

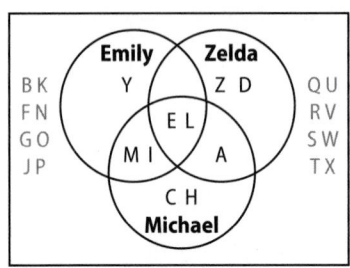

a. **In set theory, the universe is the group that contains the items that could be included in different sets. In a Venn diagram, the rectangle represents the universe. What is the universe for the Venn diagram above?**

Since all the items in the Venn diagram are letters in names, the universe consists of the letters in the English alphabet.

b. **How many sets are there in the Venn diagram above?**

A **set** is one group of items, or elements. Since the diagram represents the letters in three names, there are three sets.

c. **Are there any subsets in the Venn diagram above?**

A **subset** consists of the items that are common to related sets. Sometimes the symbol ⊂ is used to mean "is a subset of." Here is a description of one of the subsets in the Venn diagram.

{all letters common to *Emily* and *Michael*} is a subset of {all letters in *Emily* and *Michael*}
{M, I, E, L} ⊂ {E, M, I, L, Y, C, H, A}

There are three other subsets in the diagram.

{letters common to *Emily* and *Zelda*} ⊂ {all letters in *Emily* and *Zelda*}

{letters common to *Zelda* and *Michael*} ⊂ {all letters in *Zelda* and *Michael*}

{letters common to *Emily, Zelda,* and *Michael*} ⊂ {all letters in *Emily, Zelda,* and *Michael*}

Unions, Intersections, and Complements

EXAMPLE 4

Students are asked to pick 6 number cards from a deck of 20 cards numbered from 1 to 20. The Venn diagram shows the numbers on the cards that two students picked.

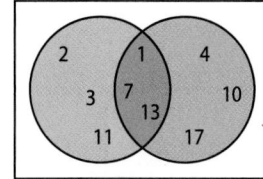

SEARCH

To see step-by-step videos of these problems, enter the page number into the SWadvantage.com Search Bar.

a. Describe the set of numbers in each circle.

orange circle: 1, 2, 3, 7, 11, 13
pink circle: 1, 4, 7, 10, 13, 17

b. What is special about the numbers 1, 7, and 13?

The numbers 1, 7, and 13 are common to both circles. They represent the **intersection** of the data in the two sets. You can use the symbol $\cap$ to describe this relationship.

orange $\cap$ pink = {1, 7, 13}

Need More
HELP

Sometimes the logic symbol $\cap$ is used to represent intersection.

Sometimes a complement is denoted by the symbol $\sim$. So, the complement of P can be written: $\sim P$.

c. What if the two sets are combined?

When sets are combined, they form a **union**. You can use the symbol $\cup$ to describe this relationship. In a union of sets, items are written only once, even if they are in both sets.

orange $\cup$ pink = {1, 2, 3, 4, 7, 10, 11, 13, 17}

d. How are the cards *not* picked by either student related to the data?

The set of cards not picked is the **complement** of the set of cards that were picked. Let P represent the cards picked. Then, P^c represents the cards not picked.

P^c = {5, 6, 8, 9, 12, 14, 15, 16, 18, 19, 20}

Got to KNOW!

Vocabulary

A **set** is a collection of distinct items.

The **universe** is the group of all the items that could be included in the sets.

An **intersection** ($\cap$) of two sets consists of all the items that are common to both sets.

A **union** ($\cup$) of two sets consists of all the items in both sets.

The **complement** (P^c) of a set is the set of items in the universe but outside the set.

Describing Data

What Came Before?
- Mean, median, mode, and range of data
- Displaying one and two data sets in graphs, plots, and diagrams

What's This About?
- Measures of the center of a data set
- Outliers and the effects of changing data
- Misleading statistics and data displays

Practical Apps
- Sports statisticians collect, analyze, and describe data to evaluate the careers of professional athletes.
- Real estate agents need to know the median prices of homes sold in each local neighborhood.

Just for FUN!

The data point was cited for jaywalking—it had apparently crossed over the median.

You can find more practice problems online by visiting:
www.SWadvantage.com

The "Center" of a Data Set

SOUTHWESTERN

What Is Average?

It is often helpful find a number that seems typical of a data set. This number may be used to summarize the data set, to compare two data sets, or to spot a trend. There are several ways to find the "center" of a data set.

The word *average* most often refers to the mean of a data set. The **mean** of a data set is the sum of the data, divided by the number of items in the set.

EXAMPLE 1

Find the mean of the data 12, 9, 11, 13, 6, 24, 15, 12.

Add the numbers: $12 + 9 + 11 + 13 + 6 + 24 + 15 + 12 = 102$.

Divide by the number of items in the set: $\frac{102}{8} = 12.75$.

The mean of the data set is 12.75.

Another number that may be used as an average is the median. The **median** of a data set is the middle number when the data are in numerical order.

Try It This Way

Put your left index finger on the first number in the ordered set and your right index finger on the last number. Move your fingers toward the center until you arrive at the median.

EXAMPLE 2

Find the median of the data 90, 87, 91, 75, 104, 88, 94, 89, 78, 92, 87.

STEP 1 Put the data in order from least to greatest.

75, 78, 87, 87, 88, 89, 90, 91, 92, 94, 104

STEP 2 Find the middle number in the list.

75, 78, 87, 87, 88, 89, 90, 91, 92, 94, 104

The median of the data set is 89.

If a data set has an even number of items, its median is the average of the two middle numbers of the set.

EXAMPLE 3

Find the median of the data in the stem-and-leaf plot.

Ages of Leah's Cousins (yr)

Stem	Leaf
0	4 7 8 9
1	0 2 5 7

Key: 1|0 represents 10

This data set has an even number of items. The data are already in numerical order. The median is the average of the fourth and fifth numbers.

$$\text{median} = \frac{9 + 10}{2} = 9.5$$

The median age of Leah's cousins is 9.5 years.

Try It This Way

It might be helpful to write the data in the stem-and-leaf plot in a list: 4, 7, 8, 9, 10, 12, 15, 17.

Another way to describe a data set is to find its *mode*. The **mode** is the number or element in a data set that appears most often in the set. If all the items of the data set are different, there is no mode. If two or more items have the same frequency, the data set may have more than one mode. Unlike mean and median, the mode can be found for nonnumerical data.

EXAMPLE 4

Find the mode of the data.

Numbers of Pets Owned by Students in 4H Club

2   5   1   3   2   1   1   2   6   2   1   4

The numbers 1 and 2 appear four times each.

The data set has two modes, 1 and 2.

EXAMPLE 5

Find the mode of the data in the bar graph.

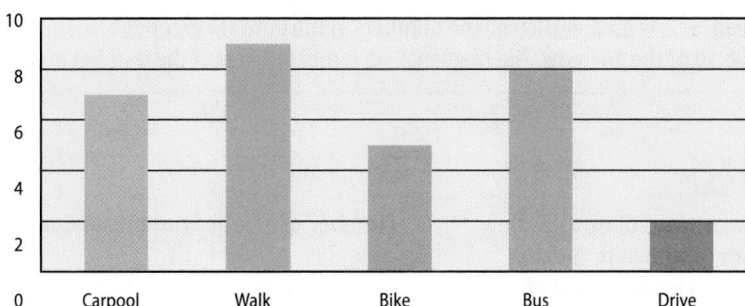

How Do You Get to School?

The bar labeled Walk is the longest one, so the mode is walking.

SEARCH

To see step-by-step videos of these problems, enter the page number into the SWadvantage.com Search Bar.

Notice that the mean and the median of a data set may be numbers that are not in the set, but the mode is always a member of the set.

EXAMPLE 6

Find the mean, the median, and the mode of the data 375, 287, 213, 401, −364, 105, −249.

STEP 1 Find the mean.

$$\frac{375 + 287 + 213 + 401 + (−364) + 105 + (−249)}{7} = \frac{768}{7} \approx 109.7$$

STEP 2 Find the median.

Put the data in order from least to greatest: −364, −249, 105, 213, 287, 375, 401.

The middle number in the list is 213.

STEP 3 Find the mode.

No number is repeated, so the data set does not have a mode.

The mean is about 109.7. The median is 213. There is no mode.

Using Mean, Median, and Mode

Some data sets are best described by their mean, others by the median or the mode. Comparing the three values can give you the best picture of the data set.

SEARCH

To see step-by-step videos of these problems, enter the page number into the SWadvantage.com Search Bar.

EXAMPLE 7

Find the mean, the median, and the mode of the data. Which one is the most typical of the data?

Donations to Save the Butterflies Campaign (Dollars)

20	175	9	13	9	8	9	15
15	10	10	9	7	20	13	10

STEP 1 Find the mean.

The sum of the data is 352. Divide by the number of donations: $\frac{352}{16} = 22$. The mean is $22.

STEP 2 Find the median.

Put the data in order: 7, 8, 9, 9, 9, 9, 10, 10, 10, 13, 13, 15, 15, 20, 20, 175. There are 16 items, so the median is the average of the eighth and the ninth items. They are both 10. The median is $10.

STEP 3 Find the mode.

The number 9 appears most frequently. The mode is $9.

STEP 4 Decide which number is most typical of the data.

The mean, $22, is greater than all the numbers in the data set except $175. The mode, $9, is less than 10 of the 16 items. The median, $10, is most typical of the data set in this case.

EXAMPLE 8

Find the mean, the median, and the mode of the data shown in the line plot. Which one is most typical of the data?

Number of Honor Students at County Schools

```
        X                       X
        X   X                   X
    X   X   X               X   X
    X   X   X           X   X   X
X   X   X   X           X   X   X   X
6   7   8   9   10  11  12  13  14
```

STEP 1 Find the mean.

The sum of the data is $6 + 3(7) + 5(8) + 4(9) + 2(11) + 3(12) + 5(13) + 14 = 240$. Count the number of X's to find the total number of schools, 24. Divide by $240 \div 24 = 10$. The mean is 10.

STEP 2 Find the median.

There are 24 items, so the median is the average of the 12th and 13th items. The median is 9.

STEP 3 Find the mode.

The numbers 8 and 13 appear most frequently. The modes are 8 and 13.

STEP 4 Decide which number is most typical of the data.

The mean, 10, is in the middle of the data set, but is not an element of the set. The data set has two peaks, or clusters. The median, 9, represents only one of the clusters. The two modes, 8 and 13, are most typical of the data set.

Some algebra problems use the formula for the mean.

EXAMPLE 9

Hiroki's test scores are 89, 93, 96, 90, and 87. What must her next test score be for the mean of her scores to be at least 90?

Hiroki will have 6 test scores. Let $x =$ the score on her sixth test.

STEP 1 Write an expression for the mean of the scores.

$$\frac{89 + 93 + 96 + 90 + 87 + x}{6}$$

STEP 2 Write an inequality. The mean must be at least 90.

$$\frac{89 + 93 + 96 + 90 + 87 + x}{6} \geq 90$$

STEP 3 Solve the inequality.

$$\frac{455 + x}{6} \geq 90$$

Multiply both sides by 6.

$$455 + x \geq 540$$

Subtract 455 from both sides.

$$x \geq 85$$

For the mean of Hiroki's test scores to be at least 90, her next test score must be at least 85.

Need More HELP?

For more about solving inequalities, go to *Two-Step Inequalities* in *Algebra* (p. 1502).

EXAMPLE 10

The product of three integers is equal to the mean of the integers. Two of the integers are 0 and -12. What is the third integer?

STEP 1 Let $x =$ the third integer.

STEP 2 Write an expression for the mean of the three integers.

$$\frac{x + 0 + (-12)}{3} = \frac{x - 12}{3}$$

STEP 3 Find the product of the three integers.

$$(-12)(0)x = 0$$

STEP 4 Write an equation showing that the product and the mean are equal.

$$\frac{x - 12}{3} = 0$$

STEP 5 Solve the equation.

Multiply both sides by 3.

$$3\left(\frac{x - 12}{3}\right) = 3(0)$$

Add 12 to both sides.

$$x - 12 = 0$$

$$x = 12$$

The third integer is 12.

GOT TO KNOW!

Mean, Median, and Mode

The mean, the median, and the mode are called *measures of central tendency.*

The **mean** of a data set $= \frac{\text{the sum of the numbers of the set}}{\text{the number of items in the set}}$.

The **median** of a data set is the middle number of a data set. If there is an even number of data items in a set, the median is the average of the middle two numbers.

The mean is also called the *arithmetic mean* or the *average.* It may be a number that is not in the data set. It is affected by very large or very small values in the set.

The **mode** is the most common element in a data set. It is always in the data set. It can be used for categorical (nonnumeric) data. A data set may have no mode or more than one mode.

Outliers

Unusual Values

A star player may have a much higher salary than all the others on a sports team. A student might miss a science test and have one score of 0. The high salary and the low test score are examples of outliers. An **outlier** is a very large or very small value that is not typical of its data set.

You can spot outliers by looking at the elements of a data set or a graph of the data.

Need More HELP ?

For more information about reading a histogram, go to *Histograms* on page 1266.

SEARCH

To see step-by-step videos of these problems, enter the page number into the SWadvantage.com Search Bar.

EXAMPLE 1

Use the graph below. Does the data set have an outlier? If so, what is it?

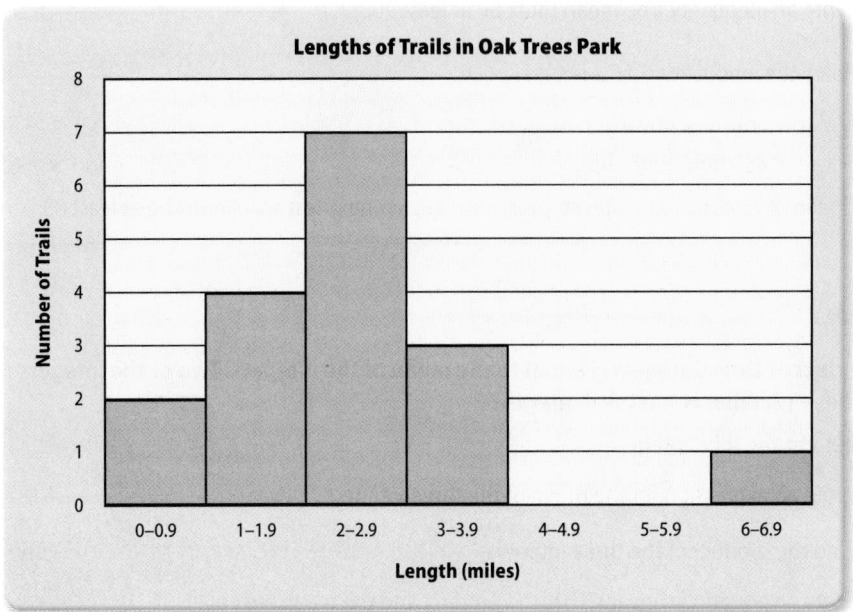

Yes, the trail that is 6 to 6.9 miles long is an outlier. It is much longer than the other trails.

EXAMPLE 2

Use the data below. Does the data set have an outlier? If so, what is it?

Try It This Way

Instead of ordering the data, circle the greatest and least values in the data set. Then scan the rest of the data for other values close to them.

Reading Test Scores

75	80	77	82	86	93	76	85	95	91
89	78	92	80	87	49	84	83	90	92
74	68	87	79	83	88	76	79	81	88

Graph the data to look for outliers. A line plot or a stem-and-leaf plot is a good choice for a data display because you can read the individual data values.

Reading Test Scores

Stem	Leaf
4	9
5	
6	8
7	4 5 6 6 7 8 9 9
8	0 0 1 2 3 3 4 5 6 7 7 8 8 9
9	0 1 2 2 3 5

Key: 9 | 0 represents 90.

Yes, the score of 49 is an outlier. It is much lower than the other scores.

EXAMPLE 3

Use the graph below. The graph shows the distances and times that 20 students travel to get to school.

a. Does the data set have an outlier?

Yes, the point at about (1.8, 5) is an outlier.

b. What is a possible explanation for the outlier?

Since the data point represents a great distance and a short travel time, the student with that distance and time may use a different form of transportation to get to school. For example, the student might drive to school while all the other students walk.

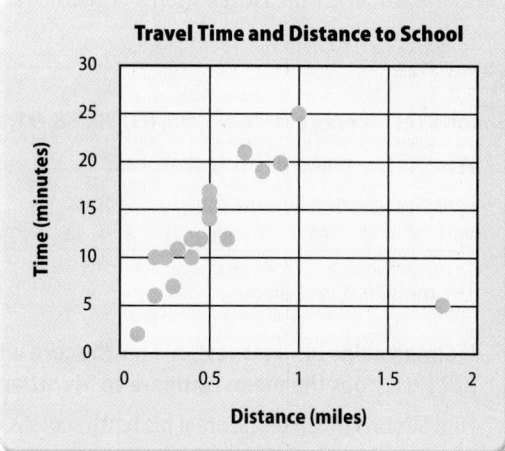

Need More

HELP?

For help with scatter plots, go to *Scatter Plots* on page 1264.

Sometimes the definition of an outlier is based on the interquartile range of the data. The **interquartile range** is the difference between the first quartile and the third quartile of the data. An outlier is considered to be any point that is less than the first quartile or greater than the third quartile by at least 1.5 times the interquartile range.

Need More

HELP?

Some people call the first quartile and the third quartile the *lower median* and the *upper median*, respectively.

EXAMPLE 4

Use the data in the table. Does the data set have an outlier? Explain why or why not.

Highest Temperature in June in Centerville (°F)									
Year 1	84	Year 2	78	Year 3	75	Year 4	81	Year 5	77
Year 6	85	Year 7	78	Year 8	80	Year 9	76	Year 10	77
Year 11	86	Year 12	98	Year 13	75				

STEP 1 Put the data in order from least to greatest to find the median and the quartiles.

75 75 76 | 77 77 78 <u>78</u> 80 81 84 | 85 86 98

There are 13 numbers in the data set. The median is the seventh number, 78.

The first quartile is the median of the lower half.   first quartile (Q1): $\frac{76 + 77}{2} = 76.5$

The third quartile is the median of the upper half.   third quartile (Q3): $\frac{84 + 85}{2} = 84.5$

STEP 2 Find the interquartile range (IQR).

IQR = Q3 − Q1 = 84.5 − 76.5 = 8.
Find 1.5 times the interquartile range: 1.5(8) = 12

STEP 3 Use the values found in Steps 1 and 2 to check for outliers. Outliers are any points that are less than Q1 − 1.5(IQR) or greater than Q3 + 1.5(IQR).

Q1 − 1.5(IQR) = 76.5 − 12 = 64.5
Q3 + 1.5(IQR) = 84.5 + 12 = 96.5

The high temperature of 98° in Year 12 is an outlier because it is greater than the sum of the third quartile and 1.5 times the interquartile range.

Try It This Way

After you arrange the numbers in order, circle the median.

Effects of Outliers

Outliers can affect measures such as the mean, median, mode, and range of the data.

SEARCH

To see step-by-step videos of these problems, enter the page number into the SWadvantage.com Search Bar.

EXAMPLE 5

Simon's test scores are 79, 85, 90, 89, 86, 88, 91, 87, and 84.

a. What is the mean of his test scores?

Find the mean of Simon's nine test scores.

$$\frac{79 + 85 + 90 + 89 + 86 + 88 + 91 + 87 + 84}{9} = \frac{779}{9} \approx 86.6$$

The mean is about 86.6.

b. If Simon skips his next test, his tenth score will be 0. What will the mean of his test scores be? How does the mean compare to his other scores?

Find Simon's mean test score if his tenth score is 0.

$$\frac{79 + 85 + 90 + 89 + 86 + 88 + 91 + 87 + 84 + 0}{10} = \frac{779}{10} = 77.9$$

If one score is 0, the mean is 77.9. This mean is lower than any of Simon's other test scores.

c. If Simon's tenth test score is 70, what will the mean of his test scores be? How does this mean compare with his other scores?

Find Simon's mean test score if his tenth score is 70.

$$\frac{79 + 85 + 90 + 89 + 86 + 88 + 91 + 87 + 84 + 70}{10} = \frac{849}{10} = 84.9$$

If the tenth score is 70, the mean is 84.9. This mean is closer to Simon's other test scores.

EXAMPLE 6

Ruby recorded how many hours she worked at her part-time job.

Hours Worked per Week
10 8 7 10 12 33 15 12 9 8
11 11 8 11 12 10 9 15 12 12

a. Find the mean, the median, and the mode of the data.

- Find the mean: $\frac{7 + 3(8) + 2(9) + 3(10) + 3(11) + 5(12) + 2(15) + 33}{20} = \frac{235}{20} = 11.75$.

- To find the median, put the data in order from least to greatest.

    7 8 8 8 9 9 10 10 10 11 11 | 11 12 12 12 12 12 15 15 33

    There are 20 numbers in the data set. The median is the mean of the tenth and eleventh elements. The median is 11.

- The mode is the value that occurs most often, 12.

b. Are there any outliers in the data? If so, remove them from the data set. Then find the mean, the median, and the mode of the new data set.

- Yes, 33 is an outlier.

- Find the new mean: $\frac{7 + 3(8) + 2(9) + 3(10) + 3(11) + 5(12) + 2(15)}{19} = \frac{202}{19} \approx 10.6$

- The median 11 and the mode 12 are the same for the new data set.

As shown in Examples 5 and 6, outliers affect the mean of a data set more than they affect the mode or the median. A statistical report that gives only one of these values may be misleading. Knowing more than one of the values gives a better picture of the whole data set. However, knowing the mean, the median, and the mode still does not tell you everything about the data set.

EXAMPLE 7

A newspaper article states that the average salary for a professional baseball team is $3,500,000. Explain why this statistic might be misleading.

The mean salary is influenced by outliers.

If one player has a very high salary, the average of the other players' salaries may be considerably lower than the overall average.

EXAMPLE 8

The median of a data set is 100, the mode is 95, and the mean is 268. What can you guess about the data set?

The data set has a large outlier, which increases the value of the mean.

EXAMPLE 9

The mean, the median, and the mode of a data set are all 10. What is a possible set of values for the data?

One possible set of values is {9, 10, 10, 10, 11}.

The data set has no outliers.

Another possible set of values is {−80, 9, 10, 10, 100}.

The data set has two outliers, −80 and 100.

Watch Out !

There is no limit to the number of data sets you can create that have a mean, median, and mode of 10.

GOT TO KNOW!

How an Outlier Affects a Data Set

An **outlier** is a value that is much larger or much smaller than the other numbers in the data set.

A data display can help find outliers.

In a set of data that is in order from least to greatest, let Q1 represent the first quartile, Q3 represent the third quartile, and IQR represent the interquartile range, Q3 − Q1.

An outlier is a value that is:

greater than (1.5(IQR) + Q3)   or   less than (Q1 − 1.5(IQR))

An outlier has a strong effect on the mean of its data set. It has a lesser effect or no effect on the median and mode.

Effects of Changing Data Values

Adding a Constant to Data Values

Sometimes the numbers in a data set must be changed, or *transformed*. If you add the same number, or constant, to every value in a data set, how will this change affect the mean, the median, the mode, and the range of the data?

Need More

HELP ?

For help with mean, median, and mode, go to *The "Center" of a Data Set* on page 1294.

EXAMPLE 1

The hourly wages of workers at the Hot Dog Palace are shown in the table.

Job	Hourly Wage ($)
Clerk 1	7.50
Clerk 2	7.50
Night crew 1	8.00
Clerk 3	7.50
Cook 1	8.50
Busboy	7.50
Cook 2	8.50
Night crew 2	8.00
Assistant manager	10.00
Clerk 4	7.50

SEARCH 🔍

To see step-by-step videos of these problems, enter the page number into the SWadvantage.com Search Bar.

The manager decides to give each employee a raise of $.25 per hour. How does this affect the mean, the median, the mode, and the range of the data?

STEP 1 Find the mean, median, mode, and range of the original data.

Put the data in order from least to greatest.

7.5 7.5 7.5 7.5 7.5 8 8 8.5 8.5 10

- Find the mean: $\dfrac{5(7.5) + 2(8) + 2(8.5) + 10}{10} = \dfrac{80.5}{10} = \$8.05$
- Find the median: $\dfrac{7.5 + 8}{2} = \$7.75$
- The mode is $7.50.
- Find the range: $10 - 7.5 = \$2.50$

STEP 2 Add 0.25 to each hourly wage.

7.75 7.75 7.75 7.75 7.75 8.25 8.25 8.75 8.75 10.25

- Find the mean: $\dfrac{5(7.75) + 2(8.25) + 2(8.75) + 10.25}{10} = \dfrac{83}{10} = \$8.30$
- Find the median: $\dfrac{7.75 + 8.25}{2} = \$8.00$
- The mode is $7.75.
- Find the range: $10.25 - 7.75 = \$2.50$

STEP 3 Compare the mean, median, mode, and range of the two data sets.

The mean, the median, and the mode of the new data are each 0.25 greater than they were for the original data.

The range of the new data equals the range of the original data.

EXAMPLE 2

Create box-and-whisker plots for the two data sets in Example 1. Compare the plots.

STEP 1 Make a box-and-whisker plot of the original data.

$$7.5 \quad 7.5 \quad 7.5 \quad 7.5 \quad 7.5 \mid 8 \quad 8 \quad 8.5 \quad 8.5 \quad 10$$

The least number in the set is 7.5, the first quartile is 7.5, the median is 7.75, the third quartile is 8.5, and the greatest number in the set is 10.

This is called the ***five-number summary*** of the data.

The box-and-whisker plot of the original data is shown below in black.

STEP 2 Make a plot of the new data.

$$7.75 \quad 7.75 \quad 7.75 \quad 7.75 \quad 7.75 \mid 8.25 \quad 8.25 \quad 8.75 \quad 8.75 \quad 10.25$$

The five-number summary of the new data is 7.75, 7.75, 8, 8.75, 10.25.

The box-and-whisker plot of the new data is shown in blue.

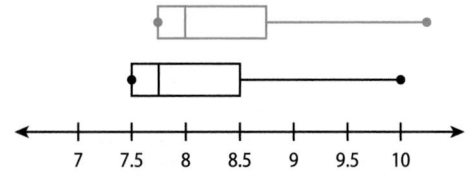

STEP 3 Compare the box-and-whisker plots.

- The box-and-whisker plots for the two data sets have boxes the same size and whiskers the same length.

- The graph of the new data is shifted 0.25 units to the right of the graph of the original data.

Need More HELP?

For more information about how to make a box-and-whisker plot, see *Box-and-Whisker Plots* on page 1280.

Watch Out !

For each data set, the first quartile equals the lowest value, so there is no left whisker.

In general, if you add a constant to every element in a data set, the mean, median, and mode of the data set will increase by the same constant. The range will not change. The graph will shift to the right if the constant is positive, or to the left if the constant is negative.

GOT TO KNOW!

Transforming Data with Addition

If you add a constant c to each element of a data set, these things happen.

- The mean increases by c.

- The median increases by c.

- The mode increases by c.

- The range does not change.

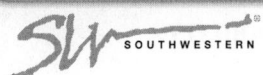

Multiplying Data Values by a Constant

Sometimes it is necessary or convenient to multiply every number in a data set by the same number. How will this affect the mean, the median, the mode, and the range of the data?

EXAMPLE 3

SEARCH

To see step-by-step videos of these problems, enter the page number into the SWadvantage.com Search Bar.

The table shows the distances in miles between locations in Yellowstone National Park.

Destination	From Lake Village (mi)
Mammoth Hot Springs	49
Tower-Roosevelt	35
Canyon Village	16
Norris Geysers	28
Grant Village	21
Old Faithful	38
Madison	42

A traveler wants to convert the distances to kilometers. How does this affect the mean, the median, the mode, and the range of the data? (Use 1 mi ≈ 1.6 km.)

STEP 1 Find the mean, the median, the mode, and the range of the original data.

Put the data in order: 16 21 28 35 38 42 49

- Find the mean: $\frac{16 + 21 + 28 + 35 + 38 + 42 + 49}{7} = \frac{229}{7} \approx 32.7$
- The median is 35.
- There is no mode.
- Find the range: $49 - 16 = 33$.

STEP 2 Multiply each element in the data set by 1.6:   25.6 33.6 44.8 56 60.8 67.2 78.4

- Find the mean: $\frac{25.6 + 33.6 + 44.8 + 56 + 60.8 + 67.2 + 78.4}{7} = \frac{366.4}{7} \approx 52.3$
- The median is 56.
- There is no mode.
- Find the range: $78.4 - 25.6 = 52.8$

STEP 3 Compare the mean, median, mode, and range of the two data sets.

- The mean of the new data is 1.6 times the mean of the original data.
  $52.3 \approx 32.7 \cdot 1.6$
- The median of the new data is 1.6 times the median of the original data.
  $56 = 35 \cdot 1.6$
- Neither data set has a mode.
- The range of the new data is 1.6 times the range of the original data.
  $52.8 = 33 \cdot 1.6$

In Step 2 of Example 3, you multiplied each length in the data set by 1.6 and then added the new lengths. Using the Distributive Property, you could instead add the original lengths and then multiply the total by 1.6. Notice that these methods give the same result.

EXAMPLE 4

Create box-and-whisker plots for the two data sets in Example 3. Compare the plots.

STEP 1 Make a box-and-whisker plot of the original data.

The five-number summary of the data is 16, 21, 35, 42, 49.

The box-and-whisker plot of the original data is shown in black below.

STEP 2 Make a plot of the new data.

The five-number summary of the new data is 25.6, 33.6, 56, 67.2, 78.4.

The box-and-whisker plot of the new data is shown in blue.

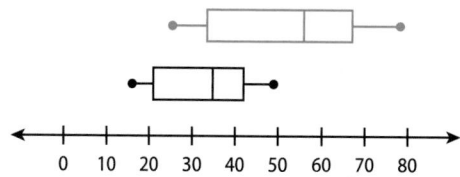

STEP 3 Compare the two box-and-whisker plots.

The box for the new data is 1.6 times as long as the box of the original plot. The whiskers for the new data are 1.6 times as long as the whiskers of the original plot.

> **Try It This Way**
>
> Think of multiplying every element in a data set by the same number as stretching the entire data set (if the constant is greater than 1) or shrinking it (if the constant is less than 1).

In general, if you multiply every element in a data set by a constant, then the mean, the median, the mode, and the range of the data set will be multiplied by the same constant.

EXAMPLE 5

A teacher gives quizzes worth 20 points each. At the end of the semester, she multiplies each score by 5 to make grading easier. The mean of the set of original quiz scores is 15.2, and the range is 10. What are the mean and the range of the revised scores?

Because the teacher multiplies each score by 5, the mean and the range are multiplied by 5.

So the mean of the new scores is $5(15.2) = 76$, and the range of the new scores is $5(10) = 50$.

GOT TO KNOW!

Transforming Data with Multiplication

If you multiply every element of a data set by a constant k, these things happen.

- The mean is multiplied by k.
- The median is multiplied by k.
- The mode is multiplied by k.
- The range is multiplied by k.

Changing the Scale

A political candidate wants to show that he is far ahead of his opponent. A business manager wants to point out that company growth has been steady. A student group wants one type of after-school activity to appear popular. In each of these situations, a graph or a statistic can be manipulated to support a point of view.

EXAMPLE 1

The results of a poll are shown in the table.

Who Will You Vote For? (% of registered voters)	
Candidate A	48
Candidate B	47
Undecided	5

a. Explain how Candidate A can use a bar graph of the data to show a significant lead.

A gap in the scale makes the bar for Candidate A appear more than one percentage point longer than the bar for Candidate B.

Leaving out the top label on the vertical axis makes it unclear that Candidate A does not have a majority (more than 50%).

Omitting the category of undecided voters makes it appear that changes in the bar lengths can occur only if a voter switches from one candidate to the other.

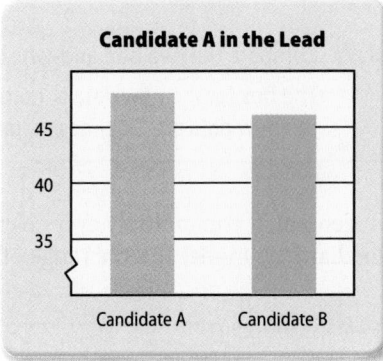

b. Explain how Candidate B can use a bar graph to show that the candidates have similar levels of support.

A larger vertical scale makes the difference between the candidates' percents of voters seem smaller.

Using an interval of 10 rather than 20 shows that Candidate A does not have 50% of the votes.

Including the category of undecided voters shows that Candidate A could lose if those voters choose Candidate B.

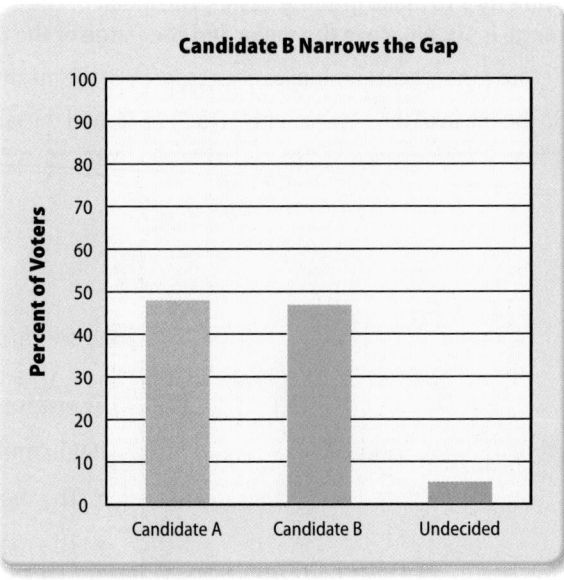

A gap in the scale on a graph or an unusual scale on a graph may indicate that the graph is misleading. When you read a graph, check whether it represents the data fairly.

Unless a bar graph is misleading, the bars should have equal widths. However, using bars of different widths in a histogram may be necessary if the data are given in uneven intervals. When using a histogram, be careful to note the width of the data intervals.

EXAMPLE 2

A survey team asked 110 students how many hours they studied for a college entrance exam. The results are shown in the data table. Make a histogram that shows these results.

Hours Spent Studying	Frequency
$0 \le h < 4$	32
$4 \le h < 5$	25
$5 \le h < 6$	23
$6 \le h < 8$	30

Notice that the intervals are not all equal. The widths of the bars of the histogram will match the sizes of the intervals.

STEP 1 Draw and label the axes. The horizontal axis represents the number of hours, and the vertical axis the frequency.

STEP 2 The first interval is 4 hours, and its frequency is 32. It is equivalent to four 1-hour intervals that are each $\frac{32}{4}$, or 8, units high. Draw a bar 4 units wide and 8 units high.

STEP 3 The second interval is 1 hour. Draw the second bar 1 unit wide and 25 units high.

STEP 4 Draw the third bar 1 unit wide and 23 units tall.

STEP 5 The fourth interval is 2 hours, and its frequency is 30. It is equivalent to two 1-hour intervals that are each $\frac{30}{2}$, or 15, units tall. Draw a bar 2 units wide and 15 units tall.

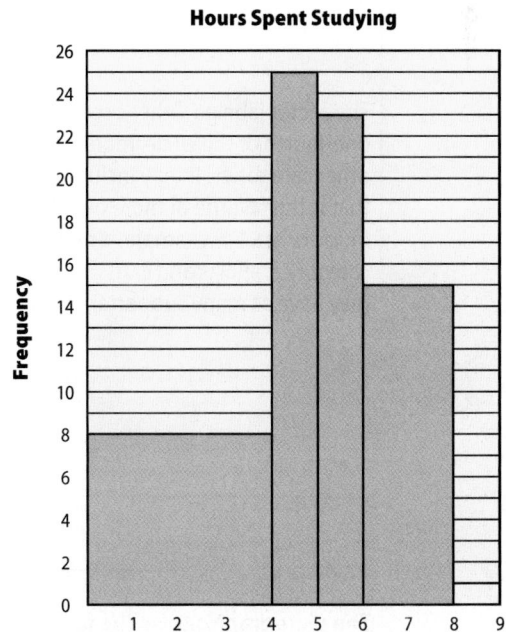

Hours Spent Studying

Need More

HELP ?

Remember that a histogram is constructed from a frequency table. For more information, see *Histograms* on page 1266.

Other Ways to Obscure Data

There are more ways to make a graph misleading. A sector of a circle graph may mask the size of some categories, or a pictograph may divert attention away from the data.

Need More
HELP ?

For more about how the sectors of a circle graph are created, go to *Circle Graphs* in *Foundations of Mathematics* (Book 1, p. 194).

EXAMPLE 3

Principal Elliot plans to add an after-school activity at her school. A group of students shows the principal the circle graph at the right to convince her that most students would prefer music or art for the activity. How might this graph be misleading?

Favorite After-School Activities

The sector labeled Other occupies about one-fourth of the circle, more than any of the other categories. It may include a category that is the favorite of more people than either music or art. For example, it might include two categories, sports and crafts, and one of them may have as many supporters as music or art.

Favorite After-School Activities

EXAMPLE 4

The pictograph shows the favorite fruits of 16 students. Explain how the graph is misleading.

Favorite Fruits

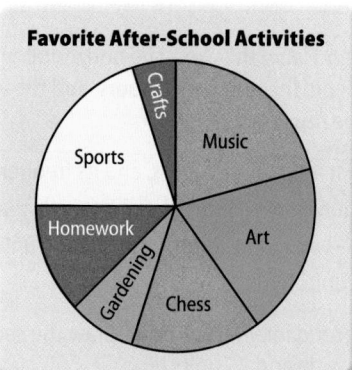

Oranges

Strawberries

Watermelon

The use of different-size symbols influences the way the choices are viewed. For example, 10 students chose strawberries and 2 chose watermelon, but the size of the watermelon symbol makes it appear more popular.

1308

EXAMPLE 5

The graph at the right gives the numbers of books and magazines sold at a book fair.

a. **Find the ratio of the number of books sold to the number of magazines sold.**

The ratio is $\frac{74}{95} \approx 0.78$.

b. **The covers of the book and the magazine are both squares. Find the ratio of the areas of the squares.**

The ratio is $\frac{74^2}{95^2} \approx 0.61$.

c. **Explain why this graph is misleading.**

The actual number of books sold is almost 80% of the number of magazines sold. Using two-dimensional figures to represent the numbers gives the impression that the number of books sold is only about 60% of the number of magazines sold.

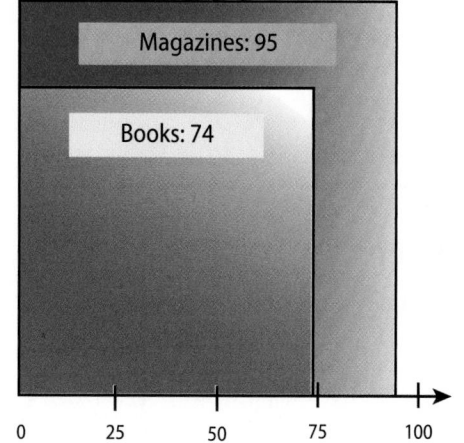

SEARCH

To see step-by-step videos of these problems, enter the page number into the SWadvantage.com Search Bar.

Using one measure of central tendency instead of another can also be misleading, especially if the numbers are not close together.

EXAMPLE 6

Lia is 14 years old. She asked her friends and her parents when they first got cell phones. The results are shown in the table.

a. **Find the mean, the median, and the mode of the data.**

The mean is

$$\frac{6(11) + 7(12) + 3(13) + 15 + 9(16) + 35 + 38}{28} = \frac{421}{28} \approx 15.$$

There are 28 numbers, so the median is the average of the fourteenth and fifteenth numbers, 13.

The mode is 16.

b. **Suppose Lia wants to get a cell phone as soon as possible. Which statistic might she use?**

Lia could use the median, the least of the three numbers.

c. **Suppose Lia's parents do not want her to have a cell phone. Which statistic might they use?**

They could use the mode, the greatest of the three numbers.

First Cell Phone

Age	Frequency
11	6
12	7
13	3
15	1
16	9
35	1
38	1

Analyzing and Using Data

What Came Before?
- Measures of the center of a data set
- Misleading statistics and data displays
- Outliers, and the effects of changing data

What's This About?
- Relationships within and between data sets
- Data distributions
- Designing experiments

Practical Apps
- Pollsters often create surveys so that the margin of error of the results is within ±3%.
- Data analysts work in many types of industries to develop means of presenting collected data as meaningful statistics.

Just for FUN!

No one believed the data value.

Most people said that it was an out and *out liar*!

You can find more practice problems online by visiting:
www.SWadvantage.com

Correlation

Is There a Pattern?

Some relationships between variables seem obvious, such as the relationship between a tree's height and its age. Others are less clear, such as whether practice really does make perfect. Making a scatter plot of a data set can help you decide what kind of pattern, if any, the data show.

EXAMPLE 1

Poppy measures the height of several palm trees from 2 to 20 years old. Her results are shown in the table.

Age (years)	2	4	6	10	11	14	17	20
Height (feet)	5	4	7	9	10	13	13.5	15

a. Make a scatter plot of the data in the table.

Draw a pair of coordinate axes. Label the horizontal axis from 0 to 20 and the vertical axis from 0 to 15.

Plot the points (age, height) on the graph.

b. What conclusion can you draw from the scatter plot?

There is a linear pattern in the data. As the age of a tree increases, the height increases also.

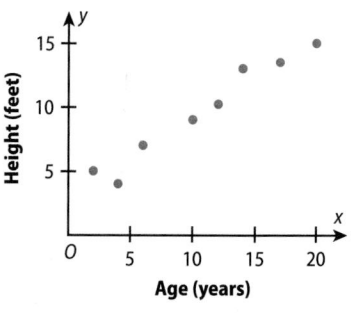

Try It This Way

You can use a spreadsheet or graphing calculator to make a scatter plot.

SEARCH

To see step-by-step videos of these problems, enter the page number into the SWadvantage.com Search Bar.

EXAMPLE 2

A placekicker on a football team attempted 20 field goals from each distance shown in the table. His coach recorded the number of goals made at each distance.

Distance (yards)	10	15	20	25	30	35	40	45	50
Goals made	20	20	17	18	17	15	12	12	10

a. Make a scatter plot of the data in the table.

Draw a pair of coordinate axes. Label the horizontal axis from 0 to 50 and the vertical axis from 0 to 20.

Plot the points (distance, goals made) on the graph.

b. What conclusion can you draw from the scatter plot?

These data also have a linear pattern. As the distance increases, the number of field goals decreases.

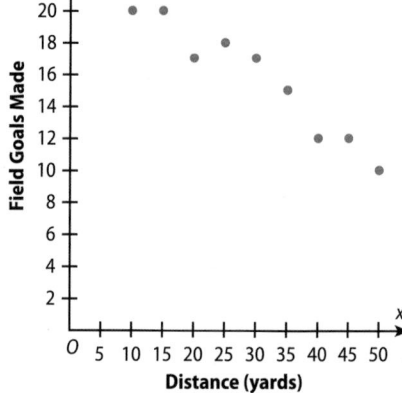

In Example 1 and Example 2, the data points in the scatter plots form linear patterns. That is, the points are not randomly distributed on the coordinate grid, but appear to lie on or near a straight line. These are examples of *linear correlations*. **Correlation** is the strength of the relationship between two variables.

Positive Correlation	**Negative Correlation**	**No Correlation**
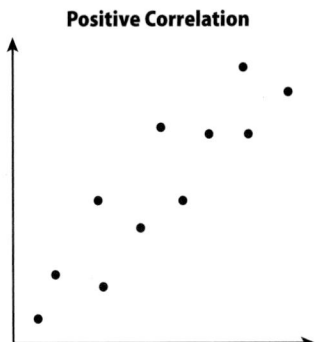	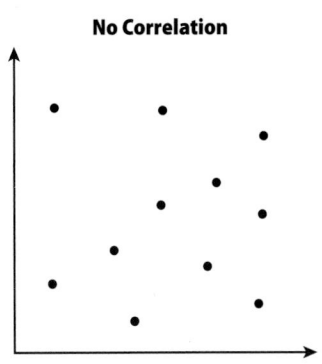	

If the points rise from left to right, the variables have a positive correlation.

If the points fall from left to right, the variables have a negative correlation.

If the points are randomly distributed on the graph, there is no correlation.

EXAMPLE 3

A keyboarding teacher asked her students to record how much time they spend practicing each week. She compares this information with the number of mistakes that the students made while typing a paper. The results are shown in the graph.

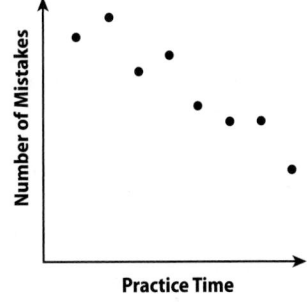

Is the relationship between the practice time and the number of mistakes a positive correlation, a negative correlation, or neither?

This is an example of a negative correlation. The data points appear to lie on or near a line with negative slope. The students who spent more time practicing made fewer mistakes.

GOT TO KNOW!

Correlation

Correlation is the strength of the relationship between two variables.

If the points on a graph rise from left to right, the variables have a **positive correlation**.

If the points on a graph fall from left to right, the variables have a **negative correlation**.

If the points on a graph are randomly distributed, there is **no correlation**.

Warnings about Correlations

The most important thing to remember when interpreting correlations is that correlation is not the same as causation. That is, if two variables show a correlation, it does not mean that change in one variable necessarily causes change in the other variable.

EXAMPLE 4

The scatter plot shows heights and reading levels of children in grades K through 5.

a. What kind of correlation does this scatter plot show?

The scatter plot shows a weak positive correlation. Taller students in the group tend to have higher reading levels.

b. Does being taller cause a student to have a higher reading level?

No, growing taller does not automatically make a student a better reader.

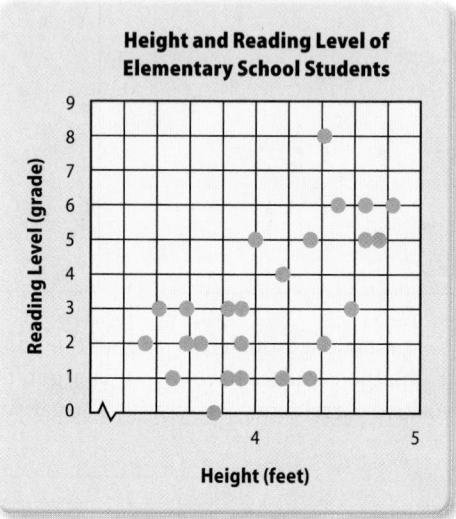

To avoid drawing an incorrect conclusion about a correlation, consider the populations the variables represent.

EXAMPLE 5

The scatter plot shows the heights and reading levels of 12 adults.

a. What kind of correlation does this show?

The scatter plot shows no correlation. The points are randomly distributed on the graph.

b. Is this a result that you might expect? Explain.

Yes. If the population contains only people less than 12 years old, you might expect taller people to have higher reading levels. If the population consists of people aged 21 and up, you would not expect reading level to be related to height.

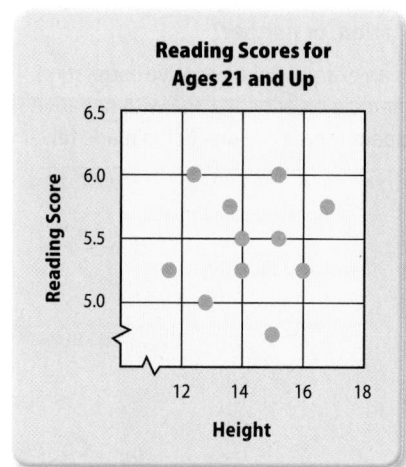

Do not assume that one part of a graph indicates what the whole graph will show. Variables may have a linear correlation for some values but have a different relationship overall.

EXAMPLE

Give an example of a pair of variables that appear to have a linear correlation for some values of the independent variable, but not for all values.

A chemist heats a solution to its boiling point, removes it from the heat source, and then measures the temperature of the solution every 5 minutes. The graph is shown at the right.

In the interval from about 5 minutes to about 25 minutes, the temperature appears to have a negative linear correlation with time. As the solution approaches room temperature, however, the graph changes and has a different shape. A single linear equation is not a good description of the cooling data.

If two variables appear to have a correlation, except for an outlier, check to see whether the outlier is reasonable.

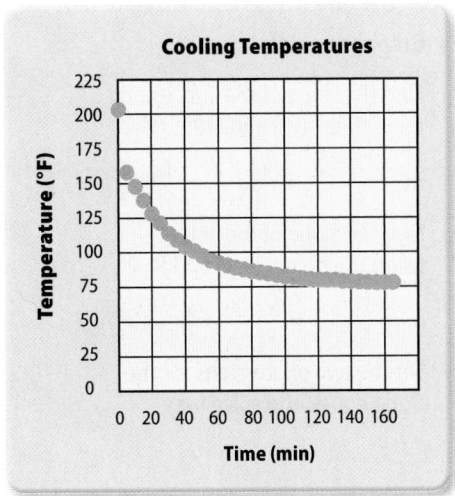

Cooling Temperatures

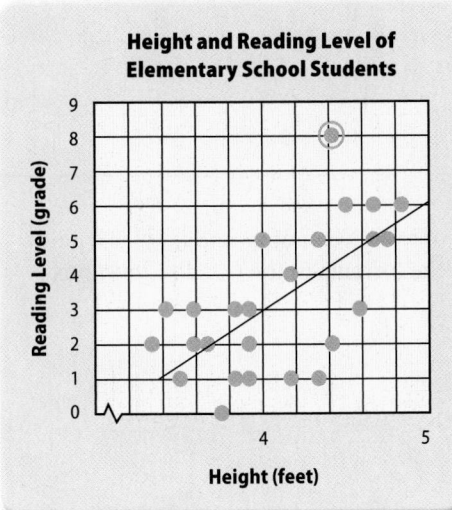

Height and Reading Level of Elementary School Students

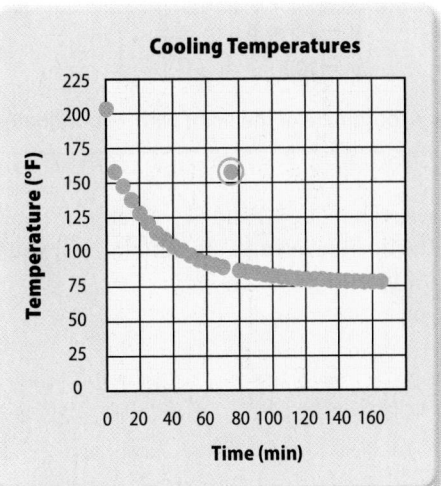

Cooling Temperatures

It seems reasonable that an elementary student might read at the eighth-grade level. The outlier is probably not an error.

It does not seem likely that a solution would have a spike in its temperature. This outlier is probably due to an error in measurement.

Need More
HELP ?

Remember that an outlier is a value that is not typical of the data set.

GOT TO KNOW!

Interpreting Correlations

Correlation is not causation.

One part of a graph may indicate a linear correlation when the graph as a whole does not.

Interpolating within a Data Set

Linear Interpolation

Suppose two variables have a linear relationship and you know the coordinates of two points on the graph. Because the slope of a line is a constant, you can use *linear interpolation* to find the coordinates of a point between the known points, as shown in Example 1.

Need More
HELP ?

For more about the slope of a line, see *Rate of Change and Slope* in *Algebra* (p. 1536).

SEARCH 🔍

To see step-by-step videos of these problems, enter the page number into the SWadvantage.com Search Bar.

EXAMPLE 1

The coordinates of two points on a line are (4, 8) and (10, 11). Find the *y*-coordinate of the point on the line whose *x*-coordinate is 9.

STEP 1 Graph the points.

STEP 2 Find the slope of the line, using the points (4, 8) and (10, 11).

$$m = \frac{y_2 - y_1}{x_2 - x_1} = \frac{11 - 8}{10 - 4} = \frac{3}{6} = \frac{1}{2}$$

STEP 3 Find the slope of the line, using the points (9, y) and (4, 8).

$$m = \frac{y_2 - y_1}{x_2 - x_1} = \frac{y - 8}{9 - 4} = \frac{y - 8}{5}$$

STEP 4 Set the two expressions for the slope equal, and solve for *y*.

$$\frac{y - 8}{5} = \frac{1}{2}$$

$$y - 8 = 5 \cdot \frac{1}{2}$$

$$y = 2.5 + 8$$

$$y = 10.5$$

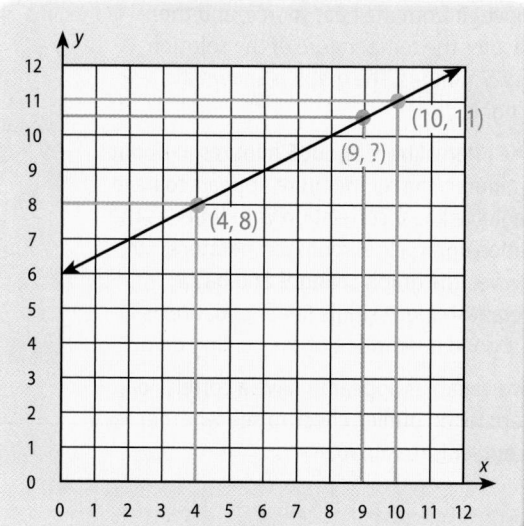

The *y*-coordinate of the point with *x*-coordinate 9 is 10.5.

In general, if (x_1, y_1) and (x_2, y_2) are the coordinates of two given points and (x, y) is a point on the line between (x_1, y_1) and (x_2, y_2), you can use the formula in the *Got To Know!* box below to find *y*.

GOT TO KNOW!

Linear Interpolation

For (x, y) on a line between (x_1, y_1) and (x_2, y_2):

$$y = y_1 + \left(\frac{y_2 - y_1}{x_2 - x_1}\right)(x - x_1)$$

If you know that the relationship between the variables in a data set is linear, you can use linear interpolation to find an unknown value. Use the two known data points closest to the point whose coordinate is unknown.

EXAMPLE 2

In the table below, Zach recorded his running time and distance each day for six days. Today Zach plans to run for 35 min. About how far can he go in that time?

Time (min)	20	48	29	14	60	42
Distance (mi)	2.7	5.8	3.8	2.0	7.0	5.1

STEP 1 Graph the data to make sure that it has a linear pattern.

To find the y-coordinate of the point with an x-coordinate of 35, use the two points with x-coordinates closest to 35: (29, 3.8) and (42, 5.1).

STEP 2 Substitute 29 for x_1, 3.8 for y_1, 42 for x_2, 5.1 for y_2, and 35 for x in the formula.

$$y = y_1 + \left(\frac{y_2 - y_1}{x_2 - x_1}\right) \cdot (x - x_1)$$

$$y = 3.8 + \left(\frac{5.1 - 3.8}{42 - 29}\right) \cdot (35 - 29)$$

$$= 3.8 + \frac{1.3}{13} \cdot 6 = 3.8 + 0.6 = 4.4$$

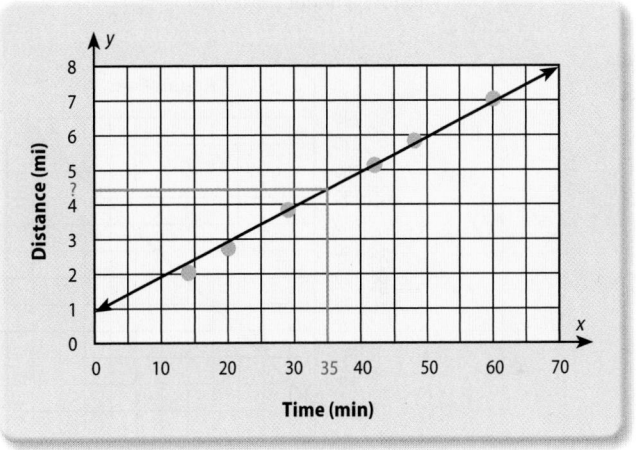

Zach can run about 4.4 mi in 35 min.

EXAMPLE 3

Use the data table in Example 2. About how long will it take Zach to run 3 mi?

Substitute 3 for y, (20, 2.7) for (x_1, y_1) and (29, 3.8) for (x_2, y_2) in the equation $\dfrac{y - y_1}{x - x_1} = \dfrac{y_2 - y_1}{x_2 - x_1}$.

Substitute. $\dfrac{3 - 2.7}{x - 20} = \dfrac{3.8 - 2.7}{29 - 20}$

Simplify. $\dfrac{0.3}{x - 20} = \dfrac{1.1}{9}$

Cross multiply. $1.1x - 22 = 2.7$

Solve for x. $1.1x = 24.7$

$x \approx 22.5$

It will take Zach about 22.5 min to run 3 mi.

Need More HELP?

Notice that the equation used in Example 3 is another form of the equation in the *Got To Know!* box. You get this form by subtracting y_1 from both sides and then dividing both sides by $x - x_1$.

Extrapolating from a Data Set

Need More

HELP ?

For more about the formula for linear interpolation, go to *Interpolating within a Data Set* on p. 1316.

Going Beyond the Data

Linear interpolation gives you an estimated value *between* two points of a linear function or relationship. **Extrapolation** gives an estimate *outside* a set of known points. If you know that data points lie on or near a line, and (x_1, y_1) and (x_2, y_2) are the coordinates of two points on the line, you can find the *y*-coordinate of a third point by using the formula for linear extrapolation. The formula is at the bottom of this page.

EXAMPLE 1

The repair fees at Herman's Bike Shop are shown in the table. How much should the shop charge for a job that takes 10 hours?

Time (hours)	Fee ($) (parts not included)
1	46
2	65
3	84
4	103
5	122

STEP 1 Graph the data to make sure they follow a linear pattern.

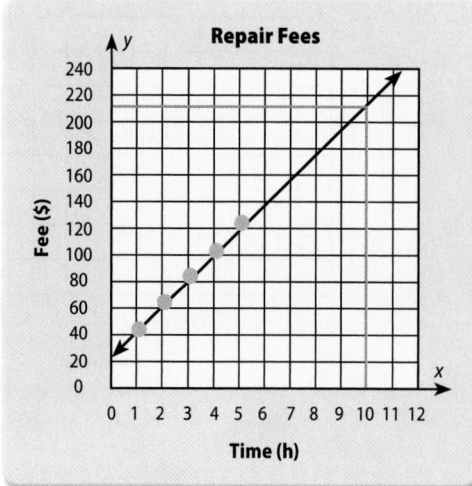

STEP 2 To find the value of *y* when $x = 10$, use the formula and the coordinates of two other points on the line.

Substitute 10 for *x*, 4 for x_1, 103 for y_1, 5 for x_2, and 122 for y_2 in the formula:

$$y = y_1 + \left(\frac{y_2 - y_1}{x_2 - x_1}\right) \cdot (x - x_1)$$

$$y = 103 + \left(\frac{122 - 103}{5 - 4}\right) \cdot (10 - 4)$$

$$= 103 + 19 \cdot 6 = 217$$

The bike shop should charge $217 for a 10-hour job.

GOT TO KNOW!

Extrapolation

You can use the formula $y = y_1 + \left(\frac{y_2 - y_1}{x_2 - x_1}\right) \cdot (x - x_1)$ to estimate the coordinates (x, y) of a point outside a data set if the data are linear or if the point (x, y) is close to the points (x_1, y_1) and (x_2, y_2).

EXAMPLE 2

Explain why the given data must be linear if you want to use the extrapolation equation to make a prediction from the data.

In Example 1, suppose the repair shop has a lower hourly rate for jobs longer than 5 hours. Then the graph at the right would give a better picture of the rates. A prediction from a straight line would not be accurate.

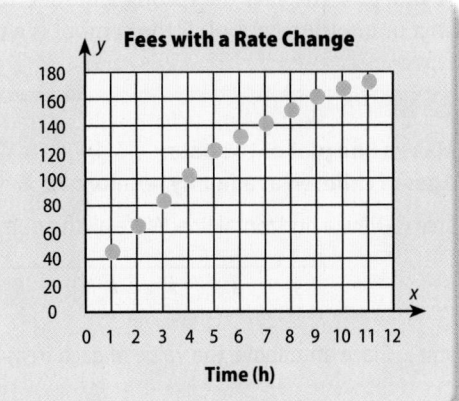

SEARCH 🔍

To see step-by-step videos of these problems, enter the page number into the SWadvantage.com Search Bar.

If the data are roughly linear, you can find the equation for the line of best fit for the data. Then you can use the equation to make an estimate.

EXAMPLE 3

The table shows the numbers of pieces in several plastic brick construction sets, along with the price of each set. Use extrapolation to estimate the price of a set with 450 pieces.

Number of Pieces	342	388	214	129	131	46	28	94	59	267	142	43	102	118	222
Price ($)	40	40	23	13	10	4	4	10	6	30	20	5	11	13	20

STEP 1 Graph the data to see whether they suggest a linear relationship.

STEP 2 Use a calculator or a spreadsheet to find the equation for the line of best fit.

The equation is $y \approx 0.11x - 0.17$.

STEP 3 Substitute 450 for x in the equation for the line of best fit.

$y \approx 0.11(450) - 0.17$

≈ 49.33

A set with 450 pieces should cost about $49.33.

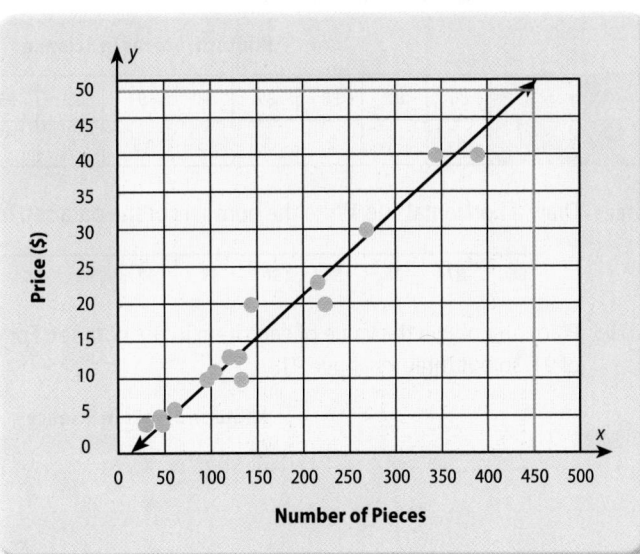

Need More

HELP ?

For more about how to find the equation for the line of best fit, go to *Linear Regression* on page 1332.

Line Plots and Data Distribution

Line Plots

A **line plot** displays data along a number line. Each number in the data set is represented by an *x* or another symbol. If the symbol is a dot, the line plot is called a *dot plot*.

SEARCH

To see step-by-step videos of these problems, enter the page number into the SWadvantage.com Search Bar.

EXAMPLE 1

Make a line plot of the data.
Ages of children at a family reunion: 12 6 11 9 12 9 12 6 12 8 11 10 9 5 16

STEP 1 Draw a horizontal line. Write all the numbers from 5 through 16 under the line.

| 5 | 6 | 7 | 8 | 9 | 10 | 11 | 12 | 13 | 14 | 15 | 16 |

STEP 2 Place an *x* above the value of each item in the data set.

```
                                        X
                        X               X
            X           X           X   X
   X    X           X   X   X   X   X               X
  ─────────────────────────────────────────────────────
   5    6    7    8    9   10   11   12   13   14   15   16
```

Notice that a line plot shows every value in the data set, and the frequency of each value. By looking at the line plot you can quickly determine the mode, 12 years; and an outlier, 16 years.

EXAMPLE 2

Make a line plot of the data in the table.

Midterm Scores in Science

Score	86	87	88	89	90	91	92	93	94	95	96	97	98
Frequency	1	1	2	3	3	3	6	5	4	1	3	2	1

STEP 1 Draw a horizontal line. Write the numbers of the data set, from 86 through 98, under the line.

| 86 | 87 | 88 | 89 | 90 | 91 | 92 | 93 | 94 | 95 | 96 | 97 | 98 |

STEP 2 Place an *x* above the value of each item in the data set. For example, there are three scores of 91, so put three *x*'s above 91.

Midterm Scores in Science

```
                              X
                              X   X
                              X   X   X
               X   X   X   X  X   X           X
           X   X   X   X   X  X   X           X   X
   X   X   X   X   X   X   X  X   X   X   X   X   X
  ──────────────────────────────────────────────────
  86  87  88  89  90  91  92 93  94  95  96  97  98
```

You can think of a line plot as a histogram with a bar (or column of *x*'s) for each number in the data set. You do not group data in intervals in a line plot.

 **EXAMPLE 3**

The line plot shows the finish times for 50 runners in a race.

Finish Times for 10K Fun Run (minutes)

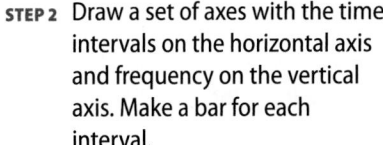

												X	X		
									X			X	X		
							X	X	X	X	X	X			
	X				X	X	X	X	X	X	X	X	X	X	
	X		X		X	X	X	X	X	X	X	X	X	X	X
X	X	X	X	X	X	X	X	X	X	X	X	X	X	X	X
36	37	38	39	40	41	42	43	44	45	46	47	48	49	50	51

a. Make a histogram from the data in the line plot, using intervals of 4 minutes.

STEP 1 Start with the least number, 36. Use it and the next three numbers, 37, 38, and 39, to make an interval of 4. There are 7 finish times in this interval, so the interval 36–39 has a frequency of 7.

Continue counting this way to the last number, 51.

Time (minutes)	Frequency
36–39	7
40–43	9
44–47	15
48–51	19

STEP 2 Draw a set of axes with the time intervals on the horizontal axis and frequency on the vertical axis. Make a bar for each interval.

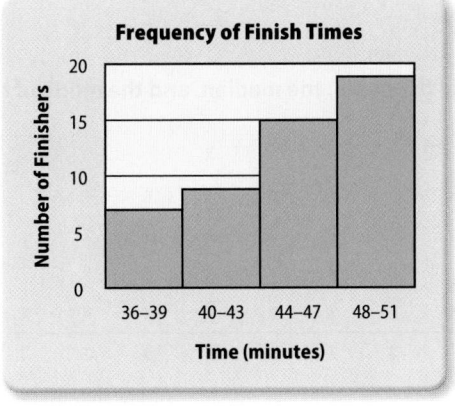

Frequency of Finish Times

b. Compare the line plot and the histogram.

The histogram shows the trend of a few runners with shorter finish times and a greater number of runners with longer times.

The line plot shows the time of every runner, but the histogram does not. For example, although the histogram shows that 7 runners had times between 36 and 39 minutes, it does not show that the fastest runner's time was 36 minutes.

The line plot was used to make the histogram, but the histogram cannot be used to make a line plot of the same data.

Try It This Way

You can use a graphing calculator to make a histogram. Check the manual for instructions.

Watch Out !

Remember that there are no spaces between the bars in a histogram.

The Shape of a Distribution

If you imagine a smooth line connecting the tops of the *x*'s in a line plot or the tops of the bars in a histogram, you can picture the shape of the distribution of data. The graphs below show some common shapes of distributions.

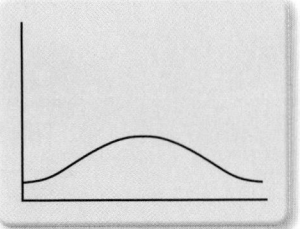

If the left half of a data set is the mirror image of its right half, the data set is called *symmetric*.

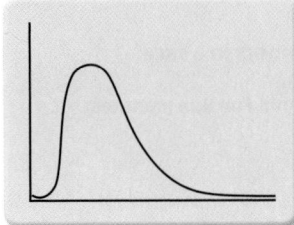

A distribution with a long tail to the right is said to be *skewed right* or *positively skewed*.

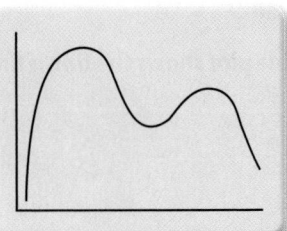

This distribution is bimodal but not symmetric. The modes have different frequencies.

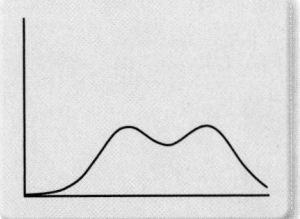

A distribution that has two distinct modes is called *bimodal*.

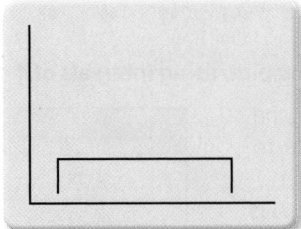

A distribution in which all the values have the same frequency is called *uniform*.

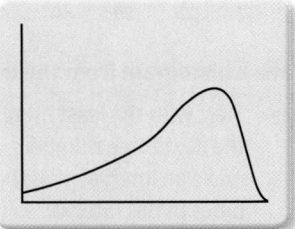

A distribution with a long tail to the left is said to be *skewed left* or *negatively skewed*.

Need More
HELP ?

For more about mean, median, and mode, go to *The Center of a Data Set* in *Describing Data* (p. 1294).

SEARCH

To see step-by-step videos of these problems, enter the page number into the SWadvantage.com Search Bar.

EXAMPLE 4

a. Find the mean, the median, and the mode of the data in the line plot.

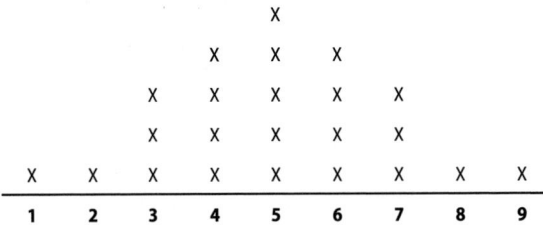

There are 23 *x*'s in the line plot, so there 23 numbers in the data set.

The mean is $\dfrac{1 + 2 + 3(3) + 4(4) + 5(5) + 4(6) + 3(7) + 8 + 9}{23} = \dfrac{115}{23} = 5$.

The median is 5, the 12th number.

The mode is 5, the most common number in the data set.

b. What is the shape of the distribution, and what do you notice about the mean, the median, and the mode?

The data are symmetrically distributed, and the mean, the median, and the mode are all equal.

EXAMPLE 5

a. **Find the mean, the median, and the mode of the data in the line plot.**

```
                                         X
                                  X      X
                        X    X    X      X
                   X    X    X    X      X
    X    X    X    X    X    X    X    X      X    X
  ─────────────────────────────────────────────────
    1    2    3    4    5    6    7    8    9    10
```

There are 22 numbers in the data set.

The mean is $\dfrac{1 + 2 + 3 + 4 + 2(5) + 3(6) + 3(7) + 4(8) + 5(9) + 10}{22} = \dfrac{146}{22} \approx 6.6$.

The median is 7, the average of the 11th and 12th numbers.

The mode is 9, the most common number in the data set.

b. **What is the shape of the distribution, and what do you notice about the mean, the median, and the mode?**

The data are skewed left. The mean is to the left of the median and the mode.

In general, if a distribution is skewed left, the mean is to the left of the median and mode on a line plot. If a distribution is skewed right, the mean is to the right of the median and mode. If a distribution is symmetric, the mean, the median, and the mode may be equal.

EXAMPLE 6

What does the line plot tell you about the distribution of the data?

Weights of White-Tailed Deer (kg)

```
              X                   X
              X                   X    X
              X    X              X    X
              X    X              X    X
         X    X    X    X    X    X
         X    X    X    X    X    X    X
    X    X    X    X    X    X    X    X    X              X
  ───────────────────────────────────────────────────────────
   40   50   60   70   80   90  100  110  120  130  140  150
```

The distribution is bimodal, with modes at 60 kg and 90 kg. The range is 110 kg, but this is influenced by an outlier of 150 kg. Most of the weights fall between 50 kg and 110 kg.

Watch Out !

The "direction" of a skewed distribution is the direction of the tail of the graph. It does not describe the location of the mode of the data set.

GOT TO KNOW !

The Shape of a Distribution

When describing a data set, include the shape of the distribution, the range, the center, and any outliers.

Shape: Tell whether the distribution is symmetric, uniform, bimodal, or skewed left or right.

Center: Tell whether the mean, the median, or the mode best describes the data, and give its value.

Range: Is the range large or small?

Outliers: Are there any unusually large or small data values? If so, what do they indicate?

Standard Deviation

Deviation from the Mean

Two data sets may have the same mean, but different distributions. For example, if the mean of a data set is 15, most of the data elements may be between 14 and 16, or there may be clusters of data near 0 and 30.

The two distributions in the diagram below have the same mean, but the data elements of the distribution shown in black cluster closer in value to the mean than are those of the distribution shown in blue.

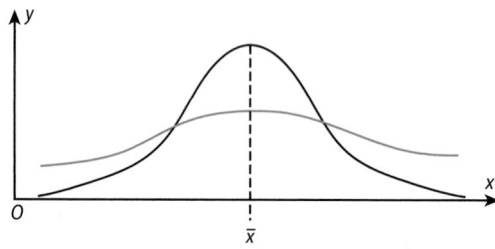

Need More
HELP ❓
The symbol $\bar{x}$ is read "x bar."

The **deviation from the mean** is the difference in value between a data element and the mean of its data set. The symbol $\bar{x}$ represents the mean of a data set, and x_i represents the ith element in the set. The expression $x_i - \bar{x}$ is the deviation from the mean of the ith element in the data set.

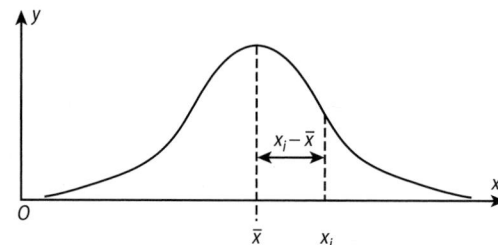

EXAMPLE 1

The mean score of a standardized test is 515. A student scores 660 on the test. Find the deviation from the mean for the student's score.

Use the formula for the deviation from the mean.

$$x_i - \bar{x} = 660 - 515$$
$$x_i - \bar{x} = 145$$

The deviation from the mean is 145.

Variance

Watch Out ⚠
The uppercase Greek letter sigma, Σ, is an operation symbol and represents a sum. The lowercase Greek letter sigma, σ, is a variable.

The *variance* of a data set is a way to average the deviations from the mean. In Example 1, a score of 370 is also 145 points from the mean, but its deviation from the mean is negative. To avoid negative values in averaging deviations, the deviations are squared first.

The **variance** of a data set is the sum of the squares of the deviations from the mean, divided by the number of elements in the data set. The symbol σ^2, read "sigma squared," is used for the variance of a population:

$$\sigma^2 = \frac{\Sigma(x_i - \bar{x})^2}{n} = \frac{1}{n}\Sigma(x_i - \bar{x})^2$$

EXAMPLE 2

Alana's test scores are 74, 88, 80, 77, and 86. What is the variance of her test scores?

STEP 1 Find the mean of the test scores.

$$\bar{x} = \frac{74 + 88 + 80 + 77 + 86}{5}$$

$$\bar{x} = 81$$

STEP 2 Make a table of the values needed to find the variance.

i	x_i	$\bar{x}$	$x_i - \bar{x}$	$(x_i - \bar{x})^2$
1	74	81	-7	49
2	88	81	7	49
3	80	81	-1	1
4	77	81	-4	16
5	86	81	5	25

STEP 3 Find the sum of the squared differences and divide by 5, the number of elements.

$$\frac{\Sigma(x_i - \bar{x})^2}{n} = \frac{49 + 49 + 1 + 16 + 25}{5}$$

$$= \frac{140}{5}$$

$$= 28$$

The variance of Alana's test scores is 28.

Try It This Way

Although it is important to know and understand the formulas for variance and standard deviation, finding the values can be tedious. Most scientific and graphing calculators can compute both values from a list of data values.

The Standard Deviation of a Population

Because the variance is an average of squares, it is difficult to interpret. So the square root of the variance, the **standard deviation**, is often used instead. The lowercase Greek letter sigma, σ, represents the standard deviation of a population.

$$\sigma = \sqrt{\frac{\Sigma(x_i - \bar{x})^2}{n}}$$

EXAMPLE 3

Find the standard deviation of the test scores in Example 2.

Use the formula for standard deviation. $\sigma = \sqrt{\frac{\Sigma(x_i - \bar{x})^2}{n}} = \sqrt{28} \approx 5.3$

The standard deviation is about 5.3 points.

SEARCH

To see step-by-step videos of these problems, enter the page number into the SWadvantage.com Search Bar.

The standard deviation is a useful measure of a data set because it is in the same unit as the original data. A small standard deviation indicates that most of the data lie close to the mean, and a large standard deviation indicates that the data are spread out.

The size of the standard deviation should be interpreted in comparison to the values of the original data. A set of annual salaries may have a standard deviation of thousands of dollars but still be grouped close to the mean.

Standard Deviation for a Sample

If a data set represents a sample instead of the entire population, the denominators of the variance and the standard deviation are slightly different. By convention, s^2 represents the variance of a sample, and s represents the standard deviation.

$$s^2 = \frac{\Sigma(x_i - \bar{x})^2}{n - 1}$$

$$s = \sqrt{\frac{\Sigma(x_i - \bar{x})^2}{n - 1}}$$

In these formulas, $\bar{x}$ represents the mean of the sample, and n is the size of the sample.

EXAMPLE 4

SEARCH

To see step-by-step videos of these problems, enter the page number into the SWadvantage.com Search Bar.

Tatsuo asks six friends what their allowances are. Find the standard deviation of the sample.

Student	1	2	3	4	5	6
Allowance ($)	15	10	12	10	14	5

STEP 1 Find the mean of the allowances.

$$\bar{x} = \frac{15 + 10 + 12 + 10 + 14 + 5}{6}$$

$$\bar{x} = 11$$

STEP 2 Make a table of the values needed to find the variance.

i	x_i	$\bar{x}$	$x_i - \bar{x}$	$(x_i - \bar{x})^2$
1	15	11	4	16
2	10	11	−1	1
3	12	11	1	1
4	10	11	−1	1
5	14	11	3	9
6	5	11	−6	36

STEP 3 Find the sum of the squared differences and divide by $n - 1$.

$$s^2 = \frac{\Sigma(x_i - \bar{x})^2}{n - 1} = \frac{16 + 1 + 1 + 1 + 9 + 36}{5}$$

$$= \frac{64}{5} = 12.8$$

The variance of the sample is 12.8.

STEP 4 The standard deviation is the square root of the variance. $s = \sqrt{\frac{\Sigma(x_i - \bar{x})^2}{n - 1}} = \sqrt{12.8} \approx 3.58$

The standard deviation of the allowance sample is about $3.58.

In Example 4, notice that four of the six allowances are within $3.58 of the mean of the allowances, $11.00.

Raw-Scores Method

It is often easier to find the variance and the standard deviation by using the raw scores instead of the deviations from the mean. The raw-scores formula for the variance of a

sample is $s^2 = \dfrac{\Sigma(x_i)^2 - \dfrac{(\Sigma x_i)^2}{n}}{n-1}$. The standard deviation is the square root of the variance.

Watch Out

The expression $\Sigma(x_i)^2$ is the sum of the squares of the data values, and $(\Sigma x_i)^2$ is the square of the sums of the data values. They are not the same.

 **EXAMPLE 5**

Use the raw-scores method to find the variance and the standard deviation of the data in Example 4.

STEP 1 Make a table of the data and the squares of the data.

i	x_i	$(x_i)^2$
1	15	225
2	10	100
3	12	144
4	10	100
5	14	196
6	5	25

STEP 2 Find $(\Sigma x_i)^2 = 225 + 100 + 144 + 100 + 196 + 25 = 790$

STEP 3 Find $(\Sigma x_i)^2 = (15 + 10 + 12 + 10 + 14 + 5)^2 = 66^2 = 4356$

STEP 4 Substitute the values from Steps 2 and 3 into the formula for the variance.

$$s^2 = \frac{\Sigma(x_i)^2 - \frac{(\Sigma x_i)^2}{n}}{n-1} = \frac{790 - \frac{4356}{6}}{6-1}$$

$$= \frac{790 - 726}{5}$$

$$= \frac{64}{5} = 12.8$$

STEP 5 The standard deviation is the square root of the variance. $s = \sqrt{12.8} \approx 3.58$

GOT TO KNOW!

	Population	Sample
Variance	$\sigma^2 = \dfrac{\Sigma(x_i - \bar{x})^2}{n}$	$s^2 = \dfrac{\Sigma(x_i - \bar{x})^2}{n-1}$
Standard deviation	$\sigma = \sqrt{\dfrac{\Sigma(x_i - \bar{x})^2}{n}}$	$s = \sqrt{\dfrac{\Sigma(x_i - \bar{x})^2}{n-1}}$
What the variables mean	x_i is the ith data value. $\bar{x}$ is the mean of the population. n is the number of elements in the population.	x_i is the ith data value. $\bar{x}$ is the mean of the sample. n is the number of elements in the sample.

Quartiles and Percentiles

Cumulative Frequencies

Owen takes a music trivia quiz and scores 18 out of 25. He would like to know how his score compares to the scores of others fans who took the quiz.

A **cumulative frequency distribution** shows how many scores are less than or equal to any given score in a data set. It is used to find percentile ranks. A **cumulative percent frequency table** shows the percent of scores less than or equal to any given score.

SEARCH

To see step-by-step videos of these problems, enter the page number into the SWadvantage.com Search Bar.

EXAMPLE 1

Make a cumulative percent frequency table of the quiz scores in the table.

Score	8	12	13	15	16	18	19	21	23
Frequency	1	1	2	2	3	4	4	2	1

STEP 1 Make a table that shows the cumulative frequency. Start with the least score. Its cumulative frequency is 1. Add the frequency of the next highest score to the cumulative frequency of the previous score. Continue this method until you reach the greatest score in the table.

Score	Frequency	Cumulative Frequency
8	1	1
12	1	$1 + 1 = 2$
13	2	$2 + 2 = 4$
15	2	$2 + 4 = 6$
16	3	$3 + 6 = 9$
18	4	$4 + 9 = 13$
19	4	$4 + 13 = 17$
21	2	$2 + 17 = 19$
23	1	$1 + 19 = 20$

Add the frequency of 16 to the cumulative frequency of 15 to find the cumulative frequency of 16.

There are 17 scores less than or equal to 19.

This is the total number of scores.

STEP 2 Add a fourth column to the table. Divide each cumulative frequency by 20, the total number of scores. Put the percent in the last column.

Score	Frequency	Cumulative Frequency	Cumulative Percent Frequency (%)
8	1	1	$\frac{1}{20} = 0.05 = 5\%$
12	1	2	10
13	2	4	20
15	2	6	30
16	3	9	45
18	4	13	65
19	4	17	85
21	2	19	95
23	1	20	100

Percentiles

You can use a cumulative percent frequency table to find percentile ranks of scores. The **percentile rank** of a given score is the percent of the total number of scores less than or equal to the score. Percentile ranks divide a data set into 100 groups of equal size.

EXAMPLE 2

Use the data in Example 1. Find the percentile rank of a score of 18 on the quiz.

Find the row that contains the score 18.

Score	Frequency	Cumulative Frequency	Cumulative Percent Frequency (%)
8	1	1	5
12	1	2	10
13	2	4	20
15	2	6	30
16	3	9	45
18	4	13	65
19	4	17	85
21	2	19	95
23	1	20	100

The table shows that 65% of the scores in the data set are less than or equal to 18. The percentile rank of 18 is 65. This is also read, "18 is at the 65th percentile."

Watch Out !

Notice that the percentile rank is not the same as the percent of questions answered correctly on the quiz.

EXAMPLE 3

Use the data in Example 1. What score has a percentile rank of 30?

Find the row that has 30 in the Cumulative Percent Frequency column.

Score	Frequency	Cumulative Frequency	Cumulative Percent Frequency (%)
8	1	1	5
12	1	2	10
13	2	4	20
15	2	6	30
16	3	9	45
18	4	13	65
19	4	17	85
21	2	19	95
23	1	20	100

The corresponding score is 15. The score 15 has a percentile rank of 30.

Finding Percentiles with Interpolation

Percentiles are often used to report an individual's rank in a large group of scores, such as those on a standardized test. The score data are often given in groups, or intervals. To find a percentile rank within an interval, you can use linear interpolation.

EXAMPLE 4

The table shows the scores for a standardized test. What score has a percentile rank of 80?

Score Interval	Frequency	Cumulative Frequency	Cumulative Percent Frequency (%)
151–200	5	5	3.3
201–250	8	13	8.7
251–300	32	45	30
301–350	60	105	70
351–400	34	139	92.7
401–450	9	148	98.7
451–500	2	150	100

None of the cumulative percent frequencies in the table is exactly 80. The score with percentile rank 80 lies in the interval 351–400.

To estimate the score, assume that the scores within each interval lie on a line. Use the upper limit of each interval as the x-coordinate and the cumulative percent frequency as the y-coordinate of each point.

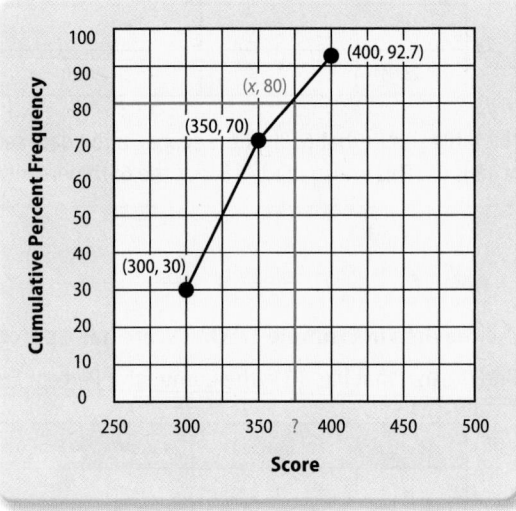

To find x, substitute 350 for x_1, 70 for y_1, 400 for x_2, 92.7 for y_2, and 80 for y in the equation below.

$$\frac{y - y_1}{x - x_1} = \frac{y_2 - y_1}{x_2 - x_1}$$

$$\frac{80 - 70}{x - 350} = \frac{92.7 - 70}{400 - 350}$$

Simplify.

$$\frac{10}{x - 350} = \frac{22.7}{50}$$

Cross-multiply.

$$22.7(x - 350) = 500$$

Divide both sides by 22.7.

$$x - 350 = \frac{500}{22.7}$$

Add 350 to both sides. Simplify.

$$x \approx 372.03$$

The score with a percentile rank of 80 is about 372.

Quartiles divide a data set into four parts, each containing an equal number of scores. The **first quartile** of a data set is its 25th percentile. The median, or **second quartile**, is the 50th percentile. The **third quartile** is the 75th percentile.

Need More

HELP

For more about quartiles, go to *Box-and-Whisker Plots* in *Displaying Data* (p. 1280) and *Outliers* in *Describing Data* (p. 1298).

EXAMPLE 5

The table shows the scores on a test. Find the first quartile and the median of the data set.

Score Interval	Frequency	Cumulative Frequency	Cumulative Percent Frequency (%)
66–70	1	1	1.25
71–75	5	6	7.5
76–80	18	24	30.0
81–85	33	57	71.25
86–90	19	76	95.0
91–95	3	79	98.75
96–100	1	80	100.0

STEP 1 Find the first quartile by finding the 25th percentile.

None of the cumulative percent frequencies in the table is exactly 25. The score with percentile rank 25 lies in the interval 76–80. Assume that the scores within the interval lie on a line. Use the upper limit of each interval as the x-coordinate and the cumulative percent frequency as the y-coordinate of each point. Substitute (75, 7.5) for (x_1, y_1), (80, 30) for (x_2, y_2), and 25 for y.

$$\frac{y - y_1}{x - x_1} = \frac{y_2 - y_1}{x_2 - x_1}$$

Substitute. $$\frac{25 - 7.5}{x - 75} = \frac{30 - 7.5}{80 - 75}$$

Simplify. $$\frac{17.5}{x - 75} = \frac{22.5}{5}$$

Solve for x. $$x \approx 78.89$$

The first quartile is about 79.

STEP 2 Find the median by finding the 50th percentile.

The score with percentile rank 50 lies in the interval 81–85. Assume that the scores within the interval lie on a line. Use the same process as in Step 1. Substitute (80, 30) for (x_1, y_1), (85, 71.25) for (x_2, y_2), and 50 for y.

$$\frac{y - y_1}{x - x_1} = \frac{y_2 - y_1}{x_2 - x_1}$$

Substitute. $$\frac{50 - 30}{x - 80} = \frac{71.25 - 30}{85 - 80}$$

Simplify. $$\frac{20}{x - 80} = \frac{41.25}{5}$$

Solve for x. $$x \approx 82.42$$

The median is about 82.

GOT TO KNOW!

Percentiles and Quartiles

Percentiles divide a data set into 100 parts, each containing an equal number of scores.

Quartiles divide a data set into 4 parts, each containing an equal number of scores.

You can find percentiles and quartiles by constructing a cumulative percent frequency table and using linear interpolation if necessary.

Linear Regression

The Line of Best Fit

The **line of best fit** is the straight line that fits most closely the trend of data points in a scatter plot. The line may contain some of the data points or none of the data points. If the data points are strictly linear, then the line of best fit will go through all the points. You can use a line of best fit to make predictions.

 **EXAMPLE 1**

The owners of an ice cream stand record the number of ice cream cones sold and the outside temperature for several days.

Ice Cream Cone Sales

Day	1	2	3	4	5	6	7	8	9
Temperature (°F)	78	82	84	86	80	75	72	77	90
Number of ice cream cones sold	131	133	152	150	149	137	122	144	158

Need More HELP

For more about graphing paired data, see *Scatter Plots,* (p. 1264).

a. Make a scatter plot of the data. What type of correlation do the data show?

Use a graphing calculator or a spreadsheet to make a scatter plot, or graph the points by hand. Use the temperatures as the *x*-values (the independent variable) and the numbers of ice cream cones sold as the *y*-values (the dependent variable).

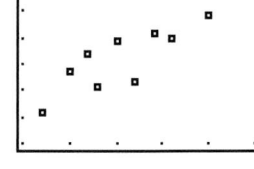

The data show a positive correlation, because the points show an upward trend from left to right.

b. Use a graphing calculator to find the equation of the line of best fit for the data.

Choose CALC from the STAT menu, and then choose LinReg or LINR. You will see a display with a linear equation and the values of its slope *a* and *y*-intercept *b*.

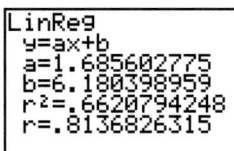

```
LinReg
 y=ax+b
 a=1.685602775
 b=6.180398959
 r²=.6620794248
 r=.8136826315
```

Need More HELP
A **regression** is a statistical analysis analyzing the association between two variables. It is used to find the relationship between two variables.

Round the decimals to the nearest hundredth, and substitute the values of *a* and *b* in the linear equation $y = ax + b$.

The equation for the line of best fit is $y = 1.69x + 6.18$.

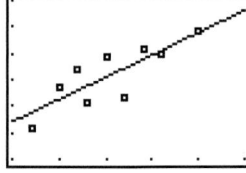

c. Use the line of best fit to predict how many ice cream cones the stand will sell if the outside temperature is 92°F.

Substitute 92 for *x* in the equation for the line of best fit.

$y = 1.69(92) + 6.18$

$y \approx 162$

The ice cream stand will sell about 162 ice cream cones if the outside temperature is 92°F.

The Correlation Coefficient

The graphing calculator screen in Example 1 that gives the slope and the y-intercept of the line of best fit also shows two other values, r and n. The second value, n, is the number of elements in the data set. The first value, r, is the *correlation coefficient*. The **correlation coefficient** measures the strength of the correlation between the two variables.

The value of r can range from -1 to 1. If r is close to 1 or -1, the correlation is strong. If r is close to 0, the correlation is weak. If $r > 0$, the slope of the line of best fit is positive. If $r < 0$, the slope of the line of best fit is negative.

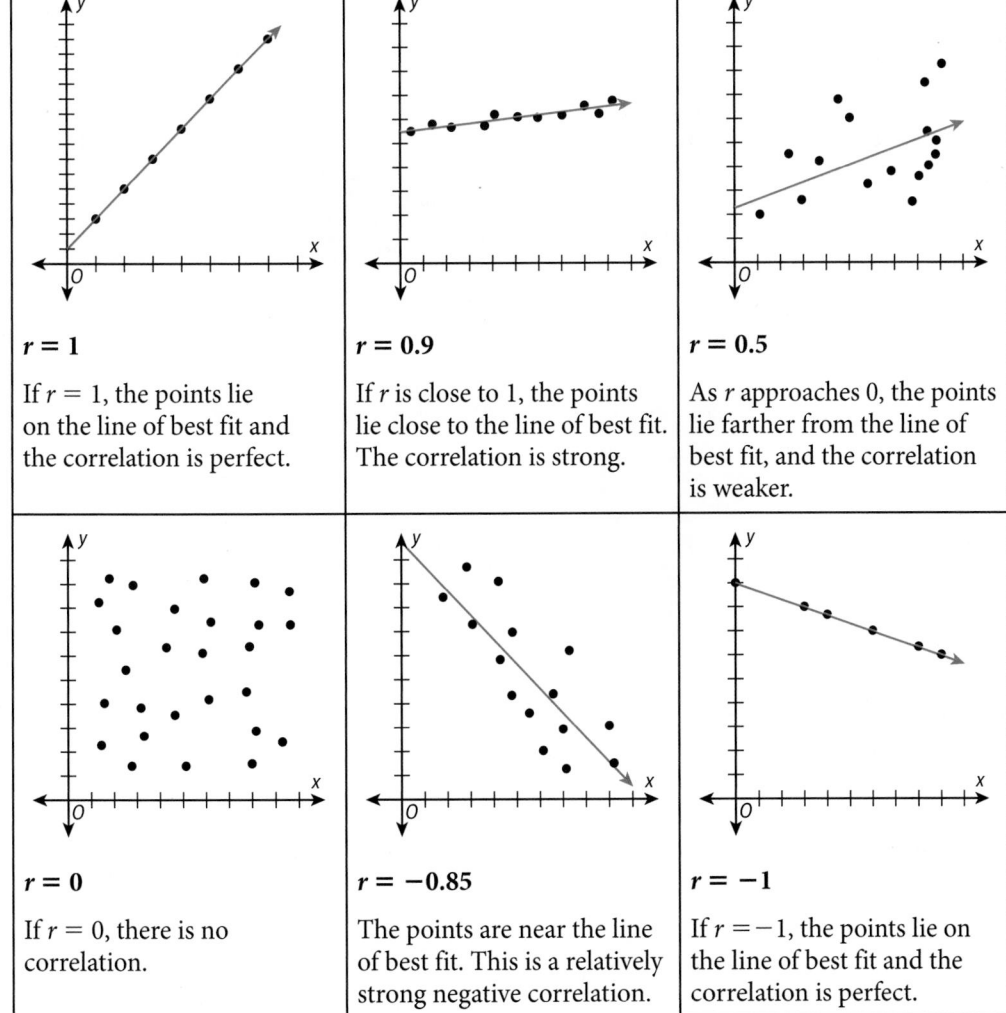

$r = 1$	$r = 0.9$	$r = 0.5$
If $r = 1$, the points lie on the line of best fit and the correlation is perfect.	If r is close to 1, the points lie close to the line of best fit. The correlation is strong.	As r approaches 0, the points lie farther from the line of best fit, and the correlation is weaker.
$r = 0$	$r = -0.85$	$r = -1$
If $r = 0$, there is no correlation.	The points are near the line of best fit. This is a relatively strong negative correlation.	If $r = -1$, the points lie on the line of best fit and the correlation is perfect.

EXAMPLE 2

Use the data in Example 1. What is the value of r? Give the strength and direction of the correlation between the outside temperature and ice cream cone sales at the stand.

Use the screen that displays the equation for the line of best fit. The value of r is about 0.81. The data are positively correlated, and the correlation between the outside temperature and the sale of ice cream cones is relatively strong.

SEARCH

To see step-by-step videos of these problems, enter the page number into the SWadvantage.com Search Bar.

Need More
HELP ?

Remember that the uppercase Greek letter sigma Σ represents a sum.

SEARCH

To see step-by-step videos of these problems, enter the page number into the SWadvantage.com Search Bar.

Formulas for the Linear Correlation Coefficient

In general, it is easiest to find the value of the correlation coefficient r by using a graphing calculator or statistics software. However, you could use a four-function calculator that can compute square roots. The *raw-score formula* for the coefficient is shown here.

$$r = \frac{n \Sigma xy - \Sigma x \Sigma y}{\sqrt{n \Sigma x^2 - (\Sigma x)^2} \cdot \sqrt{n \Sigma y^2 - (\Sigma y)^2}}$$

Although this formula looks complicated, if you store the data values in a table or the calculator's memory, it is not difficult to compute. In the formula, x represents the independent variable, y is the dependent variable, and n is the number of pairs of data.

EXAMPLE 3

A teacher gives two 10-point quizzes. The scores are shown in the table. Find the correlation coefficient for the data. Describe the direction and strength of the correlation, if any, between the sets of scores.

Quiz Score Data

Student	1	2	3	4	5
Score on Quiz 1	8	7	8	6	7
Score on Quiz 2	9	5	8	7	9

STEP 1 Use x for the Quiz 1 scores and y for the Quiz 2 scores. Make a table of the x- and y-values, their squares, and their products.

Student	x	x^2	y	y^2	xy
1	8	64	9	81	72
2	7	49	5	25	35
3	8	64	8	64	64
4	6	36	7	49	42
5	7	49	9	81	63

STEP 2 Add a row at the bottom for the sum of the entries. Add the entries in each column.

Sum	$\Sigma x = 36$	$\Sigma x^2 = 262$	$\Sigma y = 38$	$\Sigma y^2 = 300$	$\Sigma xy = 276$

STEP 3 There are 5 students, so $n = 5$. Substitute this and the values from Step 2 into the formula. Then simplify.

$$r = \frac{n \Sigma xy - \Sigma x \Sigma y}{\sqrt{n \Sigma x^2 - (\Sigma x)^2} \cdot \sqrt{n \Sigma y^2 - (\Sigma y)^2}}$$

$$= \frac{5(276) - (36)(38)}{\sqrt{5(262) - (36)^2} \cdot \sqrt{5(300) \cdot (38)^2}} = \frac{1380 - 1368}{\sqrt{1310 - 1296} \cdot \sqrt{1500 - 1444}}$$

$$= \frac{12}{\sqrt{14} \cdot \sqrt{56}} \approx \frac{12}{(3.74)(7.48)}$$

$$r \approx 0.43$$

The correlation coefficient is about 0.43. There is a weak positive correlation between the scores on the two quizzes.

Another way to find the correlation coefficient is to use the *covariance formula*. It uses the standard deviations of the data sets, and can be written in different ways.

$$r = \frac{\Sigma(x - \bar{x})(y - \bar{y})}{n s_x s_y} = \frac{1}{n} \Sigma \left(\frac{x - \bar{x}}{s_x}\right)\left(\frac{y - \bar{y}}{s_y}\right)$$

In the formulas, n is the number of data values, $\bar{x}$ and $\bar{y}$ are the means of the data sets, and s_x and s_y are the standard deviations of the data sets. The value of r has no units and does not use the units of the data sets.

EXAMPLE 4

Use the covariance formula to find the correlation coefficient for the data given in Example 3.

STEP 1   Find the values of $\bar{x}$ and $\bar{y}$.

$$\bar{x} = \frac{36}{5} = 7.2 \qquad \bar{y} = \frac{38}{5} = 7.6$$

STEP 2   Find the values of $x - \bar{x}$, $(x - \bar{x})^2$, $y - \bar{y}$, $(y - \bar{y})^2$, and $(x - \bar{x})(y - \bar{y})$ for each data set.

	x	$x - \bar{x}$	$(x - \bar{x})^2$	y	$y - \bar{y}$	$(y - \bar{y})^2$	$(x - \bar{x})(y - \bar{y})$
	8	0.8	0.64	9	1.4	1.96	1.12
	7	−0.2	0.04	5	−2.6	6.76	0.52
	8	0.8	0.64	8	0.4	0.16	0.32
	6	−1.2	1.44	7	−0.6	0.36	0.72
	7	−0.2	0.04	9	1.4	1.96	−0.28
Sum	36		2.8	38		11.2	2.4

STEP 3   Find the standard deviations for x and y.

$$s_x = \sqrt{\frac{\Sigma(x - \bar{x})^2}{n}} = \sqrt{\frac{2.8}{5}} = \sqrt{0.56} \approx 0.75 \qquad s_y = \sqrt{\frac{\Sigma(y - \bar{y})^2}{n}} = \sqrt{\frac{11.2}{5}} = \sqrt{2.24} \approx 1.5$$

STEP 4   Substitute the values from Step 3 and the last entry in the table into the formula. Then simplify.

$$r = \frac{\Sigma(x - \bar{x})(y - \bar{y})}{n s_x s_y} = \frac{2.4}{5(0.75)(1.5)} \approx 0.43$$

The correlation coefficient is about 0.43.

GOT TO KNOW!

The Line of Best Fit and the Correlation Coefficient

- To find the value of the correlation coefficient r, use a graphing calculator, statistics software, or one of these formulas.

$$r = \frac{n\Sigma xy - \Sigma x \Sigma y}{\sqrt{n\Sigma x^2 - (\Sigma x)^2} \cdot \sqrt{n\Sigma y^2 - (\Sigma y)^2}} \quad \text{or } r = \frac{\Sigma(x - \bar{x})(y - \bar{y})}{n s_x s_y} \quad \text{or } r = \frac{1}{n} \Sigma \left(\frac{x - \bar{x}}{s_x}\right)\left(\frac{y - \bar{y}}{s_y}\right)$$

- The correlation coefficient indicates how closely the variables x and y are related.

Quadratic Regression

Data are not always linear. A parabola may fit the data better than a straight line. Your graphing calculator can help you determine whether a quadratic equation models your data. The process is very similar to linear regression.

You throw a baseball into the air from a height of 4 ft and measure its height every half second. The table at the right shows the data. Use a graphing calculator or software to draw the parabola that best fits the data and to find the equation for it.

Time (s)	Height (ft)
0.0	4.0
0.5	38.7
1.0	67.1
1.5	85.6
2.0	97.2
2.5	102.0

Need More HELP

A **regression** is a statistical analysis analyzing the association between two variables. It is used to find the relationship between two variables.

STEP 1 Graph the data.

On the STAT menu of a graphing calculator, choose EDIT and enter the data in List 1 and List 2. Choose appropriate values for the viewing window. For this screen, $0 \leq x \leq 2.5$ and $0 \leq y \leq 110$. To see the graph of the data, choose GRAPH.

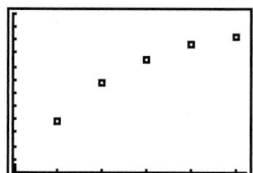

STEP 2 Find the equation for the parabola that best fits the data.

Choose STAT and then CALC on the graphing calculator, and choose QuadReg for a second-degree regression equation. Enter L1, L2, Y1 after QuadReg to make it easier to graph the equation.

Need More HELP

For help with the equation of a parabola, go to *Equations for Parabolas* (p. 1916).

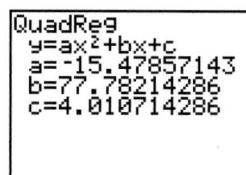

The calculator screen shows the general equation for a parabola and the values of *a*, *b*, and *c* in the equation. Round the values to the nearest hundredth, and substitute them in the equation. The equation for the parabola that best fits the data is $y = -15.48x^2 + 77.78x + 4.01$.

STEP 3 Draw the parabola.

The equation for the parabola is stored as Y1 on the Y= screen. You can use the stored equation, or you can type the equation with rounded coefficients on the Y= screen. Choose GRAPH to see the parabola.

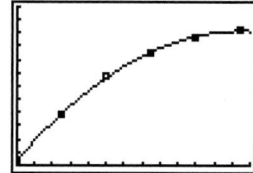

You can use a graphing calculator to find the *coefficient of determination*, r^2, for a quadratic regression equation. As with the correlation coefficient for a linear regression equation, a value that is close to 1 indicates a strong correlation. A value that is close to 0 indicates a weak correlation.

EXAMPLE 2

Find the coefficient of determination for the quadratic regression in Example 1.

After entering the data, press **VARS**, then select 5:Statistics. Move the cursor to EQ. Then select 9:R^2. Press **ENTER** twice to get the result $R^2 = 0.9998506599$.

EXAMPLE 3

a. Use the parabola in Example 1. Find the height of the ball 3 seconds after it is thrown.

METHOD 1

Use the regression equation.	$y = -15.48x^2 + 77.78x + 4.01$
Substitute 3 for x.	$y = -15.48(3)^2 + 77.78(3) + 4.01$
Simplify.	$= -15.48(9) + 77.78(3) + 4.01$
	$= -139.32 + 233.34 + 4.01$
	$y = 98.03$

The ball is about 98 ft above the ground 3 seconds after it is thrown.

METHOD 2

Use the TRACE feature of the graphing calculator. Adjust the range on the graph to include $x = 3$. If the calculator traces the data points instead of the parabola, use the up or down arrow key to get to the curve.

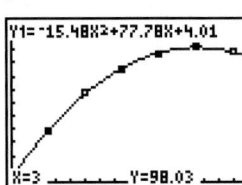

Trace the graph until the value $x = 3$ is shown.

When $x = 3$, $y \approx 98$.

The ball is about 98 ft above the ground 3 seconds after it is thrown.

b. Use the parabola in Example 1. Find the time when the ball hits the ground.

Use the TRACE feature of the graphing calculator. When the ball is on the ground, its height is 0. Adjust the range on the graph to include $y = 0$. If the calculator traces the data points instead of the parabola, use the up or down arrow key to get to the curve.

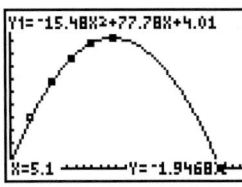

Trace the graph until the value $y = 0$ is shown.

When $y = 0$, $x \approx 5.1$.

The ball hits the ground about 5.1 seconds after it is thrown.

SEARCH

To see step-by-step videos of these problems, enter the page number into the SWadvantage.com Search Bar.

Exponential Regression

Exponential growth and decay are common in nature. You can use a graphing calculator to find an equation that models exponential data.

Need More
HELP ?

The equation $y = ab^x$ is called an exponential growth equation if $b > 1$ and an exponential decay equation if $0 < b < 1$. For more about exponential equations, go to *Exponential Growth* (p. 1996) and *Exponential Decay* (p. 2000)

EXAMPLE 4

A chemistry student records the temperature of an unknown solution every 20 minutes as it cools. The temperature of the lab is 72°F. The table shows the data. Use a graphing calculator to find an exponential equation that models the data.

Time (min)	0	20	40	60	80	100	120
Temperature (°F)	202.9	127.8	103.8	91.8	86.1	82.3	79.9

STEP 1 Graph the data.

Enter the data in List 1 and List 2. Choose appropriate values for the viewing window. This screen has a range of $0 \leq x \leq 130$ and $0 \leq y \leq 250$. To see the graph of the data, choose GRAPH.

STEP 2 Transform the data.

Notice that the graph has a horizontal asymptote at about $y = 70$. This is because the temperature of the liquid cannot fall below room temperature, 72°. The exponential regression process will yield an equation of the form $y = ab^x$, but the graph has an equation of the form $y = ab^x + c$, where c represents the room temperature. To account for this, subtract the constant 72 from each y-value in the data. In Step 4, you will add the constant to the equation.

Time (min)	0	20	40	60	80	100	120
Temperature (°F)	$202.9 - 72 = 130.9$	55.8	31.8	19.8	14.1	10.3	7.9

STEP 3 Find the equation for an exponential curve that models the transformed data.

Choose STAT and then CALC on the graphing calculator, and choose ExpReg for an exponential regression equation. Enter L1, L2, Y1 after ExpReg.

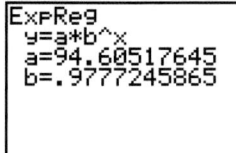

Using Y for the transformed y-values, the equation that best fits the transformed data is $Y = 94.61(0.98)^x$.

STEP 4 Adjust the regression equation to account for the data transformation, and graph it.

You decreased each data value by 72 in Step 2, so now you have to compensate for that.

$y - 72 = 94.61(0.98)^x$

$y = 94.61(0.98)^x + 72$

Choose GRAPH to see the function.

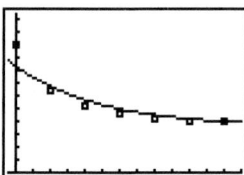

SEARCH

To see step-by-step videos of these problems, enter the page number into the SWadvantage.com Search Bar.

Choosing a Regression Model

If you are not sure whether the best model for your data is a line, a parabola, or an exponential curve, you can try all three and see which looks best.

EXAMPLE 5

The population of a bacteria strain in a culture was measured every hour. The results are given in the table. Is the relationship between time and population linear, quadratic, or exponential?

Time (hours)	0	1	2	3	4
Population	10	16	24	39	64

STEP 1 Graph the data.

Enter the data in List 1 and List 2. Choose appropriate values for the viewing window. This screen has a range of $0 \leq x \leq 5$ and $0 \leq y \leq 70$. To see the data on a graph, choose **GRAPH** .

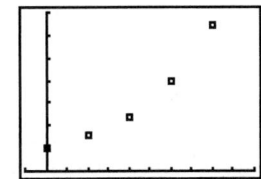

STEP 2 Test different regression models of the data.

Choose **STAT** and then CALC, and choose LinReg for a linear regression equation. Store the equation in Y1, and find the value of the correlation coefficient. Repeat the process for QuadReg and ExpReg. Store each equation in a different Y= function.

Type of regression	Linear	Quadratic	Exponential
Equation	$y = 13.1x + 4.4$	$y = 3.21x^2 + 0.24x + 10.83$	$y = 9.92(1.58)^x$
Stored in	Y1	Y2	Y3
Measure of correlation	$r = 0.958$	$R^2 = 0.997$	$r = 0.999$

STEP 3 Look at the models and the data.

Choose GRAPH to see the line, the two curves, and the data. Both the quadratic equation and the exponential equation seem to fit the data well. The value of r for the exponential equation is very close to 1, indicating that this equation is the best choice for these data.

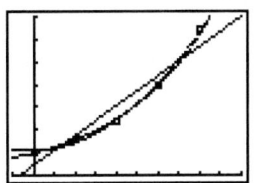

Quadratic and Exponential Regression

Use quadratic regression to find an equation in the form $y = ax^2 + bx + c$ to model a data set.

Use exponential regression to find an equation in the form $y = ab^x$ to model a data set.

If you perform a linear transformation on a data set before finding a regression equation, "undo" the transformation to find an equation for the original data.

Normal Distribution

Properties of a Normal Distribution

The **normal distribution** is used to describe many different sets of data, such as physical dimensions, test scores, and product measurements. All normal distributions have the same basic shape, called a *bell curve.*

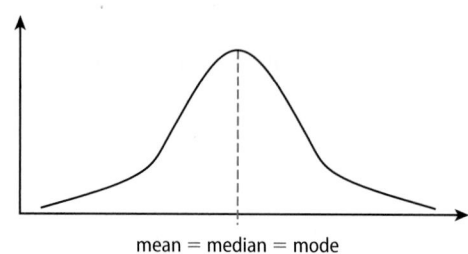

mean = median = mode

In a normal distribution, the mean, the median, and the mode are all equal. The curve is symmetrical about the mean. The *x*-axis is a horizontal asymptote of the curve.

Both the mean and the standard deviation of a normal distribution affect its graph.

Need More

HELP ?

For more about the standard deviation and the mean, see *Standard Deviation* (p. 1324).

These normal distributions have the same standard deviation but different means.

These normal distributions have the same mean but different standard deviations.

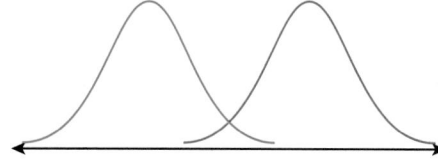
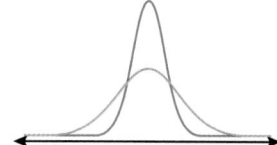

In fact, if a distribution is normal, you can describe it completely by the mean, μ (mu), and the standard deviation, σ (sigma).

The area under a normal distribution curve is proportional to the frequency of data values in the distribution. You can use calculus to find the areas of different sections of the distribution, but for convenience, they are also given in tables. Or you can use a graphing calculator or statistics software. Some benchmark areas and corresponding frequencies are given in the **Empirical Rule**.

GOT TO KNOW!

The Empirical Rule

In a normal distribution, about 68% of the data lie within one standard deviation of the mean.

About 95% of the data lie within two standard deviations of the mean.

About 99.7% of the data lie within three standard deviations of the mean.

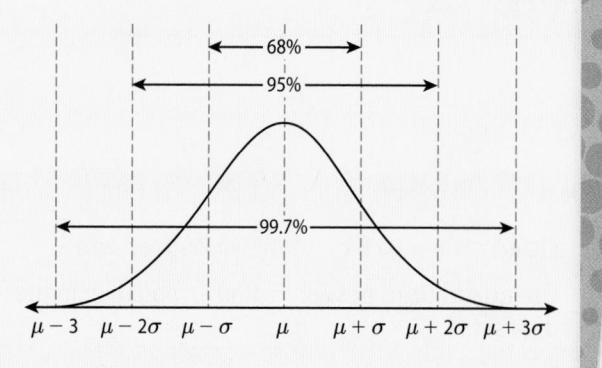

EXAMPLE 1

The mean score μ on a high school graduation exam is 120, and the standard deviation σ is 15.

a. What percent of the students scored between 105 and 135 on the exam?

The score $105 = 120 - 15$ and $135 = 120 + 15$. Therefore, 105 is one standard deviation below the mean $(\mu - \sigma)$ and 135 is one standard deviation above the mean $(\mu + \sigma)$. About 68% of the scores fall in this interval.

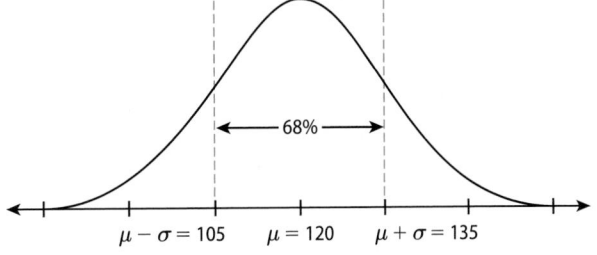

$\mu - \sigma = 105 \quad \mu = 120 \quad \mu + \sigma = 135$

SEARCH

To see step-by-step videos of these problems, enter the page number into the SWadvantage.com Search Bar.

b. Helen's score on the exam is 150. What percent of the students scored higher than she did?

The score $150 = 120 + 30$, and $30 = 15 \cdot 2$. So 150 is two standard deviations above the mean.

Since about 95% of the scores are within 2σ of the mean, 5% of the scores are in the two "tails" of the distribution.

Because the distribution is symmetric, 0.5(5%), or 2.5% of the scores are greater than $\mu + 2\sigma$. So 2.5% of the students scored higher than Helen.

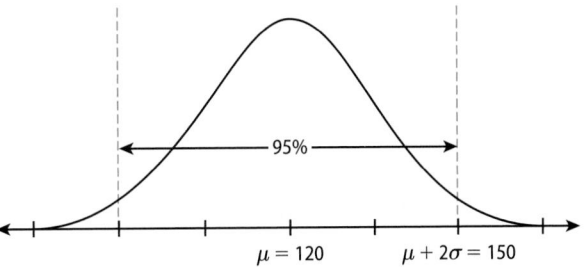

$\mu = 120 \quad \mu + 2\sigma = 150$

Standard Scores

The number of standard deviations between a data value and the mean is called the *standard score*, or **z-score**, of the data. For a data value x in a distribution with mean μ and standard deviation σ, the corresponding z-score is $z = \frac{x - \mu}{\sigma}$. The value x is called the *original score* or the **raw score**.

EXAMPLE 2

The mean height μ of a group of seventh-grade boys is 53 in. The standard deviation σ is 4 in.

a. Find the z-score of a height of 60 in.

Use the formula for a z-score. $z = \frac{x - \mu}{\sigma}$

Substitute for x, μ, and σ. $z = \frac{60 - 53}{4} = 1.75$

b. Find the raw score of a z-score of -0.25.

Substitute for z, μ, and σ in the formula. $-0.25 = \frac{x - 53}{4}$

Solve for x. $x = 52$

GOT TO KNOW!

z-Scores

The z-score of a value tells you how many standard deviations above or below the mean the value is.

Using the Standard Normal Distribution

For a standard normal distribution, you can use a table or a graphing calculator to find the portions of data above and below a certain z-score.

EXAMPLE 3

The scores on a math test have a mean μ of 50 and a standard deviation σ of 8. Levon's score is 60. What is the percentile rank of Levon's score?

STEP 1 Find the z-score of Levon's score. $\qquad z = \dfrac{x - \mu}{\sigma} = \dfrac{60 - 50}{8} = \dfrac{10}{8} = 1.25$

STEP 2 Draw a diagram. Shade the region that represents the proportion of scores you want to find.

The area to the left of Levon's score represents all the scores that are less than or equal to his.

STEP 3 Find the percent of scores that are in the shaded region.

METHOD 1 Use a table.

Standard Normal Distribution Table (for area to the left of z)

z	0.01	0.02	0.03	0.04	0.05	0.06	0.07
1.0	0.8438	0.8461	0.8485	0.8508	0.8531	0.8554	0.8577
1.1	0.8665	0.8686	0.8708	0.8729	0.8749	0.8770	0.8790
1.2	0.8869	0.8888	0.8907	0.8925	0.8944	0.8962	0.8980
1.3	0.9049	0.9066	0.9082	0.9099	0.9115	0.9131	0.9147

The first column gives the z-scores to the nearest tenth.

The first row gives the z-scores to the nearest hundredth.

Read across the 1.2 row until you get to the 0.05 column. The entry is 0.8944. This means that 89.44% of the scores are less than or equal to the z-score of 1.25, and the corresponding raw score of 60. Levon's percentile rank is about 89.

METHOD 2 Use a graphing calculator.

Press **2nd** **VARS**. Select 2:normalcdf and press **ENTER**. Input the lower limit of the interval, the upper limit, and a right parenthesis.

In this case, the original lower bound is 0, so the corresponding z-score is $\dfrac{0 - 50}{8} = -6.25$. Levon's percentile rank is about 89.

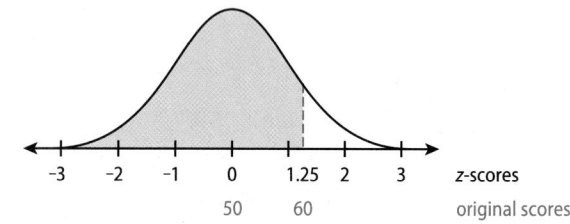

In Example 3, about 0.8944 of the scores are lower than Levon's score, so $1 - 0.8944 = 0.1056$, or about 11% of the scores are higher than Levon's.

EXAMPLE 4

The finish times for a 5 km cross-country race have a mean μ of 32.21 min and a standard deviation σ of 4.02 min. What times are in the top 10 percent? (Note that the lowest time wins the race. So the top 10 percent are the worst scores in the race.)

STEP 1 Draw a diagram.

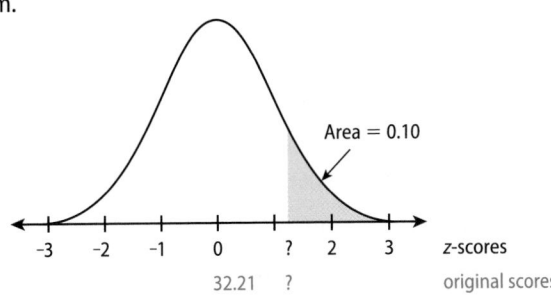

Area = 0.10

z-scores

32.21   ?   original scores

STEP 2 Use a graphing calculator to find the corresponding z-score.

Press **2nd** **VARS** and then select invNorm.
Enter 0.9 (the area left of the z-score) and a right parenthesis. The z-score is about 1.28.

```
invNorm(.9)
        1.281551567
```

STEP 3 Convert the z-score you found in Step 2 into a raw score.

Use the formula for a z-score. $z = \dfrac{x - \mu}{\sigma}$

Substitute for z, μ, and σ. $1.28 = \dfrac{x - 32.21}{4.02}$

Solve for x. $(4.02)(1.28) = x - 32.21$
$$5.1456 = x - 32.21$$
$$37.3556 = x$$

Finish times greater than about 37.36 min are in the top 10 percent.

Try It This Way

You can draw a normal curve on a graphing calculator. Press **2nd** **VARS** and then select Draw. Select ShadeNorm, and enter the variables lower bound, upper bound, mean, and standard deviation, in that order.

You can use *z*-scores to compare data.

EXAMPLE 5

Emily scored 89 on both of her physics tests. The first test has a mean of 75 and a standard deviation of 12. The second test has a mean of 77 and a standard deviation of 9. Which of Emily's scores has a higher percentile rank?

STEP 1 Find the z-score and percentile rank of the first test score.

$$z = \frac{x - \mu}{\sigma} = \frac{89 - 75}{12} \approx 1.17$$

Use a table or a graphing calculator to find the corresponding percentile rank, 0.8790.

STEP 2 Find the z-score and percentile rank of the second test score.

$$z = \frac{x - \mu}{\sigma} = \frac{89 - 77}{9} \approx 1.33$$

Use a table or a graphing calculator to find the corresponding percentile rank, 0.9082.

STEP 3 Compare the percentile ranks found in Steps 1 and 2.

Emily's second test score has a higher percentile rank, about 91% compared to 88%.

SEARCH

To see step-by-step videos of these problems, enter the page number into the SWadvantage.com Search Bar.

Pascal's Triangle and Binomial Distribution

Binomial Experiments

Toss ten coins, and count how many land heads up. Roll six dice, and count how many 1's you roll. Each of these is a binomial experiment. The trials in a **binomial experiment** have exactly two possible outcomes, one of which is called a *success*. Each trial is independent of other trials. The probability of success does not change with the number of trials.

Binomial experiments with a small number of trials can be analyzed in the same way as other compound events, as shown in Example 1.

EXAMPLE 1

You toss four coins. What is the probability that exactly two of the coins land heads up?

STEP 1 Make an organized table or a tree diagram showing the possible outcomes.

Coin 1	Coin 2	Coin 3	Coin 4	Number of heads
H	H	H	H	4
H	H	H	T	3
H	H	T	H	3
H	H	T	T	2
H	T	H	H	3
H	T	H	T	2
H	T	T	H	2
H	T	T	T	1
T	H	H	H	3
T	H	H	T	2
T	H	T	H	2
T	H	T	T	1
T	T	H	H	2
T	T	H	T	1
T	T	T	H	1
T	T	T	T	0

STEP 2 Write the ratio of the number of successes to the total number of outcomes.

$$\frac{\text{Number of times there are exactly two heads}}{\text{Number of possible outcomes}} = \frac{6}{16} = \frac{3}{8}$$

The probability of getting exactly two heads is $\frac{3}{8}$.

If a binomial experiment has a large number of trials, the calculations can be difficult. Then you can use a formula to calculate the probability of success.

GOT TO KNOW!

Probability of a Binomial Experiment

In a binomial experiment, if the probability of one success is p, then the probability of k successes in n trials is:

$P(k$ successes in n trials$) = {}_nC_k \cdot p^k(1 - p)^{n-k}$,

where ${}_nC_k = \frac{n!}{k!(n - k)!}$

Need More HELP?

For more about the formula for ${}_nC_k$, see *Combinations* (p. 1248).

1344

SEARCH 🔍

To see step-by-step videos of these problems, enter the page number into the SWadvantage.com Search Bar.

EXAMPLE 2

Apply the formula for the probability of a binomial experiment to the coin toss experiment in Example 1.

The probability p of heads is $\frac{1}{2}$ for each trial. You toss four coins, so the number of trials n is 4. You are calculating the probability that two coins land heads up, so the number of successes k is 2.

Use the formula. $P(k \text{ successes in } n \text{ trials}) = {}_nC_k \cdot p^k(1-p)^{n-k}$

Substitute. $P(2 \text{ heads in } 4 \text{ trials}) = {}_4C_2 \cdot \left(\frac{1}{2}\right)^2\left(1 - \frac{1}{2}\right)^{4-2}$

Simplify. $= \frac{4!}{2!2!} \cdot \left(\frac{1}{2}\right)^2\left(\frac{1}{2}\right)^2$

$= 6 \cdot \left(\frac{1}{2}\right)^4$

$= \frac{3}{8}$

EXAMPLE 3

You roll five dice. Find the probability of rolling a 1 on exactly three of the dice.

This is an example of a binomial experiment. The two outcomes are rolling a 1 and not rolling a 1. The probability p of rolling a 1 is $\frac{1}{6}$. The number of trials n is 5. The number of successes k is 3.

Use the formula. $P(k \text{ successes in } n \text{ trials}) = {}_nC_k \cdot p^k(1-p)^{n-k}$

Substitute. $P(3 \text{ successes in } 5 \text{ trials}) = {}_5C_3 \cdot \left(\frac{1}{6}\right)^3\left(1 - \frac{1}{6}\right)^{5-3}$

Simplify. $= \frac{5!}{3!2!} \cdot \left(\frac{1}{6}\right)^3\left(\frac{5}{6}\right)^2$

Use a calculator. $= 10 \cdot \frac{25}{6^5} \approx 0.03215$

The probability of rolling three 1's in five rolls is just over 3%.

Watch Out! ⚠️

Notice that the number on the die, 1, is not used in the formula.

EXAMPLE 4

In a packet of mixed marigold seeds, 10% of the seeds are for orange-flowering plants. The rest are for yellow-flowering plants. If 20 plants are grown from the seeds, what is the probability that exactly 2 of them will have orange flowers?

This is an example of a binomial experiment. The two outcomes are orange flowers and yellow flowers. The probability of an orange-flowering plant is $\frac{1}{10}$ for each seed.

Use the formula. $P(k \text{ successes in } n \text{ trials}) = {}_nC_k \cdot p^k(1-p)^{n-k}$

Substitute. $P(2 \text{ successes in } 20 \text{ trials}) = {}_{20}C_2 \cdot \left(\frac{1}{10}\right)^2\left(1 - \frac{1}{10}\right)^{20-2}$

Simplify. $= \frac{20!}{2!18!} \cdot \left(\frac{1}{10}\right)^2\left(\frac{9}{10}\right)^{18}$

$= 190 \cdot \frac{9^{18}}{10^{20}}$

Use a calculator. ≈ 0.2852

The probability that exactly 2 out of 20 plants will have orange flowers is about 28.5%.

Binomial Distributions

If all the outcomes of the binomial experiment in Example 1 are tallied, they form a frequency distribution. This is an example of a *binomial distribution*. The variable is the number of successes.

EXAMPLE 5

Make a histogram showing the outcomes of the coin toss in Example 1.

STEP 1 Count how many ways you can toss 0 heads, 1 head, 2 heads, and so on. Make a table of the results.

Number of heads	0	1	2	3	4
Ways this can happen	1	4	6	4	1

STEP 2 Make the histogram.

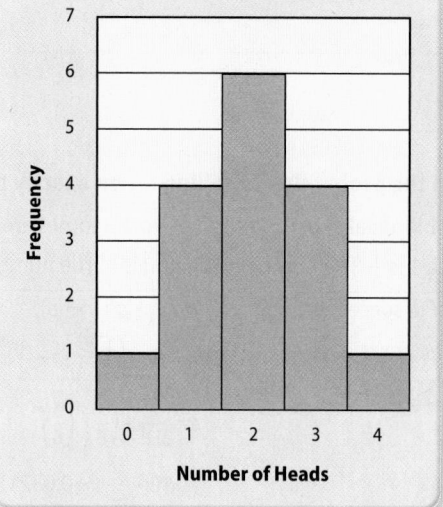

Need More

HELP ?

For more about frequency tables and histograms, see *Histograms* in *Displaying Data* (p. 1266).

In the distribution in Example 5, notice that the mean, median, and mode are all equal and the distribution is symmetric about the mean. These are the properties of a *normal distribution*. For larger values of *n*, the binomial distribution is very similar to the normal distribution.

GOT TO KNOW!

Binomial Distributions

A *binomial random variable* is the number of successes, k, in n trials of a binomial experiment.

A *binomial distribution* is the probability distribution of a binomial random variable.

If the probability of one success in a binomial experiment is p, then the mean, variance, and standard deviation of the distribution are as shown below.

Mean: $\mu = np$

Variance: $\sigma^2 = np(1 - p)$

Standard deviation: $\sigma = \sqrt{np(1 - p)}$

Pascal's Triangle

The frequencies in the table in Example 5 are also found in Pascal's Triangle. **Pascal's Triangle** is an important mathematical pattern that has many applications. The first few rows of Pascal's Triangle are shown below.

$$
\begin{array}{ccccccccccc}
\text{row 0} \rightarrow & & & & & 1 \\
\text{row 1} \rightarrow & & & & 1 & & 1 \\
\text{row 2} \rightarrow & & & 1 & & 2 & & 1 \\
\text{row 3} \rightarrow & & 1 & & 3 & & 3 & & 1 \\
\text{row 4} \rightarrow & 1 & & 4 & & 6 & & 4 & & 1 \\
\text{row 5} \rightarrow 1 & & 5 & & 10 & & 10 & & 5 & & 1
\end{array}
$$

Each row in the triangle starts and ends with 1. Each of the other numbers is the sum of the two numbers closest to it in the row above.

Notice that the numbers in row 4 are the frequencies of the outcomes of a binomial experiment with four trials. For example, the third number in row 4 is $_4C_2$. In general, the kth number in row n is $_nC_{k-1}$.

EXAMPLE 6

a. What is the 11th number in the 12th row of Pascal's Triangle?

You can find this number without writing 12 rows of the triangle. The kth number in the nth row of Pascal's Triangle is $_nC_{k-1}$. So the 11th number in the 12th row is $_{12}C_{10}$.

$$_{12}C_{10} = \frac{12!}{10!2!} = \frac{12 \cdot 11 \cdot \cancel{10!}}{\cancel{10!} \cdot 2 \cdot 1} = 66$$

b. What is the 19th number in the 25th row of Pascal's Triangle?

The 19th number in the 25th row is $_{25}C_{18}$.

Use the formula. $_{25}C_{18} = \dfrac{25!}{18!7!}$

Cancel. $= \dfrac{25 \cdot \cancel{24} \cdot 23 \cdot 22 \cdot \cancel{21} \cdot 20 \cdot 19 \cdot \cancel{18!}}{\cancel{18!} \cdot \cancel{7} \cdot \cancel{6} \cdot 5 \cdot \cancel{4} \cdot \cancel{3} \cdot 2 \cdot 1}$

Use a calculator. $= 480,700$

SEARCH

To see step-by-step videos of these problems, enter the page number into the SWadvantage.com Search Bar.

GOT TO KNOW!

Pascal's Triangle

There are many patterns in Pascal's Triangle. One of them gives the value of $_nC_k$. Also, the sum of the numbers in row n of Pascal's Triangle is 2^n. Several rows of the triangle are show below.

$$
\begin{array}{ccccccccccccc}
& & & & & & 1 \\
& & & & & 1 & & 1 \\
& & & & 1 & & 2 & & 1 \\
& & & 1 & & 3 & & 3 & & 1 \\
& & 1 & & 4 & & 6 & & 4 & & 1 \\
& 1 & & 5 & & 10 & & 10 & & 5 & & 1 \\
1 & & 6 & & 15 & & 20 & & 15 & & 6 & & 1
\end{array}
$$

$$
\begin{array}{ccccccccccccc}
& & & & & & _0C_0 \\
& & & & & _1C_0 & & _1C_1 \\
& & & & _2C_0 & & _2C_1 & & _2C_2 \\
& & & _3C_0 & & _3C_1 & & _3C_2 & & _3C_3 \\
& & _4C_0 & & _4C_1 & & _4C_2 & & _4C_3 & & _4C_4 \\
& _5C_0 & & _5C_1 & & _5C_2 & & _5C_3 & & _5C_4 & & _5C_5 \\
_6C_0 & & _6C_1 & & _6C_2 & & _6C_3 & & _6C_4 & & _6C_5 & & _6C_6
\end{array}
$$

Binomial Expansions

A polynomial that has two terms is called a **binomial**. For example, $2x + 3$, $4p - 3p^2$, and $x^5y + 10y$ are all binomials.

A binomial raised to a power, such as $(a + b)^n$, can be written in expanded form, as the sum of monomial terms. The expansions of $(a \pm b)^2$ and $(a \pm b)^3$ are used so often that you should memorize them.

> **Watch Out !**
>
> Remember that
> $(a + b)^2 \neq a^2 + b^2$.

> **SEARCH**
>
> To see step-by-step videos of these problems, enter the page number into the SWadvantage.com Search Bar.

EXAMPLE 7

a. Find $(a + b)^2$.

Write the product.	$(a + b)^2 = (a + b)(a + b)$
Use FOIL or the Distributive Property.	$= a \cdot a + ab + ab + b \cdot b$
Simplify.	$= a^2 + 2ab + b^2$

b. Find $(a + b)^3$.

Write the product.	$(a + b)^3 = (a + b)(a + b)(a + b)$
Use the result from part (a).	$= (a^2 + 2ab + b^2)(a + b)$
Use the Distributive Property.	$= (a^2 + 2ab + b^2)a + (a^2 + 2ab + b^2)b$
Distribute again.	$= a^3 + 2a^2b + ab^2 + a^2b + 2ab^2 + b^3$
Simplify.	$= a^3 + 3a^2b + 3ab^2 + b^3$

c. Explain how the coefficients in the products in parts (a) and (b) are related to Pascal's Triangle.

The coefficients of $a^2 + 2ab + b^2$ are 1, 2, 1. The coefficients of $a^3 + 3a^2b + 3ab^2 + b^3$ are 1, 3, 3, 1. These are the second and third rows of Pascal's Triangle.

The result in Example 7 is true for all values of n. In general, the nth row of Pascal's Triangle gives the coefficients of the terms in the expansion of $(a + b)^n$. The Binomial Theorem describes this pattern.

GOT TO KNOW!

The Binomial Theorem

The Binomial Theorem is a general formula for the expansion of $(a + b)^n$, where n is a positive integer.

$$(a + b)^n = \left({}_nC_0\right)a^nb^0 + \left({}_nC_1\right)a^{n-1}b + \left({}_nC_2\right)a^{n-2}b^2 + \ldots + \left({}_nC_{n-2}\right)a^2b^{n-2} + \left({}_nC_{n-1}\right)ab^{n-1} + \left({}_nC_n\right)a^0b^n$$

Notice these facts.

1. The number of terms in the expanded form is $n + 1$.

2. The sum of the exponents of a and b in each term is n.

3. The exponents of a start with n and decrease to 0. The exponents of b start with 0 and go up to n.

4. The coefficients form the nth row of Pascal's Triangle.

5. The coefficient of the kth term is ${}_nC_{k-1}$.

Applying the Binomial Theorem

Another way to write the Binomial Theorem is $(a + b)^n = \sum_{k=0}^{n} {}_nC_k a^{n-k}b^k$.

The formula for n items taken k at a time, ${}_nC_k$, is also called the **binomial coefficient**.

EXAMPLE 8

Use the Binomial Theorem to find the expanded form of $(x + y)^6$.

| Write the sixth row of Pascal's Triangle. | 1 | 6 | 15 | 20 | 15 | 6 | 1 |

Write the powers of x, starting with x^6 and decreasing.

$1x^6 \quad 6x^5 \quad 15x^4 \quad 20x^3 \quad 15x^2 \quad 6x^1 \quad 1x^0$

Write the powers of y, starting with y^0 and increasing.

$1x^6y^0 + 6x^5y^1 + 15x^4y^2 + 20x^3y^3 + 15x^2y^4 + 6x^1y^5 + 1x^0y^6$

Simplify.

$x^6 + 6x^5y + 15x^4y^2 + 20x^3y^3 + 15x^2y^4 + 6xy^5 + y^6$

Need More HELP?

Remember that $x^0 = 1$ for all nonzero values of x. For more about working with exponents, see *Exponents* in *Algebra* (p. 1396).

EXAMPLE 9

Expand $(2a - 3)^4$.

Rewrite subtraction as addition.

$(2a - 3)^4 = (2a + (-3))^4$

Use the Binomial Theorem.

$= 1(2a)^4(-3)^0 + 4(2a)^3(-3)^1 + 6(2a)^2(-3)^2 +$
$\quad 4(2a)^1(-3)^3 + 1(2a)^0(-3)^4$

$= 16a^4(1) + 4(8a^3)(-3) + 6(4a^2)(9) +$
$\quad 4(2a)(-27) + 1(1)(81)$

$= 16a^4 - 96a^3 + 216a^2 - 216a + 81$

EXAMPLE 10

Expand $(5r^2 - 2s)^3$.

Rewrite subtraction as addition.

$(5r^2 - 2s)^3 = (5r^2 + (-2s))^3$

Use the Binomial Theorem.

$= 1(5r^2)^3(-2s)^0 + 3(5r^2)^2(-2s)^1 + 3(5r^2)^1(-2s)^2 + 1(5r^2)^0(-2s)^3$

$= 125r^6(1) + 3(25r^4)(-2s) + 3(5r^2)(4s^2) + (1)(-8s^3)$

$= 125r^6 - 150r^4s + 60r^2s^2 - 8s^3$

Need More HELP?

If the terms of the binomial have coefficients or exponents, be sure to apply the exponent to the entire term.

EXAMPLE 11

Find the 6th term of $\left(4g^2 - h\right)^{10}$.

The general form for the sixth term is $\left({}_nC_5\right)a^{n-5}\,b^5$. Let $4g^2 = a$ and let $-h = b$.

Substitute for n, a, and b.

$\left({}_nC_5\right)a^{n-5}\,b^5 = \left({}_{10}C_5\right)\left(4g^2\right)^5(-h)^5 = \frac{10!}{5!5!} \cdot 4^5 \cdot g^{10}\,(-1)^5 h^5$

Simplify. Use a calculator if needed.

$= -252 \cdot 1024 \cdot g^{10}h^5 = -258{,}048g^{10}h^5$

Sample Size

Estimating a Proportion of a Population

A state governor wants to know whether voters will support a bicycle trail project. The governor can't ask every registered voter in the state, so a random sample is selected and surveyed. Of the people in the sample, 52% say they support bicycle trails. The proportion of bike trail supporters in the sample is an estimate of the proportion of bike trail supporters in the population. The variable $\hat{p}$, read "p hat," is used for the sample proportion.

Often this type of result is reported with a margin of error. The **margin of error** is an interval, or range, around a sample measure that is likely to contain the corresponding population measure. Using *ME* for the margin of error, the population proportion is expected to be between $\hat{p} - ME$ and $\hat{p} + ME$.

EXAMPLE 1

Of a random sample of 500 voters, 52% support a new bike trail project. The margin of error for the survey is 4.5%. What is the range of voters in the population that can be expected to support the bike trail project?

Add and subtract the margin of error from the sample measure.

$52\% - 4.5\% = 47.5\%$ $\qquad$ $52\% + 4.5\% = 56.5\%$

Between 47.5% and 56.5% of the population of voters can be expected to support the new bike trail project.

Watch Out !

A confidence level of 90% means that 5% of the distribution is in each "tail" of the distribution. The z-score is associated with the total area under the curve to the left of the score 0.95, not 0.90.

If *many* samples are taken from the population, and each sample is surveyed the same way, then the proportions of respondents who support bike trails form a normal distribution. Therefore, there is a numerical probability that the actual proportion of the population is within a given range.

The probability that a population measure falls in a given interval around a sample measure is called the **confidence level**. Typical values chosen for the confidence level are 90%, 95%, or 99%. If *p* represents the population proportion having a given characteristic, then the interval in which *p* lies 95% of the time is called the 95% **confidence interval**. The margin of error is based on the *z*-value, the size of the sample, and the sample proportion.

GOT TO KNOW!

The Margin of Error and Confidence Intervals

The margin of error (*ME*) for a proportion is $z_c \sqrt{\dfrac{\hat{p}(1 - \hat{p})}{n}}$.
The confidence interval is given by $\hat{p} \pm ME$.

z_c = the appropriate *z*-score from the table at the right, or from the standard normal distribution table on page 1380.

$\hat{p}$ = sample proportion

n = sample size

Confidence Level	z-Score (z_c)
90	1.64
95	1.96
99	2.57

EXAMPLE 2

A random sample of 100 students shows that 74% of them are in favor of new lunch menus. The school principal wants to use a 95% confidence level to estimate the proportion of the whole student body that favors new lunch menus.

a. Find the margin of error for this sample.

Use the formula for the margin of error.

$$ME = z_c\sqrt{\frac{\hat{p}(1-\hat{p})}{n}}$$

Substitute. Write percents as decimals.

$$= (1.96)\sqrt{\frac{(0.74)(1-0.74)}{100}}$$

Simplify. Use a calculator.

$$= (1.96)\sqrt{0.001924} \approx 0.08597$$

The margin of error is about 8.6%.

b. Find the confidence interval.

Add and subtract the margin of error from the sample proportion.

$$74\% - 8.6\% = 65.4\% \qquad 74\% + 8.6\% = 82.6\%$$

The 95% confidence interval is between 65.4% and 82.6%. This interval is also written (65.4%, 82.6%). In other words, the principal can be 95% confident that the proportion of students favoring new lunch menus is between 65.4% and 82.6%.

> **Need More HELP?**
>
> Use the chart on page 1350 to find the z-score, z_c.

Sometimes a 95% confidence level is not sufficient.

EXAMPLE 3

Suppose the principal in Example 2 wants a 99% confidence level. How does this affect the margin of error and the confidence interval?

Use the formula for the margin of error.

$$ME = z_c\sqrt{\frac{\hat{p}(1-\hat{p})}{n}}$$

Substitute. Write percents as decimals.

$$= (2.57)\sqrt{\frac{(0.74)(1-0.74)}{100}}$$

Simplify. Use a calculator.

$$= (2.57)\sqrt{0.001924} \approx 0.112729$$

The margin of error for a 99% confidence level is about 11.2%. The confidence interval is 74% ± 11.3%, or (62.7%, 85.3%). The margin of error and the confidence interval for a 99% confidence level are greater than those for a 95% confidence level.

> **SEARCH**
>
> To see step-by-step videos of these problems, enter the page number into the SWadvantage.com Search Bar.

Increasing the confidence level increases the confidence interval. To be 100% certain of the population measure, you would have to sample 100% of the population.

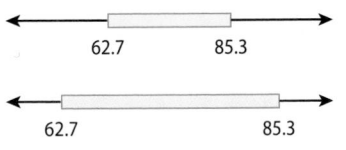

62.7   85.3

The confidence level that the population measure falls in this smaller interval is 95%.

62.7   85.3

The confidence level that the population measure falls in this larger interval is 99%.

Estimating the Mean of a Population

The state governor now wants to know how many bicycles, on average, the residents of the state own. Another random sample is chosen from the population, the results are recorded, and the mean number of bicycles per household in the sample is found. The mean from the sample can be used as an estimate of the mean for the population.

The margin of error for a mean depends on the same z-scores as the margin of error for a proportion. It also depends on the size of the sample and the standard deviation of the population. If the standard deviation of the population is not known, the standard deviation of the sample can be used as an estimate. The margin of error for a mean is found this way.

$$ME = z_c \frac{\sigma}{\sqrt{n}}$$

Need More
HELP ?

Remember that σ is used for the standard deviation of a population, and s is used for the standard deviation of a sample. For more about standard deviation, go to *Standard Deviation* (p. 1324).

EXAMPLE 4

The mean number of bicycles for a random sample of 400 households is 1.4. The standard deviation is 0.6. Find the margin of error and the confidence interval for a confidence level of 95% for the sample.

STEP 1 Find the margin of error.

Use the formula. $\qquad\qquad\qquad\qquad\qquad ME = z_c \frac{\sigma}{\sqrt{n}}$

Substitute. Use the z-score from the table below. $\qquad = (1.96) \frac{0.6}{\sqrt{400}}$

Simplify. Use a calculator. $\qquad\qquad\qquad\qquad = (1.96) \frac{0.6}{20}$

$\qquad\qquad\qquad\qquad\qquad\qquad\qquad\qquad\qquad \approx 0.0588$

The margin of error is about 0.06.

STEP 2 Find the confidence interval.

Add and subtract the margin of error from the sample mean.

$1.4 - 0.06 = 1.34 \qquad 1.4 + 0.06 = 1.46$

The 95% confidence interval for the mean number of bicycles per household in the population is (1.34, 1.46).

GOT TO KNOW!

The Margin of Error and Confidence Intervals for a Mean

For a mean, $ME = z_c \frac{\sigma}{\sqrt{n}}$. The confidence interval is given by $\bar{x} \pm ME$.

z_c = z-score from the table at the right, or from the standard normal distribution table on page 1380.

σ = population standard deviation (but s, the sample standard deviation, can be used as an estimate)

$\bar{x}$ = sample mean

n = sample size

Confidence Level	z-score (z_c)
90	1.64
95	1.96
99	2.57

EXAMPLE 5

A random sample of 4000 households is surveyed, and the mean number of bicycles per household is 1.4. The standard deviation is 0.6. Find the margin of error and the confidence interval for a confidence level of 95% for this sample.

STEP 1 Use the formula for the margin of error.

$$ME = z_c \frac{\sigma}{\sqrt{n}}$$

Substitute. Use the z-score from the table.

$$= (1.96)\frac{0.6}{\sqrt{4000}}$$

Simplify. Use a calculator.

$$= (1.96)\frac{0.6}{63.2455} \approx 0.01859$$

The margin of error is about 0.02.

STEP 2 Find the confidence interval.

Add and subtract the margin of error from the sample mean.

$$1.4 - 0.02 = 1.38 \qquad\qquad 1.4 + 0.02 = 1.42$$

The 95% confidence interval for the mean number of bicycles per household in the population is (1.38, 1.42).

SEARCH

To see step-by-step videos of these problems, enter the page number into the SWadvantage.com Search Bar.

Notice that the sample size in Example 5 is 10 times the sample size in Example 4, and the margin of error in Example 5 is about one-third the margin of error in Example 4. Increasing the sample size decreases the margin of error.

EXAMPLE 6

A quality control officer wants to estimate the mean volume of a company's 12-oz SuperSport bottles at a 99% confidence level. The standard deviation of the volumes is 0.2 oz. Find the smallest sample size that will give a margin of error of 0.04 oz from the population mean.

Use the formula.

$$ME = z_c \frac{\sigma}{\sqrt{n}}$$

Substitute the values you know.

$$0.04 = (2.57)\frac{0.2}{\sqrt{n}}$$

Solve for n.

$$0.04 = \frac{0.514}{\sqrt{n}}$$

$$0.04\sqrt{n} = 0.514$$

$$\sqrt{n} = 12.85$$

$$n = 165.1225$$

To find the sample size, always round the result up to the nearest integer. The quality control officer should use a sample of at least 166 bottles.

GOT TO KNOW!

Sample Size (n)

In general, if $n \geq 30$, the sample standard deviation is a good estimate of the population standard deviation for finding the margin of error and the confidence level for the mean.

The margin of error does not measure, and cannot correct, problems with the sampling process, such as a biased sample, biased questions, or systematic errors. A large value of n will not affect these errors.

Experimental Design

Observation or Experiment?

A soccer coach wants to find out whether increased practice time affects her players' performance. She might conduct an **observation**, a record or measure of events that occur with no intervention by the researcher. Or she could choose an **experiment**, which is a deliberate act or operation that the researcher performs in order to generate outcomes and test an assumption.

SEARCH

To see step-by-step videos of these problems, enter the page number into the SWadvantage.com Search Bar.

EXAMPLE 1

The coach decides to compare each player's amount of practice time to the player's success in making goal kicks in a drill. She records how long each player practices and makes a scatter plot showing total practice time and the number of successful goal kicks. Is this an experiment or an observation?

This is an example of an observation, because the coach records the events but does not intentionally give any of the soccer players different amounts of practice time.

EXAMPLE 2

The coach divides the players into two groups. One group is assigned 30 minutes of practice twice a week, and the other practices 30 minutes four times a week. The coach records the total practice time and the success on a goal kick drill. Is this an experiment or an observation?

This is an example of an experiment because the coach has chosen to give one group of players more practice time than the other group.

Features of a Well-Designed Experiment

The important characteristics of an experiment are that (1) subjects are assigned *randomly* to groups, (2) there are at least two groups with different *treatments*, and (3) the experiment involves *replication*.

EXAMPLE 3

Describe how the soccer coach can randomly assign players to two groups.

She can flip a coin for each name on an alphabetical list of soccer players. If the coin lands heads up, the player is assigned to the group with two practices per week. If the coin lands tails up, the player is assigned to the group with four practices per week.

Need More HELP?

For more methods of choosing a random sample, see *Random Sampling* (p. 1224).

If subjects volunteer for the groups, then the assignments are not made randomly. Assignments that are based on a characteristic, such as gender, age, or skill, are also not random.

However, a researcher may decide to divide the subjects into blocks based on some characteristic. Each block is then split randomly into groups that receive different treatments. This is called **randomized block design**.

The groups of subjects in an experiment are sometimes called the *control group* and the *experiment group*. Although a control group may have no treatment, in many experiments all the groups have some kind of treatment. For example, to test the effect of light on plants, you might use six groups of plants and six lamps of varying intensities.

Replication is the repetition of an experiment. If the results of an experiment are valid, a researcher must be able to replicate them.

Often a diagram can help you outline an experiment.

Need More
HELP ?

A sample size that is greater than 30 is considered large enough to allow generalizations to be made from a sample to the population. Go to *Sample Size* (p. 1350) for more information.

EXAMPLE 4

Make a diagram that describes how a soccer coach could test whether practicing four times per week instead of two times per week affects success in goal kicks.

Start with the number of subjects in the experiment. Show that the group assignments are random. Describe the treatments. Finally, describe what variables will be compared at the end of the experiment.

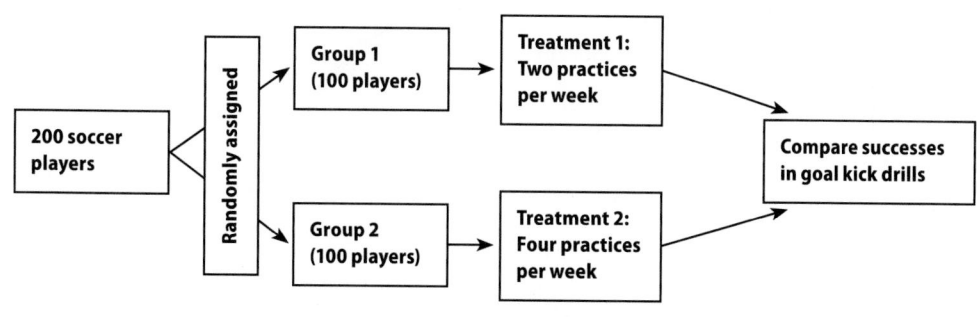

The design of an experiment can affect its validity.

EXAMPLE 5

A botanist wants to know how music affects the growth of plants. He has 80 bean plants and 80 pea plants. He plays classical music for 3 hours a day to 40 bean plants, classical music for 6 hours a day to 40 bean plants, rock music for 3 hours a day to 40 pea plants, and rock music for 6 hours per day to 40 pea plants. He finds that, on average, the bean plants produce more and are taller than the pea plants. Is there a problem with the design of this experiment? How could it be redesigned?

The experiment involves different treatments, the amount and type of music played to plants. It also uses replication, as there are 40 plants in each group.

However, the plants are not assigned to the groups randomly. The bean plants may be naturally taller than the pea plants, regardless of what music is played to them.

Compound Events and Conditional Probability

What Came Before?
- Experimental and theoretical probability
- Measures of geometric figures, such as length and area

What's This About?
- Probability of compound events
- Geometric probability
- Simulations

Practical Apps
- Operations research analysts study efficiency and use compound probabilities and simulation in analyzing the cause of a wide range of problems within a company.
- Network routing engineers use conditional probability and models to reduce the chance and duration of an outage.

just for FUN!

Q: What happened with the event and her boyfriend?

A: Well, they used to be exclusive, but now they are mutually exclusive.

1356

You can find more practice problems online by visiting:
www.SWadvantage.com

Independent and Dependent Events

Independent Events

If you toss a coin more than once, or toss two coins, and look at the possible outcomes, you are considering a compound event. A **compound event** is made up of two or more events.

SEARCH

To see step-by-step videos of these problems, enter the page number into the SWadvantage.com Search Bar.

EXAMPLE 1

Find all the possible outcomes of tossing a nickel and a dime.

There are two possible outcomes for each coin, heads (H) or tails (T). There are four possible outcomes for tossing both coins, as shown here.

nickel H, dime H   nickel H, dime T   nickel T, dime H   nickel T, dime T

The set of all possible outcomes of an experiment, with no repetition, is called the **sample space**.

Two events or trials are **independent** if the outcome of one event does not influence the outcome of the other event. The probability of two events A and B is written $P(A \text{ and } B)$. If two events are independent, you can multiply to find the probability that both events occur.

EXAMPLE 2

A coin is tossed and a number cube is rolled. What is the probability of getting heads on the coin and a 2 on the number cube?

The events are independent, because the outcome of the coin toss has no effect on the outcome of the roll of the number cube.

METHOD 1

Make a table of all possible outcomes, and count them.

Need More

HELP ?

For more about finding probabilities, go to *Theoretical Probability* in *Theoretical and Experimental Probability* (p. 1232).

Outcomes of Rolling a Number Cube

		1	2	3	4	5	6
Outcomes of Tossing a Coin	**Heads**	H and 1	H and 2	H and 3	H and 4	H and 5	H and 6
	Tails	T and 1	T and 2	T and 3	T and 4	T and 5	T and 6

There are 12 different outcomes. One of them is H and 2. So $P(\text{H and 2}) = \frac{1}{12}$.

METHOD 2

Use multiplication.

$$P(\text{H}) = \frac{1}{2} \text{ and } P(2) = \frac{1}{6}, \text{ so } P(\text{H and 2}) = \frac{1}{2} \cdot \frac{1}{6} = \frac{1}{12}.$$

EXAMPLE 3

A coin is tossed and a number cube is rolled. What is the probability of getting heads on the coin or a 2 on the number cube, or $P(\text{H or 2})$?

You can use the table in Example 2 to find the probability that either event occurs. There are 12 different outcomes. Of the 12 outcomes, 6 include getting heads and 2 include rolling a two. Of these 8 outcomes, 1 outcome, H and 2, is in both categories. Therefore,

$$P(\text{H or 2}) = P(\text{H}) + P(2) - P(\text{H and 2}) = \frac{1}{2} + \frac{1}{6} - \frac{1}{12} = \frac{7}{12}.$$

As shown in Example 3, when events A and B are independent, the probability of A or B is the sum of the probabilities of the individual events minus the probability of A and B. You can write this as $P(A \text{ or } B) = P(A) + P(B) - P(A \text{ and } B)$.

EXAMPLE 4

There are 16 girls and 14 boys in a math class. Ten of the girls and 8 of the boys are also in a physics class.

a. The math teacher selects a student at random to pass out calculators. What is the probability that the student is a boy in the physics class?

There are 30 students in the class. 18 of them are in physics.

To find $P(\text{boy and physics})$, multiply.

$$P(\text{boy and physics}) = P(\text{boy}) \cdot P(\text{physics})$$
$$= \frac{14}{30} \cdot \frac{18}{30} = \frac{7}{25}$$

b. The math teacher selects a student at random from the whole class to collect the calculators. What is the probability that the student is a girl or a physics student?

To find $P(\text{girl or physics})$, add the two probabilities and then subtract to compensate for counting an outcome twice.

$$P(\text{girl or physics}) = P(\text{girl}) + P(\text{physics}) - P(\text{girl and physics})$$
$$= P(\text{girl}) + P(\text{physics}) - P(\text{girl}) \cdot P(\text{physics})$$
$$= \frac{16}{30} + \frac{18}{30} - \frac{16}{30} \cdot \frac{18}{30} = \frac{61}{75}$$

Suppose a marble is drawn at random from a bag and returned to the bag. Then another marble is drawn at random. It is possible to select the first marble the second time around. This is called **sampling with replacement**. The two selections are independent events.

EXAMPLE 5

A bag contains 5 red marbles and 7 blue marbles. Jamie draws a marble at random, replaces it, and draws a second marble. What is the probability that the two marbles are the same color?

If the two marbles are the same color, they are both red or both blue. There is no overlap of these outcomes, so there is no need to subtract the probability of both outcomes occurring together.

$$P[(\text{red and red}) \text{ or } (\text{blue and blue})] = P(\text{red and red}) + P(\text{blue and blue})$$
$$= P(\text{red}) \cdot P(\text{red}) + P(\text{blue}) \cdot P(\text{blue})$$
$$= \frac{5}{12} \cdot \frac{5}{12} + \frac{7}{12} \cdot \frac{7}{12}$$
$$= \frac{74}{144} = \frac{37}{72}$$

The probability that the marbles are the same color is $\frac{37}{72}$.

Probabilities of Independent Events

For any two independent events A and B, probabilities are calculated as shown.

$$P(A \text{ or } B) = P(A) + P(B) - P(A \text{ and } B) \qquad P(A \text{ and } B) = P(A) \cdot P(B)$$

Dependent Events

Dependent events are another type of compound event. Two events are **dependent events** if the outcome of one event affects the outcome of the other event.

Selecting an item and then selecting another one without replacing the first item is called **sampling without replacement**. Sampling without replacement implies dependent events.

> **EXAMPLE 6**
>
> A yellow tennis ball is drawn at random from a bag containing 8 yellow balls and 10 green balls. Then, with the first ball still out, a second ball is selected at random from the bag.
>
> **a. Are these independent events or dependent events?**
>
> The outcome of the second draw is affected by the outcome of the first draw. The events are dependent.
>
> **b. What is the probability of drawing a yellow ball on the first draw?**
>
> There are 18 balls in the bag, and 8 of them are yellow. The probability is $\frac{8}{18}$ or $\frac{4}{9}$.
>
> **c. A yellow ball is drawn on the first draw. What is the probability of drawing a green ball on the second draw?**
>
> After the first draw, there are 17 balls in the bag, and 10 of them are green. The probability is $\frac{10}{17}$.

Watch Out !

The vertical line in the notation B | A is *not* a division sign.

The probability that event B occurs, given that event A has occurred, is called a **conditional probability**. It is written $P(B \mid A)$ and is read "the probability of B given A."

> **EXAMPLE 7**
>
> A card is drawn from a standard deck of 52 playing cards. Then a second card is drawn without replacement of the first. What is the probability that an ace is drawn first, and then a king?
>
> The outcome of the first draw affects the outcome of the second draw. These events are dependent.
>
> There are 4 aces. The probability of drawing an ace on the first draw is $\frac{4}{52}$ or $\frac{1}{13}$. After this draw, there are 4 kings in a deck of 51 cards. The probability of drawing a king, given that the first draw was an ace, is $\frac{4}{51}$. The probability of drawing an ace, then a king, is $\frac{1}{13} \cdot \frac{4}{51} = \frac{4}{663} \approx 0.006$, or about 0.6%.

In Example 7, the probability of drawing an ace followed by a king is the product of two probabilities, the simple probability of drawing one ace, and the conditional probability of drawing a king after an ace.

GOT TO KNOW!

The Probability of Dependent Events

For any two dependent events A and B, $P(A \text{ and } B) = P(A) \cdot P(B \mid A)$.

EXAMPLE 8

Each of the letters in the word *DEPENDENT* is written on a card. The cards are shuffled and placed face down. Two of the cards are turned over. What is the probability that both have the letter *E* written on them?

SEARCH

To see step-by-step videos of these problems, enter the page number into the SWadvantage.com Search Bar.

D E P E N D E N T

These events are dependent because the first card is not replaced before the second card is turned over. There are 9 cards, and 3 of them have the letter E written on them.

$P(E) = \frac{3}{9} = \frac{1}{3}$

After the first card is turned over, there are 8 cards remaining, and 2 of them have the letter *E* written on them.

$P(\text{second } E \mid \text{first } E) = \frac{2}{8} = \frac{1}{4}$

To find the probability of the two dependent events, multiply the probabilities.

$P(E \text{ and } E) = P(E) \cdot P(\text{second } E \mid \text{first } E)$

$= \frac{1}{3} \cdot \frac{1}{4} = \frac{1}{12}$

The probability that both cards that are turned over have *E* written on them is $\frac{1}{12}$.

Sometimes you can use a table to find conditional probabilities.

EXAMPLE 9

At Arts and Letters High School, ninth-grade students are required to participate in a fall sport. They can join the cross-country team or the soccer team, but not both. The table shows the numbers of girls and boys in each sport.

	Cross-country	Soccer	Total
Girls	34	29	63
Boys	42	35	77
Total	76	64	140

A ninth-grade student is chosen at random. What is the probability that the student is a girl, given that the student is a soccer player?

$P(A \text{ and } B) = P(A) \cdot P(B \mid A)$

$P(\text{girl and soccer}) = P(\text{soccer}) \cdot P(\text{girl} \mid \text{soccer})$

$\frac{29}{140} = \frac{64}{140} \cdot P(\text{girl} \mid \text{soccer})$

$\frac{29}{64} = P(\text{girl} \mid \text{soccer})$

The probability that the student is a girl, given that the student is a soccer player, is $\frac{29}{64}$, or about 45%.

Probability and Geometry

Using Area to Find Probabilities

Some probability problems involve geometric figures and their areas.

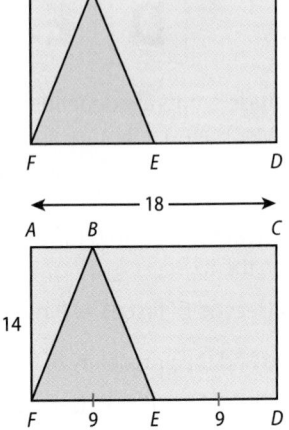

SEARCH

To see step-by-step videos of these problems, enter the page number into the SWadvantage.com Search Bar.

EXAMPLE 1

Rectangle *ACDF* has a length of 18 units and height 14 units. Point *E* is the midpoint of $\overline{FD}$. If a point is selected at random from the interior of rectangle *ACDF*, what is the probability that it lies in the interior of $\triangle FBE$?

The probability equals the ratio of the area of $\triangle FBE$ to the area of rectangle *ACDF*.

STEP 1 Label the information you know.

STEP 2 Find the areas of $\triangle FBE$ and rectangle *ACDF*.

$$\text{Area of } \triangle FBE = \frac{1}{2} \text{ base} \cdot \text{height}$$

$$= \frac{1}{2} \cdot 9 \cdot 14 = 63$$

$$\text{Area of rectangle } ACDF = \text{base} \cdot \text{height}$$

$$= 18 \cdot 14$$

$$= 252$$

STEP 3 Find the ratio.

$$\frac{\text{Area of } \triangle FBE}{\text{Area of rectangle } ACDF} = \frac{63}{252} = \frac{1}{4}$$

If a point is selected at random from the interior of the rectangle, the probability that it is in the interior of $\triangle FBE$ is $\frac{1}{4}$, or 25%.

Need More
HELP ?

For more about complementary events, see *Odds and Complements* in *Theoretical and Experimental Probability* (p. 1254).

EXAMPLE 2

Use the figure in Example 1. If a point is selected at random from the interior of rectangle *ACDF*, what is the probability that it does not lie in the interior of $\triangle FBE$?

The events "lies in the interior of $\triangle FBE$" and "does not lie in the interior of $\triangle FBE$" are complements.

$P(\text{point does not lie in the interior of } \triangle FBE) + P(\text{point lies in the interior of } \triangle FBE) = 1$

$P(\text{point does not lie in the interior of } \triangle FBE) + \frac{1}{4} = 1$

$P(\text{point does not lie in the interior of } \triangle FBE) = \frac{3}{4}$

EXAMPLE 3

Figure *PRTV* is a square. Points *Q*, *S*, *U*, and *W* are the midpoints of the sides. If a point is selected at random from the interior of the square, what is the probability that it lies inside the shaded region?

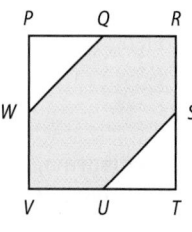

STEP 1   Label the information that you know.

When choosing expressions for the lengths of the sides of the figure, you can avoid working with fractions. For example, let $PR = 2x$. Then $PQ = x$.

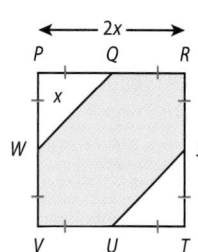

STEP 2   Write expressions in terms of x for the area of square *PRTV* and the area of the shaded region. The area of the shaded region equals the area of the square minus the area of two congruent isosceles right triangles.

Area of $PRTV = (2x)^2 = 4x^2$

Area of shaded region = Area of $PRTV - 2 \cdot$ Area of $\triangle PQW$

$$= 4x^2 - 2 \cdot \left(\frac{1}{2} x \cdot x \right)$$
$$= 4x^2 - x^2$$
$$= 3x^2$$

STEP 3   Find the ratio.

$$\frac{\text{Area of shaded region}}{\text{Area of square } PRTV} = \frac{3x^2}{4x^2} = \frac{3}{4}$$

The probability is $\frac{3}{4}$, or 75%.

EXAMPLE 4

A circle with radius 7 cm is inscribed in a square. A point is selected at random from the interior of the square. What is the probability that the point does not lie in the interior of the circle?

STEP 1   Draw a sketch.

If the point does not lie in the interior of the circle, it lies in the shaded region.

STEP 2   Find the area of the square, the circle, and the shaded region.

The area of the square is $14^2 = 196$ cm². The area of the circle is 49π cm². The area of the shaded region is $(196 - 49\pi)$ cm².

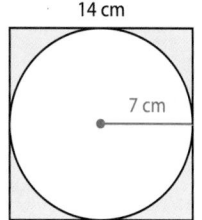

STEP 3   Find the ratio.

Use a calculator.

$$\frac{\text{Area of shaded region}}{\text{Area of square}} = \frac{(196 - 49\pi) \text{ cm}^2}{196 \text{ cm}^2} \approx 0.21$$

The probability is about 0.21, or 21%.

Need More HELP?

Remember that the area of a circle with radius r is πr^2. For more about circles, go to *Areas of Circles* in *Measurement* (Book 1, p. 548).

Using Length to Find Probabilities

Just as you can use the ratio of two areas to find a probability, you can also use the ratio of two lengths.

SEARCH

To see step-by-step videos of these problems, enter the page number into the SWadvantage.com Search Bar.

EXAMPLE 5

In the diagram, the length of $\overline{JK}$ is 9x and the length of $\overline{KL}$ is 4x. If a point is chosen at random from $\overline{JL}$, what is the probability that it lies on $\overline{JK}$?

STEP 1 Label the diagram.

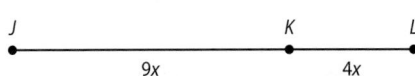

STEP 2 Find JL.

Segment Addition Postulate $JL = JK + KL = 9x + 4x = 13x$

STEP 3 Find the ratio $\frac{JK}{JL}$.

$$\frac{JK}{JL} = \frac{9x}{13x} = \frac{9}{13}$$

The probability that a point chosen at random from $\overline{JL}$ lies on $\overline{JK}$ is $\frac{9}{13}$, or about 69%.

Sometimes it is helpful to use length as a model for another continuous variable, such as time.

EXAMPLE 6

Sada and Paul start band practice sometime between 9:00 A.M. and 10:15 A.M. The practice lasts exactly 30 minutes. What is the probability that the practice ends after 10:15 A.M.?

STEP 1 Draw and label a diagram that represents the times in the problem.

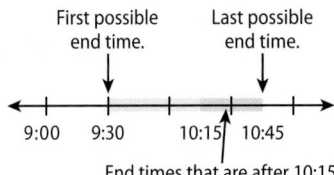

STEP 2 Find the ratio $\frac{\text{Successive end times}}{\text{All end times}}$.

$$\frac{\text{Length of segment containing possible end times after 10:15}}{\text{Length of segment containing all end times}} = \frac{30}{75} = \frac{2}{5}, \text{ or } 40\%$$

The probability the practice ends after 10:15 A.M. is 60%.

Modeling Compound Events with Area

If you choose a point at random from the interior of rectangle *LNQS*, it will lie in the interior of more than one rectangle. For example, a point that lies in the interior of rectangle *TKRS* also lies in the interior of *TPQS*. You can use this relationship to model the probability of a compound event.

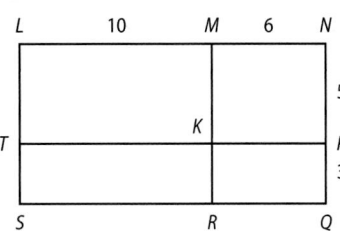

EXAMPLE 7

A point is chosen at random from rectangle *LNQS*.

a. What is the probability that the point lies in the interior of *MNQR* and the interior of *PQST*?

METHOD 1

Find the area of the intersection of the rectangles, and compare it with the area of *LNQS*.

The intersection of *MNQR* and *PQST* is rectangle *KPQR*. Its area is $6 \cdot 3 = 18$.

The area of *LNQS* is $16 \cdot 8 = 128$.

$P(\text{point in } MNQR \text{ and } PQST) = \dfrac{\text{Area of } KPQR}{\text{Area of } LNQS} = \dfrac{18}{128} = \dfrac{9}{64}$

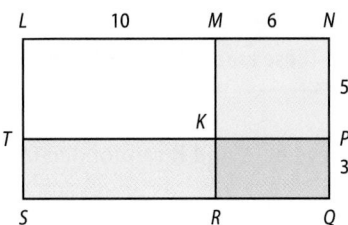

METHOD 2

Use the formula $P(A \text{ and } B) = P(A) \cdot P(B)$.

$P(\text{point in } MNQR \text{ and } PQST) = P(\text{point in } MNQR) \cdot P(\text{point in } PQST)$

$= \dfrac{\text{Area of } MNQR}{\text{Area of } LNQS} \cdot \dfrac{\text{Area of } PQST}{\text{Area of } LNQS} = \dfrac{6 \cdot 8}{128} \cdot \dfrac{16 \cdot 3}{128} = \dfrac{9}{64}$

b. What is the probability that the point lies in the interior of *MNQR* or the interior of *PQST*?

METHOD 1

Find the area of the entire shaded region, and compare it with the area of *LNQS*.

Area of shaded region = Area of *MNPK* + Area of *KPQR* + Area of *TKRS*

$= 6 \cdot 5 + 3 \cdot 6 + 10 \cdot 3$

$= 30 + 18 + 30 = 78$

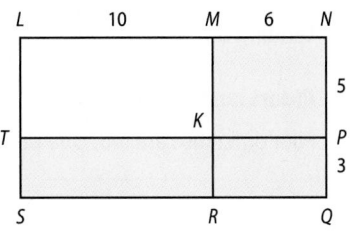

$P(\text{point in } MNQR \text{ or } PQST) = \dfrac{78}{128} = \dfrac{39}{64}$

METHOD 2

Use the formula $P(A \text{ or } B) = P(A) + P(B) - P(A \text{ and } B)$.

$P(\text{point in } MNQR \text{ or } PQST) = P(\text{point in } MNQR) + P(\text{point in } PQST) - P(\text{point in } MNQR \text{ and } PQST)$

$= \dfrac{\text{Area of } MNQR}{\text{Area of } LNQS} + \dfrac{\text{Area of } PQST}{\text{Area of } LNQS} - \dfrac{9}{64}$

$= \dfrac{6 \cdot 8}{128} + \dfrac{3 \cdot 16}{128} - \dfrac{9}{64} = \dfrac{48}{64} - \dfrac{9}{64} = \dfrac{39}{64}$

Need More HELP?

For more about the probability of compound events, go to *Independent and Dependent Events* (p. 1358).

Mutually Exclusive or Overlapping Events

Neither, Both, or Some of Each

If you throw a dart at this dartboard, it cannot hit both a black sector and a red sector. Two events that cannot happen at the same time are **mutually exclusive events**.

The dart could hit both a red sector and an even-numbered sector. Two events that can happen at the same time are **overlapping events**.

> **EXAMPLE 1**
>
> **One card is drawn from a standard deck of 52 playing cards. Tell whether each situation describes mutually exclusive events.**
>
> **a. The card is a heart. The card is a queen.**
>
> These are not mutually exclusive events. It is possible for the card to be both a heart and a queen.
>
> **b. The card is a queen. The card is a three.**
>
> These are mutually exclusive events. It is not possible for a card to be both a queen and a three.

SEARCH

To see step-by-step videos of these problems, enter the page number into the SWadvantage.com Search Bar.

If events A and B cannot occur together, then $P(A \text{ and } B) = 0$.

> **EXAMPLE 2**
>
> **Use the dartboard shown above. A dart is thrown at random at the board. Find each probability.**
>
> **a. *P*(dart lands on 6)**
>
> There are 8 outcomes, all equally likely. So $P(\text{dart lands on 6}) = \frac{1}{8}$.
>
> **b. *P*(dart lands on red)**
>
> Four outcomes are red. So $P(\text{dart lands on red}) = \frac{4}{8} = \frac{1}{2}$.
>
> **c. *P*(dart lands on red and on 6)**
>
> Landing on red and landing on 6 are mutually exclusive events. $P(\text{dart lands on red and on 6}) = 0$.
>
> **d. *P*(dart lands on red or on 6)**
>
> Four outcomes are red. One outcome is 6. $P(\text{dart lands on red or on 6}) = \frac{5}{8}$.

For two overlapping events A and B, $P(A \text{ or } B) = P(A) + P(B) - P(A \text{ and } B)$. If A and B are mutually exclusive, then $P(A \text{ and } B) = 0$, so $P(A \text{ or } B) = P(A) + P(B)$.

GOT TO KNOW!

Probability of Mutually Exclusive Events

If events A and B are mutually exclusive, then these are the probabilities.

$P(A \text{ and } B) = 0$

$P(A \text{ or } B) = P(A) + P(B)$

EXAMPLE 3

The vertices of a rectangle are (0, 0), (8, 0), (8, 6), and (0, 6). A point is selected at random from the interior of the rectangle.

a. What is the probability that the coordinates of the point satisfy the inequalities $y > x$ and $x > 6$?

Draw and label the rectangle. Shade the regions that represent $x > 6$ and $y > x$. There are no points that are in both regions. The events are mutually exclusive, so $P(x > 6$ and $y > x) = 0$.

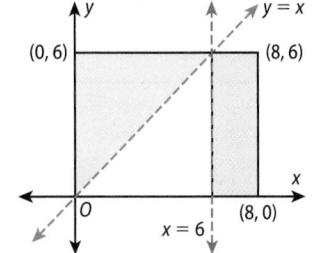

Need More

HELP?

For help with finding the area of a triangle, go to *Areas of Triangles* in *Perimeter and Area* (Book 1, p. 536).

b. What is the probability that the coordinates of the point satisfy either the inequality $y > x$ or the inequality $y < 3$?

STEP 1   Draw and label the rectangle.

Shade the regions that represent $y > x$ and $y < 3$. The events are overlapping, so
$P(y > x$ or $y < 3) = P(y > x) + P(y < 3) - P(y > x$ and $y < 3)$.

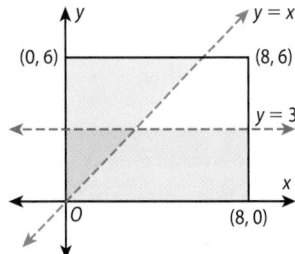

STEP 2   Find the area of each region.

The area of the big rectangle is $(6)(8) = 48$.

The region for which $y > x$ is a right triangle. Its area is $\frac{1}{2}bh = \frac{1}{2}(6)(6) = 18$.

The region for which $y < 3$ is a rectangle. Its area is $(8)(3) = 24$.

The region for which $y > x$ and $y < 3$ is a right triangle. Its area is $\frac{1}{2}bh = \frac{1}{2}(3)(3) = \frac{9}{2}$.

STEP 3   Find the probability.

$P(y > x$ or $y < 3) = P(y > x) + P(y < 3) - P(y > x$ and $y < 3)$

$$= \frac{18}{48} + \frac{24}{48} - \frac{\frac{9}{2}}{48} = \frac{25}{32}$$

EXAMPLE 4

The Central High School cafeteria may serve apple slices, orange wedges, both, or neither. The probability that apple slices are served is $\frac{3}{5}$. The probability that either apple slices or orange wedges are served is $\frac{4}{5}$. What is the probability that orange wedges are served?

Since it is possible that both apple slices and orange wedges are served, these are overlapping events.

Let $w =$ the probability that orange wedges are served. Then $P(\text{apples and oranges}) = \frac{3}{5}w$.

Use the formula. $P(\text{apples or oranges}) = P(\text{apples}) + P(\text{oranges}) - P(\text{apples and oranges})$

Substitute. $\frac{4}{5} = \frac{3}{5} + w - \frac{3}{5}w$

Solve for w. $\frac{1}{2} = w$

The probability that orange wedges are served is $\frac{1}{2}$.

Probability and Venn Diagrams

Need More

HELP ?

For more about using a Venn diagram to organize information, go to *Venn Diagrams* in *Displaying Data* (p. 1288).

Interpreting Venn Diagrams

Because Venn diagrams are a convenient way to display information about the relationships between sets, they also are a good way to organize probabilities.

Both of these diagrams show how people answered the question "Do you ski or snowboard?" In each case, the rectangle contains the sample space.

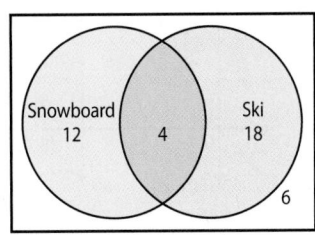

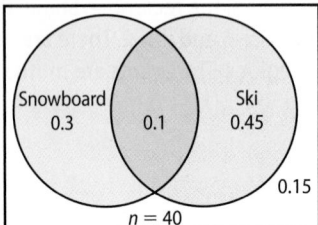

This diagram shows that 12 people snowboard, 18 people ski, 4 do both, and 6 do neither.

This diagram shows the probabilities that a person selected at random from the sample space answered in a certain way.

SEARCH 🔍

To see step-by-step videos of these problems, enter the page number into the SWadvantage.com Search Bar.

EXAMPLE 1

Make a Venn diagram to represent each situation.

a. The probability of an event A is 0.75.

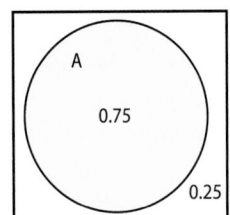

The part of the rectangle that is outside the circle represents the complement of A, written A^C.

$P(A) + P(A^C) = 1$

b. Two events R and Q are mutually exclusive.

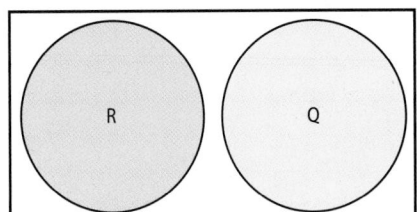

The two circles do not intersect.

$R \cap Q = \emptyset$

$P(R \text{ and } Q) = 0$

c. Two events M and N are overlapping.

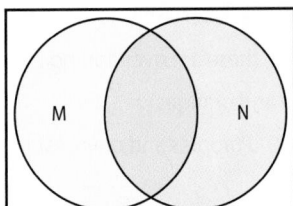

The two circles intersect.

$P(M \text{ and } N) > 0$

EXAMPLE 2

The Venn diagram shows the probabilities of customers' orders at the Coffee Stop.

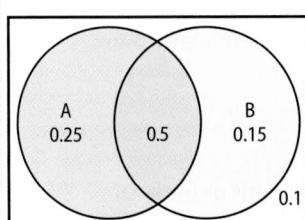

A = coffee

B = muffin

a. **What is the probability that a customer orders coffee?**

Add the two probabilities inside the circle labeled A.

$P(A) = 0.25 + 0.5 = 0.75$

The probability that a customer orders coffee is 0.75.

b. **What is the probability that a customer orders a muffin?**

Add the two probabilities inside circle B.

$P(B) = 0.15 + 0.5 = 0.65$

The probability that a customer orders a muffin is 0.65.

c. **What is the probability that a customer orders coffee or a muffin?**

METHOD 1

Add the three probabilities that are inside circles A and B. The probability is 0.9.

METHOD 2

Use the formula $P(A \text{ or } B) = P(A) + P(B) - P(A \text{ and } B)$.

$P(A) + P(B) - P(A \text{ and } B) = 0.75 + 0.65 - 0.5 = 0.9$

METHOD 3

Find the probability of the complement, and subtract it from 1.

The complement of "coffee or a muffin" is "neither." Its probability is outside the circles.

$P(A \text{ or } B) = 1 - P[(A \text{ or } B)^c] = 1 - 0.1 = 0.9$

d. **What is the probability that a customer orders a muffin, given that he or she orders coffee?**

Use the formula $P(B \mid A) = \dfrac{P(B \text{ and } A)}{P(A)}$.

$\dfrac{P(B \text{ and } A)}{P(A)} = \dfrac{0.5}{0.75} = \dfrac{2}{3} \approx 0.67$

GOT TO KNOW!

Independent Events

Two events A and B are independent if and only if $P(B \mid A) = P(B)$.

In Example 2, the probability that a customer orders a muffin, given that the customer orders coffee, is about 0.67. The probability that any customer orders a muffin is 0.65. Ordering a coffee and ordering a muffin are not independent events, because these probabilities are not equal.

Creating Venn Diagrams

To construct a Venn diagram, find the number of elements or the probability for each region. Sometimes the same label is used to represent both a region of the diagram and the number of elements in the region. Example 3 uses S to represent the region *swimming* and the number of campers who swim, 45.

EXAMPLE 3

Watch Out !

Be sure to write the value for "only S" in the part of circle S that is not part of the intersection.

At a summer day camp, every camper must sign up for swimming or tennis or both. Of 80 campers, 45 sign up for swimming and 67 sign up for tennis. A camper is then chosen at random. Use a Venn diagram to find the probability that he or she signed up only for swimming.

STEP 1 Make a Venn diagram with two overlapping circles.

Label one S for swimming and the other T for tennis.

STEP 2 Find the value for $S \cap T$.

Every camper is in at least one of the activities.

$S + T - (S \cap T) = \text{total}$

$45 + 67 - (S \cap T) = 80$

$112 - (S \cap T) = 80$

$S \cap T = 32$

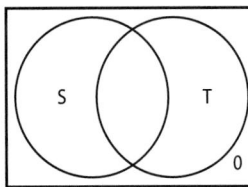

STEP 3 Find the value for only S.

$(\text{only } S) + (S \cap T) = S$

$(\text{only } S) + 32 = 45$

only $S = 13$

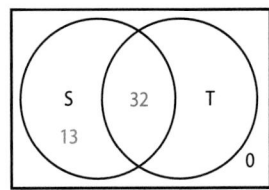

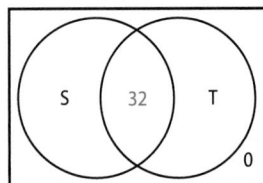

STEP 4 Find the probability.

$P(\text{only } S) = \frac{13}{80} \approx 0.16$

The probability that a camper selected at random signed up only for swimming is about 16%.

EXAMPLE 4

The table shows the number of students at West School who can drive. Make a Venn diagram that shows the values in the table. Use one circle for 11th graders and the other for drivers.

	Driving	Not Driving
11th grade	72	53
12th grade	95	12

STEP 1 Draw a Venn diagram with two overlapping circles.

STEP 2 Write the number of 11th grade drivers in the intersection of the two circles.

STEP 3 Write the number of 11th graders who do not drive here.

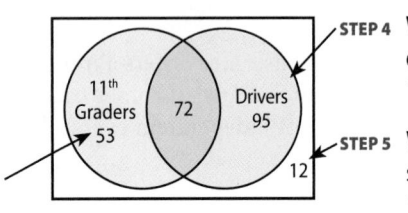

STEP 4 Write the number of drivers who are not 11th graders here.

STEP 5 Write here the number of students who are not in 11th grade and do not drive.

EXAMPLE 5

The probability that a student at Eastside School takes a bus to school is 0.7. The probability that a student takes a bus home from school is 0.75. The probability that a student takes a bus home, given that the student takes a bus to school, is 0.9.

SEARCH

To see step-by-step videos of these problems, enter the page number into the SWadvantage.com Search Bar.

a. Find the probability that a student takes a bus to school and takes a bus home.

Let T represent taking a bus to school and F represent taking a bus home from school.

Then $P(T) = 0.7$, $P(F) = 0.75$, and $P(F \mid T) = 0.9$.

Use the formula for the probability of F, given T. $P(F \mid T) = \dfrac{P(F \text{ and } T)}{P(T)}$

Substitute. $0.9 = \dfrac{P(F \text{ and } T)}{0.7}$

Solve for $P(F \text{ and } T)$. $0.63 = P(F \text{ and } T)$

The probability that a student takes the bus to and from school is 0.63.

b. Make a Venn diagram that shows the probabilities in part (a).

Because $P(F \text{ and } T) \neq 0$, draw a Venn diagram with two overlapping circles.

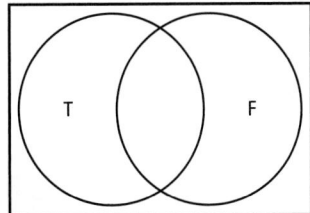

Find the probabilities of taking a bus only to school and of taking a bus only home from school.

$P(\text{only } T) = P(T) - P(F \text{ and } T) = 0.7 - 0.63 = 0.07$

$P(\text{only } F) = P(F) - P(F \text{ and } T) = 0.75 - 0.63 = 0.12$

Find the probability of not taking a bus to or from school.

$P[(T \text{ or } F)^c] = 1 - (0.07 + 0.12 + 0.63) = 0.18$

Write the probabilities in the corresponding regions of the Venn diagram.

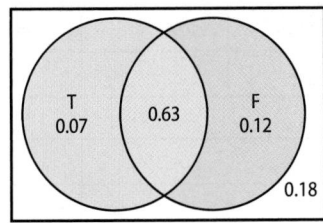

c. What is the probability of not taking a bus home from school?

Add all the probabilities that are not inside the circle labeled F.

$P(\text{not } F) = 0.07 + 0.18 = 0.25$.

d. Are taking a bus to school and home from school independent events? Explain why or why not.

No, they are not independent, because $P(F \mid T) \neq P(F)$.

Simulations and Technology

Simulating Experimental Results

If a probability experiment is difficult or time-consuming to conduct, you can use *simulation* to approximate its results. To simulate an experiment, pair an outcome with a random number found in a table or with a calculator.

SEARCH 🔍

To see step-by-step videos of these problems, enter the page number into the SWadvantage.com Search Bar.

EXAMPLE 1

Simulate tossing a coin 10 times.

In a coin toss, P(Heads) $= P$(Tails) $= 0.5$. Use this probability in the simulation.

METHOD 1

Use a random number table.

The table is made up of blocks of four digits. Choose any position within a block, such as the third digit.

Table of Random Digits									
2671	4690	1550	2262	2597	8034	0785	2978	4409	0237
9111	0250	3275	7519	9740	4577	2064	0286	3398	1348
0391	6035	9230	4999	3332	0608	6113	0391	5789	9926

If the number is even, record *H* for heads. If it is odd, record *T* for tails.

7	9	5	6	9	3	8	7	0	3
T	T	T	H	T	T	H	T	H	T

The results of this simulation are 3 heads and 7 tails.

METHOD 2

Use a scientific calculator.

Press **RAND**. A random number between 0 and 1 will be generated. If the number is less than 0.5, record heads. If it is greater than 0.5, record tails. Do not round the numbers. Repeat until you have 10 numbers.

0.45518 . . .	0.88673 . . .	0.32620 . . .	0.55993 . . .	0.65288 . . .
H	T	H	T	T

0.60213 . . .	0.20760 . . .	0.60802 . . .	0.46384 . . .	0.58053 . . .
T	H	T	H	T

The results of this simulation are 4 heads and 6 tails.

Try It This Way

You can also use a graphing calculator. Select the PRB function and use the randBin command to generate a list of 0's and 1's. Record heads if the number is 0, and tails if the number is 1.

1372

Most scientific and graphing calculators can produce a random number between 0 and 1. To produce a random number in any interval, you can use a formula.

EXAMPLE 2

A card is drawn at random from a standard deck of playing cards. The suit is recorded, and the card is replaced. Simulate six such draws.

There are four equally likely outcomes. Let 1 represent drawing a heart, 2 represent drawing a club, 3 represent drawing a diamond, and 4 represent drawing a spade.

METHOD 1

Use a calculator that does not have an integer function.

Step	Example
Use **RAND** to produce a random number between 0 and 1.	0.376827 ...
Multiply by 4 to produce a number between 0 and 4, not including 0 or 4.	1.507308 ...
Use the integer part of the number to produce a 0, 1, 2, or 3.	1
Add 1 to produce a 1, 2, 3, or 4.	2

Repeat this five more times to generate a list of six integers from 1 to 4.

METHOD 2

Use spreadsheet software to generate a list of numbers from 1 to 4.

Use the formula = INT(4*RAND()) + 1. INT will round down to the nearest integer.

	C1 ▼		f_x =INT(4*RAND())+1		
	A	B	C	D	E	F
1			3			
2			3			
3			4			
4			1			
5			2			
6			3			
7			4			

METHOD 3

Use a graphing calculator to generate a random list of numbers from 1 to 4.

Press **MATH** and select PRB. The command randInt(a, b, n) generates n integers from a to b. Use 1 for a, 4 for b, and 6 for n.

To run more trials, press **ENTER** repeatedly.

```
randInt(1,4,6)
      {4 4 1 2 1 4}
```

> **Watch Out !**
> Random numbers generated by calculators and computers are not truly random, and are called *pseudorandom*.

EXAMPLE 3

Suppose you want to simulate rolling a number cube. What change should you make to the formula in Method 3 of Example 2?

Because the outcomes of rolling a number cube are the integers 1 to 6, you should change the value of b to 6.

Probability with Simulation

EXAMPLE 4

A small commuter jet has 20 passenger seats. The airline manager has found that, on average, 10% of the people who buy seats for a flight do not arrive for the flight. The manager sells 22 seats for each flight. Use a graphing calculator to estimate the probability that a flight is overbooked because more than 20 people arrive.

The probability that a customer arrives is 90%. Let the integers 0 through 8 represent the customers who arrive. Let 9 represent customers who do not arrive.

Use randInt(0, 9, 22) to generate 22 random numbers between 0 and 9. Store the list in L1.

To count the number of customers who arrive for the flight in a trial, you can use the "sum" command on the calculator.

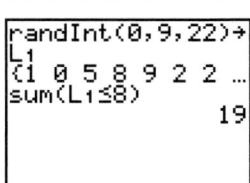

Press **2nd** **LIST** and select Math. Select 5:sum(, then enter **L1**, followed by **2nd** **TEST**. Choose the ≤ symbol. Then enter **8** **)**. Press **ENTER**. The calculator displays the number of integers in L1 that are less than or equal to 8.

In this trial, 19 of the 22 integers are less than or equal to 8, which simulates 19 out of 22 customers arriving for the flight. In this trial, the flight is not overbooked.

Repeat the trial several times, and record whether or not the flight is overbooked. Find the probability of overbooking by dividing the number of times the flight is overbooked by the total number of trials.

In each simulation, stating the probabilities of the outcomes and assigning a number for each outcome are important parts of the solution. You can use the steps below to make sure an experiment is complete.

GOT TO KNOW!

Steps in Simulation Design

- State the problem and the assumptions.
- Describe the possible outcomes.
- Assign numbers to the outcomes.
- Choose a model or a source of random numbers.
- Conduct a trial.
- Record the results of the trial.
- Repeat the trial.
- Summarize and analyze the results.

Although the list of steps on the previous page seems lengthy, using the steps is straightforward and helps you organize your results.

On average, a basketball player makes 60% of his free throws. Use simulation to estimate how often in 25 trials the player makes both of two free throws. Each trial consists of two free throws.

STEP 1 State the problem.

Find out how often in 25 trials a player makes both of two free throws.

STEP 2 Describe the outcomes.

There are two outcomes for each free throw, making it and missing it. The probability of making one free throw is 60%.

STEP 3 Assign numbers to the outcomes.

The numbers 0, 1, 2, 3, 4, and 5 will represent making a free throw. The numbers 6, 7, 8, and 9 will represent missing a free throw.

STEP 4 Choose a source of random numbers.

Use a graphing calculator to generate a list of 25 random numbers between 0 and 99. If both digits in the number are less than or equal to 5, the player makes both free throws.

STEP 5 Conduct the simulation.

Use the randInt function of the graphing calculator. Use 0 for a, 99 for b, and 25 for n. Store the list in L1.

Press **STAT**, then select EDIT and 1:Edit. Scroll through the list to see all the numbers.

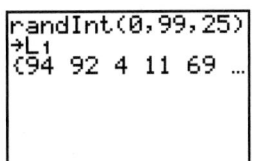

STEP 6 Record the results.

Count all the numbers in which both digits are less than or equal to 5. (The two-digit form of the number 8 is 08.)

STEP 7 Repeat the experiment. Press **ENTER** repeatedly for as many trials as you want. The new set of numbers will overwrite the numbers in L1 each time.

STEP 8 Analyze the results.

In the first experiment, the player makes both of two free throws 10 times out of 25.

Use the free-throw percentage in Example 5.

a. What is the theoretical probability of making both of two free throws?

If the events are independent, then P(two free throws) $= (0.6)(0.6) = 0.36$.

b. What is the experimental probability of making both of two free throws in the experiment shown in Example 5?

The experimental probability is $\frac{10}{25} = 0.4$.

Need More
HELP ?

Remember that if A and B are independent events, P(A and B) $=$ P(A) • P(B).

Streaks and Outcomes

What Will Happen Next?

You toss a fair coin 10 times, and each time the result is heads. Will this streak continue, or is a result of tails overdue? A family has three daughters. If they have a fourth child, is it more likely to be a boy or a girl? Sometimes your intuition about the next outcome in a sequence is not correct.

SEARCH

To see step-by-step videos of these problems, enter the page number into the SWadvantage.com Search Bar.

EXAMPLE 1

Amy tosses a fair coin 5 times.

a. **What is the probability that the result is exactly 3 heads?**

To find the number of ways that 3 tosses out of 5 can be heads, use the formula $_nC_r = \dfrac{n!}{r!(n-r)!}$.

$$_5C_3 = \frac{5!}{(3!)(2!)} = 10$$

Since there are 5 tosses and each toss has 2 possible outcomes, the total number of possible outcomes is $2^5 = 32$.

$$P(\text{exactly 3 heads}) = \frac{10}{32} = \frac{5}{16}$$

The probability of a result of exactly 3 heads is $\frac{5}{16}$, or 31.25%.

b. **What is the probability of getting 3 heads in a row?**

To get 3 heads in a row, the run of 3 could be at the beginning, in the middle, or at the end of the 5 tosses.

Beginning: HHHTT or HHHTH

Middle: THHHT

End: TTHHH or HTHHH

There are 5 different ways that 3 heads can be in a row, out of 2^5 possible outcomes.

The probability of a result of 3 heads in a row is $\frac{5}{32}$, or 15.625%.

EXAMPLE 2

Try It This Way

Instead of using the formula to find the value of $_{10}C_r$, you could use the 10th row of Pascal's Triangle.

Bae tosses a fair coin 10 times. What is the probability that the result is 3 or fewer heads?

Find the number of ways there can be 3 heads, 2 heads, 1 head, or 0 heads, and add them.

Number of ways 3 out of 10 tosses can be heads: $_{10}C_3 = \dfrac{10!}{(3!)(7!)} = 120$

Number of ways 2 out of 10 tosses can be heads: $_{10}C_2 = \dfrac{10!}{(2!)(8!)} = 45$

Number of ways 1 out of 10 tosses can be heads: $_{10}C_1 = \dfrac{10!}{(1!)(9!)} = 10$

Number of ways 0 out of 10 tosses can be heads: $_{10}C_0 = \dfrac{10!}{(0!)(10!)} = 1$

The total number of ways there can be 3 or fewer heads is $120 + 45 + 10 + 1 = 176$. The total number of outcomes is $2^{10} = 1024$.

The probability of 3 or fewer heads is $\frac{176}{1024} \approx 17\%$.

Another factor to consider when looking at compound events is whether the events are independent. Remember that sampling without replacement means the events are dependent.

EXAMPLE 3

A deck of cards has 26 red cards and 26 black cards.

a. Three cards are drawn with replacement. What is the probability that all three cards are red?

When a card is drawn, then replaced, the probability of the next draw is not affected. The events are independent.

The probability of drawing one red card is $\frac{26}{52} = \frac{1}{2}$. The probability of drawing 3 red cards is $\left(\frac{1}{2}\right)^3 = \frac{1}{8}$.

b. Three cards are dealt without replacement. What is the probability that all 3 cards are red?

When a card is drawn and not replaced, the probability of the next draw is affected.

$P(\text{red card on the first draw}) = \frac{26}{52}$

$P(\text{red card on the second draw}) = \frac{25}{51}$

$P(\text{red card on the third draw}) = \frac{24}{50}$

$P(3 \text{ red cards}) = \frac{26}{52} \cdot \frac{25}{51} \cdot \frac{24}{50} = \frac{2}{17}$

In the second part of Example 3, the number of red cards remaining in the deck is affected by each deal. On the other hand, a coin toss is not affected by the result of the last toss, or the last 20 tosses. The coin does not have a memory and cannot keep track of its results.

EXAMPLE 4

Ciara tosses a fair coin 11 times.

a. How many possible outcomes are there?

There are two possible outcomes for each toss, so the total number of outcomes is $2^{11} = 2048$.

b. What is the probability of the sequence HHHHHHHHHHT?

$P(\text{HHHHHHHHHHT}) = \frac{1}{2048}$

c. What is the probability of the sequence HHHHHHHHHHH?

$P(\text{HHHHHHHHHHH}) = \frac{1}{2048}$

d. Compare the probabilities in parts (b) and (c).

The probabilities are equal. The sequences are equally likely.

GOT TO KNOW!

Short Term and Long Term Results

The outcomes of a small number of trials of an experiment do not necessarily reflect the overall average given by many trials.

The two probabilities in Example 4 show that, after a streak of 10 heads, heads and tails are equally likely on the next toss. Over many trials, the proportion of heads is close to 0.5, but in any small run of trials, the proportion may be different.

Analyzing Outcomes

The fact that an unlikely event has occurred does not mean that it will not occur again or that it will continue to occur. When interpreting a probability experiment, keep that in mind.

SEARCH

To see step-by-step videos of these problems, enter the page number into the SWadvantage.com Search Bar.

EXAMPLE 5

David rolls a number cube 12 times. He notices that the last four rolls are all 3. He reasons that the next roll will not be a 3, because that will bring the experimental probability of rolling a 3 closer to the theoretical probability of $\frac{1}{6}$. Is his reasoning correct? Explain why or why not.

His reasoning is not correct. You can expect each number on a number cube to appear about an equal number of times during many rolls, but in a small sample the results may not necessarily be a uniform distribution. The rolls are independent, and the probability of rolling a 3 on the 13th roll is $\frac{1}{6}$.

EXAMPLE 6

The letters in the word CONSONANT are written on cards. The cards are shuffled and placed face down on a table. Three cards will be turned face up. The first two are A and O. Jessica guesses that the third card to be turned over will be a consonant. What is the probability that a consonant card is turned over?

C	O	N	S	O	N	A	N	T

The cards are sampled without replacement, so the events are dependent.

After two cards are turned over, there are 7 cards remaining, and 6 are consonants. The probability that a consonant card is turned over next is $\frac{6}{7}$.

Notice that the probability of turning over a consonant on the third try in Example 6 is high not because the probabilities are "averaging" themselves, but because of the conditions of the experiment.

EXAMPLE 7

Levon writes a spreadsheet program that simulates 24 rolls of two number cubes. The graph below shows his results. He thinks that his formula is incorrect because there are so few results of 2, 4, 11, and 12. Is Levon's reasoning correct? Explain why or why not.

```
                    X           X
                    X   X   X   X   X
        X           X   X   X   X   X   X
    X   X   X   X   X   X   X   X   X   X
    2   3   4   5   6   7   8   9   10  11  12
```

His reasoning is not correct. When two number cubes are rolled, the outcomes are not equally likely. For example, there are several different ways to roll a 7 (1 and 6, 2 and 5, or 3 and 4), but only one way to roll a 2 (1 and 1). Even if the experiment were run many times, a uniform distribution of the numbers from 2 to 12 would not be expected.

Simulation of Streaks

Baseball player Joe DiMaggio had a 56-game hitting streak in 1941. Will this record ever be broken? This is very difficult to forecast.

A binomial probability experiment can tell you *how many* hits to expect, but not in *what order* or where they may occur in a sequence. More advanced mathematical techniques can predict the length of a streak and its frequency, but not when it may occur.

Although it is difficult to calculate probabilities involving streaks of outcomes mathematically, they can be simulated using a random number table or random numbers generated by a graphing calculator.

EXAMPLE 8

Jasmine's batting average in softball is 0.250. In her first 35 at-bats of a season, she had 5 consecutive hits. Her coach wonders if Jasmine is becoming a stronger hitter, if the pitchers are becoming weaker, or if the streak is due to chance. Describe how to simulate Jasmine's batting and check for a run of 5 hits.

STEP 1 State the problem and the assumptions.

Find out how often a player has 5 hits in a row in 35 times at bat. Assume that the batting average is 0.250, that the hits are independent, and that the probability of a hit is the same each time Jasmine is at bat.

STEP 2 Describe the outcomes.

There are two possible outcomes, getting a hit and not getting a hit.

STEP 3 Assign random numbers to the outcomes.

Since Jasmine's batting average is 0.250, or 1 in 4, generate a random sequence of the numbers 1, 2, 3, and 4. 1 represents getting a hit. 2, 3, and 4 represent not getting a hit.

STEP 4 Choose a model or a source of random numbers.

Use a graphing calculator to generate a list of 35 random numbers between 1 and 4.

STEP 5 Conduct a trial.

Use the randInt function of the graphing calculator. Use 1 for *a*, 4 for *b*, and 35 for *n*. Store the list in L1.

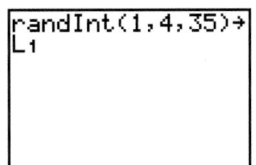

Need More

HELP

For more about simulating events with random numbers, see *Simulations and Technology*, p. 1372.

STEP 6 Record the results of the trial.

Scroll through L1 and note if 1 appears 5 times in a row anywhere in the list. If it does, count the trial as a success.

STEP 7 Repeat the trial.

Repeat the trial several times. Keep track of the total number of trials and the number of trials in which 1 appears 5 times in a row.

STEP 8 Summarize and analyze the results.

Write the ratio of successes to the total number of trials. The result is the experimental probability of a run of 5 hits in this situation.

Statistics and Probability

Think Success

Formulas

Probability (theoretical)	$P(\text{event}) = \dfrac{\text{number of favorable outcomes}}{\text{number of total outcomes}}$
Probability (experimental)	$P(\text{event}) = \dfrac{\text{number of times an event occurs}}{\text{number of trials}}$
Complement C of an Event E	$P(C) = P(\text{not } E)$ $P(C) = 1 - P(E)$ $P(\text{not } E) = 1 - P(E)$ $P(E) + P(\text{not } E) = 1$
Independent Events	$P(A \text{ and } B) = P(A) \cdot P(B)$ $P(A \text{ or } B) = P(A) + P(B) - P(A \text{ and } B)$
Dependent Events	$P(A \text{ and } B) = P(A) \cdot P(B \mid A)$
Odds for an Event	$\text{Odds in favor} = \dfrac{\text{number of favorable outcomes}}{\text{number of unfavorable outcomes}}$
Odds Against an Event	$\text{Odds against} = \dfrac{\text{number of unfavorable outcomes}}{\text{number of favorable outcomes}}$
Permutations	${}_nP_r = \dfrac{n!}{(n-r)!}$
Combinations	${}_nC_r = \dfrac{n!}{r!(n-r)!}$
Binomial Probability	$P(k \text{ successes in } n \text{ trials}) = {}_nC_r \cdot p^k(1-p)^{n-k}$
Outlier	$n < Q1 - 1.5(IQR)$ or $n > Q3 + 1.5(IQR)$
Linear Interpolation and Extrapolation	$y = y_1 + \left(\dfrac{y_2 - y_1}{x_2 - x_1}\right)(x - x_1)$
Variance	$\sigma^2 = \dfrac{\Sigma(x_i - \bar{x})^2}{n}$
Standard Deviation	$\sigma = \sqrt{\dfrac{\Sigma(x_i - \bar{x})^2}{n}}$
Margin of Error	$ME = z_c\sqrt{\dfrac{\hat{p}(1-\hat{p})}{n}} \qquad ME = z_c \cdot \dfrac{\sigma}{\sqrt{n}}$
Confidence Interval	$\hat{p} \pm ME \qquad\qquad \bar{x} \pm ME$

Theorems

Fundamental Counting Principle	If there are m ways to choose a first item and n ways to choose a second item after the first item has been chosen, then there are $m \times n$ ways to choose both items.
Binomial Theorem	$(a+b)^n = \left({}_nC_0\right)a^n + \left({}_nC_1\right)a^{n-1}b + \left({}_nC_2\right)a^{n-2}b^2 + \ldots + \left({}_nC_{n-1}\right)ab^{n-1} + \left({}_nC_n\right)b^n$ $(a+b)^n = \displaystyle\sum_{k=0}^{n} {}_nC_k a^{n-k}b^k$

Variance

$y = y_1 +$

Data Graphs

Line Plots

A *line plot* displays data along a number line. Each number in the data set is represented by an X or another symbol.

Midterm Scores in Science

```
                        X
                        X      X
                        X   X   X
        X   X   X   X   X   X
        X   X   X   X   X   X
        X   X   X   X   X   X      X
      ─────────────────────────────────
       89  90  91  92  93  94  95
```

Scatter Plots

A *scatter plot* is a graph that shows data points on a coordinate grid. Each data point represents a pair of values.

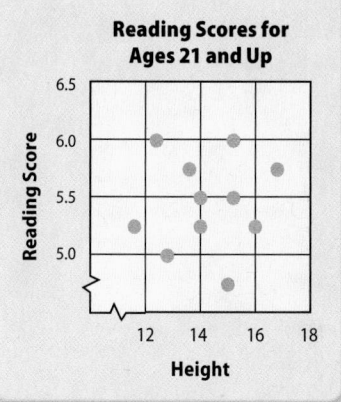

Reading Scores for Ages 21 and Up

Histograms

A *histogram* displays the frequency of a set of data in equal-size intervals, or ranges, of data.

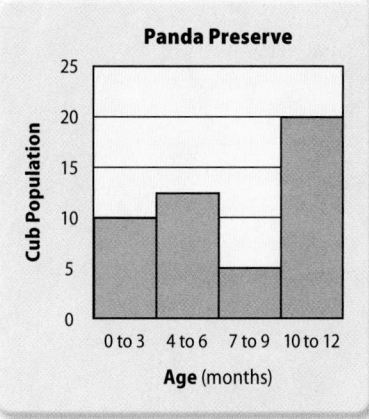

Panda Preserve

Stem-and-Leaf Plots

A *stem-and-leaf plot* is a data display that can be used to show how data are distributed. The data are in numerical order in two columns.

Cars Parked (Past 10 Days)

Stem	Leaf
0	1 2 3 6
1	0 0 3 6
2	0 9

Key: $2\,|\,9 = 29$

Box-and-Whisker Plots

A *box-and-whisker plot* is a data display that divides a set of data into four equal parts. It shows how the data are distributed among these parts.

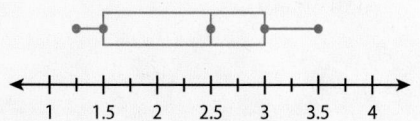

Venn Diagrams

A *Venn diagram* is a graphic display that uses overlapping circles (or squares) to show the relationship between sets and subsets of data.

Pet Owners

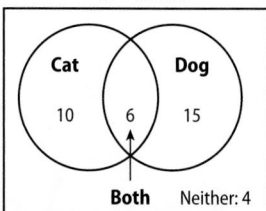

Cat 10   6   Dog 15

Both   Neither: 4

Algebra

Welders use linear inequalities to account for the expansion and contraction of metal when it is heated or cooled.

Numbers, Variables, and Expressions

What Came Before?

- Operations with whole numbers
- Finding factors and multiples

What's This About?

- Operations with integers and exponents
- Rational and irrational numbers, including square roots
- Using properties and order of operations to simplify and evaluate algebraic expressions

Practical Apps

- Workers who create complex spreadsheets use algebra to develop the formula that defines how the content of a cell is calculated.
- Civil engineers use exponents to determine minimum thicknesses of weight-bearing concrete columns.

Just for FUN!

The algebra twins often help each other. In fact, they are co-efficient.

| CONTENTS | UPLOAD | DOWNLOAD | *Algebra* |

Topics	Vocabulary		Pages
Integers and Absolute Value	*integers* *absolute value*	*opposites*	1386–1389
Adding Integers			1390–1391
Subtracting Integers			1392–1393
Multiplying and Dividing Integers			1394–1395
Exponents	*exponential notation* *power* *base* *exponent* *Product of Powers Property* *Quotient of Powers Property* *Power of a Power Property*		1396–1399
Square Roots	*square root* *radicand*	*principal square root* *perfect square*	1400–1401
The Real Number System	*natural numbers* *integers* *irrational numbers*	*whole numbers* *rational numbers* *real numbers*	1402–1405
Commutative and Associative Properties	*equivalent expressions*		1406–1409
Distributive Property	*terms* *unlike terms*	*like terms*	1410–1413
The Identity and Inverse Properties	*additive identity* *additive inverse*	*multiplicative identity* *multiplicative inverse*	1414–1417
Order of Operations			1418–1421
Variables and Algebraic Expressions	*variable* *coefficient*	*constant* *algebraic expression*	1422–1425
Evaluating Variable Expressions			1426–1429
Translating English into Algebra	*equation*		1430–1433

You can find more practice problems online by visiting: **www.SWadvantage.com**

Integers and Absolute Value

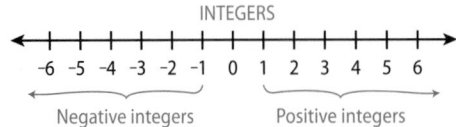

Integers

The set of whole numbers, their *opposites,* and zero are **integers**. Integers are often used in life for quantities that can have both positive and negative values, such as temperatures and elevation.

INTEGERS

-6 -5 -4 -3 -2 -1 0 1 2 3 4 5 6

Negative integers　　　Positive integers

On a number line, **opposites** are numbers that are the same distance from but on opposite sides of zero. For example, on the number line above, −4 and 4 are opposites. The sum of two opposites is zero. Zero is its own opposite.

SEARCH

To see step-by-step videos of these problems, enter the page number into the SWadvantage.com Search Bar.

EXAMPLE 1

Identify the number as an integer or non-integer. Graph the number and its opposite on the number line.

a. 3

-4 -3 -2 -1 0 1 2 3 4

The number 3 is a whole number, so it is an integer. Its opposite is −3.

b. $-2\frac{1}{2}$

-4 -3 -2 -1 0 1 2 3 4

The number $-2\frac{1}{2}$ is a fraction. It is not an integer.

Its opposite is $2\frac{1}{2}$.

Comparing Integers

The numbers on a number line increase in value from left to right. When comparing two integers, the number farther to the right is greater in value.

EXAMPLE 2

Use the number line to compare the integers.

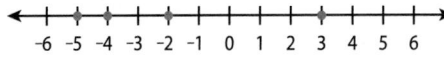

-6 -5 -4 -3 -2 -1 0 1 2 3 4 5 6

a. 3 and −4

The integer 3 is to the right of −4, so $3 > -4$.

b. −5 and −2

The integer −5 is to the left of −2, so $-5 < -2$.

Finding Absolute Value

The **absolute value** of a number is its distance from zero on a number line. A number and its opposite have the same absolute value. Since absolute value represents a distance, it is always positive.

$|-3| = 3$ The number -3 is 3 units from 0.

$|3| = 3$ The number 3 is also 3 units from 0.

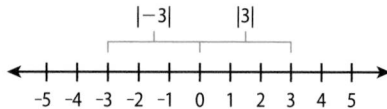

The absolute value of a number greater than zero is the number itself. The absolute value of a number less than zero is the *opposite* of the number.

Got to KNOW!

Absolute Value Symbol

The symbol for absolute value is a vertical bar on each side of the number.

$|3| = 3$

Read this equation as, "The absolute value of three is three."

EXAMPLE 3

Find each absolute value.

a. $|27|$

The absolute value is the number itself, 27.

b. $|-7.06|$

The absolute value is the *opposite* of the number, 7.06.

c. $|0|$

The absolute value is the number itself, 0.

d. $\left|-\dfrac{4}{5}\right|$

The absolute value is the *opposite* of the number, $\dfrac{4}{5}$.

Watch Out !

$-x$ looks like a negative number, but $-x$ means the opposite of x. When x is less than 0, $-x$ is **positive**! For example, if $x = -7$, then $-x = -(-7)$, which is $+7$.

Absolute Value in Variables

You can represent the general form for absolute value using variables.

Numbers greater than or equal to 0	For $x \geq 0$, $|x| = x$.	The sign is unchanged.
Numbers less than 0	For $x < 0$, $|x| = -x$.	The sign is changed.

Comparing and Ordering Absolute Value

Just as you compared integers, you can compare absolute values. First find the absolute value of each number. Then compare the numbers. You can use a number line to help visualize the numbers.

When you compare $|-4|$ and $|-2|$, you see that the distance 4 is greater than the distance 2.

$$|-4| > |-2|$$

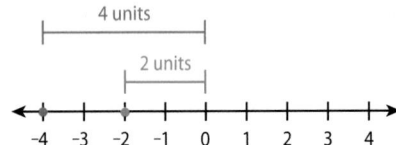

Watch Out !

Notice that −2 is an integer, not an absolute value. Do not change it to 2.

EXAMPLE 4

Order from least to greatest.

$$\left|-\frac{1}{2}\right|, |-7|, |3.5|, -2$$

STEP 1 Simplify each expression.

$$\left|-\frac{1}{2}\right| = \frac{1}{2} \qquad |-7| = 7 \qquad |3.5| = 3.5 \qquad -2$$

STEP 2 Order the numbers from least to greatest.

$$-2, \frac{1}{2}, 3.5, 7$$

STEP 3 Rewrite the numbers in their original form.

$$-2, \left|-\frac{1}{2}\right|, |3.5|, |-7|$$

EXAMPLE 5

SEARCH

To see step-by-step videos of these problems, enter the page number into the SWadvantage.com Search Bar.

The lake level dropped 9.5 feet last week, but it rose 8.9 feet this week. During which week was the change in the lake level greater?

Consider the lake level drop as a negative number, −9.5.

Find the absolute value of each change.

$$|-9.5| = 9.5 \qquad |8.9| = 8.9.$$

Compare the absolute values: $9.5 > 8.9$

The change was greater last week when the lake dropped 9.5 feet.

Simplifying Absolute-Value Expressions

You can simplify expressions that use absolute value. Think of the absolute value symbols as grouping symbols. First simplify what is inside the absolute value symbols. Then simplify any remaining absolute-value expressions and perform any operations following the order of operations.

Need More
HELP ?

Remember the order of operations.

• Parentheses
• Exponents
• Multiply or Divide
• Add or Subtract

EXAMPLE 6

Simplify each absolute value expression.

a. $|5 - 1|$

Subtract inside the symbols. $\qquad |5 - 1| = |4|$

Simplify. $\qquad\qquad = 4$

b. $|2(3)|$

Multiply inside the symbols. $\qquad |2(3)| = |6|$

Simplify. $\qquad\qquad = 6$

c. $|10| + |-10|$

Simplify each absolute value. $\qquad |10| + |-10| = 10 + 10$

Add. $\qquad\qquad = 20$

d. $3 \times |-5|$

Simplify the absolute value. $\qquad 3 \times |-5| = 3 \times 5$

Multiply. $\qquad\qquad = 15$

Positive and Negative Numbers as Absolute Values

Every positive number is the absolute value of two numbers, the number itself and the opposite of the number. For example, positive 5 is the absolute value of both 5 and −5.

No negative number is the absolute value of any number!

Adding Integers

Adding Integers on a Number Line

You can add integers by using a number line. Start at the first value. Move right when you add a positive number, and move left when you add a negative number.

EXAMPLE 1

Find each sum.

a. 6 + (−2)

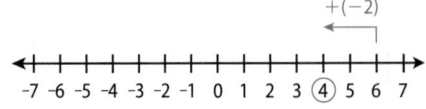

$6 + (−2) = 4$

b. −4 + 3

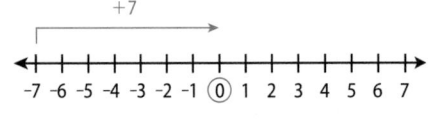

$−4 + 3 = −1$

c. −7 + 7

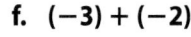

$−7 + 7 = 0$

d. 5 + (−12)

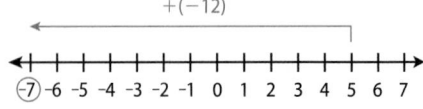

$5 + (−12) = −7$

e. −1 + (−4)

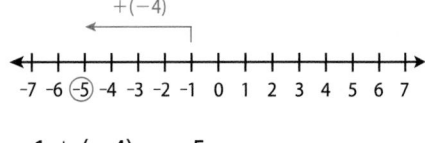

$−1 + (−4) = −5$

f. (−3) + (−2)

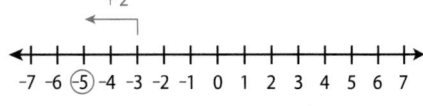

$(−3) + (−2) = −5$

Got to KNOW!

Adding Opposites

Adding a number and its opposite always gives you zero.

$6 + (−6) = 0$
$a + (−a) = 0$
$−11 + 11 = 0$
$−x + x = 0$

Two-Color Counters

Two-color counters can help you understand integer addition.

+ = 1   − = −1

Yellow counters represent positive integers.
Red counters represent negative integers.

EXAMPLE 2

Use two-color counters to find the sum 5 + (−2).

STEP 1 Show 5 counters with a value of +1 and
2 counters with a value of −1.

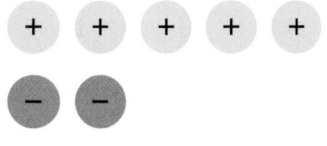

STEP 2 Combine two positive counters and two negative
counters to make pairs with a value of zero.
Remove the *zero pairs*. The sum is the remaining
counters.

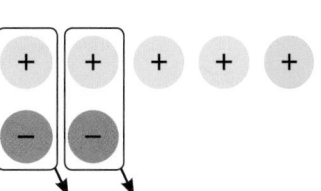

5 + (−2) = 3

SEARCH

To see step-by-step
videos of these
problems, enter the
page number into the
SWadvantage.com
Search Bar.

Using Absolute Value

Absolute value can help you decide whether the sum of two signed integers is
positive or negative.

EXAMPLE 3

**The overnight, low temperature was −12°F. By noon, the temperature had increased
by 9°F. What was the temperature at noon?**

The answer is the sum of −12 + 9. Notice that the addends have different signs.

STEP 1 Remove the signs and subtract the smaller number from the greater number.
12 − 9 = 3

STEP 2 Use the sign of the number with the greater absolute value for the sum.
$|-12| = 12$ $|9| = 9$

12 > 9, so the sum will have the same sign of −12. The sum of −12 + 9 is negative.

−12 + 9 = −3

The temperature at noon was −3°F.

Rules for Adding Two Signed Numbers

If the addends have the same sign, add the absolute values and use the sign of
the addends.

5 + 11 = 16   −5 + (−11) = −16

If the addends have different signs, subtract their absolute values and use the sign
of the addend with the greater absolute value.

−7 + 11 = 4   7 + (−11) = −4   −15 + 6 = −9   15 + (−6) = 9

Subtracting Integers

Subtracting Integers on a Number Line

You can subtract integers by using a number line. Start at the first value. Move left when you subtract a positive number and move right when you subtract a negative number.

$$3 - 2 = 1 \qquad\qquad 3 - (-2) = 5$$

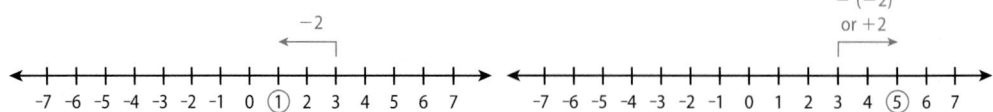

EXAMPLE 1

Find each difference.

a. $-1 - 5$

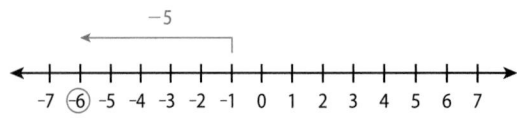

$-1 - 5 = -6$

Need More
HELP ?

When you subtract a negative number, think of turning left on the number line to subtract, but then walking *backward*.

b. $-5 - (-7)$

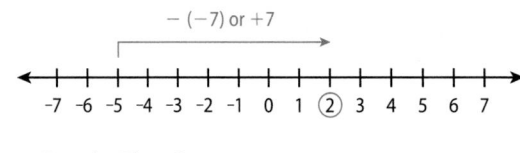

$-5 - (-7) = 2$

c. $-1 - (-1)$

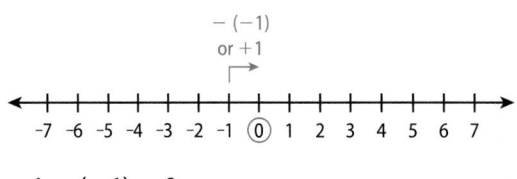

$-1 - (-1) = 0$

Got to KNOW!

Subtracting Integers

Subtracting a number is the same as adding its opposite.

$$5 - 3 = 2 \qquad\qquad a - b = a + (-b)$$
$$5 + (-3) = 2$$

To subtract a number, add its opposite. Then use the rules for adding signed numbers.

$$4 - 9 = 4 + (-9) \qquad\qquad 6 - (-7) = 6 + 7$$
$$= -5 \qquad\qquad\qquad\qquad\quad = 13$$

EXAMPLE 2

Find each difference.

a. 8 − (−5)

Add the opposite of −5. $8 − (−5) = 8 + 5$

Simplify. $= 13$

b. −4 − 7

Add the opposite of 7. $−4 − 7 = −4 + (−7)$

Simplify using the rules for adding signed numbers. $= −11$

c. 13 − 22

Add the opposite of 22. $13 − 22 = 13 + (−22)$

Simplify using the rules for adding signed numbers. $= −9$

SEARCH

To see step-by-step videos of these problems, enter the page number into the SWadvantage.com Search Bar.

When you substract negative fractions or negative decimals, you use the same process as you when you substract negative integers.

EXAMPLE 3

Subtract.

$$-\frac{1}{2} - \left(-\frac{2}{3}\right)$$

STEP 1 Add the opposite of $-\frac{2}{3}$. $-\frac{1}{2} - \left(-\frac{2}{3}\right) = -\frac{1}{2} + \frac{2}{3}$

STEP 2 Write the fractions using a common denominator. $= -\frac{3}{6} + \frac{4}{6}$

STEP 3 Simplify using the rules for adding signed numbers. $= -\frac{3}{6} + \frac{4}{6} = \frac{1}{6}$

Need More HELP?

For help with common denominators, go to *Adding Fractions with Unlike Denominators* in *Numbers and Operations* (Book 1, p. 322).

EXAMPLE 4

Francisco had a bank account balance of $236.85. The bank reverses a previous charge, and −$18.50 is subtracted from the balance. What is Francisco's new balance?

Set up a subtraction problem. $236.85 − (−18.5)$

Add the opposite of −18.5. $236.85 − (−18.5) = 236.85 + 18.5$

Simplify. $= 255.35$

Francisco's new balance is $255.35.

Multiplying and Dividing Integers

Multiplying Integers

Look at the patterns below:

$3 \times 2 = 6$	$-3 \times 2 = -6$
$3 \times 1 = 3$	$-3 \times 1 = -3$
$3 \times 0 = 0$	$-3 \times 0 = 0$
$3 \times (-1) = -3$	$-3 \times (-1) = 3$
$3 \times (-2) = -6$	$-3 \times (-2) = 6$

When you multiply integers, you multiply absolute values. The signs of the factors determine the sign of the product.

Multiplying Integers with the Same Sign

If two integers have the same sign, their product is positive.

EXAMPLE 1

Find each product.

a. 7(8)

$|7| = 7$ $|8| = 8$ $7(8) = 56$

So, $7(8) = 56$.

b. (−1)(−5)

$|-1| = 1$ $|-5| = 5$ $(1)(5) = 5$

So, $(-1)(-5) = 5$.

Multiplying Integers with Different Signs

If two integers have different signs, their product is negative.

EXAMPLE 2

Find each product.

a. 12(−9)

$|12| = 12$ $|-9| = 9$ $12(9) = 108$

So, $12(-9) = -108$.

b. (−3)(15)

$|-3| = 3$ $|15| = 15$ $(3)(15) = 45$

So, $(-3)(15) = -45$.

EXAMPLE 3

In one fantasy football league, a team scores −2 points every time its players are charged with a turnover (a fumble or an interception). If a team's players are charged with 9 turnovers, how many points are scored?

To find the total number of points, multiply the number of turnovers by the number of points scored for each turnover.

turnover	times	points for each turnover	equals	total points
9	×	−2	=	−18

The number of points scored is −18.

SEARCH 🔍

To see step-by-step videos of these problems, enter the page number into the SWadvantage.com Search Bar.

Dividing Integers

Use the same rules for the signs when you divide integers. If two integers have the same sign, their quotient is positive. If two integers have different signs, their quotient is negative.

EXAMPLE 4

Find each quotient.

a. $\dfrac{-40}{-4}$

$|40| = 40$ $|-4| = 4$ $\dfrac{40}{4} = 10$

The signs are the same. So, $\dfrac{-40}{-4} = 10$.

b. $-100 \div 5$

$|-100| = 100$ $|5| = 5$ $100 \div 5 = 20$

The signs are different. So, $-100 \div 5 = -20$.

Got to KNOW!

Multiplying or Dividing Integers with the Same Sign

If two numbers have the same sign, their product or quotient is positive.

$(-)(-) = (+)$ $(+)(+) = (+)$ $(-) \div (-) = (+)$ $(+) \div (+) = (+)$

Multiplying or Dividing Integers with Different Signs

If two numbers have different signs, their product or quotient is negative.

$(-)(+) = (-)$ $(+)(-) = (-)$ $(-) \div (+) = (-)$ $(+) \div (-) = (-)$

Exponents

Exponents and Powers

SEARCH

To see step-by-step videos of these problems, enter the page number into the SWadvantage.com Search Bar.

Sometimes it is helpful to use a shorthand way to write repeated multiplication by the same number. For example, in the following problem, 4 is a factor 3 times.

$$4 \times 4 \times 4 = \underline{?}$$

A shorter way to write this problem is to use *exponential notation*. **Exponential notation** expresses multiplication as a *power*.

- A **power** is the product written as a base and an exponent.

- The **base** is the number used as a factor.

- The **exponent** tells the number of times the factor is used. The exponent is written as a superscript to the right of the base.

$$\overbrace{4 \times 4 \times 4}^{\text{3 factors of }4} \rightarrow \underbrace{4^{\overset{\displaystyle\text{Power}}{3}}}_{\text{Base}} \text{Exponent}$$

This power is read as "the third power of four," "four to the third power," or simply, "four to the third."

EXAMPLE 1

Write each repeated multiplication as a power. Evaluate.

a. (2)(2)(2)(2)(2)(2)(2)(2)

There are 8 factors of 2, so the power is 2^8.

Use a calculator: 2 $\boxed{x^y}$ 8 $\boxed{\text{ENTER}}$ 256

b. $5 \times 5 \times 5 \times 5 \times 5 \times 5$

There are 6 factors of 5, so the power is 5^6.

Use a calculator: 5 $\boxed{x^y}$ 6 $\boxed{\text{ENTER}}$ 15,625

Try It This Way

You may need to use a different key on your calculator, such as $\boxed{y^x}$ or $\boxed{\wedge}$.

EXAMPLE 2

Write the power 3^7 as a repeated multiplication.

The base is 3, and the exponent is 7, so 3 is used as a factor 7 times.

$3^7 = (3)(3)(3)(3)(3)(3)(3)$

EXAMPLE 3

Find the number of small cubes in the figure.

There are 6 small cubes along each edge, so there are $6^3 = 216$ small cubes in the figure.

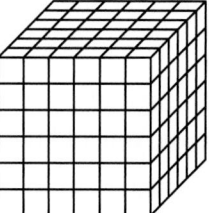

Special Exponents

The numbers 0, 1, 2, and 3 have special characteristics when used as exponents.

Exponent of 0: A power with a base $\neq 0$ and an exponent of 0 has a value of 1.

$$a^0 = 1, \text{ when } a \neq 0$$

Exponent of 1: A power with an exponent of 1 has a value equal to the base. As a result, any number equals that number to the first power.

$$a^1 = a$$

Exponent of 2: You know that a base with an exponent of 2 can be read as "(base) to the second power" or "(base) to the second." The power can also be read as "(base) squared."

Exponent of 3: You know that a base with an exponent of 3 can be read as "(base) to the third power" or "(base) to the third." It can also be read as "(base) cubed."

Need More HELP?

For help understanding why $2^0 = 1$, see Example 6 on page 1398.

EXAMPLE 4

Simplify.

a. **6^0**

$6^0 = 1$

b. **7^1**

$7^1 = 7$

c. **4 squared**

4 squared $= 4^2 = 16$

d. **2 cubed**

2 cubed $= 2^3 = 8$

Exponential Notation

$$\underset{\text{power}}{\underline{\text{base}^{\text{exponent}}}}$$

$Base^0 = 1$	$Base^2 = Base\ Squared$
$Base^1 = Base$	$Base^3 = Base\ Cubed$

Multiplying and Dividing with Exponents

Examine this example of multiplying powers with the same base.

$$5^2 \times 5^4 = (5)(5) \times (5)(5)(5)(5) = (5)(5)(5)(5)(5)(5) = 5^6$$

The **Product of Powers Property** states that to *multiply* powers that have the same base, you add the exponents and keep the same base.

Look at this example of dividing powers with the same base.

$$\frac{3^6}{3^4} = \frac{(3)(3)(3)(3)(3)(3)}{(3)(3)(3)(3)} = \frac{(3)(3)\cancel{(3)}\cancel{(3)}\cancel{(3)}\cancel{(3)}}{\cancel{(3)}\cancel{(3)}\cancel{(3)}\cancel{(3)}} = 3^2$$

The **Quotient of Powers Property** states that to *divide* powers that have the same base, you can *subtract* the exponent of the divisor from the exponent of the dividend and keep the same base.

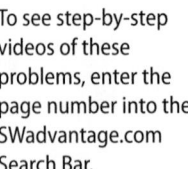

Watch Out !

You cannot apply the Product of Powers Property to $3^7 \cdot 5^7$, because the bases are different: 3 and 5. The Product of Powers and the Quotient of Powers Properties only apply when the bases are the same.

SEARCH

To see step-by-step videos of these problems, enter the page number into the SWadvantage.com Search Bar.

EXAMPLE 5

Write each product as a power with the same base.

a. $10^{12} \cdot 10^8$

Use the Product of Powers Property. $10^{12} \cdot 10^8 = 10^{12+8}$

Add the exponents, and keep the base the same. $= 10^{20}$

b. $15 \cdot 15^6$

Write 15 as 15^1. Use the Product of Powers Property. $15^1 \cdot 15^6 = 15^{1+6}$

Add the exponents, and keep the base the same. $= 15^7$

EXAMPLE 6

Write each quotient as a power with the same base.

a. $\dfrac{8^5}{8^5}$

The quotient should equal 1, because the numerator equals the denominator.

Use the Quotient of Powers Property. $\dfrac{8^5}{8^5} = 8^{5-5}$

Subtract the exponents, and keep the base the same. $= 8^0$

Simplify the exponent 0. $= 1$

b. $16^3 \div 16$

Write 16 as 16^1. Use the Quotient of Powers Property. $16^3 \div 16^1 = 16^{3-1}$

Subtract the exponents, and keep the base the same. $= 16^2$

A Power to a Power

Look at the following problem.

$$(4^3)^2 = (4^3)(4^3) = 4^{3+3} = 4^6$$

You can see that $(4^3)^2$ is 4^3 used as a factor twice. According to the Products of Powers Property, the final exponent is found by adding the exponents in each factor together.

If you look again at the initial problem and the final power, you can see that $2 \times 3 = 6$. The **Power of a Power Property** states that to raise a power to a power, you can *multiply* the exponents.

EXAMPLE 7

a. Simplify $(4^2)^3$.

METHOD 1

Use the Product of Powers Property.

Write the cube of 4^2 as a product. $(4^2)^3 = (4^2)(4^2)(4^2)$

Multiply. $= (16)(16)(16) = 4{,}096$

METHOD 2

Use the Power of a Power Property.

Write the base with one exponent. $(4^2)^3 = 4^{2 \cdot 3}$

Multiply the exponents. $= 4^6$

Simplify. $= 4{,}096$

b. Simplify $(2^0)^4$.

Use the Power of a Power Property. $(2^0)^4 = 2^{0 \times 4}$

Multiply the exponents and simplify. $= 2^0 = 1$

> **Watch Out** ⚠️
>
> These rules used to solve problems with the same base apply only to multiplication and division. They cannot be used in addition and subtraction problems involving powers.

Got to KNOW!

Rules for Exponents

For $a \neq 0$, and whole numbers m and n, the following properties are true.

Product of Powers Property

To multiply powers with the same base, use the same base and add the exponents.

$$a^m \times a^n = a^{m+n}$$

Quotient of Powers Property

To divide powers with the same base, use the same base and subtract the exponent of the divisor from the exponent of the dividend.

$$\frac{a^m}{a^n} = a^{m-n}$$

Power of a Power Property

To raise a power to a power, multiply the exponents.

$$(a^m)^n = a^{m \cdot n}$$

Square Roots

Squares and Square Roots of Integers

A number that is multiplied by itself, or squared, to form a product is a **square root** of that product. For example, $5^2 = 25$, so 5 is a square root of 25. Every positive number has two square roots.

$25 = 5^2$, so one square root of 25 is 5.

$25 = (-5)^2$, so another square root of 25 is -5.

The positive square root of the number is the **principal square root**. It is indicated with the symbol $\sqrt{}$, which is called a radical sign. The negative square root is represented by $-\sqrt{}$. The symbol $\pm\sqrt{}$ represents both square roots.

The number under the radical sign is called the **radicand**. If the square root of the radicand is an integer, the radicand is called a **perfect square**.

Try It This Way

Making a table of perfect squares can help you find integer square roots.

Number	Square
1	1
2	4
3	9
4	16
5	25
6	36
7	49
8	64
9	81
10	100
11	121
12	144

EXAMPLE 1

Simplify, if possible.

a. $\pm\sqrt{81}$

$9^2 = 81$, and $(-9)^2 = 81$, so $\pm\sqrt{81} = 9$ and -9

b. $-\sqrt{49}$

$7^2 = 49$, so $\sqrt{49} = 7$, and $-\sqrt{49} = -7$

c. $\sqrt{-16}$

There is no real solution. No square of a real number is negative.

EXAMPLE 2

There are 225 mini-squares on the game board. How many mini-squares do not touch an edge of the board?

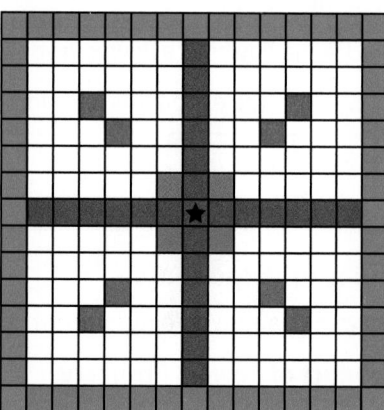

METHOD 1

There are 225 mini-squares, so the number of mini-squares along each edge is $\sqrt{225} = 15$.

There are 56 mini-squares along the edges.

The number of mini-squares that do not touch an edge of the board is $225 - 56 = 169$ mini-squares.

METHOD 2

The area of the board containing mini-squares that do not touch an edge of the board is 13 by 13.

$13^2 = 169$, so 169 mini-squares do not touch an edge of the board.

Squares and Square Roots of Other Real Numbers

Decimals and fractions also have square roots. Some square roots are not whole numbers, but they can be expressed as the quotient of two integers.

$$2.5^2 = 6.25, \text{ so } \sqrt{6.25} = 2.5 \qquad \left(\frac{1}{2}\right)^2 = \frac{1}{4}, \text{ so } \sqrt{\frac{1}{4}} = \frac{1}{2}$$

Many square roots, such as $\sqrt{2}$ and $\sqrt{3}$, cannot be expressed as a quotient of two integers. You can approximate square roots that do not have exact values.

EXAMPLE 3

A square patio has an area of 10 m², so each side is $\sqrt{10}$ m long. Approximate the length of a side to the nearest hundredth of a meter.

SEARCH

To see step-by-step videos of these problems, enter the page number into the SWadvantage.com Search Bar.

METHOD 1

Because $\sqrt{9} = 3$ and $\sqrt{16} = 4$, $\sqrt{10}$ must be between 3 and 4. You can estimate the value between 3 and 4 as shown below.

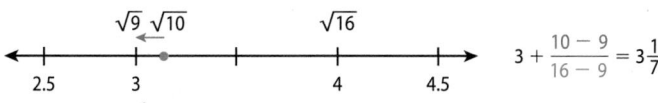

$$3 + \frac{10 - 9}{16 - 9} = 3\frac{1}{7}$$

The decimal value of this square root estimate is 3.142857…

Rounded to the nearest hundredth, the length of a side is 3.14 m.

METHOD 2

Use a calculator. ▢√ 10 = 3.16227766

Rounded to the nearest hundredth, the length of a side is 3.16 m.

Simplifying Radical Terms

You can simplify a radical term by factoring out any factors of the radicand that are perfect squares.

$$\sqrt{250} = \sqrt{25 \cdot 10}$$

Find the square root of any perfect square.

$$\sqrt{25} = 5$$

Write the expression as the product of the square root and the remaining radical term.

$$\sqrt{250} = \sqrt{25 \cdot 10} = 5\sqrt{10}$$

EXAMPLE 4

Simplify, if possible.

a. $\sqrt{242}$

$$\sqrt{242} = \sqrt{121 \cdot 2}$$
$$= \sqrt{121} \cdot \sqrt{2} = 11\sqrt{2}$$

b. $\sqrt{65}$

This term is already simplified. No factors of 65 are perfect squares.

The Real Number System

Sets of Numbers

Every real number fits into at least one number category, as described below.

- The set of numbers that includes all positive counting numbers is the set of **natural numbers**.

$$N = \{1, 2, 3, 4, 5, 6, \ldots\}$$

- The same set of numbers plus 0 is the set of **whole numbers**.

$$W = \{0, 1, 2, 3, 4, 5, 6, \ldots\}$$

- The set of whole numbers and their opposites is the set of **integers**.

$$Z = \{\ldots, -6, -5, -4, -3, -2, -1, 0, 1, 2, 3, 4, 5, 6, \ldots\}$$

- The set Q of all numbers that can be named in the form $\frac{a}{b}$, where a and b are integers and $b \neq 0$, is the set of **rational numbers**.

  Another way to define rational numbers is as the set of all terminating and repeating decimals. *Terminating decimals,* such as 4.73, 0.85, and 2.0, have a finite number of digits. *Repeating decimals,* such as 0.555..., 6.$\overline{6}$, and 1.7$\overline{263}$, have a digit or group of digits that repeats.

- The set I of all numbers that *cannot* be named in the form $\frac{a}{b}$ is the set of **irrational numbers**. For example, $\sqrt{2}$ and π are irrational numbers.

- Rational numbers and irrational numbers together make up R, the set of **real numbers**.

Real Numbers

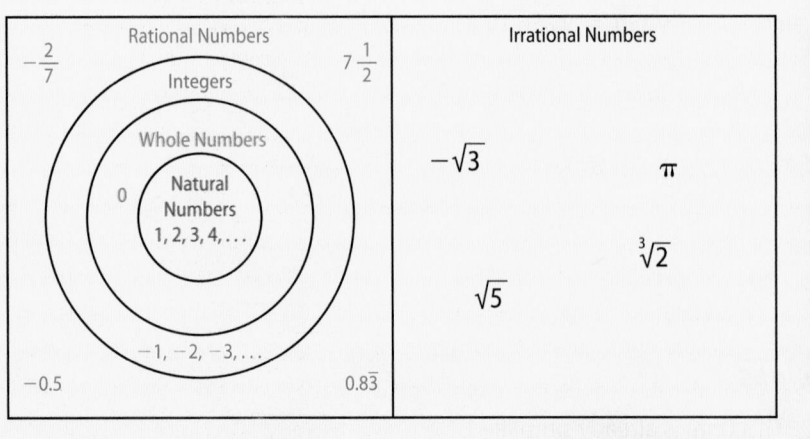

EXAMPLE 1

Name all the classifications for each real number.

a. $\sqrt{49}$

$\sqrt{49} = 7$

7 is a natural number, so $\sqrt{49}$ is also a whole number, an integer, and a rational number.

irrational number	rational number	integer	whole number	natural number

SEARCH

To see step-by-step videos of these problems, enter the page number into the SWadvantage.com Search Bar.

b. $-\dfrac{2}{3}$

$-\dfrac{2}{3}$ is the quotient of two integers, -2 and 3. It is a rational number.

irrational number	rational number	integer	whole number	natural number

c. $\sqrt{15}$

15 is not a perfect square. $\sqrt{15} \approx 3.872983\ldots$ is neither a terminating nor a repeating decimal.

$\sqrt{15}$ is an irrational number.

irrational number	rational number	integer	whole number	natural number

d. 0

0 is a whole number, so it is also an integer and a rational number, but it is not a natural number.

irrational number	rational number	integer	whole number	natural number

e. $2.61\overline{7}$

$2.61\overline{7}$ is a repeating decimal. It is a rational number.

irrational number	rational number	integer	whole number	natural number

f. -6

-6 is an integer, but it is neither a whole number nor a natural number. It is an integer and a rational number.

irrational number	rational number	integer	whole number	natural number

Real Number Flowchart

Another way to visualize the sets of numbers that make up the set of real numbers is to use a flowchart. Use the flowchart below to help you classify real numbers.

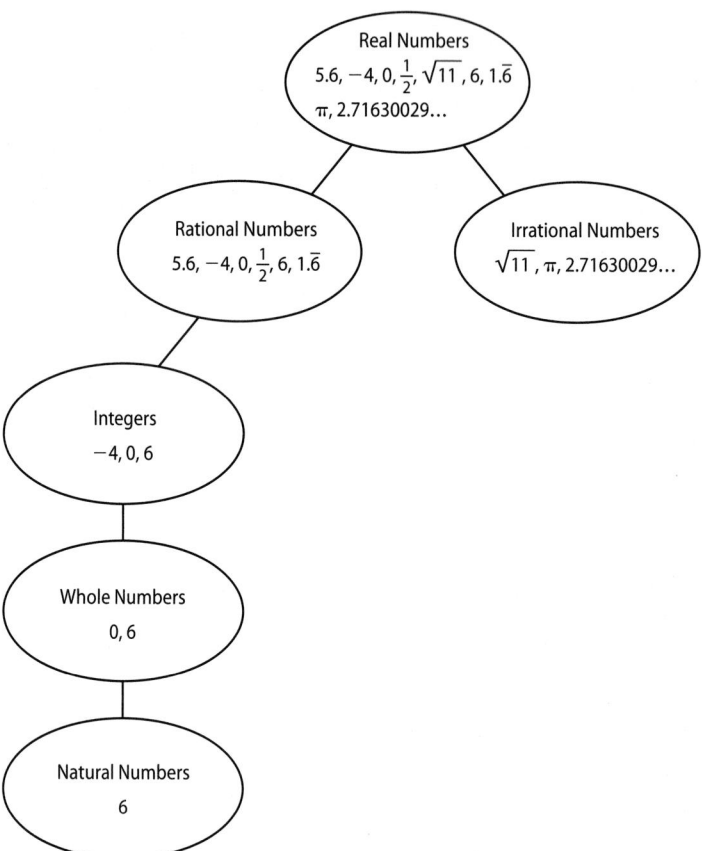

EXAMPLE 2

Tell whether each statement is true or false. If the statement is false, explain why.

a. The number 0 is the only natural number that is not a whole number.

False; 0 is not a natural number. It is the only *whole* number that is not a *natural* number.

b. All real numbers are rational numbers or irrational numbers.

True.

c. All rational numbers are integers.

False; terminating and repeating decimals are also rational numbers, but they are not integers.

d. The set of irrational numbers includes terminating decimals.

False; a terminating decimal is a rational number.

EXAMPLE 3

Give an example for each of the following.

a. a calculation with two irrational numbers where the result is a rational number

An example might be $\sqrt{2} \cdot \sqrt{8} = \sqrt{16}$; $\sqrt{16}$ is rational because it simplifies to a whole number, 4.

b. a calculation with two negative integers where the result is a whole number

An example might be $(-2)(-5) = 10$.

SEARCH

To see step-by-step videos of these problems, enter the page number into the SWadvantage.com Search Bar.

Pi—An Irrational Number

The decimal form of a rational number always either terminates or, at some point in the sequence of decimals, begins a pattern that repeats indefinitely.

You are familiar with one number whose decimal pattern never terminates or repeats. The number pi, π, is the ratio of the circumference of a circle to its diameter. Pi has been proven to be an irrational number. As shown below, the decimal value of pi does not repeat or terminate.

$\pi = 3.14159265358979323846264338327950288419716939937510582097 4944...$

Other Numbers

Not all numbers are real numbers. Some numbers are *imaginary numbers.* Real and imaginary numbers form the set of *complex numbers.* Imaginary numbers are not just made-up numbers. They are important numbers that you will find out more about in *Advanced Algebra*. Numbers like $\sqrt{-16}$ are not real numbers. However, they are complex numbers.

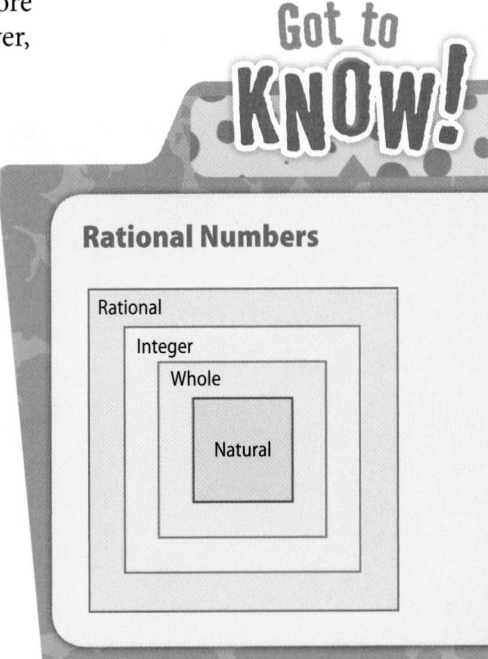

Got to KNOW!

Rational Numbers

Rational

Integer

Whole

Natural

The Commutative Properties

You know you can *add* numbers in any order, and the order does not affect the sum.

$5 + 9 = 14$ and $9 + 5 = 14$, so $5 + 9 = 9 + 5$.

You also know you can *multiply* numbers in any order, and the order does not affect the product.

$5 \cdot 9 = 45$ and $9 \cdot 5 = 45$, so $5 \cdot 9 = 9 \cdot 5$.

These relationships are expressed in the following properties.

Commutative Property of Addition
For any real numbers a and b, $a + b = b + a$.
Commutative Property of Multiplication
For any real numbers a and b, $ab = ba$.

Expressions such as $x + 7$ and $7 + x$, which have equal values for any value of x, are called **equivalent expressions**.

SEARCH

To see step-by-step videos of these problems, enter the page number into the SWadvantage.com Search Bar.

EXAMPLE 1

Find the sum $6 + \dfrac{1}{8} + 4 + \dfrac{7}{8}$.

Use the Commutative Property of Addition to rewrite the expression.	$6 + 4 + \dfrac{1}{8} + \dfrac{7}{8}$
Add the whole numbers. Then add the two fractions.	$10 + 1$
Find the sum.	$10 + 1 = 11$

EXAMPLE 2

Use a commutative property to write an equivalent expression.

a. 2w

An equivalent expression using the Commutative Property of Multiplication is $w \cdot 2$.

b. pq + 8

An equivalent expression using the Commutative Property of Multiplication is $qp + 8$.

An equivalent expression using the Commutative Property of Addition is $8 + pq$.

An equivalent expression using both commutative properties is $8 + qp$.

EXAMPLE 3

The area of a rectangle is given by $A = bh$, where b is the base and h is the height. What is another way to write the formula?

Use the Commutative Property of Multiplication.

$A = hb$

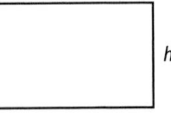

Watch Out !

There are no associative and commutative properties of subtraction and division. You can use addition properties with a subtraction problem if you think of subtraction as being addition of a negative number.

$12 - 5 = 12 + (-5)$

To use multiplication properties with a division problem, you must remember that dividing is the same thing as multiplying the dividend by the reciprocal of the divisor.

$\frac{12}{5} = 12 \cdot \frac{1}{5}$.

EXAMPLE 4

An auditorium contains 34 rows of seats, with 22 seats in each row. The number of seats can be found by multiplying the number of rows by the number of seats in each row, or by multiplying the number of seats in each row by the number of rows. Which property does this represent?

These are two orders for multiplication, 34(22) and 22(34), so this problem represents the Commutative Property of Multiplication.

The Associative Properties

Because you can add numbers in any order, you can also regroup addends without affecting the sum.

$(79 + 38) + 62$ $79 + (38 + 62)$
117 + 62   79 + 100
179   179

And because you can multiply numbers in any order, you can also regroup factors without affecting the product.

$(8.1 \cdot 3.2) \cdot 12.5$ $8.1 \cdot (3.2 \cdot 12.5)$
25.92 · 12.5   8.1 · 40
324   324

These relationships are expressed in the following properties.

Associative Property of Addition
For any real numbers a, b, and c, $(a + b) + c = a + (b + c)$.
Associative Property of Multiplication
For any real numbers a, b, and c, $(ab)c = a(bc)$.

Expressions such as $(6 + 7) + 5$ and $6 + (7 + 5)$ are equivalent expressions, as was true for expressions with equal values by the commutative properties.

Using the Properties

EXAMPLE 5

Use an associative property to write an equivalent expression.

a. $(2x + 17) + 33$

An equivalent expression using the Associative Property of Addition is $2x + (17 + 33)$.

b. $(7p)(p) + 21$

An equivalent expression using the Associative Property of Multiplication is $7(p \cdot p) + 21$.

Ways to REMEMBER

To help you remember which properties are associative and which are commutative, think about what the terms mean.

When you *commute* to work or school, you move from one place to another.

When you *associate* with people in class, you form a group.

You can use the commutative and associative properties together with mental math to solve problems quickly.

EXAMPLE 6

Find the sum or product.

a. $97 + 89 + 103 + 111$

Look for pairs of compatible numbers.

Use the Commutative Property of Addition.	$97 + 103 + 89 + 111$
Use the Associative Property of Addition.	$= (97 + 103) + (89 + 111)$
Add each group of numbers. Then find the sum.	$= 200 + 200 = 400$

b. $3\sqrt{6} \cdot 5\sqrt{24}$

Use the Commutative Property of Multiplication.	$3 \cdot 5 \cdot \sqrt{6} \cdot \sqrt{24}$
Use the Associative Property of Multiplication.	$= (3 \cdot 5) \cdot (\sqrt{6} \cdot \sqrt{24})$
Multiply each group of numbers.	$= 15 \cdot \sqrt{144}$
Simplify the radical. Then find the product.	$= 15 \cdot 12 = 180$

c. $2^5 \cdot 0.25x \cdot 2^2$

Use the Commutative Property of Multiplication.	$0.25 \cdot 2^5 \cdot 2^2 \cdot x$
Use the Associative Property of Multiplication.	$= 0.25 \cdot (2^5 \cdot 2^2) \cdot x$
Multiply the powers.	$= 0.25 \cdot 2^7 \cdot x$
Simplify the power.	$= 0.25 \cdot 128 \cdot x$
Use the Associative Property of Multiplication to find the product.	$= (0.25 \cdot 128) \cdot x = 32x$

Need More HELP?

To multiply two square roots, you multiply the numbers under the radical signs.

For every number $a \geq 0$ and $b \geq 0$,

$\sqrt{a} \cdot \sqrt{b} = \sqrt{ab}$

EXAMPLE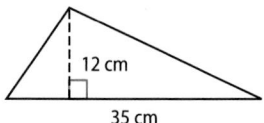

Find the area of the triangle.

12 cm

35 cm

The formula for the area of a triangle is $A = \frac{1}{2}bh$.

SEARCH 🔍

To see step-by-step videos of these problems, enter the page number into the SWadvantage.com Search Bar.

METHOD 1

Use the Associative Property of Multiplication to group the fraction with one variable.

$$A = \left(\frac{1}{2}b\right)h$$

Substitute the values for the variables.

$$= \left(\frac{1}{2} \cdot 35\right)12$$

Multiply the grouped factors. Then multiply this product by the other factor.

$$= 17.5 \cdot 12$$
$$= 210$$

METHOD 2

Use the Associative Property of Multiplication to group the variables.

$$A = \frac{1}{2}(bh)$$

Substitute the values for the variables.

$$= \frac{1}{2}(35 \cdot 12)$$

Multiply the grouped factors. Then multiply this product by the other factor.

$$= \frac{1}{2}(420)$$
$$= 210$$

The area of the triangle is 210 cm².

The Commutative and Associative Properties

For any real numbers a, b, and c:

Operation	Commutative Property	Associative Property
Addition	$a + b = b + a$	$(a + b) + c = a + (b + c)$
Multiplication	$ab = ba$	$(ab)c = a(bc)$

Distributive Property

Using the Distributive Property to Simplify

The number 27 is actually the sum of 20 and 7. When you multiply a number by 27, you are actually first multiplying the number by 7. Next, you multiply the number by 20, and then, you add these two products.

$$\begin{array}{r} 12 \\ \times\ 27 \\ \hline \end{array}$$

the product of 12 and 7	84
the product of 12 and 20	+240
the sum of these products	324

Distributing one factor over two addends of another factor is called the Distributive Property. This property is sometimes called the Distributive Property of Multiplication over Addition.

The Distributive Property states that for any real numbers *a*, *b*, and *c*:

$$a(b + c) = ab + ac$$

The Distributive Property can help you do mental math.

SEARCH

To see step-by-step videos of these problems, enter the page number into the SWadvantage.com Search Bar.

EXAMPLE 1

Use the Distributive Property to rewrite 14(1,002). Then simplify.

Rewrite 1,002 as 1,000 + 2.	$14(1,002) = 14(1,000 + 2)$
Use the Distributive Property.	$= 14(1,000) + 14(2)$
Multiply.	$= 14,000 + 28$
Add.	$= 14,028$

The Distributive Property also works for multiplication over subtraction.

For any real numbers *a*, *b*, and *c*, $a(b - c) = ab - ac$.

EXAMPLE 2

Use the Distributive Property to rewrite 8(99). Then simplify.

Rewrite 99 as 100 − 1.	$8(99) = 8(100 - 1)$
Use the Distributive Property.	$= 8(100) - 8(1)$
Multiply.	$= 800 - 8$
Subtract.	$= 792$

Use the Distributive Property if you see an easier calculation that is equivalent.

EXAMPLE 3

Simplify 2(53) + 2(47).

The numbers 53 and 47 are compatible for addition.

Use the *Distributive Property* to rewrite the expression.	$2(53) + 2(47) = 2(53 + 47)$
Add.	$= 2(100)$
Multiply.	$= 200$

The Distributive Property can be extended to apply to more than two terms.

EXAMPLE 4

The surface area of a rectangular prism is given by $SA = 2wh + 2\ell w + 2\ell h$, where w is the width, ℓ is the length, and h is the height. What is the surface area of this rectangular prism?

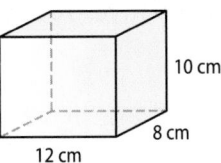

10 cm
8 cm
12 cm

METHOD 1

Substitute into the formula.

$SA = 2wh + 2\ell w + 2\ell h$
$= (2 \cdot 8 \cdot 10) + (2 \cdot 12 \cdot 8) + (2 \cdot 12 \cdot 10)$
$= 160 + 192 + 240$
$= 592$ cm^2

METHOD 2

Each term has a factor of 2. Use the Distributive Property to rewrite the formula.

$SA = 2(wh + \ell w + \ell h)$
$= 2(8 \cdot 10 + 12 \cdot 8 + 12 \cdot 10)$
$= 2(80 + 96 + 120)$
$= 2(296)$
$= 592$ cm^2

The Distributive Property

The Distributive Property of Addition over Multiplication	
For any real numbers a, b, and c, $a(b + c) = ab + ac$ $(b + c)a = ba + ca$	$4(5 + 3) = 4(5) + 4(3)$ $(5 + 3)4 = (5)4 + (3)4$
The Distributive Property of Subtraction over Multiplication	
For any real numbers a, b, and c, $a(b - c) = ab - ac$ $(b - c)a = ba - ca$	$4(5 - 3) = 4(5) - 4(3)$ $(5 - 3)4 = (5)4 - (3)4$

Variable Expressions

One important use of the Distributive Property is in writing equivalent expressions. When the Distributive Property is used to factor out the common factors of two or more *terms*, the resulting expression is equivalent to the original expression. The **terms** of an expression are the parts that are added or subtracted.

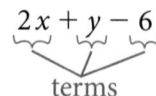

In the expression above, which terms have a common factor? The terms $2x$ and 6 have 2 as a common factor.

Use the Commutative Property to change the order of the terms. $\qquad 2x - 6 + y$

Rewrite 6 as 2(3). $\qquad 2x - 2(3) + y$

Use the Distributive Property to write an equivalent expression. $\qquad 2(x - 3) + y$

EXAMPLE 5

Use the Distributive Property to write an equivalent expression.

a. $-2(y - 5)$

Use the Distributive Property. $\qquad -2(y) + (-2)(-5)$

Multiply. $\qquad -2y + 10$

The expressions $-2(y - 5)$ and $-2y + 10$ are equivalent.

b. $4r + 8$

Write 8 as 4(2). $\qquad 4r + 4(2)$

Use the Distributive Property. $\qquad 4(r + 2)$

The expressions $4r + 8$ and $4(r + 2)$ are equivalent.

The Distributive Property can also be used to simplify expressions containing *like terms.* **Like terms** contain the same variables raised to the same powers. **Unlike terms** differ in either a variable or the power of a variable. The following table provides several examples of like terms and unlike terms.

Identifying Like Terms

Terms	Variable(s)	Power(s)	Like terms?
$3m$ and $6m$	m	1	Yes
$4x$ and $4y$	x and y	1	No
$3a$ and $4a^2$	a	1 and 2	No

EXAMPLE 6

Use the Distributive Property to simplify, if possible.

a. 11y − y

These terms are like terms. *y* is equivalent to 1*y*.

Use the Distributive Property to factor out *y*.	$11y - y = y(11 - 1)$
Add.	$= y(10)$
Use the Commutative Property.	$= 10y$

Need More HELP

Remember that the variable *y* has a coefficient of 1 and can be written as 1*y*.

b. 9x + 4y

These terms are not like terms. The variables are different.

This expression cannot be simplified.

c. 5n + 7n²

These terms are not like terms. The variables are the same, but the powers differ.

This expression cannot be simplified.

EXAMPLE 7

Simplify.

a. 3(m − 2) + 6m

Use the Distributive Property to multiply.	$3(m - 2) + 6m = 3m - 6 + 6m$
Use the Commutative Property.	$= 3m + 6m - 6$
Use the Distributive Property again.	$= m(3 + 6) - 6$
Subtract.	$= m(9) - 6$
Use the Commutative Property again.	$= 9m - 6$

b. 16 − 2(k − 2)

Use the Distributive Property to multiply.	$16 - 2(k - 2) = 16 - 2k - 2(-2)$
Multiply.	$= 16 - 2k + 4$
Use the Commutative Property.	$= 16 + 4 - 2k$
Add.	$= 20 - 2k$

SEARCH

To see step-by-step videos of these problems, enter the page number into the SWadvantage.com Search Bar.

The Identity and Inverse Properties

SOUTHWESTERN

The Additive Identity Property

When 0 is added to any number, the result is that number, so 0 is called the **additive identity**.

$$3 + 0 = 3 \qquad 0 + 6 = 6 \qquad -8 + 0 = -8 \qquad 0 + \left(-\frac{1}{2}\right) = -\frac{1}{2}$$

For any real number a:

$$a + 0 = a \qquad \text{and} \qquad 0 + a = a$$

The Multiplicative Identity Property

When any number is multiplied by 1, the result is that number, so 1 is called the **multiplicative identity**.

$$7 \cdot 1 = 7 \qquad 1 \cdot 2.5 = 2.5 \qquad -25 \cdot 1 = -25 \qquad 1 \cdot \frac{2}{3} = \frac{2}{3}$$

For any real number a:

$$a \cdot 1 = a \qquad \text{and} \qquad 1 \cdot a = a$$

SEARCH

To see step-by-step videos of these problems, enter the page number into the SWadvantage.com Search Bar.

EXAMPLE 1

Simplify each expression.

a. $75 + 98 - 75$

Use the Commutative Property.	$75 + 98 - 75 = 98 + 75 - 75$
Use the Associative Property.	$= 98 + (75 - 75)$
Subtract.	$= 98 + 0$
Use the Additive Identity Property.	$= 98$

b. $5 + h - 5$

Use the Commutative Property.	$5 + h - 5 = h + 5 - 5$
Use the Associative Property.	$= h + (5 - 5)$
Subtract.	$= h + 0$
Use the Additive Identity Property.	$= h$

c. $7p - 6p$

Use the Distributive Property.	$7p - 6p = (7 - 6)p$
Subtract.	$= 1p$
Use the Multiplicative Identity Property.	$= p$

The Additive Inverse Property

When any number and its opposite are added, the result is the additive identity, 0. As a result, the opposite of a number is also called its **additive inverse** .

$$3 + (-3) = 0$$
$$-3 + 3 = 0$$

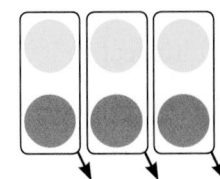

A number and its additive inverse are additive inverses of each other.

For any real number a, there is exactly one additive inverse $-a$, for which

$$a + (-a) = 0 \qquad \text{and} \qquad -a + a = 0$$

EXAMPLE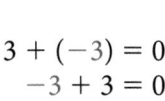

Find the additive inverse of each number.

a. 0.875

Find the opposite of 0.875. -0.875

The additive inverse of 0.875 is -0.875.

b. $-\dfrac{4}{11}$

Find the opposite of $-\dfrac{4}{11}$. $\dfrac{4}{11}$

The additive inverse of $-\dfrac{4}{11}$ is $\dfrac{4}{11}$.

c. 0

Find the opposite of 0.   0

The additive inverse of 0 is 0.

d. 5x

Find the opposite of 5x. $-5x$

The additive inverse of 5x is $-5x$.

EXAMPLE 3

Kadija babysits for her neighbor. In October, she earned \$25 one week and \$45 the next week. She then spent \$30 on a present before earning \$35 the third week. The last week of October, she earned \$30. She then spent \$25 on clothes. How much money did she have at the end of the month?

The money she earns is positive money for her. What she spends is negative. Because $-30 + 30 = 0$ and $25 - 25 = 0$, just add \$45 and \$35. She has \$80 at the end of the month.

The Multiplicative Inverse Property

When any nonzero number is multiplied by its reciprocal, the result is the multiplicative identity, 1. Thus, the reciprocal of any number is also called the **multiplicative inverse** of the number.

A number and its multiplicative inverse are multiplicative inverses of each other.

For any nonzero real number a, there is exactly one multiplicative inverse $\frac{1}{a}$, for which

$$a \cdot \frac{1}{a} = 1 \quad \text{and} \quad \frac{1}{a} \cdot a = 1$$

SEARCH

To see step-by-step videos of these problems, enter the page number into the SWadvantage.com Search Bar.

EXAMPLE 4

Find the multiplicative inverse of each number.

a. 7

Find the reciprocal of 7. $\frac{1}{7}$

The multiplicative inverse of 7 is $\frac{1}{7}$.

b. $\frac{1}{9}$

Find the reciprocal of $\frac{1}{9}$. $\dfrac{1}{\frac{1}{9}} = 1 \div \frac{1}{9} = 1 \times \frac{9}{1} = 9$

The multiplicative inverse of $\frac{1}{9}$ is 9.

c. −4

Find the reciprocal of −4. $\dfrac{1}{-4} = -\dfrac{1}{4}$

The multiplicative inverse of −4 is $-\frac{1}{4}$.

d. 0

Zero has no multiplicative inverse because division by zero is undefined.

EXAMPLE 5

Find the multiplicative inverse of 2.5.

METHOD 1

Write 2.5 as $\frac{25}{10}$. The multiplicative inverse of $\frac{25}{10}$ is $\frac{10}{25}$. Divide 10 by 25. $25 \overline{)10.0}^{\,0.4}$

METHOD 2

Use a calculator. $2.5 \;\boxed{x^{-1}} = 0.4$

EXAMPLE 6

There are about $4\frac{1}{3}$ weeks in the average month. To convert a monthly salary to a weekly salary, multiply the monthly salary by the multiplicative inverse of $4\frac{1}{3}$. Find the weekly salary for a monthly salary of $4,500 a month.

Write $4\frac{1}{3}$ as an improper fraction.

$$4\frac{1}{3} = \frac{4 \cdot 3 + 1}{3} = \frac{13}{3}$$

Find the multiplicative inverse of $\frac{13}{3}$.

$$\frac{1}{\frac{13}{3}} = \frac{3}{13}$$

Multiply $4,500 by $\frac{3}{13}$.

$$\frac{3}{13}(4,500) \approx 1,038.461538$$

The weekly salary is $1,038.46.

EXAMPLE 7

Pears are on sale at the local grocery for 3 lb for $3.29. To find the cost of a certain weight of pears, multiply the number of pounds by the multiplicative inverse of $\frac{3}{3.29}$.

Find the price of 5 lb of pears.

Write $\frac{3}{3.29}$ to include no decimals.

$$\frac{3}{3.29} = \frac{300}{329}$$

Find the multiplicative inverse of $\frac{300}{329}$.

$$\frac{1}{\frac{300}{329}} = \frac{329}{300}$$

Multiply 5 lb by $\frac{329}{300}$.

$$5\left(\frac{329}{300}\right) \approx 5.4833$$

Five pounds of pears cost $5.48.

Need More
HELP

The identity properties are sometimes known as the Addition Property of 0 and the Multiplication Property of 1.

The inverse properties were once called the Axiom of Additive Inverses and the Axiom of Multiplicative Inverses.

Got to KNOW!

Identity and Inverse Properties

For any real number a, the following properties apply:

Addition

Identity	$a + 0 = a$	and	$0 + a = a$
Inverse	$a + (-a) = 0$	and	$-a + a = 0$

Multiplication

Identity	$a \cdot 1 = a$	and	$1 \cdot a = a$
Inverse	$a \cdot \frac{1}{a} = 1$	and	$\frac{1}{a} \cdot a = 1 \ (a \neq 0)$

Order of Operations

Order of Operations

The expression $17 - 3 \times 4$ contains no grouping symbols. Without a specific order for performing the operations, the expression could be simplified in more than one way. Here are two ways someone might simplify it.

$$17 - \underbrace{3 \times 4}$$
$$\underbrace{14} \times 4$$
$$56$$

$$17 - \underbrace{3 \times 4}$$
$$17 - \underbrace{12}$$
$$5$$

To prevent confusion when simplifying expressions with addition, subtraction, multiplication, and division and no grouping symbols, always use the following order:

- Multiply and divide from left to right.
- Add and subtract from left to right.

You don't need to do all multiplications before all divisions, or all additions before subtractions. You can multiply and divide as you get to each operation.

- Divide and multiply from left to right.
- Subtract and add from left to right.

To see step-by-step videos of these problems, enter the page number into the SWadvantage.com Search Bar.

EXAMPLE 1

Simplify each expression.

a. $17 - 3 \times 4$

STEP 1 Multiply.
$$17 - 3 \times 4 = 17 - \underbrace{3 \times 4}$$
$$= 17 - 12$$

STEP 2 Subtract.
$$= 5$$

b. $100 + 50 \div 10 - 5 \times 2$

STEP 1 Divide and multiply from left to right.
$$100 + \underbrace{50 \div 10} - \underbrace{5 \times 2}$$
$$= 100 + 5 - 10$$

STEP 2 Add and subtract from left to right.
$$= 95$$

EXAMPLE 2

Lashonda uses the calculator application on her computer to evaluate the expression shown. Was the expression calculated correctly?

$$44 \boxed{-} 12 \boxed{\div} 4 \boxed{+} 20 \boxed{\times} 5 \boxed{=} 140$$

Use order of operations to check.
$$44 - 12 \div 4 + 20 \times 5$$

Divide and multiply from left to right first.
$$= 44 - 3 + 100$$

Subtract and add from left to right.
$$= 141$$

No, the correct answer is 141. The calculator evaluated all operations from left to right.

Order of Operations with Exponents

Exponents represent repeated multiplication. If an expression contains exponents, simplify any powers before performing any of the four basic operations.

- Simplify powers from left to right.
- Multiply and divide from left to right.
- Add and subtract from left to right.

Simplify each expression.

a. $54 - 3^3 \times 2$

Simplify the power first.	$54 - 3^3 \times 2 = 54 - 3^3 \times 2$
	$= 54 - 27 \times 2$
Multiply.	$= 54 - 54$
Subtract.	$= 0$

b. $(-7) + 2^7 \div 4 - 5^2$

Simplify the powers from left to right first.	$(-7) + 2^7 \div 4 - 5^2$
	$= (-7) + 128 \div 4 - 25$
Divide.	$= (-7) + \quad 32 \quad - 25$
Add and subtract from left to right.	$= 0$

Need More

HELP

For help with exponents, go to pages 1396–1399.

Order of Operations with Parentheses and Brackets

Grouping symbols such as parentheses and brackets are used to make sure that calculations are done in a specific order. Simplify expressions inside grouping symbols first.

- Perform operations inside parentheses.
- Simplify powers.
- Multiply and divide from left to right.
- Add and subtract from left to right.

This is the expression from the beginning of the lesson, with parentheses added.

$$\underbrace{(17 - 3)}_{14} \times 4$$

$$56$$

SEARCH 🔍

To see step-by-step videos of these problems, enter the page number into the SWadvantage.com Search Bar.

EXAMPLE 4

Simplify each expression.

a. $164 - (10 + 5) \times 2^3$

Perform the operation in parentheses first.	$164 - (10 + 5) \times 2^3$
	$= 164 - \quad 15 \quad \times 2^3$
Simplify the power.	$= 164 - \quad 15 \quad \times 8$
Multiply.	$= 164 - \quad\quad 120$
Subtract.	$= 44$

b. $10 + 16^{(4-3)} \div (24 \div 3)^2$

Perform the operations in parentheses first.	$10 + 16^{(4-3)} \div (24 \div 3)^2$
	$= 10 + \quad 16^{(1)} \div \quad (8)^2$
Simplify the powers.	$= 10 + \quad 16 \quad \div \quad 64$
Divide.	$= 10 + \quad\quad \frac{1}{4}$
Add.	$= 10\frac{1}{4}$

c. $22 + 3^{(1+3)} - (3 \times 2^2)^2$

Perform the operations in parentheses first.

Simplify the powers within parentheses.	$22 + 3^{(1+3)} - (3 \times 2^2)^2$
	$= 22 + 3^{(1+3)} - (3 \times 4)^2$
Simplify within the parentheses.	$= 22 + 3^4 \quad - \quad (12)^2$
Simplify the powers.	$= 22 + 81 \quad - \quad 144$
Add and subtract.	$= -41$

EXAMPLE 5

Need More

HELP ❓

When an expression has both parentheses and brackets or has nested parentheses, always start with the innermost pair first.

Felicia had $220. She bought shoes for $47.97, jeans for $34.99, four pairs of socks at $6.33 a pair, and two T-shirts at $12.50 each. Then she gave half of what she had left to her mom. Evaluate the expression below to find the amount she gave her mom.

$$[220 - (47.97 + 34.99 + 4 \cdot 6.33 + 2 \cdot 12.5)] \div 2$$

STEP 1	Multiply inside parentheses.	$[220 - (47.97 + 34.99 + 25.32 + 25)] \div 2$
STEP 2	Add inside parentheses.	$= [220 - (133.28)] \div 2$
STEP 3	You can remove the parentheses.	$= [220 - 133.28] \div 2$
STEP 4	Subtract.	$= [86.72] \div 2$
STEP 5	Divide.	$= 43.36$

Felicia gave her mom $43.36.

Order of Operations with Other Grouping Symbols

Division bars and square-root symbols are also grouping symbols.

$$\frac{\text{numerator}}{\text{denominator}} \qquad \sqrt{\text{expression}}$$

EXAMPLE 6

Simplify each expression.

a. $\dfrac{2^2 + 45}{8(11) - 3^4}$

Perform the operations in the numerator and in the denominator first.

Simplify the powers.	$\dfrac{2^2 + 45}{8(11) - 3^4} = \dfrac{4 + 45}{8(11) - 81}$
Multiply.	$= \dfrac{4 + 45}{88 - 81}$
Add and subtract.	$= \dfrac{49}{7}$
Divide.	$= 7$

b. $10^2 \sqrt{8 + 4 \cdot 2}$

Perform the operations under the radical symbol first.

Multiply under the radical.	$10^2\sqrt{8 + 4 \cdot 2} = 10^2\sqrt{8 + 8}$
Add under the radical.	$= 10^2\sqrt{16}$
Simplify the square root.	$= 10^2(4)$
Simplify the power.	$= 100(4)$
Multiply.	$= 400$

Ways to
REMEMBER

In the U.S., use the sentence **P**lease **E**xcuse **M**y **D**ear **A**unt **S**ally to remember the correct order of operations.

P Parentheses

E Exponents

M Multiply

D Divide

A Add

S Subtract

In Canada, brackets, not parentheses, are used. A helpful sentence to remember is **B**ig **E**lephants **D**estroy **M**ice **A**nd **S**nails.

Got to
KNOW!

Order of Operations

P Perform operations inside **P**arentheses.

E Simplify **E**xponents.

MD **M**ultiply and **D**ivide from left to right.

AS **A**dd and **S**ubtract from left to right.

Evaluating Expressions

With this yardstick, length can be measured in either feet or inches.

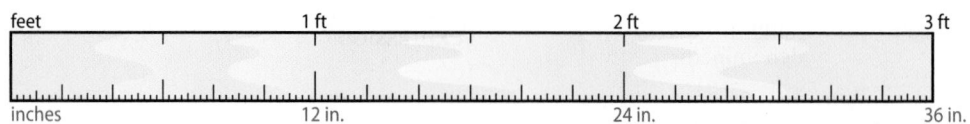

The table below shows how to convert feet to inches. You multiply the number of feet by 12. The table shows inches for 1, 2, and 3 feet. It also shows a way to change any number of feet to inches by multiplying the number of feet f by 12.

Converting Feet to Inches

Feet	1	2	3	f
Inches	12	24	36	$12 \times f$

When you use f to stand for the number of feet, you are using a variable. A **variable** is a letter or symbol that represents a quantity that can change. A **constant** is a quantity that does not change, such as 3 in the table above, or the number π (pi).

An **algebraic expression**, like $12 \times f$ above, is a mathematical phrase that uses symbols and numbers to represent mathematical operations. Expressions might contain constants, variables, and symbols for mathematical operations. Here are some examples of algebraic expressions:

$$12 \times f \qquad r^2 + 3 \qquad \sqrt{x} \qquad \frac{1}{y} - 10$$

Expressions with only constants are not algebraic expressions.

$$16 - 2 \times 7 \qquad 2 \times \pi \qquad 10 - \frac{1}{2} \cdot 4$$

The symbols used in an algebraic expression might vary. For example, multiplication with variables can be written several different ways. These algebraic expressions all show the product of 8 and t.

$$8 \cdot t \qquad 8t \qquad 8 \times t \qquad 8(t) \qquad (8)t \qquad (8)(t)$$

In the expressions above, the number 8 is the *coefficient* of the variable. A **coefficient** is the number that is multiplied by the variable in an algebraic expression.

Division with variables can be shown by a fraction, a slash mark, or a division sign. These algebraic expressions all show the quotient of 4 and s.

$$4/s \qquad 4 \div s \qquad \frac{4}{s}$$

An algebraic expression lets us determine a quantity based on a relationship, even if we don't have all the numbers. So we can say the number of inches is $12 \times f$ for f feet without needing to know what f is.

To **evaluate** an algebraic expression, substitute a number for the variable and calculate the value of the expression.

Watch Out !

The terms *expression* and *equation* are often confused with each other. They are not the same thing. You will learn about algebraic equations in *One-Variable Linear Equations* starting on page 1458.

EXAMPLE 1

Evaluate 12 × *f* for *f* = 3 to find the number of inches in 3 feet.

STEP 1 Substitute 3 for *f* in 12 × *f*. $12 \times f = 12 \times 3$

STEP 2 Multiply. $= 36$

There are 36 inches in 3 feet. The values match those in the table.

EXAMPLE 2

Evaluate each expression.

a. *x* + 7 for *x* = 3

STEP 1 Substitute 3 for *x* in *x* + 7. $x + 7 = 3 + 7$

STEP 2 Add. $= 10$

When $x = 3$, $x + 7 = 10$.

b. 20 − *z* for *z* = 14

STEP 1 Substitute 14 for *z* in 20 − *z*. $20 - z = 20 - 14$

STEP 2 Subtract. $= 6$

When $z = 14$, $20 - z = 6$.

SEARCH

To see step-by-step videos of these problems, enter the page number into the SWadvantage.com Search Bar.

EXAMPLE 3

Evaluate each expression.

a. 7*a* for *a* = 15

STEP 1 Substitute 15 for *a* in 7*a*. $7a = 7(15)$

STEP 2 Multiply. $= 105$

When $a = 15$, $7a = 105$.

b. $\frac{x}{4}$ for *x* = 10

STEP 1 Substitute 10 for *x* in $\frac{x}{4}$. $\frac{x}{4} = \frac{10}{4}$

STEP 2 Divide. $= \frac{5}{2}$, or $2\frac{1}{2}$

When $x = 10$, $\frac{x}{4} = \frac{5}{2}$, or $2\frac{1}{2}$.

Using a Table of Values to Evaluate

EXAMPLE 4

During a storm, you see a lightning strike, and soon after, you hear the thunder from the strike. An estimate for the distance d in feet is given by the expression 1,000t, where t is the number of seconds between seeing the lightning and hearing the thunder. Suppose you see lightning, and 6 seconds later you hear thunder. About how far away was the lightning strike?

Evaluate 1,000t for $t = 6$.

STEP 1 Substitute 6 for t.   1,000(6)

STEP 2 Multiply.   6,000

The lightning strike was about 6,000 feet away.

EXAMPLE 5

Evaluate each expression.

a. x^3 for $x = 1, 2, 3, 4,$ and 5

You can make a table. Substitute 1, 2, 3, 4, and 5 for x.

x	1	2	3	4	5
x^3	1^3	2^3	3^3	4^3	5^3
	↑	↑	↑	↑	↑
	1	8	27	64	125

When $x = 1, x^3 = 1$.
When $x = 2, x^3 = 8$.
When $x = 3, x^3 = 27$.
When $x = 4, x^3 = 64$.
When $x = 5, x^3 = 125$.

b. 2^x for $x = 1, 2, 3, 4,$ and 5

Make a table. Substitute 1, 2, 3, 4, and 5 for x.

x	1	2	3	4	5
2^x	2^1	2^2	2^3	2^4	2^5
	↑	↑	↑	↑	↑
	2	4	8	16	32

The values of 2^x for $x = 1, 2, 3, 4,$ and 5 are 2, 4, 8, 16, and 32.

Expressions might contain negative numbers or variables. Remember, the opposite of the opposite of a number is the number itself.

SEARCH

To see step-by-step videos of these problems, enter the page number into the SWadvantage.com Search Bar.

EXAMPLE 6

Evaluate $-x$ for $x = 0, 4, 22,$ and -10.

You can make a table. Substitute 0, 4, 22, and -10 for x.

x	0	4	22	-10
$-x$	-0	-4	-22	$-(-10)$

        0   -4 -22 10

When $x = 0$, $-x = 0$.
When $x = 4$, $-x = 4$.
When $x = 22$, $-x = -22$.
When $x = -10$, $-x = 10$.

EXAMPLE 7

Find the expression that has a value of 12 when $y = -6$.

a. $\dfrac{-72}{x}$ b. $-2y$ c. $y - 18$ d. $6 + y$

Substitute 12 for y in each expression. Then evaluate the expression.

   a. $\dfrac{-72}{x}$ does not contain y, so -6 cannot be substituted in the expression.

   b. $-2y = -2(-6) = 12$

   c. $y - 18 = -6 - 18 = -24$

   d. $6 + y = 6 + (-6) = 0$

When $y = 6$, the expression $-2y$ has a value of 12.

Evaluating an Expression with One Variable

• Determine the given value of the variable.

• Substitute that value for the variable in the expression. The result is a numerical expression.

• Use the correct order of operations to simplify the numerical expression.

• The result is the value of the expression for the given value of the variable.

Evaluating Variable Expressions

Evaluating Expressions with Several Variables and Operations

Algebraic expressions with one variable and one operation are simple to evaluate. Substitute the given value of the variable into the expression, and simplify it by performing the operation in the expression.

Expressions might also contain more than one variable. These expressions might contain several operations. Evaluating these expressions is basically the same as evaluating simpler expressions. Substitute the given values for the variables in the expression. Then simplify the expression using the correct order of operations.

EXAMPLE 1

Evaluate $x + y$ for $x = 5$ and $y = 7$.

STEP 1 Substitute 5 for x and 7 for y. $x + y = 5 + 7$

STEP 2 Add. $= 12$

When $x = 5$ and $y = 7$, $x + y = 12$.

EXAMPLE 2

Evaluate $2n - m$ for $m = 18$ and $n = 11$.

STEP 1 Substitute 18 for m and 11 for n. $2n - m = 2(11) - 18$

STEP 2 Multiply. $= 22 - 18$

STEP 3 Subtract. $= 4$

When $m = 18$ and $n = 11$, $2n - m = 4$.

When an algebraic expression has the same variable in several places, substitute the same value for *every* occurrence of that variable.

EXAMPLE 3

Evaluate $\frac{t}{t - 25}$ for $t = 30$.

STEP 1 Substitute 30 for *both* values of t. $\frac{t}{t - 25} = \frac{30}{30 - 25}$

STEP 2 Subtract. $= \frac{30}{5}$

STEP 3 Divide. $= 6$

When $t = 30$, $\frac{t}{t - 25} = 6$.

Need More

HELP ?

To decide which operation to do first, remember PEMDAS in the United States.

P   Parentheses

E   Exponents

M   Multiply

D   Divide

A   Add

S   Subtract

In Canada, remember BEDMAS.

B   Brackets

E   Exponents

D   Divide

M   Multiply

A   Add

S   Subtract

SEARCH 🔍

To see step-by-step videos of these problems, enter the page number into the SWadvantage.com Search Bar.

EXAMPLE 4

Evaluate $8(x + 12) - 32 \div x$ for $x = 4$.

STEP 1 Substitute 4 for every value of x. $8(x + 12) - 32 \div x = 8(4 + 12) - 32 \div 4$

STEP 2 Simplify inside parentheses. $= 8(16) - 32 \div 4$

STEP 3 Multiply. $= 128 - 32 \div 4$

STEP 4 Divide. $= 128 - 8$

STEP 5 Subtract. $= 120$

When $x = 4$, $8(x + 12) - 32 \div x = 120$.

EXAMPLE 5

Evaluate each expression for $a = 8$, $b = 6$, and $c = 10$.

a. $c^2 - a^2$

STEP 1 Substitute 8 for a and 10 for c. $c^2 - a^2 = 10^2 - 8^2$

STEP 2 Simplify the powers. $= 100 - 64$

STEP 3 Subtract. $= 36$

When $a = 8$ and $c = 10$, $c^2 - a^2 = 36$.

b. $\dfrac{ac - 8}{3b}$

STEP 1 Substitute 8 for a, 6 for b, and 10 for c. $\dfrac{ac - 8}{3b} = \dfrac{8(10) - 8}{3(6)}$

STEP 2 Multiply. $= \dfrac{80 - 8}{18}$

STEP 3 Subtract. $= \dfrac{72}{18}$

STEP 4 Divide. $= 4$

When $a = 8$, $b = 6$, and $c = 10$, $\dfrac{ac - 8}{3b} = 4$.

EXAMPLE 6

Evaluate $3k^2$, $3(k^2)$, and $(3k)^2$ for $k = 4$. Which results have the same value?

Substitute 4 for k. $3k^2 = 3 \cdot 4^2$ $3(k^2) = 3(4^2)$ $(3k)^2 = (3 \cdot 4)^2$

Simplify, using the order of operations. $= 3 \cdot 16$ $= 3(16)$ $= (12)^2$

                                                $= 48$ $= 48$ $= 144$

The expressions $3k^2$ and $3(k^2)$ have the same value.

Applications of Variable Expressions

EXAMPLE 7

A garden is in the shape of a trapezoid. The formula for the area of the trapezoid is $\frac{1}{2}(a + b)h$. Find the area of the garden in square feet.

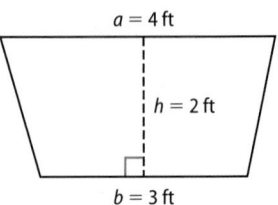

$a = 4$ ft

$h = 2$ ft

$b = 3$ ft

STEP 1 Substitute 4 for a, 3 for b, and 2 for h. $\qquad \frac{1}{2}(a + b)h = \frac{1}{2}(4 + 3)2$

STEP 2 Simplify inside parentheses. $\qquad\qquad\qquad = \frac{1}{2}(7)2$

METHOD 1

STEP 3 Multiply from left to right. $\qquad\qquad\qquad = \frac{7}{2}(2)$

$\qquad\qquad\qquad\qquad\qquad\qquad\qquad\qquad\qquad = 7$

METHOD 2

STEP 3 Use the Commutative Property of Multiplication. $\quad = (2)\frac{1}{2}(7)$

STEP 4 Multiply from left to right. $\qquad\qquad\qquad = 1(7)$

$\qquad\qquad\qquad\qquad\qquad\qquad\qquad\qquad\qquad = 7$

The area of the garden is 7 square feet.

Need More
HELP ❓

To review the Commutative Property of Multiplication, see pages 1406–1407.

Sometimes the values of the variables in an expression are not directly stated in a problem. The first step of solving such a problem is to identify the values of the variables in the expression.

EXAMPLE 8

SEARCH 🔍

To see step-by-step videos of these problems, enter the page number into the SWadvantage.com Search Bar.

Maria makes cars look almost new by "detailing" them. She is paid an amount in dollars equal to the expression $20n + 6.5t$, in which n is the number of cars she details and t is the number of hours she works. How much does Maria make if she works 72 hours detailing 24 cars?

STEP 1 Identify the values of the variables. $\qquad\qquad n = 24$ and $t = 72$

STEP 2 Substitute 24 for n and 72 for t. $\qquad 20n + 6.5t = 20(24) + 6.5(72)$

STEP 3 Multiply from left to right. $\qquad\qquad\qquad = 480 + 468$

STEP 4 Add. $\qquad\qquad\qquad\qquad\qquad\qquad\qquad = 948$

Maria earns \$948 if she works 72 hours detailing 24 cars.

Variables That Represent Different Values

Some expressions use the same letter more than once. However, the letters can represent different values if they have different numbers attached to them as subscripts.

For example, the variables x_1 and x_2 are read as "x sub 1" and "x sub 2." These variables represent different values of x. The variables y_1 and y_2 are read as "y sub 1" and "y sub 2," and they represent different values of y.

Why not just use different letters for x_1 and x_2 instead of using subscripts? Usually, variables with the same letter and different subscripts represent similar information.

For instance, in the following example, you will find the slope of a line segment. The vertical distance from 0 to one end of the line segment is y_1. The vertical distance from 0 to the other end of the segment is y_2. The values are different, but both variables show vertical distance from 0. In the same manner, x_1 and x_2 represent the horizontal distance from 0 to both ends of the segment.

EXAMPLE 9

An expression you will use to find a value called *slope* is $\frac{y_2 - y_1}{x_2 - x_1}$.

What is the slope if $x_1 = 2$, $x_2 = 10$, $y_1 = -3$, and $y_2 = 13$?

You will enter two different values for x and two different values for y.

Substitute the correct values for the variables.
$$\frac{y_2 - y_1}{x_2 - x_1} = \frac{13 - (-3)}{10 - 2}$$

Subtract to find the values of the numerator and the denominator.
$$= \frac{16}{8}$$

Divide.
$$= 2$$

The slope is 2.

Evaluating an Expression for One or More Variables

1. Determine the given value of *each* variable.
2. Substitute the same value for each occurrence of a variable, and obtain a numerical expression.
3. Use the correct order of operations to simplify the numerical expression.
4. The result is the value of the expression for the given values of the variables.

Translating English into Algebra

SOUTHWESTERN

Identifying Key Words

To solve word problems algebraically, it is first necessary to change words and phrases into mathematical expressions. You can associate certain words with mathematical operations.

The table below shows some common phrases used in problem solving and their algebraic translations.

Words	Symbols
a number	x
a number plus 5 a number increased by 5 5 more than a number the sum of 5 and a number	$x + 5$ $\}$ $+$
a number minus 16 a number decreased by 16 a number less 16 16 less than a number the difference of a number and 16	$x - 16$ $\}$ $-$
7 times a number a number multiplied by 7 the product of 7 and a number	$7 \cdot x$ $\}$ $\times$
a number divided by 2 the quotient of a number and 2 the ratio of a number and 2	$\frac{x}{2}$ $\}$ $\div$

Translating from Symbols to Words

SEARCH

To see step-by-step videos of these problems, enter the page number into the SWadvantage.com Search Bar.

EXAMPLE 1

Write two possible translations for each expression.

a. n + 50

a number *n* increased by 50   the sum of *n* and 50

b. q ÷ 8

a number *q* divided by 8   the quotient of *q* and 8

c. 12 − w

a number *w* subtracted from 12   the difference of 12 and a number *w*

d. 14y

14 times *y*   the product of 14 and *y*

An algebraic expression might contain more than one operation. Care should be taken to translate accurately.

EXAMPLE 2

Write two possible translations for each expression.

a. $3x + 10$

3 times a number x, plus 10; the sum of 3 times a number x and 10

b. $3(x + 10)$

3 multiplied by the sum of x and 10; the product of 3 and the sum x plus 10

Translating from Words to Symbols

When you translate from words to symbols, look for words that tell you what operations to perform.

combine, add	take away, reduce by	by a factor of, times as many	per, for each
Add	**Subtract**	**Multiply**	**Divide**
extra, more, expand	discount, deduct, remove	for each	into equal groups

EXAMPLE 3

Write each phrase as an algebraic expression.

a. a number r split into 3 equal parts

Split into equal parts means division. $r \div 3$

b. 17 less than a number c

Less than means subtraction. $c - 17$

Watch Out !

Other English expressions can also indicate operations, but you need to read the problem to decide the operation. "Separate into *equal groups*" indicates division. "There were 10 *equal groups* of 5" indicates multiplication.

EXAMPLE 4

a. Carol had d dollars in her account, and she added $100. Write an expression for the amount in her account now.

STEP 1 Look for a word to indicate the operation. *Added* indicates addition.

STEP 2 Write the expression. The variable d represents the amount Carol had in her account. An expression for the amount in her account now is $d + 100$.

b. Mr. Jackson took t minutes to drive to school. The time it took him to drive home was twice that long. Write an expression for the time it took him to drive home.

STEP 1 Look for a word to indicate the operation. *Twice* indicates multiplication.

STEP 2 Write the expression. The variable t represents the time it took him to drive to school. An expression for the time it took him to drive home is $2t$.

Translating Word Problems into Algebraic Expressions and Equations

1. Read the problem carefully, and determine what number or numbers need to be found.

2. Represent this unknown number with a variable, for example, x.

3. Identify key words that show what operations should be used with the numbers and variables in the problem.

4. Words like *equals* or *is* tell you to write an equation rather than just an expression.

5. Use numbers, variables, operation symbols, and a relationship stated in the problem to write any expression needed.

6. To write an equation, write two expressions and connect them with an equal sign.

Expression or Equation?

Some word problems translate to more than just an expression. They can translate to an *equation*.

An **equation** is two algebraic expressions separated by an equal sign that means that the two sides have equal value. The following examples are equations:

$$2 = 2 \qquad 3 + 7 = 10 \qquad x - 1 = 6 \qquad 2y = 10 + x$$

Usually the words *equals* and *is* translate to the equal sign, the symbol $=$. When you translate from words to algebra, look for words like *equals* or *is*. These words indicate that you should write an equation instead of an expression.

EXAMPLE 5

Write an equation for the sentence "Twice a number is 5 less than the number."

Use key terms in the sentence to determine what operations should be used. *Twice* indicates multiplication by 2. *Less than* indicates subtraction.

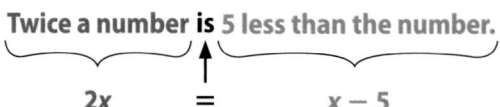

Twice a number **is** 5 less than the number.

$$2x \qquad = \qquad x - 5$$

The equation is $2x = x - 5$.

EXAMPLE 6

Write an expression or an equation to represent the problem.

Tickets to a show cost $11.50 each. How many tickets were purchased if the total cost of the tickets is $92.00?

STEP 1	What needs to be found?	the number of tickets purchased
STEP 2	Choose a variable to represent the number of tickets purchased.	t
STEP 3	What expression represents the total cost of the tickets?	$11.5t$
STEP 4	What value also represents the total cost of the tickets?	92
STEP 5	Should I represent the problem as an expression or equation?	equation
STEP 6	Write the equation.	$11.5t = 92$

The equation that can be used to determine the number of tickets purchased is $11.5t = 92$.

Sometimes translating a verbal sentence to an equation may not be straightforward. You may want to express one variable in terms of the other so that the equation has only one variable.

EXAMPLE

Write an equation to represent the problem.

A bike store has twice as many Zephyrs in stock as Falcons. The store has a total of 42 of the bikes. How many Falcons are in stock?

METHOD 1

STEP 1	What needs to be found?	the number of Falcons in stock
STEP 2	Represent the number of Falcons in stock.	f
STEP 3	Represent the number of Zephyrs in stock.	z
STEP 4	What expression represents the total number of bikes?	$f + z$
STEP 5	What value also represents the total number of bikes?	42
STEP 6	Write the equation.	$f + z = 42$
STEP 7	Express the number of Zephyrs in stock by using the variable for the number of Falcons.	$z = 2f$
STEP 8	Substitute $2f$ for z in the equation.	$f + 2f = 42$
		$3f = 42$

METHOD 2

STEP 1	What needs to be found?	the number of Falcons in stock
STEP 2	Represent the number of Falcons in stock.	f
STEP 3	Express the number of Zephyrs in stock by using the variable for the number of Falcons.	$2f$
STEP 4	What expression represents the total number of bikes?	$f + 2f$
STEP 5	What value also represents the total number of bikes?	42
STEP 6	Write the equation.	$f + 2f = 42$
		$3f = 42$

Watch Out

Most problems that you need to turn into algebraic expressions or equations don't give you the variables. You need to decide them for yourself.

- Define the variable (the unknown quantity) in the problem.
- Choose a letter to represent it.
- You might use x or the first letter of the quantity.

SEARCH

To see step-by-step videos of these problems, enter the page number into the SWadvantage.com Search Bar.

Graphing Functions

What Came Before?
- Evaluating algebraic expressions
- Making scatter plots and displaying two sets of data

What's This About?
- Understanding functions, including the domain and range of a function
- Recognizing relations that are not functions
- Evaluating linear functions and graphing them on the coordinate plane

Practical Apps
- Sales analysts make and interpret line graphs to describe sales trends.
- Medical researchers use relations and functions to compare the effects of various treatments.

just for FUN!

When *y* attends an important function, she likes to dress up as *f(x)*.

You can find more practice problems online by visiting:
www.SWadvantage.com

Relations

What Is a Relation?

When customers place an order with the Nile Company, a shipping charge is calculated for each order. These are Theo's five most recent orders.

Order amount (x)	$12.85	$38.17	$9.98	$21.57	$18.00
	↓	↓	↓	↓	↓
Shipping charge (y)	$3.99	$0	$3.99	$5.97	$4.98

Each order amount has a shipping charge, which may be $0 or an amount greater than $0. So the order amounts and shipping charges are related.

The table below shows a relationship between two other sets of numbers.

x	−2	0	1	4	6
y	−7	3	6	3	5

You can write each pair of numbers as an **ordered pair** (x, y).

$(-2, -7), (0, 3), (1, 6), (4, 3), (6, 5)$

The x-value is called the **x-coordinate**. The y-value is called the **y-coordinate**. A set of ordered pairs is called a **relation**.

Domain and Range

The **domain** of a relation is the set of all the values of x. The **range** of a relation is the set of all the values of y.

Watch Out

When you identify the domain or range of a relation, write each value in the set only once. List the numbers in order of increasing value.

EXAMPLE 1

Identify the domain and range of each relation.

a.

x	1	2	3	4	5
y	7	6	5	4	3

Domain: {1, 2, 3, 4, 5}   Range: {3, 4, 5, 6, 7}

b.

x	−2	0	1	4	6
y	−7	3	6	3	5

Domain: {−2, 0, 1, 4, 6}   Range: {−7, 3, 5, 6}

Mapping Diagrams

You can use a mapping diagram to show a relation of ordered pairs. The first number in each ordered pair is the **input**. The second number is the **output**.

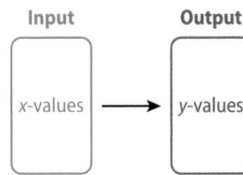

In a mapping diagram, each input points to its related output.

SEARCH

To see step-by-step videos of these problems, enter the page number into the SWadvantage.com Search Bar.

EXAMPLE 2

Show a mapping diagram for each relation. Then write the domain and range.

a. **(3, 5), (7, 12), (14, 9), (2, 17)**

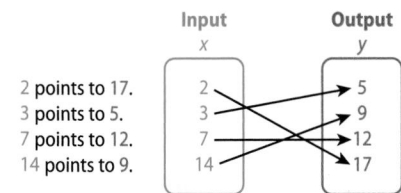

2 points to 17.
3 points to 5.
7 points to 12.
14 points to 9.

Domain: {2, 3, 7, 14}   Range: {5, 9, 12, 17}

b.

x	0	3	6	9
y	1	1	5	5

If a number is duplicated in the input or output, list it only once in the mapping diagram.

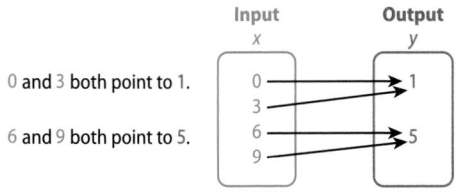

0 and 3 both point to 1.

6 and 9 both point to 5.

Domain: {0, 3, 6, 9}   Range: {1, 5}

Functions

Graphs of Relations

You can represent a relation by a set of ordered pairs, a table, a rule or algebraic expression, or a graph.

SEARCH

To see step-by-step videos of these problems, enter the page number into the SWadvantage.com Search Bar.

Look at the relation shown in the graph.

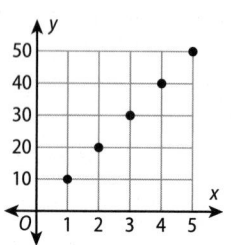

a. **What are the ordered pairs?**

(1, 10), (2, 20), (3, 30), (4, 40), (5, 50)

b. **What are the domain and range?**

Domain: {1, 2, 3, 4, 5}

Range: {10, 20, 30, 40, 50}

c. **What is a rule relating the variables?**

Each *y*-value is 10 times the corresponding *x*-value.

When the value of *y* depends on the value of *x*, *x* is the **independent variable** and *y* is the **dependent variable**.

A graph of a relation can include line segments. In that case, you cannot describe the domain or range by listing ordered pairs, but you can use inequality symbols.

EXAMPLE 2

What are the domain and range of the graph?

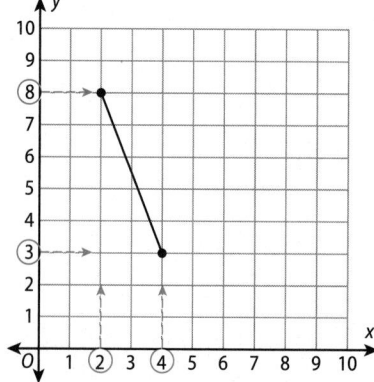

The domain is all *x*-values from 2 through 4.   Domain: $\{2 \leq x \leq 4\}$

The range is all *y*-values from 3 through 8.   Range: $\{3 \leq y \leq 8\}$

1438

Identifying Functions

Suppose you have a machine like the one below.

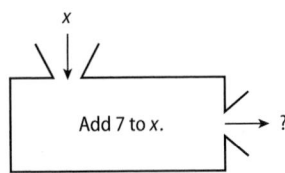

When you put a number, the input, into the machine, the machine adds 7 to the number. The output from the machine is the sum of your number and 7. If you put in 5, the output is 12. If you put in 100, the output is 107.

If you input 5, the only possible output is 12. Because any given input can have only one possible output, we call this a *function machine*.

A **function** is a relation that assigns each input *exactly one* output.

 **EXAMPLE 3**

Is *y* a function of *x*?

a. (2, 5), (4, 9), (7, 10), (4, 11)

No, when the input is $x = 4$, there are 2 different possible *y*-values.

b. (2, 1), (5, 1), (8, 7), (10, 12)

Yes, there are no *x*-values that are paired with two different *y*-values.

> **Watch Out !**
> It's still a function if different inputs generate the same output, such as (2, 1) and (5, 1).

EXAMPLE 4

Does each mapping diagram show a function?

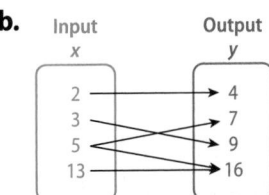

a.

No input has more than one output. The relation is a function.

b.

The input 5 has more than one output value, 7 and 16.

The relation is *not* a function.

Determining if a Relation is a Function

SEARCH

To see step-by-step videos of these problems, enter the page number into the SWadvantage.com Search Bar.

EXAMPLE 5

What are the domain and range of each relation? Is the relation a function?

a.

Diamond Prices

Weight (carats)	$\frac{3}{4}$	1	$1\frac{1}{4}$	$1\frac{1}{2}$	$1\frac{1}{2}$
Price ($)	3,500	6,500	6,800	7,500	7,500

The domain is $\left\{\frac{3}{4}, 1, 1\frac{1}{4}, 1\frac{1}{2}\right\}$. The range is {3,500, 6,500, 6,800, 7,500}.

Even though the last two columns are the same, each domain value is paired with exactly one range value. The relation is a function.

b.

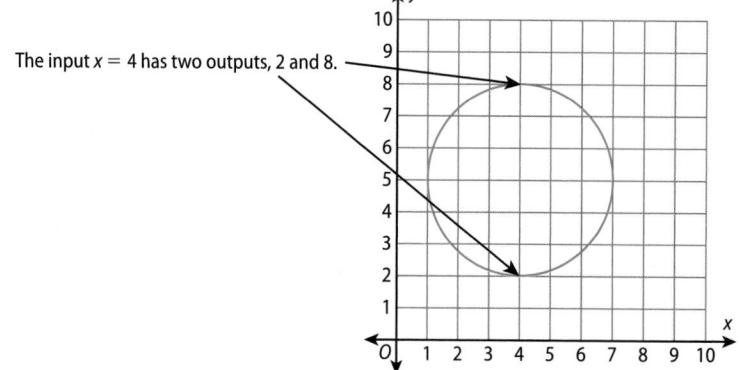

The input $x = 4$ has two outputs, 2 and 8.

Each value of x between 1 and 7 is associated with 2 y-values. This relation is *not* a function.

When the domain of a relation has an infinite number of values, you can still make a table of values to see whether you can prove that the relation is not a function.

Try It This Way

To square a negative number like -2 on a scientific calculator, first press the $(-)$ key. Then type the number.

-2

Then, press the x^2 key.

4

EXAMPLE 6

Examine the table for the relation $y^2 = x$. Is y a function of x?

When the value of x is 4, y has two values, -2 and 2.

Also, when the value of x is 1, y has two values, -1 and 1.

Either one of these conditions is proof that the relation is *not* a function.

x	y
$(-2)^2 = 4$	-2
$(-1)^2 = 1$	-1
$0^2 = 0$	0
$1^2 = 1$	1
$2^2 = 4$	2

EXAMPLE 7

If _y_ is a function of _x_, and the domain is {0, 3, 5, 8}, what value of _x_ must be shown in the red box?

If the choice is 0, when $x = 0$, there will be two _y_-values, 2 and 4.

If the choice is 5, when $x = 5$, there will be only one _y_-value, 4. ✔

If the choice is 3, when $x = 3$, there will be two _y_-values, 6 and 4.

If the choice is 8, when $x = 8$, there will be two _y_-values, 4 and 10.

A function can have only one _y_-value for each _x_-value.

So the only possible value in the red box is 5 if _y_ is a function of _x_.

x	y
0	2
5	4
3	6
	4
8	10

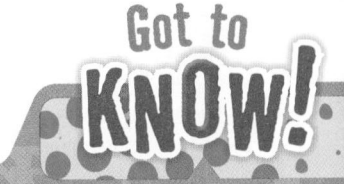

When a Relation is Not a Function

To determine whether or not a relation is a function, look for an input that has at least two different outputs. That shows the relation is *not* a function.

In a set of ordered pairs (_x_, _y_), look for the same value of _x_ with two different _y_-values.	{(10, 3), (10, 7), …}
In a mapping diagram, look for two arrows from an input that go to two different numbers in the output.	Input → Output: 5 → 4, 5 → 7
In a table of ordered pairs (_x_, _y_), look for the same _x_-value with two different _y_-values.	x: 14, 14 / y: 7, 21
In a graph, look for two points, one above the other, with the same _x_-value but two different _y_-values.	(graph with points at x = 2, y = 3 and y = 1)

The Coordinate Plane

How Can You Use the Coordinate Plane?

Many cities and towns are set up as a grid of numbered streets and avenues.

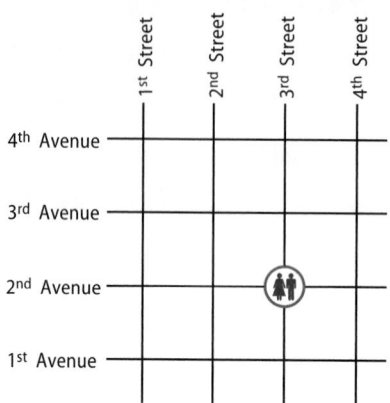

Need More

HELP

For help in understanding ordered pairs, go to *Relations* on pages 1436–1437.

If you ask a friend to meet you at the intersection shown on the map, you might say, "Meet me at the corner of 2nd Avenue and 3rd Street."

The coordinate plane is like a city map. You can use it to visualize points that represent two related variables. The **coordinate plane** is formed by two number lines that intersect at right angles. The horizontal line is the **x-axis** and the vertical line is the **y-axis**. The point where the two axes intersect is called the **origin**.

Every point on the coordinate grid is identified by an *ordered pair* (x, y).

x-coordinate ⟶
The number of units to the right from the origin

(2, 4)

⟵ **y-coordinate**
The number of units up from the origin

Finding Coordinates

To determine the location of a point on the graph, move down from the point to read the x-coordinate first. Then move left from the point to read the y-coordinate.

EXAMPLE 1

SEARCH

To see step-by-step videos of these problems, enter the page number into the SWadvantage.com Search Bar.

Find the coordinates of each point on the graph.

A is located at $(2, 1)$.

B is located at $(0, 6)$.

C is located at the origin $(0, 0)$.

D is located at $(4, 0)$.

E is located at $(7, 8)$.

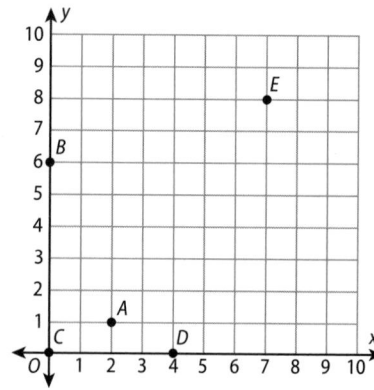

1442

Plotting Points

To plot a point (x, y) on the graph, follow these steps.

- Start at the origin.
- Move right x units.
- Then move up y units.
- Plot and label the point.

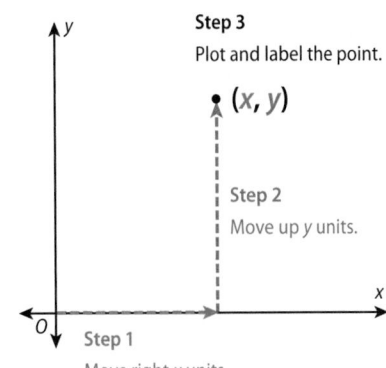

Step 3
Plot and label the point.

(x, y)

Step 2
Move up y units.

Step 1
Move right x units.

 EXAMPLE 2

Plot each point on the coordinate plane.

a. *F* at **(2, 5)**

Move right 2 units. Then move up 5 units. Label the point *F*.

b. *G* at **(8, 6)**

Move right 8 units. Then move up 6 units. Label the point *G*.

c. *H* at **(0, 2)**

Move right 0 units. Then move up 2 units. Label the point *H*.

EXAMPLE 3

The graph shows the average speed and distance traveled by 9 different cars. Which point represents a car averaging 68 miles per hour for 55 miles?

Distance is the x-variable and average speed is the y-variable.

So look for the point (55, 68).

The point *F* represents a car averaging 68 miles per hour for 55 miles.

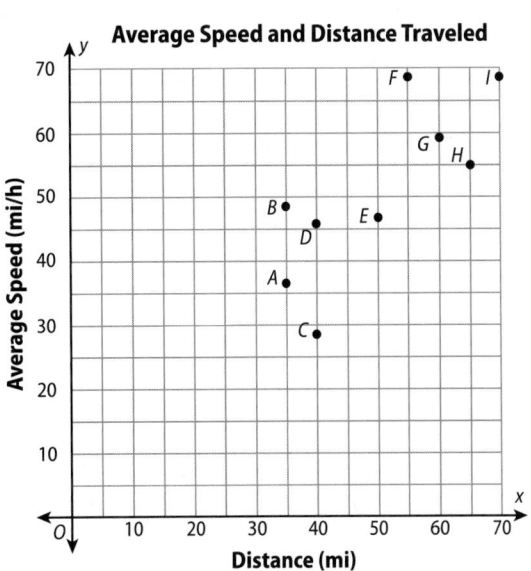

Average Speed and Distance Traveled

Different Ways to Represent a Function

You can represent a function as a set of ordered pairs, as a vertical or horizontal table of values, or as a graph.

SEARCH

To see step-by-step videos of these problems, enter the page number into the SWadvantage.com Search Bar.

EXAMPLE 4

Graph each set of data.

a.

x	y
1	3
3	5
5	7
7	9

Plot the point (1, 3).
Plot the point (3, 5).
Plot the point (5, 7).
Plot the point (7, 9).

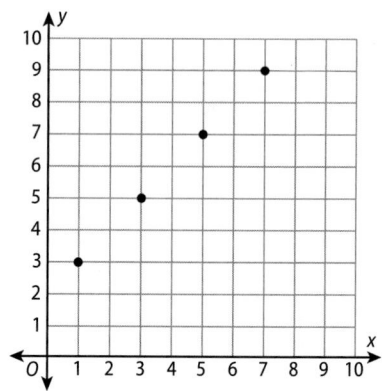

Need More

HELP ?

For help with scales of graphs, go to *Scatter Plots* in *Statistics and Probability* (p. 1264).

b.

x	5	10	15	20
y	22	8	11	6

STEP 1 First choose a scale for each axis. The *x*-axis must include values up to 20 to fit the data. The *y*-axis must include values up to 22.

A good choice is for both axes to go to 25 with intervals of 5.

STEP 2 Plot each ordered pair. The ordered pairs are (5, 22), (10, 8), (15, 11), and (20, 6).

If a *y*-value does not fall on a grid line, estimate its position.

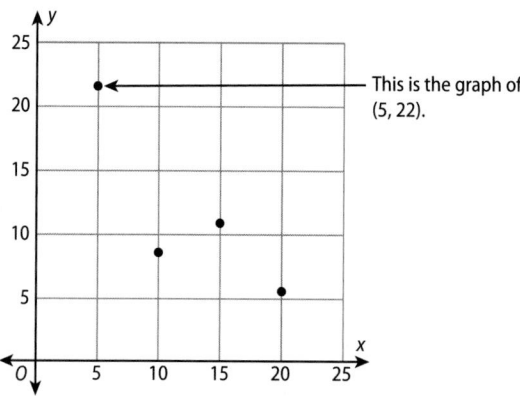

This is the graph of (5, 22).

Functions can use variables other than *x* and *y*.

EXAMPLE 5

The height of a kicked football is a function of time. The height *h* in feet of a football after *t* seconds is given in the table below. Graph each ordered pair of values.

Time (s) *t*	0	0.5	1	1.5	2	2.5	3	3.5	4
Height (ft) *h*	1	29	49	61	65	61	49	29	1

The height of the football is a function of the time elapsed since it was kicked. Time is the independent variable, and height is the dependent variable. So show the time *t* on the horizontal axis and the height *h* on the vertical axis. Each point on the graph will represent an ordered pair (*t*, *h*).

Be sure the graph fits all the data. The *t*-axis must show 0–4 seconds. The *h*-axis must show 0–65 feet.

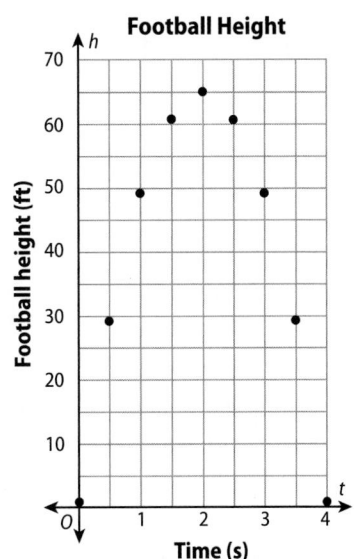

Try It
This Way

If you have access to a graphing calculator, try its point graphing function. Use **STAT** and EDIT to enter values of *x* and *y* into lists 1 and 2. Then use the STAT PLOT function to display them.

Reading and Plotting Points

To read a point (*x*, *y*) on the coordinate plane, read the *x*-value on the *x*-axis and the *y*-value on the *y*-axis.

To plot a point (*x*, *y*), on the coordinate plane, move *x* units right. Then move *y* units up. Plot and label the point.

Interpreting Line Graphs

Reading a Line Graph

A **line graph** is a data display that shows points connected by line segments. Line graphs are often used to display data that change over time.

EXAMPLE 1

Answer each question below. Support your answer with data from the line graph.

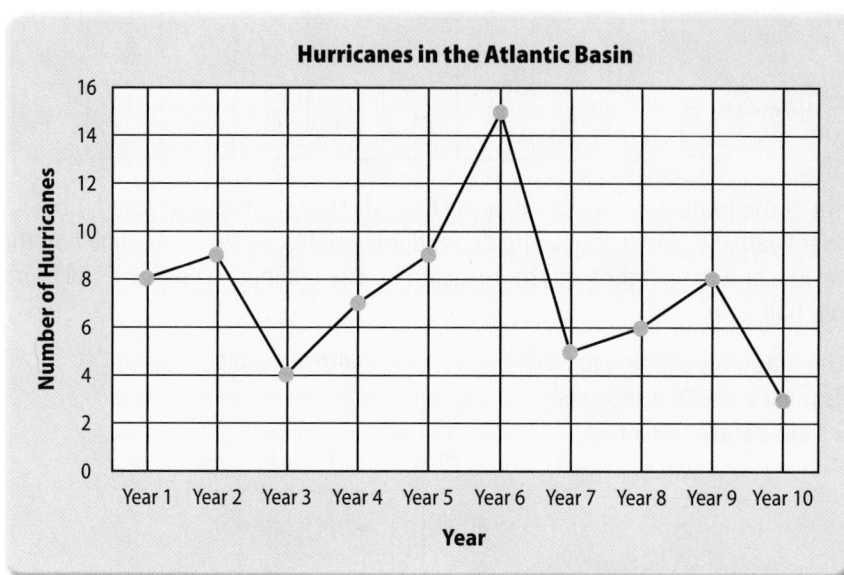

Hurricanes in the Atlantic Basin

a. Which year had the least number of hurricanes? Which year had the greatest number?

Look for the lowest point and the highest point. The least number was 3 in Year 10. The greatest number was 15 in Year 6.

b. What years had the same number of hurricanes?

Look for points on the same horizontal line. There were 8 hurricanes in both Year 1 and Year 9. There were 9 hurricanes in both Year 2 and Year 5.

c. Between which two consecutive years did the number of hurricanes increase the most?

Look for the steepest line segment rising from left to right. There were 9 hurricanes in Year 5 and 15 in Year 6, an increase of 6.

d. Between which two consecutive years did the number of hurricanes change the most?

Look for the steepest line segment. There were 15 hurricanes in Year 6 and 5 in Year 7, a decrease of 10.

e. How many hurricanes were there during the period represented by the line graph? What was the average number of hurricanes per year?

To find the total number of hurricanes, add the values represented by the points. There were a total of $8 + 9 + 4 + 7 + 9 + 15 + 5 + 6 + 8 + 3 = 74$ hurricanes during the 10-year period.

To find the average, divide the total by 10. The average number of hurricanes was $\frac{74}{10} = 7.4$.

Spotting Trends and Making Predictions

When the data in a line graph show a trend, such as a steady increase or decrease over time, you can use the graph to make predictions.

SEARCH 🔍

To see step-by-step videos of these problems, enter the page number into the SWadvantage.com Search Bar.

EXAMPLE 2

Answer each question below. Support your answer with data from the line graph.

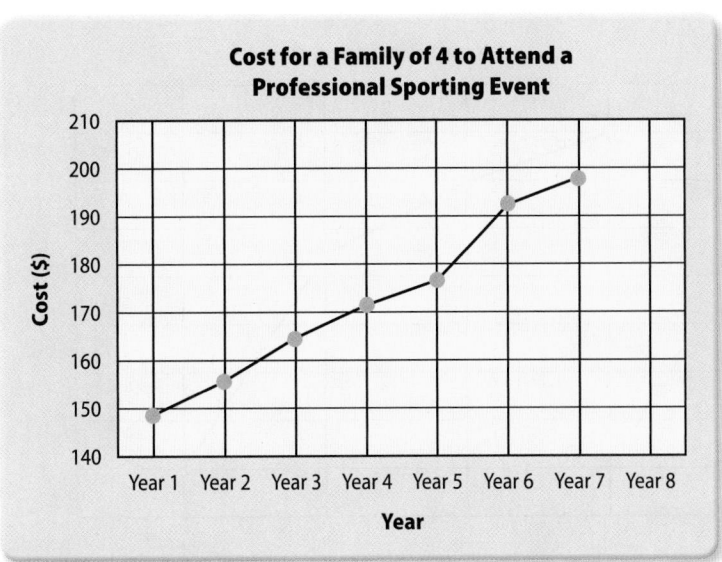

a. About how much was the cost in Year 6? in Year 7?

The cost in Year 6 was about $192.
The cost in Year 7 was about $197.

b. If the cost increased by about the same amount in Year 8, what was the cost in Year 8?

The cost in Year 7 was about $197, an increase of $5 from $192, the cost in Year 6.

So the cost in Year 8 would have been about $197 + $5 = $202.

c. About how much was the cost in Year 5?

The cost in Year 5 was about $177.

d. How much did the cost increase from Year 5 to Year 6?

The cost in Year 6 was about $192, an increase of $15 from $177 in Year 5.

e. If the cost increased by that amount from Year 7 to Year 8, what would the cost have been in Year 8?

The cost in Year 6 was $192, an increase of $15 from $177, the cost in Year 5.

So the cost in Year 8 would have been $15 more than the cost in Year 7; $197 + $15 = $212.

Misleading Line Graphs

When you interpret data from a line graph, examine the graph to see if the data display is misleading. Be sure that the scales of the graph use equal intervals.

EXAMPLE 3

Is the graph misleading? Explain.

a.

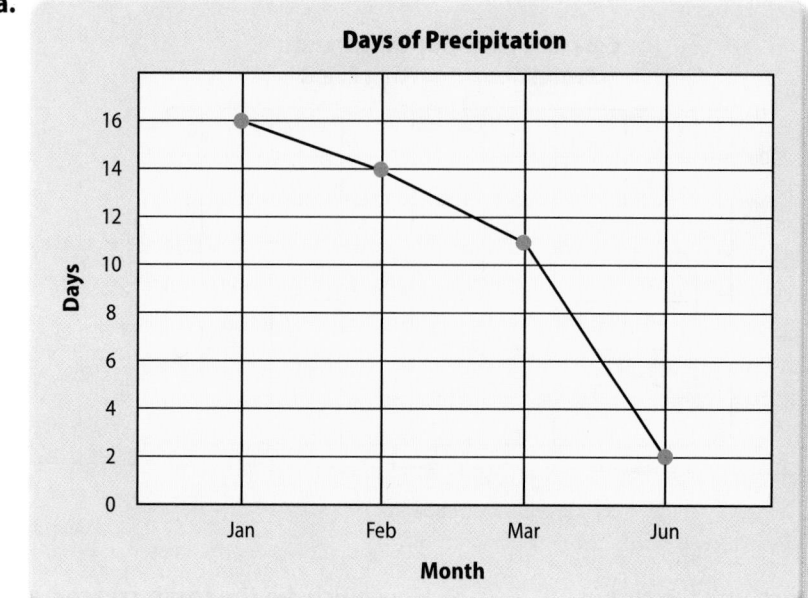

Yes; the scale of the horizontal axis must use equal intervals. The scale shows consecutive months January, February, and March, but then jumps to June.

b.

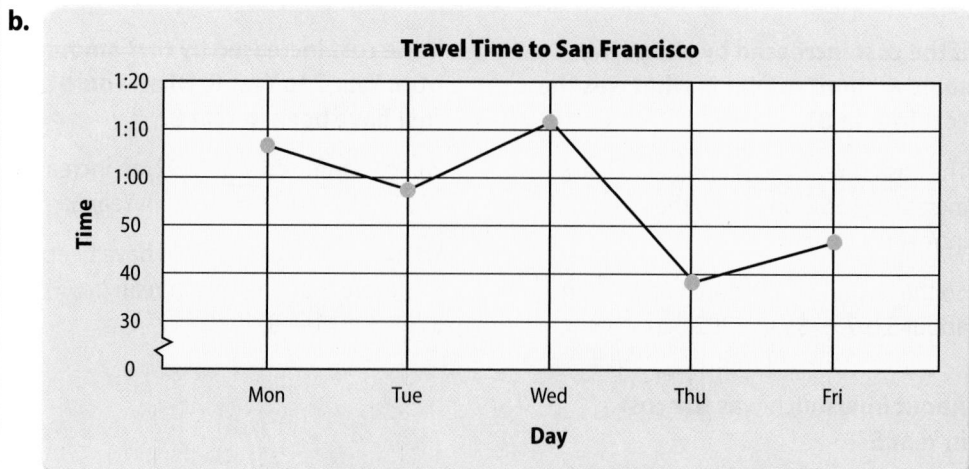

No; the scale of the vertical axis shows the times in minutes, and then changes to hours and minutes from 1:00 to 1:20. But the interval is consistently 10 minutes. The same scale could be written entirely in minutes as 50, 60, 70, 80.

Need More HELP

For help with misleading data displays, go to *Misleading Statistics, Misleading Graphs* in *Statistics and Probability* (p. 1306).

For help with multiple-line graphs, go to *Displaying Two Data Sets* in *Statistics and Probability* (p. 1284).

SEARCH

To see step-by-step videos of these problems, enter the page number into the SWadvantage.com Search Bar.

Multiple-Line Graphs

A line graph can show more than one set of data. You can analyze each data set individually. You can also compare two or more of the data sets on the graph.

EXAMPLE 4

Answer each question below. Support your answer with data from the graph.

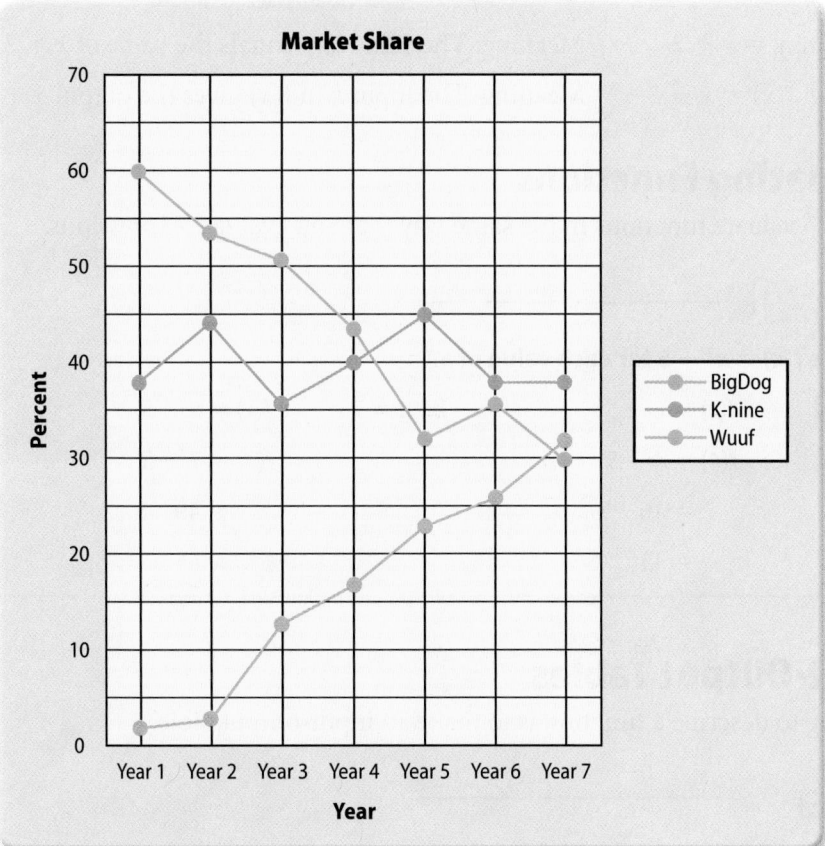

Try It This Way

You can use a spreadsheet to make a line graph. Type your data into a row or column. In Excel, select the data and click Chart. Then use the XY (Scatter) option and select the type with points and connecting lines.

Once you have a line graph, you can change the scales and labels.

a. In what year did BigDog's market share drop below 50%?

BigDog's market share was about 51% in Year 3 and about 43% in Year 4, so it dropped below 50% in Year 4.

b. Which company's market share increased the most from one year to the next?

Wuuf's market share was about 3% in Year 2 and about 13% in Year 3, an increase of 10%. This was the greatest increase from one year to the next.

c. Which company's market share stayed the same from one year to the next?

Look for the horizontal line. K-nine's market share was about 37% in both Year 6 and Year 7.

Got to KNOW!

Analyzing Line Graphs

- Look for trends so that you can make predictions.
- Think about whether the data include the line segments between the points.
- Watch out for scales that make the graph misleading.

Linear Functions

Function Notation

Functions have their own notation. In **function notation**, the output value for the input x is written as $f(x)$ and read as "f of x." The notation $f(x) =$ means "the rule applied to x is."

Input	Rule	Output
x	$\longrightarrow$	**f(x)**

Equation: $y = x + 2$ Meaning: The value of y equals the value of $x + 2$.

Function $f(x) = x + 2$ Meaning: The input x in $f(x)$ gives the output $x + 2$.

Evaluating Functions

You can evaluate functions in the same way that you evaluate expressions.

EXAMPLE 1

Evaluate $f(x) = x^2 - 5$ for each value of x.

a. $x = 4$
$$f(x) = x^2 - 5$$
$$f(4) = 4^2 - 5$$
$$= 16 - 5$$
$$= 11$$

b. $x = 7$
$$f(x) = x^2 - 5$$
$$f(7) = 7^2 - 5$$
$$= 49 - 5$$
$$= 44$$

Input-Output Tables

One way to describe a function is to make an input-output table.

Got to KNOW!

Function Rules

Functions are often written as equations.

The statement $y = f(x)$ means that y is a function of x.

So the function
$$f(x) = x^2 - 5$$
can also be written as
$$y = x^2 - 5.$$

EXAMPLE 2

Make an input-output table for the function $f(x) = 2x - 5$.

Select values for x. Then evaluate $f(x)$.

Follow the rule: Multiply the input by 2 and then subtract 5.

When $x = 1$, $f(1) = 2(1) - 5$
$$= 2 - 5$$
$$= -3$$

Input x	Rule $2x - 5$	Output $f(x)$
1	2(1) − 5	−3
2	2(2) − 5	−1
3	2(3) − 5	1
4	2(4) − 5	3
5	2(5) − 5	5

Graphing Functions

Often a function has a domain that is *continuous*. This type of function cannot be described by a set of ordered pairs because the domain is infinite.

A graph for this type of function is usually a line or curve. To graph a continuous function, plot the ordered pairs. Then connect the points by a line or smooth curve.

EXAMPLE 3

Graph the function $y = 2x^2$ for $x \geq 0$.

STEP 1 Make an input-output table.

When $x = 0$, $y = 2(0)^2 = 0$
When $x = 1$, $y = 2(1)^2 = 2$
When $x = 2$, $y = 2(2)^2 = 8$

x	0	1	2	3	4
y	0	2	8	18	32

STEP 2 Plot the points as ordered pairs.   **STEP 3** Connect the points with a smooth curve.

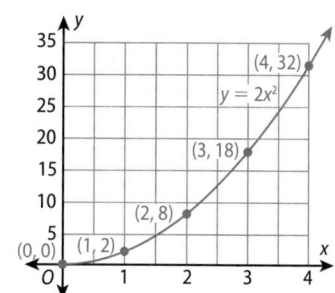

SEARCH

To see step-by-step videos of these problems, enter the page number into the SWadvantage.com Search Bar.

Linear Functions

A **linear function** is any function with a graph that is a straight line.

EXAMPLE 4

Graph the function $y = 5x$ for $x \geq 0$. Is the function linear?

STEP 1 Make an input-output table.

x	0	1	2	3	4
y	0	5	10	15	20

STEP 2 Plot the points as ordered pairs.   **STEP 3** Connect the points.

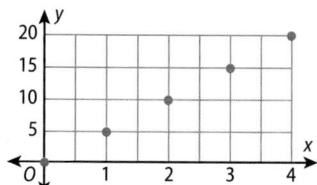   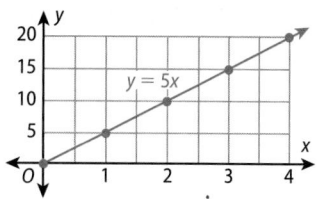

The graph is a straight line, so the function is linear.

Using Patterns to Graph

Sometimes a problem relates two sets of numbers that follow a pattern. You can graph these relationships to determine whether they are linear functions.

SEARCH

To see step-by-step videos of these problems, enter the page number into the SWadvantage.com Search Bar.

EXAMPLE 5

The diagram shows the number of chairs that fit around a row of *x* tables. Graph the number of chairs *y* as a function of the number of tables *x*. Is the function linear?

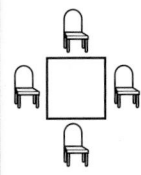 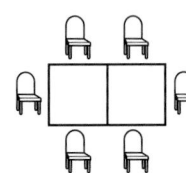 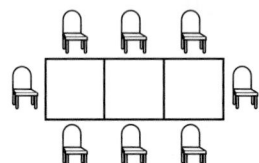 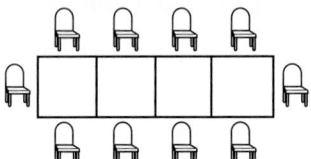

METHOD 1

Make an Input-Output Table

STEP 1 Make an input-output table with the number of tables as the input *x* and the number of chairs as the output *y*.

When $x = 1$, $y = 4$.
When $x = 2$, $y = 6$.
When $x = 3$, $y = 8$.
When $x = 4$, $y = 10$.

Tables *x*	1	2	3	4
Chairs *y*	4	6	8	10

STEP 2 Plot the points as ordered pairs.

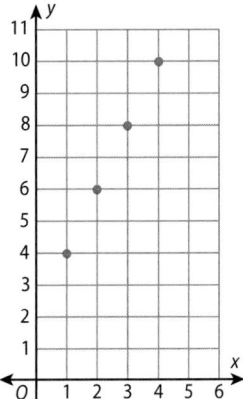

STEP 3 Connect the points.

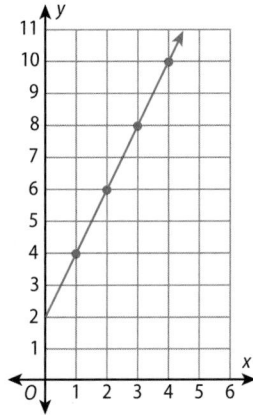

The graph of the function is a straight line, so the pattern is linear. By extending the line, you can see how many chairs are needed for each additional table.

METHOD 2

Look for a Pattern

STEP 1 Notice that the first table is surrounded by 4 chairs. Plot the point (1, 4).

STEP 2 When each additional table is added, 2 more chairs are added. Move to the right on the graph 1 unit, and move up 2 units. Plot another point at (2, 6).

STEP 3 Continue moving right 1 and up 2 from each point, and plot another point.

STEP 4 Connect the points. The graph of the function is a straight line, so the pattern is linear.

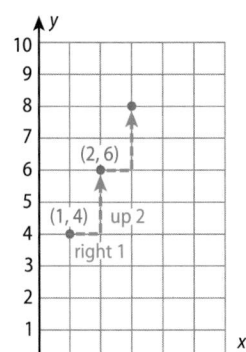

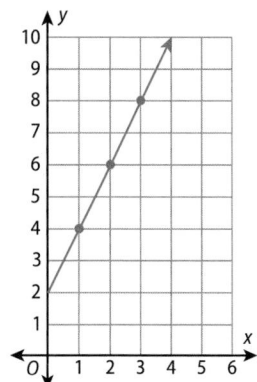

Need More

HELP ?

For help with graphing, go to *Graphing from an Equation* in *Algebra* (p. 1528).

Identifying Linear Functions

Linear functions are in the form $y = ax + b$, where a and b are real numbers.

These are linear functions.

$y = 3x$ $a = 3$ and $b = 0$
$y = -2x + 7$ $a = -2$ and $b = 7$

These are *not* linear functions.

$y = x^2$ $y = \sqrt{x}$
$y = 10^x + 5$

EXAMPLE 6

Is the function $y = 28$ linear?

Yes, the function is in the form $y = ax + b$, where $a = 0$ and $b = 28$. The graph of this function is a horizontal line at $y = 28$.

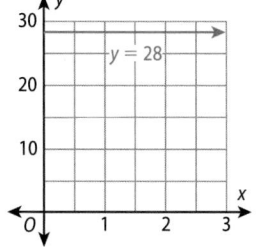

Got to KNOW!

Linear Functions

To graph a function, make an input-output table to find ordered pairs. Use at least two input values.

A linear function is any function with a graph that is a straight line.

Linear functions can be written in the form $y = ax + b$, where a and b are real numbers.

The Vertical Line Test

How Can You Use the Vertical Line Test?

Because a function has exactly one output for any input, you can use the vertical line test to decide whether a graph represents a function.

- If any vertical line can intersect the graph at more than one point, the graph does *not* represent a function.

- If no vertical line can intersect the graph at more than one point, the graph does represent a function.

Ways to REMEMBER

In basketball, it is illegal to jump with the ball and then not shoot it or pass it. This violation is called *up and down*. Remember, a graph does not represent a function if there are points "up and down."

EXAMPLE 1

Tell whether or not the graph represents a function.

Use the vertical line test.

a.
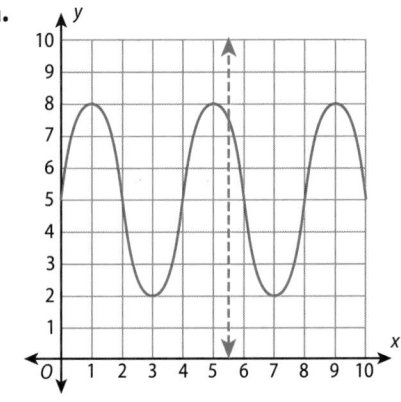

No vertical line can cross the graph at more than one point. This graph does represent a function.

b.
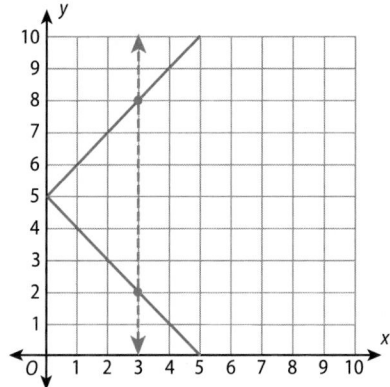

The vertical line crosses the graph at more than one point. This graph does *not* represent a function.

SEARCH

To see step-by-step videos of these problems, enter the page number into the SWadvantage.com Search Bar.

EXAMPLE 2

The graph shows the amount of water in a dog's bowl during 24 hours. Does the graph represent a function?

No vertical line can cross the graph at more than one point.

The graph does represent a function.

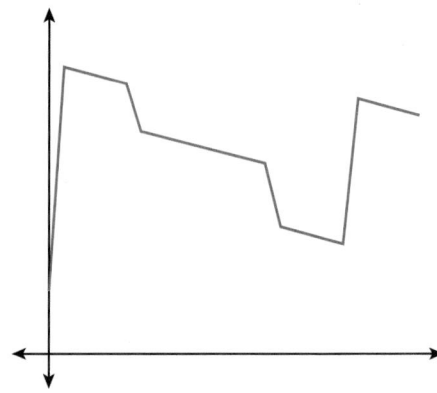

Show whether or not each relation is a function.

a. $y = 4$ **b.** $x = 7$

STEP 1 Make a table. Then use the table to make a graph.

a. Rule: For any value of x, $y = 4$.   **b.** Rule: For any value of y, $x = 7$.

x	1	2	3	4
y	4	4	4	4

x	7	7	7	7
y	1	2	3	4

STEP 2 Use the vertical line test.

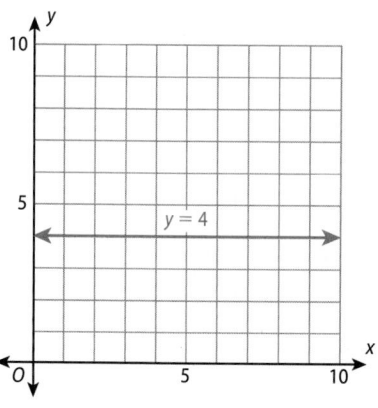

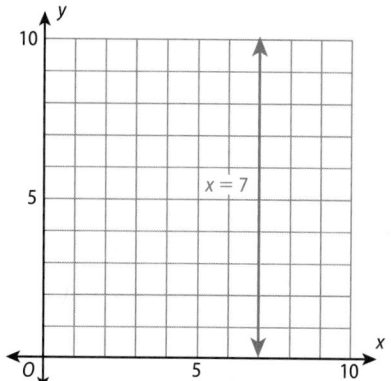

A vertical line cannot cross the graph at more than one point. The graph of $y = 4$ represents a function.

The graph is a vertical line. The graph of $x = 7$ does *not* represent a function.

An open circle at a point on a graph is *not* part of the graph. The graph on the left below does not represent a function because a vertical line can intersect both points shown. The graph on the right does represent a function because the upper segment does not contain the point at the open circle. So a vertical line cannot cross the graph at more than one point.

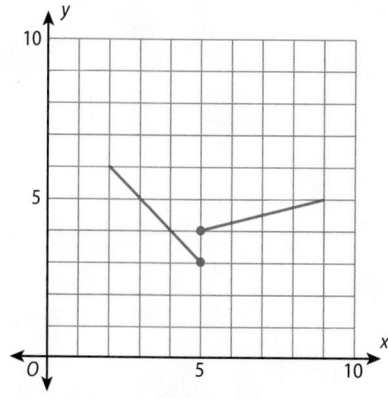

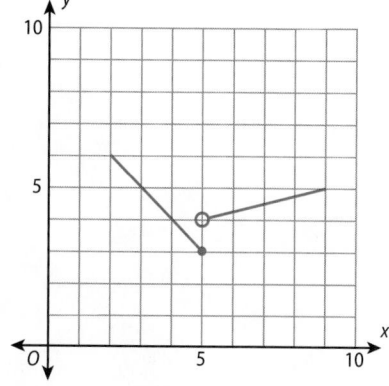

Got to KNOW!

The Vertical Line Test

If any vertical line intersects the graph at more than one point, the graph does not represent a function.

If no vertical line can intersect the graph at more than one point, the graph does represent a function.

One-Variable Linear Equations

What Came Before?
- Operations with integers, decimals, and fractions
- Evaluating variable expressions

What's This About?
- Solving one-step and two-step equations by using inverse operations
- Solving equations with fractions, decimals, and absolute value
- Using a six-step process to solve problems by writing equations

Practical Apps
- Inventory specialists use linear equations to determine the total value of the amount of product in a warehouse.
- Veterinarians use linear relationships to determine dosages of medicines for animals of different weights.

Just for FUN!

Q: Why is the equation so stuck up?

A: It considers itself an *x*-pert.

| CONTENTS | UPLOAD | DOWNLOAD | *Algebra* |

Topics	Vocabulary	Pages
Equation Concepts	*equation* *solve an equation*	1458–1459
Addition and Subtraction Equations	*inverse operations*	1460–1461
Multiplication and Division Equations		1462–1463
Two-Step Equations		1464–1467
Multi-Step Equations		1468–1471
Equations with Fractions		1472–1475
Equations with Decimals		1476–1479
Absolute-Value Equations		1480–1483
No Solution or Many Solutions		1484–1485
Solving Word Problems with Equations		1486–1489

You can find more practice problems online by visiting:
www.SWadvantage.com

Equation Concepts

True and False Equations

An **equation** is a mathematical statement that uses the symbol for equality, =, to state that two quantities are equal. An equation may be true or false.

True Equations

$2 + 2 = 4$ $\qquad$ $5(4) + 1 = 21$

False Equations

$1 + 1 = 3$ $\qquad$ $25 \div 4 = 10$

If two quantities are *not* equal, use the symbol ≠, which means "is not equal to," to make a true statement.

$$1 + 1 \neq 3 \qquad 25 \div 4 \neq 10$$

SEARCH

To see step-by-step videos of these problems, enter the page number into the SWadvantage.com Search Bar.

EXAMPLE 1

Place the correct symbol, = or ≠, in the box to make the statement true.

a. $3 + 3(7) \,\square\, 6(2 + 2)$

Simplify each expression.	$3 + 3(7) \,\square\, 6(2 + 2)$
Use order of operations.	$3 + 21 \,\square\, 6(4)$
The expressions are equal.	$24 \,\boxed{=}\, 24$

$3 + 3(7) = 6(2 + 2)$

b. $59 - \left(-\frac{27}{3}\right) \,\square\, 2(3^2 + 4^2)$

Simplify each expression.	$59 - \left(-\frac{27}{3}\right) \,\square\, 2(3^2 + 4^2)$
Use order of operations.	$59 - (-9) \,\square\, 2(9 + 16)$
	$68 \,\square\, 2(25)$
The expressions are *not* equal.	$68 \,\boxed{\neq}\, 50$

$59 - \left(-\frac{27}{3}\right) \neq 2(3^2 + 4^2)$

Solving Equations

To **solve an equation** for an unknown quantity, find the missing value that makes the equation true. There are different ways to represent the missing value in an equation. You can use a question mark, an empty box, or a variable.

$$2 + \underline{\ ?\ } = 5$$
$$2 + \square = 5$$
$$2 + x = 5$$

EXAMPLE 2

Solve each equation for the missing value.

a. 7 + ? = 10

$7 + 3 = 10$

3 makes the equation true.

b. 10(4) = ☐

$10(4) = 40$

40 makes the equation true.

c. x − 100 = 300

$400 - 100 = 300$

400 makes the equation true.

Using Guess-Check-Revise to Solve

Sometimes you can solve an equation by using the Guess-Check-Revise strategy.

EXAMPLE 3

The width of a room is 156 inches. After Tia covers the floor with as many 9-inch tiles as possible, a section of the floor that is 3 inches wide is left uncovered. How many tiles fit along the wall that measures 156 inches?

STEP 1 Write an equation to represent the problem. Let *t* equal the unknown number of tiles.

9 times the number of tiles plus 3 in. equals 156 in.
$$9(t) + 3 = 156$$

STEP 2 Guess a value for *t*. Try 20. $9(20) + 3 \overset{?}{=} 156$
Too high $183 \neq 156$

STEP 3 Adjust the guess down from 20. ↓
Try 15. $9(15) + 3 \overset{?}{=} 156$
Too low $138 \neq 156$

STEP 4 Adjust the guess up from 15. ↑
Try 17. $9(17) + 3 \overset{?}{=} 156$
Got it! $156 = 156$ ✔

A total of 17 of the 9-inch tiles fit along the wall.

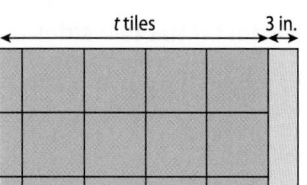

t tiles   3 in.

156 in.

Watch Out !

To solve an equation, find the value that makes the equation true. The Guess-Check-Revise strategy may not work unless the answer is a simple value, such as a small whole number.

To learn more, see other solving methods in the following pages.

Need More

HELP ?

The symbol $\overset{?}{=}$ means "does it equal?"

Isolating the Variable

To solve an equation, you must work to have the variable alone on one side of the equality symbol. This is called *isolating the variable*.

The algebra tiles at the right represent the equation $x + 3 = 5$.

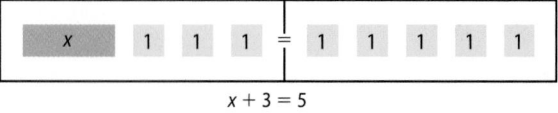

$$x + 3 = 5$$

Subtract 3 from both sides of the equation to isolate the variable.

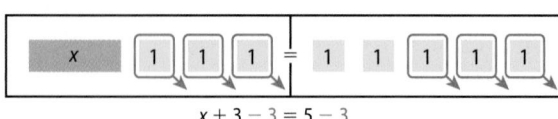

$$x + 3 - 3 = 5 - 3$$

The solution to $x + 3 = 5$ is $x = 2$.

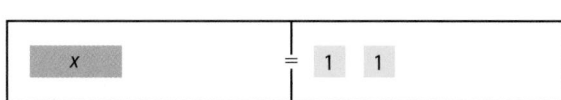

Inverse Operations

Recall that the Additive Inverse Property says that, for any real number a, there is exactly one additive inverse $-a$ for which the equations below are true.

$$a + (-a) = 0 \qquad \text{and} \qquad -a + a = 0$$

Addition and subtraction are called **inverse operations**. To reverse addition, subtract. To reverse subtraction, add.

Need More
HELP ?

For more review of inverse properties, go to *The Identity and Inverse Properties* on page 1414.

EXAMPLE 1

Use inverse operations to solve the equation $x - 16 = 21$. To check your answer, replace the variable in the original equation with the value you found. Your answer is correct if the two sides of the equation are equal.

STEP 1 Solve for x by isolating the variable.

$$x - 16 = 21$$

Because 16 is <u>subtracted</u> from x, <u>add</u> 16 to both sides.

$$x - 16 + 16 = 21 + 16$$

Use the Additive Inverse Property.

$$x + 0 = 21 + 16$$

Simplify both sides of the equation.

$$x = 37$$

STEP 2 Check the solution.

$$x - 16 = 21$$

Substitute 37 for x in the original equation.

$$37 - 16 \overset{?}{=} 21$$

Subtract.

$$21 = 21 \checkmark$$

The solution $x = 37$ is correct.

EXAMPLE 2

Solve the equation $-7 = 13 + m$. Check your answer.

STEP 1 Solve for m by isolating the variable.

Because 13 is <u>added</u> to m, <u>subtract</u> 13 from both sides.

Use the Commutative Property of Addition.

Use the Additive Inverse Property.

Simplify both sides of the equation.

$$-7 = 13 + m$$
$$-7 - 13 = 13 + m - 13$$
$$-7 - 13 = m + \underbrace{13 - 13}$$
$$-7 - 13 = m + \quad 0$$
$$-20 = m$$

STEP 2 Check the solution.

$$-7 = 13 + m$$

Substitute -20 for m in the original equation. $-7 \overset{?}{=} 13 + (-20)$

Subtract. $-7 = -7$ ✔

The solution $m = -20$ is correct.

Watch Out !

The end of the example shows $-7 = -7$, but -7 is *not* the solution of the equation. It is the value of each side of the equation when -20 is substituted for m in the equation.

In Example 2, the variable is added to a number in the original equation. If the variable is subtracted from a number, you can use one of two methods to solve.

EXAMPLE 3

Julio is on a basketball team. When the number of minutes, n, Julio played in a game is subtracted from 48, the result is 33. How many minutes did he play?

Write an equation to represent the problem. $48 - n = 33$

METHOD 1

Subtract 48 from both sides.	$48 - n - 48 = 33 - 48$
Use the Commutative Property of Addition.	$48 - 48 - n = 33 - 48$
Use the Additive Inverse Property.	$0 - n = 33 - 48$
Simplify.	$-n = -15$
If the opposite of n is -15, then n is 15.	$n = 15$

METHOD 2

Add n to both sides.	$48 - n + n = 33 + n$
Use the Additive Inverse Property.	$48 + 0 = 33 + n$
Subtract 33 from both sides.	$48 - 33 = 33 - 33 + n$
Simplify.	$15 = n$

Julio played for 15 minutes.

SEARCH

To see step-by-step videos of these problems, enter the page number into the SWadvantage.com Search Bar.

After solving an equation, remember to check your answer by substituting it for the variable in the original equation. Also be sure that your answer makes sense in the given problem situation.

Multiplication and Division Equations

Modeling Equations

SEARCH 🔍

To see step-by-step videos of these problems, enter the page number into the SWadvantage.com Search Bar.

The algebra tiles at the right represent the equation $3x = 12$.

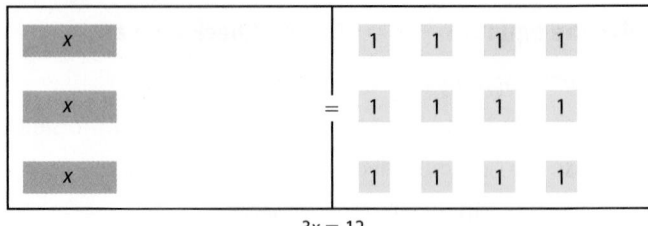

$3x = 12$

To solve the equation by isolating the variable, form 3 equal groups on each side.

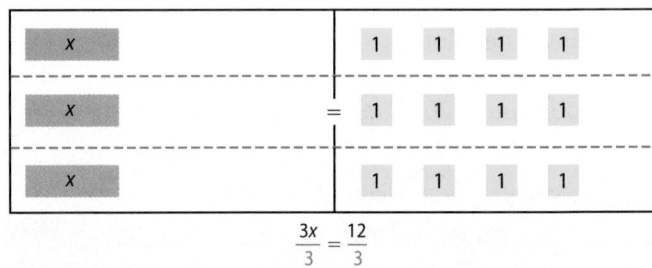

$$\frac{3x}{3} = \frac{12}{3}$$

Each x tile corresponds to a group of 4 +1 tiles. So the solution of $3x = 12$ is $x = 4$.

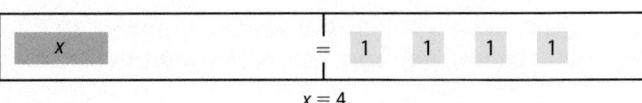

$x = 4$

Inverse Operations

Need More HELP ?

For more review of the inverse properties, go to *The Identity and Inverse Properties* on page 1414.

Recall that for any nonzero real number a, there is exactly one multiplicative inverse $\frac{1}{a}$, for which $a \cdot \frac{1}{a} = 1$ and $\frac{1}{a} \cdot a = 1$.

Multiplying by the reciprocal of a is the same as dividing by a. So to reverse multiplication, divide. To reverse division, multiply. Multiplication and division are inverse operations.

EXAMPLE 1

Use inverse operations to solve the equation $25x = 400$. To check your answer, substitute the value you find for the variable in the original equation.

STEP 1 Solve for x.

Because x is <u>multiplied</u> by 25, <u>divide</u> both sides by 25.

$$25x = 400$$

$$\frac{25x}{25} = \frac{400}{25}$$

Divide. Remember, $\frac{25}{25} = 1$.

$$\frac{\cancel{25}x}{\cancel{25}} = 16$$

Simplify.

$$1x = 16, \text{ so } x = 16$$

STEP 2 Check the solution.

Substitute 16 for x in the original equation. Multiply.

$$25(16) = 400$$
$$400 = 400 ✔$$

The solution is $x = 16$.

EXAMPLE 2

Use inverse operations to solve the equation $7 = \frac{k}{8}$. Check your answer.

STEP 1 Solve for k.

Because k is <u>divided</u> by 8, <u>multiply</u> both sides by 8.

$$7 = \frac{k}{8}$$

$$7(8) = \frac{k}{8}(8)$$

Multiply.

$$56 = \frac{8k}{8}$$

Simplify. Remember, $\frac{8}{8} = 1$.

$$56 = 1k$$

Identity Property of Multiplication

$$56 = k$$

STEP 2 Check the solution.

Substitute 56 for k in the original equation.

$$7 = \frac{56}{8}$$

Divide.

$$7 = 7 \checkmark$$

The solution is $k = 56$.

> **Watch Out !**
>
> Don't expect that an equation with division will always have a small number as an answer. Although the equation in Example 2 uses numbers that are less than 10, the solution is 56, which is much greater than 10.

EXAMPLE 3

The height of an access ramp, multiplied by 20, equals the length of the ramp. If the ramp has a length of 70 feet, what is the height?

Write an equation to represent the problem.
Let h = the height in feet.

$$20h = 70$$

Divide both sides by 20 to isolate the variable h.

$$\frac{20h}{20} = \frac{70}{20}$$

Divide. Remember, $\frac{20}{20} = 1$.

$$\frac{20h}{20} = 3.5$$

Simplify.

$$1h = 3.5, \text{ so } h = 3.5$$

The height of the ramp is 3.5 feet.

Properties of Equality

These properties apply if a, b, and c are real numbers and $a = b$.

Addition Property of Equality	$a + c = b + c$
Subtraction Property of Equality	$a - c = b - c$
Multiplication Property of Equality	$ac = bc$
Division Property of Equality	$\frac{a}{c} = \frac{b}{c} \ (c \neq 0)$

Two-Step Equations

How Can You Represent a Two-Step Equation?

When you solve an equation that has a single operation, you can use the inverse operation to solve. Some equations, such as $2x + 3 = 7$, contain more than one operation.

SEARCH

To see step-by-step videos of these problems, enter the page number into the SWadvantage.com Search Bar.

The algebra tiles below represent the equation $2x + 3 = 7$. The equation contains two operations, multiplication and addition.

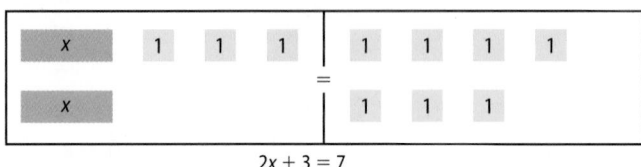

$$2x + 3 = 7$$

To begin to solve the equation, first remove 3 $\boxed{+1}$ tiles from each side to isolate the variable tiles on one side. *Subtract to reverse addition.*

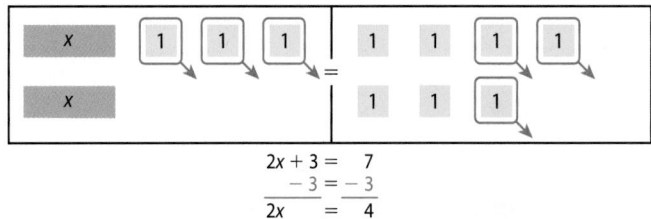

$$
\begin{array}{rcr}
2x + 3 &=& 7 \\
-3 &=& -3 \\
\hline
2x &=& 4
\end{array}
$$

The equation now contains only multiplication. To solve the equation, form equal groups with one x tile in each group. Since there are 2 x tiles, form 2 equal groups. *Divide to reverse multiplication.*

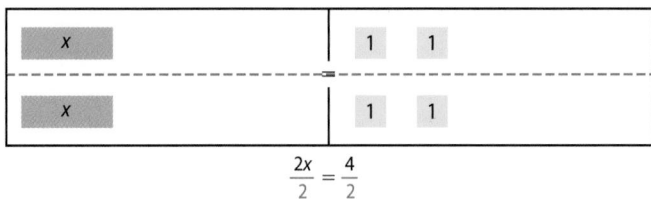

$$\frac{2x}{2} = \frac{4}{2}$$

Each x tile corresponds to a group of 2 $\boxed{+1}$ tiles.

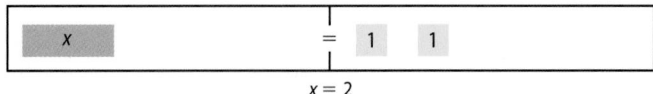

$$x = 2$$

The solution of $2x + 3 = 7$ is $x = 2$.

Two Inverse Operations

When you solve a one-step linear equation that contains one operation, you use one inverse operation to find the solution. You can solve equations with two operations by using two inverse operations.

Suppose $x = 5$. To evaluate $3x + 6$ for $x = 5$, multiply 3 by 5, and then add 6.

$$3(5) + 6$$
$$= 15 + 6$$
$$= 21$$

So $3x + 6 = 21$ when $x = 5$.

To solve the equation $3x + 6 = 21$ for x, *reverse* the process.

1. Subtract 6 from both sides.

2. Divide both sides by 3.

$$3x + 6 = 21$$
$$3x + 6 - 6 = 21 - 6$$
$$\frac{3x}{3} = \frac{15}{3}$$
$$x = 5$$

You "undo" the operations in an equation by reversing the order of operations.

Perform additions and subtractions first. Then use multiplication or division to isolate the variable.

Try It

This Way

Think of solving a two-step equation as reversing your path.

Getting there:

Turn right.

Go east 3 blocks.

Reversing your path:

Go west 3 blocks.

Turn left.

EXAMPLE 1

Use inverse operations to solve $5x - 3 = 27$. To check your answer, substitute the value you find for the variable in the original equation.

In this equation, x is multiplied by 5. Then 3 is subtracted. Work backward to solve.

STEP 1 Add 3 to both sides to reverse subtraction.

$$\begin{aligned} 5x - 3 &= 27 \\ + 3 &= +3 \\ \hline 5x &= 30 \end{aligned}$$

STEP 2 Divide both sides by 5 to reverse multiplication.

$$\frac{5x}{5} = \frac{30}{5}$$
$$1x = 6, \text{ so } x = 6$$

The solution is $x = 6$.

STEP 3 Check the solution.

Substitute 6 for x in the original equation.
Multiply.
Subtract.

$$5x - 3 = 27$$
$$5(6) - 3 \stackrel{?}{=} 27$$
$$30 - 3 \stackrel{?}{=} 27$$
$$27 = 27 ✔$$

Equations with Multiplication

Need More HELP ?

For more review of dividing integers, go to *Multiplying and Dividing Integers* on page 1394.

EXAMPLE 2

Use inverse operations to solve $18 = 6 - 3h$. Check your answer.

In this equation, h is multiplied by -3. Then 6 is added. Work backward to solve.

STEP 1 Subtract 6 from both sides to reverse addition.

$$\begin{array}{rl} 18 = & 6 - 3h \\ -6 = & -6 \\ \hline 12 = & -3h \end{array}$$

STEP 2 Divide both sides by -3 to reverse multiplication.

$$\frac{12}{-3} = \frac{-3h}{-3}$$

$$-4 = 1h, \text{ so } h = -4.$$

The solution is $h = -4$.

STEP 3 Check the solution.
Substitute -4 for h in the original equation.
Multiply.
Add.

$$18 = 6 - 3h$$
$$18 \stackrel{?}{=} 6 - 3(-4)$$
$$18 \stackrel{?}{=} 6 + 12$$
$$18 = 18 ✔$$

EXAMPLE 3

A soccer team receives 3 points for each win plus a point for each draw. The Tornadoes have a total of 35 points, which includes 8 points for draws. How many wins do they have?

Translate to an equation and then solve. Let w equal the number of wins.

3 times the number of wins plus the number of draws equals 35

$$3w \qquad + \qquad 8 \qquad = 35$$

Subtract 8 from both sides to reverse addition.

$$\begin{array}{rl} 3w + 8 = & 35 \\ -8 = & -8 \\ \hline 3w = & 27 \end{array}$$

Divide both sides by 3 to reverse multiplication.

$$\frac{3w}{3} = \frac{27}{3}$$

$$w = 9$$

The Tornadoes have 9 wins.

CHECK Check your result by using substitution.

$$3w + 8 = 35$$
$$3(9) + 8 \stackrel{?}{=} 35$$
$$35 = 35 ✔$$

Equations with Division

Perform additions and subtractions first. Then multiply to reverse division.

EXAMPLE 4

Use inverse operations to solve each equation. Check your answer.

a. $10 + \frac{n}{5} = 23$

In this equation, *n* is divided by 5. Then 10 is added. Work backward to solve.

STEP 1 Subtract 10 from both sides to reverse addition.

$$10 + \frac{n}{5} = 23$$
$$\underline{-10 \qquad = -10}$$
$$\frac{n}{5} = 13$$

STEP 2 Multiply both sides by 5 to reverse division.

$$(5)\frac{n}{5} = (5)13$$
$$n = 65$$

The solution is $n = 65$.

STEP 3 Check the solution.

$$10 + \frac{n}{5} = 23$$

Substitute 65 for *n* in the original equation.

$$10 + \frac{65}{5} \overset{?}{=} 23$$

Simplify.

$$10 + 13 \overset{?}{=} 23$$
$$23 = 23 ✔$$

b. $-14 = \frac{d}{7} - 11$

In this equation, *d* is divided by 7. Then 11 is subtracted. Work backward to solve.

STEP 1 Add 11 to both sides to reverse subtraction.

$$-14 = \frac{d}{7} - 11$$
$$\underline{+11 = \qquad +11}$$
$$-3 = \frac{d}{7}$$

STEP 2 Multiply both sides by 7 to reverse division. The solution is $d = -21$.

$$(7)(-3) = (7)\frac{d}{7}$$
$$-21 = d$$

STEP 3 Check the solution.

$$-14 = \frac{d}{7} - 11$$

Substitute −21 for *d* in the original equation.

$$-14 \overset{?}{=} \frac{-21}{7} - 11$$

Simplify.

$$-14 \overset{?}{=} -3 - 11$$
$$-14 = -14 ✔$$

SEARCH

To see step-by-step videos of these problems, enter the page number into the SWadvantage.com Search Bar.

Multi-Step Equations

Using the Distributive Property to Solve Equations

You know that if $5x = 10$, then $x = 2$.
Because $5x$ is the same as $2x + 3x$ by the
Distributive Property, you also know that
the solution to $2x + 3x = 10$ is also $x = 2$.

$$5x = 10$$
$$(2 + 3)x = 10$$
$$2x + 3x = 10$$

You can solve many multi-step equations by using the Distributive Property.

Need More

HELP

For more review, go to
The Distributive Property
on page 1410.

EXAMPLE 1

Solve $3x + 7x = 50$ and check.

First, use the Distributive Property
to combine the like terms x and $7x$.

$$3x + 7x = 50$$
$$(3 + 7)x = 50$$

Add inside the parentheses.

$$(10)x = 50$$

Divide both sides by 10.

$$\frac{10x}{10} = \frac{50}{10}$$
$$x = 5$$

CHECK Check the solution.
Substitute 5 for x in the original equation.
Multiply.
Then add.

$$3(5) + 7(5) \stackrel{?}{=} 50$$
$$15 + 35 \stackrel{?}{=} 50$$
$$50 = 50 \checkmark$$

The solution is $x = 5$.

EXAMPLE 2

Cal goes to the cash register with 16 cans of tomato soup and a coupon that gives him 4 cans free. So the cost of 4 cans is taken off the bill. The total Cal pays is $6. What was the price marked on each can?

Translate to an equation and solve. Let p equal the marked price in dollars on each can.

16 times the marked price minus 4 times the marked price equals 6

$$16p \qquad - \qquad 4p \qquad = 6$$

$$16p - 4p = 6$$

Use the Distributive Property.

$$(16 - 4)p = 6$$

Subtract.

$$12p = 6$$

Divide both sides by 12.

$$p = 0.5$$

The price marked on each can was $.50.

Equations with Parentheses

EXAMPLE 3

Solve 2(4y + 1) = 26. Check the solution.

SEARCH

To see step-by-step videos of these problems, enter the page number into the SWadvantage.com Search Bar.

METHOD 1

When you solve equations with parentheses, you can use the Distributive Property first to remove the parentheses.

Use the Distributive Property. $2(4y + 1) = 26$

$2(4y) + 2(1) = 26$

Multiply. $8y + 2 = 26$

Subtract 2 from both sides. $8y = 24$

Divide both sides by 8. $y = 3$

METHOD 2

As an alternative method, first isolate the expression inside the parentheses on one side of the equation.

$2(4y + 1) = 26 \longrightarrow 2\boxed{?} = 26$

Divide both sides by 2. $\dfrac{2(4y + 1)}{2} = \dfrac{26}{2}$

Simplify. $4y + 1 = 13$

Now you've found the value of the expression inside the parentheses. Continue to find the solution by isolating the variable.

Subtract 1 from both sides. $4y = 12$

Divide both sides by 4. $y = 3$

CHECK Check the solution $y = 3$. $2(4y + 1) = 26$

Substitute 3 for y in the original equation. $2(4 \cdot 3 + 1) \overset{?}{=} 26$

Multiply inside the parentheses. $2(12 + 1) \overset{?}{=} 26$

Add inside the parentheses and simplify. $2(13) \overset{?}{=} 26$

$26 = 26$ ✔

The solution is $y = 3$.

Distributive Property

For any numbers a, b, and c, the equations below are true.

$a(b + c) = ab + ac \qquad a(b - c) = ab - ac \qquad a[b + (-c)] = ab + a(-c) = ab - ac$

$(b + c)a = ba + ca \qquad (b - c)a = ba - ca \qquad [b + (-c)]a = ba + (-c)a = ba - ca$

EXAMPLE 4

The area of the entire rectangle is 56 square inches. What is the value of *x*? Check the solution.

The length times the width equals the area.

$(x + 5) \times 4 = 56$

Use the Distributive Property.
$$(x + 5)4 = 56$$
$$4x + 4(5) = 56$$

Multiply. $\qquad 4x + 20 = 56$

Subtract 20 from both sides. $\qquad 4x = 36$

Divide both sides by 4. $\qquad x = 9$

CHECK Check the solution by using a diagram.

The value of *x* is 9 inches.

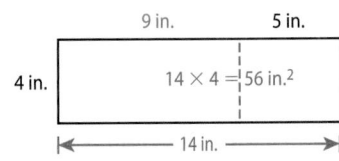

EXAMPLE 5

Solve $17 - 3(2y - 5) = 20$.

METHOD 1

Use the Distributive Property.
$$17 - 3(2y - 5) = 20$$
$$17 - 3(2y) - 3(-5) = 20$$

Multiply. $\qquad 17 - 6y + 15 = 20$

Add 6*y* to both sides. $\qquad 17 + 15 = 20 + 6y$

Subtract 20 from both sides. $\qquad 17 + 15 - 20 = 6y$

Simplify. $\qquad 12 = 6y$

Divide both sides by 6. $\qquad y = 2$

METHOD 2

Use inverse operations first. $\qquad 17 - 3(2y - 5) = 20$
Subtract 17 from both sides. $\qquad -3(2y - 5) = 3$

Divide both sides by -3. $\qquad 2y - 5 = -1$

Add 5 to both sides. $\qquad 2y = 4$

Divide both sides by 2. $\qquad y = 2$

The solution is $y = 2$.

EXAMPLE 6

If $2 - (x - 7) = 0$, find the value of $200x - 1$.

METHOD 1

Find the value of x.

Rewrite $2 - (x - 7) = 0$ as the addition of the opposite of $(x - 7)$.	$2 - (x - 7) = 0$ $2 + (-1)(x - 7) = 0$
Use the Distributive Property to multiply.	$2 + (-1)x + (-1)(-7) = 0$
Simplify.	$2 - x + 7 = 0$
Add x to both sides and simplify.	$9 = x$

Find the value of $200x - 1$ when $x = 9$.	$200x - 1$
Substitute 9 for the variable in $200x - 1$.	$= 200(9) - 1$
Simplify.	$= 1{,}799$

The value of $200x - 1$ is 1,799.

METHOD 2

Find the value of x.

	$2 - (x - 7) = 0$
Add $x - 7$ to both sides.	$\dfrac{x - 7 = x - 7}{2 \qquad = x - 7}$
Add 7 to both sides and simplify.	$9 = x$

Find the value of $200x - 1$ when $x = 9$.	$200x - 1$
Substitute 9 for the variable in $200x - 1$.	$= 200(9) - 1$
Simplify.	$= 1{,}799$

The value of $200x - 1$ is 1,799.

Need More HELP ?

Remember, subtracting is the same as adding the opposite. The opposite of x is $(-1)x$.

For more review of subtracting integers, go to *Subtracting Integers* on page 1392.

Got to KNOW!

Properties of Equality

These properties apply if a, b, and c are real numbers and $a = b$.

Addition Property of Equality	$a + c = b + c \qquad a + (-c) = b + (-c)$
Subtraction Property of Equality	$a - c = b - c$
Multiplication Property of Equality	$ac = bc$
Division Property of Equality	$\dfrac{a}{c} = \dfrac{b}{c}\ (c \neq 0)$

One-Step Equations with Fractions

You can solve one-step equations that involve fractions in the same way as you solve equations with whole numbers. Use inverse operations to undo the operation so that you isolate the variable on one side of the equation.

SEARCH

To see step-by-step videos of these problems, enter the page number into the SWadvantage.com Search Bar.

EXAMPLE 1

Solve $\frac{6}{7} = x + \frac{2}{7}$.

Write the equation.	$\frac{6}{7} = x + \frac{2}{7}$
Subtract $\frac{2}{7}$ from both sides.	$\frac{6}{7} - \frac{2}{7} = x + \frac{2}{7} - \frac{2}{7}$
Subtract the numerators.	$\frac{4}{7} = x$

To solve an equation in which the only fraction is the coefficient of the variable, you can treat the term as division or as multiplication.

EXAMPLE 2

Solve and check $\frac{1}{6}x = 8$.

$\frac{1}{6}x = 8$ is the same as $\frac{x}{6} = 8$. Compare the steps for solving both versions of the equation.

	Multiplication	**Division**
	$\frac{1}{6}x = 8$	$\frac{x}{6} = 8$
Multiply both sides by 6.	$6\left(\frac{1}{6}\right)x = 6(8)$	$6\left(\frac{x}{6}\right) = 6(8)$
Simplify.	$\left(\frac{6}{6}\right)x = 6(8)$	$\left(\frac{6x}{6}\right) = 6(8)$
	$x = 48$	$x = 48$

CHECK Check the solution in the original equation. $\quad \frac{1}{6}x = 8$

Substitute 48 for x in the original equation. $\quad \frac{1}{6}(48) = 8$

$$8 = 8 \checkmark$$

The solution is $x = 48$.

Two-Step Equations with Fractions

When you solve an equation with a single fraction, you can use inverse operations, or you can multiply both sides by the denominator of the fraction to clear the equation of fractions.

EXAMPLE 3

Solve $\frac{2}{3}x + 5 = 11$. Check the solution.

METHOD 1

Use inverse operations.

Write the equation.	$\frac{2}{3}x + 5 = 11$
Subtract 5 from both sides to isolate the variable term.	$\frac{2}{3}x + 5 - 5 = 11 - 5$
Simplify.	$\frac{2}{3}x = 6$
Multiply both sides by $\frac{3}{2}$.	$\left(\frac{3}{2}\right)\frac{2}{3}x = \left(\frac{3}{2}\right)6$
Simplify.	$1x = \frac{18}{2}$, so $x = 9$

CHECK Check the solution in the original equation. $\frac{2}{3}x + 5 = 11$

Substitute 9 for x in the original equation. $\frac{2}{3}(9) + 5 = 11$

Simplify. $6 + 5 = 11$

$11 = 11$ ✔

The solution is $x = 9$.

METHOD 2

Clear the equation of the fraction first.

Write the equation.	$\frac{2}{3}x + 5 = 11$
Multiply both sides by 3 to clear the fraction.	$3\left(\frac{2}{3}x + 5\right) = 3(11)$
Use the Distributive Property.	$3\left(\frac{2}{3}x\right) + 3(5) = 3(11)$
Subtract 15 from both sides.	$2x + 15 = 33$
Simplify.	$2x = 18$, so $x = 9$

Check as in Method 1.

The solution is $x = 9$.

Watch Out !

Don't forget to multiply *every* term by the denominator of the fraction, not just the term with the fraction.

SOUTHWESTERN

Equations with Several Fractions

When you solve an equation with several fractions, you can use inverse operations. Another way to begin solving is to multiply both sides by the least common denominator (LCD) of the fractions to clear the equation of fractions.

SEARCH

To see step-by-step videos of these problems, enter the page number into the SWadvantage.com Search Bar.

EXAMPLE 4

Solve $\frac{1}{35}x - \frac{3}{7} = \frac{2}{7}$.

METHOD 1

Use inverse operations first.

$$\frac{1}{35}x - \frac{3}{7} = \frac{2}{7}$$

Add $\frac{3}{7}$ to both sides to isolate the variable term.

$$\frac{+\frac{3}{7} \quad +\frac{3}{7}}{\frac{1}{35}x = \frac{5}{7}}$$

Multiply both sides by 35.

$$35\left(\frac{1}{35}x\right) = 35\left(\frac{5}{7}\right)$$

Simplify.

$$x = \frac{35 \cdot 5}{7} = \frac{{}^5\cancel{35} \cdot 5}{\cancel{7}_1} = 25$$

$$x = 25$$

METHOD 2

Clear the equation of fractions first by using the LCD.

Need More HELP?

To review finding the LCD, go to *Multiples* in *Numbers and Operations* (Book 1, p. 288).

The LCD of 35, 7, and 7 is 35.

$$\frac{1}{35}x - \frac{3}{7} = \frac{2}{7}$$

Multiply both sides by 35 to clear the fraction.

$$35\left(\frac{1}{35}x - \frac{3}{7}\right) = 35\left(\frac{2}{7}\right)$$

Use the Distributive Property.

$$35\left(\frac{1}{35}x\right) - 35\left(\frac{3}{7}\right) = (35)\left(\frac{2}{7}\right)$$

Simplify each term.

$$x - \frac{35 \cdot 3}{7} = \frac{35 \cdot 2}{7}$$

Simplify.

$$x - \frac{{}^5\cancel{35} \cdot 3}{\cancel{7}_1} = \frac{{}^5\cancel{35} \cdot 2}{\cancel{7}_1}$$

$$x - 15 = 10$$

Add 15 to both sides to find the value of x.

$$x = 25$$

The solution is $x = 25$.

Sometimes you need to combine like terms when solving an equation.

EXAMPLE 5

Solve $\dfrac{11}{12}x - \dfrac{5}{8}x = \dfrac{1}{6}$.

Clear the equation of fractions. Use the LCD.

Write the equation. Then find the LCD of all the fractions. $\dfrac{11}{12}x - \dfrac{5}{8}x = \dfrac{1}{6}$

$12 = 2 \cdot 2 \cdot 3$ $8 = 2 \cdot 2 \cdot 2$ $6 = 2 \cdot 3$

The LCD of 12, 8, and 6 is $2 \cdot 2 \cdot 2 \cdot 3 = 24$.

Multiply each fraction by a fraction equal to 1 to make each denominator 24. $\dfrac{2 \cdot 11}{2 \cdot 12}x - \dfrac{3 \cdot 5}{3 \cdot 8}x = \dfrac{4 \cdot 1}{4 \cdot 6}$

Simplify. $\dfrac{22}{24}x - \dfrac{15}{24}x = \dfrac{4}{24}$

Multiply both sides by 24 to eliminate the fractions. $22x - 15x = 4$

Combine like terms to simplify. $7x = 4$

Divide both sides by 7 to find the value of x. $x = \dfrac{4}{7}$

The solution is $x = \dfrac{4}{7}$.

Need More

HELP ?

Remember, the LCD of two or more fractions is the product of factors in the denominators. Each factor of the LCD is used the *greatest* number of times that it appears in any denominator.

Methods to Solve Equations with Fractions

Clearing the Equation of Fractions

- First multiply both sides by the LCD to clear the equation of fractions.
- Then combine like terms or simplify if needed.
- Use inverse operations to solve.

Using Inverse Operations

- First multiply each term by a fraction equal to 1 to get the LCD as the denominator of all fractions.
- Use inverse operations to isolate the variable term.
- Then multiply both sides of the equation by the LCD, and simplify.

Equations with Decimals

Need More

HELP

For a review of
operations with
decimals, go to these
topics in *Numbers and
Operations* (Book 1,
pp. 226–257).

Adding Decimals

Subtracting Decimals

*Multiplying Decimals
by Whole Numbers*

*Multiplying Decimals
by Decimals*

*Dividing Decimals by
Whole Numbers*

*Dividing Whole
Numbers by Decimals*

*Dividing Decimals by
Decimals*

One-Step Equations with Decimals

You can use what you know about inverse operations and decimals to solve equations with decimal numbers.

EXAMPLE 1

Solve each equation and check the answer.

a. $x + 0.09 = 1.07$

Subtract 0.09 from both sides.

$$\begin{aligned} x + 0.09 &= 1.07 \\ -\,0.09 &\;\; -\,0.09 \\ \hline x &= 0.98 \end{aligned}$$

CHECK Check the solution.

Substitute 0.98 for x in the original equation. $0.98 + 0.09 = 1.07$ ✓

The solution is $x = 0.98$.

b. $7.5x = 30$

METHOD 1

Use inverse operations. $7.5x = 30$

Divide both sides by 7.5. $\dfrac{7.5x}{7.5} = \dfrac{30}{7.5}$

Remember, $\dfrac{7.5}{7.5} = 1$. $\dfrac{\cancel{7.5}x}{\cancel{7.5}} = 4$

Simplify. $x = 4$

CHECK Check the solution. $7.5x = 30$

Substitute 4 for x. $7.5(4) \stackrel{?}{=} 30$

$30 = 30$ ✓

The solution is $x = 4$.

METHOD 2

Clear the equation of decimals first. $7.5x = 30$

Multiply both sides by 10. $10(7.5x) = 10(30)$

$75x = 300$

Divide both sides by 75. $\dfrac{\cancel{75}x}{\cancel{75}} = \dfrac{300}{75}$

Simplify. $x = 4$

Check as shown in Method 1.

The solution is $x = 4$.

Two-Step Equations with Decimals

In Example 1b, you can see that multiplying both sides by 10 will result in an equation without decimals. In equations with decimals, the easiest way to clear the equation of decimals is to multiply both sides by the same power of 10.

EXAMPLE 2

Solve $2.4x - 1.7 = 45.1$. Check the solution.

METHOD 1

Use inverse operations.

Write the equation.	$2.4x - 1.7 = 45.1$
Add 1.7 to both sides.	$\underline{+\ 1.7 \quad +\ 1.7}$
	$2.4x = 46.8$
Divide both sides by 2.4.	$\dfrac{2.4x}{2.4} = \dfrac{46.8}{2.4}$
Simplify.	$x = 19.5$

CHECK Check the solution in the original equation.

$$2.4x - 1.7 = 45.1$$

Substitute 19.5 for x in the original equation. $2.4(19.5) - 1.7 \overset{?}{=} 45.1$

Multiply. $46.8 - 1.7 \overset{?}{=} 45.1$

Subtract. $45.1 = 45.1 \checkmark$

The solution is $x = 19.5$.

METHOD 2

Clear the equation of decimals first. No decimal number has more than one decimal place. So multiply both sides by 10 to the first power, or 10.

$$2.4x - 1.7 = 45.1$$

Multiply both sides by 10.	$10(2.4x - 1.7) = 10(45.1)$
Use the Distributive Property.	$10(2.4x) - 10(1.7) = 10(45.1)$
Simplify.	$24x - 17 = 451$
Add 17 to both sides.	$24x - 17 + 17 = 451 + 17$
	$24x = 468$
Divide both sides by 24.	$\dfrac{24x}{24} = \dfrac{468}{24}$
	$x = 19.5$

Check as shown in Method 1.

The solution is $x = 19.5$.

SEARCH

To see step-by-step videos of these problems, enter the page number into the SWadvantage.com Search Bar.

Need More HELP?

To review multiplying by powers of 10, go to *Multiplying Decimals by Whole Numbers* in *Numbers and Operations* (Book 1, p. 240).

Equations with Negative Decimals or Percents

SEARCH

To see step-by-step videos of these problems, enter the page number into the SWadvantage.com Search Bar.

EXAMPLE 3

Solve $22.31 - 6.7a = -5.83$. Check the solution.

METHOD 1

Use inverse operations.

Write the equation.	$22.31 - 6.7a = -5.83$
Subtract 22.31 from both sides.	$-22.31 \qquad -22.31$
	$-6.7a = -28.14$
Divide both sides by -6.7.	$\dfrac{-6.7a}{-6.7} = \dfrac{-28.14}{-6.7}$
Simplify.	$a = 4.2$

CHECK Check the solution in the original equation.

$$22.31 - 6.7a = -5.83$$

Substitute 4.2 for x in the original equation. $\quad 22.31 - 6.7(4.2) \stackrel{?}{=} -5.83$

Multiply. $\quad 22.31 - 28.14 \stackrel{?}{=} -5.83$

Subtract. $\quad -5.83 = -5.83 \ \checkmark$

The solution is $a = 4.2$.

METHOD 2

Clear the equation of decimals first.

No decimal number has more than two decimal places. So multiply both sides by 10 to the second power, or 100.

Multiply both sides by 100.	$22.31 - 6.7a = -5.83$
	$100(22.31 - 6.7a) = 100(-5.83)$
Use the Distributive Property.	$100(22.31) - 100(6.7a) = 100(-5.83)$
Simplify.	$2{,}231 - 670a = -583$
Subtract 2,231 from both sides.	$2{,}231 - 670a - 2{,}231 = -583 - 2{,}231$
	$-670a = -2{,}814$
Divide both sides by -670.	$\dfrac{-670a}{-670} = \dfrac{-2{,}814}{-670}$
	$a = 4.2$

Check as shown in Method 1.

The solution is $a = 4.2$.

You may need to convert percents to decimals before solving an equation.

EXAMPLE 4

A chemist combines two ingredients to make 28 milliliters of a substance. She has one ingredient that is 23.7% of a bottle. She adds 12.7 milliliters of another liquid to the bottle. What is the total capacity c of the bottle holding the first ingredient, to the nearest tenth of a milliliter?

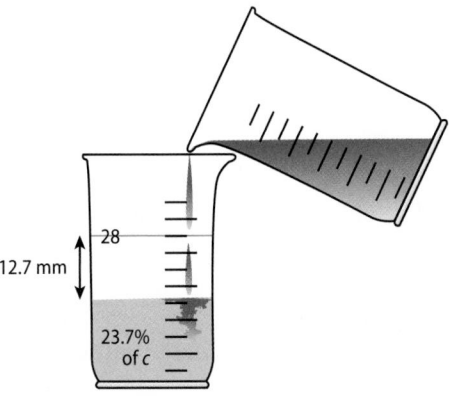

STEP 1 First convert 23.7% to a decimal.

$$23.7\% = \frac{23.7}{100} = 0.237$$

STEP 2 Translate the problem to an equation and solve.

23.7% of bottle capacity plus 12.7 equals 28

$$0.237c \qquad + \quad 12.7 \quad = \quad 28$$

$$0.237c + 12.7 = 28$$

Subtract 12.7 from both sides. $\qquad 0.237c + 12.7 - 12.7 = 28 - 12.7$

$$0.237c = 15.3$$

Multiply both sides by 1,000. $\qquad 1{,}000(0.237c) = 1{,}000(15.3)$

Simplify. $\qquad 237c = 15{,}300$

Divide both sides by 237.
Use a calculator. $\qquad c = \frac{15{,}300}{237} \approx 64.55696$

Round to the nearest tenth. $\qquad c \approx 64.6$

The capacity of the bottle is about 64.6 milliliters.

Try It This Way

If you're comfortable with powers of 10 in exponential form, you can represent 1,000 as 10^3.

Methods to Solve Equations with Decimals

- Use inverse operations.
- Multiply both sides of the equation by a power of 10. Use the greatest power of 10 necessary to clear all the decimals. Then use order of operations.
- Convert percents to decimals, if necessary, as a first step.

Absolute-Value Equations

Solving Absolute-Value Equations

Need More

HELP?

For more review of absolute value, go to *Integers and Absolute Value* on page 1386.

The absolute value of a number is its distance from 0 on a number line. Both 3 and −3 are 3 units from 0, so both numbers have an absolute value of 3.

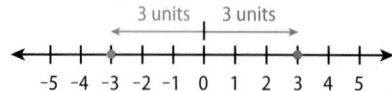

You can write this as an equation.

The absolute value of a number x equals 3.

$$|x| = 3$$

The equation above has two solutions, $x = 3$ and $x = -3$. Because either number is a solution, but not at the same time, state the solution as:

$$x = 3 \; or \; x = -3$$

SEARCH 🔍

To see step-by-step videos of these problems, enter the page number into the SWadvantage.com Search Bar.

EXAMPLE 1

Solve $|x| = 6$ and check the solution.

Think: What numbers are 6 units from 0 on a number line?

$x = 6$ or $x = -6$

CHECK Check both solutions in the equation.

$$|x| = 6 \qquad\qquad |x| = 6$$
$$|6| \overset{?}{=} 6 \qquad\qquad |-6| \overset{?}{=} 6$$
$$6 = 6 \checkmark \qquad\qquad 6 = 6 \checkmark$$

The solution is $x = 6$ or $x = -6$.

Because absolute value is distance, and distance cannot be negative, some absolute-value equations have no solution.

EXAMPLE 2

Solve $|x| = -4$.

Think: What numbers are a distance of −4 units from 0 on a number line? None are.

Absolute value cannot be negative.

There is no solution.

To solve an equation involving absolute value, you may need to perform inverse operations. First undo the operations to isolate the absolute value expression on one side of the equation. Then find the values of the variable that make the equation true.

EXAMPLE 3

Solve and check the solution.

a. **2 |x| = 10**

$$2|x| = 10$$

Divide both sides by 2. $|x| = 5$

$$x = 5 \text{ or } x = -5$$

CHECK $2|x| \overset{?}{=} 10$ $2|x| \overset{?}{=} 10$

Substitute both solutions. $2|5| \overset{?}{=} 10$ $2|-5| \overset{?}{=} 10$

$$10 = 10 \checkmark \qquad\qquad 10 = 10 \checkmark$$

The solution is $x = 5$ or $x = -5$.

Need More HELP ?

Remember to undo multiplication by using division. Undo subtraction by adding the same number to both sides of an equation.

b. **|x| − 3 = −3**

$$|x| - 3 = -3$$

Add 3 to both sides. $|x| = 0$

There is only one solution. $x = 0$

CHECK $|x| - 3 \overset{?}{=} -3$

Substitute 0 for x. $|0| - 3 \overset{?}{=} -3$

$$-3 = -3 \checkmark$$

The solution is $x = 0$.

Got to KNOW!

Absolute-Value Equations

Rule	**Examples**
If $a > 0$, then $|x| = a$ has **2** solutions, a and $-a$.	$|x| = 3$ has two solutions, $x = 3$ and $x = -3$.
If $a = 0$, then $|x| = a$ has **1** solution, $a = 0$.	$|x| = 0$ has one solution, $x = 0$.
If $a < 0$, then $|x| = a$ has **0** solutions.	$|x| = -2$ has no solution.

Operations Within Absolute-Value Bars

To solve an equation like $|x - 3| = 5$, remember that the expression inside the absolute-value bars is equal to 5 or -5. Think: "What numbers are located a distance of 5 units from the number 3 on the number line?"

EXAMPLE 4

Solve $|x - 3| = 5$. Then check and graph the solution.

STEP 1 Write two equations to solve. $\quad x - 3 = 5 \quad$ or $\quad x - 3 = -5$

   Add 3 to both sides. $\qquad\qquad\qquad x = 8 \quad$ or $\qquad x = -2$

STEP 2 Check in the original equation. $\quad |x - 3| = 5 \qquad\qquad |x - 3| = 5$

   Substitute both solutions. $\qquad |8 - 3| \overset{?}{=} 5 \qquad\quad |-2 - 3| \overset{?}{=} 5$

$$|5| \overset{?}{=} 5 \qquad\qquad\quad |-5| \overset{?}{=} 5$$

$$5 = 5 \checkmark \qquad\qquad\quad 5 = 5 \checkmark$$

STEP 3 Graph the solution on a number line.

$$|x - 3| = 5$$

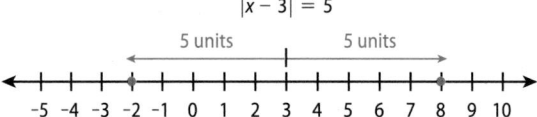

Both values are a distance of 5 units from 3 on the number line.

The solution is $x = 8$ or $x = -2$.

EXAMPLE 5

Solve $7 + |x + 9| = 4$.

Use inverse operations to get the absolute-value expression isolated on one side of the equation.

$$7 + |x + 9| = 4$$

Subtract 7 from both sides. $\qquad \dfrac{-7 \qquad\qquad -7}{|x + 9| = -3}$

Absolute value cannot be negative!

There is no solution.

To solve more complicated absolute-value equations, isolate the absolute-value expression first. Then use the absolute-value expression to write and solve two equations.

EXAMPLE 6

Solve $5 - 10\left|\dfrac{2}{3}x - 6\right| + 8 = -7$. Check the solution.

STEP 1 Isolate the absolute-value expression.

$$5 - 10\left|\dfrac{2}{3}x - 6\right| + 8 = -7$$

Subtract 5 and 8 from both sides.

$$5 - 10\left|\dfrac{2}{3}x - 6\right| - 5 + 8 - 8 = -7 - 5 - 8$$

Simplify.

$$-10\left|\dfrac{2}{3}x - 6\right| = -20$$

Divide both sides by -10.

$$\left|\dfrac{2}{3}x - 6\right| = 2$$

STEP 2 Write two equations to solve.

$$\dfrac{2}{3}x - 6 = 2 \quad \text{or} \quad \dfrac{2}{3}x - 6 = -2$$

Add 6 to both sides.

$$\dfrac{2}{3}x = 8 \quad \text{or} \quad \dfrac{2}{3}x = 4$$

Multiply both sides by $\dfrac{3}{2}$.

$$\dfrac{3}{2}\left(\dfrac{2}{3}x\right) = \dfrac{3}{2}(8) \quad \text{or} \quad \dfrac{3}{2}\left(\dfrac{2}{3}x\right) = \dfrac{3}{2}(4)$$

Simplify.

$$x = 12 \quad \text{or} \quad x = 6$$

CHECK

$$5 - 10\left|\dfrac{2}{3}x - 6\right| + 8 = -7 \qquad 5 - 10\left|\dfrac{2}{3}x - 6\right| + 8 = -7$$

Substitute 12 and 6 for x.

$$5 - 10\left|\dfrac{2}{3}(12) - 6\right| + 8 = -7 \qquad 5 - 10\left|\dfrac{2}{3}(6) - 6\right| + 8 = -7$$

Simplify.

$$5 - 10|2| + 8 = -7 \qquad 5 - 10|-2| + 8 = -7$$

$$13 - 10|2| = -7 \qquad 13 - 10|-2| = -7$$

$$13 - 10(2) = -7 \qquad 13 - 10(2) = -7$$

$$13 - 20 = -7 \qquad 13 - 20 = -7$$

$$-7 = -7 \checkmark \qquad -7 = -7 \checkmark$$

The solution is $x = 12$ or $x = 6$.

Try It This Way

To solve a simpler problem in Step 1, let $\left|\dfrac{2}{3}x - 6\right| = y$. Then solve the equation $5 - 10y + 8 = -7$. The solution is $y = 2$. So, then write $\left|\dfrac{2}{3}x - 6\right| = 2$, and solve for x in Step 2.

SEARCH

To see step-by-step videos of these problems, enter the page number into the SWadvantage.com Search Bar.

No Solution or Many Solutions

SOUTHWESTERN

Variables on Both Sides

To solve an equation with variables on both sides, use inverse operations to write an equation with all the variable terms on the same side.

EXAMPLE 1

SEARCH

To see step-by-step videos of these problems, enter the page number into the SWadvantage.com Search Bar.

Solve each equation.

a. $9x = 5x + 8$

Subtract $5x$ from both sides to get an equation with the variable term on the *left* side only.

$$\begin{array}{rl} 9x = & 5x + 8 \\ \underline{-5x} & \underline{-5x} \\ 4x = & 8 \end{array}$$

Divide both sides by 4.

$$\frac{4x}{4} = \frac{8}{4}$$
$$x = 2$$

CHECK Substitute 2 for x.

$$9(2) = 5(2) + 8$$
$$18 = 10 + 8 \checkmark$$

The solution is $x = 2$.

b. $2x + 3 = 4x - 5$

METHOD 1

Subtract $4x$ from both sides to get an equation with the variable term on the *left* side only.

$$\begin{array}{rl} 2x + 3 = & 4x - 5 \\ \underline{-4x} & \underline{-4x} \\ -2x + 3 = & -5 \end{array}$$

Subtract 3 from both sides to isolate the variable term.

$$\begin{array}{rl} & \underline{-3} \quad\quad \underline{-3} \\ -2x = & -8 \end{array}$$

Divide both sides by -2.

$$x = 4$$

METHOD 2

Subtract $2x$ from both sides to get an equation with the variable term on the *right* side only.

$$\begin{array}{rl} 2x + 3 = & 4x - 5 \\ \underline{-2x} & \underline{-2x} \\ 3 = & 2x - 5 \end{array}$$

Add 5 to both sides to isolate the variable term.

$$\begin{array}{rl} \underline{+5} & \underline{+5} \\ 8 = & 2x \end{array}$$

Divide both sides by 2.

$$4 = x$$

CHECK Substitute 4 for x.

$$2(4) + 3 = 4(4) - 5$$
$$8 + 3 = 16 - 5$$
$$11 = 11 \checkmark$$

The solution is $x = 4$.

How Many Solutions?

When an equation has a variable on both sides, it may have one solution, no solution, or infinitely many solutions.

EXAMPLE 2

Solve each equation.

a. $x + 10 = x$

Subtract x from both sides.

$$\begin{array}{r} x + 10 = x \\ \underline{-x -x} \\ 10 = 0 \text{ ✗} \end{array}$$

This equation is always false!

So, the original equation has no solution.

b. $3(x - 6) = 4x - 18 - x$

$$3(x - 6) = 4x - 18 - x$$

Use the Distributive Property. $3(x) - 3(6) = 4x - 18 - x$

Multiply. Use the Commutative Property. $3x - 18 = 4x - x - 18$

Combine like terms. $4x - x$ means $4x - 1x$. $3x - 18 = 3x - 18$

Subtract $3x$ from both sides.

$$\begin{array}{r} \underline{-3x -3x} \\ -18 = -18 \text{ ✔} \end{array}$$

This equation is always true!

Any value of x can be a solution. Test with values of 0, −8, and 1.

Let $x = 0$.

$3(0 - 6) = 4(0) - 18 - 0$

$-18 = -18$ ✔

Let $x = -8$.

$3(-8 - 6) = 4(-8) - 18 - (-8)$

$-42 = -42$ ✔

Let $x = 1$.

$3(1 - 6) = 4(1) - 18 - 1$

$-15 = -15$ ✔

So, the original equation has infinitely many solutions.

> **Watch Out !**
>
> Whether you're dealing with numbers or variables, remember to use inverse operations to move them to the other side of the equation.
>
> The equation $3x - 18 = 3x - 18$ cannot be rewritten as $6x - 18 = -18$.

Method to Solve Equations with Variables on Both Sides

- Use inverse operations to write an equation with all variable terms on one side of the equation.

- Combine like terms on each side of the equation.

The final equation you find will tell you the number of solutions the original equation has.

Resulting Equation	Sample	Number of Solutions
True for one value	$x = 2$	one solution
Never true	$3 = 2$	no solution
Always true	$3 = 3$	infinitely many solutions

Solving Word Problems with Equations

Need More

HELP ?

For more review of translating words to algebraic expressions, go to *Translating English into Algebra* on page 1430.

Translating Words to Equations

To solve a word problem, follow these steps.

- Determine what number or numbers you need to find.
- Let a variable represent the number you are trying to find.
- Write an equation that describes the conditions of the problem.
- Solve the equation.
- Check the solution to see if it is reasonable in the problem.

EXAMPLE 1

The difference between three times a number and 15 is 60. Find the number.

STEP 1 Choose a variable.

Let k = the number.

STEP 2 Write an equation.

This is a problem about the difference between two values. The phrase "three times a number" occurs before the phrase "and 15," so write "three times a number" first.

Three times a number minus 15 is 60.

$$3k \quad - \quad 15 = 60$$

STEP 3 Solve the equation.

Add 15 to both sides first to isolate the variable term on the left side.

$$
\begin{aligned}
3k - 15 &= 60 \\
+ 15 \quad &+ 15 \\
\hline
3k \quad &= 75
\end{aligned}
$$

Divide both sides by 3 to isolate k.

$$\frac{3k}{3} = \frac{75}{3}$$

The number is 25.

$$k = 25$$

CHECK Check the solution in the problem.

Read the word problem to see whether the answer is reasonable.

Replace words with numbers, where appropriate.

The difference between 3 times 25 and 15 is 60.

$$
\begin{aligned}
3(25) - 15 &\overset{?}{=} 60 \\
75 - 15 &\overset{?}{=} 60 \\
60 &= 60 \checkmark
\end{aligned}
$$

The number 25 is correct.

EXAMPLE 2

The difference between 15 and three times a number is 60. Find the number.

SEARCH

To see step-by-step videos of these problems, enter the page number into the SWadvantage.com Search Bar.

STEP 1 Choose a variable, and translate the problem into an equation.

Let n = the number. Notice that 15 occurs before "three times a number."

Fifteen **minus** three times a number **is** 60.

$$15 \quad - \quad 3n \quad = 60$$

STEP 2 Solve the equation.

Subtract 15 from both sides first to isolate the variable term on the left side.

$$
\begin{array}{r}
15 - 3n = 60 \\
-15 -15 \\
\hline
-3n = 45
\end{array}
$$

Divide both sides by -3 to isolate n.

$$\frac{-3n}{-3} = \frac{45}{-3}$$

The number is -15.

$$n = -15$$

CHECK Check the solution in the problem. Replace words with numbers, where appropriate.

The difference between 15 and 3 times -15 is 60.

$$15 - 3(-15) = 60$$
$$15 + 45 \overset{?}{=} 60$$

The number -15 is correct.

$$60 = 60 \; ✔$$

EXAMPLE 3

When the sum of a number and 5 is divided by 3, the quotient is 14. Find the number.

STEP 1 Choose a variable, and translate the problem into an equation.

Let m = the number. Then break the statement into parts.

The quotient (when the sum of a number and 5 is divided by 3) is 14.

The quotient ... is 14. $\boxed{} = 14$

What is the quotient? the sum of a number and 5 divided by 3

$$\frac{m + 5}{3}$$

Write the equation.

$$\frac{m + 5}{3} = 14$$

STEP 2 Solve the equation.

Multiply both sides of the equation by 3 to clear the fraction.

$$3\left(\frac{m + 5}{3}\right) = 3(14)$$

Simplify.

$$m + 5 = 42$$

Subtract 5 from both sides to isolate the variable.

$$m + 5 - 5 = 42 - 5$$

The number is 37.

$$m = 37$$

CHECK Check the solution in the problem.

The quotient when the sum of 37 and 5 is divided by 3 is 14.

$$\frac{37 + 5}{3} \overset{?}{=} 14$$

$$\frac{42}{3} \overset{?}{=} 14$$

The number 37 is correct.

$$14 = 14 \; ✔$$

Translating Problem Situations into Equations

EXAMPLE 4

SEARCH

To see step-by-step videos of these problems, enter the page number into the SWadvantage.com Search Bar.

Four-fifths of the students in a PE class chose to play dodgeball. After 2 more students joined the game, 26 were playing. How many students are in the PE class?

STEP 1 Choose a variable, and translate the problem into an equation.

Let s = the number of students in the PE class.

Four-fifths of the students plus 2 students is 26 students.

$$\frac{4}{5}s \quad + \quad 2 \quad = \quad 26$$

STEP 2 Solve the equation.

Subtract 2 from both sides of the equation.

$$\frac{4}{5}s + 2 = 26$$
$$\underline{\quad -2 \quad -2 \quad}$$
$$\frac{4}{5}s = 24$$

Multiply both sides of the equation by $\frac{5}{4}$.
There are 30 students in the PE class.

$$\frac{5}{4}\left(\frac{4}{5}s\right) = \frac{5}{4}(24)$$
$$s = 30$$

CHECK Check the solution in the problem.

Four-fifths of 30 students plus 2 students is 26 students.

$$\frac{4}{5}(30) + 2 \overset{?}{=} 26$$
$$24 + 2 \overset{?}{=} 26$$
$$26 = 26 \checkmark$$

The number of students, 30, is correct.

There are 30 students in PE class.

EXAMPLE 5

Carly paid for 3 tubes of lip gloss with a $10 bill and got $1.15 in change. How much does 1 tube of lip gloss cost?

Let c equal the cost in dollars of 1 tube of lip gloss. Translate to an equation and solve.

3 times the cost of 1 tube equals $10 minus change of $1.15

$$3c \quad = \quad 10 \quad - \quad 1.15$$

$$3c = 10 - 1.15$$

Simplify by subtracting. $\quad 3c = 8.85$

Divide both sides by 3. $\quad \dfrac{3c}{3} = \dfrac{8.85}{3}$

$$c = 2.95$$

One tube of lip gloss costs $2.95.

EXAMPLE 6

A baseball team had played *g* games before January and had won 25% of them. Then they won the next 4 games. By then, the team had won 40% of their games.

a. How many games had the team played before January?

STEP 1 First convert the percents to decimals.

$$25\% = \frac{25}{100} = 0.25 \qquad 40\% = \frac{40}{100} = 0.4$$

STEP 2 Translate into an equation and solve.

25% of *g* games plus 4 equals 40% of the number of games *g* plus 4

$$0.25g \quad + \ 4 \ = \ 0.4 \ \cdot \qquad (g + 4)$$

	$0.25g + 4 = 0.4(g + 4)$
Multiply both sides by 100.	$100(0.25g + 4) = 100(0.4)(g + 4)$
Use the Distributive Property and simplify.	$25g + 400 = 40g + 160$
Subtract 160 from both sides.	$25g + 400 - 160 = 40g + 160 - 160$
	$25g + 240 = 40g$
Subtract 25*g* from both sides.	$25g - 25g + 240 = 40g - 25g$
	$240 = 15g$
Divide both sides by 15.	$\frac{240}{15} = \frac{15g}{15}$
	$16 = g$

The team had played 16 games before January.

b. How many games have they now played? How many have they won?

The team has now played *g* + 4 games. $\qquad 16 + 4 = 20$

The team has now won 40% of its 20 games. $\qquad 0.4(20) = 8$

The team has now played 20 games and has won 8 of them.

Try It This Way

To get the variable term on one side and the constant on the other, you can subtract 160 and 25*g* from both sides in a single step.

$$25g + 400 =$$
$$\underline{-25g - 160}$$

$$40g + 160$$
$$\underline{-25g - 160}$$

$$240 = 15g$$

Six Steps to Solving Word Problems

STEP 1 Read the problem carefully and determine what number or numbers you need to find.

STEP 2 Represent one unknown number with a variable.

STEP 3 Use a condition stated in the problem to write an expression for a second number.

STEP 4 Use a second condition to find two expressions that are equal. Then write these two expressions algebraically and connect them with an equals sign.

STEP 5 Solve the equation.

STEP 6 Check to make sure the result matches the conditions stated in the problem.

One-Variable Linear Inequalities

What Came Before?
- Graphing points on a number line
- Solving one-variable linear equations

What's This About?
- Graphing inequalities on a number line
- Solving one-step and two-step linear inequalities
- Solving compound inequalities, including inequalities with absolute value

Practical Apps
- Mechanical engineers use absolute-value inequalities to see whether machine parts may be interchangeable.
- Welders use linear inequalities to account for the expansion and contraction of metal when it is heated or cooled.

Just for FUN!

TEACHER: "Ricky, solve $3k > 6$."

RICKY: "Easy, it's always true."

TEACHER: "Why is that?"

RICKY: "Well, 3(1,000) is a lot more than 6."

You can find more practice problems online by visiting:
www.SWadvantage.com

Inequalities

An **inequality** is a mathematical statement that two quantities are not or may not be equal. An inequality may be true or false. There are five inequality symbols.

$\neq$	$<$	$>$	$\leq$	$\geq$
is not equal to	is less than	is greater than	is less than or equal to	is greater than or equal to

True Inequalities

$3 < 4 \qquad 4 + 2 > 5 \qquad 7(2) \geq 14$
$3 \leq 4 \qquad 4 + 2 \geq 5 \qquad 8 - 3 \neq 7$

False Inequalities

$7 < 5 \qquad 7(2) > 14 \qquad 10 - 3 \neq 7$

An **algebraic inequality** is an inequality with a variable. A value of the variable that makes the inequality true is a **solution of the inequality**.

The value 5 is a solution of $2x > 7$ because when $x = 5$, $2x > 7$ is true.

The value 0 is not a solution of $2x > 7$ because when $x = 0$, $2x > 7$ is false.

EXAMPLE 1

Tell whether 0.5 is a solution of each inequality.

a. $6x \leq 3$

$6(0.5) \leq 3$ Substitute 0.5 for x.

$3 \leq 3$ Simplify.

$3 \leq 3$ is true, so 0.5 is a solution.

b. $27 - 15x > 20$

$27 - 15(0.5) > 20$

$27 - 7.5 > 20$

$19.5 > 20$

$19.5 > 20$ is false, so 0.5 is *not* a solution.

EXAMPLE 2

Evaluate $4x - 6$ and $2(x + 5)$ for $x = 7$, 8, and 9. Place the correct symbol, $<$, $=$, or $>$, in the box to make a true statement.

For $x = 7$:

$4x - 6 \;\Box\; 2(x + 5)$

$4(7) - 6 \qquad 2(7 + 5)$ Substitute.

$28 - 6 \qquad 2(12)$ Simplify.

$22 < 24$ Compare.

$4x - 6 \;\boxed{<}\; 2(x + 5)$

For $x = 8$:

$4x - 6 \;\Box\; 2(x + 5)$

$4(8) - 6 \qquad 2(8 + 5)$ Substitute.

$32 - 6 \qquad 2(13)$ Simplify.

$26 = 26$ Compare.

$4x - 6 \;\boxed{=}\; 2(x + 5)$

For $x = 9$:

$4x - 6 \;\Box\; 2(x + 5)$

$4(9) - 6 \qquad 2(9 + 5)$

$36 - 6 \qquad 2(14)$

$30 > 28$

$4x - 6 \;\boxed{>}\; 2(x + 5)$

Translating Words into Inequalities

 EXAMPLE 3

Write an inequality for each situation.

a. The cable TV company offers more than two hundred channels.

The words "more than" indicate a *greater than* symbol.

Number of channels > 200

b. The express lane is for fifteen items or fewer.

The word "fewer" indicates a *less than* symbol or a *less than or equal to* symbol. The word "or" tells you that it should be *less than or equal to*.

Number of items ≤ 15

 EXAMPLE 4

Translate each sentence into an inequality.

a. Seventy-two is no more than twice the number of children c.

Seventy-two is no more than twice the number of children *c*.

$$72 \qquad \leq \qquad 2 \cdot \qquad c$$

The inequality is $72 \leq 2c$.

b. A number r plus 2.75 has a maximum value of 6.25.

A number *r* plus 2.75 has a maximum value of 6.25.

$$r \qquad + \quad 2.75 \qquad \leq \qquad 6.25$$

The inequality is $r + 2.75 \leq 6.25$.

Watch Out ⚠

Maximum and *no more than* may make you think of "greater," but these are expressions that indicate something is *less* than or equal to another value.

No more than is the opposite of *more than*.

Inequality Symbols

Look for key words to help you choose the inequality symbol.

Symbol	Key Words
$>$	is greater than, is more than, exceeds
$<$	is less than, are fewer than
$\geq$	is no less than, is at least, has a minimum of
$\leq$	is no more than, is at most, has a maximum value of

Solutions of Inequalities

The inequality $x \geq 2$ has an infinite number of solutions. The numbers 2, 3, 5.5, and 100 are all solutions. The *solution set* includes all numbers that are equal to or greater than 2.

A **solution set** is the set of all solutions of an inequality. Because all solutions cannot be listed, the best way to show the solutions of an inequality is with a graph. The **graph of an inequality** is the graph of all solutions on a number line.

When graphing an inequality that relates a variable to a number, follow these rules.

- An open circle ○ shows a number that is *not* a solution.

- A closed circle ● shows a number that is a solution.

- An arrow ← or → shows that the solution set includes numbers beyond the extent of the graph.

SEARCH

To see step-by-step videos of these problems, enter the page number into the SWadvantage.com Search Bar.

EXAMPLE 5

Graph $x \geq 2$.

STEP 1 Because 2 is a solution, make a *closed* circle at 2.

STEP 2 Test a point to the left of 2.

> $0 > 2$ is false, so 0 is not a solution. Don't shade this side.

STEP 3 Test a point to the right of 2.

> $5 > 2$ is true, so 5 is a solution. Shade this side and make an arrow to the right.

EXAMPLE 6

Graph each inequality.

a. $y < -1$

b. $35 \leq t$

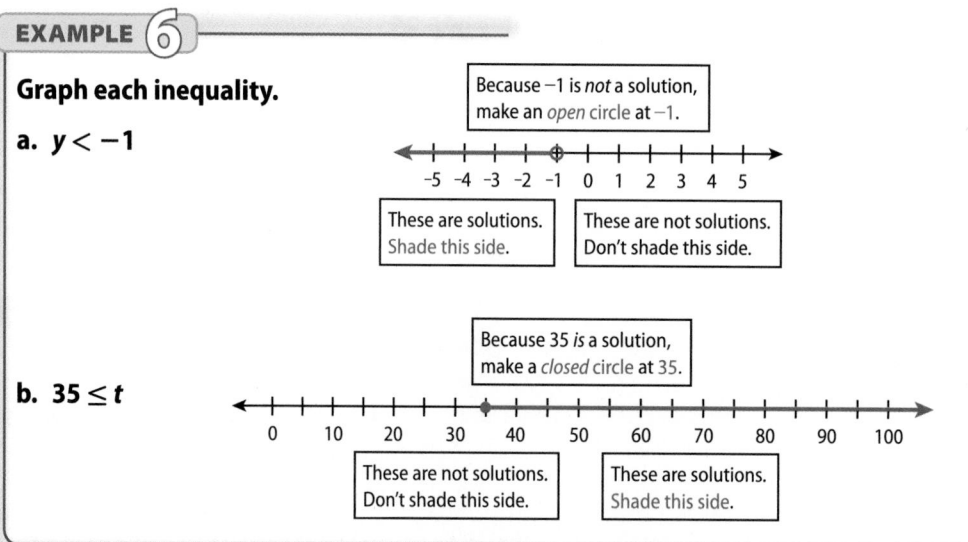

Because −1 is *not* a solution, make an *open* circle at −1.

These are solutions. Shade this side.

These are not solutions. Don't shade this side.

Because 35 *is* a solution, make a *closed* circle at 35.

These are not solutions. Don't shade this side.

These are solutions. Shade this side.

Watch Out !

To graph $35 \leq t$, you need to graph all numbers *greater than or equal to* 35. The inequality can also be written as $t \geq 35$.

EXAMPLE 7

Graph the inequality $-2.5 > p$.

METHOD 1

Make an open circle at -2.5.

Test 0 in the inequality. $-2.5 > 0$ is false.

Test -5 in the inequality. $-2.5 > -5$ is true.

Shade the part of the number line to the left of -2.5.

-7 -6 -5 -4 -3 -2 -1 0 1 2 3

METHOD 2

Flip the inequality, including the symbol.

$-2.5 > p$ means $p < -2.5$

Test 0 in the inequality. Because $0 < -2.5$ is false, shade the number line on the side of -2.5 opposite from 0.

-7 -6 -5 -4 -3 -2 -1 0 1 2 3

The graph of $-2.5 > p$ is the same as the graph of $p < -2.5$.

The solutions of the inequalities $2 < x < 4$ and $4 > x > 2$ are the values of x between 2 and 4. To graph the solutions, shade the interval on the graph between the values. Use the rules for open and closed circles at each end of the interval.

EXAMPLE 8

a. Graph the inequality $-3 \leq x < 5$.

There is a closed circle at -3 and an open circle at 5.

Shade the interval between the two points.

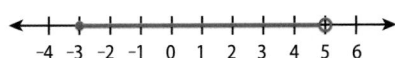

-4 -3 -2 -1 0 1 2 3 4 5 6

b. Write the inequality for the graph below.

15 16 17 18 19 20 21 22 23 24 25

There is an open circle at 17 and a closed circle at 24.

The inequality is $17 < x \leq 24$.

Need More HELP ?

For more help with inequalities of this type, go to *Compound Inequalities* on page 1512.

Solving Inequalities

What happens when you add or subtract the same number to or from both sides of a true inequality?

$$
\begin{array}{cc}
5 & > \quad 4 \\
+\,3 & +\,3 \\
\hline
8 & > \quad 7
\end{array}
\qquad
\begin{array}{cc}
1 & \le \quad 3 \\
+\,5 & +\,5 \\
\hline
6 & \le \quad 8
\end{array}
\qquad
\begin{array}{cc}
10 & < \quad 11 \\
-\,2 & -\,2 \\
\hline
8 & < \quad 9
\end{array}
\qquad
\begin{array}{cc}
13 & \ge \quad 10 \\
-\,10 & -\,10 \\
\hline
3 & \ge \quad 0
\end{array}
$$

All True!

The resulting inequality is always true. So adding or subtracting the same quantity from both sides of an algebraic inequality never changes the solution set.

When you solve an inequality, you isolate the variable on one side of the inequality, just as you do for equations. To check the solution of an inequality, substitute a number from the solution set.

Inequalities with Addition

> **EXAMPLE 1**
>
> **Solve. Graph the solution on a number line and check.**
>
> **a.** $x + 7 > 16$
>
> $$x + 7 > 16$$
>
> Subtract 7 from both sides. $-\,7 \quad\quad -\,7$
>
> Simplify. $x \quad > \quad 9$
>
>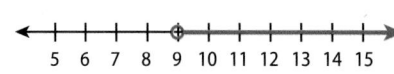
>
> **CHECK**   Substitute a number greater than 9. $x + 7 > 16$
>
>   Substitute 10 for x. $10 + 7 \overset{?}{>} 16$
>
>   Simplify. The inequality is true. $17 > 16 \checkmark$
>
> **b.** $2 \ge 13 + k$
>
> $$2 \ge 13 + k$$
>
> Subtract 13 from both sides. $-\,13 \quad\quad -\,13$
>
> Simplify. $-11 \ge \quad k$
>
>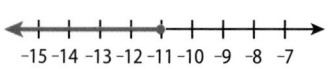
>
> **CHECK**   Substitute a number less than -11. $2 \ge 13 + k$
>
>   Substitute -13 for k. $2 \overset{?}{\ge} 13 + (-13)$
>
>   Simplify. The inequality is true. $2 \ge 0 \checkmark$

Need More HELP

When you check the solution of an inequality, you can choose any number in the solution set. So choose a number that is easy to work with in the original inequality.

For example, if the solution is $x < 5$, testing 0 in the original inequality may be easy to do.

EXAMPLE 2

Manuel needs at least 280 points on his exams to earn an A in the class. He has 237 exam points before his final exam. How many points does he need on his final exam to earn an A?

SEARCH

To see step-by-step videos of these problems, enter the page number into the SWadvantage.com Search Bar.

The number of points needed plus 237 is at least 280.

$$p \qquad + \ 237 \quad \geq \quad 280$$

$$p + 237 \geq \quad 280$$

Subtract 237 from both sides. $\qquad - \ 237 \qquad - \ 237$

Simplify. $\qquad p \qquad \geq \qquad 43$

Manuel needs at least 43 points on his final exam to get an A.

Inequalities with Subtraction

EXAMPLE 3

Solve $x - \frac{2}{3} < 1\frac{1}{3}$. Graph the solution on a number line.

$$x - \frac{2}{3} < 1\frac{1}{3}$$

Write $1\frac{1}{3}$ as an improper fraction. $\qquad x - \frac{2}{3} < \quad \frac{4}{3}$

Add $\frac{2}{3}$ to both sides. $\qquad x - \frac{2}{3} + \frac{2}{3} < \frac{4}{3} + \frac{2}{3}$

Simplify. $\qquad x < 2$

```
    ◄─┼──┼──┼──┼──┼──┼──◌──┼──┼──┼─►
     -5 -4 -3 -2 -1  0  1  2  3  4  5
```

Properties of Inequality

If $a > b$, these properties are true.

Addition Property of Inequality $\qquad a + c > b + c$

Subtraction Property of Inequality $\qquad a - c > b - c$

These properties are also true for the other inequality symbols: $\leq, >, \geq$.

One-Step Multiplication and Division Inequalities

Multiplying or Dividing by a Positive Number

What happens if you multiply or divide both sides of a true inequality by the same *positive* number?

$6 > 2$	$2 \le 4$	$10 < 15$	$2 < 5$
$3(6) > 3(2)$	$\frac{1}{2}(2) \le \frac{1}{2}(4)$	$\frac{10}{5} < \frac{15}{5}$	$\frac{2}{0.5} < \frac{5}{0.5}$
All true! $18 > 6$	$1 \le 2$	$2 < 3$	$4 < 10$

The resulting inequality is *always* true. So multiplying or dividing both sides of an algebraic inequality by the same positive number does not change the solution set.

SEARCH

To see step-by-step videos of these problems, enter the page number into the SWadvantage.com Search Bar.

EXAMPLE 1

Solve. Graph the solution on a number line and check.

a. $2x < 30$

$$2x < 30$$

Divide both sides by 2. $\dfrac{2x}{2} < \dfrac{30}{2}$

Simplify. $x < 15$

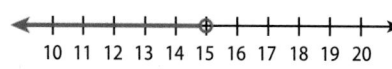

CHECK Substitute a number less than 15. $2x < 30$

Substitute 10 for x. $2(10) \stackrel{?}{<} 30$

Multiply. The inequality is true. $20 < 30$ ✔

b. $\frac{3}{4}x \ge 6$

$$\frac{3}{4}x \ge 6$$

Multiply both sides by $\frac{4}{3}$. $\frac{4}{3}\left(\frac{3}{4}x\right) \ge \frac{4}{3}(6)$

Simplify. $x \ge 8$

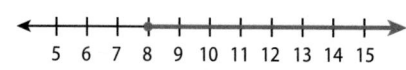

CHECK Substitute a number greater than 8. $\frac{3}{4}x \ge 6$

Substitute 12 for x. $\frac{3}{4}(12) \stackrel{?}{\ge} 6$

Simplify. $\frac{36}{4} \stackrel{?}{\ge} 6$

The inequality is true. $9 \ge 6$ ✔

EXAMPLE 2

The perimeter of a playground shaped like a regular hexagon cannot exceed 200 ft. What is the length of each side of the playground?

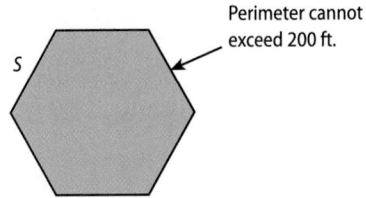

Perimeter cannot exceed 200 ft.

The playground has 6 sides of equal length.

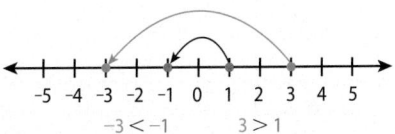

6 times the length of each side cannot exceed 200

$$6 \quad \cdot \quad s \quad \leq \quad 200$$

$$6s \leq 200$$

Divide both sides by 6. $\dfrac{6s}{6} \leq \dfrac{200}{6}$

Simplify. $s \leq 33\dfrac{1}{3}$

The length of each side of the playground is less than or equal to $33\dfrac{1}{3}$ ft, or 33 ft 4 in.

Multiplying or Dividing by a Negative Number

The number 3 is *greater than* 1. The opposite of 3 is *less than* the opposite of 1.

-5 -4 -3 -2 -1 0 1 2 3 4 5

$-3 < -1$ $3 > 1$

Remember, finding the opposite of a number is the same as multiplying by -1.

What happens if you multiply or divide both sides of a true inequality by the same *negative* number?

$6 > 2$	$-3 \leq 1$	$-40 < -30$
$-3(6) > -3(2)$	$-2(-3) \leq -2(1)$	$\dfrac{-40}{-10} < \dfrac{-30}{-10}$
All false! $-18 > -6$	$6 \leq -2$	$4 < 3$

The resulting inequality is *never* true. To make the inequalities true, **reverse** the inequality symbol when you multiply or divide both sides by a negative number.

$6 > 2$	$-3 \leq 1$	$-40 < -30$
Reverse it! $-3(6) < -3(2)$	$-2(-3) \geq -2(1)$	$\dfrac{-40}{-10} > \dfrac{-30}{-10}$
All true! $-18 < -6$	$6 \geq -2$	$4 > 3$

Reversing the Inequality Symbol

SEARCH

To see step-by-step videos of these problems, enter the page number into the SWadvantage.com Search Bar.

EXAMPLE 3

Solve $-x < 5$. Graph the solution on a number line.

$$-x < 5$$

Multiply both sides by -1, and reverse the inequality symbol. $-1(-x) > -1(5)$

Simplify. $x > -5$

If the opposite of a number is less than 5, the number is greater than -5.

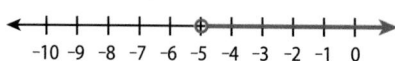

EXAMPLE 4

Solve. Graph the solution on a number line. Check the solution.

a. $-15z \geq 105$

$$-15z \geq 105$$

Divide both sides by -15, and reverse the inequality symbol. $\dfrac{-15z}{-15} \leq \dfrac{105}{-15}$

Simplify. $z \leq -7$

CHECK Substitute a number less than -7. $-15z \geq 105$

Substitute -10 for z. $-15(-10) \overset{?}{\geq} 105$

Multiply. **The inequality is true.** $150 \geq 105$ ✔

b. $-0.25x < 1$

$$-0.25x < 1$$

Multiply both sides by -4, and reverse the inequality symbol. $-4(-0.25x) > -4(1)$

Simplify. $x > -4$

CHECK Substitute a number greater than -4. $-0.25x < 1$

Substitute 0 for x. $-0.25(0) \overset{?}{<} 1$

The inequality is true. $0 < 1$ ✔

EXAMPLE 5

Solve $-16 < -24x$.

METHOD 1

Solve as is.	$-16 < -24x$
Divide both sides by -24. Reverse the inequality symbol.	$\dfrac{-16}{-24} > \dfrac{-24x}{-24}$
Simplify.	$\dfrac{2}{3} > x$

METHOD 2

Isolate the variable on the left side of the inequality.	$-16 < -24x$
Add $24x$ and add 16 to both sides.	$\dfrac{+24x + 16}{24x} < \dfrac{+24x + 16}{16}$
Divide both sides by 24.	$\dfrac{24x}{24} < \dfrac{16}{24}$
Simplify.	$x < \dfrac{2}{3}$

CHECK Substitute a number less than $\dfrac{2}{3}$. $-16 < -24x$

Substitute -2 for x. $-16 \overset{?}{<} -24(-2)$

The inequality is true. $-16 < 48$ ✔

Watch Out !

Don't let a negative number confuse you. To solve an inequality like $-10 < 2x$, you would divide by the *positive* number 2. So don't automatically reverse the inequality symbol whenever you see a negative sign.

Properties of Inequality

	For $a > b$:	For $a < b$:
Multiplication Property of Inequality	$ac > bc$ if $c > 0$	$ac < bc$ if $c > 0$
	$ac < bc$ if $c < 0$	$ac > bc$ if $c < 0$
Division Property of Inequality	$\dfrac{a}{c} > \dfrac{b}{c}$ if $c > 0$	$\dfrac{a}{c} < \dfrac{b}{c}$ if $c > 0$
	$\dfrac{a}{c} < \dfrac{b}{c}$ if $c < 0$	$\dfrac{a}{c} > \dfrac{b}{c}$ if $c < 0$

Similar properties hold for $\leq$ and $\geq$.

Multi-Step Inequalities

Two-Step Inequalities

Solve multi-step inequalities in the same way you solve two-step equations.

EXAMPLE 1

Solve. Graph the solution on a number line. Check the solution.

a. $7x - 5 < 65$

	$7x - 5 < 65$
Add 5 to both sides.	$+5 \phantom{<} +5$
	$7x \phantom{- 5<} < 70$
Divide both sides by 7.	$\dfrac{7x}{7} < \dfrac{70}{7}$
Simplify.	$x < 10$

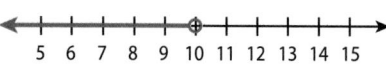

CHECK Substitute a number less than 10. $7x - 5 < 65$

Substitute 9 for x. $7(9) - 5 \overset{?}{<} 65$

Multiply. $63 - 5 \overset{?}{<} 65$

Subtract. $58 < 65$

The inequality is true.

> ### Watch Out !
> Remember, a fraction indicates division. So use multiplication to undo the operation.

b. $\dfrac{m}{2} + 3 \geq 21$

	$\dfrac{m}{2} + 3 \geq 21$
Subtract 3 from both sides.	$\phantom{\dfrac{m}{2} +}-3 -3$
	$\dfrac{m}{2} \geq 18$
Multiply both sides by 2.	$(2)\dfrac{m}{2} \geq (2)18$
Simplify.	$m \geq 36$

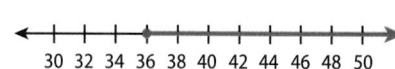

CHECK Substitute a number greater than 36. $\dfrac{m}{2} + 3 \geq 21$

Substitute 40 for m. $\dfrac{40}{2} + 3 \overset{?}{\geq} 21$

Divide and add. $20 + 3 \geq 21$

The inequality is true. $23 \geq 21$ ✔

EXAMPLE 2

A school club wants to make a profit of at least $800 on a raffle. The club has spent $250 for the prizes. How many $5 tickets must the club members sell?

SEARCH

To see step-by-step videos of these problems, enter the page number into the SWadvantage.com Search Bar.

STEP 1 Translate into an inequality.

To determine the profit, subtract the costs from the ticket sales.

$5 times the number of tickets sold minus $250 must be at least 800

$$5 \cdot t - 250 \geq 800$$

$$5t - 250 \geq 800$$

Add 250 to both sides. $+\ 250\quad +\ 250$

$$5t \geq 1{,}050$$

Divide both sides by 5. $\dfrac{5t}{5} \geq \dfrac{1{,}050}{5}$

Simplify. $t \geq 210$

The club members need to sell at least 210 raffle tickets.

STEP 2 Make a table to check possible solutions.

Tickets sold	200	210	220
Sales	5(200) = $1,000	5(210) = $1,050	5(220) = $1,100
Costs	$250	$250	$250
Profit = Sales − Costs	$750	$800 ✔	$850 ✔

Numbers from the solution set meet the conditions in the problem.

EXAMPLE 3

Solve $1.2(k + 3) \leq 24$.

METHOD 1

Use the Distributive Property.

$$1.2(k + 3) \leq 24$$

Multiply. $1.2(k) + 1.2(3) \leq 24$

Simplify. $1.2k + 3.6 \leq 24$

Multiply both sides by 10 to clear the decimals. $10(1.2k + 3.6) \leq 10(24)$

Simplify. $12k + 36 \leq 240$

Subtract 36 from both sides. $12k + 36 - 36 \leq 240 - 36$

Divide both sides by 12. $12k \leq 204$

$$k \leq 17$$

METHOD 2

Find the value of $k + 3$.

$$1.2(k + 3) \leq 24$$

Divide both sides by 1.2.

$$\dfrac{1.2(k + 3)}{1.2} \leq \dfrac{24}{1.2}$$

Subtract 3 from both sides.

$$k + 3 \leq 20$$

$$k \leq 17$$

Multiplying or Dividing by a Negative Number

When multiplying or dividing both sides of an inequality by a negative number, reverse the inequality symbol. This rule applies to multi-step inequalities as well as to one-step inequalities.

EXAMPLE 4

SEARCH

To see step-by-step videos of these problems, enter the page number into the SWadvantage.com Search Bar.

Solve. Graph the solution on a number line. Check the solution.

a. $-2x - 1 \geq 5$

Add 1 to both sides.

$$\begin{array}{rcl} -2x - 1 & \geq & 5 \\ +1 & & +1 \\ \hline -2x & \geq & 6 \end{array}$$

Divide both sides by -2. *Reverse* the symbol.

$$\frac{-2x}{-2} \leq \frac{6}{-2}$$

Simplify.

$$x \leq -3$$

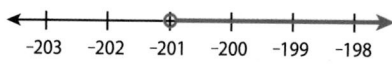

CHECK Substitute a number less than -3.

$$-2x - 1 \geq 5$$

Substitute -4 for x.

$$-2(-4) - 1 \overset{?}{\geq} 5$$

Multiply and then subtract.

$$8 - 1 \overset{?}{\geq} 5$$

The inequality is true.

$$7 \geq 5$$

b. $\dfrac{-1 - x}{2} < 100$

$$\frac{-1 - x}{2} < 100$$

Multiply both sides by 2.

$$2\left(\frac{-1 - x}{2}\right) < 2(100)$$

$$-1 - x < 200$$

Add 1 to both sides to isolate the variable.

$$-1 - x + 1 < 200 + 1$$

$$-x < 201$$

Multiply both sides by -1. Reverse the symbol.

$$x > -201$$

CHECK Substitute a number greater than -201.

$$\frac{-1 - x}{2} \overset{?}{<} 100$$

Substitute 1 for x.

$$\frac{-1 - (1)}{2} \overset{?}{<} 100$$

Subtract and then divide.

$$\frac{-2}{2} \overset{?}{<} 100$$

The inequality is true.

$$-1 < 100 \ ✔$$

EXAMPLE 5

Solve $1 > 13 - 2w$. Graph the solution.

METHOD 1

$$1 > \quad 13 - 2w$$

Subtract 13 from both sides.

$$\underline{-13 \quad -13}$$
$$-12 > \qquad -2w$$

Divide both sides by -2 and flip the inequality symbol.

$$\frac{-12}{-2} < \frac{-2w}{-2}$$

Simplify.

$$6 < w$$

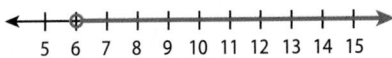

METHOD 2

Multiply both sides by -1 and reverse the inequality symbol.

$$1 > 13 - 2w$$

$$(-1)1 < (-1)13 - (-1)2w$$

Simplify.

$$-1 < -13 + 2w$$

Add 13 to both sides.

$$\underline{+13 \quad +13}$$
$$12 < \qquad 2w$$

Divide both sides by 2.

$$\frac{12}{2} < \frac{2w}{2}$$

$$6 < w$$

Try It

This Way

You know that multiplying both sides of an inequality by -1 changes the sign of each term and reverses the inequality symbol. Use what you know to rewrite $1 > 13 - 2w$ as $-1 < -13 + 2w$.

Steps for Solving a Two-Step Inequality

To solve inequalities like $ax + b < c$, $ax + b > c$, $ax + b \leq c$, or $ax + b \geq c$, where b is a positive or negative number,

1. Add or subtract a constant on both sides to isolate the variable term.

2. Divide both sides by the coefficient of the variable term to isolate the variable. If the coefficient is negative, reverse the inequality symbol.

3. Use order of operations to isolate the variable.

4. Check your solution by testing values of the solution set in the original inequality.

You can graph the solution as a set of numbers on a number line.

Solving Inequalities by Using Tables

If the variable occurs on both sides of an inequality, you may be able to find the solution set by using a table. Find the value that makes the related equation true. Check points on both sides of that value to find which values satisfy the inequality.

SEARCH

To see step-by-step videos of these problems, enter the page number into the SWadvantage.com Search Bar.

EXAMPLE 1

Use a table to solve $5x \geq 3x + 4$. Graph the solution on a number line.

STEP 1 Make a table.

x	Left side 5x	Right side 3x + 4	Is the equation true? 5x = 3x + 4	Is the inequality true? 5x ≥ 3x + 4
0	5(0)	3(0) + 4		
1	5(1)	3(1) + 4		
2	5(2)	3(2) + 4		
3	5(3)	3(3) + 4		
4	5(4)	3(4) + 4		
5	5(5)	3(5) + 4		

STEP 2 Evaluate each side of the inequality for the given value of x. Determine when the equation and the inequality is true.

x	Left side 5x	Right side 3x + 4	Is the equation true? 5x = 3x + 4	Is the inequality true? 5x ≥ 3x + 4
0	0	4	No	No
1	5	7	No	No
2	10	10	Yes	Yes
3	15	13	No	Yes
4	20	16	No	Yes
5	25	19	No	Yes

STEP 3 Graph the solution of the inequality.

Because the solution of the related equation is an integer, that value 2 is the endpoint of the graph of the inequality.

Because the inequality symbol is $\geq$, make a closed circle at $x = 2$.

Notice the values that make the inequality true are greater than or equal to 2, so make the solution arrow point to the right.

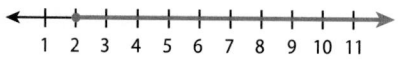

You can make your table horizontal or vertical.

EXAMPLE 2

Use a table to solve 21 + x > 7x − 9. Graph the solution on a number line.

STEP 1 Make a table. Determine when the related equation and the inequality are true.

x	0	1	2	3	4	5	6
21 + x	21 + 0 = 21	22	23	24	25	26	27
7x − 9	7(0) − 9 = −9	−2	5	12	19	26	33
21 + x = 7x − 9	No	No	No	No	No	Yes	No
21 + x > 7x − 9	Yes	Yes	Yes	Yes	Yes	No	No

STEP 3 Graph the solution of the inequality.

Because the solution of the related equation is an integer, that value 5 is the endpoint of the graph of the inequality.

Because the inequality symbol is >, not ≥, make an open circle at $x = 5$.

Notice the values that make the inequality true are less than 5, so make the solution arrow point to the left.

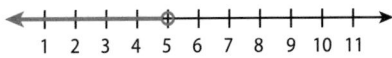

Making a table such as the one above works to find a solution set for an inequality only when the solution of the related equation is an integer that appears as a value of x in the table. When the equation solution is not a value in the table, you cannot determine the endpoint of the inequality.

EXAMPLE 3

Can you use a table to solve 4(x − 1) ≥ x + 7?

x	0	1	2	3	4	5	6
4(x − 1)	−4	0	4	8	12	16	20
x + 7	7	8	9	10	11	12	13
4(x − 1) = x + 7	No	No	No	No	No	No	No
4(x − 1) ≥ x + 7	No	No	No	No	Yes	Yes	Yes

You cannot find the solution from this table because there is no integer value of x for which the expressions $4(x - 1)$ and $x + 7$ are equal. The two expressions are equal for some value of x between 3 and 4.

To solve this inequality, you can use the process shown on page 1510.

Solving Inequalities Algebraically

You can solve inequalities with variables on both sides in the same way that you solve equations with variables on both sides. Just remember to reverse the inequality symbol when you multiply or divide by a negative number.

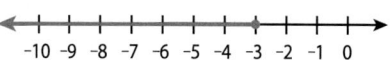

Solve each inequality. Graph the solution on a number line, and check.

a. $3x \geq 7x + 12$

STEP 1 Solve.

To put the variable terms on the same side, first subtract $3x$ from both sides and simplify.

Subtract 12 from both sides to isolate the variable term on the right side, and simplify.

Divide both sides by 4 and simplify.

$$3x \geq 7x + 12$$
$$3x - 3x \geq 7x + 12 - 3x$$
$$0 \geq 4x + 12$$
$$0 - 12 \geq 4x + 12 - 12$$
$$-12 \geq 4x$$
$$\frac{-12}{4} \geq \frac{4x}{4}$$
$$-3 \geq x, \text{ or } x \leq -3$$

STEP 2 Graph.

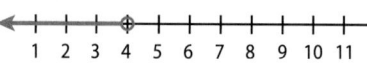

STEP 3 Check that 0 is not a solution of the original inequality.

$$3x \geq 7x + 12$$

Substitute 0 for x and then multiply.

$$3(0) \overset{?}{\geq} 7(0) + 12$$

0 is *not* a solution of the original inequality.

$$0 \overset{?}{\geq} 12 \; ✗$$

The correct side of the graph is shaded.

b. $\frac{x}{2} < 5 - \frac{3x}{4}$

Solve.

$$\frac{x}{2} < 5 - \frac{3x}{4}$$

Multiply both sides by the LCD, 4.

$$4\left(\frac{x}{2}\right) < 4\left(5 - \frac{3x}{4}\right)$$

Use the Distributive Property.

$$\frac{4x}{2} < 4(5) - 4\left(\frac{3x}{4}\right)$$

Simplify.

$$2x < 20 - 3x$$

Add $3x$ to both sides.

$$2x + 3x < 20 - 3x + 3x$$

Simplify.

$$5x < 20$$

Divide both sides by 5.

$$x < 4$$

Graph.

You can check by substitution that 0 is a solution: $\frac{0}{2} < 5 - \frac{3(0)}{4} \longrightarrow 0 < 5$

Try It This Way

You could also subtract $7x$ from both sides as a first step, to put the variable term on the left side. This will result in the inequality $-4x \geq 12$.

To find the value of x, you will then need to reverse the inequality symbol when you divide both sides of the inequality by -4.

EXAMPLE 5

E-Glou Communications offers two text messaging plans. The monthly fees are shown below.

Plan A: $9.99 plus $.03 per message   **Plan B: $4.99 plus $.05 per message**

For how many messages is plan A cheaper than plan B? Graph the solution.

SEARCH

To see step-by-step videos of these problems, enter the page number into the SWadvantage.com Search Bar.

STEP 1 Translate into an inequality.

Let m be the number of text messages.

Cost of Plan A				<		Cost of Plan B			
$9.99	plus	$.03	times	number of messages	is less than	4.99	plus	$.05	times	number of messages
9.99	+	0.03	·	m	<	4.99	+	0.05	·	m

STEP 2 Solve.

$$9.99 + 0.03m < 4.99 + 0.05m$$

Subtract 4.99 from both sides.

$$\begin{array}{r} 9.99 + 0.03m < 4.99 + 0.05m \\ -4.99 \qquad\qquad -4.99 \\ \hline 5 + 0.03m < \qquad 0.05m \end{array}$$

Subtract 0.03m from both sides.

$$5 + 0.03m - 0.03m < 0.05m - 0.03m$$

Simplify.

$$5 < 0.02m$$

Divide both sides by 0.02.

$$\frac{5}{0.02} < \frac{0.02m}{0.02}$$

Simplify.

$$250 < m$$

$$m > 250$$

Plan A is cheaper for more than 250 text messages.

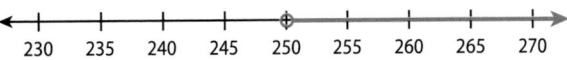

STEP 3 Make a table to check the solution.

Text Messages m	240	250	260
Cost of plan A	$9.99 + $.03(240) = $17.19	$9.99 + $.03(250) = $17.49	$9.99 + $.03(260) = $17.79
Cost of plan B	$4.99 + $.05(240) = $16.99	$4.99 + $.05(250) = $17.49	$4.99 + $.05(260) = $17.99
Cheaper Plan	B	neither	A

The table verifies the solution.

Try It This Way

When you use the Distributive Property to simplify one side of the inequality, use a ruler to cover the other side. What you're simplifying won't look as complicated.

Simplifying Each Side Before Solving

You may be able to simplify on one or both sides of the given inequality as a first step of your solution.

Solve $4(x - 1) \geq x + 7$. Graph the solution.

Use the Distributive Property on the left side of the inequality.	$4(x - 1) \geq x + 7$
	$4(x) - 4(1) \geq x + 7$
Simplify.	$4x - 4 \geq x + 7$
Add 4 to both sides to isolate $4x$.	$4x - 4 + 4 \geq x + 7 + 4$
Simplify.	$4x \geq x + 11$
Subtract x from both sides.	$4x - x \geq x + 11 - x$
	$3x \geq 11$
Divide both sides by 3.	$\dfrac{3x}{3} \geq \dfrac{11}{3}$
Simplify.	$x \geq 3\dfrac{2}{3}$

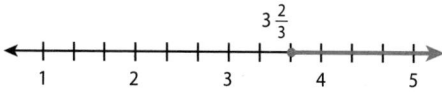

SEARCH

To see step-by-step videos of these problems, enter the page number into the SWadvantage.com Search Bar.

EXAMPLE 6

Both triangles are equilateral. The perimeter of triangle _D_ is less than the perimeter of triangle _C_. What is the minimum value of _x_ if _x_ is a whole number? What is the maximum value?

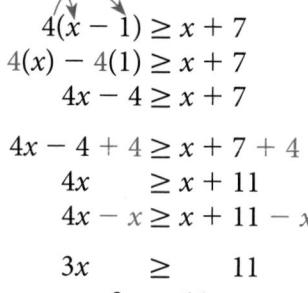

Because the perimeter of triangle _D_ is less than the perimeter of triangle _C_, the side length of triangle _D_ is less than the side length of triangle _C_.

Use the Distributive Property.	$30 - 2x < 2(x + 4) - 6$
	$30 - 2x < 2(x) + 2(4) - 6$
Simplify the right side.	$30 - 2x < 2x + 8 - 6$
	$30 - 2x < 2x + 2$
Subtract 2 from both sides.	$30 - 2x - 2 < 2x + 2 - 2$
	$28 - 2x < 2x$
Add $2x$ to both sides.	$28 - 2x + 2x < 2x + 2x$
Simplify.	$28 < 4x$
Divide both sides by 4 and simplify.	$\dfrac{28}{4} < \dfrac{4x}{4}$

The value of x is greater than 7. $\qquad\qquad 7 < x$, or $x > 7$

So the minimum value of x is 8.

Notice that for $x = 15$, the side length of triangle _D_ becomes $30 - 2(15)$, or 0. Since the side length of triangle _D_ must be greater than 0, the maximum value of x is 14.

No Solutions or All Solutions

An inequality may have no solutions, or every real number may be a solution.

Need More

HELP

For more review of combining like terms, go to *Multi-Step Equations* on page 1468.

EXAMPLE 7

Solve each inequality.

a. $x + 2x + 5 \geq 3(x + 2)$

	$x + 2x + 5 \geq 3(x + 2)$
Use the Distributive Property.	$x + 2x + 5 \geq 3(x) + 3(2)$
Simplify.	$x + 2x + 5 \geq 3x + 6$
Combine like terms on the left side of the inequality.	$3x + 5 \geq 3x + 6$
Subtract $3x$ from both sides.	$3x + 5 - 3x \geq 3x + 6 - 3x$
The inequality is never true.	$5 \geq 6$ ✗
There is no solution.	

b. $-(2 - x) - 1 < x - 2$

	$-(2 - x) - 1 < x - 2$
Use the Distributive Property.	$-(1)(2) - (-1)(x) - 1 < x - 2$
Simplify.	$-2 + x - 1 < x - 2$
Use the Commutative Property to add.	$x - 3 < x - 2$
Subtract x from both sides.	$x - 3 - x < x - 2 - x$
The equation is always true.	$-3 < -2$ ✔
Every real number is a solution.	

Got to KNOW!

To Solve Inequalities with Variables on Both Sides

1. Simplify each side of the inequality.

2. Use inverse operations to isolate variable terms on one side of the inequality.

3. If you multiply or divide both sides by a negative number, reverse the inequality symbol.

4. When solving, if you get an inequality that is *never* true, like $2 > 3$, there is *no solution* to the original inequality.

5. If you get an inequality that is *always* true, like $5 \geq 4$, every real number is a solution of the original inequality.

Compound Inequalities

The Words *And* and *Or*

A **compound statement** is formed by using the word *and* or *or* to combine two simple statements. A compound statement may be true or false, depending on whether each simple statement is true or false.

Two simple statements are given below.

Statement *P*: Figure 1 is a triangle.   Statement *Q*: Figure 2 is a circle.

Two compound statements can be made, using the two simple statements.

1. *P* and *Q*: Figure 1 is a triangle and Figure 2 is a circle.

2. *P* or *Q*:   Figure 1 is a triangle or Figure 2 is a circle.

The truth table below shows all four possibilities for the truth of each compound statement.

> **Watch Out !**
>
> Any false statement in an *and* compound statement makes the entire statement false.
>
> For more help with truth values, see *Conditionals* in *Geometry* (Book 1, p. 612).

Figure 1	Figure 2	*P* is	*Q* is	*P* and *Q* is	*P* or *Q* is
△	○	true	true	true	true
△	□	true	false	false	true
□	○	false	true	false	true
□	□	false	false	false	false

When two simple inequalities are joined by *and* or *or*, the result is a **compound inequality**.

Compound Statement	Compound Inequality	Graph
Solution set is all real numbers greater than 3 and less than 5.	$3 < x$ and $x < 5$ $3 < x < 5$	Only $x < 5$ true $x > 3$ and $x < 5$ true Only $x > 3$ true 2 3 4 5 6 *And* compound: Both need to be true.
Solution set is all real numbers less than or equal to 3 or greater than or equal to 5.	$x \leq 3$ or $x \geq 5$	$x \leq 3$ true Neither is true. $x \geq 5$ true 2 3 4 5 6 *Or* compound: Only one needs to be true.

EXAMPLE 1

What compound inequality is graphed below?

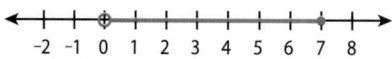

Each number graphed satisfies both $x > 0$ and $x \leq 7$. The compound inequality is $0 < x \leq 7$.

Solving *And* Inequalities—Conjunctions

A compound statement with two inequalities separated by the word *and* is a conjunction. Solve conjunctions the same way you would solve simple inequalities. Because both simple inequalities must be true for a conjunction to be true, the graph of a conjunction is the *intersection* of the graphs of the simple inequalities.

EXAMPLE 2

Solve $3 < x + 1 < 6$. Graph the solution on a number line.

STEP 1 Separate the inequality into two statements with the word *and*.
The inequality is a conjunction. $\qquad 3 < x + 1$ and $x + 1 < 6$

STEP 2 Solve each simple inequality.

Subtract 1 from both sides
of each inequality.

$$
\begin{array}{ccc}
3 < x + 1 & \text{and} & x + 1 < 6 \\
\underline{-1 \quad -1} & & \underline{-1 \quad -1} \\
2 < x & \text{and} & x < 5
\end{array}
$$

STEP 3 Graph the intersection of the two inequalities: $2 < x < 5$.

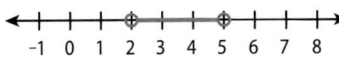

SEARCH
To see step-by-step videos of these problems, enter the page number into the SWadvantage.com Search Bar.

Notice that the same operation was used to solve both inequalities in Example 2.

EXAMPLE 3

Solve $-8 \le 3x - 5 < 13$. Graph the solution on a number line.

You can solve the compound inequality without separating it. The goal is to isolate x between the two inequality signs.

The inequality is a conjunction.

STEP 1 Add 5 to each part of the inequality.

$$
\begin{array}{ccc}
-8 \le 3x - 5 < & 13 \\
\underline{+5 \qquad +5} & \underline{+5} \\
-3 \le 3x < & 18
\end{array}
$$

STEP 2 Divide each part by 3 to isolate x.

$$\frac{-3}{3} \le \frac{3x}{3} < \frac{18}{3}$$

$$-1 \le x < 6$$

STEP 3 Graph the solution.

Need More

HELP

Remember, the union of two sets A and B is the set of all elements that are in A or B. The intersection of A and B is the set of all elements that are in both A and B.

For more help with sets, see *Venn Diagrams* in *Statistics and Probability* (p. 1288).

Solving *Or* Inequalities—Disjunctions

A compound statement with two inequalities separated by the word *or* is a **disjunction**. Solve disjunctions the same way you would solve conjunctions. Because only one of the simple inequalities must be true for a disjunction to be true, the graph of a disjunction is the *union* of the graphs of the simple inequalities.

EXAMPLE 4

Solve $x - 6 > -3$ or $x + 15 < 11$. Graph the solution on a number line.

STEP 1 Notice that the inequality is two statements connected by the word *or*. The inequality is a disjunction.

$$x - 6 > -3 \text{ or } x + 15 < 11$$

STEP 2 Solve each simple inequality.

Use inverse operations to isolate x in each inequality.

$$
\begin{array}{rcl}
x - 6 > -3 & \text{or} & x + 15 < 11 \\
\underline{+6 \quad +6} & & \underline{-15 \quad -15} \\
x \quad > \quad 3 & \text{or} & x \quad < \quad -4
\end{array}
$$

STEP 3 Graph the union of the two inequalities.

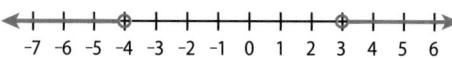

SEARCH

To see step-by-step videos of these problems, enter the page number into the SWadvantage.com Search Bar.

EXAMPLE 5

Solve $2 > 4 - \frac{2x}{5}$ or $6 \geq 2x$. Graph the solution on a number line.

The inequality is a disjunction. Solve each simple inequality.

$$2 > 4 - \frac{2x}{5} \quad \text{or} \quad 6 \geq 2x$$

Use inverse operations.

$$5(2) > 5\left(4 - \frac{2x}{5}\right) \quad \text{or} \quad \frac{6}{2} \geq \frac{2x}{2}$$

Use the Distributive Property on the first inequality.

$$10 > 20 - 2x \quad \text{or} \quad 3 \geq x$$

Subtract 20 from both sides.

$$10 - 20 > 20 - 20 - 2x$$
$$-10 > -2x$$

Divide by -2 and reverse the inequality symbol.

$$\frac{-10}{-2} < \frac{-2x}{-2}$$
$$5 < x$$

Graph the disjunction $5 < x$ or $3 \geq x$.

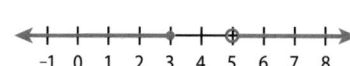

EXAMPLE 6

After a penalty, the distance of the football from the goal line will be half the current distance minus 3 yards. The football will be between 1 and 2 yards from the goal line. How far is the football from the goal line now?

STEP 1 Translate into a compound inequality.

Let d = current distance to the goal line. The word *between* means a conjunction.

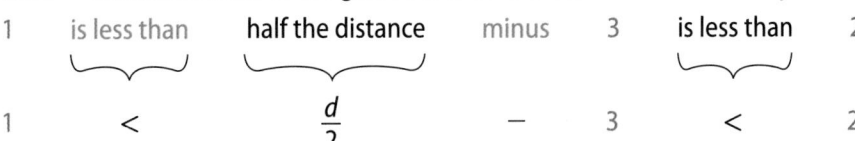

1	is less than	half the distance	minus	3	is less than	2

1	$<$	$\dfrac{d}{2}$	$-$	3	$<$	2

STEP 2 Solve.

$$1 < \frac{d}{2} - 3 < 2$$

Add 3 to each part to isolate $\dfrac{d}{2}$.

$$\begin{array}{ccc} +\,3 & +\,3 & +\,3 \\ \hline 4 < & \frac{d}{2} & < 5 \end{array}$$

Multiply each part by 2 to isolate d. $$2(4) < 2\left(\frac{d}{2}\right) < 2(5)$$

Simplify. $$8 < d < 10$$

The football is between 8 yards and 10 yards from the goal line.

EXAMPLE 7

Solve.

a. $x < 1$ and $x > 3$

There is no solution.

b. $x < 3$ or $x > 1$

Every value of x is a solution.

c. $x > 1$ and $x > 3$

The solution is $x > 3$.

d. $x > 1$ or $x > 3$

The solution is $x > 1$.

Try It This Way

Graph the two simple inequalities in each part of Example 7 above each other. Use a kind of vertical line test to see where both inequalities are true for the conjunctions and where either is true for the disjunctions.

Conjunctions and Disjunctions

Conjunctions are *and* statements. Both statements must be true for the conjunction to be true.

$x > 1$ and $x < 2$
$1 < x < 2$

Disjunctions are *or* statements. Only one statement must be true for the conjunction to be true.

$x < 1$ or $x > 2$

Absolute-Value Inequalities

Absolute Value with "Less than"

Remember that the absolute value of a number is its distance from 0 on a number line. The graph shows all values of x with an absolute value less than 3.

The distance from 0 is less than 3.

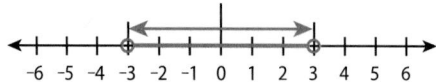

The graph shows all points that are less than 3 units from 0. Notice that the graph matches the graph of the conjunction $-3 < x < 3$. You can solve a "less than" absolute-value inequality by solving the related conjunction. Check your solution by choosing two points in different intervals and substituting into the original inequality.

SEARCH

To see step-by-step videos of these problems, enter the page number into the SWadvantage.com Search Bar.

EXAMPLE 1

Solve. Graph the solution on a number line.

a. $|x| + 7 < 9$

Isolate the absolute value. Because 7 is added to $|x|$, subtract 7 from both sides.
The distance from 0 to x is less than 2.

$$\begin{array}{rcr} |x| + 7 &<& 9 \\ -7 && -7 \\ \hline |x| &<& 2 \end{array}$$

Graph $-2 < x < 2$.

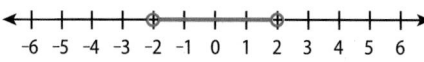

CHECK Substitute $x = 1$ and $x = -3$.

$|x| + 7 < 9$	$|x| + 7 < 9$
$|1| + 7 < 9$	$|-3| + 7 < 9$
$1 + 7 < 9$	$3 + 7 < 9$
$8 < 9$ ✔	$10 < 9$ ✘

The value $x = 1$ works and $x = -3$ does not. The solution is $-2 < x < 2$.

b. $|x| - 24 \leq -15$

Isolate the absolute value. Because 24 is subtracted from $|x|$, add 24 to both sides.
The distance from 0 to x is less than or equal to 9.

$$\begin{array}{rcr} |x| - 24 &\leq& -15 \\ +24 && +24 \\ \hline |x| &\leq& 9 \end{array}$$

Graph $-9 \leq x \leq 9$.

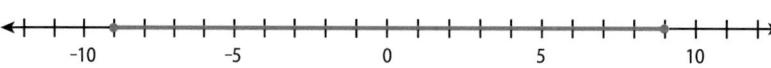

CHECK Substitute $x = -5$ and $x = 10$.

$|x| - 24 \leq -15$	$|x| - 24 \leq -15$
$|-5| - 24 \leq -15$	$|10| - 24 \leq -15$
$5 - 24 \leq -15$	$10 - 24 \leq -15$
$-19 \leq -15$ ✔	$-14 \leq -15$ ✘

The value $x = -5$ works and $x = 10$ does not. The solution is $-9 \leq x \leq 9$.

EXAMPLE 2

Solve $\frac{|x|}{10} < 0.55$. Graph the solution on a number line.

Isolate the absolute value. Because $|x|$ is divided by 10, multiply both sides by 10.

$$\frac{|x|}{10} < 0.55$$

$$10 \cdot \frac{|x|}{10} < 10 \cdot 0.55$$

The distance from 0 to x is less than 5.5.

$$|x| < 5.5$$

Graph $-5.5 < x < 5.5$.

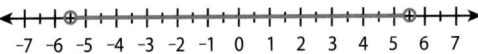

CHECK Substitute $x = 4$ and $x = -6$.

$$\frac{|x|}{10} < 0.55 \qquad \frac{|x|}{10} < 0.55$$

$$\frac{|4|}{10} < 0.55 \qquad \frac{|-6|}{10} < 0.55$$

$$\frac{4}{10} < 0.55 \qquad \frac{6}{10} < 0.55$$

Divide to convert fractions to decimals.

$$0.4 < 0.55 \ ✔ \qquad 0.6 < 0.55 \ ✗$$

The value $x = 4$ works and $x = -6$ does not. The solution is $-5.5 < x < 5.5$.

If the absolute value is on the right side of the inequality, you can reverse the inequality before solving.

EXAMPLE 3

Solve $60 \geq 15|x|$.

$$60 \geq 15|x|$$

Reverse the entire inequality.

$$15|x| \leq 60$$

Divide by 15 to isolate the absolute value.

$$\frac{15|x|}{15} \leq \frac{60}{15}$$

Simplify.

$$|x| \leq 4$$

The solution is $-4 \leq x \leq 4$.

CHECK Substitute $x = 0$ and $x = 5$.

$$60 \geq 15|x| \qquad 60 \geq 15|x|$$
$$60 \geq 15|0| \qquad 60 \geq 15|5|$$
$$60 \geq 15(0) \qquad 60 \geq 15(5)$$
$$60 \geq 0 \ ✔ \qquad 60 \geq 75 \ ✗$$

The value $x = 0$ works and $x = 5$ does not. The solution is $-4 \leq x \leq 4$.

Watch Out !

Don't confuse reversing an entire inequality with reversing only the inequality symbol when multiplying or dividing by a negative number.

Expressions Within Absolute-Value Bars

An expression within absolute-value bars also represents distance.

The inequality $|x - 6| < 5$ means that the value of $x - 6$ is between -5 and 5.

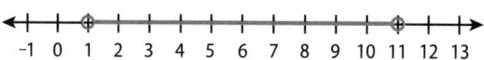

EXAMPLE 4

Solve $|x - 6| < 5$. Graph the solution on a number line.

The inequality is a conjunction.	$-5 < x - 6 < \quad 5$
Add 6 to each part of the inequality to isolate x.	$\underline{+6 \qquad +6 \quad +6}$
	$1 < x \qquad < \quad 11$

Graph the conjunction $1 < x < 11$.

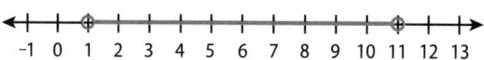

CHECK Test values of x greater than and less than 6.

$|x - 6| < 5$	$|x - 6| < 5$
$|4 - 6| < 5$	$|9 - 6| < 5$
$|-2| < 5$	$|3| < 5$
$2 < 5$ ✔	$3 < 5$ ✔

The solution is $1 < x < 11$.

Watch Out !

Don't use inverse operations within the absolute-value bars. Wait until the absolute-value expression is isolated and written as a conjunction with the absolute-value bars removed.

EXAMPLE 5

Solve $3 \geq |0.5x - 1|$. Check whether the endpoints of the solution are correct.

Reverse the entire inequality.	$|0.5x - 1| \leq 3$
The inequality is a conjunction.	$-3 \leq \quad 0.5x - 1 \leq 3$
Multiply the inequality by 2 to clear the decimal.	$2(-3) \leq 2(0.5x - 1) \leq 2(3)$
Simplify.	$-6 \leq \quad x - 2 \leq 6$
Add 2 to each part to isolate x.	$\underline{+2 \qquad\qquad +2 \quad +2}$
	$-4 \leq \quad x \qquad \leq 8$

CHECK Substitute $x = -4$ and $x = 8$.

$3 \geq |0.5x - 1|$	$3 \geq |0.5x - 1|$
$3 \geq |0.5(-4) - 1|$	$3 \geq |0.5(8) - 1|$
$3 \geq |-2 - 1|$	$3 \geq |4 - 1|$
$3 \geq |-3|$	$3 \geq |3|$
$3 \geq 3$ ✔	$3 \geq 3$ ✔

The endpoints are correct.

The solution is $-4 \leq x \leq 8$.

SEARCH

To see step-by-step videos of these problems, enter the page number into the SWadvantage.com Search Bar.

EXAMPLE 6

Solve $|4x - 2| + 6 \leq 12$. Graph the solution on a number line.

Isolate the absolute-value expression. Because 6 is added, subtract 6 from both sides.

$$
\begin{array}{r}
|4x - 2| + 6 \leq\ \ 12 \\
-6 \quad -6 \\
\hline
|4x - 2| \ \ \leq\ \ \ 6
\end{array}
$$

The inequality is a conjunction.

Add 2 to each part of the inequality to isolate $4x$.

$$
\begin{array}{r}
-6 \leq 4x - 2 \leq\ \ \ 6 \\
+2 \qquad +2 \quad +2 \\
\hline
-4 \leq 4x \quad\ \ \ \leq\ \ \ 8
\end{array}
$$

Divide each part by 4 to isolate x.

$$\frac{-4}{4} \leq \frac{4x}{4} \leq \frac{8}{4}$$

$$-1 \leq x \leq 2$$

Graph the conjunction $-1 \leq x \leq 2$.

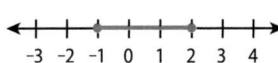

Absolute Value with "Greater than"

The graph below represents all values of x with an absolute value greater than 3.

Each point on the graph has a distance from 0 that is greater than 3 units. The graph matches the graph of the disjunction $x < -3$ or $x > 3$. You can solve a "greater than" absolute-value inequality by solving the related disjunction.

The distance from 0 is greater than 3.

EXAMPLE 7

Solve $|x| + 2 > 3$.

Isolate the absolute value. Because 2 is added to $|x|$, subtract 2 from both sides.

$$
\begin{array}{r}
|x| + 2 >\ \ \ 3 \\
-2 \quad -2 \\
\hline
\end{array}
$$

The distance from 0 to x is greater than 1.

$$|x| \quad\ \ > \quad 1$$

The inequality is a disjunction.

$$x < -1 \text{ or } x > 1$$

CHECK Substitute $x = 2$, $x = -2$, and $x = 0$.

$|x| + 2 > 3$	$|x| + 2 > 3$	$|x| + 2 > 3$
$|2| + 2 > 3$	$|-2| + 2 > 3$	$|0| + 2 > 3$
$2 + 2 > 3$	$2 + 2 > 3$	$0 + 2 > 3$
$4 > 3$ ✔	$4 > 3$ ✔	$2 > 3$ ✘

The values $x = 2$ and $x = -2$ work, and $x = 0$ does not.

The solution is $x < -1$ or $x > 1$.

Disjunctions

SEARCH 🔍

To see step-by-step videos of these problems, enter the page number into the SWadvantage.com Search Bar.

> **EXAMPLE** 8

Solve. Graph the solution on a number line.

a. $|x| + 5 > 12$

Isolate the absolute value. Because 5 is added to $|x|$, subtract 5 from both sides.

$$|x| + 5 > 12$$
$$\underline{\quad -5 \quad\quad -5}$$
$$|x| \quad > \quad 7$$

The distance from 0 to x is greater than 7.

The inequality is a disjunction.

$$x < -7 \text{ or } x > 7$$

Graph $x < -7$ or $x > 7$.

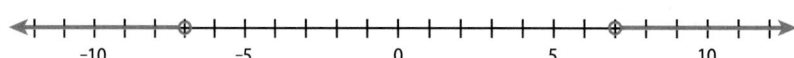

b. $|2x| - 13 \geq -5$

Isolate the absolute value. Because 13 is subtracted from $|2x|$, add 13 to both sides.

$$|2x| - 13 \geq -5$$
$$\underline{\quad +13 \quad\quad +13}$$
$$|2x| \quad \geq \quad 8$$

The inequality is a disjunction.

$$2x \leq -8 \text{ or } 2x \geq 8$$

Divide by 2 to isolate x.

$$\frac{2x}{2} \leq -\frac{8}{2} \text{ or } \frac{2x}{2} \geq \frac{8}{2}$$

The distance from 0 to x is greater than or equal to 4.

$$x \leq -4 \text{ or } x \geq 4$$

Graph $x \leq -4$ or $x \geq 4$.

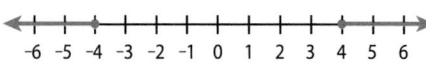

c. $3|x - 8| > 6$

Isolate the absolute value. Divide both sides by 3.

$$\frac{3|x-8|}{3} > \frac{6}{3}$$

The distance from x to 8 is greater than 2.

$$|x - 8| > 2$$

The inequality is a disjunction. Add 8 to each part to isolate x.

$$x - 8 < -2 \text{ or } x - 8 > 2$$
$$\underline{\quad +8 \quad +8 \quad\quad +8 \quad +8}$$
$$x \quad < \quad 6 \text{ or } x \quad > \quad 10$$

Graph $x < 6$ or $x > 10$.

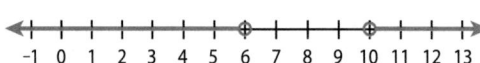

Got to KNOW!

Inequalities with the Same Solution

The inequalities $|x| > 2$ and $|-x| > 2$ have the same solution because opposites have the same absolute value.

So $|x - 8| > 2$ and $|8 - x| > 2$ also have the same solution for that reason.

EXAMPLE 9

In a survey of likely voters, 52% were in favor of a proposal. The survey is accurate within 3%. If 1,500 people vote, how many can be expected to vote for the proposal?

STEP 1 Find each percent.

52% of 1,500 voters = 0.52(1,500) = 780 voters

3% of 1,500 voters = 0.03(1,500) = 45 voters

STEP 2 Write an absolute-value inequality.

Let v be the number expected to vote for the proposal. The word *within* indicates a conjunction. The number of voters is within 45 of 780.

$$|v - 780| \leq 45$$

STEP 3 Solve.

The inequality is a conjunction.

Add 780 to each part of the inequality to isolate v.

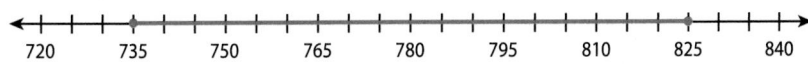

$$-45 \leq v - 780 \leq 45$$
$$+780 \qquad +780 \qquad +780$$
$$735 \leq v \qquad \leq 825$$

From 735 and 825 voters can be expected to vote for the proposal.

You can graph the solution on a number line.

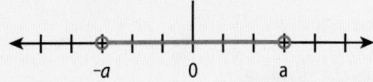

720 735 750 765 780 795 810 825 840

Try It This Way

Finding percents can be time-consuming. Use your calculator to find percents such as 52% of 1,500.

You can also use mental math to find some percents, such as 3% of 1,500. To find 1% of a number, move the decimal point to the left 2 places. So 1% of 1,500 is 15, and 3% is 3 times 15, or 45.

Got to KNOW!

Absolute-Value Inequalities

For a constant a, where $a > 0$, each inequality below has the given meaning, equivalent inequalities, and graph.

$|x| < a$ — the values of x with an absolute value less than a — $-a < x < a$
$x > -a$ and $x < a$

The distance from 0 is less than a.

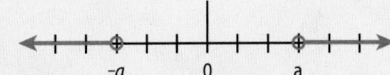

$-a$ 0 a

Similar properties hold true for $|x| \leq a$.

$|x| > a$ — the values of x with an absolute value greater than a — $x < -a$ or $x > a$

The distance from 0 is greater than a.

$-a$ 0 a

Similar properties hold true for $|x| \geq a$.

Two-Variable Linear Equations and Inequalities

What Came Before?

- Graphing points and linear functions in the first quadrant
- Solving one-variable linear equations and inequalities

What's This About?

- Graphing points, linear equations, and linear inequalities in all four quadrants of the coordinate plane
- Understanding and using slopes and intercepts of lines
- Using and converting the three forms of linear equations to solve and graph two-variable equations

Practical Apps

- Pilots use two-variable linear equations to determine "glide" slopes from ground speeds and wind conditions.
- Bank tellers use two-variable linear equations to convert currencies.

Just for FUN!

As the equation ran up the slope, it intercepted the pass.

"Good form!" cheered its teammates.

You can find more practice problems online by visiting:
www.SWadvantage.com

Four Quadrants

Need More
HELP ?
For help remembering ordered pairs, go to *The Coordinate Plane* on page 1442.

Extending the Coordinate Plane

You can graph ordered pairs with negative values on a coordinate plane.

Ordered Pair

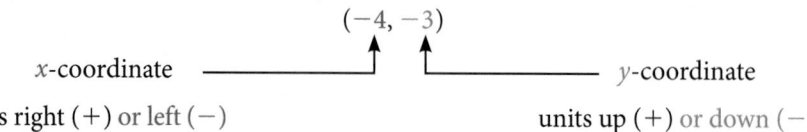

x-coordinate ⟶ $(-4, -3)$ ⟵ y-coordinate

units right $(+)$ or left $(-)$ units up $(+)$ or down $(-)$

The coordinate plane extends infinitely in four directions to include positive and negative numbers. The x- and y-axes divide the plane into four regions called **quadrants**. The quadrants are numbered as shown, counterclockwise from the upper right.

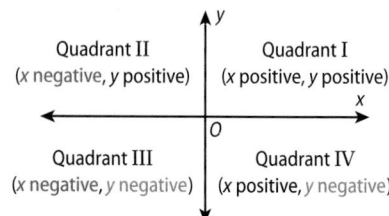

Quadrant II (x negative, y positive)   Quadrant I (x positive, y positive)

Quadrant III (x negative, y negative)   Quadrant IV (x positive, y negative)

SEARCH
To see step-by-step videos of these problems, enter the page number into the SWadvantage.com Search Bar.

EXAMPLE 1

Locate each point on the coordinate plane.

Point	Location	Coordinates
A	Quadrant I	(2, 1)
B	Quadrant II	(−3, 2)
C	Quadrant III	(−4, −2)
D	Quadrant IV	(1, −3.5)
E	on the negative x-axis	(−2.5, 0)

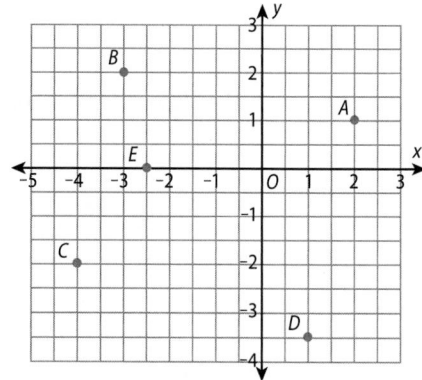

Graphing Points in Four Quadrants

To graph a point, start at the origin. Move left or right the number of units in the x-coordinate. Then move up or down the number of units in the y-coordinate.

EXAMPLE 2

Graph each point on the coordinate plane. Describe its location.

a. **F at (−2, 3)**

Start at the origin. Move left 2 units and then up 3 units. Label the point *F*. The point is in Quadrant II.

b. **G at (5, −4)**

Start at the origin. Move right 5 units and then down 4 units. Label the point *G*. The point is in Quadrant IV.

c. **H at (0, −3)**

Start at the origin. Move down 3 units. Label the point *H*. The point is on the negative y-axis.

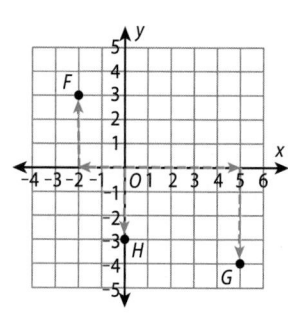

ALGEBRA

Variable Linear Equations and Inequalities **ALGEBRA**

Horizontal and Vertical Distance

To find the horizontal distance between two points (x_1, y_1) and (x_2, y_2) on the coordinate plane, find the difference between the x-coordinates and take the absolute value.

$$\text{Horizontal Distance} = |x_2 - x_1|$$

Either point can be chosen as (x_1, y_1).

To find the vertical distance between two points (x_1, y_1) and (x_2, y_2) on the coordinate plane, find the difference between the y-coordinates and take the absolute value.

$$\text{Vertical Distance} = |y_2 - y_1|$$

EXAMPLE 3

Find the base length and the height of the right triangle. Then find the area of the triangle.

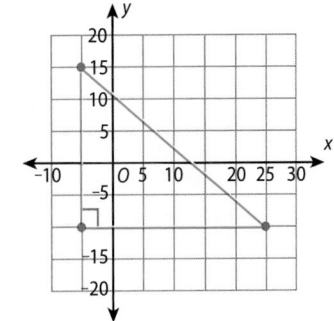

STEP 1 Find the base length.

The endpoints of the base are $(-5, -10)$ and $(25, -10)$.

Subtract the x-coordinates. $|-5 - 25| = |-30|$

Take the absolute value. $= 30$

The base length b is 30 units.

STEP 2 Find the height.

The endpoints of the height are $(-5, 15)$ and $(-5, -10)$.

Subtract the y-coordinates. $|15 - (-10)| = |25|$

Take the absolute value. $= 25$

The height h is 25 units.

STEP 3 Find the area.

Use the formula for area of a triangle. $A = \frac{1}{2}bh = \frac{1}{2}(30)(25) = 375$

The area of the triangle is 375 square units.

GOT TO KNOW!

Graphing (x, y) on the Coordinate Plane

Value of x	Value of y	Location of Point
+	+	Quadrant I
−	+	Quadrant II
−	−	Quadrant III
+	−	Quadrant IV
0	+ or −	on the y-axis
+ or −	0	on the x-axis

Graphing from a Table of Values

Using a Table of Ordered Pairs

You can use tables of ordered pairs to graph points on the coordinate plane.

Need More
HELP ?

For help in working with ordered pairs, go to *The Coordinate Plane* on page 1442.

EXAMPLE 1

Graph each set of data.

a.

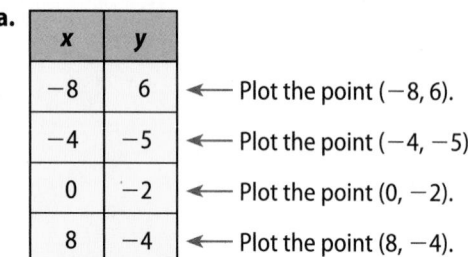

x	y
−8	6	← Plot the point (−8, 6).
−4	−5	← Plot the point (−4, −5).
0	−2	← Plot the point (0, −2).
8	−4	← Plot the point (8, −4).

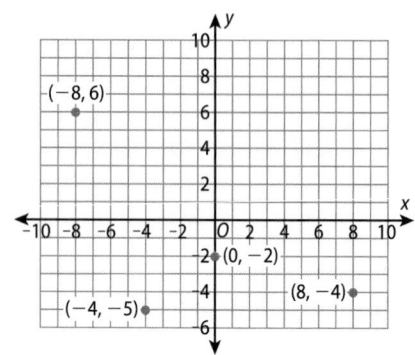

b.

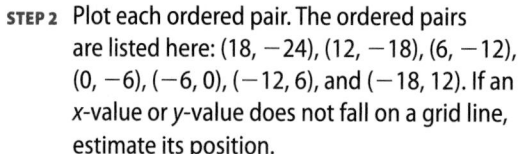

x	18	12	6	0	−6	−12	−18
y	−24	−18	−12	−6	0	6	12

STEP 1 First choose a scale for each axis. The *x*-axis must include values from −18 to 18 to fit the data. The *y*-axis must include values from −24 to 12.

A good choice is for both axes to go from −25 to 25 with intervals of 5.

STEP 2 Plot each ordered pair. The ordered pairs are listed here: (18, −24), (12, −18), (6, −12), (0, −6), (−6, 0), (−12, 6), and (−18, 12). If an *x*-value or *y*-value does not fall on a grid line, estimate its position.

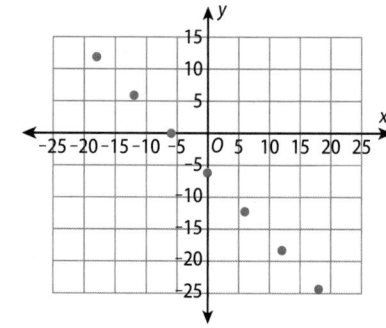

EXAMPLE 2

Graph the function $y = x − 7$ for $x = −5, 0, 5,$ and 10.

STEP 1 Evaluate the function for each value of *x*. You can make a table.

STEP 2 Choose a scale, and plot each ordered pair.

x	x − 7	y	(x, y)
−5	−5 − 7	−12	(−5, −12)
0	0 − 7	−7	(0, −7)
5	5 − 7	−2	(5, −2)
10	10 − 7	3	(10, 3)

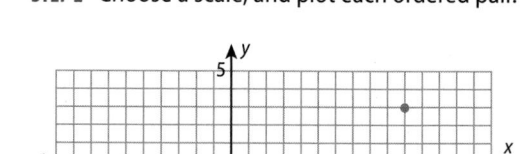

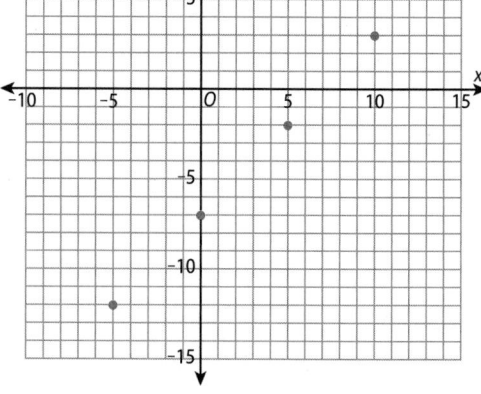

Reversing the Variables

Generally, the value of *y* depends on the value of *x*. When you graph two related sets of data, you can sometimes choose which set of values to represent on the *x*-axis.

SEARCH

To see step-by-step videos of these problems, enter the page number into the SWadvantage.com Search Bar.

EXAMPLE 3

The table shows the equivalent temperature in degrees Celsius for various temperatures in degrees Fahrenheit.

Temperature (°F)	−58	−40	−22	−4	14	32	50	68
Temperature (°C)	−50	−40	−30	−20	−10	0	10	20

a. Graph the temperature in degrees Celsius as a function of the temperature in degrees Fahrenheit.

STEP 1 Place the Fahrenheit temperature on the *x*-axis and the Celsius temperature on the *y*-axis. The *x*-axis must include values from −58 to 68 to fit the data. The *y*-axis must include values from −50 to 20.

STEP 2 Plot each ordered pair (Fahrenheit temperature, Celsius temperature). The ordered pairs are (−58, −50), (−40, −40), (−22, −30), (−4, −20), (14, −10), (32, 0), (50, 10), and (68, 20).

Temperature in Degrees Celsius

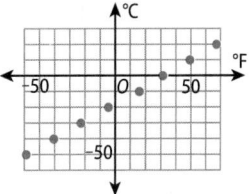

b. Graph the temperature in degrees Fahrenheit as a function of the temperature in degrees Celsius.

STEP 1 Place the Celsius temperature on the *x*-axis and the Fahrenheit temperature on the *y*-axis. The *x*-axis must include values from −50 to 20 to fit the data. The *y*-axis must include values from −58 to 68.

STEP 2 Reverse each ordered pair in part (a). Plot each ordered pair (Celsius temperature, Fahrenheit temperature). The ordered pairs are (−50, −58), (−40, −40), (−30, −22), (−20, −4), (−10, 14), (0, 32), (10, 50), and (20, 68).

Temperature in Degrees Fahrenheit

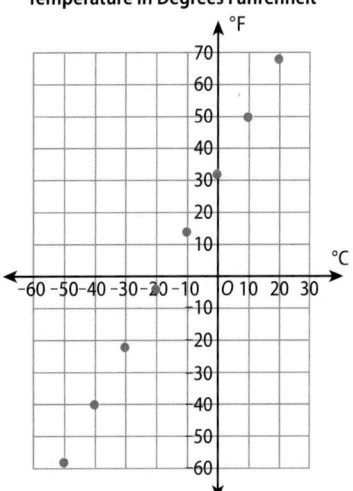

GOT TO KNOW!

Using a Table to Graph on the Coordinate Plane

Determine which set of values to represent on each axis.

Determine the scale of each axis to fit the data. Plot each point.

Graphing from an Equation

Solutions of Equations in Two Variables

Equations with one variable, such as $2x + 3 = 7$, generally have one solution. Equations with two variables, such as $2x + y = 7$, have a set of infinitely many solutions that are ordered pairs. For the equation $2x + y = 7$, some of the solutions are $(2, 3)$, $(1, 5)$, $(5, -3)$, and $(2.5, 2)$.

To determine whether an ordered pair is a solution of a two-variable equation, substitute the x- and y-values for x and y in the equation and see whether the result is true.

Watch Out !

Make sure you substitute the first coordinate in the point for x, and the second coordinate in the point for y.

EXAMPLE 1

Determine whether the ordered pair is a solution of the equation $2x + 3 = y$.

a. (5, 13)

$2x + 3 = y$

$2(5) + 3 \overset{?}{=} 13$

$10 + 3 \overset{?}{=} 13$

$13 = 13$ ✔

$(5, 13)$ is a solution.

b. (−5, −7)

$2x + 3 = y$

$2(-5) + 3 \overset{?}{=} -7$

$-10 + 3 \overset{?}{=} -7$

$-7 = -7$ ✔

$(-5, -7)$ is a solution.

c. (−2, 1)

$2x + 3 = y$

$2(-2) + 3 \overset{?}{=} 1$

$-4 + 3 \overset{?}{=} 1$

$-1 \neq 1$ ✗

$(-2, 1)$ is not a solution.

EXAMPLE 2

Determine whether the ordered pair is a solution of the equation $-3y + 5x = 15$.

a. (−5, 3)

$-3y + 5x = 15$

$-3(3) + 5(-5) \overset{?}{=} 15$

$-9 + (-25) \overset{?}{=} 15$

$-34 \neq 15$ ✗

$(-5, 3)$ is not a solution.

b. (0, −5)

$-3y + 5x = 15$

$-3(-5) + 5(0) \overset{?}{=} 15$

$15 + 0 \overset{?}{=} 15$

$15 = 15$ ✔

$(0, -5)$ is a solution.

c. (−1.5, −7.5)

$-3y + 5x = 15$

$-3(-7.5) + 5(-1.5) \overset{?}{=} 15$

$22.5 + (-7.5) \overset{?}{=} 15$

$15 = 15$ ✔

$(-1.5, -7.5)$ is a solution.

To find ordered pairs that are solutions of a two-variable equation, solve the equation for one variable in terms of the other. Substitute values for the other variable, and simplify to find values for the variable you solved for.

EXAMPLE 3

Find three solutions of the equation $3x + y = 5$.

It is easier to solve for y.

$$3x + y = 5$$
$$\underline{-3x \quad\quad = -3x}$$
$$y = -3x + 5$$

Need More HELP

You can choose any convenient values for x.

Substitute values for x, and simplify to find values for y.

If $x = 0$, then $y = -3(0) + 5 = 5$.   solution: $(0, 5)$

If $x = 1$, then $y = -3(1) + 5 = 2$.   solution: $(1, 2)$

If $x = 2$, then $y = -3(2) + 5 = -1$.   solution: $(2, -1)$

Linear Equations

An equation with a graph that is a straight line is called a **linear equation**. In a linear equation, each variable is to the first power, there are no variables in the denominator of a fraction, and there are no products of variables.

Linear equations	$y = 2x + 7$	$3x + 2y = 10$	$-6 = 2y$
Nonlinear equations	$y = x^2 + 7$	$\frac{3}{x} + 2y = 10$	$-6 = 2xy$

Graphing Linear Equations

The graph of a linear equation is a straight line. After finding two ordered-pair solutions, you can graph those points and then draw the line passing through them. All points on the line are solutions.

Only two points are needed to graph a linear equation. Using a third point can sometimes help you draw the line more accurately.

EXAMPLE 4

Graph the linear equation $x - 2y = -3$.

STEP 1 Solve $x - 2y = -3$ for a variable.

It is easier to solve for x.
$$\begin{aligned} x - 2y &= -3 \\ +2y &= +2y \\ \hline x &= 2y - 3 \end{aligned}$$

STEP 2 Substitute values for y to find values for x.

If $y = 0$, then $x = 2(0) - 3 = -3$.   solution: $(-3, 0)$

If $y = 4$, then $x = 2(4) - 3 = 5$.   solution: $(5, 4)$

If $y = 2$, then $x = 2(2) - 3 = 1$.   solution: $(1, 2)$

STEP 3 Graph the points. Then use a straightedge or ruler to draw a line through the points.

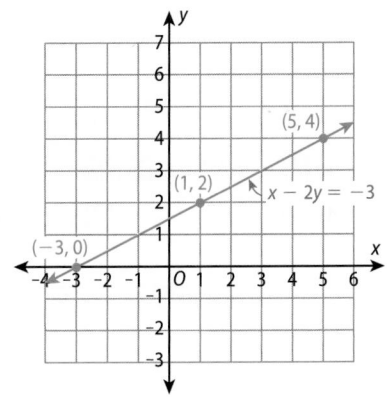

Need More

HELP ?

For more help in graphing lines, see *Linear Functions* on page 1450.

SEARCH 🔍

To see step-by-step videos of these problems, enter the page number into the SWadvantage.com Search Bar.

Methods of Graphing Linear Equations

If you solve a linear equation for y, you can use the function-graphing capability of a graphing calculator to graph the equation.

EXAMPLE 5

Graph the linear equation $4y = 3x - 4$.

METHOD 1

Need More HELP?

The values of x chosen in Example 5 are multiples of 4 so that the calculations are easier.

STEP 1 Solve $4y = 3x - 4$ for y.

$$4y = 3x - 4$$
$$\frac{4y}{4} = \frac{3x}{4} - \frac{4}{4}$$
$$y = \frac{3}{4}x - 1$$

STEP 2 Make a table.

x	$\frac{3}{4}x - 1$	y	(x, y)
0	$\frac{3}{4}(0) - 1$	-1	$(0, -1)$
4	$\frac{3}{4}(4) - 1$	2	$(4, 2)$
8	$\frac{3}{4}(8) - 1$	5	$(8, 5)$

STEP 3 Plot the points. Draw the line through the points.

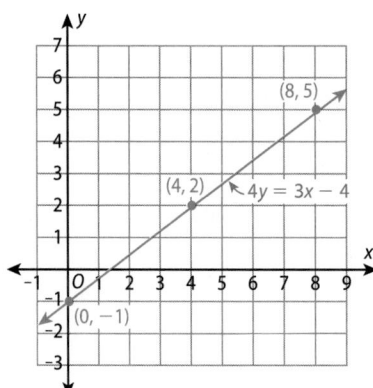

METHOD 2

Use a graphing calculator.

STEP 1 Solve $4y = 3x - 4$ for y as in Method 1 to get $y = \frac{3}{4}x - 1$.

STEP 2 Press [Y=] and type [(] [3] [÷] [4] [)] [X,T,θ,n] [−] [1] as Y1.

STEP 3 To graph, press [ZOOM], choose **4:ZDecimal** and press [ENTER]. You can press [TRACE] and the left or right arrow to see solutions.

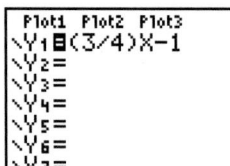 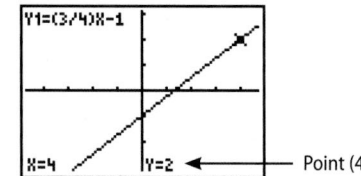

Point (4, 2) is a solution.

Try It This Way

Instead of dividing the right side of the equation by 4 yourself, let the calculator do it. Enter $(3X - 4) \div 4$ as Y1.

Pressing [ZOOM] and selecting **4:ZDecimal** is only one way to graph. If you press [GRAPH], the calculator will use its most recent graphing window.

Dependent and Independent Variables

If an equation contains variables other than x and y, you need to determine which variable *depends* on the other variable. This variable is the **dependent variable** . The other variable is called the **independent variable** . Write the equation so that the dependent variable is a function of the independent variable.

EXAMPLE 6

A company reimburses employees who use their own cars for work-related trips. The rate paid is $.478 per mile. Use a graph to estimate the amount the company will pay for a trip of 79 miles.

STEP 1 Translate into an equation.

Let m be the number of miles, and let p be the amount in dollars the company pays.

The amount paid p depends on the number of miles m. So p is the dependent variable, and m is the independent variable.

Write an equation: $p = 0.478m$. The equation is linear.

STEP 2 Make a table of values for m and p.

Miles m	$0.478m$	Amount Paid ($) p
0	0.478(0)	0
50	0.478(50)	23.90
100	0.478(100)	47.80

STEP 3 Plot the points (m, p) and graph the line.

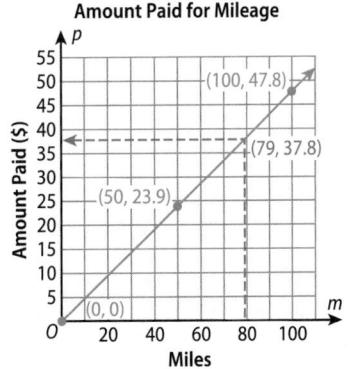

STEP 4 Locate $m = 79$ on the m-axis. Find the point on the graph where $m = 79$.

Use the scale on the p-axis to read the estimated value of p at that point.

The company will pay about $38.

CHECK Multiply: $0.478(79) = 37.762$, which rounds to $38.

SEARCH

To see step-by-step videos of these problems, enter the page number into the SWadvantage.com Search Bar.

Graphing a Linear Equation

1. Solve for a variable.

2. Substitute to find two or more ordered pairs.

3. Plot the points.

4. Draw the line through the plotted points.

Each point on the line is a solution of the linear equation.

The *y*-Intercept and the *x*-Intercept

The *y*-Intercept

The **y-intercept** is the value of *y* where a graph crosses the *y*-axis. To find the *y*-intercept, let $x = 0$ and solve for *y*.

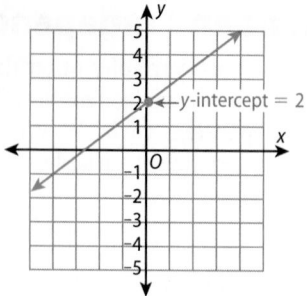

y-intercept = 2

GOT TO KNOW!

Intercepts

The intercept is a single value, but some books and exams may refer to the point itself as the intercept.

EXAMPLE 1

Find the *y*-intercept.

a. $y = 4x + 8$

Let $x = 0$.	$y = 4x + 8$
Substitute 0 for *x*.	$y = 4(0) + 8$
Solve for *y*.	$y = 0 + 8$
	$y = 8$

The *y*-intercept is 8.

The point where the line crosses the *y*-axis is (0, 8).

b. $6x + 8y = 24$

Let $x = 0$.	$6x + 8y = 24$
Substitute 0 for *x*.	$6(0) + 8y = 24$
Solve for *y*.	$0 + 8y = 24$
	$8y = 24$
	$y = 3$

The *y*-intercept is 3.

The point where the line crosses the *y*-axis is (0, 3).

The *x*-Intercept

The **x-intercept** is the value of *x* where a graph crosses the *x*-axis. To find the *x*-intercept, let $y = 0$ and solve for *x*.

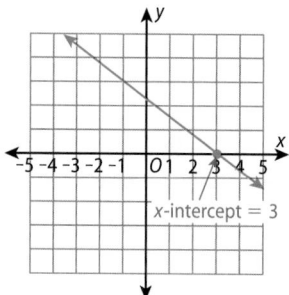

x-intercept = 3

EXAMPLE 2

Find the *x*-intercept.

a. $y = 4x + 8$

Let $y = 0$.	$y = 4x + 8$
Substitute 0 for *y*.	$0 = 4x + 8$
Solve for *x*.	$-8 = 4x$
	$-2 = x$

The *x*-intercept is -2.

The point where the line crosses the *x*-axis is $(-2, 0)$.

b. $6x + 8y = 24$

Let $y = 0$.	$6x + 8y = 24$
Substitute 0 for *y*.	$6x + 8(0) = 24$
Solve for *x*.	$6x = 24$
	$x = 4$

The *x*-intercept is 4.

The point where the line crosses the *x*-axis is (4, 0).

Graphing with Intercepts

The *x*- and *y*-intercepts identify two points on the graph of a linear equation, one on each axis. So once you have found the intercepts, you can use the points to graph the line.

EXAMPLE 3

Use the intercepts to graph the linear equation $5y - 4x - 20 = 0$.

STEP 1 Find the intercepts.

Let $x = 0$.	$5y - 4(0) - 20 = 0$	Let $y = 0$.	$5(0) - 4x - 20 = 0$
Add 20 to both sides.	$5y - 4(0) = 20$		$5(0) - 4x = 20$
	$5y = 20$		$-4x = 20$
	$y = 4$		$x = -5$

The *y*-intercept is 4. Plot the point $(0, 4)$.

The *x*-intercept is -5. Plot the point $(-5, 0)$.

STEP 2 Graph the line.

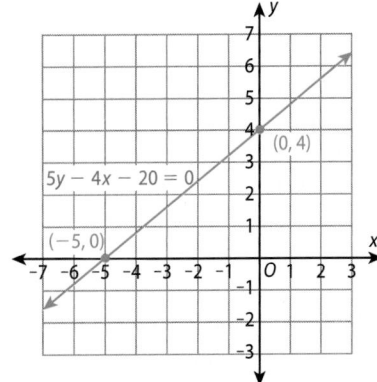

SEARCH

To see step-by-step videos of these problems, enter the page number into the SWadvantage.com Search Bar.

GOT TO KNOW!

Intercepts of a Linear Equation Graph

The ***x*-intercept** is the *x*-coordinate of the point where the graph intercepts the *x*-axis.

- To find the *x*-intercept, let $y = 0$ and solve for *x*.

The ***y*-intercept** is the *y*-coordinate of the point where the graph intercepts the *y*-axis.

- To find the *y*-intercept, let $x = 0$ and solve for *y*.

Intercepts When a Line Goes through the Origin

For a line like $y = 3x$, the *x*-intercept is 0 and the *y*-intercept is 0.

This means that both intercepts occur at the same point, $(0, 0)$, the origin.

- You need to find a second point to graph the line.

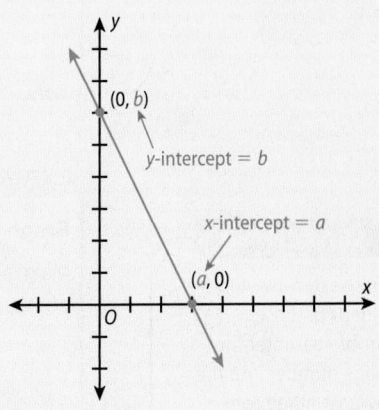

Horizontal and Vertical Lines

Horizontal Lines

You can rewrite a linear equation with a single variable, such as $y = 5$, as a linear equation with two variables. Write a coefficient of 0 for the second variable. For example, the equation $y = 5$ can be rewritten as $y = 0x + 5$. The solution set of $y = 5$ is all ordered pairs $(x, 5)$. The value of y is 5 for all values of x.

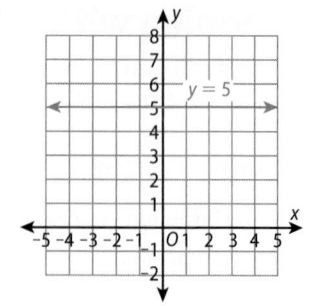

EXAMPLE 1

Graph $y = 1$.

METHOD 1

STEP 1 Evaluate the function $y = 0x + 1$ for several values of x.

x	$0x + 1$	y	(x, y)
0	$0(0) + 1$	1	$(0, 1)$
4	$0(4) + 1$	1	$(4, 1)$
-2	$0(-2) + 1$	1	$(-2, 1)$

STEP 2 Graph the points.

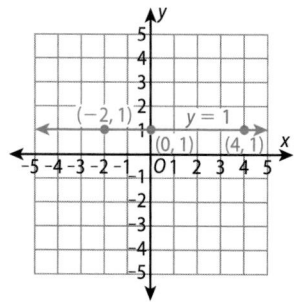

METHOD 2

Because a horizontal line is a function, you can use the function-graphing capability of a graphing calculator to graph the equation.

STEP 1 Press [Y=] and type [1] as Y1.

STEP 2 To graph, press [ZOOM], choose **4:ZDecimal** and press [ENTER]. You can press [TRACE] and the left or right arrow to see solutions.

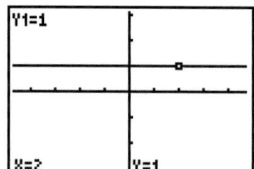

EXAMPLE 2

Graph $y = -4$.

Make a table to find some points on the line.

x	y
-3	-4
1	-4
3	-4

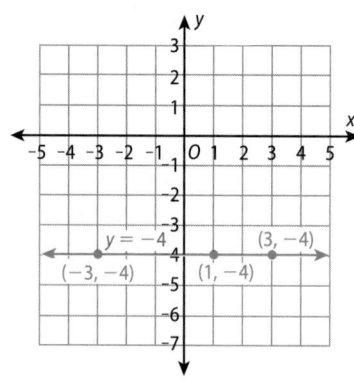

Vertical Lines

The linear equation $x = 2$ can be written as $x = 0y + 2$. The solution set of $x = 2$ consists of all ordered pairs $(2, y)$. The value of x is 2 for all values of y.

Because a vertical line is not a function, you cannot use the function-graphing capability of a graphing calculator to graph the equation.

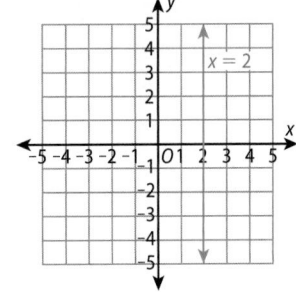

EXAMPLE 3

Graph $x = -2.75$.

The x-value is always -2.75. Find some points on the line.

x	y
-2.75	2
-2.75	0
-2.75	-1

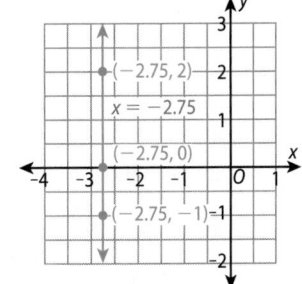

EXAMPLE 4

Graph $x = 14$ and $y = 11$. Where do the graphs intersect?

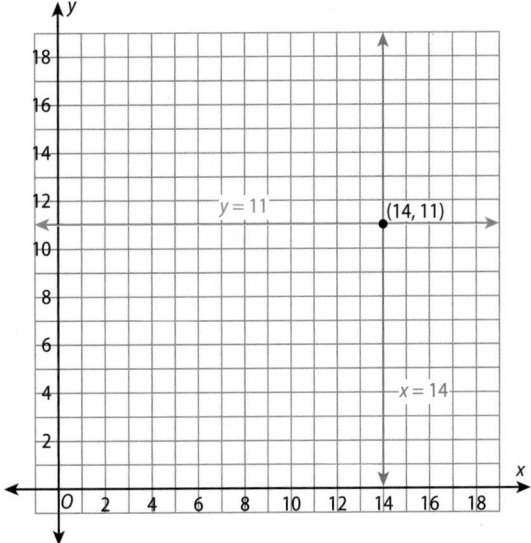

The graphs intersect at the point $(14, 11)$.

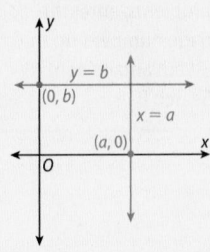

GOT TO KNOW!

Horizontal Lines

The graph of $y = b$ is a horizontal line parallel to the x-axis with a y-intercept of b.

The graph of the line $y = 0$ is the x-axis.

Vertical Lines

The graph of $x = a$ is a vertical line parallel to the y-axis with an x-intercept of a.

The graph of the line $x = 0$ is the y-axis.

Rate of Change and Slope

Rate of Change

The **rate of change** is a ratio that compares the change in the dependent variable with the change in the independent variable.

$$\text{rate of change} = \frac{\text{change in dependent variable}}{\text{change in independent variable}}$$

EXAMPLE 1

The table shows the average June price of 1 kilowatt-hour of electricity in U.S. cities for several years. Between which years was the rate of change the greatest?

Year	Year 1	Year 4	Year 5	Year 7	Year 9
Price ($)	0.95	1.04	1.18	1.28	1.32

The price depends on the year, so price is the dependent variable and time is the independent variable.

STEP 1 Find each rate of change.

from Year 1 to Year 4 $\dfrac{\text{change in price}}{\text{change years}} = \dfrac{1.04 - 0.95}{4 - 1} = \dfrac{0.09}{3} = \dfrac{\$\,.03}{1\text{ year}}$

from Year 4 to Year 5 $= \dfrac{1.18 - 1.04}{5 - 4} = \dfrac{0.14}{1} = \dfrac{\$\,.14}{1\text{ year}}$ ✔

from Year 5 to Year 7 $= \dfrac{1.28 - 1.18}{7 - 5} = \dfrac{0.10}{2} = \dfrac{\$\,.05}{1\text{ year}}$

from Year 7 to Year 9 $= \dfrac{1.32 - 1.28}{9 - 7} = \dfrac{0.04}{2} = \dfrac{\$\,.02}{1\text{ year}}$

STEP 2 Find the greatest rate of change.
The greatest rate of change in price was $.14 per year from Year 4 to Year 5.

Need More
HELP ?

When time is one of the variables, it is almost always the independent variable.

Rate of change can be positive, negative, or 0.

EXAMPLE 2

Find the rate of change represented by each segment of the graph.

segment AB $\dfrac{\text{change in } y}{\text{change in } x} = \dfrac{+4}{+2} = \dfrac{2}{1} = 2$

segment BC $\dfrac{\text{change in } y}{\text{change in } x} = \dfrac{-2}{+2} = \dfrac{-1}{1} = -1$

segment CD $\dfrac{\text{change in } y}{\text{change in } x} = \dfrac{0}{+3} = \dfrac{0}{1} = 0$

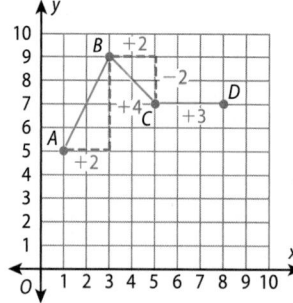

SEARCH

To see step-by-step videos of these problems, enter the page number into the SWadvantage.com Search Bar.

Slope

The *slope* of a line describes its steepness. The **slope** is a rate of change, expressed as a ratio.

The change in *y* is called the **rise**. The change in *x* is called the **run**. The slope of a line is the change in *y* divided by the change in *x*.

$$\text{slope} = \frac{\text{rise} \leftarrow \text{change in } y}{\text{run} \leftarrow \text{change in } x}$$

The slope ratio for a given line is constant. That is, it is the same between any two points on the line.

The slope of the line shown on the graph is 2.

$$\frac{2}{1} = \frac{4}{2} = \frac{6}{3} = \frac{8}{4} = 2$$

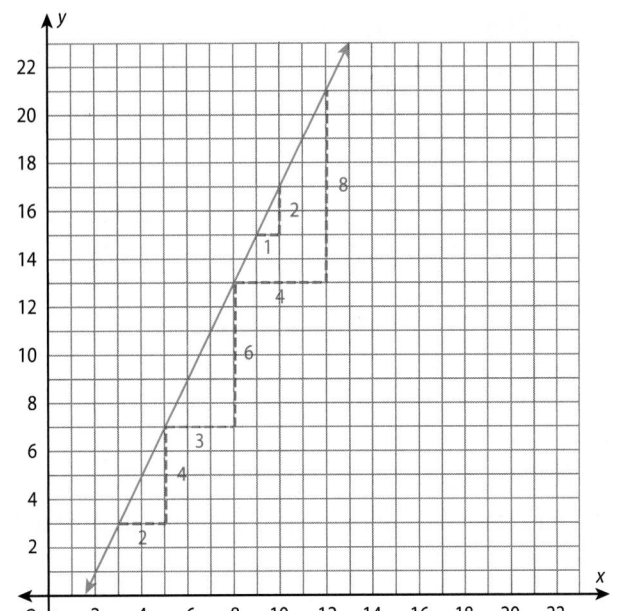

The sign of the slope tells whether the line rises or falls from left to right.

- A line with a positive slope rises from left to right.
- A line with a negative slope falls from left to right.
- A line with a slope of 0 is horizontal.

EXAMPLE 3

Explain whether the slope is positive, negative, or 0. Then find the slope.

a.

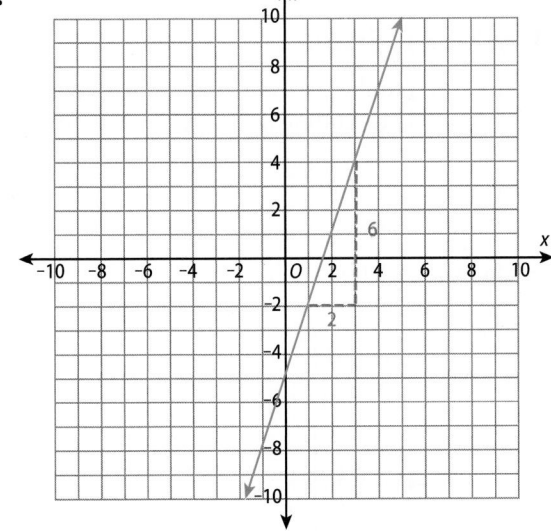

The line rises from left to right, so the slope is positive.

$$\text{slope} = \frac{\text{rise}}{\text{run}} = \frac{6}{2} = 3$$

b.

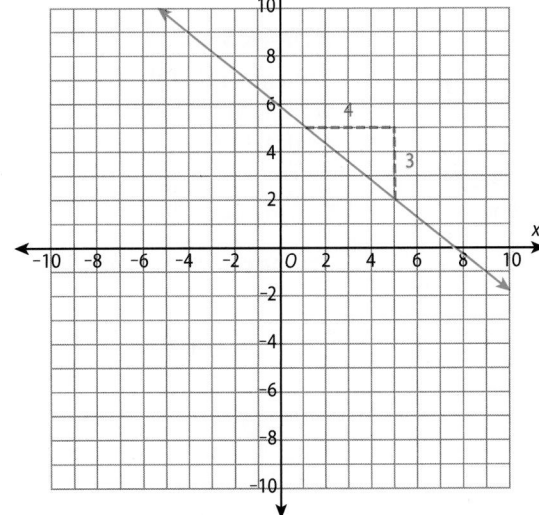

The line falls from left to right, so the slope is negative.

$$\text{slope} = \frac{\text{rise}}{\text{run}} = \frac{-3}{4} = -\frac{3}{4}$$

The Slope Formula

You can find the slope of a line by using the coordinates of any two points on the line, (x_1, y_1) and (x_2, y_2).

$$\text{slope} = \frac{y_2 - y_1}{x_2 - x_1}$$

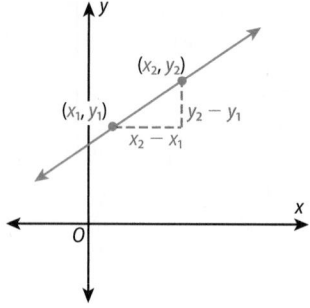

SEARCH

To see step-by-step videos of these problems, enter the page number into the SWadvantage.com Search Bar.

EXAMPLE 4

Use the coordinates of the points to find the slope of the line.

METHOD 1

Choose $(1, 2)$ as (x_1, y_1) and $(3, -2)$ as (x_2, y_2).

$$\frac{y_2 - y_1}{x_2 - x_1} = \frac{-2 - 2}{3 - 1} = \frac{-4}{2} = -2$$

METHOD 2

Choose $(1, 2)$ as (x_2, y_2) and $(3, -2)$ as (x_1, y_1).

$$\frac{y_2 - y_1}{x_2 - x_1} = \frac{2 - (-2)}{1 - 3} = \frac{4}{-2} = -2$$

The slope of the line is -2.

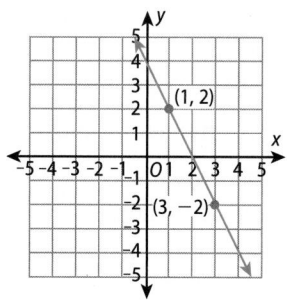

Slopes of Horizontal and Vertical Lines

Remember that the result of dividing 0 by a nonzero number is always 0. But dividing a nonzero number by 0 is undefined. These results apply to finding the slope of a horizontal or vertical line.

Watch Out !

Sometimes the term "no slope" is incorrectly used to describe an undefined slope.

Remember, a line with a slope of 0 has a slope. A slope of 0 does *not* mean "no slope."

EXAMPLE 5

Use the coordinates of the points to find the slope of each line.

a.

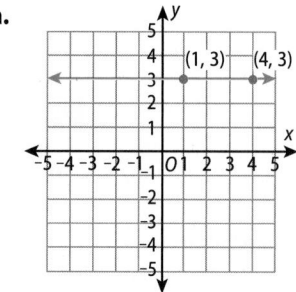

$$\text{slope} = \frac{y_2 - y_1}{x_2 - x_1} = \frac{3 - 3}{4 - 1} = \frac{0}{3} = 0$$

b.

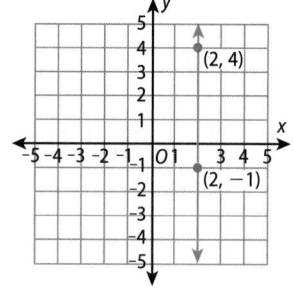

$$\text{slope} = \frac{y_2 - y_1}{x_2 - x_1} = \frac{4 - (-1)}{2 - 2} = \frac{5}{0} = \text{undefined}$$

Parallel Lines Have Equal Slopes

If two lines have equal slopes, then the lines are parallel. If two lines have unequal slopes, then the lines are not parallel.

The *converse* of each statement above is also true. If two lines are parallel, then they have equal slopes. If two lines are not parallel, then they have unequal slopes.

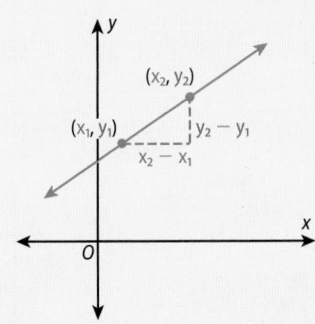

Need More HELP?

The converse of the statement "If *A* is true, then *B* is true" is the statement "If *B* is true, then *A* is true."

See *Conditionals* in *Geometry* (Book 1, p. 612).

Determine whether the two lines are parallel.

STEP 1 Find two points on each line.

Line *m* goes through (1, 4) and (5, 6).
Line *n* goes through (4, 0) and (8, 2).

STEP 2 Find the slope of each line.

slope of line $m = \dfrac{y_2 - y_1}{x_2 - x_1} = \dfrac{6-4}{5-1} = \dfrac{2}{4} = \dfrac{1}{2}$

slope of line $n = \dfrac{y_2 - y_1}{x_2 - x_1} = \dfrac{2-0}{8-4} = \dfrac{2}{4} = \dfrac{1}{2}$

The slopes of the lines are equal, so the lines are parallel.

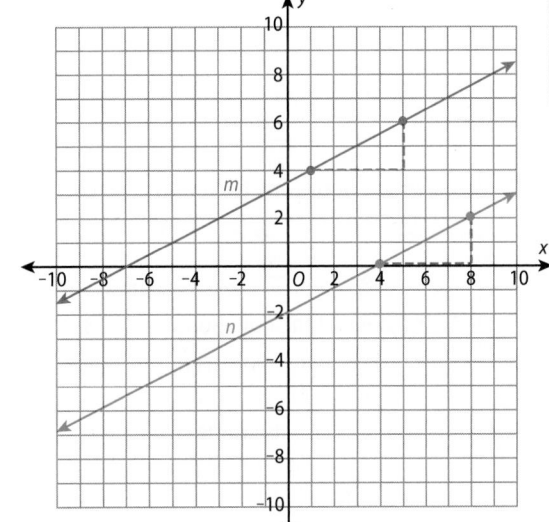

All vertical lines are parallel to each other. All horizontal lines are parallel to each other.

GOT TO KNOW!

Slope of a Line

The slope of a line is $\dfrac{\text{rise}}{\text{run}}$.

The slope of a line containing two points (x_1, y_1) and (x_2, y_2) is $\dfrac{y_2 - y_1}{x_2 - x_1}$.

The slope of a horizontal line is 0.

The slope of a vertical line is undefined.

Lines with equal slopes are parallel. Lines with unequal slopes are not parallel.

The Slope-Intercept Form of a Linear Equation

Finding the Slope, Given a Linear Equation

To find the slope of a line, use the linear equation to find two points on the line. Then use the coordinates of the points to calculate the slope.

SEARCH

To see step-by-step videos of these problems, enter the page number into the SWadvantage.com Search Bar.

EXAMPLE 1

Use the linear equation to find the slope of each line.

a. $y = 2 - 3x$

STEP 1 Make a table. Substitute values of x into the equation $y = 2 - 3x$.

x	0	1	2	3
y	$2 - 3(0) = 2$	$2 - 3(1) = -1$	$2 - 3(2) = -4$	$2 - 3(3) = -7$

STEP 2 Choose any two points and use the coordinates to find the slope.

Use $(0, 2)$ as (x_1, y_1) and $(3, -7)$ as (x_2, y_2).

$$\text{slope} = \frac{y_2 - y_1}{x_2 - x_1} = \frac{-7 - 2}{3 - 0} = \frac{-9}{3} = -3$$

The slope of the equation $y = 2 - 3x$ is -3.

CHECK Graph the line to check the slope. The line falls from left to right, so the slope is negative. To move from $(0, 2)$ to $(1, -1)$, move right 1 and down 3. So the slope is -3.

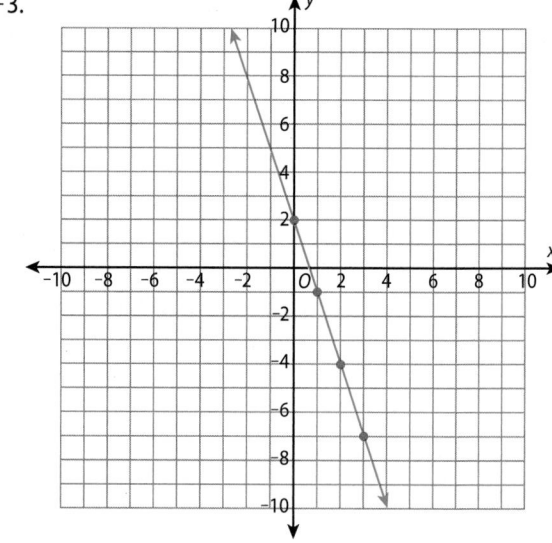

b. $2x + 5y = 8$

STEP 1 Find the x- and y-intercepts.

Let $x = 0$.	$2x + 5y = 8$	Let $y = 0$.	$2x + 5y = 8$
Substitute 0 for x.	$2(0) + 5y = 8$	Substitute 0 for y.	$2x + 5(0) = 8$
Solve for y.	$5y = 8$	Solve for x.	$2x = 8$
	$y = \frac{8}{5} = 1.6$		$x = 4$

The y-intercept is 1.6. One point is $(0, 1.6)$. The x-intercept is 4. Another point is $(4, 0)$.

STEP 2 Find the slope.

Let $(0, 1.6)$ equal (x_1, y_1) and $(4, 0)$ equal (x_2, y_2).

$$\text{slope} = \frac{y_2 - y_1}{x_2 - x_1} = \frac{0 - 1.6}{4 - 0} = \frac{-1.6}{4} = -0.4$$

The slope of the equation $2x + 5y = 8$ is -0.4 or $-\frac{2}{5}$.

Using the Slope and the *y*-Intercept to Graph an Equation

EXAMPLE 2

Use the slope and the *y*-intercept to graph each linear equation.

a. *y*-intercept = −3, slope = 2

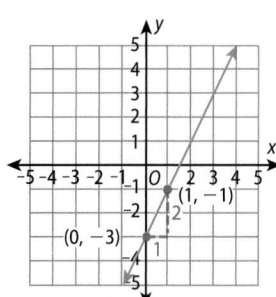

STEP 1 Plot on the *y*-axis the point represented by the *y*-intercept.

Plot the point (0, −3).

STEP 2 Use the slope to find a second point.

$$\frac{\text{change in } y}{\text{change in } x} = \frac{2}{1}$$

From (0, −3), move 1 unit right and 2 units up.

Plot the point (1, −1).

STEP 3 Draw the line through the two points.

b. *y*-intercept = 2, slope = $-\frac{4}{5}$

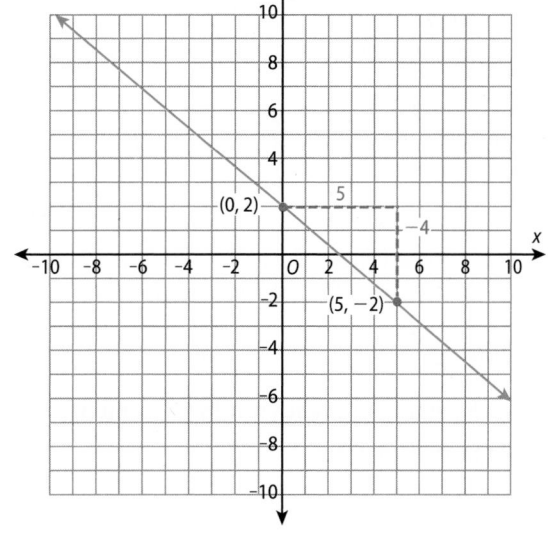

STEP 1 Plot on the *y*-axis the point represented by the *y*-intercept.

Plot the point (0, 2).

STEP 2 Use the slope to find a second point.

$$\frac{\text{change in } y}{\text{change in } x} = \frac{-4}{5}$$

From (0, 2), move 5 units right and 4 units down.

Plot the point (5, −2).

STEP 3 Draw the line through the two points.

Need More HELP?

In Example 2(b), you can continue the *right 5, down 4* pattern to plot any number of points.

Because $\frac{-4}{5}$ is equal to $\frac{4}{-5}$, you can also use the pattern *left 5, up 4* to plot points.

If you know the slope and the coordinates of one point, you don't need the *y*-intercept to graph a linear equation.

EXAMPLE 3

The point (25, 60) is on a line that has a slope of 12. Find two more points on the line.

A slope of 12, or $\frac{12}{1}$, means the change in *y* is 12 and the change in *x* is 1.

The point (25 + 1, 60 + 12), or (26, 72), is also on the line.

The point (26 + 1, 72 + 12), or (27, 84), is a third point on the line.

Slope-Intercept Form: $y = mx + b$

In the slope-intercept form of a linear equation, the letter m represents the slope of the line.

$$m = \frac{y_2 - y_1}{x_2 - x_1}$$

The letter b represents the y-intercept of the line. If you know the slope and the y-intercept of a line, you can write the equation of the line.

SEARCH 🔍

To see step-by-step videos of these problems, enter the page number into the SWadvantage.com Search Bar.

EXAMPLE 4

The slope of a line is 2 and the y-intercept is 3. Write the equation of the line.

STEP 1 Find the point represented by the y-intercept. The point on the line where $x = 0$ represents the y-intercept. The y-intercept is 3, so the point is (0, 3).

STEP 2 Use the equation for the slope of a line. Solve for y.

Substitute the coordinates (0, 3) for (x_1, x_2). $\dfrac{y - 3}{x - 0} = m$

Substitute 2 for m. $\dfrac{y - 3}{x} = 2$

Multiply both sides by x. $y - 3 = 2x$

Add 3 to both sides to isolate y. $y = 2x + 3$

In Example 4, the equation $y = 2x + 3$ represents a line with slope 2 and y-intercept 3. Any line with slope m and y-intercept b can be represented by the equation below.

$$y = mx + b$$

Suppose you are given the slope and y-intercept of a line. To write the linear equation for the line, substitute the given values for m and b in the equation $y = mx + b$.

EXAMPLE 5

Write the equation of each line in slope-intercept form.

a. slope = 4, y-intercept = 1

$y = mx + b$

$y = 4x + 1$

b. slope = −1, y-intercept = 0

$y = mx + b$

$y = -1x + 0$

$y = -x$

c. slope = $\dfrac{3}{5}$, y-intercept = −4

$y = mx + b$

$y = \dfrac{3}{5}x + (-4)$

$y = \dfrac{3}{5}x - 4$

d. slope = 0, y-intercept = −2

$y = mx + b$

$y = 0x + (-2)$

$y = -2$

GOT TO KNOW!

The Slope-Intercept Form of a Linear Equation

$$y = mx + b$$

where m is the slope of the line and b is the y-intercept

To make it easier to graph a linear equation, first write it in slope-intercept form.

EXAMPLE 6

Write the equation $3x + 4y + 20 = 0$ in slope-intercept form. Then graph the line.

STEP 1 Solve the equation for y.

$$3x + 4y + 20 = 0$$

Subtract 20 from both sides. $3x + 4y = -20$

Subtract $3x$ from both sides. $4y = -3x - 20$

Divide both sides by 4. $\dfrac{4y}{4} = \dfrac{-3x}{4} - \dfrac{20}{4}$

Simplify. $y = -\dfrac{3}{4}x - 5$

STEP 2 Graph the line.

The slope is $-\dfrac{3}{4}$, and the y-intercept is -5.

Plot the point $(0, -5)$.

Move 4 units right and 3 units down.

Plot the point $(4, -8)$ and draw the line.

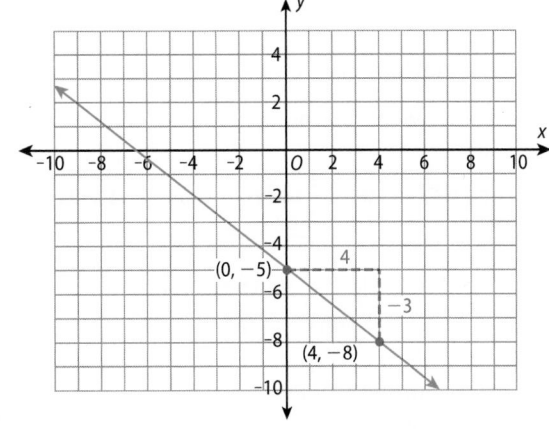

Try It This Way

Use a graphing calculator to graph a linear equation. Once you have the equation in slope-intercept form, enter it into Y= to graph it as a function. You can then make a table of ordered pairs from the equation by pressing 2nd GRAPH.

EXAMPLE 7

A landscaper charges \$200 for a spring cleanup and \$35 for each weekly visit after that. The cost as a function of the number of visits is shown in the graph.

a. Write a linear equation to represent the cost.

cost is \$35 times the number of weekly visits plus \$200

   y = 35 · x +   200

The linear equation is $y = 35x + 200$.

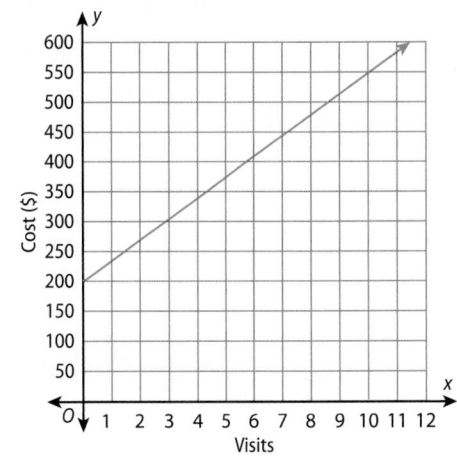

b. Identify what the slope and y-intercept represent.

The y-intercept, 200, is the initial cleanup cost with no weekly visits.

The slope, 35, is the cost for each weekly visit.

c. Find the total cost after 6 weekly visits.

$y = 35x + 200$

$y = 35(6) + 200 = 410$

The cost after 6 visits is \$410.

The Point-Slope Form of a Linear Equation

Using a Point and the Slope to Graph a Line

To graph a line, you need two points. If you know the *y*-intercept and the slope, you can find two points on the line. If, instead, you are given the slope and any point on the line, you can find a second point.

EXAMPLE 1

SEARCH

To see step-by-step videos of these problems, enter the page number into the SWadvantage.com Search Bar.

Graph each line.

a. a line with slope 2 that contains the point (3, 1)

  STEP 1 Plot the point (3, 1).

  STEP 2 Use the slope to find a second point.

  $$m = \frac{\text{change in } y}{\text{change in } x} = \frac{2}{1}$$

  From (3, 1), move 1 unit right and 2 units up.

  Plot the point (4, 3).

  STEP 3 Draw the line through the two points.

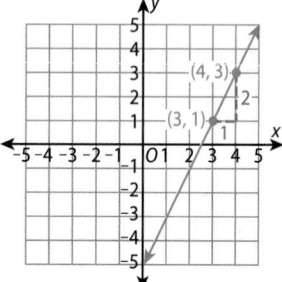

b. a line with slope $-\frac{2}{3}$ that contains the point (−1, 4)

  STEP 1 Plot the point (−1, 4).

  STEP 2 Use the slope to find a second point.

  $$m = \frac{\text{change in } y}{\text{change in } x} = \frac{-2}{3}$$

  From (−1, 4), move 3 units right and 2 units down.

  Plot the point (2, 2).

  STEP 3 Draw the line through the two points.

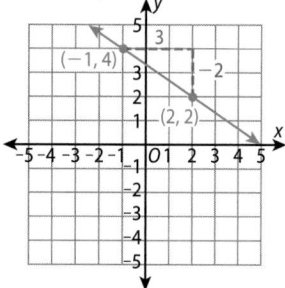

c. a line with slope 0 that contains the point (4, −3)

  STEP 1 Plot the point (4, −3).

  STEP 2 A horizontal line has slope 0.

  Draw a horizontal line through (4, −3).

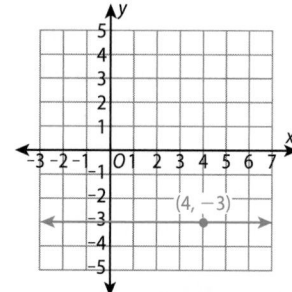

The Line Represented by $y = mx$

The line represented by the equation $y = mx$ has slope m and passes through the origin.

For $y = 2x$, the *y*-intercept is 0, and the slope is 2.

When $x = 0$, $y = 2x = 2(0) = 0$. When $x = 1$, $y = 2x = 2(1) = 2$.

So the points (0, 0) and (1, 2) are both points on the line.

Finding Point-Slope Form

In Example 1a, you graphed the equation of a line with a slope of 2 containing the point (3, 1). Suppose (x, y) is any other point on the line. Write an equation representing the line.

Write the formula for the slope.

$$\frac{y_2 - y_1}{x_2 - x_1} = m$$

Substitute the given coordinates and the slope into the formula.

$$\frac{y - 1}{x - 3} = 2$$

Multiply both sides by $x - 3$.

$$y - 1 = 2(x - 3)$$

The Point-Slope Equation of a Line

The equation below represents the line with slope m that contains the point (x_1, y_1).

$$y - y_1 = m(x - x_1)$$

EXAMPLE 2

Write an equation in point-slope form for each line.

a. a line with slope 6 that contains the point (5, 2)

Write the point-slope equation. $y - y_1 = m(x - x_1)$

Substitute for $x_1, y_1,$ and m. $y - 2 = 6(x - 5)$

b. a line with slope −4 that contains the point (4, −2)

Write the point-slope equation. $y - y_1 = m(x - x_1)$

Substitute for $x_1, y_1,$ and m. $y - (-2) = -4(x - 4)$

You can use the identity properties in some cases to simplify point-slope form.

EXAMPLE 3

Write an equation for each line in point-slope form.

a. a line with slope $\frac{4}{7}$ that contains the point (0, 12)

Write the point-slope equation. $y - y_1 = m(x - x_1)$

Substitute for $x_1, y_1,$ and m. $y - 12 = \frac{4}{7}(x - 0)$

Simplify the right side. $y - 12 = \frac{4}{7}x$

b. a line with slope 0 that contains the point (3, 5)

Write the point-slope equation. $y - y_1 = m(x - x_1)$

Substitute for $x_1, y_1,$ and m. $y - 5 = 0(x - 3)$

Simplify the right side. $y - 5 = 0$

Need More HELP?

The line with slope m that goes through the origin is $y = mx$.

Another way to show the point-slope equation is

$y - k = m(x - h)$,

where (h, k) is the given point on the line.

Think of the line as a slide, or translation, of the line $y = mx$ that goes through (h, k).

Using Point-Slope Form

You can identify the point and the slope from an equation in point-slope form.

EXAMPLE 4

Use the equation to identify the slope and one point on the line.

a. $y - 8 = -5(x - 1)$

slope: -5 point: $(1, 8)$

b. $y + 4 = -(x - 3)$

Rewrite this equation in point-slope form.

$y - (-4) = -1(x - 3)$

slope: -1 point: $(3, -4)$

Watch Out !

In the point-slope equation of a line, the numerical coordinates are subtracted from x and y.

In Example 4(b), the expression $y + 4$ is the same as $y - (-4)$. So the y-coordinate of the point is negative.

Writing a Point-Slope Equation, Given Two Points

You can write the equation of a line in point-slope form, given two points, by first finding the slope. Then use either point to write the equation.

EXAMPLE 5

Write a point-slope equation for the line that contains points (3, 7) and (6, 8).

STEP 1 Use the two points to find the slope.

Let $(3, 7)$ be (x_1, y_1) and $(6, 8)$ be (x_2, y_2). $m = \dfrac{y_2 - y_1}{x_2 - x_1} = \dfrac{8 - 7}{6 - 3} = \dfrac{1}{3}$

STEP 2 Substitute the slope and one point in the point-slope equation.

Write the point-slope equation. $y - y_1 = m(x - x_1)$

Choose $(3, 7)$. Substitute for $x_1, y_1,$ and m. $y - 7 = \dfrac{1}{3}(x - 3)$

The equation in point-slope form is $y - 7 = \dfrac{1}{3}(x - 3)$.

SEARCH

To see step-by-step videos of these problems, enter the page number into the SWadvantage.com Search Bar.

When two points are given, you can use the coordinates of either point in the point-slope equation.

In Example 5, if you choose $(6, 8)$, the equation in point-slope form is $y - 8 = \dfrac{1}{3}(x - 6)$.

By simplifying, you can see that the two equations are equivalent.

$y - 7 = \dfrac{1}{3}(x - 3)$ $y - 8 = \dfrac{1}{3}(x - 6)$

$y - 7 = \dfrac{1}{3}x - 1$ Use the Distributive Property. $y - 8 = \dfrac{1}{3}x - 2$

$y = \dfrac{1}{3}x + 6$ Isolate y by adding on both sides. $y = \dfrac{1}{3}x + 6$

EXAMPLE 6

The table shows the cost of an airport shuttle service for different trips. Show that the relationship between distance and cost is linear. Write an equation in point-slope form relating cost and distance. Then use the equation to find the cost of a 45-mile trip.

Distance (mi)	13.5	18	27
Cost ($)	19	23	31

STEP 1 Show that the relationship is linear.

Find each rate of change and compare.

$$\frac{\text{change in cost}}{\text{change in distance}} = \frac{31 - 23}{27 - 18} = \frac{8}{9}$$

$$\frac{\text{change in cost}}{\text{change in distance}} = \frac{23 - 19}{18 - 13.5} = \frac{4}{4.5} = \frac{8}{9}$$

The rates of change are equal, so the relationship is linear.

STEP 2 Write an equation relating cost and distance.

Cost is dependent on distance, so use distance as the x-variable, and cost as the y-variable.
The rate of change $\frac{8}{9}$ represents the slope of the line that graphs the data.
Write the point-slope equation. $y - y_1 = m(x - x_1)$

Choose (18, 23). Substitute for x_1, y_1, and m. $y - 23 = \frac{8}{9}(x - 18)$

The point-slope equation that represents the data is $y - 23 = \frac{8}{9}(x - 18)$.

STEP 3 Find the cost of a 45-mile trip.

Substitute 45 for x. $y - 23 = \frac{8}{9}(45 - 18)$

Subtract. $y - 23 = \frac{8}{9}(27)$

Multiply. $y - 23 = 24$

Add 23 to both sides. $y = 47$

The cost of a 45-mile trip is $47.

Try It This Way

You can use a graphing calculator to find some points by entering the point-slope equation as a function.

Add 23 to both sides to isolate y.

$y = \frac{8}{9}(x - 18) + 23$

Press [Y=] and enter $(8 \div 9)(X - 18) + 23$.

Then press [2nd] TBLSET and use these numbers.

   TblStart $= 13.5$

   ΔTbl $= 4.5$

Then press [2nd] [GRAPH] to see a table of values.

X	Y1
13.5	19
18	23
22.5	27
27	31

and so on

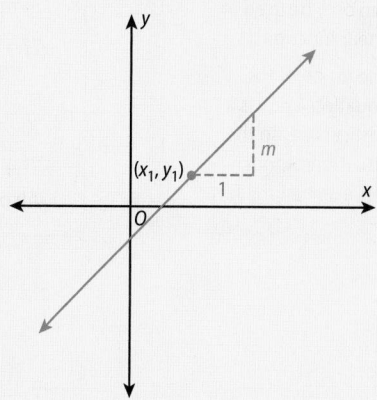

GOT TO KNOW!

The Point-Slope Equation of a Line

The equation of a line with slope m that contains the point (x_1, y_1) can be written this way.

$y - y_1 = m(x - x_1)$

Standard Form

If an equation is linear, it can be written in *standard form*.

The **standard form** of a linear equation is shown below.

$$Ax + By = C$$

In this form, A and B are integers that are not both 0; A, B, and C have no common factors; and A is positive or zero.

SEARCH

To see step-by-step videos of these problems, enter the page number into the SWadvantage.com Search Bar.

EXAMPLE 1

Is the equation linear? If so, write the equation in standard form.

a. $y = 2x + 5$

Write the equation.	$y = 2x + 5$
Subtract $2x$ from both sides.	$y - 2x = 2x + 5 - 2x$
The coefficient of x is negative.	$-2x + y = 5$
Multiply both sides by -1.	$-1(2x) + (-1)(y) = -1(5)$
Simplify.	$2x - y = -5$

The equation can be written in standard form, so it is linear.

b. $x = 9$

The equation can be written in standard form as $1x + 0y = 9$, so it is linear.

c. $x + 4 = \dfrac{y}{3}$

Write the equation.	$x + 4 = \dfrac{y}{3}$
Subtract 4 from both sides.	$x + 4 - 4 = \dfrac{y}{3} - 4$
Both x and y must be on the same side.	$x = \dfrac{y}{3} - 4$
Subtract $\dfrac{y}{3}$ from both sides.	$x - \dfrac{y}{3} = \dfrac{y}{3} - 4 - \dfrac{y}{3}$
The coefficient of y is $\dfrac{1}{3}$.	$x - \dfrac{y}{3} = -4$
Multiply both sides by 3.	$3(x) - 3\left(\dfrac{y}{3}\right) = 3(-4)$
Simplify to write in standard form.	$3x - y = -12$

The equation can be written in standard form as $3x - 1y = -12$, so it is linear.

d. $\dfrac{3}{x} - y^2 - 8 = 0$

The equation cannot be written in standard form because there is a variable in a denominator. Also, the equation is not linear because a variable is squared.

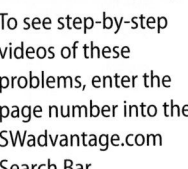

GOT TO KNOW!

Linear Equations and Vertical Lines

In Example 1b, the equation $x = 9$ is linear, but it cannot be written in slope-intercept form. Slope-intercept form can only be used for linear functions.

The graph of the equation $x = 9$ is a vertical line, so the equation cannot represent a function.

Using Standard Form to Find Intercepts

Writing a two-variable linear equation in standard form makes it easy to find the intercepts and graph the equation.

EXAMPLE 2

Write $7 - 2(x + 1) = 5y$ in standard form. Then graph.

STEP 1 Rewrite the equation in standard form.

Write the given equation.	$7 - 2(x + 1) = 5y$
Use the Distributive Property.	$7 - 2x - 2(1) = 5y$
Simplify.	$7 - 2x - 2 = 5y$
Combine like terms.	$5 - 2x = 5y$
Add $2x$ to both sides.	$5 - 2x + 2x = 5y + 2x$
Simplify.	$5 = 2x + 5y$
Use the Symmetric Property to reverse sides.	$2x + 5y = 5$

The equation $2x + 5y = 5$ is in standard form.

STEP 2 Find the intercepts, and graph the equation.

Find the y-intercept.

$$2x + 5y = 5$$
$$2(0) + 5y = 5$$
$$5y = 5$$
$$y = 1$$

Find the x-intercept.

$$2x + 5y = 5$$
$$2x + 5(0) = 5$$
$$2x = 5$$
$$x = 2.5$$

Plot the points $(0, 1)$ and $(2.5, 0)$. Draw the line through them.

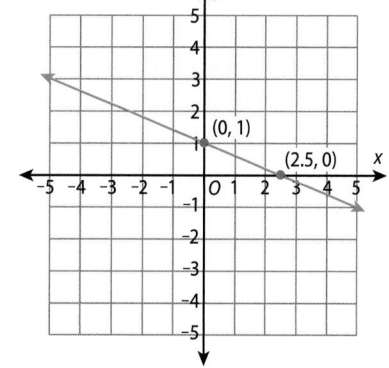

GOT TO KNOW!

Standard Form of a Linear Equation

The standard form of a linear equation is

$$Ax + By = C$$

where A and B are integers and not both 0; A, B, and C have no common factors; and A is positive or 0.

The x-intercept of the graph is $\frac{C}{A}$. The y-intercept of the graph is $\frac{C}{B}$.

Forms of a Linear Equation

You can determine which form of a linear equation is most appropriate depending on what you are given or what you know.

- **Slope-intercept form,** $y = mx + b$, is useful when you want to solve for y in terms of x. Also, you can easily graph an equation in that form by using a graphing calculator or by graphing the y-intercept and using slope to find another point.
- **Point-slope form,** $y - y_1 = m(x - x_1)$, is useful when you know both the slope and a point on the graph. Also, you can easily read that information from an equation given in that form.
- **Standard form,** $Ax + By = C$, is useful for finding the intercepts and graphing. This form can be used for a linear equation that is not a function.

EXAMPLE 1

SEARCH

To see step-by-step videos of these problems, enter the page number into the SWadvantage.com Search Bar.

Write the most appropriate form of the linear equation. Simplify if necessary.

a. a line with slope 0.5 that contains the point (5, −1)

One point and the slope are given. Point-slope form is appropriate.

$$y - y_1 = m(x - x_1)$$
$$y - (-1) = 0.5(x - 5)$$
$$y + 1 = 0.5(x - 5)$$

b. a line with undefined slope that contains the point (3, 4)

The slope is undefined, so the line must be vertical. A vertical line cannot be a function. So, only standard form is appropriate. The line contains the point (3, 4). So the line includes all points where x equals 3.

$$Ax + By = C$$
$$1x + 0y = 3$$
$$x = 3$$

c. a line with y-intercept −7 and slope $-\frac{6}{7}$

The slope and intercept are given. Slope-intercept form is appropriate.

$$y = mx + b$$
$$y = -\frac{6}{7}x + (-7)$$
$$y = -\frac{6}{7}x - 7$$

GOT TO KNOW!

Forms of a Linear Equation

slope-intercept form	$y = mx + b$
point-slope form	$y - y_1 = m(x - x_1)$
standard form	$Ax + By = C$

Converting to Slope-Intercept Form

EXAMPLE 2

Convert the equation $4x + 5y = 20$ to slope-intercept form, if possible.

The equation is in standard form.

Write the equation.	$4x + 5y = 20$
Add $-4x$ to both sides to isolate $5y$.	$\underline{+ (-4x) \qquad + (-4x)}$
	$5y = -4x + 20$
Divide both sides by 5 to solve for y.	$\dfrac{5y}{5} = \dfrac{-4x + 20}{5}$
Use the Distributive Property.	$y = \dfrac{-4x}{5} + \dfrac{20}{5}$
Simplify. The equation is in slope-intercept form.	$y = -\dfrac{4}{5}x + 4$

Need More

HELP ?

Remember that these forms are equivalent.

$$-\frac{4}{5}x \qquad \frac{-4}{5}x \qquad \frac{4}{-5}x$$

$$-\frac{4x}{5} \qquad \frac{-4x}{5} \qquad \frac{4x}{-5}$$

EXAMPLE 3

The revenue from the sale of x adult tickets at $7.50 each plus y discount tickets at $3.75 each is $750. Write the standard-form equation for the revenue. Then convert the equation to slope-intercept form and graph. What does the graph mean?

STEP 1 Write the standard form of the equation.

Translate the given information into an equation.	$7.5x + 3.75y = 750$
Multiply by 100 to clear decimals.	$100(7.5x) + 100(3.75y) = 100(750)$
Simplify.	$750x + 375y = 75,000$

The equation is in standard form.

STEP 2 Convert to slope-intercept form.

Add $-750x$ to both sides to isolate $375y$.	$750x + (-750x) + 375y = -750x + 75,000$
Simplify.	$375y = -750x + 75,000$
Divide both sides by 375 to solve for y.	$\dfrac{375y}{375} = \dfrac{-750x}{375} + \dfrac{75,000}{375}$
Simplify.	$y = -2x + 200$

The equation is in slope-intercept form.

STEP 3 Graph the equation.

The y-intercept is 200, so one point is (0, 200).

Find a second point. If $x = 50$,
$y = -2(50) + 200 = 100$.

Graph the line through (0, 200) and (50, 100).

Only graph in Quadrant 1 since a negative number of tickets does not make sense.

STEP 4 Explain the meaning.

The graph shows the combinations of tickets sold that would generate $750 in revenue.

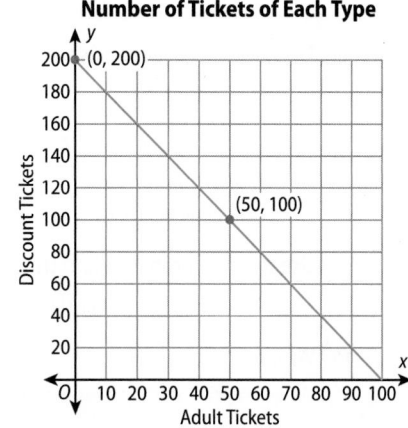

Number of Tickets of Each Type

Converting between Forms

EXAMPLE 4

Convert the equation to slope-intercept form, if possible.

a. $y - 2 = -3(x - 6)$

The equation is in point-slope form.

Write the equation.	$y - 2 = -3(x - 6)$
Add 2 to both sides to isolate y.	$y - 2 + 2 = -3(x - 6) + 2$
Simplify.	$y = -3(x - 6) + 2$
Use the Distributive Property.	$y = -3x + (-3)(-6) + 2$
Simplify and combine terms.	$y = -3x + 18 + 2$
The equation is in slope-intercept form.	$y = -3x + 20$

b. $3x = 10$

The equation is in standard form $Ax + By = C$, where $B = 0$.
The equation cannot be written in slope-intercept form because the coefficient of y is 0 (the equation does not have a y-term).

EXAMPLE 5

Convert the equation to point-slope form.

a. $y = 10x + 15$

The equation is in slope-intercept form.

Because the y-intercept is 15, one point on the line is (0, 15).

Write the point-slope equation.	$y - 15 = 10(x - 0)$
Use the identity property.	$y - 15 = 10x$

The equation is in point-slope form.

Other point-slope forms are possible, depending on which point is chosen.

b. $-8x + 6y = 36$

The equation is in standard form.

STEP 1 Find the intercepts to use as the points.

Write the equation.	$-8x + 6y = 36$	$-8x + 6y = 36$
Substitute 0 for x and for y.	$-8(0) + 6y = 36$	$-8x + 6(0) = 36$
Simplify.	$6y = 36$	$-8x = 36$
A second point is (0, 6).	$y = 6$	$x = -4.5$

STEP 2 Use the two points to find the slope.

Choose (0, 6) as (x_1, y_1) and $(-4.5, 0)$ as (x_2, y_2). $\quad m = \frac{y_2 - y_1}{x_2 - x_1} = \frac{0 - 6}{-4.5 - 0} = \frac{-6}{-4.5} = \frac{12}{9} = \frac{4}{3}$

STEP 3 Write in point-slope form.

Write the point-slope equation.	$y - y_1 = m(x - x_1)$
Substitute for m, x_1, and y_1.	$y - 6 = \frac{4}{3}(x - 0)$, or $y - 6 = \frac{4}{3}x$

Converting to Standard Form

EXAMPLE 6

Convert the equation to standard form.

a. $y = \frac{2}{7}x - 5$

The equation is in slope-intercept form.	$y = \frac{2}{7}x - 5$
Multiply both sides by 7 to clear the fraction.	$7y = 7\left(\frac{2}{7}x\right) - 7(5)$
Simplify.	$7y = 2x - 35$
Subtract $2x$ from both sides.	$7y - 2x = 2x - 35 - 2x$
	$-2x + 7y = -35$
Multiply each term by -1.	$2x - 7y = 35$
The equation is in standard form.	

b. $y - 5 = 8(x - 1)$

The equation is in point-slope form.	$y - 5 = 8(x - 1)$
Use the Distributive Property to multiply.	$y - 5 = 8x - 8(1)$
Subtract y from both sides.	$y - 5 - y = 8x - 8 - y$
	$-5 = 8x - 8 - y$
Add 8 to both sides.	$-5 + 8 = 8x - 8 - y + 8$
Simplify.	$3 = 8x - y$
Use the Symmetric Property.	$8x - y = 3$
The equation is in standard form.	

Need More

HELP

Changing the sign of each term is the same as multiplying by -1.

$-x + y = 4$
$(-1)(-x) + (-1)y = (-1)4$
$x - y = -4$

GOT TO KNOW!

Converting between Forms of a Linear Equation

From	To	Method
Any form	Slope-intercept form	Solve the equation for y.
Standard form	Point-slope form	Use the intercept points to find the slope. Then substitute a point.
Slope-intercept form	Point-slope form	Use the y-intercept point and the given slope.
Any form	Standard form	Use properties to transform the equation.

Writing an Equation of a Line

Write an Equation, Given a Table

EXAMPLE 1

Write the slope-intercept equation that fits the data in the table.

x	2	5	8
y	10	7	4

STEP 1 First, check that the data have a linear relationship. Find the slope.

Find each rate of change.

$$\frac{\text{change in } y}{\text{change in } x} = \frac{7 - 10}{5 - 2} = \frac{-3}{3} = -1$$

$$\frac{\text{change in } y}{\text{change in } x} = \frac{4 - 7}{8 - 5} = \frac{-3}{3} = -1$$

The rates of change are equal, so the relationship is linear. The slope is -1.

METHOD 1

STEP 2 Substitute the slope and one point in the point-slope equation.

Write the point-slope equation. $y - y_1 = m(x - x_1)$

Choose (2, 10). Substitute. $y - 10 = -1(x - 2)$

STEP 3 Solve for y.

Use the Distributive Property. $y - 10 = -1(x) - (-1)(2)$

Simplify. $y - 10 = -x + 2$

Add 10 to both sides. $y = -x + 12$

The equation $y = -x + 12$ is in slope-intercept form.

Need More HELP?

You can write $-1(x - 2)$ as $-(x - 2)$.

When you use the Distributive Property to simplify, write the opposite of both terms inside parentheses.

$-(x - 2) = -x + 2$

METHOD 2

STEP 2 Substitute the slope and one point in the slope-intercept equation.

Write the slope-intercept equation. $y = mx + b$

Choose (2, 10). Substitute. $10 = -1(2) + b$

STEP 3 Solve for b.

Simplify. $10 = -2 + b$

Add 2 to both sides. $12 = b$

STEP 4 Substitute m and b in the slope-intercept equation. $y = mx + b$

Substitute -1 for m and 12 for b. $y = -1x + 12$

Simplify. $y = -x + 12$

The equation $y = -x + 12$ is in slope-intercept form.

Write an Equation, Given a Graph

Given a graph, you can write the equation of the line. First, use two points to find the slope. Then substitute one point and the slope in either the point-slope equation or the slope-intercept equation, and simplify.

EXAMPLE

Write the slope-intercept equation for the line shown.

STEP 1 Choose two points on the line, and use the coordinates to calculate the slope.

Two of the points on the line appear to be (40, 70) and (60, 45).

STEP 2 Find the slope.

Choose (40, 70) as (x_1, y_1) and (60, 45) as (x_2, y_2).

$$m = \frac{y_2 - y_1}{x_2 - x_1}$$

$$= \frac{45 - 70}{60 - 40} = \frac{-25}{20} = -\frac{5}{4}$$

STEP 3 Substitute the slope and one point in the point-slope equation.

Write the point-slope equation. $y - y_1 = m(x - x_1)$

Choose (40, 70). Substitute. $y - 70 = -\frac{5}{4}(x - 40)$

STEP 4 Solve for y.

Use the Distributive Property. $y - 70 = -\frac{5}{4}(x) - \frac{5}{4}(-40)$

Multiply. $y - 70 = -\frac{5}{4}x + \frac{200}{4}$

Divide. $y - 70 = -\frac{5}{4}x + 50$

Add 70 to both sides. $y = -\frac{5}{4}x + 120$

A y-intercept of 120 is reasonable.

The equation is in slope-intercept form.

CHECK Substitute the other point in the equation.

$$y = -\frac{5}{4}x + 120$$

$$45 \stackrel{?}{=} -\frac{5}{4}(60) + 120$$

$$45 \stackrel{?}{=} -\frac{300}{4} + 120$$

$$45 \stackrel{?}{=} -75 + 120$$

$$45 = 45 ✔$$

The equation $y = -\frac{5}{4}x + 120$ is in slope-intercept form and represents the given graph.

(40, 70)

(60, 45)

Watch Out !

Try not to use two points that are very close together on the line. If any of the coordinates are inaccurate, the error in the equation will be large. If possible, choose points that are located where the grid lines of the graph intersect.

Modeling a Line of Best Fit

Many data sets are very close to linear. In that case, you can use a **line of best fit**, the line that most closely fits the data and make predictions.

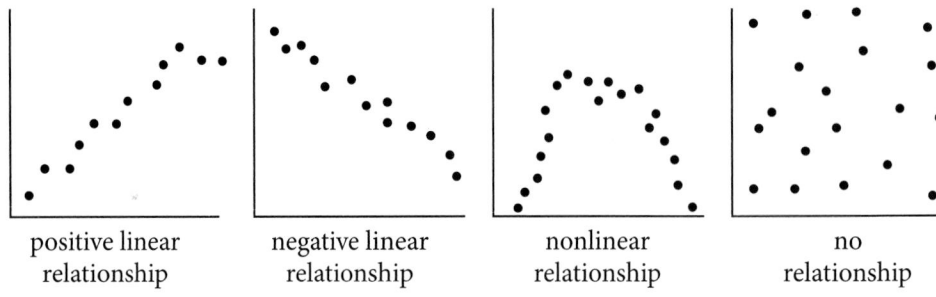

positive linear relationship   negative linear relationship   nonlinear relationship   no relationship

EXAMPLE 3

The table shows the average January temperature in 11 non-coastal U.S. cities. Determine whether there is a relationship between latitude and temperature. Sketch a line of best fit, and find its equation.

Make a scatter plot of the data.

There is a negative linear relationship between latitude and temperature.

Sketch a line of best fit to model the data.

Draw a line that splits the data equally above and below the line.

City	Latitude (degrees)	Avg. Jan Temp (°F)
Austin	30	50
Cleveland	41	26
Columbia	34	45
Denver	40	29
Fargo	47	7
Indianapolis	40	27
Jackson	32	45
Minneapolis	44	13
Oklahoma City	35	37
Phoenix	33	54
San Antonio	29	50

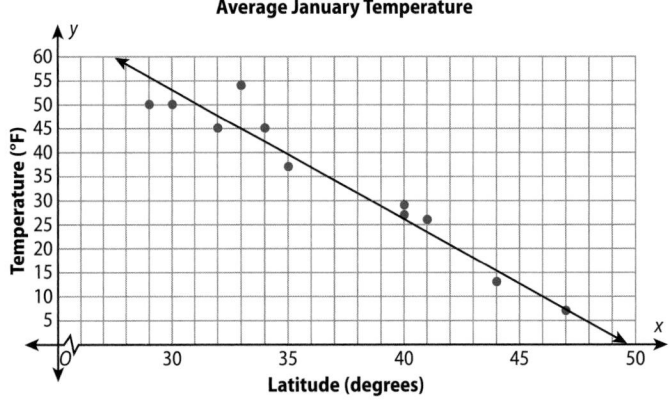

Average January Temperature

Follow the steps in the *Got To Know!* box. Using the points (33, 45) and (46, 10), an equation of a line of best fit is $y = -2.69x + 133.7$.

EXAMPLE 4

Use the linear regression function of your graphing calculator to find the line of best fit for the temperature data in Example 3. Use the line to predict the average January temperature for a non-coastal U.S. city at latitude 37°.

STEP 1 Enter the data.

Press **STAT** and choose **1:Edit.**

Enter each ordered pair in lists L1 and L2.

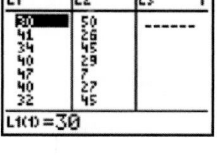

STEP 2 Find the linear regression line.

Press **STAT** and choose **CALC** and **4: LinReg(ax+b)**. Press **ENTER** twice.

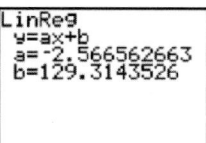

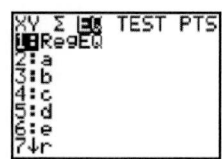

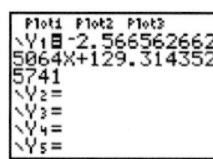

STEP 3 Enter the linear regression line into the function grapher.

Press **Y=**, then **VARS**. Choose **5:Statistics...** . Choose **EQ and 1:RegEQ**, and press **ENTER**.

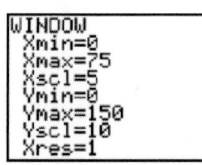

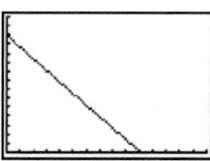

STEP 4 Choose a window to fit the data, and graph.

Press **WINDOW**, enter the values shown, and press **GRAPH**.

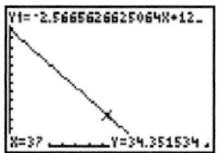

STEP 5 Substitute 37 for x to predict the temperature.

Press **CALC** and choose **1:value.**
Type 37 for **X=** and press **ENTER**.

The predicted average January temperature for a non-coastal U.S. city at latitude 37° is about 34.4°F.

Graphing a Linear Inequality

Linear Inequalities

The solution of an inequality in one variable is a set of points. The solution of a linear inequality in two variables is a set of ordered pairs.

SEARCH

To see step-by-step videos of these problems, enter the page number into the SWadvantage.com Search Bar.

EXAMPLE 1

Tell whether the ordered pair is a solution of the linear inequality.

a. (2, 1) $5x + 3y \overset{?}{>} 12$

$5(2) + 3(1) \overset{?}{>} 12$ Substitute.

$10 + 3 \overset{?}{>} 12$ Simplify.

$13 > 12 \checkmark$

The ordered pair is a solution.

b. (−7, −4) $-2x + 7y \overset{?}{\le} -15$

$-2(-7) + 7(-4) \overset{?}{\le} -15$

$14 + (-28) \overset{?}{\le} -15$

$-14 \le -15 \; ✗$

The ordered pair is not a solution.

Need More

HELP ?

Graphs of linear inequalities are similar to graphs of one-variable inequalities.

If the symbol is < or >, the graph has an open circle or dashed line.

If the symbol is ≤ or ≥, the graph has a closed circle or solid line.

In the graph of a linear inequality with two variables, the **boundary line** is the graph of the related equation. The graph of the inequality is the region on one side of the line and is called a **half-plane**. A solid boundary line is part of the solution of the inequality. A dashed line is not part of the solution.

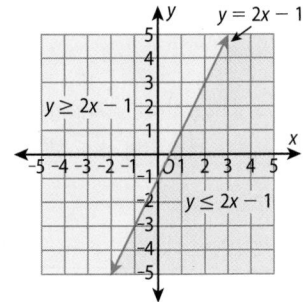

EXAMPLE 2

Match each inequality with its graph: $y > x + 2$, $y < x + 2$, $y \ge x + 2$, and $y \le x + 2$.

a.

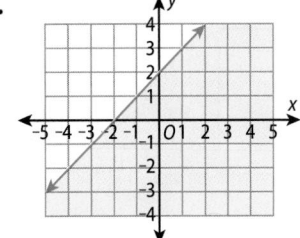

The half-plane below the line is shaded, and the line is solid; $y \le x + 2$.

b.

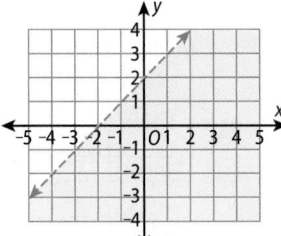

The half-plane below the line is shaded, and the line is dashed; $y < x + 2$.

c.

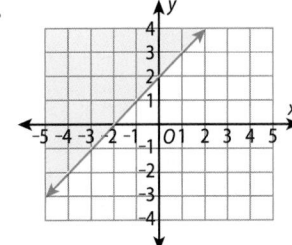

The half-plane above the line is shaded, and the line is solid; $y \ge x + 2$.

d.

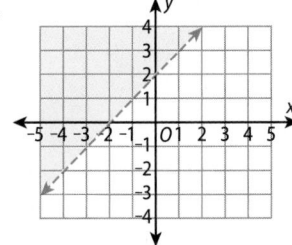

The half-plane above the line is shaded, and the line is dashed; $y > x + 2$.

EXAMPLE 3

Graph each linear inequality.

a. $y - 13 > 4x - 16$

STEP 1 Solve the inequality for y.

Write the inequality. $y - 13 > 4x - 16$

Add 13 to both sides. $y > 4x - 3$

STEP 2 Graph the boundary line.

Graph $y = 4x - 3$. Use a dashed line for $>$.

STEP 3 Shade the correct half-plane.

The inequality symbol is $>$, so shade *above* the line.

CHECK The point $(0, 0)$ is in the shaded region. Substitute $(0, 0)$ in the inequality to see whether the correct region is shaded.

Write the inequality. $y - 13 > 4x - 16$

Substitute $(0, 0)$. $0 - 13 \overset{?}{>} 4(0) - 16$

$0 > -3$ ✔

The ordered pair $(0, 0)$ is a solution. The correct region is shaded.

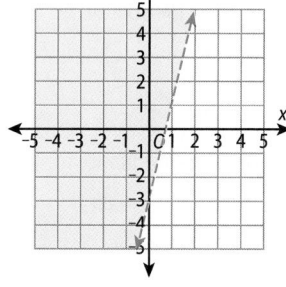

b. $-2y \geq x + 4$

STEP 1 Solve the inequality for y.

Write the inequality. $-2y \geq x + 4$

Divide by -2 and reverse the inequality symbol. $\dfrac{-2y}{-2} \leq \dfrac{x + 4}{-2}$

Simplify. $y \leq -\dfrac{1}{2}x - 2$

STEP 2 Graph the boundary line.

Graph $y = -\dfrac{1}{2}x - 2$. Use a solid line for $\leq$.

STEP 3 Shade the correct half-plane.

The inequality is $\leq$, so shade *below* the line.

CHECK The point $(0, 0)$ is not in the shaded region. Substitute $(0, 0)$ in the inequality to make sure the correct region is shaded.

Write the inequality. $-2y \geq x + 4$

Substitute $(0, 0)$. $-2(0) \overset{?}{\geq} 0 + 4$

$0 \geq 4$ ✘

The ordered pair $(0, 0)$ is not a solution. The correct region is shaded.

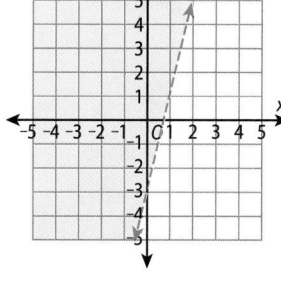

Need More HELP?

When the boundary line is very steep, shading above will look more like shading the left or right side.

GOT TO KNOW!

To Graph a Linear Inequality

1. Solve the inequality for y.

2. Graph the boundary line as solid (for $y \geq$ or $y \leq$) or dashed (for $y >$ or $y <$).

3. Shade above the boundary line (for $y \geq$ or $y >$) or below (for $y \leq$ or $y <$).

Graphing Linear Inequalities to Solve Problems

EXAMPLE 4

One part of an exam has 2-point questions and 3-point questions. The total number of points earned for that part of the exam can be no more than 90.

a. Write an inequality for the situation.

Let x be the number of 2-point questions, and y be the number of 3-point questions.

Write an inequality.

The points from 2-point questions plus the points from 3-point questions total no more than 90.

| $2x$ | $+$ | $3y$ | $\leq$ | 90 |

Solve the inequality for y.

Write the inequality.	$2x + 3y \leq 90$
Subtract $2x$ from both sides to isolate $2y$.	$2x + 3y - 2x \leq 90 - 2x$
Divide both sides by 3 to solve for y.	$\dfrac{3y}{3} \leq \dfrac{90 - 2x}{3}$
Simplify.	$y \leq 30 - \dfrac{2}{3}x$

The inequality is $y \leq 30 - \dfrac{2}{3}x$.

b. Graph the inequality.

STEP 1 Graph the boundary line.

The number of questions of each type cannot be negative. So graph the line in the first quadrant only. Use a solid line for $\leq$.

STEP 2 Shade the correct region.

The symbol used is $\leq$, so shade below the line.

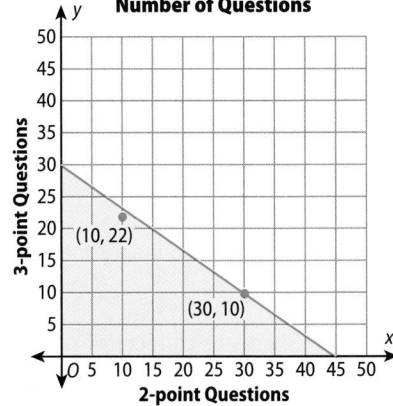

c. Describe two combinations of questions that could be used on the exam.

All points in the shaded region or on the boundary line are solutions to the inequality. However, only whole-number ordered pairs make sense as solutions to the problem.

One possible combination is 30 2-point questions and 10 3-point questions.

$30(2) + 10(3) = 60 + 30 = 90, 90 \leq 90$

Another possible combination is 10 2-point questions and 22 3-point questions.

$10(2) + 22(3) = 20 + 66 = 86, 86 \leq 90$

Vertical and Horizontal Boundary Lines

EXAMPLE

Write an inequality for each graph.

a.

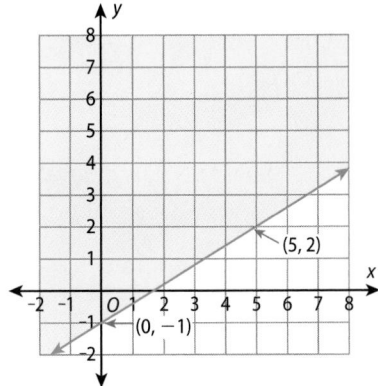

The y-intercept is -1. Two points on the boundary line are $(0, -1)$ and $(5, 2)$.

$$m = \frac{y_2 - y_1}{x_2 - x_1} = \frac{2 - (-1)}{5 - 0} = \frac{3}{5}$$

Write the equation for the boundary line:
$y = \frac{3}{5}x - 1$.

The graph is shaded above the solid line, so replace $=$ with the $\geq$ symbol: $y \geq \frac{3}{5}x - 1$.

SEARCH

To see step-by-step videos of these problems, enter the page number into the SWadvantage.com Search Bar.

GOT TO KNOW!

Graph of $y \neq$

The graph of a linear inequality that uses the "is not equal to" symbol $\neq$ is a dashed line with both sides of the line shaded.

For example, the graph of $y \neq 2$ is a dashed line at $y = 2$ with shading both above and below the dashed line.

b.

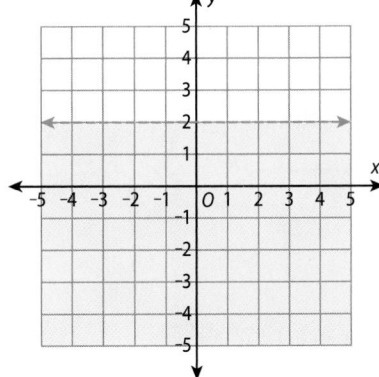

There is no x-intercept.

The boundary line is a horizontal line at $y = 2$.

The graph is shaded below the dashed line, so replace $=$ with the $<$ symbol: $y < 2$.

c.

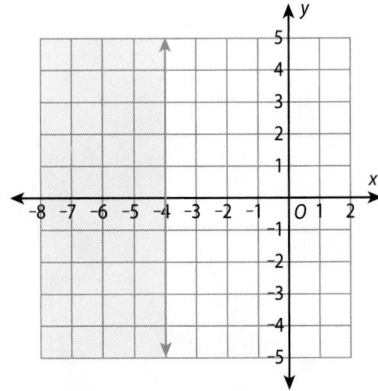

There is no y-intercept.

The boundary line is a vertical line at $x = -4$.

The graph is shaded to the left of the solid line, so replace $=$ with the $\leq$ symbol: $x \leq -4$.

Systems of Linear Equations and Inequalities

What Came Before?
- Solving equations, inequalities, and conjunctions
- Graphing linear equations and linear inequalities

What's This About?
- Solving systems of equations by graphing or algebraic methods
- Recognizing systems with no solution or with infinitely many solutions
- Graphing systems of linear inequalities to solve linear programming problems

Practical Apps
- Transportation analysts use linear programming to analyze and improve the flow of traffic.
- Video game programmers use systems of equations to determine whether a moving target has been hit.

just for FUN!

TESSA: "Your feasible region is too big."

NANCY: "I guess it broke free from its constraints!"

| CONTENTS | UPLOAD | DOWNLOAD | *Algebra* |

You can find more practice problems online by visiting:
www.SWadvantage.com

Solving a System by Graphing

Solutions of Linear Systems

When more than one equation is needed to describe a situation, the set of equations is called a *system of equations*. A **system of linear equations** is a set of two or more linear equations with two or more variables. A solution of a system of linear equations is any ordered pair that is a solution of every linear equation in the system.

EXAMPLE 1

SEARCH

To see step-by-step videos of these problems, enter the page number into the SWadvantage.com Search Bar.

Tell whether the ordered pair is a solution of the system of linear equations.

a. $(-3, 2)$ $\begin{cases} 4x - y = -14 \\ 5y - 2x = 16 \end{cases}$

Substitute the ordered pair in each equation.

$$4x - y = -14 \qquad\qquad 5y - 2x = 16$$
$$4(-3) - 2 \overset{?}{=} -14 \qquad 5(2) - 2(-3) \overset{?}{=} 16$$
$$-12 - 2 \overset{?}{=} -14 \qquad\qquad 10 + 6 \overset{?}{=} 16$$
$$-14 = -14 \;✔ \qquad\qquad 16 = 16 \;✔$$

The ordered pair is a solution.   The ordered pair is a solution.

The ordered pair $(-3, 2)$ makes both equations true, so it is a solution of the system.

b. $(6, -1)$ $\begin{cases} y = 17 - 3x \\ -x - 4y = -10 \end{cases}$

Substitute the ordered pair in each equation.

$$y = 17 - 3x \qquad\qquad -x - 4y = -10$$
$$-1 \overset{?}{=} 17 - 3(6) \qquad -(6) - 4(-1) \overset{?}{=} -10$$
$$-1 \overset{?}{=} 17 - 18 \qquad\qquad -6 + 4 \overset{?}{=} -10$$
$$-1 = -1 \;✔ \qquad\qquad\qquad -2 = -10 \;✗$$

The ordered pair is a solution.   The ordered pair is not a solution.

The ordered pair $(6, -1)$ makes one equation false, so it is *not* a solution of the system.

c. $(8, 10)$ $\begin{cases} y = 6x \\ -7x + 5y = 4 \end{cases}$

Substitute 8 for x in $y = 6x$: $y = 6(8) = 48$

Compare the result with the value of y in the given ordered pair, $(8, 10)$. $48 \neq 10$

The ordered pair $(8, 10)$ is not a solution of the first equation. Since the ordered pair $(8, 10)$ makes the first equation false, it is *not* a solution of the system. There is no need to check the second equation!

You can use a table to find a solution of some linear systems.

1. Be sure that each equation shows an expression equal to y.

2. Make a table of values for x, and record the corresponding values of y for each equation.

3. Look for an x-value that has the same y-value in both equations. That ordered pair is the solution of the system.

EXAMPLE 2

Use a table to find a solution of the linear system.

$$\begin{cases} y = 6 - x \\ y = 2x \end{cases}$$

Both equations are already solved for y. Make a table to find solutions of each equation.

x	1	2	3	4	5	6
$y = 6 - x$	5	4	3	2	1	0
$y = 2x$	2	4	6	8	10	12

When $x = 2$, $y = 4$ in both equations. The ordered pair (2, 4) is a solution of the system.

Graphs of Linear Systems

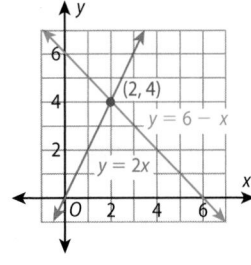

In the table in Example 2, the ordered pair common to both equations is a solution of the system. In a graph of the system, this is the point where the graphs of the two linear equations intersect. The graphs intersect at (2, 4), so (2, 4) is a solution of the system.

EXAMPLE 3

Use a graph to find a solution of the linear system.

$$\begin{cases} 3x - y = 3 \\ x + y = 5 \end{cases}$$

Both equations are in standard form.

STEP 1 Find the intercept points for each equation.

$$3x - y = 3$$
$$3(0) - y = 3 \qquad 3x - 0 = 3$$
$$-y = 3 \qquad\quad 3x = 3$$
$$y = -3 \qquad\quad\; x = 1$$
Intercept points are (0, −3) and (1, 0).

$$x + y = 5$$
$$0 + y = 5 \qquad x + 0 = 5$$
$$y = 5 \qquad\quad x = 5$$
Intercept points are (0, 5) and (5, 0).

STEP 2 Graph the system.

Use the intercepts to graph each line.

STEP 3 Look for the intersection point.

The solution appears to be (2, 3).

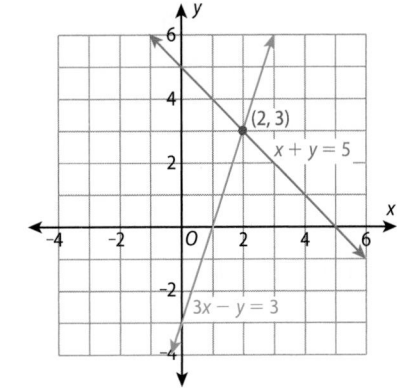

STEP 4 Check the solution in each equation.

$$3x - y = 3 \qquad\quad x + y = 5$$
$$3(2) - 3 \overset{?}{=} 3 \qquad 2 + 3 \overset{?}{=} 5$$
$$6 - 3 \overset{?}{=} 3 \qquad\qquad 5 = 5 \checkmark$$
$$3 = 3 \checkmark$$

The ordered pair (2, 3) is a solution of the system.

Need More
HELP ?

On some graphs, it may be difficult to identify the coordinates of the intersection point. Changing the scales of the axes may help.

Solving Systems with Graphing Technology

You can use a graphing calculator to solve linear systems. Whether you graph by hand or with a calculator, make sure that the scale or window you use includes the intersection point. Remember that two lines in the same plane that are not parallel have different slopes, so they must intersect somewhere.

EXAMPLE 4

Solve the system of linear equations.

$$\begin{cases} y = 26 - 3x \\ 3x = 2y - 16 \end{cases}$$

STEP 1 Solve the second equation for y.

$$3x = 2y - 16$$

Add 16 to both sides. $3x + 16 = 2y$

Divide both sides by 2. $\dfrac{3x}{2} + \dfrac{16}{2} = y$

Simplify. $\dfrac{3}{2}x + 8 = y,$

                 or $y = \dfrac{3}{2}x + 8$

STEP 2 Press [Y=] and enter the right sides of the equations into **Y1** and **Y2**.

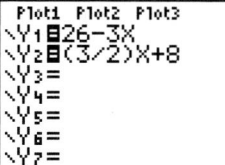

STEP 3 Press [ZOOM] and choose **6:ZStandard** to graph the system in the standard window. It has a scale of -10 to 10 for each variable.

The intersection point is above the graphing window.

STEP 4 Change the graphing window.

Press [WINDOW] and change **YMax** to 20. Press [GRAPH].

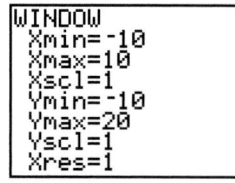

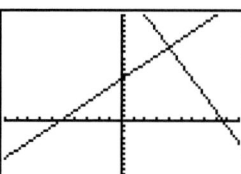

STEP 5 Look for the intersection point.

Press [2nd] [CALC], choose **5:intersect**, and press [ENTER] several times until the solution is shown.

The solution is (4, 14).

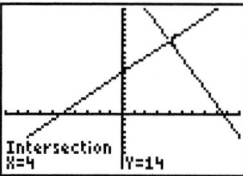

Try It This Way

Another way to see the intersection point is to press [ZOOM] and select **3:Zoom Out** to zoom out on the graph.

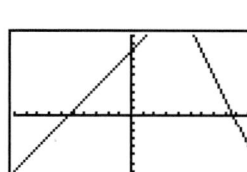

Using Systems to Solve Word Problems

When a word problem can be represented by systems of linear equations, the *x*- and *y*-values of the intersection point of the graph usually relate to the solution of the problem.

EXAMPLE 5

An athletic club has two payment options. Option A has a membership fee of $49 and weekly dues of $10.50. Option B has a membership fee of $10 and weekly dues of $12. After how many weeks would the cost be the same for Options A and B? What is the cost for that many weeks?

STEP 1 Write a system of equations for the situation.

Let *x* be the number of weeks and *y* be the cost.

The total cost is the membership fee plus the dues per week.

Option A	y	$=$	49	$+$	$10.5x$
Option B	y	$=$	10	$+$	$12x$

STEP 2 Use a graphing calculator to graph the system.

$$\begin{cases} y = 49 + 10.5x \\ y = 10 + 12x \end{cases}$$

The lines intersect at (26, 322).

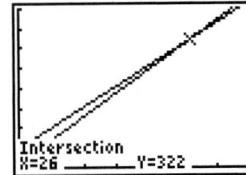

STEP 3 Use the solution to answer the questions.

The *x*-value of the intersection point is the number of weeks. The *y*-value is the total cost.

For a 26-week membership, Option A and Option B cost the same amount, $322.

STEP 4 **CHECK** Substitute the coordinates of the point of intersection into each equation.

$y = 49 + 10.5x$	$y = 10 + 12x$
$322 \overset{?}{=} 49 + 10.5(26)$	$322 \overset{?}{=} 10 + 12(26)$
$322 \overset{?}{=} 49 + 273$	$322 \overset{?}{=} 10 + 312$
$322 = 322$ ✔	$322 = 322$ ✔

The solution makes the system of equations true.

For a 26-week membership, Option A and Option B cost the same amount, $322.

Option B is cheaper for up to 25 weeks.

Option A is cheaper for more than 26 weeks.

Need More

HELP ?

You can also use the differences in fees and dues to find the number of weeks.

The difference in membership fees is $49 − $10 = $39.

The difference in weekly dues is $12 − $10.50 = $1.50.

Divide to find the number of weeks at which the cost is the same.

$\frac{39}{1.5}$ = 26 weeks

SEARCH

To see step-by-step videos of these problems, enter the page number into the SWadvantage.com Search Bar.

GOT TO KNOW!

To Solve a System of Two Linear Equations by Graphing

1. Solve each equation for *y*.

2. Graph each equation as a line, and find the intersection point.

3. The solution of the system is the ordered pair at the intersection point.

4. If it is difficult to find the intersection point, try using a different method to find the solution.

Solving a System by Substitution

SOUTHWESTERN

The Substitution Method

It may be difficult to find the solution of a system of linear equations by graphing. One way to solve a system algebraically is by substitution. The **substitution method** finds an expression for the value of a variable from one equation and substitutes the expression for that variable in the other equation.

EXAMPLE 1

Use the substitution method to solve the system.

$$\begin{cases} y = x + 3 \\ y = 2x \end{cases}$$

STEP 1 Solve an equation for a variable.

Both equations already express a value for y, so there are two choices for substitution for y.

STEP 2 Substitute an expression for y from one equation into the other equation.

Write the equation you choose to use. $\qquad y = x + 3$

Substitute $2x$ for y. $\qquad 2x = x + 3$

STEP 3 Solve for x.

$$\begin{array}{r} 2x = x + 3 \\ -x \quad -x \\ \hline x = \quad 3 \end{array}$$

Subtract x from both sides.

STEP 4 Solve for y in one of the original equations.

Choose the second equation. $\qquad y = 2x$

Substitute 3 for x. $\qquad y = 2(3)$

$\qquad y = 6$

You found that $x = 3$ and $y = 6$. So the solution is $(3, 6)$.

CHECK Substitute the solution into each equation.

$$y = x + 3 \qquad y = 2x$$
$$6 \stackrel{?}{=} 3 + 3 \qquad 6 \stackrel{?}{=} 2(3)$$
$$6 = 6 ✔ \qquad 6 = 6 ✔$$

The ordered pair $(3, 6)$ is a solution of the system.

It does not matter which equation you use first. Look back at Step 2 in Example 1. You can choose to substitute in the second equation the value of y from the first equation. The solution will remain the same.

STEP 2 Substitute an expression for y from one equation into the other equation.

Write the equation you choose to use. $\qquad y = 2x$

Substitute $x + 3$ for y. $\qquad x + 3 = 2x$

When you solve for x, the value will still be 3. By substitution, $y = 6$, and so the solution will still be $(3, 6)$.

When you have a choice of equations to use for substitution, choose the one that is easiest to simplify, or one that already expresses a value for a variable.

EXAMPLE 2

Use the substitution method to solve the system.

$$\begin{cases} y = x - 2 \\ 3x + y = 10 \end{cases}$$

STEP 1 Solve an equation for a variable.

The first equation already expresses a value for y.

STEP 2 Substitute the expression for y from the first equation into the second equation.

$$3x + y = 10$$

Substitute $x - 2$ for y. $3x + x - 2 = 10$

STEP 3 Simplify and solve for x.

Use the Associative Property.	$(3x + x) - 2 = 10$
Combine like terms.	$4x - 2 = 10$
Add 2 to both sides.	$4x - 2 + 2 = 10 + 2$
Simplify.	$4x = 12$
Divide both sides by 4.	$\dfrac{4x}{4} = \dfrac{12}{4}$
	$x = 3$

STEP 4 Solve for y in one of the original equations.

Choose the first equation.	$y = x - 2$
Substitute 3 for x.	$y = 3 - 2$
Simplify.	$y = 1$

You found that $x = 3$ and $y = 1$. So the solution is (3, 1).

CHECK Substitute the solution into each equation.

$y = x - 2$	$3x + y = 10$
$1 \overset{?}{=} 3 - 2$	$3(3) + 1 \overset{?}{=} 10$
$1 = 1$ ✔	$10 = 10$ ✔

The ordered pair (3, 1) is a solution of the system.

SEARCH 🔍

To see step-by-step videos of these problems, enter the page number into the SWadvantage.com Search Bar.

Watch Out ❗

Remember, the solution is an ordered pair, not a value of x. Continue solving until you find the values of both x and y.

GOT TO KNOW!

To Solve a System of Two Linear Equations by Substitution

1. Solve one equation to form an expression for one variable in terms of the other.

2. Substitute the expression for that variable in the other equation.

3. Solve that equation for the other variable.

4. Substitute the resulting value for that variable in one of the original equations to find the value of the other variable.

5. Check the solution in each original equation.

Using the Substitution Method

EXAMPLE 3

Use the substitution method to solve the system.
$$\begin{cases} 2x - 5y = 23 \\ 3x + 4y = 0 \end{cases}$$

STEP 1 Solve an equation for a variable.

The second equation is easier to solve for a variable. Solve for y.

$$4y = -3x$$

Divide both sides by 4. $\quad \dfrac{4y}{4} = \dfrac{-3x}{4}$

$$y = -\dfrac{3}{4}x$$

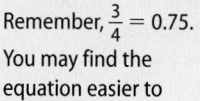

Need More
HELP ?

Remember, $\dfrac{3}{4} = 0.75$.
You may find the equation easier to simplify if you convert $-\dfrac{3}{4}$ to the decimal -0.75.

STEP 2 Substitute the expression for y from the second equation into the first equation.

$$2x - 5y = 23$$

Substitute $-\dfrac{3}{4}x$ for y. $\quad 2x - 5\left(-\dfrac{3}{4}x\right) = 23$

STEP 3 Simplify and solve for x.

Rewrite subtraction of a negative as addition.	$2x + \dfrac{15}{4}x = 23$
Multiply both sides by 4 to clear the fraction.	$4\left(2x + \dfrac{15}{4}x\right) = 4(23)$
Use the Distributive Property.	$4(2x) + 4\left(\dfrac{15}{4}x\right) = 4(23)$
Simplify.	$8x + 15x = 92$
Combine like terms.	$23x = 92$
Divide both sides by 23.	$\dfrac{23x}{23} = \dfrac{92}{23}$
	$x = 4$

SEARCH

To see step-by-step videos of these problems, enter the page number into the SWadvantage.com Search Bar.

STEP 4 Solve for y in one of the original equations.

The second equation looks easier to use.	$3x + 4y = 0$
Substitute 4 for x.	$3(4) + 4y = 0$
Simplify.	$12 + 4y = 0$
Subtract 12 from both sides.	$12 + 4y - 12 = 0 - 12$
Simplify.	$4y = -12$
Divide both sides by 4.	$\dfrac{4y}{4} = \dfrac{-12}{4}$
	$y = -3$

You found that $x = 4$ and $y = -3$. So the solution is $(4, -3)$.

CHECK Substitute the solution into each equation.

$2x - 5y = 23$	$3x + 4y = 0$
$2(4) - 5(-3) \stackrel{?}{=} 23$	$3(4) + 4(-3) \stackrel{?}{=} 0$
$8 + 15 \stackrel{?}{=} 23$	$12 + (-12) \stackrel{?}{=} 0$
$23 = 23 \checkmark$	$0 = 0 \checkmark$

The ordered pair $(4, -3)$ is a solution of the system.

Problem Solving with Substitution

EXAMPLE 4

A restaurant offers two specials: the $5.00 meat plate and the $3.50 vegetarian plate. One day the restaurant sold 125 specials for a total revenue of $550. How many of each type were sold?

STEP 1 Write a system of equations to represent the situation.

Let x be the number of meat plates sold. Let y be the number of vegetarian plates sold.

Total number sold: $x + y = 125$ $\begin{cases} x + y = 125 \\ 5x + 3.5y = 550 \end{cases}$

Total revenue ($): $5x + 3.5y = 550$

STEP 2 Solve an equation for a variable.

Solve the first equation for x. $x = 125 - y$

STEP 3 Substitute the expression for x into the second equation.

$$5x + 3.5y = 550$$

Substitute $125 - y$ for x. $5(125 - y) + 3.5y = 550$

STEP 4 Simplify and solve for y.

$$5(125 - y) + 3.5y = 550$$

Use the Distributive Property. $625 - 5y + 3.5y = 550$

Subtract 625 from both sides. $625 - 5y + 3.5y - 625 = 550 - 625$

Combine like terms. $(-5 + 3.5)y = -75$

$$-1.5y = -75$$

Divide both sides by -1.5. $\dfrac{-1.5y}{-1.5} = \dfrac{-75}{-1.5}$

$$y = 50$$

STEP 5 Solve one of the original equations for x.

Choose the first equation. $x + y = 125$

Substitute 50 for y. $x + 50 = 125$

Subtract 50 from both sides. $x = 75$

You found that $x = 75$ and $y = 50$. So the solution of the system is (75, 50).

STEP 6 Interpret the solution in the problem situation.

The restaurant sold 75 meat plates and 50 vegetarian plates.

CHECK Substitute the solution to check that it meets the conditions of the problem.

The total number of specials sold was $75 + 50 = 125$. ✔

The total revenue was $75(\$5) = \$375$ for meat plates plus $50(\$3.50) = \$175$ for vegetarian plates, or $\$375 + \$175 = \$550$. ✔

Need More HELP?

In a system of equations, each equation can represent an amount in a different category. In Example 4, one equation represents the total number sold. The second equation represents the total revenue in dollars. Both equations use the same variables.

GOT TO KNOW!

To Solve a Problem Using a System of Two Linear Equations

1. Write a system of equations to represent the situation.

2. Solve the system of equations for the variables, one at a time.

3. Interpret the ordered-pair solution in the problem situation.

4. Check the solution to see that it meets the conditions in the problem.

Solving a System by Addition or Subtraction

The Addition Method

There are several ways to solve a system of linear equations. One way to solve a system algebraically is by addition. The **addition method** involves adding the equations to eliminate a variable.

Remember that both sides of any equation have the same value. So when you add two equations of a system of linear equations, you are adding the same value on each side to make another true equation.

SEARCH 🔍

To see step-by-step videos of these problems, enter the page number into the SWadvantage.com Search Bar.

EXAMPLE 1

Use the addition method to solve the system.

$$\begin{cases} 2x + y = 9 \\ x - y = 3 \end{cases}$$

STEP 1 Be sure that the same variables align vertically before adding.

The equations already have the variables lined up.

In the given equations, $+y$ is directly above its opposite, $-y$.

STEP 2 Add the equations to eliminate one variable.

Write a plus sign to indicate addition.

$$\begin{array}{r} 2x + y = 9 \\ + \; x - y = 3 \\ \hline 3x \qquad = 12 \end{array}$$

$\quad y + (-y) = 0$

STEP 3 Solve the new equation.

Divide both sides by 3. $\qquad \dfrac{3x}{3} = \dfrac{12}{3}$

Simplify. $\qquad x = 4$

STEP 4 Solve for the second variable by substituting that solution for the first variable in one of the original equations.

Choose the first equation. $\qquad 2x + y = 9$

Substitute 4 for x. $\qquad 2(4) + y = 9$

Multiply. $\qquad 8 + y = 9$

Subtract 8 from both sides. $\qquad 8 + y - 8 = 9 - 8$

$\qquad y = 9 - 8$

$\qquad y = 1$

You found that $x = 4$ and $y = 1$, so the solution is (4, 1).

CHECK Substitute the solution into each equation.

$$2x + y = 9 \qquad\qquad x - y = 3$$
$$2(4) + 1 \overset{?}{=} 9 \qquad\quad 4 - 1 \overset{?}{=} 3$$
$$9 = 9 \; ✔ \qquad\qquad 3 = 3 \; ✔$$

Both equations are true. So the ordered pair (4, 1) is the solution of the system of equations.

Try It This Way

Use a graphing calculator. Find the intercepts and graph each equation to verify the solution.

EXAMPLE 2

Use the addition method to solve the system.

$$\begin{cases} 3y = 4x - 30 \\ 4x + 5y = 14 \end{cases}$$

STEP 1 Write the equations in standard form.

$$3y = 4x - 30$$
$$-4x + 3y = 30$$

STEP 2 Be sure that the same variables align vertically before adding.

The equations already have the variables lined up.

Notice that $-4x$ is directly above its opposite, $4x$.

STEP 3 Add the equations to eliminate one variable.

$$-4x + 3y = -30$$
$-4x + 4x = 0$
$$\underline{+\ \ 4x + 5y = \ \ \ 14}$$
$$8y = -16$$

STEP 4 Solve the new equation.

Divide both sides by 8.

$$\frac{8y}{8} = \frac{-16}{8}$$
$$y = -2$$

STEP 5 Solve for the other variable by substituting that solution for the first variable in one of the original equations.

Choose the second equation.	$4x + 5y = 14$
Substitute -2 for y.	$4x + 5(-2) = 14$
Multiply.	$4x + (-10) = 14$
Add 10 to both sides.	$4x + (-10) + 10 = 14 + 10$
Simplify.	$4x = 24$
Divide both sides by 4.	$\frac{4x}{4} = \frac{24}{4}$
	$x = 6$

You found that $x = 6$ and $y = -2$, so the solution of the system of equations is $(6, -2)$.

CHECK Substitute the solution into the original equations.

$-4x + 3y = -30$	$4x + 5y = 14$
$-4(6) + 3(-2) \stackrel{?}{=} -30$	$4(6) + 5(-2) \stackrel{?}{=} 14$
$-24 + (-6) \stackrel{?}{=} -30$	$24 + (-10) \stackrel{?}{=} 14$
$-30 = -30$ ✔	$14 = 14$ ✔

Both equations are true. So the ordered pair $(6, -2)$ is the solution of the system of equations.

GOT TO KNOW!

To Solve a System of Two Linear Equations by Using Addition

1. Write the equations so that the same variables are lined up.

2. If two terms above one another are opposites, add the two equations to eliminate one variable and solve for the other variable.

3. Substitute the resulting value into one of the original equations to find the value of the other variable.

4. Check the solution in each original equation.

The Subtraction Method

Just as you can add equations to eliminate a variable, you can also subtract equations. When you subtract equations, you are subtracting the same value on each side and producing another true equation.

EXAMPLE 3

Use the subtraction method to solve the system.

$$\begin{cases} 3x + y = 23 \\ 2x + y = 17 \end{cases}$$

STEP 1 Write the equations so that the same variables are lined up.

The equations already have the equal quantities $+y$ and $+y$ lined up.

STEP 2 Subtract the second equation from the first equation to eliminate one variable and solve for the other.

$$\begin{array}{rcl} 3x + y = 23 & \rightarrow & 3x + y = 23 \\ -(2x + y = 17) & \rightarrow & -2x - y = -17 \\ \hline & & x = 6 \quad \rightharpoondown y - y = 0 \end{array}$$

STEP 3 Solve for the other variable in one of the original equations.

Choose the first equation. $3x + y = 23$

Substitute 6 for x. $3(6) + y = 23$

Multiply. $18 + y = 23$

Subtract 18 from both sides to solve for y. $18 + y - 18 = 23 - 18$

$y = 5$

You found that $x = 6$ and $y = 5$, so the solution is $(6, 5)$.

CHECK Substitute the solution into the original equations.

$$\begin{array}{cc} \mathbf{3x + y = 23} & \mathbf{2x + y = 17} \\ 3(6) + 5 \overset{?}{=} 23 & 2(6) + 5 \overset{?}{=} 17 \\ 18 + 5 \overset{?}{=} 23 & 12 + 5 \overset{?}{=} 17 \\ 23 = 23 \; \checkmark & 17 = 17 \; \checkmark \end{array}$$

Both equations are true. So the ordered pair $(6, 5)$ is the solution of the system of equations.

EXAMPLE 4

Use the subtraction method to solve the system.

$$\begin{cases} x = -6 + y \\ x = 3y - 2 \end{cases}$$

STEP 1 Write the equations so that the same variables are lined up above each other.

$$x = -6 + y \rightarrow x = y - 6$$
$$x = 3y - 2 \rightarrow x = 3y - 2 \qquad \text{Equal quantities } x \text{ and } x \text{ are directly lined up.}$$

STEP 2 You can reverse the order of the equations.

$$x = y - 6 \qquad x = 3y - 2$$
$$x = 3y - 2 \qquad x = y - 6$$

STEP 3   Subtract the second equation from the first equation to eliminate one variable and solve for the other.

$$x = 3y - 2 \quad \longrightarrow \quad x = 3y - 2$$
$$\underline{- (x = y - 6)} \quad \longrightarrow \quad \underline{- x = - y - (-6)}$$
$$0 = 2y + 4$$

Subtract 4 from both sides. $0 - 4 = 2y + 4 - 4$

Simplify. $-4 = 2y$

Divide both sides by 2. $\dfrac{-4}{2} = \dfrac{2y}{2}$

$$-2 = y$$

STEP 4   Solve for x in one of the original equations.

Choose the second equation. $x = 3y - 2$

Substitute -2 for y. $x = 3(-2) - 2$

Multiply. $x = -6 - 2$

Subtract. $x = -8$

So $x = -8$ and $y = -2$, and the solution is $(-8, -2)$. You can check by substitution.

 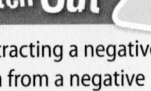

EXAMPLE 5

Two angles are complementary. The measure of one angle is 4 times the measure of the other. What are the measures of the two angles?

STEP 1   Write a system of equations for the situation.

Let x be the measure of the smaller angle and y be the measure of the larger angle.

The sum of the measures is 90°.
One angle measures 4 times the other:
$$\begin{cases} x + y = 90 \\ y = 4x \end{cases}$$

STEP 2   Write the first equation in slope-intercept form to match the second equation. Then subtract.

$$x + y = 90 \quad \longrightarrow \quad y = -x + 90$$
$$\underline{-1(y = 4x)} \quad \longrightarrow \quad \underline{(-1)y = (-1)4x}$$
$$0 = -5x + 90$$

Add 5x to both sides. $0 + 5x = -5x + 90 + 5x$

Simplify. $5x = 90$

Solve for x. $x = \dfrac{90}{5} = 18$

STEP 3   Solve for y in one of the original equations.

Choose the second equation. Substitute 18 for x. $y = 4x = 4(18) = 72$

You found that $x = 18$ and $y = 72$, so the solution is $(18, 72)$.

STEP 4   Interpret the solution in the problem situation.

The smaller angle measures 18°, and the larger angle measures 72°.

CHECK   Substitute the solution into the equations: $18 + 72 = 90$ and $72 = 4(18)$.

The angle measures have a sum of 90°. ✔ One angle measures 4 times the other one. ✔

Need More HELP?

If two angles are complementary, the sum of their measures is **90°**.

GOT TO KNOW!

To Solve a System of Two Linear Equations by Using Subtraction

Write the equations so that the same variables are lined up.

If a term is equal to the one above it, subtract equations to eliminate one variable and solve for the other variable.

Substitute the resulting value into one of the original equations to find the value of the other variable.

Check the solution in each original equation.

Solving a System by Elimination

The Elimination Method

An extension of the addition method allows you to solve a system by elimination. The **elimination method** is the adding of equations, or their multiples, to eliminate a variable. This method of solving systems is sometimes called using **linear combinations**.

EXAMPLE 1

Solve. $\begin{cases} 2x + 5y = 20 \\ 2x - 3y = 4 \end{cases}$

METHOD 1

Use the elimination method to solve the system.

STEP 1 Write the equations so that the same variables are lined up.

The equations already have the same variables lined up.

Notice that the equal quantities $2x$ and $2x$ are directly lined up.

Need More

HELP ?

For help adding like terms, go to *Distributive Property* on page 1410.

STEP 2 Multiply either equation by -1.

$(-1)(2x + 5y = 20) \longrightarrow -2x - 5y = -20$

$2x - 3y = 4 \longrightarrow 2x - 3y = 4$ $-2x$ and $2x$ are opposites.

STEP 3 Add the equations to eliminate the x terms, and solve for y.

$$\begin{aligned} -2x - 5y &= -20 \\ + \quad 2x - 3y &= 4 \\ \hline -8y &= -16 \end{aligned}$$

Note that $-2x + 2x = 0$.

Divide both sides by -8. $\dfrac{-8y}{-8} = \dfrac{-16}{-8}$

$$y = 2$$

SEARCH

To see step-by-step videos of these problems, enter the page number into the SWadvantage.com Search Bar.

STEP 4 Solve one of the original equations for x.

Choose the first equation.	$2x + 5y = 20$
Substitute 2 for y.	$2x + 5(2) = 20$
Multiply.	$2x + 10 = 20$
Subtract 10 from both sides.	$2x + 10 - 10 = 20 - 10$
Simplify.	$2x = 10$
Divide both sides by 2.	$\dfrac{2x}{2} = \dfrac{10}{2}$
	$x = 5$

You found that $x = 5$ and $y = 2$, so the solution is (5, 2).

CHECK Substitute the solution into each original equation.

$2x + 5y = 20$	$2x - 3y = 4$
$2(5) + 5(2) \stackrel{?}{=} 20$	$2(5) - 3(2) \stackrel{?}{=} 4$
$10 + 10 \stackrel{?}{=} 20$	$10 - 6 \stackrel{?}{=} 4$
$20 = 20 \checkmark$	$4 = 4 \checkmark$

Both equations are true.

The ordered pair (5, 2) is the solution of the system of equations.

METHOD 2

Use the subtraction method to solve the system.

Subtracting an equation is the same as multiplying it by -1 and adding.

Subtract the equations to eliminate the x-terms and solve for y.

$$
\begin{array}{rcl}
2x + 5y = 20 & \rightarrow & 2x + 5y = 20 \\
-(2x - 3y = 4) & \rightarrow & -2x - (-3y) = -4 \\
\hline
& & 8y = 16
\end{array}
$$

Note: $-(-3y) = +3y$

Divide both sides by 8.

$$\frac{8y}{8} = \frac{16}{8}$$

$$y = 2$$

Solve one of the original equations for x and check as in Method 1.

Using Multiplication First

Because the values on both sides of an equation are equal, you can multiply an equation by any constant and the equation will still be true. For some systems, multiplying an equation by a multiple of one of the coefficients will cause one variable to have opposite coefficients in two equations. You can use the opposite coefficients to eliminate that variable.

EXAMPLE 2

Use the elimination method to solve the system.

$$\begin{cases} 3x + 2y = 8 \\ 5x - 4y = -38 \end{cases}$$

STEP 1 Since $4y$ is a multiple of $2y$, multiply the first equation by 2.

$$
\begin{array}{rcl}
2(3x + 2y = 8) & \rightarrow & 6x + 4y = 16 \\
5x - 4y = -38 & \rightarrow & 5x - 4y = -38 \qquad \text{$4y$ and $-4y$ are opposites.}
\end{array}
$$

STEP 2 Add the equations to eliminate the y terms, and solve for x.

$$
\begin{array}{rcl}
& & 6x + 4y = 16 \\
& + & 5x - 4y = -38 \\
\hline
& & 11x = -22
\end{array}
$$

Note that $4y + (-4y) = 0$.

Divide both sides by 11.

$$\frac{11x}{11} = -\frac{22}{11}$$

$$x = -2$$

STEP 3 Solve one of the original equations for y.

Choose the first equation. $3x + 2y = 8$

Substitute -2 for x. $3(-2) + 2y = 8$

Multiply. $-6 + 2y = 8$

Add 6 to both sides. $-6 + 2y + 6 = 8 + 6$

Simplify. $2y = 14$

Divide both sides by 2. $y = 7$

You found that $x = -2$ and $y = 7$, so the solution is $(-2, 7)$.

You should check the solution by substituting the solution into each original equation.

Linear Combinations

For some systems of equations, multiplying each equation by a different number will result in opposite coefficients in the two equations.

Multiply one or both equations by integers so that the coefficients of terms with the same variable are opposites. Finding the LCM of two aligned coefficients can be helpful. (Don't worry about the signs.)

Need More

HELP ❓

There are many ways to eliminate a variable in Example 3. Here are a few alternatives for Step 1:

$\boxed{1}$ = 1st equation

$\boxed{2}$ = 2nd equation

To eliminate y:

$$4\boxed{1} + 6\boxed{2}$$

or

$$-2\boxed{1} + 3\boxed{2}$$

To eliminate x:

$$3\boxed{1} + (-5)\boxed{2}$$

or

$$-3\boxed{1} + 5\boxed{2}$$

EXAMPLE 3

Solve the system.

$$\begin{cases} 5x - 6y = -9 \\ 3x - 4y = -7 \end{cases}$$

Notice that none of the aligned coefficients are multiples of one another. The LCM of 6 and 4 is 12.

STEP 1 Multiply the first equation by 2 and the second equation by -3 to get opposite coefficients.

$$2(5x - 6y = -9) \longrightarrow 10x - 12y = -18$$
$$-3(3x - 4y = -7) \longrightarrow -9x + 12y = 21$$

STEP 2 Add the equations to eliminate the y terms, and solve for x.

$$\begin{aligned} 10x - 12y &= -18 \\ + (-9x) + 12y &= 21 \\ \hline 1x \phantom{{}+12y} &= 3 \end{aligned}$$

Use the Identity Property of Multiplication. $\qquad x = 3$

STEP 3 Solve for y in one of the original equations.

Choose the second equation.	$3x - 4y = -7$
Substitute 3 for x.	$3(3) - 4y = -7$
Multiply.	$9 - 4y = -7$
Subtract 9 from both sides.	$9 - 4y - 9 = -7 - 9$
Simplify.	$-4y = -16$
Divide both sides by -4.	$\dfrac{-4y}{-4} = \dfrac{-16}{-4}$
Simplify.	$y = 4$

So $x = 3$ and $y = 4$, and the solution is $(3, 4)$. Check by substitution in the original equations.

EXAMPLE 4

Find a possible first step in solving each system by using elimination.

a. $\begin{cases} 3x + 5y = 17 \\ 8x - 13y = 44 \end{cases}$

Use the x-coefficients: The LCM of 3 and 8 is 24.

Multiply the first equation by -8. Multiply the second equation by 3.

b. $\begin{cases} 1.25x + 1.5y = 1 \\ 1.75x - 3y = 2 \end{cases}$

Use the y-coefficients: $2(1.5) = 3$.

Multiply the first equation by 2. Leave the second equation as it is.

EXAMPLE 5

An airline offers a short flight with tickets at two prices, business class and coach. The revenue from a flight with 12 people in business class and 40 in coach is $3,308. The revenue from a flight with 16 people in business class and 32 in coach is $3,152. How much does each type of ticket cost?

SEARCH

To see step-by-step videos of these problems, enter the page number into the SWadvantage.com Search Bar.

STEP 1 Write a system of equations for the situation.

Let x be the price of a business class ticket and y be the price of a coach ticket.

First flight revenue ($): $\quad\quad\begin{cases} 12x + 40y = 3,308 \\ 16x + 32y = 3,152 \end{cases}$
Second flight revenue ($):

None of the aligned coefficients is a multiple of another. The LCM of 12 and 16 is 48.

STEP 2 Multiply the first equation by 4 and the second equation by −3.

$$4(12x + 40y = 3,308) \longrightarrow 48x + 160y = 13,232$$
$$-3(16x + 32y = 3,152) \longrightarrow -48x - 96y = -9,456$$

STEP 3 Add the equations to eliminate the x terms, and solve for y.

$$\begin{array}{r} 48x + 160y = 13,232 \\ + (-48x) - 96y = -9,456 \\ \hline 64y = 3,776 \end{array}$$

$$y = \frac{3,776}{64} = 59$$

STEP 4 Solve one of the original equations for x.

Choose the first equation.	$12x + 40y = 3,308$
Substitute 59 for y.	$12x + 40(59) = 3,308$
Multiply.	$12x + 2,360 = 3,308$
Subtract 2,360 from both sides.	$12x = 948$
Divide both sides by 12.	$x = 79$

You found that $x = 79$ and $y = 59$, so the solution is (79, 59).

STEP 5 Interpret the solution in the problem situation.

A business class ticket costs $79, and a coach ticket costs $59.

CHECK Substitute the solution into the problem equations.

The revenue from the first flight is 12(79) + 40(59) = $948 + $2,360 = $3,308. ✔
The revenue from the second flight is 16(79) + 32(59) = $1,264 + $1,888 = $3,152. ✔

GOT TO KNOW!

To Solve a System of Two Linear Equations by Using Linear Combinations

1. Write the equations so that the same variables are lined up.

2. Find the LCM of the coefficients of one variable.

3. Multiply one or both equations by integers so that the coefficients of one variable are opposites.

4. Add the two equations to eliminate one variable, and solve for the other.

5. Substitute that solution in one equation, and solve for the eliminated variable.

6. Check the solution in each original equation.

Need More
HELP ?

For more help with parallel lines, go to *Rate of Change and Slope* on page 1536.

For more help with equations with no solutions, go to *No Solution or Many Solutions* on page 1484.

Systems of Equations with No Solution

Lines with equal slopes are parallel and do not intersect. So a system of equations that represent parallel lines has no solution.

A system of equations with no solution is called an **inconsistent system**. A system of equations with at least one solution is called a **consistent system**.

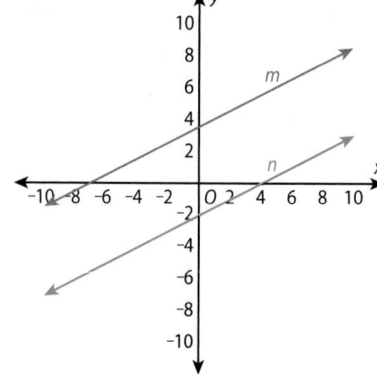

EXAMPLE 1

Solve. $\begin{cases} x + y = 1 \\ y = 3 - x \end{cases}$

METHOD 1

Write each equation in slope-intercept form. Then compare slopes and y-intercepts.

$$x + y = 1 \longrightarrow y = -x + 1$$
$$y = 3 - x \longrightarrow y = -x + 3$$

Both equations have the same slope, -1, but they have different y-intercepts, 1 and 3. The equations in the system represent two parallel lines. So it has no solution. The system is inconsistent.

CHECK Graph the equations to check.

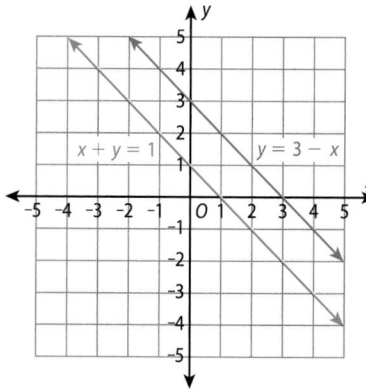

METHOD 2

Use the substitution method.

Substitute the expression for y from the second equation into the first equation.

$$x + y = 1$$

Substitute $3 - x$ for y in the first equation. $x + 3 - x = 1$

Use the Commutative Property. $x + (-x) + 3 = 1$

The equation is false. $3 = 1 ✗$

The system has no solution.

SEARCH

To see step-by-step videos of these problems, enter the page number into the SWadvantage.com Search Bar.

A system of two linear equations whose lines intersect at a single point has one solution and is called an **independent system**. A system of linear equations that represent the same line is called a **dependent system**. Because all the points on the line are solutions to both equations, the system has infinitely many solutions.

$$\begin{cases} y = x + 1 \longrightarrow y = x + 1 \\ y - 1 = x \quad \text{Add 1 to both sides.} \longrightarrow y = x + 1 \end{cases}$$

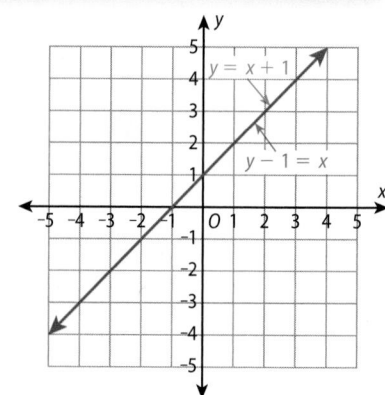

Systems of Equations with Many Solutions

EXAMPLE 2

Solve. $\begin{cases} 4(y-1) = -3x \\ y = -\frac{3}{4}x + 1 \end{cases}$

METHOD 1

Write the equations in slope-intercept form, and compare slopes and y-intercepts.

Use the Distributive Property.   Add 4 to both sides.   Divide both sides by 4.

$4(y-1) = -3x \longrightarrow 4y - 4 = -3x \longrightarrow 4y = -3x + 4 \longrightarrow y = -\frac{3}{4}x + 1$

$y = -\frac{3}{4}x + 1 \longrightarrow\qquad\qquad\qquad\qquad\qquad\qquad\qquad y = -\frac{3}{4}x + 1$

Both equations have the same slope, $-\frac{3}{4}$, and they have the same y-intercept, 1. The system is dependent. Every point on the line $y = -\frac{3}{4}x + 1$ is a solution.

CHECK Graph the original equations.

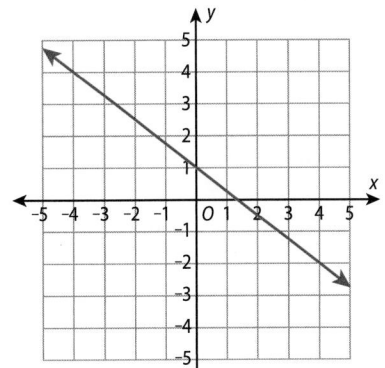

METHOD 2

Use the substitution method.

Substitute the expression for y from the second equation into the first equation.

Write the first equation. $4(y-1) = -3x$

Substitute $-\frac{3}{4}x + 1$ for y in the first equation. $4(-\frac{3}{4}x + 1 - 1) = -3x$

Simplify. $4(-\frac{3}{4}x) = -3x$

The equation is always true. $-3x = -3x$ ✔

There are infinitely many solutions. Every point on the line $y = -\frac{3}{4}x + 1$ is a solution.

> **Watch Out !**
>
> Finding equal slopes only indicates that the system does not have exactly one solution.
>
> You still need to find the y-intercepts to see whether the equations represent parallel lines (no solution) or the same line (infinitely many solutions).

GOT TO KNOW!

Solutions of a System of Two Linear Equations

One Solution	No Solution	Infinitely Many Solutions
consistent system independent system	inconsistent system	consistent system dependent system
intersecting lines	parallel lines	same line
different slopes	same slope different y-intercepts	same slope same y-intercept

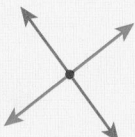

Systems of Inequalities

Solutions of Systems of Inequalities

A **system of linear inequalities** is a set of two or more linear inequalities with two or more variables. The solution of a system of linear inequalities is the set of ordered pairs that make every linear inequality in the system true.

SEARCH

To see step-by-step videos of these problems, enter the page number into the SWadvantage.com Search Bar.

EXAMPLE 1

Tell whether the ordered pair is a member of the solution set for the system of linear inequalities.

a. $(0, 4)$ $\begin{cases} y < -x + 7 \\ y > x - 5 \end{cases}$

Substitute the ordered pair into each inequality.

$y < -x + 7$ $y > x - 5$

$4 \overset{?}{<} -0 + 7$ $4 \overset{?}{>} 0 - 5$

$4 < 7$ ✔ $4 > -5$ ✔

The ordered pair $(0, 4)$ makes both inequalities true, so it is a member of the solution set.

b. $(3, 4)$ $\begin{cases} x + 2y \leq 12 \\ 3x - 2y \leq -1 \end{cases}$

Substitute the ordered pair in each equation.

$x + 2y \leq 12$ $3x - 2y \leq -1$

$3 + 2(4) \overset{?}{\leq} 12$ $3(3) - 2(4) \overset{?}{\leq} -1$

$3 + 8 \overset{?}{\leq} 12$ $9 - 8 \overset{?}{\leq} -1$

$11 \leq 12$ ✔ $1 \leq -1$ ✗

The ordered pair $(3, 4)$ makes one inequality false, so it is *not* a member of the solution set.

c. $(-1, 2)$ $\begin{cases} y \geq -3x \\ -5x + 17y > 45 \end{cases}$

Substitute -1 for x and 2 for y in $y \geq -3x$: $2 \geq -3(-1)$, or $2 \geq 3$ ✗

The ordered pair $(-1, 2)$ makes the first inequality false, so it is *not* a member of the solution set.

There is no need to check the second inequality.

Need More

HELP ?

For help with conjunctions, go to *Compound Inequalities* on page 1512.

The solution of a system of two linear inequalities makes both inequalities true, so it is like an *and* statement, or a conjunction. Just like the solution of a compound inequality, the solution of a system of inequalities is the intersection, the overlapping region.

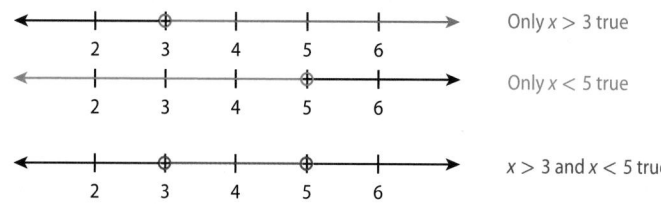

Only $x > 3$ true

Only $x < 5$ true

$x > 3$ and $x < 5$ true

Graphing Solutions of Systems of Linear Inequalities

To graph a system of two linear inequalities, use a different color or shading method for each inequality. The shaded region representing both inequalities is the solution region.

Need More

HELP ?

For help graphing linear inequalities, go to *Graphing a Linear Inequality* on page 1558.

EXAMPLE 2

a. Graph the system of linear inequalities.

$$\begin{cases} x + y < 3 \\ y \geq x + 1 \end{cases}$$

STEP 1 Write the first inequality in slope-intercept form. Slope-intercept form helps you decide whether to shade above or below the line.

$$x + y < 3 \;\longrightarrow\; y < -x + 3$$
$$y \geq x + 1 \;\longrightarrow\; y \geq x + 1$$

STEP 2 Graph each inequality. Remember to graph the boundary line first.

b. Find three ordered pairs that are members of the solution set of the system.

The region where both inequalities are shaded is the solution region. Choose points inside that region.

The ordered pairs $(-3, 4)$, $(0, 1)$, and $(-4, -1)$ are all solutions.

Note that the point $(2, 3)$ is *not* a solution.

To graph a system, you need to graph only the solution region.

EXAMPLE 3

Graph the system of linear inequalities.

$$\begin{cases} -2y < -x \\ y + 1 < 2x \end{cases}$$

STEP 1 Write each inequality in slope-intercept form.

$$-2y < -x \;\longrightarrow\; y > 0.5x \qquad \text{Reverse the inequality symbol when dividing by } -2.$$
$$y + 1 < 2x \;\longrightarrow\; y < 2x - 1$$

STEP 2 Graph each line. Use arrows to remind you of the side to shade.

STEP 3 Shade the solution region.

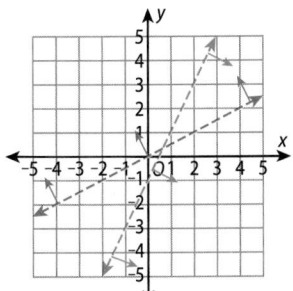

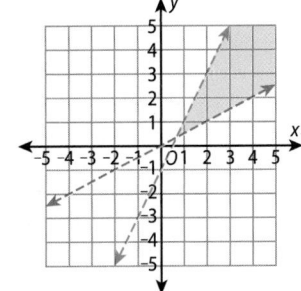

Vertical, Horizontal, and Parallel Boundary Lines

Boundary lines in a system of linear inequalities may be vertical or horizontal.

EXAMPLE 4

Graph the system of linear inequalities.

$$\begin{cases} 3 \leq x \\ y < 2x \end{cases}$$

STEP 1 Reverse the first inequality so that the variable is on the left.

$$3 \leq x \longrightarrow x \geq 3$$
$$y < 2x \longrightarrow y < 2x$$

STEP 2 Graph each line, and shade the solution region.

Use arrows to remind you which side of each line to shade.

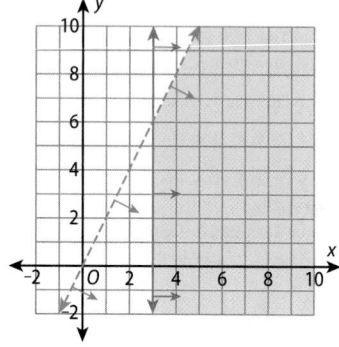

When the boundary lines of a system of inequalities are parallel, there are three possibilities for the solution.

One possibility is that the solution region may be shaped like a strip instead of a wedge.

EXAMPLE 5

Graph the system of linear inequalities.

$$\begin{cases} y < \frac{1}{3}x + 4 \\ 3y - 3 \geq x \end{cases}$$

STEP 1 Write the second inequality in slope-intercept form.

$$y < \frac{1}{3}x + 4 \longrightarrow y < \frac{1}{3}x + 4$$
$$3y - 3 \geq x \longrightarrow y \geq \frac{1}{3}x + 1$$

STEP 2 Graph each line, and shade the solution region.

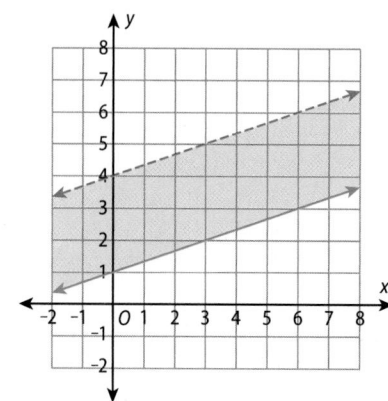

GOT TO KNOW!

Systems with the Same Boundary Line

If the boundary lines for the two inequalities are the same line, both symbols must be "or equal to" symbols for the system to have a solution.

The points on the line are the solution.

A second possibility is that the system of inequalities may have no solution.

EXAMPLE 6

Graph the system of linear inequalities.

$$\begin{cases} 2y \le -3x + 4 \\ y \ge -1.5x + 5 \end{cases}$$

STEP 1 Write the first inequality in slope-intercept form.

$$2y \le -3x + 4 \quad \longrightarrow \quad y \le -1.5x + 2$$
$$y \ge -1.5x + 5 \quad \longrightarrow \quad y \ge -1.5x + 5$$

STEP 2 Graph each line, and look for the solution region.

The regions do not overlap, so there is no solution.

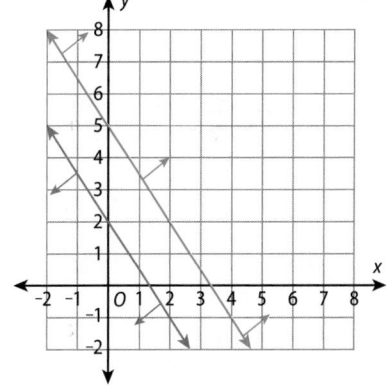

SEARCH

To see step-by-step videos of these problems, enter the page number into the SWadvantage.com Search Bar.

The third possibility when the boundary lines are parallel is that the solutions of the inequalities reach in the same direction. In that case, the solution of one linear inequality is completely inside the other. Because the overlapping region is the solution of the system, the graph of the inside inequality is the solution.

EXAMPLE 7

Graph the system of linear inequalities.

$$\begin{cases} y < x - 1 \\ 2y \le 2x + 7 \end{cases}$$

STEP 1 Write the second inequality in slope-intercept form.

$$y < x - 1 \quad \longrightarrow \quad y < x - 1$$
$$2y \le 2x + 7 \quad \longrightarrow \quad y \le x + 3.5$$

STEP 2 Graph each line, and look for the solution region.

Notice that the inequality symbols $<$ and $\le$ are in the same direction.

The graph of $y < x - 1$ is completely inside the graph of $2y \le 2x + 7$. Only points within the solution region for $y < x - 1$ make both inequalities in the system true.

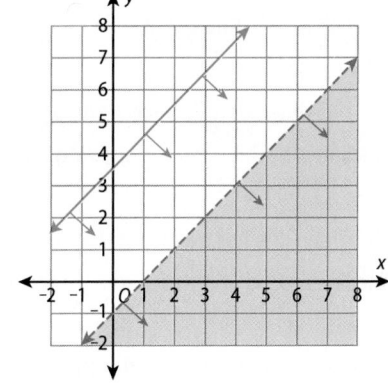

Need More

HELP

When one set is completely within another, the inside set is a *subset* of the larger set.

More Than Two Inequalities

A system can include more than two inequalities. The solution region is the region where all of the inequalities are true.

EXAMPLE 8

Graph the system of linear inequalities. What geometric figure does the solution region represent?

$$\begin{cases} y \geq x + 1 \\ y \leq 3x \\ y \leq 4 \end{cases}$$

STEP 1 Graph the boundary line $y = x + 1$. The solution region is above this line.

STEP 2 Graph $y = 3x$ and $y = 4$. The solution region is below these lines.

STEP 3 Use arrows to remind you of the side to shade. Shade the solution.

The figure is a triangle.

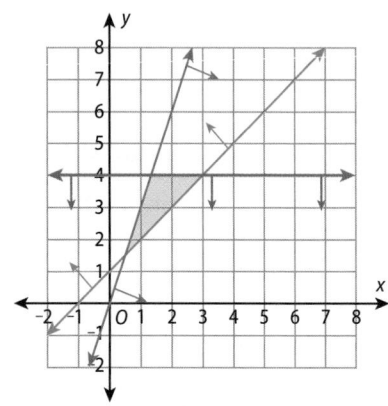

Writing a System of Linear Inequalities from a Graph

You can write a system of linear inequalities when given a graph of the system. Use the slope and y-intercept of each boundary line to write an equation. Use the way the line is drawn and the direction of the shading to choose an inequality symbol.

EXAMPLE 9

Write a system of linear inequalities for the graph.

The red line has a slope of -2 and a y-intercept of 0.

The line is solid and the shading is below it.

$$y \leq -2x$$

The blue line has a slope of 1 and a y-intercept of -3.

The line is dashed and the shading is above it.

$$y > x - 3$$

The green line has a slope of 0 and a y-intercept of -4.

The line is solid and the shading is above it.

$$y \geq -4$$

A system of linear inequalities for the graph is shown here.

$$\begin{cases} y \leq -2x \\ y > x - 3 \\ y \geq -4 \end{cases}$$

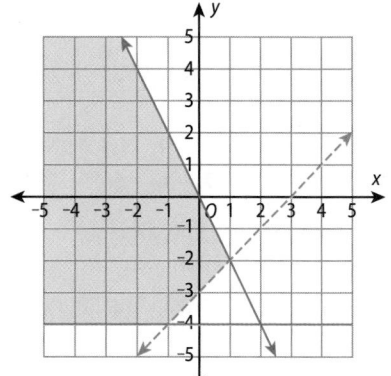

EXAMPLE 10

The football team is selling T-shirts and sweatshirts to raise funds. For each T-shirt sold, the team makes $5. For each sweatshirt sold, the team makes $8. There are only 80 sweatshirts to sell.

a. **Write and graph a system of inequalities to show how many of each type of shirt the team can sell to make at least $1,000 from sales.**

STEP 1 Write a system of inequalities for the situation.

Let x be the number of T-shirts sold. Let y be the number of sweatshirts sold.

Amount of money from sales ($):
Number of sweatshirts team can sell:

$$\begin{cases} 5x + 8y \geq 1,000 \\ y \leq 80 \end{cases}$$

STEP 2 Solve the first inequality for y.

$$5x + 8y \geq 1,000 \longrightarrow y \geq -\frac{5}{8}x + 125$$

$$y \leq 80 \longrightarrow y \leq 80$$

STEP 3 Graph each line, and shade the solution region.

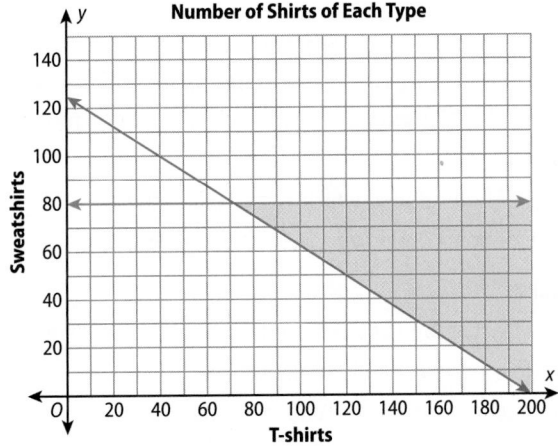

Number of Shirts of Each Type

b. **Give three possible combinations that satisfy the conditions of the problem.**

Using points in the solution region, the team could sell any of these combinations.

100 T-shirts and 70 sweatshirts for $500 + $560 = $1,060

80 T-shirts and 80 sweatshirts for $400 + $640 = $1,040

160 T-shirts and 40 sweatshirts for $800 + $320 = $1,120

SEARCH

To see step-by-step videos of these problems, enter the page number into the SWadvantage.com Search Bar.

Need More HELP?

For help with solving linear inequalities, go to *Graphing a Linear Inequality* on page 1558.

Constraints

Writing Linear Programming Constraints

Linear programming is a useful branch of mathematics that maximizes or minimizes the value of a function, within the restrictions of a system of linear inequalities. The function that is maximized or minimized is called the **optimization function**. The linear inequalities that restrict the solution are called **constraints**. Constraints are usually written in standard form, that is, with the constant on the right side of the inequality.

EXAMPLE 1

Write a constraint to represent each situation.

a. The number of plates cannot be negative.

    Let x be the number of plates. $x \geq 0$

b. The total spent on hats costing $7 each and coats costing $19 each must be less than $300.

    Let x be the number of hats, and let y be the number of coats. $7x + 19y < 300$

EXAMPLE 2

Write the constraints for the situation. Then graph.

Two scientists, Jim and Vicky, require the use of a lab. Jim needs the lab for at least as long as Vicky needs it but, at most, for 12 hours. The lab is available for no more than 20 hours.

STEP 1 Define the variables.

    Let x be the number of hours during which Vicky can use the lab.

    Let y be the number of hours during which Jim can use the lab.

STEP 2 Write each constraint.

Jim needs the lab at least as long as Vicky needs it.	$y \geq x$, or $y - x \geq 0$
The lab is available for no more than 20 hours.	$x + y \leq 20$
The number of hours Jim needs the lab is no more than 12.	$y \leq 12$
The number of hours Jim can use the lab is nonnegative.	$y \geq 0$
The number of hours Vicky can use the lab is nonnegative.	$x \geq 0$

STEP 3 Graph each line, and shade the solution region.

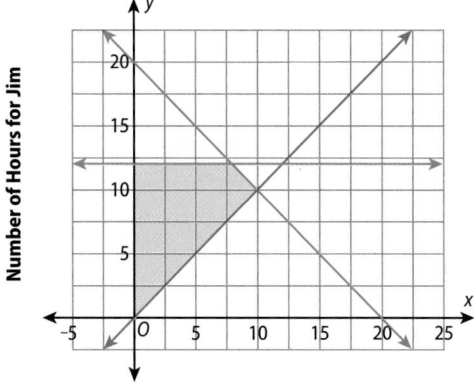

Number of Hours for Jim

Number of Hours for Vicky

EXAMPLE 3

Write the constraints for the situation. Then graph.

A gardening company is buying bags of fertilizer with nitrogen and potash to use in its own mixture. The company needs at least 300 pounds of nitrogen and 80 pounds of potash. It can buy Brand X bags, which have 8 pounds of nitrogen and 3 pounds of potash, or Brand Y bags, with 12 pounds of nitrogen and 2 pounds of potash. Brand X costs $15 and Brand Y costs $18. The company wants to spend no more than $750.

STEP 1 Define the variables.

Let x be the number of bags of Brand X the company should buy.

Let y be the number of bags of Brand Y the company should buy.

So, $8x$ represents the number of pounds of nitrogen in Brand X bags.

STEP 2 Write each constraint.

Amount of nitrogen is at least 300 pounds. $8x + 12y \geq 300$

Amount of potash is at least 80 pounds. $3x + 2y \geq 80$

Number of Brand X bags is nonnegative. $x \geq 0$

Number of Brand Y bags is nonnegative. $y \geq 0$

The cost is, at most, $750. $15x + 18y \leq 750$

> **Watch Out** !
>
> Don't assume that numbers given together in the problem situation, such as 8 pounds and 3 pounds, go together in the same constraint.

STEP 3 Graph each line, and shade the solution region.

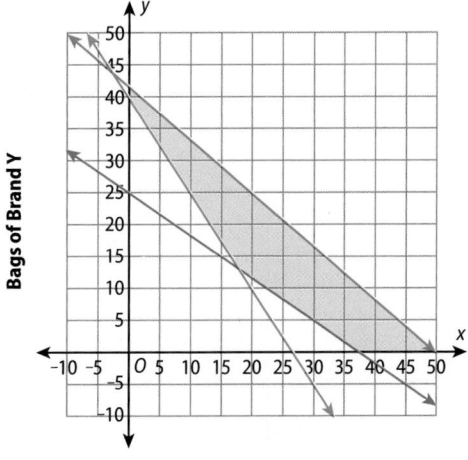

Bags of Brand Y

Bags of Brand X

GOT TO KNOW!

Writing and Graphing Constraints

1. Translate each condition into an inequality.

2. Write the inequality with the constant alone on the right side.

3. Graph the constraints as a system of inequalities.

Feasible Regions

Feasible Solutions

In linear programming, the graph of the solution of the system of linear inequalities that form the constraints is called the **feasible region**. The points in the feasible region make up the set of feasible solutions. Every point in the feasible region satisfies all of the constraints.

A feasible region is **bounded** if it is completely enclosed by line segments and forms a polygon. If it extends infinitely in any direction, it is **unbounded**.

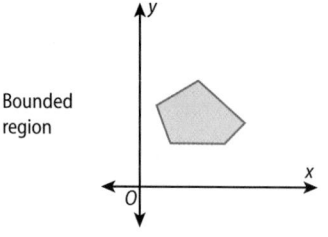

Bounded region

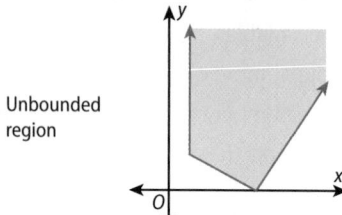

Unbounded region

EXAMPLE 1

Graph the feasible region. Determine whether it is bounded or unbounded.

a. $\begin{cases} x + y \leq 5 \\ y \geq 2x \\ x \geq 0 \end{cases}$

The feasible region is a triangle, so it is bounded.

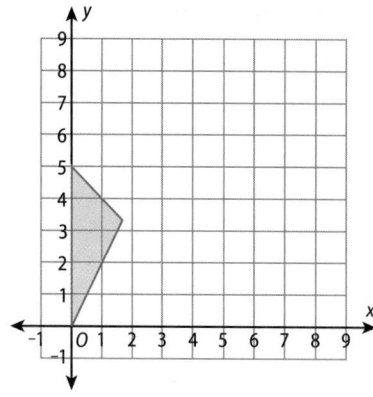

b. $\begin{cases} x + y \geq 6 \\ 2y - x \leq 0 \\ y \geq 0 \end{cases}$

The feasible region extends infinitely to the right, so it is unbounded.

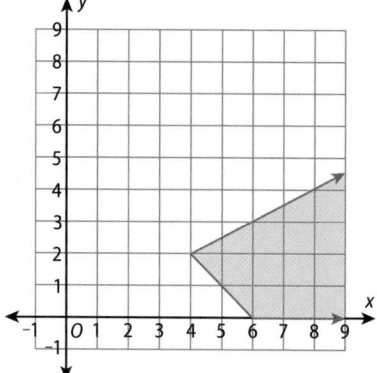

Finding Vertices

The points where the lines of the equations of two constraints intersect are **vertices** of the feasible region. You can find the coordinates of a vertex by looking at the graph or by solving the system of the two equations that intersect there.

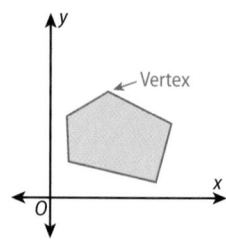

Vertex

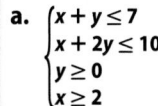

Graph the feasible region. Find the coordinates of the vertices.

a. $\begin{cases} x + y \le 7 \\ x + 2y \le 10 \\ y \ge 0 \\ x \ge 2 \end{cases}$

From the graph, you can see that the coordinates of the vertices are (2, 0), (2, 4), (4, 3), and (7, 0).

Verify the coordinates (4, 3).

This is where the lines $x + y = 7$ and $x + 2y = 10$ intersect. Substitute (4, 3) into each equation.

$x + y = 7$		$x + 2y = 10$
$4 + 3 \stackrel{?}{=} 7$	Substitute (4, 3).	$4 + 2(3) \stackrel{?}{=} 10$
$7 = 7 ✔$	Simplify.	$4 + 6 \stackrel{?}{=} 10$
		$10 = 10 ✔$

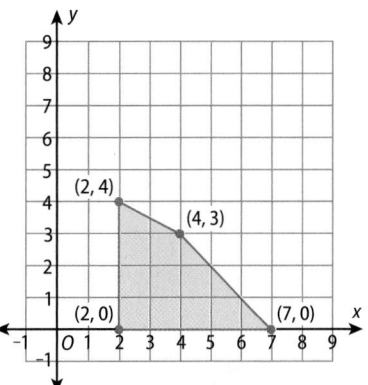

Try It

This Way

Subtract the first equation from the second to eliminate y, or use a graphing calculator's intersect feature to find the vertex.

b. $\begin{cases} y - x \ge 3 \\ -5x + y \ge -2 \\ y \le 8 \end{cases}$

You can verify that the upper two vertices have coordinates (2, 8) and (5, 8).

Find the third vertex by solving the system of the first two equations.

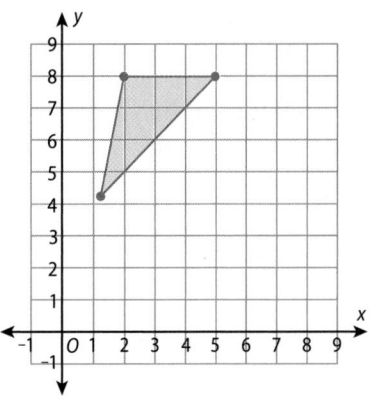

Solve each equation for y.

$$y - x = 3 \longrightarrow y = x + 3$$
$$-5x + y = -2 \longrightarrow y = 5x - 2$$

Substitute $5x - 2$ for y in the first equation to solve for x.

$$5x - 2 = x + 3$$

Use inverse operations to isolate the variable on the left and the constant on the right.

$$5x - x = 3 + 2$$
$$4x = 5$$

Solve for x.

$$x = 1.25$$

Substitute 1.25 for x in the first equation to solve for y.

$$y = x + 3$$
$$y = 1.25 + 3 = 4.25$$

The coordinates of the third vertex are (1.25, 4.25).

GOT TO KNOW!

Finding the Feasible Region Defined by a Set of Constraints

- Graph the constraints as a system of inequalities.

- The feasible region may be bounded or unbounded.

- To find the vertices, solve the system of equations corresponding to each pair of constraints.

Objective Functions and Linear Programming

Objective Functions

Linear programming is useful for finding the best solution to a problem that can be represented by a system of linear inequalities, or constraints. The feasible region for the graph of the system represents all possible solutions.

When you maximize or minimize the value of a function in linear programming, subject to the constraints, that function is called the **objective function**. In linear programming, the objective function is a linear equation.

An objective function can be used to solve such problems as the following:

- maximizing profit
- minimizing cost
- maximizing total quantities
- minimizing resource use

Maximum and Minimum Values

Need More HELP ? For help with constraints and feasible regions, see pages 1590–1591.

If the feasible region is bounded, then the objective function has a maximum value and a minimum value. These occur at vertices of the feasible region.

Suppose the feasible region is the rectangle shown in the figure, and the objective is to maximize or minimize the value of C when $C = 3x + 4y$.

Think of sliding the line from the lower left to the upper right. As the line slides from one edge of the region to the other, the value of $3x + 4y$ increases.

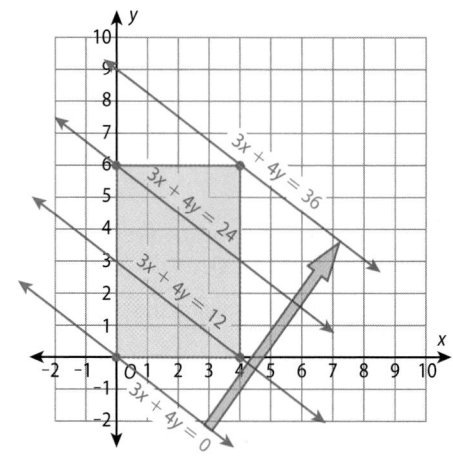

The minimum value of $3x + 4y$ is 0, which occurs at the lower left vertex.

The maximum value of $3x + 4y$ is 36, which occurs at the upper right vertex.

SEARCH 🔍 To see step-by-step videos of these problems, enter the page number into the SWadvantage.com Search Bar.

EXAMPLE 1

Find the maximum and minimum value of the objective function $C = 5x + 2y$ for the feasible region shown.

Substitute each ordered pair in the function.

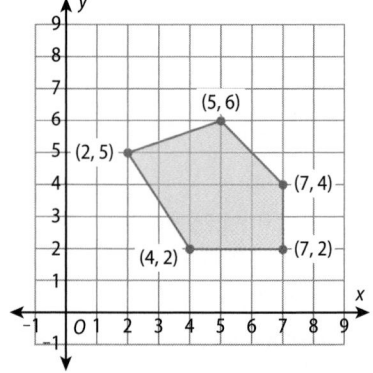

(x, y)	C = 5x + 2y
(2, 5)	$C = 5(2) + 2(5) = 20$
(5, 6)	$C = 5(5) + 2(6) = 37$
(7, 4)	$C = 5(7) + 2(4) = 43$
(7, 2)	$C = 5(7) + 2(2) = 39$
(4, 2)	$C = 5(4) + 2(2) = 24$

The maximum value is 43. It occurs when $x = 7$ and $y = 4$.
The minimum value is 20. It occurs when $x = 2$ and $y = 5$.

Maximizing an Objective Function

EXAMPLE 2

Locate the maximum value of $P = 3x + 7y$ for the given constraints.

$$\begin{cases} x + y \le 10 \\ 4x + 3y \le 36 \\ x \ge 0 \\ y \ge 0 \end{cases}$$

STEP 1 Graph the constraints, and shade the feasible region.

STEP 2 Find the value of P at each vertex.

Find each vertex. Substitute each ordered pair in the function.

(x, y)	$P = 3x + 7y$
$(0, 0)$	$P = 3(0) + 7(0) = 0$
$(0, 10)$	$P = 3(0) + 7(10) = 70$
$(6, 4)$	$P = 3(6) + 7(4) = 46$
$(9, 0)$	$P = 3(9) + 7(0) = 27$

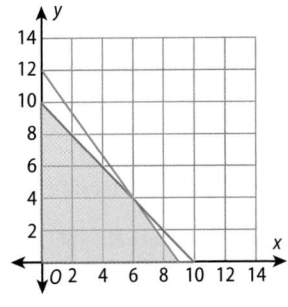

The maximum value, 70, is at $(0, 10)$.

Need More HELP?

The vertex $(6, 4)$ is the solution of the system of equations.

$$x + y = 10$$
$$4x + 3y = 36$$

For help with solving systems, go to *Solving a System by Elimination* on page 1576.

If an objective function has the same maximum value at two vertices, any point on the segment that connects the vertices will give you that maximum value. This is also true for the minimum value.

EXAMPLE 3

Locate the maximum value of $R = x + 2y$ for the given constraints.

$$\begin{cases} 2x + y \le 10 \\ 0.5x + y \le 4 \\ x \ge 0 \\ y \ge 0 \end{cases}$$

STEP 1 Graph the constraints, and shade the feasible region.

STEP 2 Find each vertex. Substitute each ordered pair in the function R.

(x, y)	$R = x + 2y$
$(0, 0)$	$R = 0 + 2(0) = 0$
$(0, 4)$	$R = 0 + 2(4) = 8^*$
$(4, 2)$	$R = 4 + 2(2) = 8^*$
$(5, 0)$	$R = 5 + 2(0) = 5$

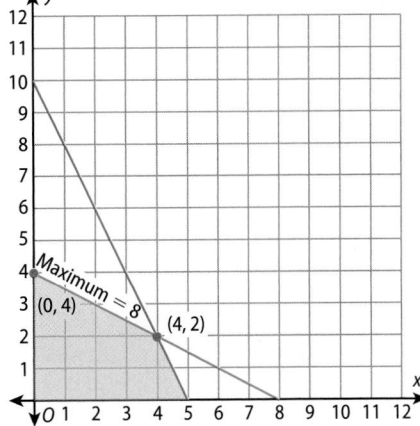

Two vertices both give the maximum value. So the maximum value, 8, occurs at any point on the segment from $(0, 4)$ to $(4, 2)$.

Minimizing an Objective Function

The same procedure used to find the maximum value can also be used to find the minimum value within a bounded feasible region. When the feasible region is unbounded, you may still be able to use this procedure to find the *optimal value* (the maximum or minimum).

EXAMPLE 4

SEARCH

To see step-by-step videos of these problems, enter the page number into the SWadvantage.com Search Bar.

Locate the minimum value of $Q = 2x + 3y$ for the given constraints.

$$\begin{cases} x + 3y \geq 6 \\ 2x + y \leq 12 \\ x \geq 3 \\ y \geq 0 \end{cases}$$

STEP 1 Graph the feasible region.

STEP 2 Find the value of Q at each vertex.

Find each vertex. Substitute each ordered pair in the function.

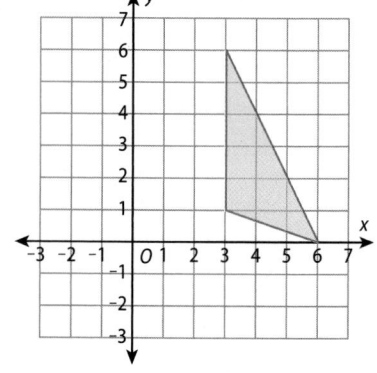

(x, y)	$Q = 2x + 3y$
$(3, 1)$	$Q = 2(3) + 3(1) = 9$
$(3, 6)$	$Q = 2(3) + 3(6) = 24$
$(6, 0)$	$Q = 2(6) + 3(0) = 12$

The minimum value, 9, is at (3, 1).

EXAMPLE 5

Locate the minimum value of $A = 5x + 4y$ for the given constraints.

$$\begin{cases} 5x + 2y \geq 14 \\ 2x + 3y \geq 10 \\ x \geq 0 \\ y \geq 0 \end{cases}$$

STEP 1 Graph the feasible region.

The feasible region is unbounded.

STEP 2 Find the value of A at each vertex.

Find each vertex. Substitute each ordered pair in the function.

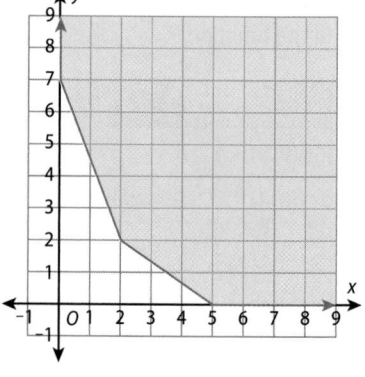

(x, y)	$A = 5x + 4y$
$(0, 7)$	$A = 5(0) + 4(7) = 28$
$(2, 2)$	$A = 5(2) + 4(2) = 18$
$(5, 0)$	$A = 5(5) + 4(0) = 25$

GOT TO KNOW!

No Maximum Value

Sometimes the objective function has no maximum value for the given constraints.

The minimum value, 18, is at (2, 2). Notice that the graph shows that there is no maximum value.

Finding the Minimum Cost

EXAMPLE 6

a. **A furnace supplier needs to send at least 80 furnaces from its distribution center to its two warehouses. The north warehouse has room for 60 furnaces. The south warehouse has room for 45 furnaces. It costs $20 to send a furnace to the north warehouse, and $16 to send a furnace to the south warehouse. How many furnaces should be shipped to each warehouse to minimize cost? What is the minimum cost?**

STEP 1 Write the constraints and the cost function.

Let x be the number of furnaces to send to the north warehouse.
Let y be the number of furnaces to send to the south warehouse.

$x + y \geq 80$	At least 80 furnaces need to be sent.
$x \leq 60$	The number sent to the north warehouse must be no more than 60.
$y \leq 45$	The number sent to the south warehouse must be no more than 45.
$C = 20x + 16y$	The cost to send a furnace to the north warehouse is $20. The cost to send a furnace to the south warehouse is $16.

STEP 2 Graph the feasible region on a coordinate plane. Find the vertices of the region.

The vertices are (35, 45), (60, 20), and (60, 45).

STEP 3 Substitute each ordered pair in the cost function.

Look for the minimum cost.

(x, y)	$C = 20x + 16y$
(35, 45)	$C = 20(35) + 16(45) = 1420$
(60, 20)	$C = 20(60) + 16(20) = 1520$
(60, 45)	$C = 20(60) + 16(45) = 1920$

The supplier can minimize the cost by sending 35 furnaces to the north warehouse and 45 to the south warehouse, for a minimum cost of $1420.

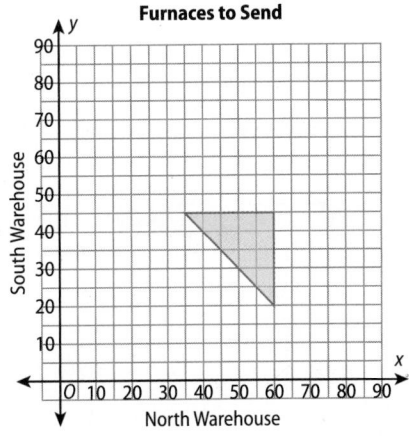

Furnaces to Send

South Warehouse / North Warehouse

Need More HELP ?

When you look for the vertex that maximizes or minimizes the value of an objective function, you may be able to rule out vertices by looking at the graph first, before finding and testing coordinates.

b. **Suppose the cost is actually found to be $20 to send a furnace to either warehouse. How many furnaces should be sent to each warehouse to minimize costs?**

The feasible region does not change. So you need to revise only the cost function in Step 3 above.

Substitute each ordered pair in the cost function $C = 20x + 20y$. Look for the minimum cost.

(x, y)	$C = 20x + 20y$
(35, 45)	$C = 20(35) + 20(45) = 1600$
(60, 20)	$C = 20(60) + 20(20) = 1600$
(60, 45)	$C = 20(60) + 20(45) = 2100$

The points (35, 45) and (60, 20) both give the minimum cost of $1600. Any integer coordinates on the segment between them are solutions.
The points (35, 45), (36, 44), (37, 43), . . . , (59, 21), (60, 20) all represent solutions.

Of the 80 furnaces the supplier will send, any number from 35 to 60 can be sent to the north warehouse, and the rest can be sent to the south warehouse.

SOUTHWESTERN

Finding the Maximum Profit

EXAMPLE 7

Need More
HELP ?
Assume that in a given week, Sam's Company sells every vono and jowd that it produces.

Sam's Company produces and sells two products. The company makes a profit of $24 on each vono sold and $18 on each jowd sold. The company can produce no more than 72 vonos per week and no more than 90 jowds per week. In addition, the company can produce no more than a total of 140 vonos and jowds in one week.

What is the maximum profit that the company can make in one week? How many vonos and how many jowds should the company produce to maximize the weekly profit?

Let x be the number of vonos produced. Let y be the number of jowds produced.

STEP 1 Write the constraints and the profit function.

$x \leq 72$	The company can produce no more than 72 vonos in one week.
$y \leq 90$	The company can produce no more than 90 jowds in one week.
$x + y \leq 140$	The company can produce no more than a total of 140 products in one week.
$x \geq 0, y \geq 0$	Both the number of vonos and the number of jowds are nonnegative.
$P = 24x + 18y$	The company makes a profit of $24 on each vono and $18 on each jowd sold.

STEP 2 Graph the feasible region on a coordinate plane. Find the vertices of the region.

The vertices are (0, 0), (0, 90), (50, 90), (72, 68), and (72, 0).

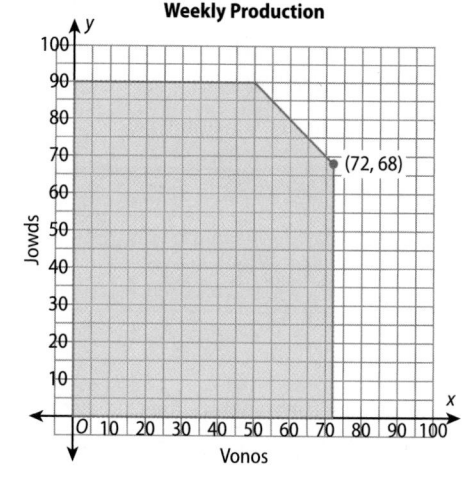

Weekly Production

STEP 3 Substitute each ordered pair in the profit function. Find the maximum profit.

(x, y)	$P = 24x + 18y$
(0, 0)	$P = 24(0) + 18(0) = 0$
(0, 90)	$P = 24(0) + 18(90) = 1620$
(50, 90)	$P = 24(50) + 18(90) = 2820$
(72, 68)	$P = 24(72) + 18(68) = 2952$
(72, 0)	$P = 24(72) + 18(0) = 1728$

The company can make a maximum profit of $2952 in a week.

It can do so by producing and selling 72 vonos and 68 jowds.

GOT TO KNOW!

To Solve a Linear Programming Problem

1. Write the constraints and the objective function from the problem.

2. Graph the feasible region, and find the coordinates of the vertices.

3. Evaluate the objective function at the vertices.

4. The solution is the vertex coordinates that give the maximum or minimum value.

EXAMPLE 8

SEARCH

To see step-by-step videos of these problems, enter the page number into the SWadvantage.com Search Bar.

A golf club manufacturer makes two types of putters, a mallet and a blade. The mallet needs 2 hours in the assembly room and 0.5 hour in the finishing room. The blade model needs 3 hours in the assembly room and 1.5 hours in the finishing room. The assembly room is available for 84 hours a week, and the finishing room is available for 36 hours a week.

a. The profit for each mallet is $18, and the profit for each blade is $45. How many of each type should be produced to maximize profit?

STEP 1 Organize the information in a table.

	Mallet	Blade	Time available (h)
Assembly Room (h)	2	3	84
Finishing Room (h)	0.5	1.5	36
Profit ($)	18	45	

STEP 2 Write the constraints and the profit function.

Let x be the number of mallets produced. Let y be the number of blades produced.

$2x + 3y \leq 84$	The assembly room is available for no more than 84 hours weekly.
$0.5x + 1.5y \leq 36$	The finishing room is available for no more than 36 hours weekly.
$x \geq 0, y \geq 0$	Both the number of mallets and blades are nonnegative.
$P = 18x + 45y$	The profit for each mallet is $18. The profit for each blade is $45.

STEP 3 Graph the feasible region on a coordinate plane. Find the vertices of the region.

The vertices are (0, 0), (0, 24), (12, 20), (42, 0).

STEP 4 Substitute each ordered pair in the profit function. Find the maximum profit.

(x, y)	P = 18x + 45y
(0, 0)	$P = 18(0) + 45(0) = 0$
(0, 24)	$P = 18(0) + 45(24) = 1080$
(12, 20)	$P = 18(12) + 45(20) = 1116$
(42, 0)	$P = 18(42) + 45(0) = 756$

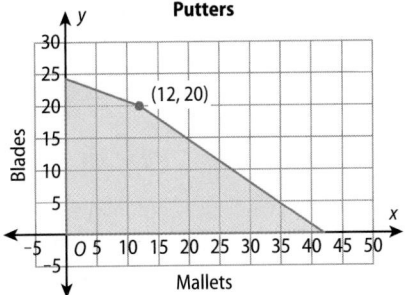

Putters

The maximum weekly profit of $1116 occurs by producing and selling 12 mallets and 24 blades.

b. Suppose the profit for each blade increases to $55. How many of each type of putter should the company produce to maximize profit?

The feasible region does not change. Revise Step 4 above.

Substitute each ordered pair in the profit function $P = 18x + 55y$. Look for the maximum profit.

(x, y)	P = 18x + 55y
(0, 0)	$P = 18(0) + 55(0) = 0$
(0, 24)	$P = 18(0) + 55(24) = 1320$
(12, 20)	$P = 18(12) + 55(20) = 1316$
(42, 0)	$P = 18(42) + 55(0) = 756$

The maximum profit of $1320 per week occurs by producing and selling *no mallets at all* and 24 blades.

Try It This Way

Find the vertex (12, 20) by using your graphing calculator.

Let the calculator solve the corresponding linear equations for y.

Y1 = (84−2X)/3

Y2 = (36−0.5X)/1.5

Graph the functions in a large enough window, and use the **CALC** key and the intersection feature.

Operations with Polynomials

What Came Before?
- Multiplying or dividing expressions by using the rules of exponents
- Dividing numbers by using long division

What's This About?
- Adding and subtracting monomial and binomial expressions
- Multiplying algebraic expressions, including the FOIL method
- Dividing polynomials by using long division

Practical Apps
- Postal workers can use polynomials to determine if a letter or package meets the postal service's minimum and maximum dimensions for shipping.
- Roller coaster designers can use polynomials to design and model sections of a ride.

just for FUN!

I think the parrot in the math teacher's office is hungry.

Q: Why?

A: He keeps saying, "Polly no meal!"

CONTENTS | UPLOAD | DOWNLOAD | *Algebra*

Monomials

Types of Polynomials

A **monomial** is an algebraic expression consisting of a number, a variable, or a product of numbers and variables. Each variable in a monomial has a whole-number exponent, and no variable appears in a denominator.

The following are examples of monomials:

$2x$ $5x^2y^2$ $-17x^2b$ mn y 4

Tell whether the expression is a monomial.

a. $7xy^4$

This is a monomial.

b. $-\frac{3}{4}xy$

This is a monomial.

c. $5p + q$

Two terms are added.

This is not a monomial.

d. $3a^{-1}b^4$

-1 is not a whole number.

This is not a monomial.

A **polynomial** is an algebraic expression that is the sum of one or more monomials.

The following are examples of polynomials:

$2xy + 6x^2y^9$ $3x + 7y - 8$ $5 - 2r - 9r^2$

Each monomial that is added to form a polynomial is a **term** of the polynomial. A **binomial** is a polynomial with two terms. A **trinomial** is a polynomial with three terms.

Classify each expression as a type of polynomial, if possible.

a. $3x^3y^2 - 4$

This is a polynomial with two terms.

binomial

b. $9 + 9y - 3xy^4$

This is a polynomial with three terms.

trinomial

c. $\frac{x}{4}(y)$

This is the same as $\frac{1}{4}xy$.

This is a polynomial with one term.

monomial

d. $-\frac{1}{x} + 8xy$

The variable x is in a denominator.

This is not a polynomial.

Watch Out !

The polynomial $5 - 2x - 9x^2$ does not look like a sum. Remember that subtraction of a number is addition of its opposite.

$5 - 2x - 9x^2$ equals $5 + (-2x) + (-9x^2)$

Ways to REMEMBER

The prefix *bi-* means 2.

bicycle – two-wheel vehicle

biweekly – every two weeks

bilingual – speaking two languages

The prefix *tri-* means 3.

tricycle – three-wheel vehicle

tripod – three-leg support

triangle – polygon with three angles

Degree of a Polynomial

The **degree** of a term of a polynomial is the sum of the exponents of the variables. These terms all have a degree of 5. The degree of a nonzero constant is 0.

$$10y^5 \qquad 7x^2y^3 \qquad x^4y \qquad xyz^3$$

degree: 5   2 + 3   4 + 1   1 + 1 + 3

The **degree of a polynomial** is the greatest degree of all the terms in the polynomial.

Need More
HELP ?
Remember that y is the same as y^1. So x^4y is the same as x^4y^1. The degree of x^4y is the sum $4 + 1$, or 5.

EXAMPLE 3

Find the degree of each term and the degree of the polynomial.

a. $x^2 + 6x$

terms: 2   1   ← degrees →

polynomial: 2

b. $-12 + 3x^4 + y^8$

terms: 0   4   8

polynomial: 8

c. $12x^3y^2 + 7x^4 - y$

terms: 5   4   1   ← degrees →

polynomial: 5

d. $-9xy + \dfrac{x}{2} + 5$

terms: 2   1   0

polynomial: 2

The terms of polynomials are usually written in descending order of degree.

EXAMPLE 4

Write the polynomial in descending order of degree.

a. $-12 + 3x^4 + y^8$

0   4   8   ← degrees →

$y^8 + 3x^4 - 12$ ← rearrange terms →

b. $-4x^4y + y - 15x^3y^3$

5   1   6

$-15x^3y^3 - 4x^4y + y$

SEARCH
To see step-by-step videos of these problems, enter the page number into the SWadvantage.com Search Bar.

The only operation in a monomial term is multiplication. (Division is multiplication of the reciprocal.) Each number or variable in a monomial is a factor of the term. The factors of $-7x^2y$ are -7, x (twice), and y.

The number that is multiplied by the variables of a term is called the **coefficient**. The coefficient of $-7x^2y$ is -7.

EXAMPLE 5

Find the coefficient of each monomial.

a. $3x^4$ b. $-4x^4y$ c. 76 d. y^5 e. $-x^2y^2$ f. $2\pi x$

3   -4   76   1   -1 2π

Watch Out !
The number π is a constant. So the coefficient of $2\pi x$ is 2π.

Need More

HELP

For more review of combining like terms, go to *Multi-Step Equations* on page 1468.

Like Terms

Recall that like terms are terms that have the same variables raised to the same powers.

like terms: $-7x^2y$, $3x^2y$, and $-x^2y$

Each term has the same variable factors, x^2 and y.

unlike terms: $4x^3y$, $4xy^3$, and $-3xy$

Each term has different variable factors.

You can combine like terms. Use the Distributive Property to add or subtract.

EXAMPLE 6

Combine like terms, if possible.

a. $4x^2y + 7x^2y$

Use the Distributive Property. $4x^2y + 7x^2y = (4 + 7)x^2y$

Add. $= 11x^2y$

b. $-3xy + 5xy$

Use the Distributive Property. $-3xy + 5xy = (-3 + 5)xy$

Add. $= 2xy$

c. $a^2 - 7a^2$

Use the Distributive Property. $a^2 - 7a^2 = (1 - 7)a^2$

Subtract. $= -6a^2$

d. $7x^9y + (-2x^9y)$

Use the Distributive Property. $7x^9y + (-2x^9y) = [7 + (-2)]x^9y$

Add. $= 5x^9y$

e. $6xy^2 - 2x^2y$

These are not like terms. The terms cannot be combined.

SEARCH

To see step-by-step videos of these problems, enter the page number into the SWadvantage.com Search Bar.

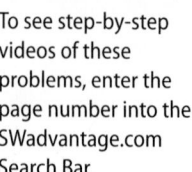

EXAMPLE 7

a. Find the perimeter of the triangle.

Write the sum of the side lengths.

$5xy^2 + 6xy^2 + 2xy^2 = (5 + 6 + 2)xy^2$

Add. $= 13xy^2$

The perimeter is $13xy^2$ units.

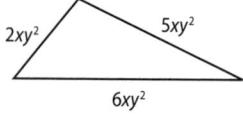

b. What is the perimeter if $x = 1$ and $y = 2$?

Evaluate $13xy^2$ for $x = 1$ and $y = 2$.

$13(1)(2)^2 = 52$

The perimeter is 52 units.

Multiplying Monomials

To multiply monomials, use the same rules of multiplication that you use for numbers. Use the Commutative Property to multiply constants and variables separately.

To multiply expressions with exponents, use the Product of Powers Property. It is shown in the *Got to Know* box below.

Need More
HELP

You do not need like terms in order to multiply. You can multiply unlike terms.

EXAMPLE 8

Multiply.

a. $5x \cdot 7x^4$

Use the Commutative Property.	$5x \cdot 7x^4 = 5 \cdot 7 \cdot x \cdot x^4$
Multiply constants.	$= 35 \cdot x \cdot x^4$
Use Product of Powers Property.	$= 35 \cdot x^{1+4}$
Simplify the exponent.	$= 35x^5$

b. $3x^2y^3 \cdot x^8y^4$

Use the Commutative Property.	$3x^2y^3 \cdot x^8y^4 = 3 \cdot x^2 \cdot x^8 \cdot y^3 \cdot y^4$
Use Product of Powers Property.	$= 3 \cdot x^{2+8} \cdot y^{3+4}$
Simplify the exponents.	$= 3x^{10}y^7$

c. $-10x^{12} \cdot (-xy)$

Write $-xy$ as $-1xy$.	$-10x^{12} \cdot (-xy) = -10x^{12} \cdot (-1xy)$
Use the Commutative Property.	$= -10 \cdot (-1) \cdot x^{12} \cdot x \cdot y$
Multiply constants.	$= 10 \cdot x^{12} \cdot x \cdot y$
Use Product of Powers Property.	$= 10 \cdot x^{12+1} \cdot y$
Simplify the exponent.	$= 10x^{13}y$

GOT TO KNOW!

Properties of Powers

For $a \neq 0$ and whole numbers m and n, you can use these properties of powers.

Product of Powers Property

$a^m \times a^n = a^{m+n}$

Quotient of Powers Property

$\dfrac{a^m}{a^n} = a^{m-n}$

Power of a Power Property

$(a^m)^n = a^{m \cdot n}$

Power of a Quotient Property

$\left(\dfrac{a}{b}\right)^m = \dfrac{a^m}{b^m}$

Binomials

Modeling Polynomial Addition

You can use algebra tiles to model polynomial addition.

EXAMPLE 1

SEARCH

To see step-by-step videos of these problems, enter the page number into the SWadvantage.com Search Bar.

Use algebra tiles to model the sum $(2x^2 - x + 2) + (-x^2 + 3x - 1)$.

STEP 1 Model both expressions.

$(2x^2 - x + 2) + (-x^2 + 3x - 1)$

STEP 2 Rearrange to group same-size tiles together.

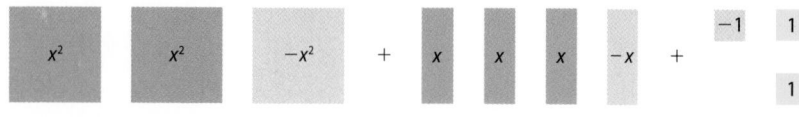

$2x^2 + (-x^2) + 3x + (-x) + 2 + (-1)$

STEP 3 Remove zero pairs.

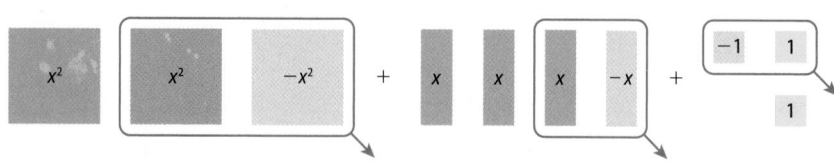

$x^2 + x^2 + (-x^2) + 2x + x + (-x) + 1 + 1 + (-1)$

Need More HELP?

A *zero pair* is a pair of tiles that have the sum of 0.

STEP 4 Write the sum.

The sum is $x^2 + 2x + 1$.

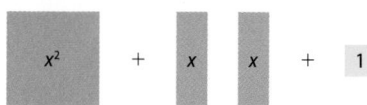

Adding Binomials

You can add two or more polynomials by using a horizontal format or by grouping like terms in vertical columns. Then you can add the like terms.

EXAMPLE 2

Add $2x^2 + 5y$ and $x^2 + 3y$.

Add vertically.

Arrange like terms in vertical columns.

$$\begin{array}{r} 2x^2 + 5y \\ + \ x^2 + 3y \\ \hline \end{array}$$

Add the coefficients of like terms.

$$3x^2 + 8y$$

EXAMPLE 3

Add $-4x^2 + 7xy$ and $6x^2 - 7xy$.

METHOD 1

Add horizontally.	$(-4x^2 + 7xy) + (6x^2 - 7xy)$
Use the Associative Property.	$-4x^2 + 7xy + 6x^2 - 7xy$
Use the Commutative Property.	$-4x^2 + 6x^2 + 7xy - 7xy$
Use the Distributive Property.	$(-4 + 6)x^2 + (7 - 7)xy$
Simplify.	$2x^2$

METHOD 2

Add vertically.

Arrange like terms in vertical columns.

$$-4x^2 + 7xy$$
$$\underline{+\ 6x^2 - 7xy}$$

Add the coefficients of like terms.　　$2x^2$

EXAMPLE 4

Add $10x^2 + 5y^2$ and $15x + 6y^2$.

METHOD 1

Add horizontally.	$(10x^2 + 5y^2) + (15x + 6y^2)$
Use the Associative Property.	$10x^2 + 5y^2 + 15x + 6y^2$
Use the Commutative Property.	$10x^2 + 15x + 5y^2 + 6y^2$
Use the Distributive Property.	$10x^2 + 15x + (5 + 6)y^2$
Simplify.	$10x^2 + 15x + 11y^2$

METHOD 2

Add vertically.

Arrange like terms in vertical columns.

$$10x^2 \qquad + 5y^2$$
$$\underline{+ \qquad 15x + 6y^2}$$

Add the coefficients of like terms.　　$10x^2 + 15x + 11y^2$

You may need to rearrange the terms before adding.

EXAMPLE 5

Add $x^2 - 7xy$, $9y^2 - 2x^2$, and $6xy - 6y^2$.

Arrange like terms in vertical columns.

Use the Commutative Property to rearrange $9y^2 - 2x^2$.

$$x^2 - 7xy$$
$$-2x^2 \qquad + 9y^2$$
$$\underline{+ \qquad 6xy - 6y^2}$$

Add the coefficients of like terms.　　$-x^2 - xy + 3y^2$

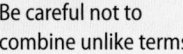

Watch Out !

Be careful not to combine unlike terms.

Try It This Way

For Method 2, write the variables at the top and just add the coefficients.

x^2	x	y^2
10	0	5
0	15	6
10	15	11

Then write the solution, using each sum as the coefficient of the variable expression at the top of its column.

$10x^2 + 15x + 11y^2$

Subtracting Binomials

You can subtract one binomial from another either horizontally or vertically in the same way that you add binomials.

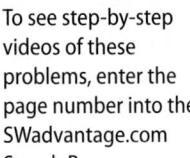
EXAMPLE 6

Subtract $x^2 + 3y$ from $2x^2 + 5y$.

METHOD 1

Subtract horizontally.	$(2x^2 + 5y) - (x^2 + 3y)$
Use the Distributive Property.	$2x^2 + 5y - x^2 - 3y$
Use the Commutative Property.	$2x^2 - x^2 + 5y - 3y$
Use the Distributive Property.	$(2 - 1)x^2 + (5 - 3)y$
Simplify.	$x^2 + 2y$

METHOD 2

Subtract vertically.

Arrange like terms in vertical columns.

$$2x^2 + 5y$$
$$\underline{- (x^2 + 3y)}$$

Subtract like terms. $x^2 + 2y$

Adding and Subtracting Polynomials

You can use similar methods to add or subtract any polynomials. To subtract a polynomial, you can add its opposite.

EXAMPLE 7

Find the sum and difference of $5p^2 + 2pq + 4q^2$ and $-p^2 - 9q^2 + 2pq$.

Find the sum. Add vertically.

Arrange like terms in vertical columns. $5p^2 + 2pq + 4q^2$

Use the Commutative Property to rearrange terms. $\underline{+ \; -p^2 + 2pq - 9q^2}$

Add like terms. $4p^2 + 4pq - 5q^2$

Find the difference. Subtract vertically.

To subtract the second polynomial, add its opposite to the first polynomial.

Arrange like terms in vertical columns. $5p^2 + 2pq + 4q^2 \longrightarrow 5p^2 + 2pq + 4q^2$

Distribute the negative on each term. $\underline{-(-p^2 + 2pq - 9q^2)} \longrightarrow \underline{+ \; p^2 - 2pq + 9q^2}$

Add like terms. $6p^2 \qquad + 13q^2$

The sum is $4p^2 + 4pq - 5q^2$ and the difference is $6p^2 + 13q^2$.

Polynomial Functions

You can add or subtract polynomial functions to solve problems.

EXAMPLE 8

A football is kicked twice. On the first kick, the height in feet after t seconds is given by the polynomial function $h = -16t^2 + 64t + 1$. On the second kick, the height is given by $h = -16t^2 + 60t + 2$.

a. What polynomial function gives the difference of the heights?

Write the function for the first kick. $h = -16t^2 + 64t + 1$

Write the function for the second kick. $h = -16t^2 + 60t + 2$

Subtract the second kick from the first kick.

$$
\begin{array}{r}
-16t^2 + 64t + 1 \\
- (-16t^2 + 60t + 2) \\
\hline
4t - 1
\end{array}
$$

Let d represent the difference in height. Then $d = 4t - 1$ is the function that gives the difference in height.

b. What is the difference in height after 3 seconds?

Evaluate $d = 4t - 1$ for $t = 3$. $d = 4(3) - 1$

$\qquad\qquad\qquad\qquad\qquad\qquad\qquad\quad = 11$ feet

CHECK   Substitute 3 for t in the original functions.

First kick	**Second kick**
$h = -16t^2 + 64t + 1$	$h = -16t^2 + 60t + 2$
$\quad = -16(3)^2 + 64(3) + 1$	$\quad = -16(3)^2 + 60(3) + 2$
$\quad = -16(9) + 192 + 1$	$\quad = -16(9) + 180 + 2$
$\quad = -144 + 193$	$\quad = -144 + 182$
$\quad = 49$	$\quad = 38$

The difference in height is $49 - 38 = 11$ feet. ✔

Need More

HELP ?

You could use h_1 to represent the height of the first kick and h_2 to represent the height of the second kick. Then $h_1 - h_2 = 4t - 1$ is the polynomial function that represents the difference in height.

For more information on polynomial functions, go to *Graphing Polynomial Functions* on page 1624.

To Add or Subtract Polynomials

1. To add or subtract horizontally, use properties to combine like terms.

2. To add or subtract vertically, arrange like terms in vertical columns.

3. To subtract a polynomial, you can add its opposite.

Multiplying Polynomials

Multiplying Binomials

You can use algebra tiles to model multiplication of binomials. First, make a **+** grid on your paper as shown in Example 1. Then model each binomial by placing the correct numbers of x and 1 tiles along one edge of the grid. Finally, complete the grid to find the product.

- Place tiles for one factor across the top and tiles for the other factor along the left side.
- To find a tile to place within the grid, multiply a column tile value by a row tile value.
- Place each tile so that its length matches the length of the factor tile in the top row and its height matches the length of the factor tile on the left side.

EXAMPLE 1

Use algebra tiles to model each product.

a. $(x + 3)(x + 2)$

Place the factors across the top and down the side. Fill in the grid with tiles.

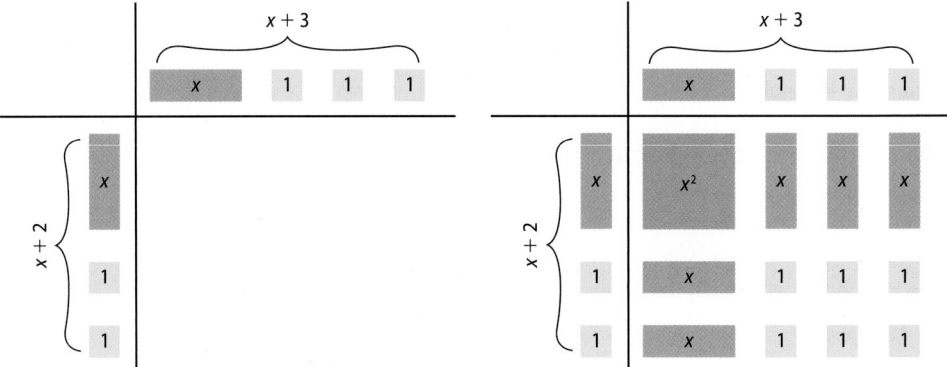

Write an expression for the tiles within the grid. $x^2 + 3x + 2x + 6$

Add like terms. $x^2 + 5x + 6$

$(x + 3)(x + 2) = x^2 + 5x + 6$

b. $(x + 3)(x - 2)$

Place the factors across the top and down the side. Fill in the grid with tiles.

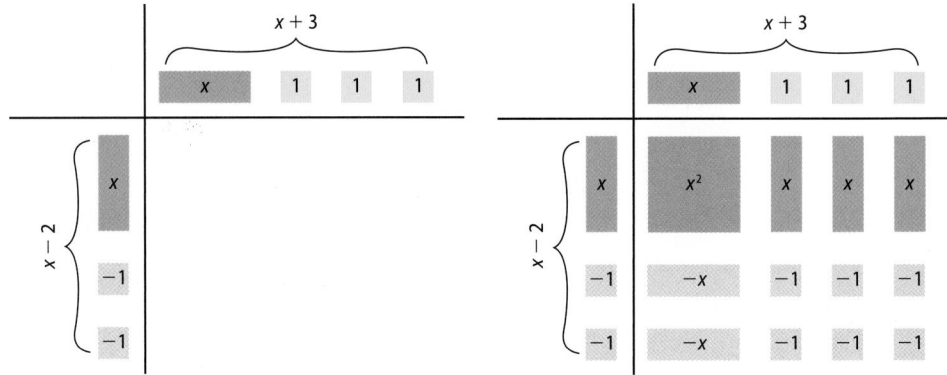

Write an expression for the tiles within the grid. $x^2 + 3x - 2x - 6$

Add like terms. $x^2 + x - 6$

$(x + 3)(x - 2) = x^2 + x - 6$

To multiply a monomial by a polynomial, use the Distributive Property.

$$4x^2y(x + 5y + 2) = 4x^2y(x) + 4x^2y(5y) + 4x^2y(2)$$
$$= 4x^3y \quad + 20x^2y^2 \quad + 8x^2y$$

To multiply binomials algebraically, you can use the Distributive Property twice to multiply each term of one binomial by each term of the other binomial. Then find the sum of the four resulting terms and combine like terms to simplify.

> ### GOT TO KNOW!
>
> Remember the rule for multiplying powers with the same base.
>
> $x^4 \cdot x^3 = x^{4+3} = x^7$
>
> A variable written without an exponent has an exponent of 1.
>
> $x \cdot x^4 = x^{1+4} = x^5$

EXAMPLE 2

Find each product. Use a horizontal format.

a. $(3x - 2)(x + 5)$

Multiply each term in the first binomial by $x + 5$.	$(3x - 2)(x + 5) = 3x(x + 5) - 2(x + 5)$
Distribute both $3x$ and -2.	$= 3x(x) + 3x(5) - 2(x) - 2(5)$
Multiply.	$= 3x^2 + 15x - 2x - 10$
Add like terms.	$= 3x^2 + 13x - 10$

b. $(4x + 7)(-x - 2)$

Multiply each term in the first binomial by $-x - 2$.	$(4x + 7)(-x - 2) = 4x(-x - 2) + 7(-x - 2)$
Distribute both $4x$ and 7.	$= 4x(-x) + 4x(-2) + 7(-x) + 7(-2)$
Multiply.	$= -4x^2 - 8x - 7x - 14$
Add like terms.	$= -4x^2 - 15x - 14$

EXAMPLE 3

Find the product $(6x + 5)(5x - 3)$. Use a vertical format.

Write the binomials one above the other. Multiply each term in the bottom polynomial by each term in the top polynomial.

This method is similar to multiplying whole numbers.

Multiply $6x + 5$ by each term in the second binomial.

$$
\begin{array}{r}
6x + 5 \\
\times\ 5x - 3 \\
\hline
-18x - 15 \\
30x^2 + 25x \\
\hline
\end{array}
$$

Add like terms. $\overline{30x^2 + 7x - 15}$

The FOIL Method

The **FOIL** method is a way of using the Distributive Property to multiply binomials. Its name can help you remember the process.

Ways to REMEMBER

Use *FOIL* to remember how to multiply two binomials.

F = first

O = outside

I = inside

L = last

EXAMPLE 5

Multiply $(2x - 1)(3x + 1)$.

Use the FOIL method.

Multiply the **First** terms.	$(2x - 1)(3x + 1) \longrightarrow 2x \cdot 3x = 6x^2$
Multiply the **Outside** terms.	$(2x - 1)(3x + 1) \longrightarrow 2x \cdot 1 = 2x$
Multiply the **Inside** terms.	$(2x - 1)(3x + 1) \longrightarrow -1 \cdot 3x = -3x$
Multiply the **Last** terms.	$(2x - 1)(3x + 1) \longrightarrow -1 \cdot 1 = -1$
Add the resulting terms.	$6x^2 + 2x - 3x - 1$
Combine like terms.	$6x^2 - x - 1$

Watch Out !

Remember to include the sign with the term when multiplying.

EXAMPLE 6

Multiply $(5a - 3b)(2a - 4b)$.

Use the FOIL method.

Multiply the **F**irst terms.	$(5a - 3b)(2a - 4b) \longrightarrow 5a \cdot 2a = 10a^2$
Multiply the **O**uter terms.	$(5a - 3b)(2a - 4b) \longrightarrow 5a \cdot (-4b) = -20ab$
Multiply the **I**nner terms.	$(5a - 3b)(2a - 4b) \longrightarrow -3b \cdot 2a = -6ab$
Multiply the **L**ast terms.	$(5a - 3b)(2a - 4b) \longrightarrow -3b \cdot (-4b) = 12b^2$
Add the resulting terms.	$10a^2 - 20ab - 6ab + 12b^2$
Combine like terms.	$10a^2 - 26ab + 12b^2$

SEARCH

To see step-by-step videos of these problems, enter the page number into the SWadvantage.com Search Bar.

EXAMPLE 7

Multiply $(8m - 5n)(8m + 5n)$.

Use the FOIL method.

Multiply the **F**irst terms.	$(8m - 5n)(8m + 5n) \longrightarrow 8m \cdot 8m = 64m^2$
Multiply the **O**uter terms.	$(8m - 5n)(8m + 5n) \longrightarrow 8m \cdot 5n = 40mn$
Multiply the **I**nner terms.	$(8m - 5n)(8m + 5n) \longrightarrow -5n \cdot 8m = -40mn$
Multiply the **L**ast terms.	$(8m - 5n)(8m + 5n) \longrightarrow -5n \cdot 5n = -25n^2$
Add the resulting terms.	$64m^2 + 40mn - 40mn - 25n^2$
Combine like terms.	$64m^2 - 25n^2$

Multiplying Binomials and Trinomials

Multiplying two polynomials is similar to multiplying two binomials. You can use the Distributive Property to multiply each term of one polynomial by each term of the other polynomial. Then add the resulting sums.

EXAMPLE

Multiply $(4x - 2)(6x^2 - 3x + 7)$.

METHOD 1

Use a horizontal format.

Multiply each term of the first polynomial by $6x^2 - 3x + 7$.

$$(4x - 2)(6x^2 - 3x + 7) = 4x(6x^2 - 3x + 7) - 2(6x^2 - 3x + 7)$$

Distribute $4x$ and -2.

$$= 4x(6x^2) + 4x(-3x) + 4x(7) - 2(6x^2) - 2(-3x) - 2(7)$$

Multiply.

$$= 24x^3 - 12x^2 + 28x - 12x^2 + 6x - 14$$

Combine like terms.

$$= 24x^3 - 24x^2 + 34x - 14$$

> **Watch Out !**
> You cannot use FOIL with polynomials other than binomials. FOIL works only when there are two terms in each factor.

METHOD 2

Use a box model.

Place the terms of one polynomial above a row of boxes. Place the terms of the other at the left of a column of boxes. Multiply each pair of terms, and write the sum of the monomial products.

	$6x^2$	$-3x$	$+7$
$4x$	$24x^3$	$-12x^2$	$28x$
-2	$-12x^2$	$6x$	-14

Combine terms inside the box. $24x^3 - 12x^2 + 28x - 12x^2 + 6x - 14$

Simplify by adding like terms. $24x^3 - 24x^2 + 34x - 14$

METHOD 3

Use a vertical format.

Write the polynomials one above the other. Multiply each term in the bottom polynomial by each term in the top polynomial. This format is similar to multiplying whole numbers.

Multiply each term in the top polynomial by -2.

Multiply each term by $4x$. Align like terms.

Combine like terms.

$$
\begin{array}{r}
6x^2 - 3x + 7 \\
\times \quad\quad 4x - 2 \\
\hline
-12x^2 + 6x - 14 \\
24x^3 - 12x^2 + 28x \\
\hline
24x^3 - 24x^2 + 34x - 14
\end{array}
$$

Applying Binomial Multiplication

EXAMPLE 9

The deep part of a swimming pool is *x* meters square. It is in one corner of the pool. From the deep part, the pool extends 19 meters in one direction and 7 meters in the other direction.

a. Draw a diagram of the swimming pool.

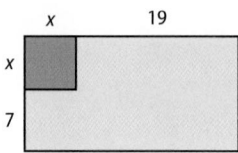

b. Write and simplify an expression for the area of the swimming pool.

The length of the swimming pool is $(x + 19)$ meters. The width of the pool is $(x + 7)$ meters.

Use the area formula.	$A = \ell w$
Substitute for ℓ and w.	$= (x + 19)(x + 7)$
Use FOIL.	$= x(x) + 7x + 19x + 19(7)$
Multiply.	$= x^2 + 7x + 19x + 133$
Combine like terms.	$= x^2 + 26x + 133$

The area of the swimming pool can be expressed as $x^2 + 26x + 133$ square meters.

c. Suppose *x* = 6 meters. Verify that the expression in part b gives the same area as the area formula.

If $x = 6$, the pool has length $6 + 19$, or 25 meters, and width $6 + 7$, or 13 meters.

$A = \ell w = 25(13) = 325 \text{ m}^2$

Substitute 6 for x in $x^2 + 26x + 133$. $x^2 + 26x + 133 = 6^2 + 26(6) + 133$

$= 36 + 156 + 133$

$= 325 \text{ m}^2 ✔$

Watch Out !

When you multiply binomials like $x + 19$ and $x + 7$, there are always four product terms before you combine like terms. Do not just multiply the first terms, x and x, and the last terms, 19 and 7.

EXAMPLE 10

SEARCH

To see step-by-step videos of these problems, enter the page number into the SWadvantage.com Search Bar.

Mary has a rectangular garden and wants to add a path around it. The garden is *x* feet wide and (*x* + 5) feet long. The path will be 2 feet wide all the way around the garden.

a. Draw a diagram of the garden and path.

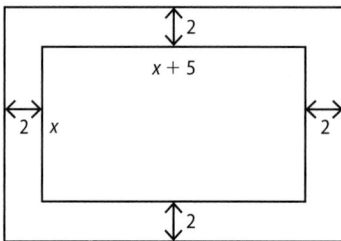

b. Write and simplify an expression for the area of the garden.

The width of the garden is x ft. The length of the garden is $(x + 5)$ ft.

Use the area formula.	$A = \ell w$
Substitute for ℓ and w.	$= (x + 5) \cdot x$
Use the Distributive Property.	$= (x)x + (5)x$
Multiply.	$= (x^2 + 5x)$ ft^2

c. Write and simplify an expression for the area of the garden and path combined.

Add the width of the path on each side of the garden to the sides of the garden.

Width of the combined garden and path:	$x + 2 + 2 = x + 4$
Length of the combined garden and path:	$(x + 5) + 2 + 2 = x + 9$
Use the area formula.	$A = \ell w$
Substitute for ℓ and w.	$= (x + 9)(x + 4)$
Use FOIL method.	$= x(x) + x(4) + 9(x) + 9(4)$
Multiply.	$= x^2 + 4x + 9x + 36$
Add like terms.	$= (x^2 + 13x + 36)$ ft^2

d. Suppose $x = 11$ feet. Verify that the expressions in parts b and c give the same areas as the area formulas.

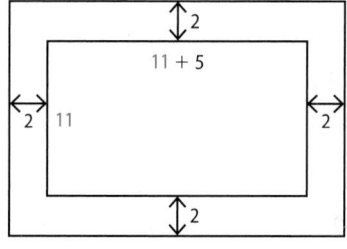

If $x = 11$, the garden has length $11 + 5$, or 16 ft, and width 11 ft.

$A = \ell w = 16(11) = 176$ ft^2

Substitute 11 for x in $x^2 + 5x$.

$$x^2 + 5x = 11^2 + 5(11)$$
$$= 121 + 55$$
$$= 176 \text{ ft}^2 ✔$$

If $x = 11$, the garden with the path has length $11 + 5 + 4$, or 20 ft, and width $11 + 4$, or 15 ft.

$$A = \ell w = 20(15) = 300 \text{ ft}^2$$

Substitute 11 for x in $x^2 + 13x + 36$.

$$x^2 + 13x + 36 = 11^2 + 13(11) + 36$$
$$= 121 + 143 + 36$$
$$= 300 \text{ ft}^2 ✔$$

GOT TO KNOW!

To Multiply Polynomials

Use the Distributive Property. Multiply each term of one polynomial by each term of the other, and write the sum of the terms. Combine like terms to simplify the sum.

$$(a + b)(c + d + e) = a(c + d + e) + b(c + d + e)$$
$$= ac + ad + ae + bc + bd + be$$

Use FOIL to help you remember how to use the Distributive Property to multiply binomials.

Special Products of Binomials

Squaring a Binomial Sum

Suppose the side length of a large square is expressed as $a + b$. Then the area is expressed as $(a + b)(a + b)$, or $(a + b)^2$.

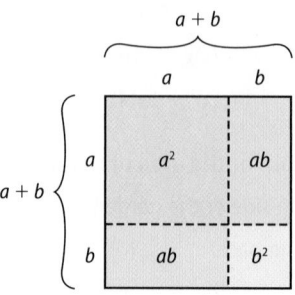

Notice that the area of the large square is the sum of the areas of two small squares plus the sum of the areas of two rectangles.

$$(a + b)^2 = a^2 + \underbrace{ab + ab} + b^2$$
$$= a^2 + 2ab + b^2$$

A polynomial that is the result of squaring a binomial is called a **perfect-square trinomial**.

EXAMPLE 1

Simplify.

a. $(x + 6)^2$

METHOD 1

Expand the square.

Write the square as a product.	$(x + 6)(x + 6)$
Use the Distributive Property.	$(x + 6)(x + 6) = x(x + 6) + 6(x + 6)$
Multiply.	$= x^2 + \underbrace{6x + 6x} + 36$
Combine like terms.	$= x^2 + 12x + 36$

METHOD 2

Use the formula.

Use the formula.	$(a + b)^2 = a^2 + 2ab + b^2$
Substitute x for a and 6 for b.	$(x + 6)^2 = x^2 + 2(x)(6) + 6^2$
Multiply.	$= x^2 + 12x + 36$

b. $(3x + 5)^2$

METHOD 1

Expand the square.

Write the square as a product.	$(3x + 5)(3x + 5)$
Use FOIL.	$(3x + 5)(3x + 5) = (3x)(3x) + (3x)(5) + 5(3x) + 5(5)$
Multiply. $(3x)(3x) = 3 \cdot 3 \cdot x \cdot x = 9x^2$	$= 9x^2 + \underbrace{15x + 15x} + 25$
Combine like terms.	$= 9x^2 + 30x + 25$

METHOD 2

Use the formula. $(a + b)^2 = a^2 + 2ab + b^2$

Substitute $3x$ for a and 5 for b. $(3x + 5)^2 = (3x)^2 + 2(3x)(5) + 5^2$

Multiply. $= 9x^2 + 30x + 25$

c. $(7x^2 + 5y)^2$

METHOD 1

Use a box model.

Multiply. $(7x^2)(7x^2) = 7 \cdot 7 \cdot x^2 \cdot x^2 = 49x^4$

	$7x^2$	$5y$
$7x^2$	$49x^4$	$35x^2y$
$5y$	$35x^2y$	$25y^2$

Add the four terms inside the box. $49x^4 + \underbrace{35x^2y + 35x^2y} + 25y^2$

Combine like terms. $= 49x^4 + 70x^2y + 25y^2$

METHOD 2

Use the formula. $(a + b)^2 = a^2 + 2ab + b^2$

Substitute $7x^2$ for a and $5y$ for b. $(7x^2 + 5y)^2 = (7x^2)^2 + 2(7x^2)(5y) + (5y)^2$

Multiply. $= 49x^4 + 70x^2y + 25y^2$

Squaring a Binomial Difference

Just as you can square a binomial sum by using a formula, you can also square a binomial difference. The result is again a perfect-square trinomial.

$$(a - b)^2 = a^2 - \underbrace{ab - ab} + b^2$$
$$= a^2 - 2ab + b^2$$

Watch Out !

The last term of the formula is $+ b^2$. The last term in the square of a binomial difference is *positive* because it is the product of two negative numbers.

EXAMPLE 2

Simplify $(4x - 3)^2$.

METHOD 1

Expand the square.

Write the square as a product. $(4x - 3)(4x - 3)$

Use FOIL. $(4x - 3)(4x - 3) = (4x)(4x) + (4x)(-3) + (-3)(4x) + (-3)(-3)$

Multiply. $(4x)(4x) = 4 \cdot 4 \cdot x \cdot x = 16x^2$ $= 16x^2 - 12x - 12x + 9$

Combine like terms. $= 16x^2 - 24x + 9$

METHOD 2

Use the formula. $(a - b)^2 = a^2 - 2ab + b^2$

Substitute $4x$ for a and 3 for b. $(4x - 3)^2 = (4x)^2 - 2(4x)(3) + 3^2$

Multiply. $= 16x^2 - 24x + 9$

Squaring a Binomial Difference

EXAMPLE 3

Simplify $(2xy^2 - 9x^3y)^2$.

SEARCH

To see step-by-step videos of these problems, enter the page number into the SWadvantage.com Search Bar.

METHOD 1

Use a vertical format.

Multiply each term in the top polynomial by $-9x^3y$.

Multiply each term by $2xy^2$. Align like terms.

Add like terms.

$$
\begin{array}{r}
2xy^2 - 9x^3y \\
\times\ 2xy^2 - 9x^3y \\
\hline
-18x^4y^3 + 81x^6y^2 \\
4x^2y^4 - 18x^4y^3 \\
\hline
4x^2y^4 - 36\,x^4y^3 + 81x^6y^2
\end{array}
$$

METHOD 2

Use the formula.

Substitute $2xy^2$ for a and $9x^3y$ for b.

Simplify.

$$(a - b)^2 = a^2 - 2ab + b^2$$
$$(2xy^2 - 9x^3y)^2 = (2xy^2)^2 - 2(2xy^2)(9x^3y) + (9x^3y)^2$$
$$= 4x^2y^4 - 36\,x^4y^3 + 81x^6y^2$$

The Difference of Two Squares

When you multiply a binomial of the form $a + b$ and a binomial of the form $a - b$, the product is the **difference of two squares**, $a^2 - b^2$.

$$(a + b)(a - b) = a^2 - ab + ab - b^2$$
$$= a^2 - \quad 0 \quad + b^2$$
$$= a^2 - b^2$$

EXAMPLE 4

Multiply $(2x + 1)(2x - 1)$.

Need More

HELP ?

Remember the Power of a Power Property.

$(a^m)^n = a^{mn}$

Practice squaring monomial terms.

$(8)^2 = 64$

$(2x)^2 = 4x^2$

$(x^5)^2 = x^{10}$

$(x^4y)^2 = x^8y^2$

$(x^4y^6)^2 = x^8y^{12}$

METHOD 1

Expand the product.

Use FOIL.

Multiply. $(2x)(2x) = 2 \cdot 2 \cdot x \cdot x = 4x^2$

Combine like terms.

$$(2x + 1)(2x - 1) = (2x)(2x) + (2x)(-1) + 1(2x) + 1(-1)$$
$$= 4x^2 - 2x + 2x - 1$$
$$= 4x^2 - 1$$

METHOD 2

Use the formula.

Substitute $2x$ for a and 1 for b.

Multiply.

$$(a + b)(a - b) = a^2 - b^2$$
$$(2x + 1)(2x - 1) = (2x)^2 - 1^2$$
$$= 4x^2 - 1$$

Applying Differences of Two Squares

EXAMPLE 5

A deck was designed to be square. The design was revised to extend the length by 3.5 feet and to reduce the width by 3.5 feet.

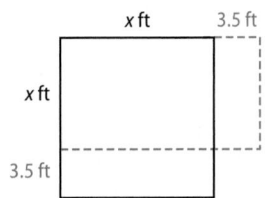

a. **Write expressions for the original area of the deck and the revised area.**

Let the original side length of the deck be x ft. The original area was x^2 ft².

The revised design has a length of $(x + 3.5)$ ft and a width of $(x - 3.5)$ ft.

The revised area is $(x + 3.5)(x - 3.5)$ ft².

b. **How does the revised perimeter compare with the original perimeter?**

The original perimeter is $4x$ ft.

The revised perimeter is $2(x + 3.5) + 2(x - 3.5) = 2x + 7 + 2x - 7 = 4x$ ft.

The perimeters are equal.

c. **How does the revised area compare with the original area?**

Expand the expression representing the revised area.

Use the difference of squares formula. $\qquad (a + b)(a - b) = a^2 - b^2$

Substitute x for a and 3.5 for b. $\qquad (x + 3.5)(x - 3.5) = x^2 - 3.5^2$

Simplify. $\qquad\qquad\qquad\qquad\qquad\qquad = x^2 - 12.25$ ft²

The difference between the original area and the revised area is $x^2 - (x^2 - 12.25) = 12.25$ ft².

The revised area is 12.25 ft² less than the original area.

d. **Suppose the original plan was for a square deck with a side length of 16.5 feet. Check the differences in area.**

The original area was $16.5^2 = 272.25$ ft².

The revised area is $(16.5 + 3.5)(16.5 - 3.5) = 272.25 - 12.25 = 260$ ft².

The difference between the original area and the revised area is $272.25 - 260 = 12.25$ ft². ✔

Special Products of Binomials

Perfect-Square Trinomials	$(a + b)^2 = a^2 + 2ab + b^2$
	$(a - b)^2 = a^2 - 2ab + b^2$
Difference of Two Squares	$(a + b)(a - b) = a^2 - b^2$

Polynomial Long Division

Dividing Monomials

To divide monomials, use the same rules of division that you use for numbers. Use the Commutative Property to divide constants and variables separately. When you divide expressions with exponents, use the Quotient of Powers Property.

EXAMPLE 1

Divide.

a. $\dfrac{6x^5}{2x^2}$

Divide constants and variables separately.

$$\frac{6 \cdot x^5}{2 \cdot x^2} = \frac{6}{2} \cdot \frac{x^5}{x^2}$$

Simplify and use the Quotient of Powers Property.

$$= \frac{\overset{3}{6}}{\underset{1}{2}} \cdot x^{5-2}$$

Simplify the exponent.

$$= 3x^3$$

b. $\dfrac{24xy^3}{16xy^2}$

Divide constants and variables separately.

$$\frac{24 \cdot x \cdot y^3}{16 \cdot x \cdot y^2} = \frac{24}{16} \cdot \frac{x}{x} \cdot \frac{y^3}{y^2}$$

Simplify, and use the Quotient of Powers Property.

$$= \frac{\overset{3}{24}}{\underset{2}{16}} \cdot 1 \cdot y^{3-2}$$

Simplify the exponent.

$$= \frac{3}{2} y$$

c. $\dfrac{2x^2y^6}{8xy^4}$

Divide constants and variables separately.

$$\frac{2 \cdot x^2 \cdot y^6}{8 \cdot x \cdot y^4} = \frac{2}{8} \cdot \frac{x^2}{x} \cdot \frac{y^6}{y^4}$$

Simplify, and use the Quotient of Powers Property.

$$= \frac{\overset{1}{2}}{\underset{4}{8}} \cdot x^{2-1} \cdot y^{6-4}$$

Simplify the exponent.

$$= \frac{1}{4} xy^2$$

EXAMPLE 2

Divide $\dfrac{8x^2(4y^2)}{4x(2y)}$.

METHOD 1

Multiply first.

Use the Commutative and Associative properties.

$$\frac{8x^2(4y^2)}{4x(2y)} = \frac{8 \cdot 4 \cdot x^2y^2}{4 \cdot 2 \cdot xy} = \frac{32x^2y^2}{8xy}$$

Simplify, and use the Quotient of Powers Property.

$$= \frac{\overset{4}{32}}{\underset{1}{8}} x^{2-1}y^{2-1}$$

Simplify each exponent.

$$= 4xy$$

METHOD 2

Divide first.

Divide. $x^2 \div x = x$

$$\frac{8x^2(4y^2)}{4x(2y)} = \frac{{}^2\cancel{8}x^{2\,2}}{{}_1\cancel{4}x_1} \cdot \frac{{}^2\cancel{4}y^{\,2}}{{}_1\cancel{2}y_1}$$

Simplify.

$$= 2 \cdot x \cdot 2 \cdot y$$

Use the Commutative Property and multiply.

$$= 4xy$$

Dividing a Polynomial by a Monomial

To divide a polynomial by a monomial, write the division as a fraction. Then divide each term of the polynomial by the monomial, and write the result as a sum of the quotient terms.

EXAMPLE 3

a. $(15x^3 + 21x^2 - 9x) \div 3x$

Write the division as a fraction.

$$\frac{15x^3 + 21x^2 - 9x}{3x}$$

Use the Distributive Property.

$$= \frac{15x^3}{3x} + \frac{21x^2}{3x} - \frac{9x}{3x}$$

Simplify, and use the Quotient of Powers Property.

$$= \frac{{}^5\cancel{15}}{{}_1\cancel{3}}x^{3-1} + \frac{{}^7\cancel{21}}{{}_1\cancel{3}}x^{2-1} - \frac{{}^3\cancel{9}}{{}_1\cancel{3}}x^{1-1}$$

Simplify each exponent.

$$= 5x^2 + 7x - 3$$

b. $(12x^5y^7 + 18x^8y^3) \div 6x^3y^2$

Write the division as a fraction.

$$\frac{12x^5y^7 + 18x^8y^3}{6x^3y^2}$$

Use the Distributive Property.

$$= \frac{12x^5y^7}{6x^3y^2} + \frac{18x^8y^3}{6x^3y^2}$$

Simplify, and use the Quotient of Powers Property.

$$= \frac{{}^2\cancel{12}}{{}_1\cancel{6}}x^{5-3}y^{7-2} + \frac{{}^3\cancel{18}}{{}_1\cancel{6}}x^{8-3}y^{3-2}$$

Simplify each exponent.

$$= 2x^2y^5 + 3x^5y$$

c. $(6x^4y + 8x^3y^7) \div 12x^3y$

Write the division as a fraction.

$$\frac{6x^4y + 8x^3y^7}{12x^3y}$$

Use the Distributive Property.

$$= \frac{6x^4y}{12x^3y} + \frac{8x^3y^7}{12x^3y}$$

Simplify, and use the Quotient of Powers Property.

$$= \frac{{}^1\cancel{6}}{{}_2\cancel{12}}x^{4-3}y^{1-1} + \frac{{}^2\cancel{8}}{{}_3\cancel{12}}x^{3-3}y^{7-1}$$

Simplify each exponent.

$$= \frac{1}{2}x + \frac{2}{3}y^6$$

SEARCH

To see step-by-step videos of these problems, enter the page number into the SWadvantage.com Search Bar.

Using Long Division

Long division of polynomials is very similar to arithmetic long division. Compare the following.

$$\begin{array}{r} 32 \\ 21\overline{)673} \\ 63 \\ \hline 43 \\ 42 \\ \hline 1 \end{array}$$ quotient
divisor 21)673 dividend
remainder

$$\begin{array}{r} 3x + 2 \\ 2x + 1\overline{)6x^2 + 7x + 3} \\ 6x^2 + 3x \\ \hline 4x + 3 \\ 4x + 2 \\ \hline 1 \end{array}$$ quotient
divisor 2x + 1)6x² + 7x + 3 dividend
remainder

EXAMPLE 4

SEARCH

To see step-by-step videos of these problems, enter the page number into the SWadvantage.com Search Bar.

Divide $6x^2 + 7x + 3$ by $2x + 1$.

STEP 1 Set up the problem as you would a long division problem in arithmetic.

$$2x + 1\overline{)6x^2 + 7x + 3}$$

STEP 2 Divide the first term of the trinomial by the first term of the binomial to get a partial quotient.

$$6x^2 \div 2x = 3x \qquad \begin{array}{r} 3x \\ 2x + 1\overline{)6x^2 + 7x + 3} \end{array}$$

STEP 3 Multiply the partial quotient and the binomial.

$$\begin{array}{r} 3x \\ 2x + 1\overline{)6x^2 + 7x + 3} \\ 6x^2 + 3x \end{array}$$

$$3x(2x + 1) = 6x^2 + 3x$$

STEP 4 Subtract that product from the trinomial, and bring down the next term of the dividend.

$$\begin{array}{r} 3x \\ 2x + 1\overline{)6x^2 + 7x + 3} \\ 6x^2 + 3x \downarrow \\ \hline 4x + 3 \end{array}$$

STEP 5 Divide the first term of the bottom expression by the first term of the binomial. Multiply and then subtract.

$$\begin{array}{r} 3x + 2 \\ 2x + 1\overline{)6x^2 + 7x + 3} \\ 6x^2 + 3x \\ \hline 4x + 3 \\ 4x + 2 \\ \hline 1 \end{array}$$

STEP 6 Write the quotient. Include the remainder as a fraction of the divisor.

The quotient of $6x^2 + 7x + 3$ divided by $2x + 1$ is $3x + 2$ R1, or $3x + 2 + \dfrac{1}{2x + 1}$.

Operations with Polynomials   **ALGEBRA**

EXAMPLE 5

Divide $3x^3 + 2x^2 - 5$ by $x + 2$.

STEP 1 Divide the first term of the polynomial by the first term of the binomial. Multiply the partial quotient and the binomial. Then subtract. Bring down the next term of the dividend.

Write $0x$ for the missing x term.

$$\begin{array}{r} 3x^2 \\ x + 2\overline{)3x^3 + 2x^2 + 0x - 5} \\ \underline{3x^3 + 6x^2} \downarrow \\ -4x^2 + 0x \end{array}$$

$2x^2 - 6x^2 = -4x^2$

STEP 2 Continue dividing, subtracting, and bringing down the next term.

$$\begin{array}{r} 3x^3 - 4x + 8 \\ x + 2\overline{)3x^4 + 2x^2 + 0x - 5} \\ \underline{3x^3 + 6x^2} \\ -4x^2 + 0x \\ \underline{-4x^2 - 8x} \downarrow \\ 8x - 5 \\ \underline{8x + 16} \\ -21 \end{array}$$

$-4x^2 \div x = -4x$

$0x - (-8x) = 8x$

Multiply the partial quotient and the binomial and subtract.

STEP 3 Write the quotient. Include the remainder as a fraction of the divisor.

The quotient of $3x^3 + 2x^2 - 5$ divided by $x + 2$ is $3x^2 - 4x + 8$ R -21, or $3x^2 - 4x + 8 - \dfrac{21}{x + 2}$.

Need More

HELP?

For more help dividing polynomials by binomials of the form $x + a$, go to *Synthetic Division* on page 1678.

EXAMPLE 6

Divide $-18x^2 + 33x - 5$ by $-3x + 5$.

$$\begin{array}{r} 6x - 1 \\ -3x + 5\overline{)-18x^2 + 33x - 5} \\ \underline{-18x^2 + 30x} \downarrow \\ 3x - 5 \\ \underline{3x - 5} \\ 0 \end{array}$$

$3x \div (-3x) = -1$

There is no remainder.

The quotient of $-18x^2 + 33x - 5$ divided by $-3x + 5$ is $6x - 1$.

GOT TO KNOW!

Polynomial Long Division

1. Set up the problem as you would set up a long division problem in arithmetic.

2. Divide the first term of the dividend by the first term of the divisor to get a partial quotient.

3. Multiply the partial quotient and the divisor.

4. Subtract that product from the dividend, and bring down the next term.

5. Continue dividing, subtracting, and bringing down the next term.

6. Write the quotient with the remainder as a fraction of the divisor.

Polynomial Functions and Equations

What Came Before?

- Solving and graphing linear functions and equations
- Performing operations with polynomials

What's This About?

- Graphing polynomial functions
- Using theorems to find real zeros, roots, and solutions of polynomial functions and equations
- Finding imaginary zeros of polynomial functions

Practical Apps

- Roadway engineers solve polynomial equations to determine the up-and-down curvature of an elevated portion of a road.
- Aerospace engineers use polynomial equations to design the wings of airplanes for optimum aerodynamics.

just for FUN!

Q: Why did the function like the zero?

A: It always behaved rationally.

CONTENTS	UPLOAD	DOWNLOAD	*Algebra*

Graphing Polynomial Functions

Polynomial Functions

A polynomial is a monomial or a sum of monomials. A **polynomial function** in one variable is a function of degree n, where n is a nonnegative integer, and the degrees of the terms are decreasing from n to 0.

The function below is a polynomial function of degree 3. Notice that the highest exponent of the variable x is 3, which determines the degree. The exponents decrease from 3 to 0.

$$f(x) = 5x^3 + 2x^2 - 7x + 10$$

The standard form of a polynomial function of degree n is shown here.

$$f(x) = a_n x^n + a_{n-1} x^{n-1} + a_{n-2} x^{n-2} + \ldots + a_1 x + a_0$$

Types of Polynomial Functions

GOT TO KNOW!

Higher-Order Polynomials

Polynomials of degree greater than 5 are generally referred to as *higher-order polynomials*.

Degree	Type	Standard Form	Example
0	Constant	$f(x) = a_0$	$f(x) = 5$
1	Linear	$f(x) = a_1 x + a_0$	$f(x) = -2x + 3$
2	Quadratic	$f(x) = a_2 x^2 + a_1 x + a_0$	$f(x) = 2x^2 - 9x + 14$
3	Cubic	$f(x) = a_3 x^3 + a_2 x^2 + a_1 x + a_0$	$f(x) = 3x^3 + 14$
4	Quartic	$f(x) = a_4 x^4 + a_3 x^3 + a_2 x^2 + a_1 x + a_0$	$f(x) = x^4 + 2x^3 + 3x$
5	Quintic	$f(x) = a_5 x^5 + a_4 x^4 + a_3 x^3 + a_2 x^2 + a_1 x + a_0$	$f(x) = 4x^5 - 3x + 10$

Some coefficients of a polynomial function in standard form may equal 0, as shown above. For example, in the function $f(x) = 3x^3 + 14$, the coefficients of x^2 and x both equal 0.

The **leading coefficient** of a polynomial function is the coefficient of the term of greatest degree, which is called the **leading term**. The leading coefficient cannot be 0.

EXAMPLE 1

Determine whether the function is a polynomial function. If it is, write it in standard form and give its type.

a. $f(x) = x^4 - 6x^2 - 0.5$

The polynomial function is in standard form. $f(x) = x^4 - 6x^2 - 0.5$

The greatest degree is 4, so it is a quartic function.

b. $f(x) = 1 - \dfrac{x^3}{4}$

Use the Commutative Property. $f(x) = 1 - \dfrac{x^3}{4} = -\dfrac{x^3}{4} + 1$

Write division as multiplication. $= -\dfrac{1}{4}x^3 + 1$

In standard form, the function is $f(x) = -\dfrac{1}{4}x^3 + 1$. The greatest degree is 3, so it is a cubic function.

c. $f(x) = 8x^2 + \dfrac{1}{x} - 7$

There is a variable in the denominator. So this is not a polynomial function.

SEARCH

To see step-by-step videos of these problems, enter the page number into the SWadvantage.com Search Bar.

Parent Polynomial Functions

The **parent functions** for polynomials of degree n are the functions $f(x) = x^n$. The graphs of the parent functions are shown below.

Linear	Quadratic	Cubic	Quartic	Quintic
$f(x) = x$	$f(x) = x^2$	$f(x) = x^3$	$f(x) = x^4$	$f(x) = x^5$

End Behavior

Polynomial functions are classified by degree. Polynomial functions of degree 1, 3, 5, and so on are called **odd functions**. Polynomial functions of degree 2, 4, 6, and so on are called **even functions**.

Notice the end behavior in the graphs of the parent functions above.

Odd parent functions – The ends of the graph point in opposite directions. The graph goes from the lower left to the upper right.

Even parent functions – The ends of the graph point in the same direction. The graph goes from the upper left to the upper right.

All polynomial functions with positive leading coefficients have these end behaviors.

When the leading coefficient is negative, the end behavior changes.

Odd parent functions – The graph goes from the upper left to the lower right.

Even parent functions – The graph goes from the lower left to the lower right.

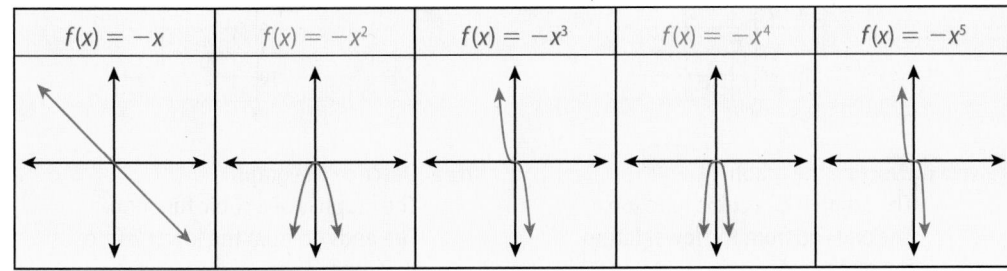

$f(x) = -x$	$f(x) = -x^2$	$f(x) = -x^3$	$f(x) = -x^4$	$f(x) = -x^5$

Graphs of Polynomial Functions

The graphs of polynomial functions of degree 2 or greater are smooth curves. Graphs of polynomial functions of degree 3 or greater may also have **turning points**, places where the direction of the curve changes. Turning points are also known as *points of inflection*.

Need More

HELP ?

For help graphing lines, go to *Linear Functions* on page 1450.

For more help graphing quadratic functions, go to *Quadratic Functions* on page 1688.

SEARCH

To see step-by-step videos of these problems, enter the page number into the SWadvantage.com Search Bar.

EXAMPLE 2

Graph each polynomial function. Describe the graph and its end behavior, and tell whether it has any turning points.

a. $f(x) = x^3 + x$

STEP 1 Make a table.

x	$x^3 + x$	y
-2	$(-2)^3 + (-2)$	-10
-1	$(-1)^3 + (-1)$	-2
0	$(0)^3 + (0)$	0
1	$(1)^3 + (1)$	2
2	$(2)^3 + (2)$	10

STEP 2 Graph the ordered pairs. Connect the ordered pairs with a smooth curve.

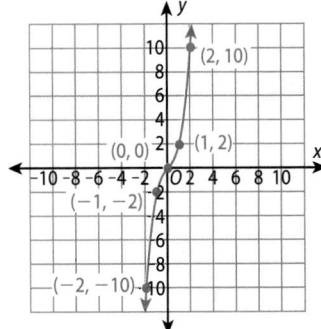

STEP 3 Describe the graph.
The graph is of a cubic function.
The ends go from the lower left to the upper right.

The graph has no turning points.

b. $f(x) = x^3 - 2x$

STEP 1 Make a table.

x	$x^3 - 2x$	y
-2	$(-2)^3 - 2(-2)$	-4
-1	$(-1)^3 - 2(-1)$	1
0	$(0)^3 - 2(0)$	0
1	$(1)^3 - 2(1)$	-1
2	$(2)^3 - 2(2)$	4

STEP 2 Graph the ordered pairs. Connect the ordered pairs with a smooth curve.

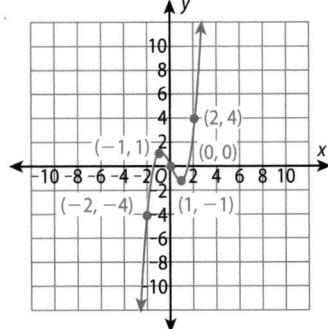

STEP 3 Describe the graph.
The graph is of a cubic function.
The ends go from the lower left to the upper right.

The graph has two turning points.

More than a few points are often needed to draw the curves accurately. Try evaluating polynomial functions for noninteger values of x and then plot those points to see whether a graph that appears to flatten, or to have a diminishing slope, actually has turning points.

EXAMPLE 3

Use the polynomial function below to model the change in total attendance, in millions, at Yankee Stadium from one decade to the next, beginning with the 1920s.

$$A(d) = 0.0118d^4 - 0.0324d^3 - 0.6444d^2 + 4.5962d + 6.5848$$

a. Graph the function.

METHOD 1

STEP 1 Use a calculator to evaluate the function $A(d)$ for $d = 0$ to 8. Round each value of $A(d)$ to the nearest tenth.

Number of decades since the 1920s (d)	0	1	2	3	4	5	6	7	8
Attendance in millions A(d)	6.6	10.5	13.1	14.7	15.6	16.8	19.3	24.4	33.9

STEP 2 Graph the points and connect them with a smooth curve.

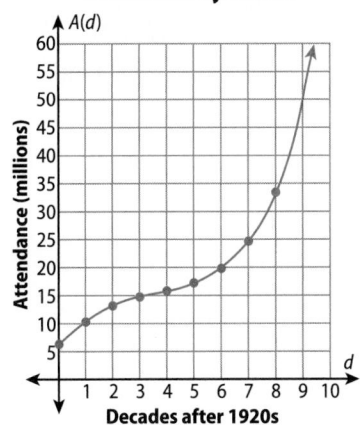

Yankee Stadium Attendance by Decade

METHOD 2

Use a graphing calculator.

Enter the function into the Y= editor, set the window to fit the data, and graph.

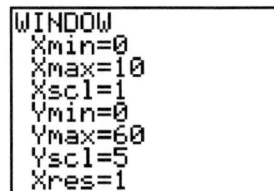
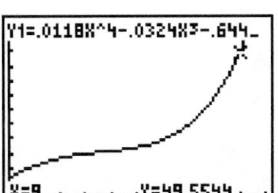

b. Predict attendance to the nearest million for the decade that began with 2010.

Use the graph, or evaluate the polynomial function for $d = 9$.

The calculator graph shows the calculated value for $A(9)$ as 49.5544 million, so the model predicts about 50 million.

Zeros and Roots

Zeros of a Polynomial Function

A **zero of a function** is an input value with a corresponding output value equal to 0. The maximum number of zeros of a polynomial function is the degree of the function.

EXAMPLE 1

Need More

HELP

Remember these facts.

Odd powers of negative numbers are negative.

Even powers of negative numbers are positive.

Odd	Even
$(-1)^1 = -1$	$(-1)^2 = 1$
$(-1)^3 = -1$	$(-1)^4 = 1$
$(-1)^5 = -1$	$(-1)^6 = 1$
$(-1)^7 = -1$	$(-1)^8 = 1$

Determine whether the given value is a zero of the polynomial function.

a. $3; f(x) = x^3 + 2x^2 - 17x + 6$

Evaluate the function for $x = 3$. $f(x) = x^3 + 2x^2 - 17x + 6$

Substitute 3 for x. $= 3^3 + 2(3)^2 - 17(3) + 6$

Simplify. $= 27 + 18 - 51 + 6$

                                      $= 0$

When $x = 3$, $f(x) = 0$, so 3 is a zero of the polynomial function.

b. $-3; f(x) = x^4 + 3x^3 - 2x^2 - 9x - 9$

Evaluate the function for $x = -3$. $f(x) = x^4 + 3x^3 - 2x^2 - 9x - 9$

Substitute -3 for x. $= (-3)^4 + 3(-3)^3 - 2(-3)^2 - 9(-3) - 9$

Simplify. $= 81 - 81 - 18 + 27 - 9$

                                       $= 0$

When $x = -3$, $f(x) = 0$, so -3 is a zero of the polynomial function.

c. $-2; f(x) = 2x^4 + x^3 + 6x - 6$

Evaluate the function for $x = -2$. $f(x) = 2x^4 + x^3 + 6x - 6$

Substitute -2 for x. $= 2(-2)^4 + (-2)^3 + 6(-2) - 6$

Simplify. $= 32 - 8 - 12 - 6$

                                       $= 6$

When $x = -2$, $f(x) \neq 0$, so -2 is not a zero of the function.

A function may have more than one zero.

EXAMPLE 2

SEARCH

To see step-by-step videos of these problems, enter the page number into the SWadvantage.com Search Bar.

Given the domain $D = \{0, 1, 2, 3\}$, which values are zeros of the function $f(x) = x^3 - 4x^2 + 3x$?

You can use a table.

Domain Value	$f(x) = x^3 - 4x^2 + 3x$
0	$f(x) = 0^3 - 4(0)^2 + 3(0) = 0 - 0 + 0 = 0$ ✔
1	$f(x) = 1^3 - 4(1)^2 + 3(1) = 1 - 4 + 3 = 0$ ✔
2	$f(x) = 2^3 - 4(2)^2 + 3(2) = 8 - 16 + 6 = -2$ ✘
3	$f(x) = 3^3 - 4(3)^2 + 3(3) = 27 - 36 + 9 = 0$ ✔

The domain values 0, 1, and 3 are zeros of the polynomial function.

Finding Zeros from a Graph

The zeros of a polynomial function are the *x*-intercepts of the graph of the function.

Graph each polynomial function. Find any zeros.

a. $f(x) = x^2 - 4x - 5$

STEP 1 Graph the polynomial function.
This is a quadratic function.

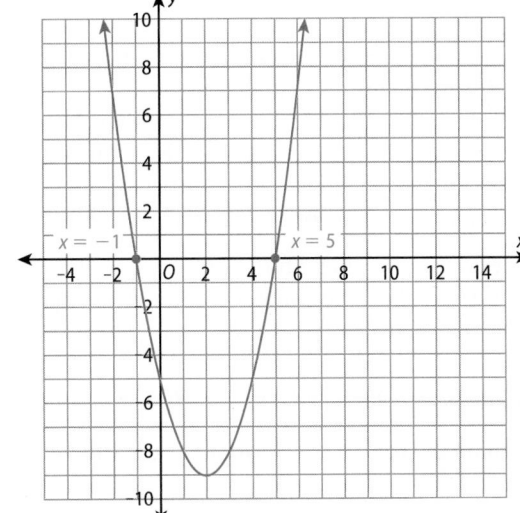

> **Watch Out** !
>
> You may not be able to read the zeros of a polynomial function from a graph. Many polynomial functions have zeros that are irrational numbers.

STEP 2 Estimate the zeros, and check the estimates.
The zeros appear to be $x = -1$ and $x = 5$.

CHECK Substitute each value into the polynomial function.

$$f(x) = x^2 - 4x - 5 \qquad\qquad f(x) = x^2 - 4x - 5$$
$$= (-1)^2 - 4(-1) - 5 \qquad\qquad = (5)^2 - 4(5) - 5$$
$$= 1 + 4 - 5 \qquad\qquad\qquad = 25 - 20 - 5$$
$$= 0 ✔ \qquad\qquad\qquad\qquad = 0 ✔$$

b. $f(x) = x^3 + 3x^2 - 6x - 8$

STEP 1 Graph the polynomial function.
This is a cubic function.

STEP 2 Estimate the zeros, and check the estimates.
The zeros appear to be $x = -4$, $x = -1$, and $x = 2$.

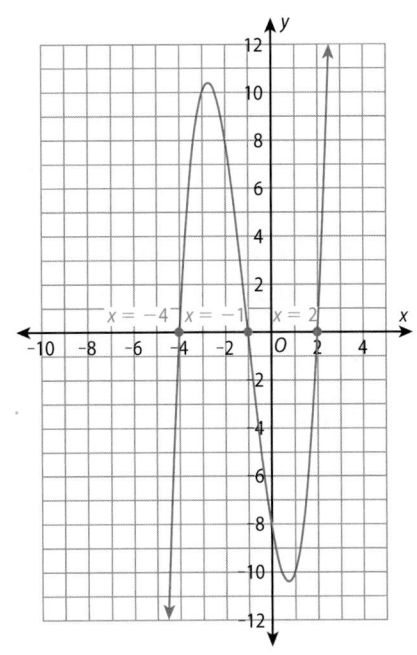

CHECK Substitute each value into the polynomial function.

Value	$f(x) = x^3 + 3x^2 - 6x - 8$
-4	$f(x) = (-4)^3 + 3(-4)^2 - 6(-4) - 8$ $= -64 + 48 + 24 - 8 = 0$ ✔
-1	$f(x) = (-1)^3 + 3(-1)^2 - 6(-1) - 8$ $= -1 + 3 + 6 - 8 = 0$ ✔
2	$f(x) = 2^3 + 3(2)^2 - 6(2) - 8$ $= 8 + 12 - 12 - 8 = 0$ ✔

Need More
HELP ?

Think of an elevator. If the elevator travels from the basement to the second floor, or from the second floor to the basement, it passes ground level during each trip.

SEARCH 🔍

To see step-by-step videos of these problems, enter the page number into the SWadvantage.com Search Bar.

Finding Roots

A **root of an equation** is a domain value that makes the equation true. The roots of the equation $x^3 + 3x^2 - 6x - 8 = 0$ are the same values as the zeros of the function $f(x) = x^3 + 3x^2 - 6x - 8$.

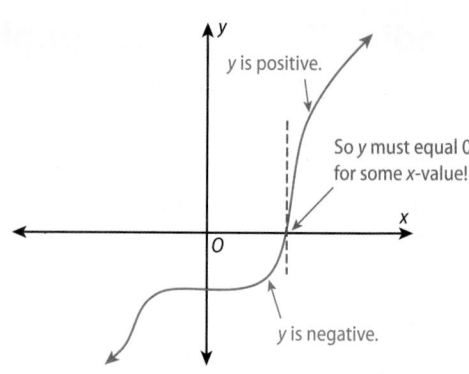

y is positive.

So y must equal 0 for some x-value!

y is negative.

Polynomial functions are continuous functions, which have no breaks in their graphs. If a continuous function $f(x)$ has opposite signs for two values of the independent variable x, then it has a value of 0 for some value of x between these two values. So a zero, or root, exists between the two values of x. This is the **location principle**.

For example, the linear function $y = 2x - 1$ has a value of -1 when $x = 0$ and a value of 1 when $x = 1$. Because you know the sign changed from negative to positive, you know that a root exists between $x = 0$ and $x = 1$. (The root is $x = 0.5$, because $2(0.5) - 1 = 0$.)

EXAMPLE 4

Estimate the root of the polynomial equation $y + 5 = x^3$ to the nearest hundredth.

METHOD 1

Guess, check, and revise.

STEP 1 Isolate the variable y. $y = x^3 - 5$

STEP 2 Make a table of values.

x	$x^3 - 5$	y
-1	$(-1)^3 - 5$	-6
0	$(0)^3 - 5$	-5
1	$(1)^3 - 5$	-4
2	$(2)^3 - 5$	3
3	$(3)^3 - 5$	22

Sign change! The root is between $x = 1$ and $x = 2$.

STEP 3 Make a guess, and check it.

Guess $x = 1.5$. $y = x^3 - 5$
$y = 1.5^3 - 5$
$= -1.625$ too low

STEP 4 Revise the guess, and check again.

Guess $x = 1.8$. $y = x^3 - 5$
$y = 1.8^3 - 5$
$= 0.832$ too high

STEP 5 Revise the guess, and check again.

Guess $x = 1.7$. $y = x^3 - 5$
$y = 1.7^3 - 5$
$= -0.087$ too low

STEP 6 Revise the guess, and check again.

Guess $x = 1.75$. $y = x^3 - 5$
$y = 1.75^3 - 5$
$= 0.359$ too high

STEP 7 Continue to revise the guess and narrow the interval.

Guess $x = 1.72$.   Guess $x = 1.71$.

$y = 1.72^3 - 5 = 0.088$ too high $y = 1.71^3 - 5 = 0.0002$

The root of the equation, to the nearest hundredth, is $x = 1.71$.

METHOD 2

Use a graphing calculator.

STEP 1 Isolate y. $y = x^3 - 5$

STEP 2 Enter the expression $x^3 - 5$ in **Y1**.

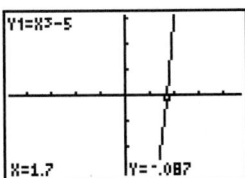

STEP 3 Press ZOOM , choose **4:ZDecimal**, and press ENTER to graph.

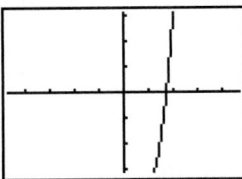

STEP 4 Press TRACE and the right arrow repeatedly.

$x = 1.7$ is too low.

$x = 1.8$ is too high.

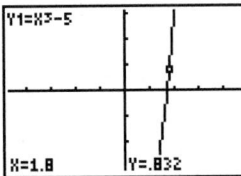

STEP 5 Press 2nd CALC , choose **2:zero**, and press ENTER . Press the left arrow key once to use $x = 1.7$ as the left bound, and press ENTER . Press the right arrow key once to use $x = 1.8$ as the right bound, and press ENTER .

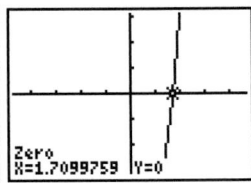

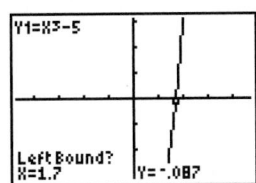

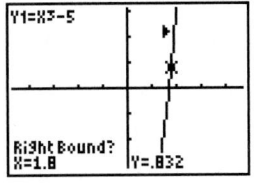

For the estimate, press ENTER again. The root of the equation, to the nearest hundredth, is 1.71.

GOT TO KNOW!

Zeros and Roots of Polynomials

zero – A value of x that gives a polynomial function $f(x)$ a value of 0.

root – A value of x in a polynomial equation that makes the dependent variable y equal to 0.

There are at most n zeros or roots for a polynomial of degree n.

Solutions of a Polynomial Equation

Roots and Solutions

Need More

HELP

The phrase *if and only if* forms a biconditional statement. In a biconditional, when the first part of the statement is true, the second part is also true. When the first part is false, the second part is also false.

For more help, go to *Biconditionals* in *Geometry* (Book 1, p. 616).

For more help with the Zero-Product Property, go to *The Zero-Product Property* on page 1700.

Any root of an equation is a solution of the equation. So roots, solutions, and zeros are often interchangeable. When an equation is not a function, there are no zeros, but there may be roots and solutions.

Recall the Zero-Product Property. It is true for any number of factors.

$ab = 0$ if and only if $a = 0$ or $b = 0$

If a is a solution of a polynomial equation $P(x) = 0$, then $(x - a)$ is a factor of the equation.

EXAMPLE 1

Write a polynomial equation that has 8 as a solution.

If 8 is a solution, then $x - 8$ is a factor. So $x - 8 = 0$ is a polynomial equation with 8 as a solution.

EXAMPLE 2

Write a polynomial equation with the given solutions.

a. 3 and −4

If 3 is a solution, then $x - 3$ is a factor. If -4 is a solution, then $x - (-4)$, or $x + 4$, is a factor.

Use the Zero-Product Property.	$(x - 3)(x + 4) = 0$
When $x = 3$, the binomial on the left equals 0.	$(3 - 3)(x + 4) = 0$
When $x = -4$, the binomial on the right equals 0.	$(x - 3)(-4 + 4) = 0$
Use FOIL to multiply $(x - 3)(x + 4)$.	$x(x) + 4x - 3x - 12 = 0$
Combine like terms and simplify.	$x^2 + x - 12 = 0$

CHECK

$x^2 + x - 12 = 0$
For $x = 3$ $3^2 + 3 - 12 \stackrel{?}{=} 0$
$9 + 3 - 12 \stackrel{?}{=} 0$
$0 = 0$ ✔

$x^2 + x - 12 = 0$
For $x = -4$ $(-4)^2 + (-4) - 12 \stackrel{?}{=} 0$
$16 - 4 - 12 \stackrel{?}{=} 0$
$0 = 0$ ✔

A polynomial equation with solutions 3 and -4 is $x^2 + x - 12 = 0$.

b. 0, 1, and −1

Solutions:	0	1	−1
Factors:	$x - 0$	$x - 1$	$x - (-1)$

Simplify each factor. Set the product equal to 0.	$x(x - 1)(x + 1) = 0$
Multiply the binomial terms as a special product.	$x(x^2 - 1) = 0$
Multiply.	$x^3 - x = 0$

CHECK

$x^3 - x = 0$
$0^3 - 0 \stackrel{?}{=} 0$
$0 - 0 \stackrel{?}{=} 0$
$0 = 0$ ✔

$x^3 - x = 0$
$1^3 - 1 \stackrel{?}{=} 0$
$1 - 1 \stackrel{?}{=} 0$
$0 = 0$ ✔

$x^3 - x = 0$
$(-1)^3 - (-1) \stackrel{?}{=} 0$
$-1 + 1 \stackrel{?}{=} 0$
$0 = 0$ ✔

A polynomial equation with solutions 0, 1, and -1 is $x^3 - x = 0$.

Finding Solutions

There are many methods to use to solve polynomial equations.

SEARCH

To see step-by-step videos of these problems, enter the page number into the SWadvantage.com Search Bar.

EXAMPLE

Solve $x^2 - 25 = 0$.

METHOD 1

STEP 1 Analyze the equation.
The equation is quadratic.
It is the difference of two squares, x^2 and 5^2. $x^2 - 25 = 0$

STEP 2 Factor the quadratic expression.
Remember, $a^2 - b^2 = (a + b)(a - b)$. $(x + 5)(x - 5) = 0$

STEP 3 Set each factor equal to 0.
Use the Zero-Product Property. $x + 5 = 0$ or $x - 5 = 0$

STEP 4 Solve.
Find the values of x. $x = -5$ or $x = 5$

METHOD 2

Solve for x. $x^2 - 25 = 0$

Add 25 to both sides. $x^2 = 25$

Take the square root of both sides. $\sqrt{x^2} = \pm\sqrt{25}$

Simplify. $x = \pm 5$

$x = 5$ or $x = -5$

METHOD 3

STEP 1 Write the related function for the equation.
$y = x^2 - 25$

STEP 2 Graph the function.

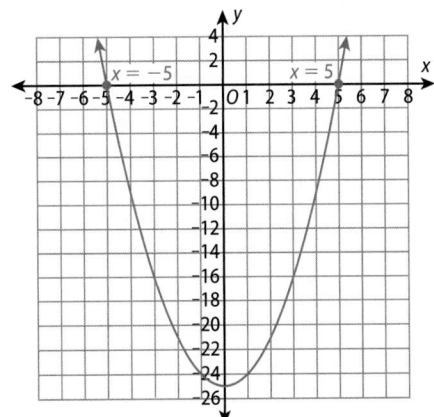

STEP 3 Find the values of x where the value of y is 0.
$x = -5$ or $x = 5$

Try It This Way

Use a graphing calculator to graph the function $y = x^2 - 25$ in the standard window.
Use **2nd** **CALC** **2:zero** to find each zero.

Factoring to Solve Polynomial Equations

You can factor out a common factor from each term to solve some polynomial equations.

 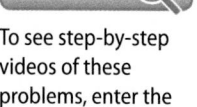
EXAMPLE 4

Solve $x^5 - 2x^4 = 0$.

Factor out x^4.	$x^4(x - 2) = 0$
Use the Zero-Product Property.	$x^4 = 0$ or $x - 2 = 0$
Solve.	$x = 0$ or $x = 2$

Some polynomial equations have no real solutions.

EXAMPLE 5

Solve $x^4 + 16x^2 + 4 = 0$.

METHOD 1

STEP 1 Analyze the equation.

The equation is quartic. The leading coefficient is positive, so the graph will go from the upper left to the upper right.

The values of x^4 and x^2 cannot be negative, so $x^4 + 16x^2$ cannot be negative.

STEP 2 Isolate the variable terms on one side of the equation. $x^4 + 16x^2 + 4 = 0$

Subtract 4 from both sides of the equation. $x^4 + 16x^2 = -4$

For the equation to be true, $x^4 + 16x^2$ must equal -4. But $x^4 + 16x^2$ cannot be negative. This is a contradiction.

The equation $x^4 + 16x^2 + 4 = 0$ has no real solutions.

METHOD 2

Make a table of values.

x	-3	-2	-1	0	1	2	3
$x^4 + 16x^2 + 4$	229	84	21	4	21	84	229

The value of the expression is never less than 4. There is no real solution.

METHOD 3

Graph the equation.

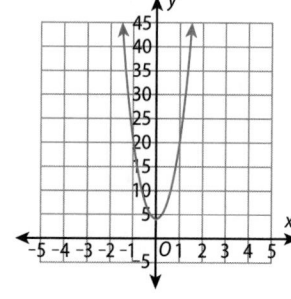

The equation has no x-intercepts, so there are no real roots. The equation has no real solution.

EXAMPLE 6

The difference in volume between the two cubes is 37 cm³.
Find the length of a side of the larger cube.

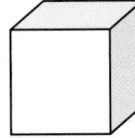 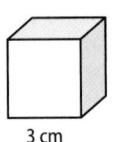

3 cm

x cm

METHOD 1

Solve algebraically.

Write the cubic equation.	$x^3 - 3^3 = 37$
Simplify.	$x^3 - 27 = 37$
Add 27 to both sides.	$x^3 = 64$
Take the cube root of both sides.	$\sqrt[3]{x^3} = \sqrt[3]{64}$
64 is a perfect cube. $64 = 4^3$.	$x = 4$

The length of a side is 4 cm.

CHECK Substitute $x = 4$ into the problem.

The volume of the larger cube is $(4 \text{ cm})^3 = 64 \text{ cm}^3$. The volume of the smaller cube is
$(3 \text{ cm})^3 = 27 \text{ cm}^3$. The difference in volume is $64 - 27 = 37 \text{ cm}^3$. ✔

METHOD 2

Use a graphing calculator.

Enter the expression $x^3 - 3^3$ in **Y1**, and enter 37 in **Y2**.   Set your WINDOW to include Y2.

```
Plot1 Plot2 Plot3
\Y1▉X3-3³
\Y2▉37
\Y3=
\Y4=
\Y5=
\Y6=
\Y7=
```

```
WINDOW
Xmin=-10
Xmax=10
Xscl=1
Ymin=-50
Ymax=50
Yscl=10
Xres=1
```

Press **2nd** **CALC** and choose **5:intersect**. Press **ENTER** three times, until the intersection point is shown.

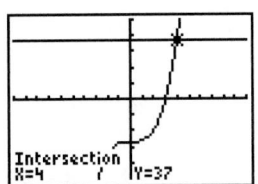

The *x*-value is the length of a side, 4 cm. The *y*-value is the difference of the volumes.

Factoring to Find Zeros

Recall that a *zero* of a function is an input value with a corresponding output value equal to 0. You can find zeros of a polynomial function $P(x)$ by first factoring the polynomial expression. Then use the Zero-Product Property to set each factor equal to 0 and solve.

EXAMPLE 1

Find the zeros of $f(x) = x^2 + 3x - 28$.

Factor the expression into two binomials, $(x + ?)(x + ?)$.

Recall that when you multiply two binomial factors using FOIL, the last term of the resulting expression is the product of the last terms of the binomials. Also, the middle term is the sum of the outside product and the inside product.

So when you factor the polynomial expression, you need to find factors that generate those products.

STEP 1 First find factors of the last term of the expression.

The factors of -28 are ± 1, ± 2, ± 4, ± 7, ± 14, and ± 28.

STEP 2 Then look for factor pairs that have a product of -28 and a sum equal to the coefficient of the middle term of the expression.

Make a table. Continue listing factor pairs until you find the pair with a sum of 3.

Factor Pairs with Product -28	28 and -1	14 and -2	7 and -4
Sum	27	12	3

STEP 3 Write the factors of the polynomial expression and set the product equal to 0.

$(x + 7)(x - 4) = 0$

You can verify the factors by using FOIL to multiply.

$$(x + 7)(x - 4) = x^2 - 4x + 7x - 28$$
$$= x^2 \quad + 3x \quad - 28$$

STEP 4 Find the zeros of the polynomial function.

Use the Zero-Product Property. $x + 7 = 0$ or $x - 4 = 0$

Solve. $x = -7$ or $x = 4$

CHECK -7; $x^2 + 3x - 28$ 4; $x^2 + 3x - 28$

$(-7)^2 + 3(-7) - 28 \overset{?}{=} 0$ $(4)^2 + 3(4) - 28 \overset{?}{=} 0$

$49 - 21 - 28 \overset{?}{=} 0$ $16 + 12 - 28 \overset{?}{=} 0$

$0 = 0$ ✔ $0 = 0$ ✔

The zeros of the polynomial are -7 and 4.

Recall that the maximum number of zeros is the degree n of the polynomial. When a polynomial function has integer coefficients, the number of possible rational zeros is limited.

Rational factors may be fractions or integers (fractions with a denominator of 1).

Rational Zeros of Polynomial Functions

By the Zero-Product Property, the function $f(x) = (5x - 2)(2x - 3)$ has zeros $\frac{2}{5}$ and $\frac{3}{2}$.

Multiplying the binomials, you get $(5x - 2)(2x - 3) = 10x^2 - 19x + 6$.

So, the trinomial function $f(x) = 10x^2 - 19x + 6$ also has zeros $\frac{2}{5}$ and $\frac{3}{2}$.

The numerators, 2 and 3, are factors of the constant term, 6.

The denominators, 5 and 2, are factors of the leading coefficient, 10.

The Rational Zeros Theorem

If the polynomial function $f(x) = a_n x^n + a_{n-1} x^{n-1} + a_{n-2} x^{n-2} + \ldots + a_1 x + a_0$ has integer coefficients, then every rational zero of f has the form shown below.

$$\frac{p}{q} \begin{array}{l} \leftarrow \text{a factor of the constant term } a_0 \\ \leftarrow \text{a factor of the leading coeficient } a_n \end{array}$$

This is called the **Rational Zeros Theorem**. Because this theorem also applies to roots of polynomial equations, it is also known as the **Rational Roots Theorem**.

EXAMPLE 2

List the possible rational zeros.

a. $f(x) = x^3 + 10x^2 - 4x + 18$

Always include both positive and negative factors.

Factors of the constant term 18: $\pm 1, \pm 2, \pm 3, \pm 6, \pm 9, \pm 18$

Factors of the leading coefficient 1: ± 1

Possible rational zeros: $\pm\frac{1}{1}, \pm\frac{2}{1}, \pm\frac{3}{1}, \pm\frac{6}{1}, \pm\frac{9}{1}, \pm\frac{18}{1}$

Simplify: $\pm 1, \pm 2, \pm 3, \pm 6, \pm 9, \pm 18$

b. $f(x) = 4x^3 - 120x^2 + 90x - 6$

Factors of the constant term -6: $\pm 1, \pm 2, \pm 3, \pm 6$

Factors of the leading coefficient 4: $\pm 1, \pm 2, \pm 4$

Possible rational zeros: $\pm\frac{1}{1}, \pm\frac{2}{1}, \pm\frac{3}{1}, \pm\frac{6}{1},$

$\pm\frac{1}{2}, \pm\frac{2}{2}, \pm\frac{3}{2}, \pm\frac{6}{2},$

$\pm\frac{1}{4}, \pm\frac{2}{4}, \pm\frac{3}{4}, \pm\frac{6}{4}$

Simplify: $\pm 1, \pm 2, \pm 3, \pm 6, \pm\frac{1}{2}, \pm\frac{3}{2}, \pm\frac{1}{4}, \pm\frac{3}{4}$

GOT TO KNOW!

A **theorem** is a mathematical statement that is proved by using mathematical reasoning. A **property** or **axiom** is assumed to be true and requires no proof.

SEARCH

To see step-by-step videos of these problems, enter the page number into the SWadvantage.com Search Bar.

Testing Rational Zeros of Polynomial Functions

Polynomial functions may not have any rational zeros. Use the Rational Zeros Theorem to test the possible rational zeros. If you test all possible rational zeros and none are actual zeros, the polynomial function has no rational zeros.

EXAMPLE 3

Find the rational zeros of the function.

a. $f(x) = x^2 - 8x + 15$

Factors of the constant term 15: $\pm 1, \pm 3, \pm 5, \pm 15$

Factors of the leading coefficient 1: ± 1

Possible rational zeros: $\pm 1, \pm 3, \pm 5, \pm 15$

Test 1.

$f(x) = 1^2 - 8(1) + 15$

$= 1 - 8 + 15$

$= 8$ ✗

Test 3.

$f(x) = 3^2 - 8(3) + 15$

$= 9 - 24 + 15$

$= 0$ ✔

So 3 is a zero, and $(x - 3)$ is a factor of the function.

The function is a quadratic function, so there is one other binomial linear factor. Use the factor you just found to find the other factor, which will give the other zero.

$(x - 3)(x + ?) = x^2 - 8x + 15$. The product of the last terms is 15, so the missing value must be $\frac{15}{-3} = -5$. Therefore, the other term is $x - 5$, and the second zero is 5.

The two zeros are 3 and 5.

b. $f(x) = 2x^3 - x^2 + 1$

Factors of the constant term 1: ± 1

Factors of the leading coefficient 2: $\pm 1, \pm 2$

Possible rational zeros: $\pm 1, \pm \frac{1}{2}$

Test 1.

$f(x) = 2(1)^3 - (1)^2 + 1$

$= 2 - 1 + 1$

$= 2$ ✗

Test -1.

$f(x) = 2(-1)^3 - (-1)^2 + 1$

$= -2 - 1 + 1$

$= -2$ ✗

Test $\frac{1}{2}$.

$f(x) = 2\left(\frac{1}{2}\right)^3 - \left(\frac{1}{2}\right)^2 + 1$

$= \frac{1}{4} - \frac{1}{4} + 1$

$= 1$ ✗

Test $-\frac{1}{2}$.

$f(x) = 2\left(-\frac{1}{2}\right)^3 - \left(-\frac{1}{2}\right)^2 + 1$

$= -\frac{1}{4} - \frac{1}{4} + 1$

$= \frac{1}{2}$ ✗

None of the four possible rational zeros are actual zeros of the polynomial function.

The function has no rational zeros.

EXAMPLE 4

A small baking dish has a length that is 2 inches longer than the width and a height that is 1 inch less than the width. The volume of the baking dish is 30 in.³. What are the dimensions of the dish?

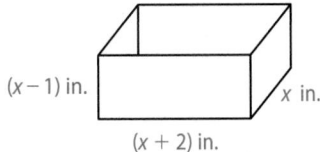

$(x-1)$ in. x in.

$(x+2)$ in.

SEARCH

To see step-by-step videos of these problems, enter the page number into the SWadvantage.com Search Bar.

STEP 1 Write an equation for the volume of the dish.

Let x = the width of the dish in inches.

The length of the dish is $(x+2)$ inches, and the height is $(x-1)$ inches.

The volume $V = \ell wh = (x+2)(x)(x-1)$, or $x(x+2)(x-1)$ in.³.

The given volume is 30 in.³.

So the equation to find the width is $x(x+2)(x-1) = 30$.

STEP 2 Write the equation in polynomial form with 0 on one side.

First, multiply the factors. $x(x+2)(x-1) = 30$

Multiply the binomial factors. $x(x^2 + x - 2) = 30$

Multiply x by the trinomial. $x^3 + x^2 - 2x = 30$

Subtract 30 from both sides. $x^3 + x^2 - 2x - 30 = 0$

STEP 3 Solve the equation.

Factors of the constant term -30: $\pm 1, \pm 2, \pm 3, \pm 5, \pm 6, \pm 10, \pm 15, \pm 30$

Factors of the leading coefficient 1: ± 1

Possible rational roots: $\pm 1, \pm 2, \pm 3, \pm 5, \pm 6, \pm 10, \pm 15, \pm 30$

Because the width must be positive, the possible roots are 1, 2, 3, 5, 6, 10, 15, and 30. Test the possible roots in $x^3 + x^2 - x - 30 = 0$ until you find the one that satisfies the equation.

Test 1.

$1^3 + 1^2 - 2(1) - 30 \stackrel{?}{=} 0$

$1 + 1 - 2 - 30 \stackrel{?}{=} 0$

$-30 = 0$ ✗

Test 2.

$2^3 + 2^2 - 2(2) - 30 \stackrel{?}{=} 0$

$8 + 4 - 4 - 30 \stackrel{?}{=} 0$

$-22 = 0$ ✗

Test 3.

$3^3 + 3^2 - 2(3) - 30 \stackrel{?}{=} 0$

$27 + 9 - 6 - 30 \stackrel{?}{=} 0$

$0 = 0$ ✔

STEP 3 Solve the problem.

The width x is 3 inches. The length is $3 + 2 = 5$ inches. The height is $3 - 1 = 2$ inches.

CHECK The volume of the dish is $V = \ell wh = 5(3)(2) = 30$ in.³. ✔

GOT TO KNOW!

Rational Zeros Theorem

The **Rational Zeros Theorem** is used to find all of the possible rational zeros of a polynomial function. If the polynomial function has integer coefficients, then every rational zero has this form.

$\dfrac{p}{q}$ ← a factor of the constant term

← a factor of the leading coefficient

Roots and Complex Conjugates

Irrational Conjugates

Recall the formula for the difference of two squares: $(a + b)(a - b) = a^2 - b^2$. There is no middle term in the product. This also is true when the value of b is an irrational number.

The **conjugate** of the irrational number $a + \sqrt{c}$ is $a - \sqrt{c}$, and the conjugate of $a - \sqrt{c}$ is $a + \sqrt{c}$.

SEARCH

To see step-by-step videos of these problems, enter the page number into the SWadvantage.com Search Bar.

EXAMPLE 1

Multiply $(x + \sqrt{7})(x - \sqrt{7})$.

METHOD 1

Expand.

Use FOIL.

$$(x + \sqrt{7})(x - \sqrt{7}) = x^2 - x\sqrt{7} + x\sqrt{7} + \sqrt{7} \cdot (-\sqrt{7})$$

Multiply $\sqrt{7} \cdot (-\sqrt{7})$.

$$= x^2 + x\sqrt{7} - x\sqrt{7} - 7$$

Combine like terms.

$$= x^2 - 7$$

METHOD 2

Use the formula for the difference of two squares.

$$(a + b)(a - b) = a^2 - b^2$$

Substitute x for a and $\sqrt{7}$ for b.

$$(x + \sqrt{7})(x - \sqrt{7}) = x^2 - (\sqrt{7})^2$$

Multiply.

$$= x^2 - 7$$

EXAMPLE 2

a. Solve $x^2 - 23 = 0$.

Factor the difference of two squares.

$$x^2 - 23 = (x + \sqrt{23})(x - \sqrt{23})$$

Use the Zero-Product Property.

$$x + \sqrt{23} = 0 \text{ or } x - \sqrt{23} = 0$$

Solve.

$$x = -\sqrt{23} \text{ or } x = \sqrt{23}$$

b. Solve $9x^2 - 48 = 0$.

Factor the difference of two squares.

$$9x^2 - 48 = (3x + \sqrt{48})(3x - \sqrt{48})$$

Use the Zero-Product Property.

$$3x + \sqrt{48} = 0 \text{ or } 3x - \sqrt{48} = 0$$

Simplify the square root.

$$3x + 4\sqrt{3} = 0 \text{ or } 3x - 4\sqrt{3} = 0$$

Isolate the variable term.

$$3x = -4\sqrt{3} \text{ or } 3x = 4\sqrt{3}$$

Divide both sides by 3 to solve for x.

$$x = -\frac{4}{3}\sqrt{3} \text{ or } x = \frac{4}{3}\sqrt{3}$$

CHECK Substitute the possible solutions into $9x^2 - 48 = 0$.

$$9\left(-\frac{4}{3}\sqrt{3}\right)^2 - 48 \overset{?}{=} 0 \qquad 9\left(\frac{4}{3}\sqrt{3}\right)^2 - 48 \overset{?}{=} 0$$

$$9\left(\frac{16}{9}\right)(3) - 48 \overset{?}{=} 0 \qquad 9\left(\frac{16}{9}\right)(3) - 48 \overset{?}{=} 0$$

$$48 - 48 = 0 \checkmark \qquad 48 - 48 = 0 \checkmark$$

GOT TO KNOW!

The Irrational Zeros Theorem

If the polynomial function $f(x)$ has rational coefficients and has a zero of the form $x = a + b\sqrt{c}$, where $\sqrt{c}$ is irrational and a and b are rational, then $x = a - b\sqrt{c}$ is also a zero.

In other words, if the coefficients of a polynomial function are rational, and an irrational zero is found, then its conjugate must also be a zero.

Complex Conjugates

The **complex conjugate** of the number $a + bi$ is $a - bi$, and vice versa.

The product of complex conjugates $a + bi$ and $a - bi$ is shown below.

$$(a + bi)(a - bi) = a^2 - abi + abi - (bi)^2$$
$$= a^2 \quad + 0 \quad - b^2i^2$$
$$= a^2 \quad\quad - b^2(-1) = a^2 + b^2$$

If a complex number is a root of a polynomial equation, then its complex conjugate is also a root of the equation.

Watch Out

Remember, i represents $\sqrt{-1}$, so $i^2 = -1$.

Need More HELP

For more help with complex numbers, go to *The Symbol* i in *Advanced Algebra* (p. 1894).

 **EXAMPLE 3**

Solve $x^2 + 25 = 0$.

Factor the sum of two squares.	$x^2 + 25 = (x + 5i)(x - 5i)$
Use the Zero-Product Property.	$x + 5i = 0$ or $x - 5i = 0$
Solve.	$x = -5i$ or $x = 5i$

EXAMPLE 4

Find an equation that has $3 - 2i$ as a root.

If the equation has $3 - 2i$ as a root, then the complex conjugate $3 + 2i$ is also a root.

	$x = 3 - 2i$ or $x = 3 + 2i$
Get 0 on one side of the equations.	$x - (3 - 2i) = 0$ or $x - (3 + 2i) = 0$
Simplify.	$x - 3 + 2i = 0$ or $x - 3 - 2i = 0$
Use the Zero-Product Property.	$(x - 3 + 2i)(x - 3 - 2i) = 0$
Substitute a for $x - 3$ temporarily.	$(a + 2i)(a - 2i) = 0$
This is the difference of two squares.	$a^2 - (2i)^2 = 0$
	$a^2 - 4i^2 = 0$
$i^2 = -1$	$a^2 + 4 = 0$
Return $x - 3$ to the equation.	$(x - 3)^2 + 4 = 0$
Expand the square.	$x^2 - 6x + 9 + 4 = 0$
Add.	$x^2 - 6x + 13 = 0$

GOT TO KNOW!

Complex Conjugates

If a polynomial equation has a complex root $a + bi$, then its conjugate $a - bi$ is also a root of the equation.

The Fundamental Theorem of Algebra

Multiplicity

The polynomial equation $x^3 - 2x^2 + x = 0$ can be factored as $x(x - 1)(x - 1) = 0$. By the Zero-Product Property, the solutions are $x = 0$, $x = 1$, and $x = 1$ again. The value 1 appears more than once, so it is a **repeated solution**. There are only two distinct solutions, 0 and 1.

In the example above, the root 1 is called a *multiple root*. The binomial $(x - 1)$ is a factor two times. So the multiplicity of the root is 2. The **multiplicity** of a root r is the number of times that $(x - r)$ is a factor of *the equation*.

When a root has *even* multiplicity, the graph of the polynomial equation touches, but does not cross, the x-axis at the root. It reverses direction.

When a root has *odd* multiplicity, the graph of the polynomial function crosses the x-axis at the root. It may appear to flatten, or decrease in slope, at the root, but it continues in the same direction after crossing the x-axis.

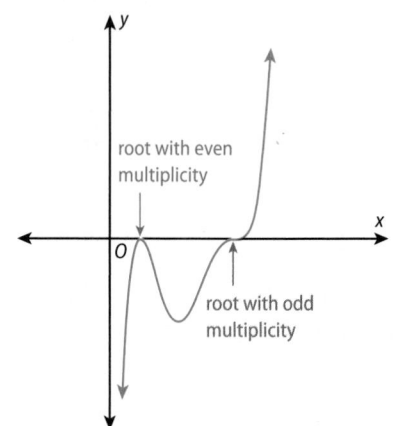

Ways to REMEMBER

In the movie *Multiplicity*, the main character, Doug Kinney, clones copies of himself.

The total number of Doug Kinneys was his multiplicity.

SEARCH

To see step-by-step videos of these problems, enter the page number into the SWadvantage.com Search Bar.

EXAMPLE 1

Solve. Find the multiplicity of each root of the equation. Then graph the function.

a. $x^2 + 8x + 16 = 0$

Factor the perfect square trinomial.	$(x + 4)(x + 4) = 0$
Use the Zero-Product Property.	$x + 4 = 0$ or $x + 4 = 0$
Solve for x.	$x = -4$ or $x = -4$

The root $x = -4$ has multiplicity 2, which is even.

The degree of the polynomial is 2, so this is the only root.

Graph the function.

The graph touches but does not cross the x-axis at $x = -4$. It reverses direction.

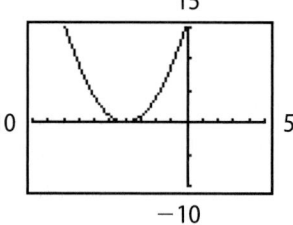

b. $2x^5 - 12x^4 + 18x^3 = 0$

Factor out the GCF.	$2x^3(x^2 - 6x + 9) = 0$
Factor the perfect square trinomial.	$2x^3(x - 3)^2 = 0$
Use the Zero-Product Property.	$2x^3 = 0$ or $(x - 3)^2 = 0$
Solve for x.	$x = 0$ or $x = 3$

The factor x^3 is raised to the third power, so the root $x = 0$ has multiplicity 3, which is odd.

The factor $(x - 3)^2$ is squared, so the root $x = 3$ has multiplicity 2, which is even.

Because $3 + 2 = 5$ and the degree of the polynomial is 5, these are the only roots.

Graph the function.

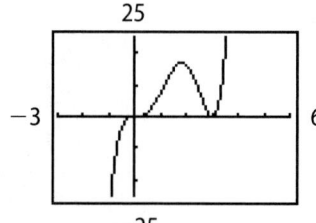

The graph crosses the x-axis at $x = 0$. It touches the axis and reverses direction at $x = 3$.

The Fundamental Theorem of Algebra

If $P(x)$ is a polynomial of degree n, then the equation $P(x) = 0$ has at least one root, which is a complex number.

The Fundamental Theorem of Algebra deals with distinct roots. The corollary below takes multiplicities into account.

Corollary to the Fundamental Theorem of Algebra

If $P(x)$ is a polynomial of degree n, then the equation $P(x) = 0$ has exactly n complex roots when multiplicities are taken into account.

EXAMPLE 2

How many roots does each equation have?

a. $x^3 + 2x^2 + 9x + 18 = 0$

The degree is 3, so there are 3 complex roots, which may not be distinct.

b. $x^4 - 2x^3 + 17x^2 - 32x + 16 = 0$

The degree is 4, so there are 4 complex roots, which may not be distinct.

EXAMPLE 3

Find all the roots of the equation $x^2 - 4x + 5 = 0$.

The equation is quadratic.

The discriminant, $b^2 - 4ac$ is $(-4)^2 - 4(1)(5) = 16 - 20 = -4$, so the equation has no real roots. It must have 2 imaginary roots that are complex conjugates.

Use the quadratic formula. $\dfrac{-b \pm \sqrt{b^2 - 4ac}}{2a} \rightarrow \dfrac{-(-4) \pm \sqrt{-4}}{2} = \dfrac{4 \pm 2i}{2} = 2 \pm i$

The roots are $2 + i$ and $2 - i$.

Because the roots are conjugates, you only need to check one root.

CHECK

$$x^2 \quad - \quad 4x \quad + 5 = 0$$

Substitute $2 + i$ for x. $\qquad (2 + i)^2 - 4(2 + i) + 5 \stackrel{?}{=} 0$

$$4 + 4i + i^2 - 8 - 4i + 5 \stackrel{?}{=} 0$$

$$4 - 1 - 8 + 5 \stackrel{?}{=} 0$$

$$0 = 0 ✔$$

Need More HELP?

For help with factoring, go to *Factoring to Solve Quadratics* on page 1702.

The Fundamental Theorem of Algebra and Its Corollary

Theorem: If $P(x)$ is a polynomial of degree n, then the equation $P(x) = 0$ has at least one root, which is complex.

Corollary: If $P(x)$ is a polynomial of degree n, then the equation $P(x) = 0$ has exactly n roots when multiplicities are taken into account.

Remainders and Function Values

You know that if a is a zero of a polynomial function $P(x)$, then $x - a$ is a factor of the polynomial, with no remainder when you divide. Suppose a is a number that might *not* be a zero.

Consider $P(x) = x^2 - 16$ when $x = 5$.

$$P(5) = 5^2 - 16$$
$$= 25 - 16$$
$$= 9.$$

Now divide $P(x)$ by $x - 5$.

Use $0x$ for the missing x term.
Multiply the partial quotient and the binomial, and subtract.

$$\begin{array}{r} x + 5 \\ x - 5 \overline{)\, x^2 + 0x - 16} \\ \underline{x^2 - 5x } \\ 5x - 16 \\ \underline{5x - 25} \\ \end{array}$$

remainder   9

The remainder when $P(x)$ is divided by $x - 5$ is the same as the value of $P(5)$.

The Remainder Theorem

The **Remainder Theorem** allows you to use long division or synthetic division to evaluate polynomial functions.

> If a polynomial function $P(x)$ is divided by $x - a$, then the remainder r is equal to $P(a)$.

 **EXAMPLE** 1

Need More
HELP?
For help with synthetic division, go to *Synthetic Division* on page 1678.

a. Evaluate $x^2 + 5x + 10$ for $x = -2$.

To evaluate, use synthetic division to find the remainder when $x^2 + 5x + 10$ is divided by $x + 2$.

	x^2	x	constant
$-2\rfloor$	1	5	10
		-2	-6
	1	3	$\boxed{4}$ remainder

The remainder is 4, so for $f(x) = x^2 + 5x + 10$, $f(-2) = 4$.

CHECK

$$f(x) = x^2 + 5x + 10$$
$$f(-2) \stackrel{?}{=} (-2)^2 + 5(-2) + 10$$
$$\stackrel{?}{=} 4 - 10 + 10$$
$$= 4 ✔$$

b. Evaluate $2x^5 - 15x^4 - x^3 - 12x^2 + 45x - 200$ for $x = 8$.

To evaluate, use synthetic division to find the remainder when the function is divided by $x - 8$.

$8\rfloor$	2	-15	-1	-12	45	-200
		16	8	56	352	3,176
	2	1	7	44	397	$\boxed{2,976}$ remainder

The remainder is 2,976, so for $f(x) = 2x^5 - 15x^4 - x^3 - 12x^2 + 45x - 200$, $f(8) = 2,976$.

You can check by substituting and evaluating as in part (a).

Remember that if the remainder is 0 when a polynomial function $P(x)$ is divided by $x - a$, then $P(a) = 0$, and a is a zero of the function. You can use long division or synthetic division to find $P(a)$. If $P(a) = 0$, then a is a zero of the polynomial function.

EXAMPLE 2

Determine whether the given value is a zero of the function.

a. $2; f(x) = -3x^4 + 1.5x^3 - x^2 + 12x + 16$

If $x = 2$ is a zero of $f(x)$, then the remainder will be 0 when $f(x)$ is divided by $x - 2$.

Use synthetic division to find the remainder.

2 $\rfloor$	-3	1.5	-1	12	16	
		-6	-9	-20	-16	
	-3	-4.5	-10	-8	$\lfloor 0$	remainder

The remainder is 0, so 2 is a zero of $f(x) = -3x^4 + 1.5x^3 - x^2 + 12x + 16$.

b. $-3; f(x) = -x^5 + 5x^3 - 2x^2 - 18x + 144$

If $x = -3$ is a zero of $f(x)$, then the remainder will be 0 when $f(x)$ is divided by $x + 3$.

Use synthetic division to find the remainder.

-3 $\rfloor$	-1	0	5	-2	-18	144	
		3	-9	12	-30	144	
	-1	3	-4	10	-48	$\lfloor 288$	remainder

The remainder is not 0, so -3 is not a zero of $f(x) = -x^5 + 5x^3 - 2x^2 - 18x + 144$.

EXAMPLE 3

The dimensions of a cube with side length x in. are increased to form a new rectangular prism. The length is doubled, the width is increased by 2 in., and the height is increased by 3 in. The volume of the new prism is 336 in.^{3}. Can the cube have a length of 4 in.?

STEP 1 Write an equation to find x, the length of the cube.

The volume of the new prism is $(2x)(x + 2)(x + 3) = 336$, or $2x^3 + 10x^2 + 12x = 336$.

So the equation $2x^3 + 10x^2 + 12x - 336 = 0$ can be used to find x, the length of the cube.

STEP 2 Find the value of the polynomial when $x = 4$.

If $x = 4$ is a solution of the equation, then the remainder will be 0 when $f(x)$ is divided by $x - 4$.

Use synthetic division to find the remainder.

4 $\rfloor$	2	10	12	-336	
		8	72	336	
	2	18	84	$\lfloor 0$	remainder

The remainder is 0, so 4 is a solution of $2x^3 + 10x^2 + 12x - 336 = 0$.

The cube can have a length of 4 in.

You can check by substituting the result into the conditions of the problem.

Watch Out !

The Rational Zeros Theorem only applies to polynomials with integer coefficients. So you cannot use that theorem on the polynomial function in Example 2(a). Doing so will give the incorrect result that 2 is not a possible zero.

SEARCH

To see step-by-step videos of these problems, enter the page number into the SWadvantage.com Search Bar.

The Factor Theorem

Suppose the remainder is 0 when a polynomial $P(x)$ is divided by $x - a$. Then:

$$P(x) = \text{quotient} + \text{remainder}$$
$$= (x - a)q(x) + \frac{0}{x - a}$$
$$= (x - a)q(x)$$

The **Factor Theorem** follows from the Remainder Theorem.

    A polynomial $P(x)$ has a factor of $x - a$ if and only if $P(a) = 0$.

To determine whether a binomial of the form $x - a$ is a factor of a polynomial $P(x)$, you can use synthetic division to test whether $P(a) = 0$ by checking whether the remainder is 0.

SEARCH

To see step-by-step videos of these problems, enter the page number into the SWadvantage.com Search Bar.

EXAMPLE 4

Determine whether the binomial is a factor of the polynomial $P(x)$.

a. $x - 4$; $P(x) = x^3 + 4x^2 - 35x + 12$

For $x - 4$ to be a factor of $P(x)$, then the quotient must have a remainder of 0.

Use synthetic division to find the remainder.

4	1	4	-35	12
		4	32	-12
	1	8	-3	$\boxed{0}$ remainder

The remainder is 0, so $x - 4$ is a factor of $P(x) = x^3 + 4x^2 - 35x + 12$.

b. $x - \frac{1}{2}$; $P(x) = 6x^3 - 3x^2 - 10x + 8$

For $x - \frac{1}{2}$ to be a factor of $P(x)$, then the quotient must have a remainder of 0.

Use synthetic division to find the remainder.

$\frac{1}{2}$	6	-3	-10	8
		3	0	-5
	6	0	-10	$\boxed{3}$ remainder

The remainder is 3, so $x - \frac{1}{2}$ is not a factor of $P(x) = 6x^3 - 3x^2 - 10x + 8$.

c. $x + 2.5$; $P(x) = 4x^4 + 8x^3 - 5x^2 - 2x - 5$

For $x + 2.5$ to be a factor of $P(x)$, then $P(-2.5)$ must equal 0.

Use synthetic division to find the remainder.

-2.5	4	8	-5	-2	-5
		-10	5	0	5
	4	-2	0	-2	$\boxed{0}$ remainder

The remainder is 0, so $x + 2.5$ is a factor of $P(x) = 4x^4 + 8x^3 - 5x^2 - 2x - 5$.

EXAMPLE 5

Two zeros of the function $f(x) = x^4 - x^3 + 7x^2 - 9x - 18$ are 2 and -1. Factor the polynomial completely.

STEP 1 Determine the known factors.

Because 2 is a zero, $x - 2$ is a factor. Because -1 is a zero, $x + 1$ is a factor.

STEP 2 Use synthetic division to divide by one known factor.

Choose the factor $x - 2$.

	x^4	x^3	x^2	x	constant
2⌋	1	-1	7	-9	-18
		2	2	18	18
	1	1	9	9	⌊0 remainder

The remainder is 0, so 2 is verified as a zero, and $x - 2$ is a factor.

Read the remaining factor from the synthetic division table.

1	1	9	9
x^3	x^2	x	constant

The remaining factor is $x^3 + x^2 + 9x + 9$.

Rewrite the function, using the two factors: $f(x) = (x - 2)(x^3 + x^2 + 9x + 9)$

STEP 3 Use synthetic division to divide $x^3 + x^2 + 9x + 9$ by the other known factor, $x + 1$.

	x^3	x^2	x	constant
-1⌋	1	1	9	9
		-1	0	-9
	1	0	9	⌊0 remainder

The remainder is 0, so -1 is verified as a zero, and $x + 1$ is a factor.

Read the remaining factor from the synthetic division table.

1	0	9
x^2	x	constant

The remaining factor is $x^2 + 9$.

Rewrite the function, using the three factors: $f(x) = (x - 2)(x + 1)(x^2 + 9)$

STEP 4 Set $x^2 + 9$ equal to 0 and factor to find the complex roots.

$$x^2 + 9 = 0$$
$$x^2 = -9$$
$$x = \pm 3i$$

The factored form of the polynomial function is $f(x) = (x - 2)(x + 1)(x + 3i)(x - 3i)$.

GOT TO KNOW!

Zeros, Roots, Solutions

You can find zeros, roots, or solutions, depending on whether the polynomial is written as a function or as an equation.

You can find factors, given any of the forms above, or find one of the forms above when given factors.

GOT TO KNOW!

The Remainder Theorem

If a polynomial function $P(x)$ is divided by $x - a$, then the remainder r is equal to $P(a)$.

The Factor Theorem

A polynomial $P(x)$ has a factor of $x - a$ if and only if $P(a) = 0$.

Real and Imaginary Zeros

Sign Changes in Polynomial Functions

The number of sign changes in a polynomial function can help you determine the number of positive real zeros.

EXAMPLE 1

Determine the number of sign changes in each polynomial function.
Compare the sign of each term with the sign of the one before it.

a. $f(x) = -x^3 + 2x^2 + 7x - 10$

2 sign changes

b. $f(x) = x^4 + 5x^2 + 7$

no sign changes

c. $f(x) = x^5 + 4x^3 - 3x^2 + x - 1$

3 sign changes

In 1637, mathematician René Descartes, who also developed the Cartesian plane, discovered a rule about sign changes in polynomial functions.

Positive Real Zeros

Descartes's Rule of Signs for Positive Real Zeros
The number of positive real zeros of the polynomial function $P(x)$ is either • equal to the number of sign changes in $P(x)$ or • less than the number of sign changes in $P(x)$ by an even number.

Note that a zero of multiplicity m is counted m times when this rule is applied.

GOT TO KNOW!

Positive Real Zeros

The table shows the number of positive real zeros of a polynomial function, based on the number of sign changes in the function.

Sign Changes	Zeros
0	0
1	1
2	2 or 0
3	3 or 1
4	4, 2, or 0
5	5, 3, or 1
6	6, 4, 2, or 0
7	7, 5, 3, or 1

Count down by two from the number of sign changes.

EXAMPLE 2

Determine the number of positive real zeros.

a. $f(x) = 3x^5 - 8x^2 + 3x + 60$

There are 2 sign changes.

The number of positive real zeros is equal to 2 or is less than 2 by an even number. So the number of positive real zeros is 2 or 2 – 2 = 0. The number of positive real zeros is 2 or 0.

b. $f(x) = 2 - x - 2x^3 - 3x^5 + 5x^2 + 6x^4$

Use the Commutative Property to arrange the polynomial terms in decreasing order.

$f(x) = -3x^5 + 6x^4 - 2x^3 + 5x^2 - x + 2$

There are 5 sign changes.

The number of positive real zeros is equal to 5 or is less than 5 by an even number. So the number of zeros is 5, 5 − 2 = 3, or 5 − 4 = 1. The number of positive real zeros is 5, 3, or 1.

When the number of sign changes is odd, there must be at least one positive real zero.

Negative Real Zeros

Descartes's Rule of Signs for Negative Real Zeros
The number of negative real zeros of the polynomial function $P(x)$ is either • equal to the number of sign changes in $P(-x)$ or • less than the number of sign changes in $P(-x)$ by an even number.

EXAMPLE 3

Determine the number of negative real zeros for the functions in Example 2.

a. $f(x) = 3x^5 - 8x^2 + 3x + 60$

Replace x with $-x$. $f(-x) = 3(-x)^5 - 8(-x)^2 + 3(-x) + 60$

Simplify. $= -3x^5 - 8x^2 - 3x + 60$

Count the number of sign changes. There is 1 sign change.

The number of negative real zeros is equal to 1.

b. $f(x) = 2 - x - 2x^3 - 3x^5 + 5x^2 + 6x^4$

Write the terms in decreasing order: $f(x) = -3x^5 + 6x^4 - 2x^3 + 5x^2 - x + 2$

Replace x with $-x$. $f(-x) = -3(-x)^5 + 6(-x)^4 - 2(-x)^3 + 5(-x)^2 - (-x) + 2$

Simplify. $= 3x^5 + 6x^4 + 2x^3 + 5x^2 + x + 2$

Count the number of sign changes. There are no sign changes.

There are no negative real zeros.

> **Need More**
> **HELP?**
> When you go from $f(x)$ to $f(-x)$, the signs of the even-powered terms stay the same, and the signs of the odd-powered terms reverse.

EXAMPLE 4

Determine the numbers of positive real zeros, negative real zeros, and nonreal complex zeros for the function $f(x) = x^5 + 7x^4 + 10x^3 - 4x^2 + 3x - 8$.

STEP 1   Write the signs of each term of $f(x)$ and of $f(-x)$. Then find the numbers of sign changes and the numbers of positive and negative real zeros.

$f(x) = x^5 + 7x^4 + 10x^3 - 4x^2 + 3x - 8$ $f(-x) = -x^5 + 7x^4 - 10x^3 - 4x^2 - 3x - 8$
$\quad\quad\ +\ \ \ +\ \ \ +\ \ -\ \ \ +\ \ -$ $\quad\quad\quad\ -\ \ \ \ +\ \ \ -\ \ \ -\ \ \ -\ \ -$

There are 3 sign changes.   There are 2 sign changes.

There are 3 or 1 positive real zeros.   There are 2 or 0 negative real zeros.

STEP 2   Make a table to show all possible numbers of nonreal complex zeros.

The degree is 5, so the total number of zeros is 5.

Positive Real Zeros (3 or 1)	Negative Real Zeros (2 or 0)	Nonreal Complex Zeros	Total
3	2	0	5
3	0	2	5
1	2	2	5
1	0	4	5

STEP 3   Make a graph to determine which of the possible combinations is true for $f(x)$.

There are 2 negative real zeros and 1 positive. So there are 2 nonreal complex zeros.

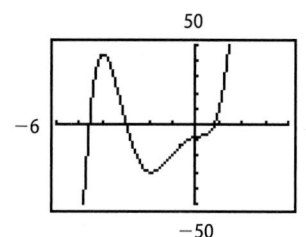

SOUTHWESTERN

Irrational Zero Pairs

Just like complex zeros, irrational zeros come in pairs.

The Irrational Zeros Theorem

If a polynomial function $P(x)$ with rational coefficients has a zero of the form $x = a + b\sqrt{c}$, then it also has a zero of the form $x = a - b\sqrt{c}$.

EXAMPLE 5

Need More
HELP ?

Remember,

$$\frac{3 - \sqrt{11}}{4} = \frac{3}{4} - \frac{\sqrt{11}}{4}$$

$$\frac{3 + \sqrt{11}}{4} = \frac{3}{4} + \frac{\sqrt{11}}{4}$$

For more help with irrational conjugates, go to *Roots and Complex Conjugates* on page 1640.

One zero of a polynomial function is given. What is another zero of the function?

a. $3 + \sqrt{5}$ 　　　　**b.** $-\sqrt{5}$ 　　　　**c.** $\sqrt{17} - 4$ 　　　　**d.** $\dfrac{3 - \sqrt{11}}{4}$

$3 - \sqrt{5}$ is a zero. 　　$\sqrt{5}$ is a zero. 　　$-\sqrt{17} - 4$ is a zero. 　　$\dfrac{3 + \sqrt{11}}{4}$ is a zero.

The product of the irrational zeros will form a sum or difference of two squares.

EXAMPLE 6

Find the polynomial function of least degree that has $2 - 5\sqrt{3}$ as a zero.

If $2 - 5\sqrt{3}$ is a zero, then $2 + 5\sqrt{3}$ is a zero. So $x - (2 - 5\sqrt{3})$ and $x - (2 + 5\sqrt{3})$ are factors.

Simplify the factors. 　　　　　　　　　$x - 2 + 5\sqrt{3}$ and $x - 2 - 5\sqrt{3}$

Write the product. 　　　　　　　　　$(x - 2 + 5\sqrt{3})(x - 2 - 5\sqrt{3})$

Use the formula for the difference 　　　　　$(a + b)(a - b) = a^2 - b^2$
of two squares.

Substitute $x - 2$ for a and $5\sqrt{3}$ for b. 　$(x - 2 + 5\sqrt{3})(x - 2 - 5\sqrt{3}) = (x - 2)^2 - (5\sqrt{3})^2$

Multiply. 　　　　　　　　　　　　　　$= x^2 - 4x + 4 - 5^2(3)$

Simplify. 　　　　　　　　　　　　　　$= x^2 - 4x + 4 - 75$

　　　　　　　　　　　　　　　　　　$= x^2 - 4x - 71$

CHECK Substitute into the quadratic formula.

$a = 1, b = -4,$ and $c = -71$ 　　$\dfrac{-b \pm \sqrt{b^2 - 4ac}}{2a} \rightarrow \dfrac{-(-4) \pm \sqrt{(-4)^2 - 4(1)(-71)}}{2(1)}$

Simplify. 　　　　　　　　　　　　　　　　$= \dfrac{4 \pm \sqrt{16 - (-284)}}{2} = \dfrac{4 \pm \sqrt{300}}{2}$

$\sqrt{300} = \sqrt{3 \cdot 100} = \sqrt{100} \cdot \sqrt{3}$ 　　　　　　　$= \dfrac{4 \pm 10\sqrt{3}}{2}$

　　　　　　　　　　　　　　　　　　　　　　$= 2 \pm 5\sqrt{3}$ ✔

The function of least degree with the given zero is $f(x) = x^2 - 4x - 71$.

EXAMPLE 7

Find the polynomial function of least degree that has 5, $-1 + \sqrt{3}$, and $4 - 3\sqrt{2}$ as zeros.

The conjugate of each irrational zero is also a zero. So the polynomial should be of degree 5. One factor is $x - 5$.

If $-1 + \sqrt{3}$ is a zero, then $-1 - \sqrt{3}$ is a zero. So, two factors are $x - (-1 + \sqrt{3})$ and $x - (-1 - \sqrt{3})$.

Simplify the factors. $\quad x + 1 - \sqrt{3}$ and $x + 1 + \sqrt{3}$

Write the product. $\quad (x + 1 - \sqrt{3})(x + 1 + \sqrt{3})$

If $4 - 3\sqrt{2}$ is a zero, then $4 + 3\sqrt{2}$ is a zero. So, two factors are $x - (4 - 3\sqrt{2})$ and $x - (4 + 3\sqrt{2})$.

Simplify the factors. $\quad x - 4 + 3\sqrt{2}$ and $x - 4 - 3\sqrt{2}$

Write the product. $\quad (x - 4 + 3\sqrt{2})(x - 4 - 3\sqrt{2})$

Write the product of all factors. $\quad (x - 5)(x + 1 - \sqrt{3})(x + 1 + \sqrt{3})(x - 4 + 3\sqrt{2})(x - 4 - 3\sqrt{2})$

Use the formula $(a + b)(a - b) = a^2 - b^2$ for the irrational zero pairs.

Substitute for a and b. $\quad (x - 5)[(x + 1)^2 - (\sqrt{3})^2][(x - 4)^2 - (3\sqrt{2})^2]$

Multiply. $\quad (x - 5)(x^2 + 2x + 1 - 3)(x^2 - 8x + 16 - 9(2))$

Simplify. $\quad (x - 5)(x^2 + 2x - 2)(x^2 - 8x - 2)$

Multiply the trinomials. $\quad (x - 5)(x^4 - 6x^3 - 20x^2 + 12x + 4)$

Multiply the binomial and the polynomial. $\quad x^5 - 11x^4 + 10x^3 + 112x^2 - 56x - 20$

To check, use a calculator. Enter the polynomial in **Y1**. Store each zero in **X**. Use the exact calculator value for each zero. Then find the value of **Y1** for each stored zero.

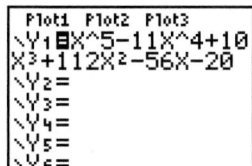

Each value of Y1 is 0, so the polynomial function has the given zeros.

SEARCH
To see step-by-step videos of these problems, enter the page number into the SWadvantage.com Search Bar.

Need More HELP?
For more help finding products of polynomials, go to *Multiplying Polynomials* (p. 1608).

GOT TO KNOW!

Descartes's Rule of Signs

The number of positive real zeros of $P(x)$ is either

- equal to the number of sign changes in $P(x)$ **or**
- less than the number of sign changes in $P(x)$ by an even number.

The number of negative real zeros of $P(x)$ is either

- equal to the number of sign changes in $P(-x)$ **or**
- less than the number of sign changes in $P(-x)$ by an even number.

The Irrational Zeros Theorem

If $P(x)$ has a zero of the form $a + b\sqrt{c}$, it also has a zero of the form $a - b\sqrt{c}$.

Approximating Real Zeros

Approximating Zeros by Using a Table

Need More
HELP ?

For more help with determining the number of zeros by the number of sign changes and Descartes's Rule, go to *Real and Imaginary Zeros* (p. 1648).

SEARCH

To see step-by-step videos of these problems, enter the page number into the SWadvantage.com Search Bar.

EXAMPLE

Approximate the zero or zeros of the polynomial function $f(x) = x^3 - 3x^2 - 2x - 7$ to the nearest hundredth.

STEP 1 Determine the number of positive and negative real roots.

Use Descartes's Rule of Signs.

$f(x) = x^3 - 3x^2 - 2x - 7$
1 sign change, 1 positive zero

$f(-x) = -x^3 - 3x^2 + 2x - 7$
2 sign changes, 2 or 0 negative zeros

STEP 2 Graph the function.

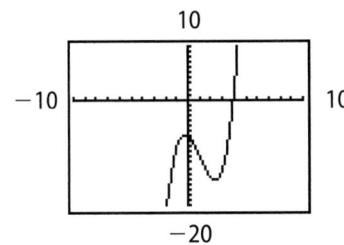

The graph indicates that there is only one real zero, at about 4.

STEP 3 Use the calculator's **TABLE** function to make a table of values. Press **2nd** **WINDOW**, and set **TblStart=0** and the step value △**Tbl=1.** Press **2nd** **GRAPH** to see the table of values.

X	Y₁	
0	-7	
1	-11	
2	-15	
3	-13	
4	1	
5	33	
6	89	

X=4

The closest value of x to the zero is 4.

The sign changes just before x reaches 4.

STEP 4 Repeat Step 3, but use **TblStart=3.5** and set the step value △**Tbl=0.1.**

X	Y₁	
3.5	-7.875	
3.6	-6.424	
3.7	-4.817	
3.8	-3.048	
3.9	-1.111	
4	1	
4.1	3.291	

X=4

The sign changes between $x = 3.9$ and $x = 4$.

STEP 5 Repeat Step 3, but use **TblStart=3.9** and set the step value △**Tbl=0.01.**

X	Y₁	
3.9	-1.111	
3.91	-.9078	
3.92	-.7029	
3.93	-.4962	
3.94	-.2878	
3.95	-.0776	
3.96	.13434	

X=3.95

Because -0.0776 is closer to 0 than 0.13434, 3.95 is closer to the zero than 3.96 is.

The zero of the function, to the nearest hundredth, is 3.95.

Approximating Zeros by Graphing

EXAMPLE 2

Approximate the zero or zeros of the polynomial function $f(x) = x^6 - 5x^3 + 7x - 10$ to the nearest hundredth.

STEP 1 Determine the number of positive and negative real roots.

Use Descartes's Rule of Signs.

$f(x) = x^6 - 5x^3 + 7x - 10$
3 sign changes, 3 or 1 positive zero

$f(-x) = x^6 + 5x^3 - 7x - 10$
1 sign change, 1 negative zero

STEP 2 Graph the function. Use TRACE and the arrow key to go as close to a zero as possible.

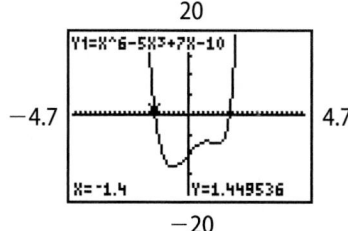

The graph indicates that there is one zero near -1.4.

STEP 3 Use the calculator's zoom function to zoom in on the zero. Press **ZOOM** and **2:ZoomIn,** and press **ENTER** twice to zoom in. Press **TRACE**, move as close to the zero as possible, and zoom in again until you have the zero to the nearest hundredth.

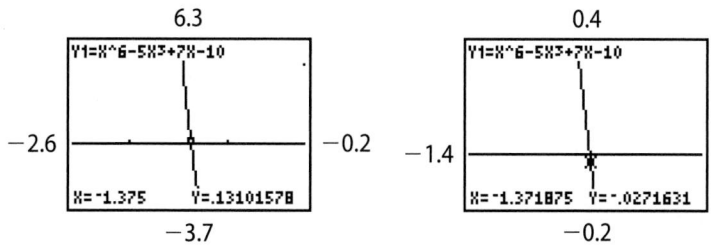

STEP 4 Using the original window, repeat Steps 2 and 3 for the other zero.

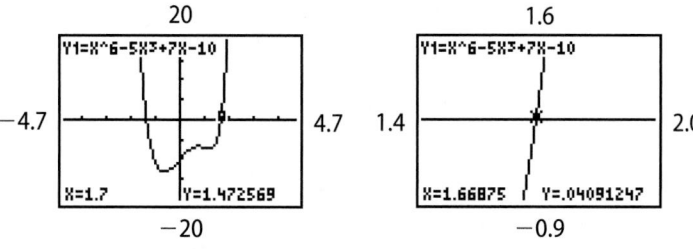

The zeros, to the nearest hundredth, are -1.37 and 1.67.

Try It This Way

You can also use the Zero function on a graphing calculator. Go to the CALC menu and choose **2:zero**.

GOT TO KNOW!

Approximating Zeros

Use a graphing calculator to graph the function.

Use the table feature to find approximate zeros. Change the settings to find more precise values.

Use the zoom and trace functions or the zero function to find more precise values on the graph.

The Behavior of a Polynomial Function

Intercepts of Polynomial Functions

You can use the intercepts to graph polynomial functions.

EXAMPLE 1

Use the intercepts to graph the function $f(x) = (x + 2)(x - 3)^2$.

STEP 1 Determine the *x*-intercepts.

The *x*-intercepts are the zeros of the function. Use the Zero-Product Property.

When $f(x) = 0$, then either $x + 2 = 0$ or $x - 3 = 0$. So $x = -2$ is one intercept, and $x = 3$ is the other intercept. Note that the zero 3 is of multiplicity 2.

STEP 2 Plot the *x*-intercepts.

Plot the points $(-2, 0)$ and $(3, 0)$.

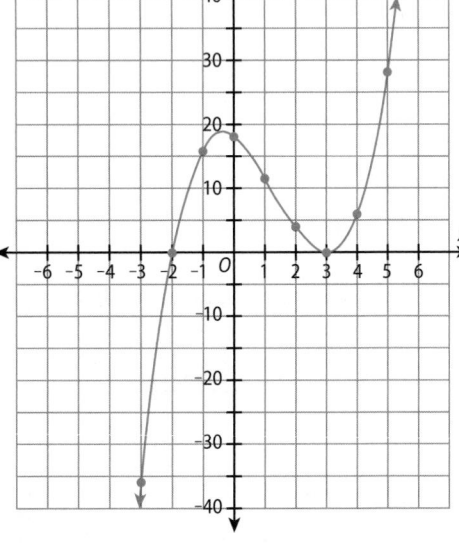

STEP 3 Find and plot points between and on both sides of the intercepts.

x	−3	−2	−1	0	1	2	3	4	5
y	−36	0	16	18	12	4	0	6	28

STEP 4 Draw a smooth curve through the points.

Turning Points of Polynomial Functions

A turning point on a graph is a point where the graph changes direction. The value of the function at a turning point is called a **local minimum** or **local maximum**.

GOT TO KNOW!

Zeros, Roots, Solutions, Intercepts, and Factors

Consider the function $P(x) = a_n x^n + a_{n-1} x^{n-1} + a_{n-2} x^{n-2} + \ldots + a_1 x + a_0$.

If $P(x) = 0$ and r is a zero of $P(x)$, these statements are equivalent.

zero	r is a zero of the function $P(x)$.
root	r is a root of the equation $P(x) = 0$.
solution	r is a solution of the equation $P(x) = 0$.
***x*-intercept**	r is an *x*-intercept of the graph of $P(x)$, and the graph passes through $(r, 0)$.
factor	$x - r$ is a factor of the polynomial $P(x)$.

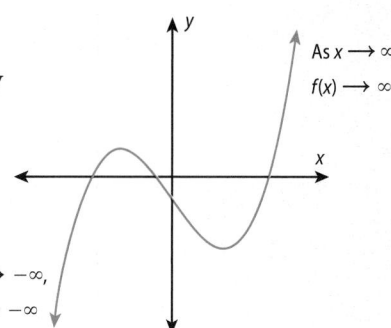

If the *y*-coordinate of a turning point is higher than the nearby points, then it is a local maximum. If the *y*-coordinate of a turning point is lower than all nearby points, then it is a local minimum.

A polynomial function of degree *n* has at most $n - 1$ turning points. If the function has *n* distinct real zeros, then it has exactly $n - 1$ turning points.

EXAMPLE 2

Graph the polynomial function $f(x) = 3x^3 + 8x^2 - 5x - 6$. For any local minima or maxima, estimate the values of *x* and of the function to the nearest hundredth.

STEP 1   Use a graphing calculator to graph the function.

STEP 2   Determine the intercepts.

The possible rational zeros, or *x*-intercepts, are ± 1, ± 2, ± 3, ± 6, $\pm\frac{1}{3}$, and $\pm\frac{2}{3}$.
Verify that the intercept points $(-3, 0)$, $\left(-\frac{2}{3}, 0\right)$, and $(1, 0)$ are on the graph.

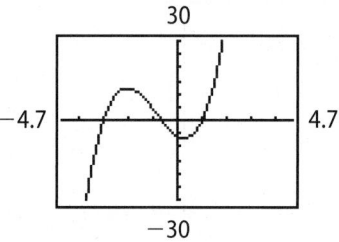

STEP 3   Determine the number of turning points.

The maximum number of turning points is $3 - 1 = 2$. There are 2 turning points, one local maximum between $x = -3$ and $x = -\frac{2}{3}$, and one local minimum between $x = -\frac{2}{3}$ and $x = 1$.

STEP 4   Use the calculator to find the first turning point.

Press 2nd CALC, choose **4:maximum,** and press ENTER. Press the left arrow key, move to the left of the "hump," and press ENTER for the left bound. Press the right arrow key, move to the right of the "hump," and press ENTER for the right bound.

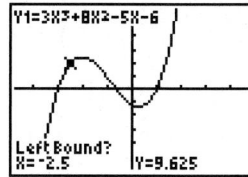   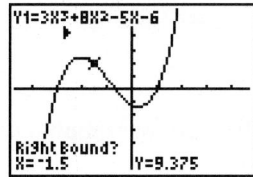

For the "guess," move anywhere between the bounds and press ENTER.

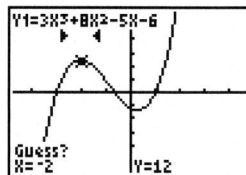   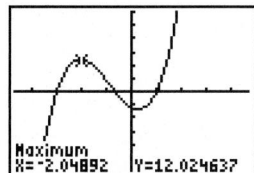

The local maximum, to the nearest hundredth, is 12.02, and is located at $x \approx -2.05$.

STEP 5   Use the calculator to find the second turning point.

To find the local minimum between $-\frac{2}{3}$ and 1, repeat the above procedure, but choose **3:minimum** instead of **4:maximum.** Use bounds to the left and right of the ∪. The local minimum, to the nearest hundredth, is -6.71, and is located at $x \approx 0.27$.

GOT TO KNOW!

Exact Values

The exact values of *x* at the turning points can be found only by using calculus.

The exact values in Example 2 are
$$x = -\frac{8}{9} \pm \frac{\sqrt{109}}{9}.$$

Ways to REMEMBER

The faces of positive even-degree functions "smile," while negative even-degree functions "frown."

End Behavior

The end behavior of the graph of a polynomial function is the direction the graph "points" as it approaches $-\infty$ on the left side of the graph and $+\infty$ on the right side of the graph.

The end behavior of a polynomial function is determined by its degree and by the sign of the leading coefficient.

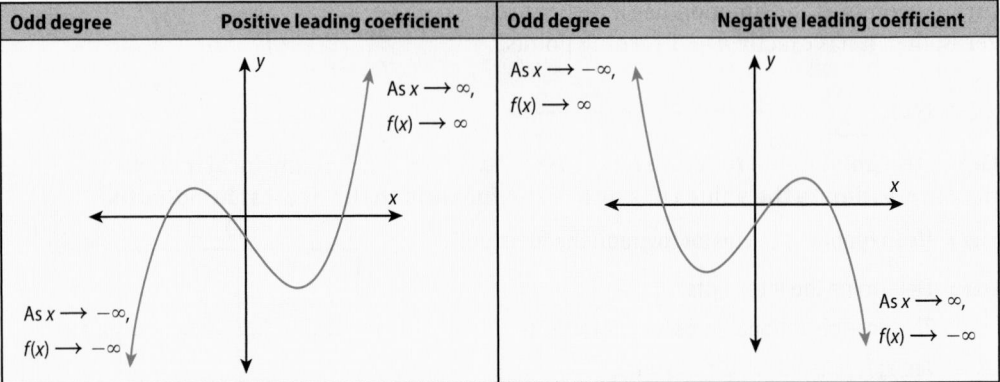

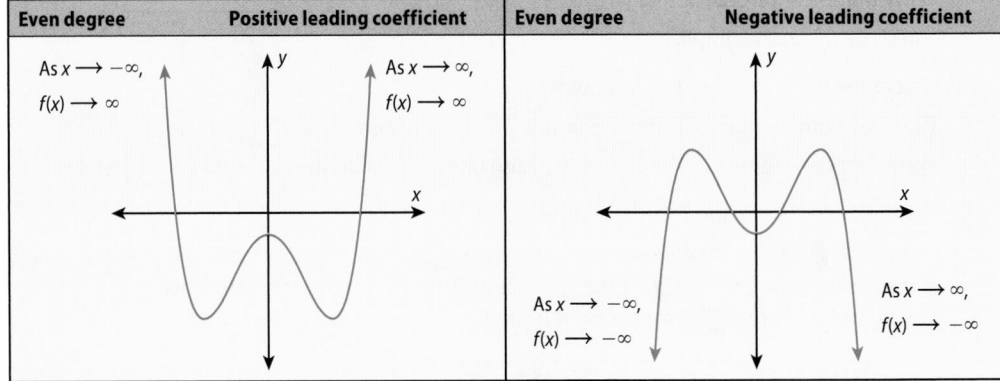

EXAMPLE 3

Describe the end behavior of each function without graphing.

a. $f(x) = -2x^7 + 4x^2 - 1$

The polynomial function has degree 7, an odd degree. The leading coefficient is negative. The graph will go from the upper left to the lower right.
As $x \to -\infty$, $f(x) \to \infty$, and as $x \to \infty$, $f(x) \to -\infty$.

b. $f(x) = (x - 2)^3(x + 10)$

The polynomial function has degree $3 + 1 = 4$, an even degree. The leading coefficient is positive. The graph will go from the upper left to the upper right.
As $x \to -\infty$, $f(x) \to \infty$, and as $x \to \infty$, $f(x) \to \infty$.

EXAMPLE 4

A sheet of cardboard 3 ft by 4.5 ft will be made into a box by cutting equal-size squares from each corner and folding up the four edges. What are the dimensions of the box with the maximum volume?

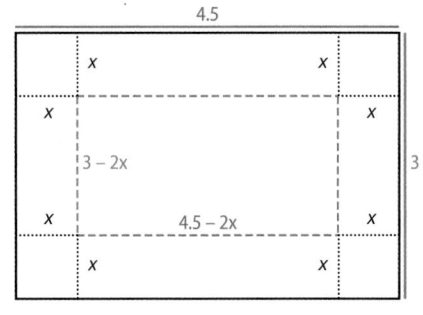

SEARCH

To see step-by-step videos of these problems, enter the page number into the SWadvantage.com Search Bar.

STEP 1 Write a polynomial function for the volume of the box.

Volume formula. $V = $ length $\ell \cdot$ width $w \cdot$ height h

Volume in terms of x. $V(x) = x(4.5 - 2x)(3 - 2x)$

STEP 2 Determine the x-intercepts of the function.

Zero-Product Property $x = 0$ or $4.5 - 2x = 0$ or $3 - 2x = 0$

Solve each equation. $x = 0$ or $x = 2.25$ or $x = 1.5$

STEP 3 Write and simplify the polynomial function to represent the problem.

$$V(x) = x(4.5 - 2x)(3 - 2x)$$

Use FOIL to multiply the binomials. $= x(13.5 - 9x - 6x + 4x^2)$

Combine like terms. $= x(13.5 - 15x + 4x^2)$

Multiply. $= 13.5x - 15x^2 + 4x^3$

Write the terms in descending order. $= 4x^3 - 15x^2 + 13.5x$

Need More HELP?

For more help with finding products of polynomials, go to *Multiplying Polynomials* in *Algebra* (p. 1608).

STEP 4 Determine the end behavior of the graph, and verify the number of positive real roots.

The function is cubic (odd) with a positive leading coefficient.
As $x \rightarrow -\infty$, $f(x) \rightarrow -\infty$, and as $x \rightarrow \infty$, $f(x) \rightarrow \infty$.
There are 2 sign changes, so there are 2 or 0 positive real roots. ✔

STEP 5 Graph the equation to find the maximum value of the function.

Although the function has no maximum value, values of x equal to or greater than 1.5 do not make sense in the problem. Find the local maximum between the intercepts 0 and 1.5.

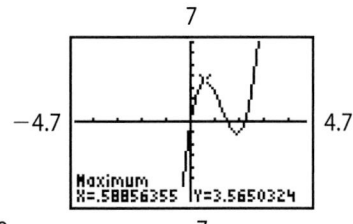

Use the method from Example 2.

The local maximum of the function is about 3.57 at $x \approx 0.59$.

STEP 6 Interpret the local maximum in the problem situation, and solve the problem.
The maximum volume of the box is about 3.57 cu ft when squares of length $x \approx 0.59$ feet (about 7.1 inches) are cut from the corners of the cardboard and the flaps are folded up.

Dimensions of the box x ft by $(4.5 - 2x)$ ft by $(3 - 2x)$ ft

Substitute 0.59 for x. 0.59 ft by $[4.5 - 2(0.59)]$ ft by $[3 - 2(0.59)]$ ft

Simplify. 0.59 ft by 3.32 ft by 1.82 ft

The dimensions of the box with the maximum volume are about 0.59 ft by 3.32 ft by 1.82 ft.

Factoring Polynomials

What Came Before?
- Factoring out common factors and combining like terms
- Finding zeros of a polynomial function

What's This About?
- Factoring binomials, trinomials, and expressions to the 3rd and nth powers
- Finding all rational roots of a polynomial equation
- Using synthetic division to represent polynomial long division

Practical Apps
- Topologists use polynomial functions and equations to study and describe mathematical knots.
- Fish tank designers use polynomial equations to find the sturdiest dimensions of large tanks, such as saltwater aquariums.

Just for FUN!

Q: What do you call the earliest polynomials?

A: Dinomials.

Q: What do you call male polynomials?

A: Guynomials.

You can find more practice problems online by visiting:
www.SWadvantage.com

Factoring Binomials

Using the GCF and the Distributive Property to Factor Binomials

Factoring an expression means rewriting the expression as the product of its factors. For example, the trinomial $x^2 + 4x + 3$ is equal to the product $(x + 1)(x + 3)$.

One method of factoring begins by finding the greatest common factor (GCF). The GCF of two or more monomials is the common factor with the greatest numerical factor and the greatest degree of the variables.

EXAMPLE 1

Find the greatest common factor of $10x^2$, $6x$, and $4x^3$.

Factor each term.
$$10x^2 = 2 \cdot 5 \cdot x \cdot x$$
$$6x = 2 \cdot 3 \cdot x$$
$$4x^3 = 2 \cdot 2 \cdot x \cdot x \cdot x$$

The product of the two common factors, 2 and x, is $2x$, the greatest common factor, or GCF.

The Distributive Property, $ab + ac = a(b + c)$, allows you to factor out common factors of a binomial. Use the Distributive Property to factor out the GCF of the terms. The remaining expression is the other factor.

Need More
HELP ?

Remember, the Distributive Property is true for a sum or a difference.

$ab + ac = a(b + c)$
$ab - ac = a(b - c)$

EXAMPLE 2

Write each binomial in factored form.

a. $18x + 24$

There is a common factor of 6 in each term. The GCF is 6. Write the terms as products with the GCF as a factor.

Use the Distributive Property to factor out the GCF.

$18x + 24$

$6(3x) + 6(4)$

$6(3x + 4)$

$18x + 24 = 6(3x + 4)$

b. $5x^2 - 7x$

There is a factor of x in each term. The GCF is x. Write the terms as products with the GCF as a factor.

Use the Distributive Property to factor out the GCF.

$5x^2 - 7x$

$x(5x) - x(7)$

$x(5x - 7)$

$5x^2 - 7x = x(5x - 7)$

c. $12x^2 + 8x$

There is a factor of 4 and a factor of x in each term. The GCF is $4x$. Write the terms as products with the GCF as a factor.

Use the Distributive Property to factor out the GCF.

$12x^2 + 8x$

$4x(3x) + 4x(2)$

$4x(3x + 2)$

$12x^2 + 8x = 4x(3x + 2)$

You can use the GCF and the Distributive Property to factor binomials with more than one variable.

SEARCH

To see step-by-step videos of these problems, enter the page number into the SWadvantage.com Search Bar.

EXAMPLE 3

Write $4x^3y^5 + 10x^2y^4$ in factored form.

The factors 2, x^2, and y^4 are found in each term. The GCF is $2x^2y^4$. Write the terms as products with the GCF as a factor.

$$4x^3y^5 + 10x^2y^4$$

$$2x^2y^4(2xy) + 2x^2y^4(5)$$

Use the Distributive Property to factor out the GCF.

$$2x^2y^4(2xy + 5)$$

Using Algebra Tiles to Factor Binomials

You can model the process of factoring binomials by using algebra tiles.

Need More HELP?

A 1 or −1 tile has the dimensions 1 by 1.

An x or $-x$ tile has the dimensions 1 by x.

An x^2 tile has the dimensions x by x.

EXAMPLE 4

Use algebra tiles to factor $3x + 6$.

STEP 1 Model $3x + 6$ with the tiles.

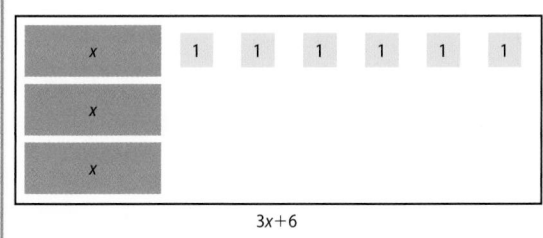

STEP 2 Arrange the tiles to form a rectangle.

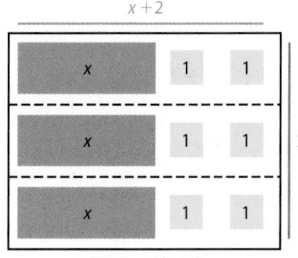

The rectangle has a width of 3 and a length of $x + 2$. The area is $3(x + 2)$. So $3x + 6 = 3(x + 2)$.

EXAMPLE 5

Use algebra tiles to factor $x^2 - 4x$.

STEP 1 Model $x^2 - 4x$ with the tiles.

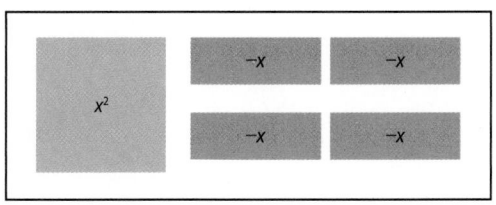

STEP 2 Arrange the tiles to form a rectangle.

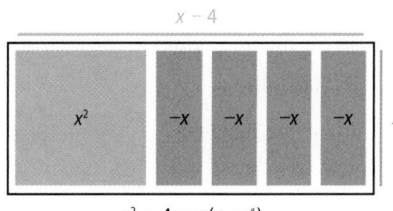

The rectangle has a width of x and a length of $x - 4$. The area is $x(x - 4)$. So $x^2 - 4x = x(x - 4)$.

GOT TO KNOW!

Factoring Binomials

Find the GCF. Then use the Distributive Property to factor out the GCF.

Factoring $x^2 + bx + c$

Factoring $x^2 + bx + c$ When c Is Positive

You can find the product of two binomials, such as $(x + 5)(x + 3)$, by using FOIL or the Distributive Property.

Need More HELP ?

For more help with FOIL, go to *Multiplying Polynomials* in *Algebra* (p. 1608).

$$\overset{\text{F} \quad \text{O} \quad \text{I} \quad \text{L}}{(x + 5)(x + 3) = x^2 + 3x + 5x + 15}$$

$$= x^2 + 8x + 15$$

The result is a trinomial of the form $x^2 + bx + c$, a quadratic expression with a leading coefficient of 1. Recall that a quadratic expression is an expression in which the highest power of the variable is 2.

To factor a trinomial expression, you must reverse the multiplication process. For example, to factor $x^2 + 8x + 15$, find the two factors, $(x + 5)$ and $(x + 3)$, whose product is $x^2 + 8x + 15$.

To find the factors of a quadratic trinomial, use FOIL in reverse. Look for two binomial factors that meet these requirements.

1. The product of their first terms is the FIRST term of the quadratic expression.
2. The product of their last terms is the LAST term of the quadratic expression.
3. The sum of the products of their INSIDE and OUTSIDE terms is the middle term of the quadratic expression.

EXAMPLE 1

Factor $x^2 + 5x + 6$.

STEP 1 Write the factored expression with missing values.

The first term of the trinomial is x^2, so the first term of each binomial factor is x.

$(x + ?)(x + ?)$

STEP 2 Find the pairs of numbers that have a product equal to the last term of the trinomial.

The last term of the trinomial is 6. $x^2 + 5x + 6$

Look for pairs of integers with a product of 6.

1 and 6   2 and 3   −1 and −6   −2 and −3

STEP 3 Find the pair with a sum equal to the middle coefficient of the trinomial.

The middle coefficient is 5, a positive number. $x^2 + 5x + 6$

1 and 6   2 and 3   −1 and −6   −2 and −3

Sums: 7   5   −7   −5

STEP 4 Fill in the missing values in the factored expression, using the factors of 6 with a sum of 5.

$(x + 2)(x + 3)$

CHECK Multiply by using FOIL. $(x + 2)(x + 3) = x^2 + 3x + 2x + 6$

$= x^2 + 5x + 6$ ✔

GOT TO KNOW!

Order of Binomial Factors

The order of the factors in the factored expression does not matter.

$(x + 2)(x + 3) =$
$(x + 3)(x + 2)$

When you factor a trinomial of the form $x^2 + bx + c$, you look for factors of c that have a sum of b. If b is negative, then both factors must be negative if their product c is positive.

EXAMPLE 2

Factor each trinomial. Check your answer.

a. $x^2 + 9x + 18$

Write the factored expression with missing values. $(x + ?)(x + ?)$

The trinomial $x^2 + 9x + 18$ is in the form $x^2 + bx + c$. Determine the values of b and c.

$x^2 + 9x + 18$

$b = 9$ and $c = 18$

Make a table to look for factors of 18 that have a sum of 9. Since the product 18 and the sum 9 are both positive, you need to look for factor pairs that are both positive.

Factors of 18	Sum
1 and 18	19
2 and 9	11
3 and 6	9

The factors are 3 and 6.

Fill in the missing values in the factored expression, using the factor pair you found. $(x + 3)(x + 6)$

CHECK Multiply by using FOIL. $(x + 3)(x + 6) = x^2 + 6x + 3x + 18$

$= x^2 + 9x + 18$ ✔

b. $x^2 - 13x + 36$

Write the factored expression with missing values. $(x + ?)(x + ?)$

The trinomial $x^2 - 13x + 36$ is in the form $x^2 + bx + c$. Determine the values of b and c.

$x^2 - 13x + 36$

$b = -13$ and $c = 36$

Make a table to look for factors of 36 that have a sum of -13. Since the product 36 is positive, but the sum -13 is negative, you need to look for factors pairs that are both negative.

Factors of 36	Sum
-1 and -36	-37
-2 and -18	-20
-3 and -12	-15
-4 and -9	-13

The factors are -4 and -9.

Fill in the missing values in the factored expression. $[x + (-4)][x + (-9)]$

Simplify the expression by writing each factor as a difference. $(x - 4)(x - 9)$

CHECK Multiply by using FOIL. $(x - 4)(x - 9) = x^2 - 9x - 4x + 36$

$= x^2 - 13x + 36$ ✔

Factoring $x^2 + bx + c$ When c Is Negative

When the constant term of a trinomial is negative, the middle term can be positive or negative. Consider the following products.

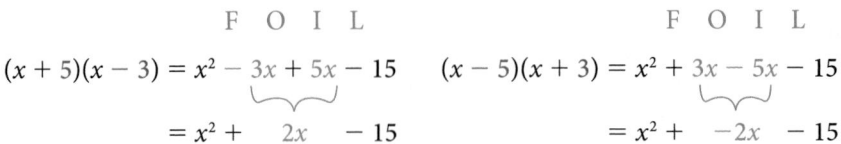

F O I L   F O I L

$(x + 5)(x − 3) = x^2 − 3x + 5x − 15$ $(x − 5)(x + 3) = x^2 + 3x − 5x − 15$

$= x^2 + \quad 2x \quad − 15$ $= x^2 + \quad −2x \quad − 15$

When c in the trinomial $x^2 + bx + c$ is negative, the factors of c have opposite signs. The factor with the greater absolute value has the same sign as b.

In $(x + 5)(x − 3) = x^2 + 2x − 15$, $|5| > |−3|$, so the middle term is $+ 2x$.

In $(x − 5)(x + 3) = x^2 − 2x − 15$, $|−5| > |3|$, so the middle term is $− 2x$.

Need More
HELP ?

For more help with absolute value, go to *Integers and Absolute Value* in *Algebra* (p. 1386).

SEARCH 🔍

To see step-by-step videos of these problems, enter the page number into the SWadvantage.com Search Bar.

EXAMPLE 3

Factor each trinomial. Check your answer.

a. $x^2 + 2x − 35$

Write the factored expression with missing values. $(x + ?)(x + ?)$

For the given trinomial in the form $x^2 + bx + c$, $b = 2$ and $c = −35$.

Make a table to look for factors of $−35$ that have a sum of 2.

Only list factor pairs with opposite signs where the positive number has the greater absolute value.

Factors of −35	Sum
−1 and 35	34
−5 and 7	2

The factors are −5 and 7.

Fill in the missing values in the factored expression. $(x − 5)(x + 7)$

CHECK Multiply by using FOIL. $(x − 5)(x + 7) = x^2 + 7x − 5x − 35 = x^2 + 2x − 35$ ✔

b. $x^2 − 8x − 48$

Write the factored expression with missing values. $(x + ?)(x + ?)$

For the given trinomial, $b = −8$ and $c = −48$.

Make a table to look for factors of $−48$ that have a sum of $−8$.

Only list factor pairs with opposite signs where the negative number has the greater absolute value.

Factors of −48	Sum
1 and −48	−47
2 and −24	−22
3 and −16	−13
4 and −12	−8

The factors are 4 and −12.

Fill in the missing values in the factored expression. $(x + 4)(x − 12)$

CHECK $(x + 4)(x − 12) = x^2 − 12x + 4x − 48 = x^2 − 8x − 48$ ✔

EXAMPLE 4

The diagram shows a square garden that was increased in length and reduced in width. The original garden was x feet on a side. The new garden has the area given in the diagram.

a. **Find the missing lengths indicating changes in dimensions in the diagram.**

The original side length of the garden is x ft. The area of the new garden is $(x^2 + 5x - 84)$ ft².

Factor the expression for the area of the new garden.

Write the factored expression with missing values.
    $(x + ?)(x + ?)$

The trinomial $x^2 + 5x - 84$ is in the form $x^2 + bx + c$, where $b = 5$ and $c = -84$.

Make a table to look for factors of -84 that have a sum of 5.

Factors of -84	Sum
-1 and 84	83
-2 and 42	40
-3 and 28	25
-4 and 21	17
-6 and 14	8
-7 and 12	5

The factors are -7 and 12.

Fill in the missing values in the factored expression. $(x - 7)(x + 12)$.

So the length of the garden was increased by 12 feet, and the width was decreased by 7 feet.

b. **If the original garden was 32 feet on a side, how does the area of the new garden compare with the area of the original garden?**

The original area is $32^2 = 1{,}024$ ft²

The new area is $(x - 7)(x + 12) = (32 - 7)(32 + 12)$

$$= 25 \cdot 44$$
$$= 1{,}100 \text{ ft}^2$$

The area of the new garden is $1{,}100 - 1{,}024 = 76$ ft² greater than the area of the original garden.

(diagram, top right)
— x ft — [?]
x ft
$A = x^2 + 5x - 84$
[?]

Need More
HELP ?

Instead of using the factored expression to find the area of the new garden in Example 4(b), substitute 32 for x in the trinomial shown in the diagram. Then evaluate.

GOT TO KNOW!

Factoring $x^2 + bx + c$

Find factors of c that have a sum of b.

When c is positive   The factors have the same sign.

When c is negative   The factors have opposite signs.

The factor with the greater absolute value has the same sign as b.

Factoring $ax^2 + bx + c$

SOUTHWESTERN

Factoring Trinomials When the Coefficient of x^2 Is Not 1

The first step in factoring a trinomial of the form $ax^2 + bx + c$, where a is not 1, is to try to factor out a common factor. Then the remaining trinomial may be in the form $x^2 + bx + c$.

EXAMPLE 1

Factor each trinomial. Check your answer.

a. $2x^2 + 12x + 18$

Factor out 2 from each term.	$2(x^2 + 6x + 9)$
Write the factored expression with missing values.	$2(x + ?)(x + ?)$
Determine the values of b and c in the trinomial $x^2 + 6x + 9$.	$b = 6$ and $c = 9$
The factors of 9 that have a sum of 6 are 3 and 3.	
Fill in the missing values in the factored expression.	$2(x + 3)(x + 3)$

CHECK Multiply by using FOIL. $\quad 2(x + 3)(x + 3) = 2(x^2 + 3x + 3x + 9)$
$$= 2(x^2 + 6x + 9)$$
$$= 2x^2 + 12x + 18 \checkmark$$

b. $x^3 - 10x^2 + 21x$

Factor out x from each term.	$x(x^2 - 10x + 21)$
Write the factored expression with missing values.	$x(x + ?)(x + ?)$
Determine the values of b and c in the trinomial $x^2 - 10x + 21$.	$b = -10$ and $c = 21$
Look for factors of 21 that have a sum of -10.	

Factors of 21	Sum
-1 and -21	-22
-3 and -7	-10 ✔

The factors are -3 and -7.

Write the sums as differences. $\qquad\qquad\qquad\qquad x(x - 3)(x - 7)$

CHECK Multiply by using FOIL. $\quad x(x - 3)(x - 7) = x(x^2 - 7x - 3x + 21)$
$$= x(x^2 - 10x + 21)$$
$$= x^3 - 10x^2 + 21x \checkmark$$

c. $-x^2 + x + 6$

Factor out -1 from each term.	$-1(x^2 - x - 6)$
Write the factored expression with missing values.	$-1(x + ?)(x - ?)$
Determine the values of b and c in the trinomial $x^2 - x - 6$.	$b = -1$ and $c = -6$
Look for factors of -6 that have a sum of -1.	

Factors of -6	Sum
1 and -6	-5
2 and -3	-1 ✔

The factors are 2 and -3.

Fill in the missing values in the factored expression. $\qquad -1(x + 2)(x - 3)$

CHECK Multiply by using FOIL. $\quad -1(x + 2)(x - 3) = -1(x^2 - 3x + 2x - 6)$
$$= -1(x^2 - x - 6)$$
$$= -x^2 + x + 6 \checkmark$$

Middle Terms of Binomial Products

When you multiply two binomials like $(2x + 3)(3x + 1)$, in which the first coefficient of one or both binomials is *not* 1, then the coefficient of the x^2 term of the product is the product of the coefficients of the first terms.

$$(2x + 3)(3x + 1) = \overset{F}{6x^2} + \overset{O}{2x} + \overset{I}{9x} + \overset{L}{3}$$

$$= 6x^2 + 11x + 3$$

The result is a trinomial of the form $ax^2 + bx + c$, a quadratic expression, with a nonzero leading coefficient *not* equal to 1.

Two binomial products can have the same first and last terms but different middle terms. Finding the product that has the correct middle term is the key to factoring trinomials of this type.

EXAMPLE 2

The products of the two pairs of binomials have the same first term and the same last term. Find the first and last term for both pairs. Then find the middle term for each pair.

SEARCH

To see step-by-step videos of these problems, enter the page number into the SWadvantage.com Search Bar.

a. $(2x + 5)(4x + 3)$ and $(2x + 15)(4x + 1)$

The product of the first terms for both pairs is $8x^2$.	$2x \cdot 4x = 8x^2$	$2x \cdot 4x = 8x^2$
The product of the last terms for both pairs is 15.	$5 \cdot 3 = 15$	$15 \cdot 1 = 15$
Use FOIL. Find the outside and inside products.	$(2x + 5)(4x + 3)$	$(2x + 15)(4x + 1)$
Add the products to find the middle term.	$2x \cdot 3 + 5 \cdot 4x$	$2x \cdot 1 + 15 \cdot 4x$
	$26x$	$62x$

b. $(8x + 3)(2x − 7)$ and $(2x + 3)(8x − 7)$

The product of the first terms for both pairs is $16x^2$.	$8x \cdot 2x = 16x^2$	$2x \cdot 8x = 16x^2$
The product of the last terms for both pairs is $−21$.	$3 \cdot (−7) = −21$	$3 \cdot (−7) = −21$
Use FOIL. Find the outside and inside products.	$(8x + 3)(2x − 7)$	$(2x + 3)(8x − 7)$
Add the products to find the middle term.	$8x \cdot (−7) + 3 \cdot 2x$	$2x \cdot (−7) + 3 \cdot 8x$
	$−50x$	$10x$

c. $(x − 24)(20x − 9)$ and $(5x − 12)(4x − 18)$

The product of the first terms for both pairs is $20x^2$.	$x \cdot 20x = 20x^2$	$5x \cdot 4x = 20x^2$
The product of the last terms for both pairs is 216.	$(−24)(−9) = 216$	$(−12)(−18) = 216$
Use FOIL. Find the outside and inside products.	$(x − 24)(20x − 9)$	$(5x − 12)(4x − 18)$
Add the products to find the middle term.	$x \cdot (−9) + (−24) \cdot 20x$	$5x \cdot (−18) + (−12) \cdot 4x$
	$−489x$	$−138x$

Using FOIL in Reverse to Factor

To find the factors of a quadratic trinomial of the form $ax^2 + bx + c$, use FOIL in reverse.

EXAMPLE 3

Factor $15x^2 + 19x + 6$.

STEP 1 Write the factored expression with missing values.

There are two missing values in each binomial. $(?x + ?)(?x + ?)$

STEP 2 Find the pairs of numbers whose product is equal to the coefficient of the first term.

The first term of the trinomial is 15, a positive number.

Possible pairs: 1 and 15   3 and 5

STEP 3 Write a factor pair as the coefficients of the first terms in the factors.

Use 1 and 15. $(1x + ?)(15x + ?)$

STEP 4 Find the pairs of numbers that have a product equal to the last term.

The last term of the trinomial is 6, a positive number.

Possible pairs: 1 and 6   2 and 3

STEP 5 Substitute each of these possible pairs into the factored expression $(1x + ?)(15x + ?)$. Try to find a set that gives a coefficient of 19 for the middle term of the trinomial product.

In this case, the order of the factors does matter, so try 6 and 1 as well as 1 and 6.

Factors of 15	Factors of 6	Product	Trinomial
1 and 15	1 and 6	$(1x + 1)(15x + 6)$	$15x^2 + 21x + 6$ ✘
1 and 15	2 and 3	$(1x + 2)(15x + 3)$	$15x^2 + 33x + 6$ ✘
1 and 15	3 and 2	$(1x + 3)(15x + 2)$	$15x^2 + 47x + 6$ ✘
1 and 15	6 and 1	$(1x + 6)(15x + 1)$	$15x^2 + 91x + 6$ ✘

Now try 3 and 5 as the first terms in the factored expression. $(3x + ?)(5x + ?)$

3 and 5	1 and 6	$(3x + 1)(5x + 6)$	$15x^2 + 23x + 6$ ✘
3 and 5	2 and 3	$(3x + 2)(5x + 3)$	$15x^2 + 19x + 6$ ✔

The factored expression is $(3x + 2)(5x + 3)$.

Watch Out !

When the coefficient of the x^2 term is not 1, you need to consider the factors of both the first term and the last term to identify the missing values in each binomial.

Factoring $ax^2 + bx + c$

If possible, factor out a common factor. Then look for two binomial factors that meet these requirements.

- The product of their FIRST terms is the first term of the quadratic expression.

- The product of their LAST terms is the last term of the quadratic expression.

- The sum of the products of their INSIDE and OUTSIDE terms is the middle term of the quadratic expression.

EXAMPLE 4

Factor each trinomial.

SEARCH

To see step-by-step videos of these problems, enter the page number into the SWadvantage.com Search Bar.

a. $2x^2 + 11x + 12$

Write the factored expression with missing values. $(?x + ?)(?x + ?)$

Find the pairs of numbers whose product is the coefficient of the first term, 2.

   1 and 2

Write the factor pair as the first terms in the factored expression. $(1x + ?)(2x + ?)$

You can omit the coefficient of 1. $(x + ?)(2x + ?)$

Find the pairs of numbers that have a product of the last term, 12.

   1 and 12   2 and 6   3 and 4

Try each of these possible factor pairs to find a set that gives a coefficient of 11 for the middle term of the product.

Product	Coefficient of Middle Term
$(x + 1)(2x + 12)$	$12 + 2 = 14$ ✗
$(x + 2)(2x + 6)$	$6 + 4 = 10$ ✗
$(x + 3)(2x + 4)$	$4 + 6 = 10$ ✗
$(x + 4)(2x + 3)$	$3 + 8 = 11$ ✔

The factored expression is $(x + 4)(2x + 3)$.

b. $3x^2 - 2x - 8$

Write the factored expression with missing values. $(?x\ ?)(?x\ ?)$

Find the pairs of numbers whose product is the coefficient of the first term, 3.

   1 and 3

Write the factor pair as the first terms in the factored expression.

   $(1x\ ?)(3x\ ?)$ or $(x\ ?)(3x\ ?)$

Find all pairs of numbers that have a product equal to the last term, -8. Because the constant term is negative, write all possible pairs with opposite signs.

1 and -8	2 and -4	4 and -2	8 and -1
-1 and 8	-2 and 4	-4 and 2	-8 and 1

Substitute each of these possible pairs into the factored expression $(x\ ?)(3x\ ?)$. Try to find a set that gives a coefficient of -2 for the middle term of the trinomial product.

Product	Coefficient of Middle Term
$(x + 1)(3x - 8)$	$-8 + 3 = -5$ ✗
$(x + 2)(3x - 4)$	$-4 + 6 = 2$ ✗
$(x + 4)(3x - 2)$	$-2 + 12 = 10$ ✗
$(x + 8)(3x - 1)$	$-1 + 24 = 23$ ✗
$(x - 1)(3x + 8)$	$8 - 3 = 5$ ✗
$(x - 2)(3x + 4)$	$4 - 6 = -2$ ✔

The factored expression is $(x - 2)(3x + 4)$.

Watch Out

When the last term of the trinomial is negative and the first terms of the binomials are different, omit the signs inside the parentheses as you work through the solution. You don't know which term will end up with the minus sign until you have tested each possible factor pair!

Prime Polynomials

Not every trinomial of the form $x^2 + bx + c$ or $ax^2 + bx + c$ is factorable. A polynomial that cannot be factored is called a **prime polynomial**.

EXAMPLE 5

SEARCH

To see step-by-step videos of these problems, enter the page number into the SWadvantage.com Search Bar.

Factor, if possible.

a. $x^2 + 4x + 9$

Write the factored expression with missing values. $(x + ?)(x + ?)$

Find the pairs of numbers whose product is equal to the last term, 9.

   1 and 9   3 and 3

Try each of these factor pairs, looking for one that gives a coefficient of 4 for the middle term of the product.

Product	Coefficient of Middle Term
$(x + 1)(x + 9)$	$9 + 1 = 10$ ✗
$(x + 3)(x + 3)$	$3 + 3 = 6$ ✗

The trinomial is prime and cannot be factored.

b. $4x^2 - 11x - 7$

Write the factored expression with missing values. $(x\ ?)(x\ ?)$

Find the pairs of numbers whose product is equal to the coefficient of the first term, 4.

   1 and 4   2 and 2

Write a factor pair as the first terms in the factored expression.

   $(1x\ ?)(4x\ ?)$ or $(x\ ?)(4x\ ?)$

Find all pairs of numbers that have a product equal to the last term, -7. Because the constant term is negative, write all possible pairs with opposite signs.

   1 and -7 7 and -1 -1 and 7 -7 and 1

Substitute each of these pairs into the factored expression $(x\ ?)(4x\ ?)$. Try to find a set that gives a coefficient of -11 for the middle term of the trinomial product.

Product	Coefficient of Middle Term
$(x + 1)(4x - 7)$	$-7 + 4 = -3$ ✗
$(x + 7)(4x - 1)$	$-1 + 28 = 27$ ✗
$(x - 1)(4x + 7)$	$7 - 4 = 3$ ✗
$(x - 7)(4x + 1)$	$1 - 28 = -27$ ✗

Change the first terms.

$(2x + 1)(2x - 7)$	$-14 + 2 = -12$ ✗
$(2x + 7)(2x - 1)$	$-2 + 14 = 12$ ✗
$(2x - 1)(2x + 7)$	$14 - 2 = 12$ ✗
$(2x - 7)(2x + 1)$	$2 - 14 = -12$ ✗

The trinomial is prime and cannot be factored.

Factoring $ax^2 + bx + c$ When a Is Negative

In Example 1(c), you factored a trinomial of the form $ax^2 + bx + c$ in which a was equal to -1. You can factor trinomials of the form $ax^2 + bx + c$ for other negative values of a.

EXAMPLE 6

Factor $-25x^2 + 20x - 4$.

Factor out -1 from each term.	$-1(25x^2 - 20x + 4)$
Write the factored expression with missing values.	$-1(?x\ \ ?)(?x\ \ ?)$
Because the constant term is positive and the middle term is negative, you can write in minus signs.	$-1(x - ?)(25x - ?)$

Find the pairs of numbers whose product is equal to the coefficient of the first term, 25.

> 1 and 25   5 and 5

Write one factor pair as the first terms in the factored expression. $-1(1x - ?)(25x - ?)$ or $-1(x - ?)(25x - ?)$

Find all pairs of numbers that have a product equal to the last term, 4. Because the middle term is negative, and the factors of 4 have the same sign, only look for pairs of negative numbers.

> -1 and -4 -2 and -2 -4 and -1

Try each of these factor pairs, looking for one that gives a coefficient of -20 for the middle term of the binomial product.

Product	Coefficient of Middle Term
$(x - 1)(25x - 4)$	$-4 - 25 = -29$ ✘
$(x - 2)(25x - 2)$	$-2 - 50 = -52$ ✘
$(x - 4)(25x - 1)$	$-1 - 100 = -101$ ✘
Change the first terms.	
$(5x - 1)(5x - 4)$	$-20 - 5 = -25$ ✘
$(5x - 2)(5x - 2)$	$-10 - 10 = -20$ ✔
$(5x - 4)(5x - 1)$	$-5 - 20 = -25$ ✘

The factored expression is $-1(5x - 2)(5x - 2)$, or $-1(5x - 2)^2$.

Need More
HELP **?**

Because $5x - 2$ and $2 - 5x$ are opposites, $-1(5x - 2)$ and $(2 - 5x)$ are equal.

So you could write the product in Example 6 as $(2 - 5x)(5x - 2)$.

GOT TO KNOW!

Factoring $ax^2 + bx + c$

When $a > 1$, follow one of these procedures.

1. If $b > 0$ and $c > 0$, find pairs of positive factors of a and c.

2. If $b < 0$ and $c > 0$, find pairs of positive factors of a and negative factors of c.

3. If $b < 0$ and $c < 0$, find pairs of positive factors of a and opposite-sign factors of c.

When $a < 1$, factor out -1 first. Then find factors as above.

Factoring by Grouping

Factoring Out a Common Binomial Factor

When you use the Distributive Property to multiply $x^2 + 5$ and $x + 3$, the result is an expression in which pairs of terms have common factors.

$$(x^2 + 5)(x + 3) = x^2(x + 3) \quad + \quad 5(x + 3)$$

$$= x^3 + 3x^2 \quad + \quad 5x + 15$$

Both pairs of terms have $x + 3$ as a common binomial factor.

Need More

HELP ?

You could also distribute this way:

$(x^2 + 5)(x + 3) =$

$(x^2 + 5)x + (x^2 + 5)3 =$

$x^3 + 5x + 3x^2 + 15$

In this case, both pairs of terms have $x^2 + 5$ as a common factor.

EXAMPLE 1

Factor each expression.

a. $2x(x - 8) - 7(x - 8)$

The terms have a common binomial factor of $x - 8$. $2x(x - 8) - 7(x - 8)$

Use the Distributive Property. $(2x - 7)(x - 8)$

b. $x^2(3x + y) - 11(3x + y)$

The terms have a common binomial factor of $3x + y$. $x^2(3x + y) - 11(3x + y)$

Use the Distributive Property. $(x^2 - 11)(3x + y)$

Factoring by Grouping

If a polynomial has 4 terms, it may be possible to find a common factor in pairs of terms.

For the expression $x^3 + 3x^2 + 5x + 15$ at the top of the page, the first two terms have a common factor of x^2, and the last two terms have a common factor of 5.

You can use the Distributive Property in reverse to factor the resulting expression.

$$x^3 + 3x^2 + 5x + 15$$

Factor the GCF from each pair of terms. $x^2(x + 3) + 5(x + 3)$

$$(x^2 + 5)(x + 3)$$

SEARCH

To see step-by-step videos of these problems, enter the page number into the SWadvantage.com Search Bar.

EXAMPLE 2

Factor each expression.

a. $x^3 + x^2 + 2x + 2$

$$x^3 + x^2 + 2x + 2$$

Factor each binomial pair. $x^2(x + 1) + 2(x + 1)$

Use the Distributive Property. $(x^2 + 2)(x + 1)$

b. $x^2y - 3xy + 2x - 6$

$$x^2y - 3xy + 2x - 6$$

Factor each binomial pair. $xy(x - 3) + 2(x - 3)$

Use the Distributive Property. $(xy + 2)(x - 3)$

In some cases, you can group the binomials and treat the expression as a sum or difference of binomials before factoring.

EXAMPLE 3

Factor each expression.

a. $15 - 12x - 10x^3 + 8x^4$

Group the binomials and treat the expression as a sum.

$$15 - 12x - 10x^3 + 8x^4$$

$$(15 - 12x) + (-10x^3 + 8x^4)$$

Factor each binomial pair. $3(5 - 4x) + (-2x^3)(5 - 4x)$

Use the Distributive Property. $(3 - 2x^3)(5 - 4x)$

b. $xy - 4x - 5y + 20$

Group the binomials and treat the expression as a difference.

$$xy - 4x - 5y + 20$$

$$(xy - 4x) - (5y - 20)$$

Factor each binomial pair. $x(y - 4) - 5(y - 4)$

Use the Distributive Property. $(x - 5)(y - 4)$

Be careful to consider all signs before trying to factor by grouping.

EXAMPLE 4

Factor $2x^3 - 6x^2 + 3x + 9$ by grouping, if possible.

$$2x^3 - 6x^2 + 3x + 9$$

Factor each binomial pair. $2x^2(x - 3) + 3(x + 3)$

The polynomial cannot be factored by grouping.

You may be able to factor again after factoring by grouping.

EXAMPLE 5

Factor $x^3 + 5x^2 - x - 5$ by grouping.

$$x^3 + 5x^2 - x - 5$$

Factor each binomial pair. $x^2(x + 5) - 1(x + 5)$

Use the Distributive Property. $(x^2 - 1)(x + 5)$

Factor the difference of squares. $(x + 1)(x - 1)(x + 5)$

GOT TO KNOW!

Factoring Polynomials by Grouping

1. Look for common factors in pairs of terms.

2. Use the Distributive Property to factor.

Factoring Special Polynomials

SOUTHWESTERN

Factoring Perfect Trinomial Squares

When you square a binomial of the form $x + B$, the product has the form $x^2 + 2Bx + B^2$.

$B = 5$ F   O   I   L

$$(x + 5)(x + 5) = x^2 + \underbrace{5x + 5x} + 5^2$$

$$= x^2 + 2(5x) + 5^2$$

If you recognize a polynomial as a perfect trinomial square, you can factor it easily.

$$x^2 + 10x + 25 = x^2 + 2(5x) + 5^2$$

$$= (x + 5)^2$$

For trinomials of the form $x^2 + bx + c$, if c is a perfect square of some number B and $b = \pm 2B$, then the trinomial is a perfect trinomial square and can be factored as $(x \pm B)^2$.

Need More

HELP ?

For more help with perfect trinomial squares and the differences of squares, go to *Special Products of Binomials* (p. 1614).

EXAMPLE 1

Factor each expression as a perfect trinomial square, if possible.

a. $x^2 + 24x + 144$

    STEP 1   Determine whether the last term is the square of some number B.

            Yes, $144 = (\pm 12)^2$, so $B = 12$ or $B = -12$.

    STEP 2   Determine whether the coefficient b of the middle term is $\pm 2B$.

            Yes, $24 = 2(12)$, so $B = 12$.

    STEP 3   Factor the perfect square trinomial.

            $x^2 + 24x + 144 = (x + 12)^2$

    CHECK

         Multiply by using FOIL. $(x + 12)(x + 12) = x^2 + 12x + 12x + 144$

                                           $= x^2 + 24x + 144$ ✔

     $x^2 + 24x + 144 = (x + 12)^2$

b. $x^2 - 14x + 49$

     The last term, 49, is the square of 7 and the square of -7. $B = 7$ or $B = -7$

     The coefficient of the middle term, $-14x$, is $2(-7)$. $B = -7$

     $x^2 - 14x + 49 = (x - 7)^2$

    CHECK

         Multiply by using FOIL. $(x - 7)(x - 7) = x^2 - 7x - 7x + 49$

                                           $= x^2 - 14x + 49$ ✔

     $x^2 - 14x + 49 = (x - 7)^2$

c. $x^2 - 10x + 100$

     The last term, 100, is the square of 10 and the square of -10. $B = 10$ or $B = -10$

     The coefficient of the middle term is -10, and is *not* $\pm 2(10)$.

     The trinomial is not a perfect square.

You can also factor a perfect trinomial square of the form $A^2x^2 + 2ABx + B^2$ where the leading coefficient is not equal to 1.

The trinomial is a perfect square if the first and last terms are perfect squares and the coefficient of the middle term is $\pm 2AB$.

SEARCH

To see step-by-step videos of these problems, enter the page number into the SWadvantage.com Search Bar.

EXAMPLE 2

Factor each perfect trinomial square.

a. $16x^2 + 24x + 9$

$16x^2 + 24x + 9$

Find the square roots of the first and last terms.

$(4x)^2 \quad (3)^2$

$2(4x)(3)$

Check the middle term. The trinomial is a perfect square.

$16x^2 + 24x + 9 = (4x + 3)^2$

CHECK

Multiply by using FOIL.

$(4x + 3)(4x + 3) = 16x^2 + 12x + 12x + 9$
$= 16x^2 + 24x + 9 ✔$

b. $36x^2 - 12xy + y^2$

$36x^2 - 12xy + y^2$

Find the square roots of the first and last terms.

$(6x)^2 \quad y^2$

$-2(6x)(y)$

Check the middle term. The trinomial is a perfect square.

$36x^2 - 12xy + y^2 = (6x - y)^2$

CHECK

Multiply by using FOIL.

$(6x - y)(6x - y) = 36x^2 - 6xy - 6xy + y^2$
$= 36x^2 - 12xy + y^2 ✔$

Factoring a Difference of Two Squares

Recall that when you multiply a binomial of the form $a + b$ and a binomial of the form $a - b$, the product is the difference of two squares $a^2 - b^2$. If you recognize a polynomial as a difference of two squares, you can factor it.

$$a^2 - b^2 = (a + b)(a - b)$$

EXAMPLE 3

Factor $25x^2 - 81y^4$.

$25x^2 - 81y^4$

Find the square roots of the absolute values.

$(5x)^2 \quad (9y^2)^2$

Factor: $(5x + 9y^2)(5x - 9y^2)$

$25x^2 - 81y^4 = (5x + 9y^2)(5x - 9y^2)$

Factoring $a^3 \pm b^3$

When you multiply $x + 2$ by $x^2 - 2x + 2^2$, the result is a sum of two cubes.

$$(x + 2)(x^2 - 2x + 2^2) = x^3 - 2x^2 + 2^2x + 2x^2 - 2^2x + 2^3$$
$$= x^3 - 2x^2 + 2x^2 + 2^2x - 2^2x + 2^3$$
$$= x^3 \qquad\qquad\qquad + 2^3$$

When you multiply $x - 2$ by $x^2 + 2x + 2^2$, the result is a difference of two cubes.

$$(x - 2)(x^2 + 2x + 2^2) = x^3 + 2x^2 + 2^2x - 2x^2 - 2^2x - 2^3$$
$$= x^3 + 2x^2 - 2x^2 + 2^2x - 2^2x - 2^3$$
$$= x^3 \qquad\qquad\qquad - 2^3$$

To factor a polynomial of the form $a^3 + b^3$, use the following formulas.

Sum of two cubes	$a^3 + b^3 = (a + b)(a^2 - ab + b^2)$
Difference of two cubes	$a^3 - b^3 = (a - b)(a^2 + ab + b^2)$

EXAMPLE 4

Factor the sum or difference of cubes. Check your answer.

a. $x^3 + 1$

This is a sum of two cubes, $a^3 + b^3$, where $a = x$ and $b = 1$.

Use the sum formula. $a^3 + b^3 = (a + b)(a^2 - ab + b^2)$

Substitute. $x^3 + 1^3 = (x + 1)(x^2 - x \cdot 1 + 1^2)$

Simplify. $x^3 + 1 = (x + 1)(x^2 - x + 1)$

CHECK

Use the Distributive Property. $(x + 1)(x^2 - x + 1) = x^3 - x^2 + x + x^2 - x + 1$

Use the Commutative Property. $= x^3 - x^2 + x^2 + x - x + 1$

Simplify. $= x^3 + 1$ ✔

$x^3 + 1 = (x + 1)(x^2 - x + 1)$

b. $8x^3 - 125$

This is a difference of two cubes, $a^3 - b^3$, where $a = 2x$ and $b = 5$.

Use the difference formula. $a^3 - b^3 = (a - b)(a^2 + ab + b^2)$

Substitute. $(2x)^3 - 5^3 = (2x - 5)[(2x)^2 + 2x \cdot 5 + 5^2]$

Simplify. $8x^3 - 125 = (2x - 5)(4x^2 + 10x + 25)$

CHECK

Use the Distributive Property. $(2x - 5)(4x^2 + 10x + 25) = 8x^3 + 20x^2 + 50x - 20x^2 - 50x - 125$

Use the Commutative Property. $= 8x^3 + 20x^2 - 20x^2 + 50x - 50x - 125$

Simplify. $= 8x^3 - 125$ ✔

$8x^3 - 125 = (2x - 5)(4x^2 + 10x + 25)$

GOT TO KNOW!

Sum or Difference of Cubes

The formulas for the sum and the difference of two cubes can be written as a single formula.

$a^3 \pm b^3 =$
$(a \pm b)(a^2 \mp ab + b^2)$

The $\mp$ is a "minus or plus" symbol. It indicates that you use the opposite symbol of the one in the binomial factor.

Factoring $a^n \pm b^n$

To factor $a^n \pm b^n$ when n is an odd number, you can use a sequential pattern of exponents as shown below. Notice the alternating-sign pattern for $a^n + b^n$. Look back at Example 4(a) to see how this pattern applies to the sum of two cubes.

$$a^n + b^n = (a + b)(a^{n-1} - a^{n-2}b + a^{n-3}b^2 - a^{n-4}b^3 + \ldots - ab^{n-2} + b^{n-1})$$

$$a^n - b^n = (a - b)(a^{n-1} + a^{n-2}b + a^{n-3}b^2 + a^{n-4}b^3 + \ldots + ab^{n-2} + b^{n-1})$$

When n is an even number, you can factor $a^n - b^n$ as a difference of squares.

EXAMPLE 5

Factor each polynomial.

a. $x^5 + 1$

This is a sum $a^5 + b^5$, where $a = x$ and $b = 1$.

Use the formula. $a^5 + b^5 = (a + b)(a^4 - a^3b + a^2b^2 - ab^3 + b^4)$

Substitute. $x^5 + 1^5 = (x + 1)(x^4 - x^3 \cdot 1 + x^2 \cdot 1^2 - x \cdot 1^3 + 1^4)$

Simplify. $x^5 + 1 = (x + 1)(x^4 - x^3 + x^2 - x + 1)$

b. $x^7 - 1$

This is a difference $a^7 - b^7$, where $a = x$ and $b = 1$.

Use the formula. $a^7 - b^7 = (a - b)(a^6 + a^5b + a^4b^2 + a^3b^3 + a^2b^4 + ab^5 + b^6)$

Substitute. $x^7 - 1^7 = (x - 1)(x^6 + x^5 \cdot 1 + x^4 \cdot 1^2 + x^3 \cdot 1^3 + x^2 \cdot 1^4 + x \cdot 1^5 + 1^6)$

Simplify. $x^7 - 1 = (x - 1)(x^6 + x^5 + x^4 + x^3 + x^2 + x + 1)$

c. $x^8 - 256$

This is a difference of two squares.

Factor. $(x^4)^2 - 16^2 = (x^4 + 16)(x^4 - 16)$

Factor the difference of squares $x^4 - 16$. $= (x^4 + 16)(x^2 + 4)(x^2 - 4)$

Factor the difference of squares $x^2 - 4$. $= (x^4 + 16)(x^2 + 4)(x + 2)(x - 2)$

SEARCH

To see step-by-step videos of these problems, enter the page number into the SWadvantage.com Search Bar.

GOT TO KNOW!

Factoring Special Binomials and Trinomials

Squares of Binomials

$a^2 + 2ab + b^2 = (a + b)^2$

$a^2 - 2ab + b^2 = (a - b)^2$

Difference of Squares

$a^2 - b^2 = (a + b)(a - b)$

$a^{2n} - b^{2n} = (a^n + b^n)(a^n - b^n)$

Sum of Two Cubes

$a^3 + b^3 = (a + b)(a^2 - ab + b^2)$

Difference of Two Cubes

$a^3 - b^3 = (a - b)(a^2 + ab + b^2)$

Sum and Difference of Powers, when n is odd

$a^n + b^n = (a + b)(a^{n-1} - a^{n-2}b + a^{n-3}b^2 - a^{n-4}b^3 + \ldots - ab^{n-2} + b^{n-1})$

$a^n - b^n = (a - b)(a^{n-1} + a^{n-2}b + a^{n-3}b^2 + a^{n-4}b^3 + \ldots + ab^{n-2} + b^{n-1})$

Synthetic Division

The Synthetic Division Method

To divide a polynomial in standard form by a linear binomial in the form $x - a$, you can use a shorthand process called **synthetic division**.

Because polynomial factors $x - a$ are related to the zeros of polynomial functions and the solutions of polynomial equations, synthetic division is an extremely useful tool.

Synthetic division is a way of using addition and multiplication to evaluate polynomials for specific values of x. To find the value of a polynomial $f(x)$ when $x = a$, divide $f(x)$ by $x - a$, using synthetic division. The remainder is $f(a)$.

EXAMPLE 1

Use synthetic division to divide the polynomial $2x^3 + 3x^2 - 17x - 25$ by $x - 3$. Check by using long division.

STEP 1 Write the value of a, 3, in the upper-left corner, and write the coefficients of the polynomial on the same line. Then skip a line and draw an addition bar under the coefficients. Bring the first coefficient, 2, below the line.

$$3 \underline{|\ \ } \quad 2 \quad\quad 3 \quad\quad -17 \quad\quad -25$$
$$2$$

STEP 2 Multiply the divisor by the first coefficient below the line ($3 \cdot 2$), and write the product under the next coefficient. Then add the new column ($3 + 6 = 9$).

$$3 \underline{|\ \ } \quad 2 \quad\quad 3 \quad\quad -17 \quad\quad -25$$
$$\quad\quad\quad\quad 6$$
$$2 \quad\quad 9$$

STEP 3 Multiply the divisor by the sum of the second column, and write the product under the next coefficient. Then add the new column.

$$3 \underline{|\ \ } \quad 2 \quad\quad 3 \quad\quad -17 \quad\quad -25$$
$$\quad\quad\quad\quad 6 \quad\quad 27$$
$$2 \quad\quad 9 \quad\quad 10$$

STEP 4 Multiply the divisor by the sum of the third column, and write the product under the next coefficient. Then add the last column, and box this sum. This is the remainder.

$$3 \underline{|\ \ } \quad 2 \quad\quad 3 \quad\quad -17 \quad\quad -25$$
$$\quad\quad\quad\quad 6 \quad\quad 27 \quad\quad 30$$
$$2 \quad\quad 9 \quad\quad 10 \quad\quad \boxed{5}$$

STEP 5 Read the quotient from the bottom line. The quotient has a degree 1 less than the degree of the dividend.

The quotient is $2x^2 + 9x + 10 + \dfrac{5}{x - 3}$.

CHECK

$$\begin{array}{r} 2x^2 + 9x + 10 + \dfrac{5}{x-3} \;\checkmark \\[4pt] x - 3 \overline{)\,2x^3 + 3x^2 - 17x - 25} \end{array}$$

Multiply $2x^2$ by $x - 3$.	$2x^3 - 6x^2$
Subtract.	$9x^2 - 17x$
Multiply $9x$ by $x - 3$.	$9x^2 - 27x$
Subtract.	$10x - 25$
Multiply 10 by $x - 3$.	$10x - 30$
Subtract.	5

When the remainder is 0, the polynomial is evenly divisible by the divisor.

EXAMPLE 2

Use synthetic division to divide $3x^4 + 21x^3 - 4x^2 - 26x + 14$ by $x + 7$. Determine whether the polynomial is evenly divisible by the divisor. Check by multiplying.

SEARCH

To see step-by-step videos of these problems, enter the page number into the SWadvantage.com Search Bar.

STEP 1 Set up synthetic division.

When the divisor $x + 7$ is written in the form $x - a$, $a = -7$.

The degree of the dividend is 4, so the degree of the quotient will be 3.

	x^4	x^3	x^2	x	constant
$-7\rfloor$	3	21	-4	-26	14
					$\llcorner$

STEP 2 Use synthetic division to complete the table.

$-7\rfloor$	3	21	-4	-26	14
		-21	0	28	-14
	3	0	-4	2	$\lfloor 0$ remainder
	x^3	x^2	x	constant	

STEP 3 Read the quotient and remainder from the table.

The quotient is $3x^3 + 0x^2 - 4x + 2$, or $3x^3 - 4x + 2$. The remainder is 0, so the polynomial is evenly divisible by the divisor.

STEP 4 **CHECK**

Leave spaces to keep powers aligned.

$$
\begin{array}{r}
3x^3 - 4x + 2 \\
\times \quad x + 7 \\
\hline
21x^3 \qquad - 28x + 14 \\
3x^4 \qquad - 4x^2 + 2x \\
\hline
3x^4 + 21x^3 - 4x^2 - 26x + 14 \ ✔
\end{array}
$$

EXAMPLE 3

Use synthetic division to divide $\dfrac{-4x^3 + 5x^2 + 3x - 8}{x + 1}$. Determine whether the polynomial is evenly divisible by the divisor. Check by multiplying.

When the divisor $x + 1$ is written in the form $x - a$, $a = -1$. The degree of the dividend is 3, so the degree of the quotient will be 2.

$-1\rfloor$	-4	5	3	-8
		4	-9	6
	-4	9	-6	-2 $\lfloor -2$ remainder

The quotient is $-4x^2 + 9x - 6 - \dfrac{2}{x + 1}$. The remainder is -2, so the polynomial is not evenly divisible by the divisor.

CHECK $\left(-4x^2 + 9x - 6 - \dfrac{2}{x + 1}\right)(x + 1) = -4x^2(x + 1) + 9x(x + 1) - 6(x + 1) - \dfrac{2}{x + 1}(x + 1)$

$$= -4x^3 - 4x^2 + 9x^2 + 9x - 6x - 6 - 2$$

$$= -4x^3 + 5x^2 + 3x - 8 \ ✔$$

Special Cases When Dividing

When you set up synthetic division, be sure to include a column for each power of the variable, even when a variable term is missing because its coefficient is 0. Sometimes the value of a in $x - a$ does not have to be an integer.

EXAMPLE 4

Use synthetic division to divide.

a. $2x^4 - 15x^2 - 22 \div (x - 4)$

Since $x - 4$ is in the form $x - a$, $a = 4$. The degree of the dividend is 4, so the degree of the quotient will be 3.

The x^3 term and x term are missing, so write the coefficient 0 in these columns.

	x^4	x^3	x^2	x	constant	
4⌋	2	0	−15	0	−22	
		8	32	68	272	
	2	8	17	68	⌊250	remainder

The quotient is $2x^3 + 8x^2 + 17x + 68 + \dfrac{250}{x - 4}$.

b. $\dfrac{x^6 - 1}{x + 2}$

When the divisor $x + 2$ is written in the form $x - a$, $a = -2$. The degree of the dividend is 6, so the degree of the quotient will be 5. Write 0 in the appropriate columns.

	x^6	x^5	x^4	x^3	x^2	x	constant	
−2⌋	1	0	0	0	0	0	−1	
		−2	4	−8	16	−32	64	
	1	−2	4	−8	16	−32	⌊63	remainder

The quotient is $x^5 - 2x^4 + 4x^3 - 8x^2 + 16x - 32 + \dfrac{63}{x + 2}$.

EXAMPLE 5

Use synthetic division to divide.

$x^3 + \dfrac{7}{2}x^2 - 12x + 5 \div \left(x - \dfrac{1}{2}\right)$

Since $x - \dfrac{1}{2}$ is in the form $x - a$, $a = \dfrac{1}{2}$. The degree of the dividend is 3, so the degree of the quotient will be 2.

	x^3	x^2	x	constant	
$\frac{1}{2}$⌋	1	$\frac{7}{2}$	−12	5	
		$\frac{1}{2}$	2	−5	
	1	4	−10	⌊0	remainder

The quotient is $x^2 + 4x - 10$.

To write a divisor in the form $x - a$, you may need to factor out a common factor from the dividend and divisor. Or you may need to multiply both dividend and divisor by the same number.

EXAMPLE ⑥

Use synthetic division to divide.

a. $\dfrac{-2x^3 - 4x^2 + 16x + 42}{2x - 6}$

Because the coefficient of x in the denominator is 2, factor out 2 from both the numerator and denominator.

$$\frac{-2x^3 - 4x^2 + 16x + 42}{2x - 6} = \frac{2(-x^3 - 2x^2 + 8x + 21)}{2(x - 3)}$$

$$= \frac{-x^3 - 2x^2 + 8x + 21}{x - 3}$$

Now you can use synthetic division to divide.

$$
\begin{array}{r|rrrr}
3 & -1 & -2 & 8 & 21 \\
  &   & -3 & -15 & -21 \\
\hline
  & -1 & -5 & -7 & \underline{|0} \quad \text{remainder}
\end{array}
$$

The quotient is $-x^2 - 5x - 7$.

b. $\dfrac{6x^5 + 2x^4 - 15x - 5}{3x + 1}$

There is no common factor. Because the coefficient of x in the denominator is 3, multiply both the numerator and denominator by $\frac{1}{3}$.

$$\frac{6x^5 + 2x^4 - 15x - 5}{3x + 1} = \frac{\frac{1}{3}(6x^5 + 2x^4 - 15x - 5)}{\frac{1}{3}(3x + 1)}$$

$$= \frac{2x^5 + \frac{2}{3}x^4 - 5x - \frac{5}{3}}{x + \frac{1}{3}}$$

Now you can use synthetic division to divide. Remember to use 0's as placeholders in the dividend.

$$
\begin{array}{r|rrrrrr}
-\frac{1}{3} & 2 & \frac{2}{3} & 0 & 0 & -5 & -\frac{5}{3} \\
             &   & -\frac{2}{3} & 0 & 0 & 0 & \frac{5}{3} \\
\hline
             & 2 & 0 & 0 & 0 & -5 & \underline{|0} \quad \text{remainder}
\end{array}
$$

The quotient is $2x^4 - 5$.

Synthetic Division

To divide P by $x - a$, use this diagram to help you remember the process.

$$
\begin{array}{l|l}
\underline{a} & \text{C o e f f i c i e n t s   o f   } P \\
\hline
 & \text{C o e f f i c i e n t s   o f   Q u o t i e n t   } |\text{Remainder}
\end{array}
$$

The Rational Roots Theorem

Factoring to Find Roots and Solve Equations

You can find roots of a polynomial equation $P(x) = 0$ by factoring the polynomial, using the Zero-Product Property to set each factor equal to 0, and solving.

Find the roots to solve each equation.

a. $x^3 + 2x^2 - 63x = 0$

Remove a common factor of x. $\qquad\qquad\qquad\qquad\qquad\qquad$ $x(x^2 + 2x - 63) = 0$

Write the factored expression with missing values. $\qquad\qquad$ $x(x\ \ ?)(x\ \ ?) = 0$

For the trinomial $x^2 + 2x - 63$ in the form $x^2 + bx + c$, the values of b and c are $b = 2$ and $c = -63$.

Make a table to look for factors of -63 that have a sum of 2.

Only list factor pairs in which the positive number has a greater absolute value.

Factors of -63	Sum
-1 and 63	62
-3 and 21	18
-7 and 9	2

The factors are -7 and 9.

Fill in the missing values in the factored expression. $\qquad$ $x(x - 7)(x + 9) = 0$

Use the Zero-Product Property to solve. $\qquad$ $x = 0$ or $x - 7 = 0$ or $x + 9 = 0$

Roots of the equation: $\qquad\qquad\qquad\qquad$ $x = 0$ or $x = 7$ or $x = -9$

CHECK $\quad x^3 + 2x^2 - 63x = 0 \qquad\qquad x^3 + 2x^2 - 63x = 0 \qquad\qquad x^3 + 2x^2 - 63x = 0$

$\qquad\qquad 0^3 + 2(0)^2 - 63(0) = 0 \qquad 7^3 + 2(7)^2 - 63(7) = 0 \qquad (-9)^3 + 2(-9)^2 - 63(-9) = 0$

$\qquad\qquad\qquad\qquad 0 + 0 - 0 = 0 \qquad\qquad 343 + 98 - 441 = 0 \qquad\qquad -729 + 162 + 567 = 0$

$\qquad\qquad\qquad\qquad\qquad\qquad 0 = 0 ✔ \qquad\qquad\qquad\qquad 0 = 0 ✔ \qquad\qquad\qquad\qquad\qquad 0 = 0 ✔$

The roots are $x = 0$, $x = 7$, and $x = -9$.

b. $49x^2 - 256 = 0$

Use the formula for the difference of two squares to factor. $\qquad$ $(7x + 16)(7x - 16) = 0$

Use the Zero-Product Property to solve. $\qquad$ $7x + 16 = 0$ or $7x - 16 = 0$

Roots of the equation: $\qquad\qquad\qquad\qquad$ $x = -\dfrac{16}{7}$ or $x = \dfrac{16}{7}$

CHECK $\qquad 49x^2 - 256 = 0 \qquad\qquad\qquad 49x^2 - 256 = 0$

$\qquad\qquad 49\left(-\dfrac{16}{7}\right)^2 - 256 = 0 \qquad\quad 49\left(-\dfrac{16}{7}\right)^2 - 256 = 0$

$\qquad\qquad \overset{1}{\cancel{49}}\left(\dfrac{256}{\cancel{49}}\right) - 256 = 0 \qquad\quad \overset{1}{\cancel{49}}\left(\dfrac{256}{\cancel{49}}\right) - 256 = 0$

$\qquad\qquad\qquad 256 - 256 = 0 \qquad\qquad\qquad 256 - 256 = 0$

$\qquad\qquad\qquad\qquad\qquad 0 = 0 ✔ \qquad\qquad\qquad\qquad\qquad 0 = 0 ✔$

The roots are $x = \pm\dfrac{16}{7}$.

Watch Out !

Remember that opposites raised to even powers are equal.

The roots in Example 1(b) are opposites. So their squares are equal. You only need to check the positive root in the equation to verify both roots.

There are a limited number of possibilities for the rational roots of an equation.

Rational Roots of Polynomial Functions

For an equation $(ax - b)(cx - d) = 0$, the following is true by the Zero-Product Property.

$$ax - b = 0 \quad \text{or} \quad cx - d = 0$$
$$ax = b \quad \text{or} \quad cx = d$$
$$x = \frac{b}{a} \quad \text{or} \quad x = \frac{d}{c}$$

The product of the binomials $(ax - b)(cx - d)$ is $acx^2 - (ad + bc)x + bd$.

So the trinomial equation $acx^2 - (ad + bc)x + bd = 0$ also has roots $\frac{b}{a}$ and $\frac{d}{c}$.

The numerators, b and d, are factors of the constant term, bd.

The denominators, a and c, are factors of the leading coefficient, ab.

The Rational Zeros Theorem

If the polynomial equation $a_n x^n + a_{n-1}x^{n-1} + a_{n-2}x^{n-2} + \ldots + a_1 x + a_0 = 0$ has integer coefficients, then every rational root of the equation has the form $\frac{p}{q}$ shown below.

$$\frac{p}{q} \begin{array}{l} \leftarrow \text{a factor of the constant term } a_0 \\ \leftarrow \text{a factor of the leading coefficient } a_n \end{array}$$

This is the Rational Roots Theorem. Because it also applies to zeros of polynomial functions, it is also known as the **Rational Zeros Theorem** .

Need More HELP

For more help with rational roots and rational zeros, go to *Rational Zeros of a Polynomial Function* (p. 1636).

EXAMPLE 2

List the possible rational roots.

a. $x^4 - 16x^2 + 3x + 7 = 0$

Always include both positive and negative factors.

Factors of the constant term, 7: $\pm 1, \pm 7$

Factors of the leading coefficient term, 1: ± 1

Possible rational roots: $\pm\frac{1}{1}, \pm\frac{7}{1}$, or $\pm 1, \pm 7$

b. $-9x^3 + 14x^2 - 90x - 12 = 0$

Factors of the constant term, -12: $\pm 1, \pm 2, \pm 3, \pm 4, \pm 6, \pm 12$

Factors of the leading coefficient, -9: $\pm 1, \pm 3, \pm 9$

Possible rational roots:
$$\pm\frac{1}{1}, \pm\frac{2}{1}, \pm\frac{3}{1}, \pm\frac{4}{1}, \pm\frac{6}{1}, \pm\frac{12}{1}$$
$$\pm\frac{1}{3}, \pm\frac{2}{3}, \pm\frac{3}{3}, \pm\frac{4}{3}, \pm\frac{6}{3}, \pm\frac{12}{3}$$
$$\pm\frac{1}{9}, \pm\frac{2}{9}, \pm\frac{3}{9}, \pm\frac{4}{9}, \pm\frac{6}{9}, \pm\frac{12}{9} \quad \text{Simplify and remove duplicates.}$$

Possible rational roots: $\pm 1, \pm 2, \pm 3, \pm 4, \pm 6, \pm 12, \pm\frac{1}{3}, \pm\frac{2}{3}, \pm\frac{4}{3}, \pm\frac{1}{9}, \pm\frac{2}{9}, \pm\frac{4}{9}$

SEARCH

To see step-by-step videos of these problems, enter the page number into the SWadvantage.com Search Bar.

Factoring to Find Roots and Solve Equations

You may be able to find the roots of a polynomial equation $P(x) = 0$ by finding the possible rational roots and testing them by using synthetic division, the Factor Theorem, and the Remainder Theorem. When you find a root, you can factor the corresponding binomial out of the polynomial. Then test possible roots of the quotient.

Need More
HELP
Test the easiest values first. There's no reason to test a fraction first if an integer can be tested and found to be a root.

EXAMPLE 3

Find all roots of $3x^3 - 2x^2 - 12x + 8 = 0$, if possible.

STEP 1 First, find the possible rational roots.

Factors of the constant term: $\pm 1, \pm 2, \pm 4, \pm 8$

Factors of the leading coefficient term: $\pm 1, \pm 3$

Possible rational roots: $\pm 1, \pm 2, \pm 4, \pm 8, \pm\frac{1}{3}, \pm\frac{2}{3}, \pm\frac{4}{3}, \pm\frac{8}{3}$

STEP 2 Use synthetic division to test possible roots. If the remainder is 0, the number is a root and you can factor out the expression ($x -$ the root).

Test 1:

$$\underline{1|} \quad 3 \quad -2 \quad -12 \quad 8$$
$$\qquad \quad 3 \quad \; 1 \quad -11$$
$$\overline{\quad 3 \quad \; 1 \quad -11 \quad \underline{|-3}}$$

Test 2:

$$\underline{2|} \quad 3 \quad -2 \quad -12 \quad 8$$
$$\qquad \quad 6 \quad \; 8 \quad -8$$
$$\overline{\quad 3 \quad \; 4 \quad \; -4 \quad \underline{|0} \checkmark}$$

Because 2 is a root, $(x - 2)$ is a factor of the polynomial.

From the synthetic division, the factored equation is $(x - 2)(3x^2 + 4x - 4) = 0$. The possible rational roots of $3x^2 + 4x - 4 = 0$ are $\pm 1, \pm 2, \pm 4, \pm\frac{1}{3}, \pm\frac{2}{3}, \pm\frac{4}{3}$

Test 4:

$$\underline{4|} \quad 3 \quad 4 \quad -4$$
$$\qquad \quad 12 \quad 64$$
$$\overline{\quad 3 \quad 16 \quad \underline{|60}}$$

Test -1:

$$\underline{-1|} \quad 3 \quad 4 \quad -4$$
$$\qquad \quad \; -3 \quad -1$$
$$\overline{\quad 3 \quad 1 \quad \underline{|-5}}$$

Test -2:

$$\underline{-2|} \quad 3 \quad 4 \quad -4$$
$$\qquad \quad \; -6 \quad 4$$
$$\overline{\quad 3 \quad -2 \quad \underline{|0} \checkmark}$$

Because -2 is a root, $(x + 2)$ is a factor of the polynomial.

From the synthetic division, the remaining factor is $3x - 2$. Find the remaining root.

$3x - 2 = 0$

$x = \frac{2}{3}$. The roots are 2, -2, and $\frac{2}{3}$. $(x - 2)(x + 2)(3x - 2) = 0$.

GOT TO KNOW!

Rational Roots Theorem

If a polynomial equation $P(x) = 0$ has integer coefficients, then every rational zero has this form.

$\dfrac{p}{q}$ $\leftarrow$ a factor of the constant term
     $\leftarrow$ a factor of the leading coefficient

EXAMPLE 4

A funnel is made up of a cylinder and a portion of a cone called a frustum. The formula for the volume of a frustum of a cone is $\frac{1}{3}\pi h(a^2 + ab + b^2)$, where h is the height, a is the radius of one base, and b is the radius of the other. The volume of the funnel is 300π cm³. Find x, the radius of the cylinder and of the lower base of the frustum.

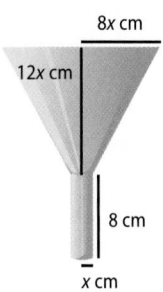

8x cm

12x cm

8 cm

x cm

SEARCH

To see step-by-step videos of these problems, enter the page number into the SWadvantage.com Search Bar.

STEP 1 Write a polynomial for the volume of the funnel.

Funnel volume = volume of the cone frustum + volume of the cylinder

Volume in terms of x: $V(x) = \frac{1}{3}\pi(12x)[x^2 + x(8x) + (8x)^2] + \pi x^2(8)$

Multiply. $= 4\pi x \cdot (x^2 + 8x^2 + 64x^2) + 8\pi x^2$

Simplify. $= 4\pi x \cdot \quad 73x^2 \quad + 8\pi x^2$

Multiply. $= 292\pi x^3 + 8\pi x^2$

STEP 2 Write and simplify the polynomial equation to represent the problem situation.

Set the volume equal to 300π cm³. $\qquad 292\pi x^3 + 8\pi x^2 = 300\pi$

Subtract 300π from both sides. $\qquad 292\pi x^3 + 8\pi x^2 - 300\pi = 0$

Divide both sides by the constant 4π. $\qquad 73x^3 + 2x^2 - 75 = 0$

STEP 3 Determine the possible rational roots.

Factors of constant term: $\pm 1, \pm 3, \pm 5, \pm 15, \pm 25, \pm 75$; Factors of leading term: $\pm 1, \pm 73$.

Possible rational roots: $\pm 1, \pm 3, \pm 5, \pm 15, \pm 25, \pm 75, \pm\frac{1}{73}, \pm\frac{3}{73}, \pm\frac{5}{73}, \pm\frac{15}{73}, \pm\frac{25}{73}, \pm\frac{75}{73}$.

Since x represents a length, you can eliminate all possible negative roots.

STEP 4 Graph $y = 73x^3 + 2x^2 - 75$ to see whether any of the possible rational roots may be roots.

There appears to be only one root, at $x = 1$ or at $x = \frac{75}{73}$. Use synthetic division to test $x = 1$ in the equation $73x^3 + 2x^2 - 75 = 0$.

```
1| 73    2    0   -75
         73   75   75
   ─────────────────
   73   75   75   |0  remainder
```

The remainder is 0, so 1 is a root, and $x - 1$ is a factor.

$(x - 1)(73x^2 + 75x + 75) = 0$

The discriminant of $73x^2 + 75x + 75$ is $-16{,}275$.
So there are no other real roots.

500

−4.7 | 4.7

−500

Need More HELP?

For help with discriminants, go to *Using the Discriminant*, (p. 1714).

STEP 5 **CHECK** Volume of the funnel $V = \frac{1}{3}\pi(12)(1)[1^2 + 1(8 \cdot 1) + (8 \cdot 1)^2] + \pi 1^2(8)$

$= 4\pi \cdot 73 + 8\pi$

$= 292\pi + 8\pi$

$= 300\pi$ cm³ ✔

Quadratic Functions and Equations

What Came Before?

- Square roots and properties of numbers, including the Multiplication Property of Zero
- Factoring binomials and trinomials

What's This About?

- Graphs, properties, and transformations of quadratic functions
- Solving quadratic and higher-order equations, including using the Quadratic Formula
- Using quadratic functions to solve word problems that involve the motion of objects through the air

Practical Apps

- Fireworks technicians can use quadratic functions to predict the arcs of various types of fireworks.
- Police investigators can determine the speed of a braking car by measuring the length of skid marks, finding the road surface's coefficient for friction, and then applying a quadratic equation.

just for FUN!

Q: Why was the polynomial equation jealous of the quadratic equation?

A: It had more than one solution!

CONTENTS | UPLOAD | DOWNLOAD | *Algebra*

You can find more practice problems online by visiting:
www.SWadvantage.com

Quadratic Functions

Graphing Quadratic Functions

A *parabola* is a cuplike shape somewhat like a U and somewhat like a V. Every *quadratic function* has a graph with this shape.

A **quadratic function** is any function that can be written in the standard form $y = ax^2 + bx + c$, where $a \neq 0$. The **parent quadratic function** is $y = x^2$, which can be written as $y = 1x^2 + 0x + 0$.

The **axis of symmetry** is the line that can be drawn through the parabola so that one side of the parabola is a reflection of the other. The **vertex** is the point where the line of symmetry intersects the parabola. In the parabola shown above, the axis of symmetry is the y-axis, and the vertex is the origin.

To graph a quadratic function, make a table of ordered pairs.

SEARCH

To see step-by-step videos of these problems, enter the page number into the SWadvantage.com Search Bar.

EXAMPLE

Each equation below is in the form $y = ax^2$. Find the value of *a*. Then graph each quadratic function. Describe the direction in which the parabola opens.

a. $y = 2x^2$

STEP 1 Find the value of *a*.

a is the coefficient of x^2. $a = 2$

STEP 2 Make a table.

x	$2x^2$	y
-2	$2(-2)^2$	8
-1	$2(-1)^2$	2
0	$2(0)^2$	0
1	$2(1)^2$	2
2	$2(2)^2$	8

STEP 3 Graph the ordered pairs. Connect the ordered pairs with a smooth curve.

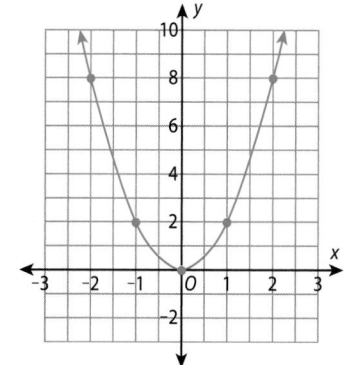

b. $y = -x^2$

STEP 1 Find the value of *a*.

a is the coefficient of x^2. $a = -1$.

STEP 2 Make a table.

x	-3	-2	-1	0	1	2	3
y	-9	-4	-1	0	-1	-4	-9

STEP 3 Graph the ordered pairs. Connect the ordered pairs with a smooth curve.

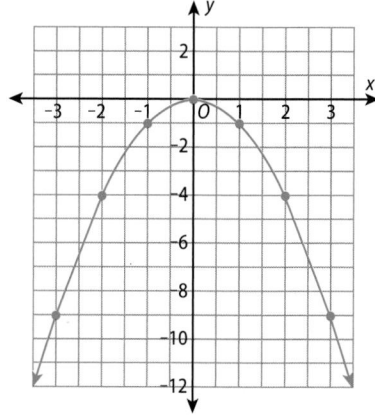

GOT TO KNOW!

Parabolas

A U is not a parabola because its sides are parallel.

A V is not a parabola because its sides and vertex form an angle.

From the graphs, you can see that when the value of *a* is positive, the parabola opens upward. When the value of *a* is negative, the parabola opens downward.

EXAMPLE 2

Explain whether the graph of each function opens upward or downward. Then graph.

a. $y = -2x^2 + 4x - 1$

The function is in the form $y = ax^2 + bx + c$. The value of a is -2, which is negative, so the graph opens downward.

Make a table.

x	$-2x^2 + 4x + 1$	y
-2	$-2(-2)^2 + 4(-2) + 1$	-15
-1	$-2(-1)^2 + 4(-1) + 1$	-5
0	$-2(0)^2 + 4(0) + 1$	1
1	$-2(1)^2 + 4(1) + 1$	3
2	$-2(2)^2 + 4(2) + 1$	1
3	$-2(3)^2 + 4(3) + 1$	-5
4	$-2(4)^2 + 4(4) + 1$	-15

Graph the ordered pairs.

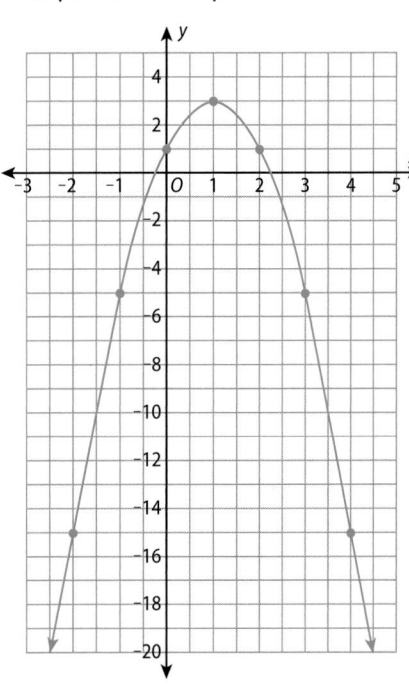

Notice that the left and right sides are symmetric.

Need More HELP?

To graph the curve more accurately, find more ordered pairs between the integers. For example, when $x = -1.5$, $y = -9.5$.

b. $y = \frac{1}{2}x^2 - 4$

The function is in the form $y = ax^2 + bx + c$. The value of a is positive, so the graph opens upward.

Make a table.

x	$\frac{1}{2}x^2 - 4$	y
-3	$\frac{1}{2}(-3)^2 - 4$	$\frac{1}{2}$
-2	$\frac{1}{2}(-2)^2 - 4$	-2
-1	$\frac{1}{2}(-1)^2 - 4$	$-3\frac{1}{2}$
0	$\frac{1}{2}(0)^2 - 4$	-4
1	$\frac{1}{2}(1)^2 - 4$	$-3\frac{1}{2}$
2	$\frac{1}{2}(2)^2 - 4$	-2
3	$\frac{1}{2}(3)^2 - 4$	$\frac{1}{2}$

Graph the ordered pairs.

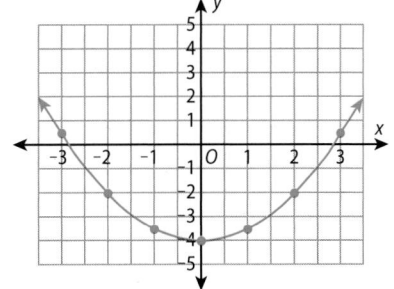

GOT TO KNOW!

Graphing Quadratic Functions

When $y = ax^2 + bx + c$, the sign of a determines the direction in which the parabola opens.

Plot enough ordered pairs to draw a smooth, symmetric curve.

Recognizing Quadratic Functions

A function is a quadratic function if and only if it can be written in the form $y = ax^2 + bx + c$, where $a \neq 0$.

In a linear function, the change in y is constant for a constant change in x. The differences between values of y for consecutive values of x, the **first-order differences**, are constant.

x	0	1	2	3	4
$y = 2x - 1$	−1	1	3	5	7

$\searrow +2 \nearrow \searrow +2 \nearrow \searrow +2 \nearrow \searrow +2 \nearrow$ First-order differences

In a quadratic function, the first-order differences are linear for a constant change in x. The differences between these linear differences, the **second-order differences**, are constant.

x	0	1	2	3	4
$y = x^2 - 1$	−1	0	3	8	15

$\searrow +1 \nearrow \searrow +3 \nearrow \searrow +5 \nearrow \searrow +7 \nearrow$ First-order differences

$\searrow +2 \nearrow \searrow +2 \nearrow \searrow +2 \nearrow$ Second-order differences

---

EXAMPLE 1

SEARCH

To see step-by-step videos of these problems, enter the page number into the SWadvantage.com Search Bar.

Determine whether each function is linear, quadratic, or neither.

a. $y + (x + 1)^2 = 5$

Simplify and solve for y.

$$y + x^2 + 2x + 1 = 5$$
$$y = -x^2 - 2x + 4$$

The function can be written in the form $y = ax^2 + bx + c$, so this is a quadratic function.

b.

x	−3	−2	−1	0	1
y	5	11	14	14	11

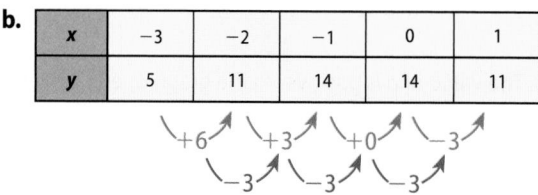

The second-order differences are constant, so the function is quadratic.

c.

x	5	10	15	20	25
y	1	4	9	14	17

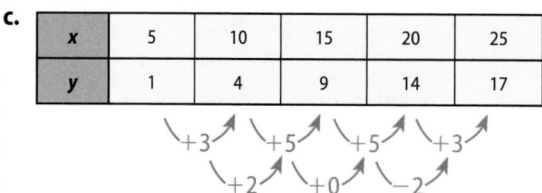

Neither the first-order differences nor the second-order differences are constant, so the function is neither linear nor quadratic.

Minimum and Maximum Values

The highest or lowest point on a parabola is called the vertex. The domain of a quadratic function is all real numbers $\mathcal{R}$. The range is determined by the location of the vertex and whether the parabola opens upward or downward.

A quadratic function that opens upward has a **minimum value** at the vertex.

The range is all y-values greater than or equal to the y-value at the vertex.

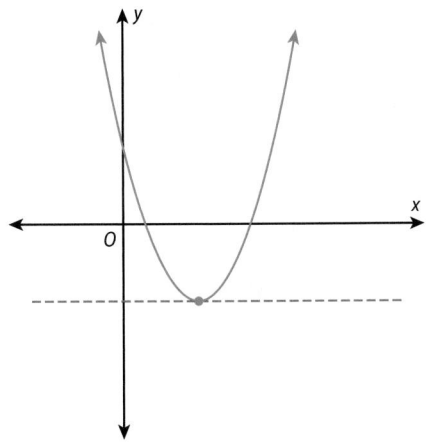

A quadratic function that opens downward has a **maximum value** at the vertex.

The range is all y-values less than or equal to the y-value at the vertex.

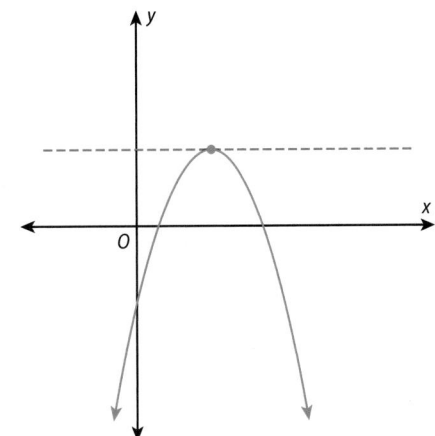

EXAMPLE 2

Identify the vertex, the minimum or maximum value of the quadratic function, and the domain and range for each parabola.

a.

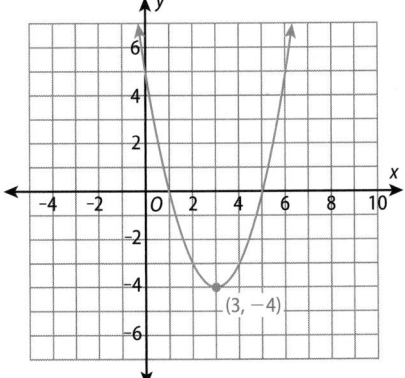

The vertex is $(3, -4)$. The minimum value is -4.

Domain: the set of real numbers $\mathcal{R}$

Range: $\{y \mid y \geq -4\}$

b.

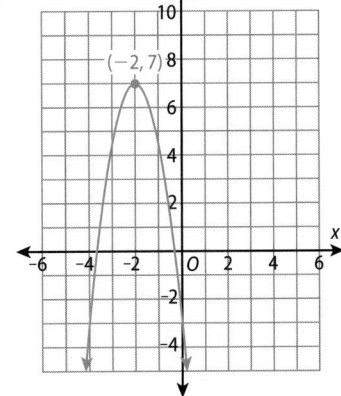

The vertex is $(-2, 7)$. The maximum value is 7.

Domain: the set of real numbers $\mathcal{R}$

Range: $\{y \mid y \leq 7\}$

GOT TO KNOW!

Properties of a Quadratic Function

1. For a constant change in x-values, y-values change as follows:
   - First differences are linear.
   - Second differences are constant.

2. A quadratic function has a maximum or minimum value at the vertex of the parabola.

3. The range is determined by the location of the vertex and whether the parabola opens up or down.

SW SOUTHWESTERN

Zeros of a Quadratic Function

A quadratic function can intersect the x-axis in three different ways.

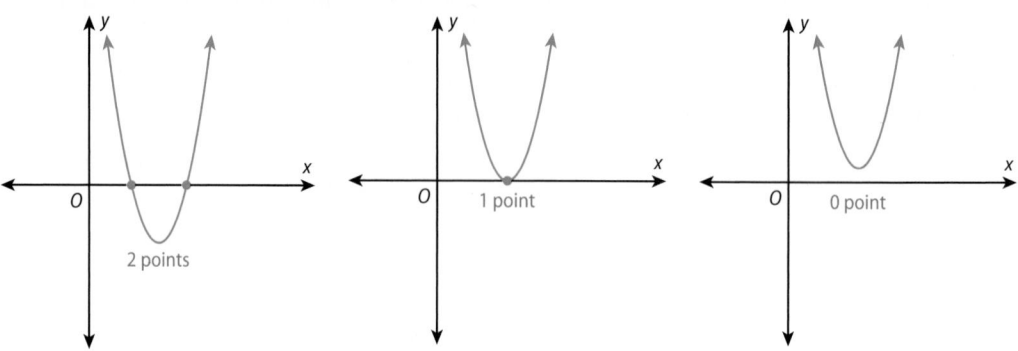

2 points   1 point   0 point

EXAMPLE 3

Find any zeros of the quadratic function from its graph. Check in the function.

a. $y = x^2 - 2x - 3$

b. $y = -x^2 - 8x - 16$

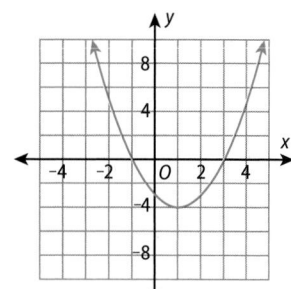   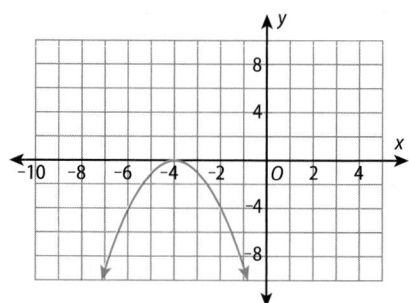

The zeros are $x = -1$ and $x = 3$.

The only zero is $x = -4$.

CHECK Substitute into $y = x^2 - 2x - 3$.

$y = (-1)^2 - 2(-1) - 3$ $y = 3^2 - 2(3) - 3$

    $= 1 + 2 - 3$ $= 9 - 6 - 3$

    $= 0$ ✔ $= 0$ ✔

CHECK Substitute into $y = -x^2 - 8x - 16$.

$y = -(-4)^2 - 8(-4) - 16$

    $= -16 + 32 - 16$

    $= 0$ ✔

Watch Out !

The value of $-x^2$ when $x = -4$ is $-(-4)^2$, not $(-4)^2$.

Vertex and Line of Symmetry of a Quadratic Function

The x-value of the vertex of the quadratic function
$y = ax^2 + bx + c$ is given by $x = -\dfrac{b}{2a}$.

The line $x = -\dfrac{b}{2a}$ is called the line of symmetry
because it divides the graph into two congruent reflections.

If a quadratic function has one zero, the line of symmetry
goes through the zero. If it has two zeros, the line of
symmetry passes through a point halfway between
the zeros on the x-axis.

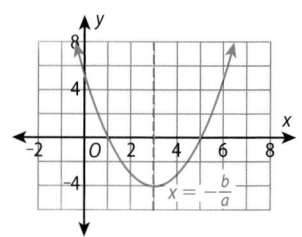

Need More HELP ?

Axis of Symmetry

Some books refer to the line of symmetry of a quadratic function as the axis of symmetry.

1692

EXAMPLE 4

Find the line of symmetry and the vertex of the quadratic function.

$y = x^2 - 2x + 8$

SEARCH

To see step-by-step videos of these problems, enter the page number into the SWadvantage.com Search Bar.

METHOD 1

Graph the function.

The coordinates of the vertex are (1, 7). Since the line of symmetry passes through the vertex, it must be $x = 1$.

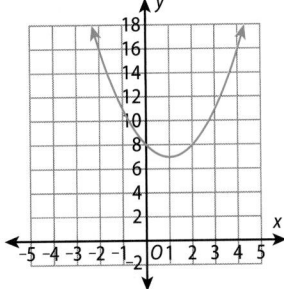

METHOD 2

Use the function.

STEP 1 The line of symmetry is $x = -\dfrac{b}{2a} = -\dfrac{-2}{2(1)} = 1$.

STEP 2 Find the vertex.

The x-coordinate of the vertex is 1.

To find the y-coordinate, evaluate the function at $x = 1$.

$$\begin{aligned} y &= x^2 - 2x + 8 \\ &= 1^2 - 2(1) + 8 \\ &= 1 - 2 + 8 \\ &= 7 \end{aligned}$$

The coordinates of the vertex are (1, 7).

METHOD 3

Use a graphing calculator.

Graph the function in Y1. Press **2nd** **CALC** , choose **3:minimum**, and press **ENTER**. Press the left arrow key, move to the left of the vertex, and press **ENTER** for the left bound. Press the right arrow key, move to the right of the vertex, and press **ENTER** for the right bound. For the "Guess," move anywhere between the bounds and press **ENTER**.

The coordinates of the vertex are (1, 7). Since the line of symmetry passes through the vertex, it must be $x = 1$.

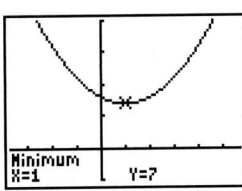

GOT TO KNOW!

Properties of Quadratic Functions

Quadratic functions can have 0, 1, or 2 zeros.

The graph of the quadratic function $y = ax^2 + bx + c$ has a line of symmetry at $x = -\dfrac{b}{2a}$.

The maximum or minimum value is the value of the function at $x = -\dfrac{b}{2a}$.

Transforming Quadratics

Stretching and Shrinking Quadratic Functions

The sign of a in the function $y = ax^2$ determines whether the parabola opens upward or downward. The value of a also affects how the graph of the function differs from the graph of the parent function $y = x^2$. The graph of $y = ax^2$ is called a **transformation** of $y = x^2$.

When $|a| > 1$, the graph of the parent function is *compressed* by the factor a.

When $|a| < 1$, the graph of the parent function is *stretched* by the factor a.

When a is negative, the graph of the parent function is reflected across the x-axis.

Ways to REMEMBER

Use the inequality symbols to help you remember how a parent function is transformed.

When $|a| > 1$, the graph of the parent function is **compressed** ($>$).

When $|a| < 1$, the graph of the parent function is **stretched** ($<$).

EXAMPLE 1

Graph each quadratic function along with the parent quadratic function $y = x^2$. Describe how the graph is a transformation of the graph of the parent function.

a. $y = 2x^2$

b. $y = -\dfrac{1}{3}x^2$

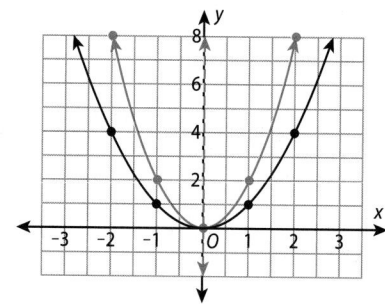

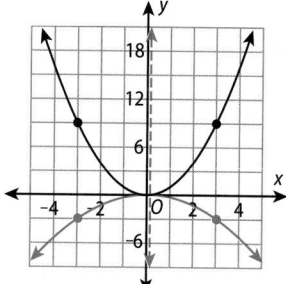

The parent graph is compressed by a factor of 2. The vertex, (0, 0), and the line of symmetry, $x = 0$, are the same.

The parent graph is stretched by a factor of $\dfrac{1}{3}$ and reflected across the x-axis. The vertex, (0, 0) and the line of symmetry, $x = 0$, are the same.

Need More HELP ?

Compressing the graph along the x-axis by a given value is the same as multiplying the y-value of each point by that value. Stretching the graph along the x-axis by a given factor is the same as dividing the y-value of each point by that value.

Compressing the graph of a function appears to narrow the graph along the x-axis. Stretching it appears to widen the graph along the x-axis.

The graph of $y = ax^2$ where $|a| > 1$ is *narrower* than the graph of $y = x^2$. The graph of $y = ax^2$ where $|a| < 1$ is *wider* than the graph of $y = x^2$. So as $|a|$ increases, the graph becomes increasingly narrow.

EXAMPLE 2

Order the quadratic functions from the narrowest graph to the widest.

$$y = -x^2 \qquad y = 3x^2 \qquad y = \frac{2}{3}x^2 \qquad y = -0.2x^2 \qquad y = -25x^2$$

STEP 1 Write each function in the form $y = |a|x^2$ by omitting the sign of the coefficient.

$$y = x^2 \qquad y = 3x^2 \qquad y = \frac{2}{3}x^2 \qquad y = 0.2x^2 \qquad y = 25x^2$$

STEP 2 Order the functions in Step 1 by their coefficients, from greatest to least.

$$y = 25x^2 \qquad y = 3x^2 \qquad y = 1x^2 \qquad y = \frac{2}{3}x^2 \qquad y = 0.2x^2$$

STEP 3 Restore the sign of the coefficient to write each function in the form $y = ax^2$.

Narrowest graph ————————————→ Widest graph

$$y = -25x^2 \qquad y = 3x^2 \qquad y = -x^2 \qquad y = \frac{2}{3}x^2 \qquad y = -0.2x^2$$

Vertical Translations

The value of k in the function $y = x^2 + k$ also affects how the graph of the function differs from the graph of the parent function $y = x^2$. This transformation is called a **vertical translation** of the parent function.

When $k > 0$, the graph of the parent function is *translated up* $|k|$ units.

When $k < 0$, the graph of the parent function is *translated down* $|k|$ units.

EXAMPLE 3

Graph each quadratic function along with the parent quadratic function $y = x^2$. Describe how the graph is a transformation of the graph of the parent function.

a. $y = x^2 + 3$

b. $y = x^2 - 4$

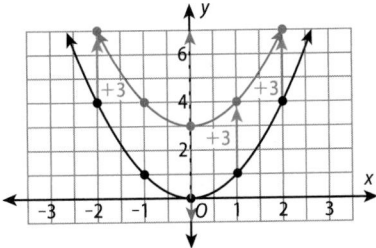

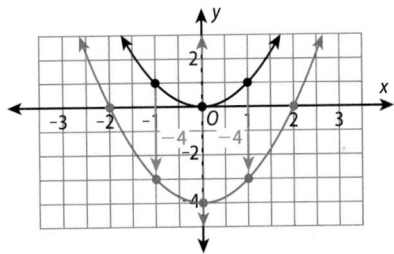

The graph is translated up 3 units.

The graph is translated down 4 units.

SEARCH

To see step-by-step videos of these problems, enter the page number into the SWadvantage.com Search Bar.

Horizontal Translations

The value of h in the function $y = (x - h)^2$ also affects how the graph of the function differs from the graph of the parent function $y = x^2$. This transformation is called a **horizontal translation** of the parent function.

When $h > 0$, the graph of the parent function is translated right $|h|$ units.

When $h < 0$, the graph of the parent function is translated left $|h|$ units.

EXAMPLE 4

Graph each quadratic function along with the parent quadratic function $y = x^2$. Describe how the graph is transformed from the graph of the parent function.

a. $y = (x - 4)^2$

b. $y = (x + 2)^2$

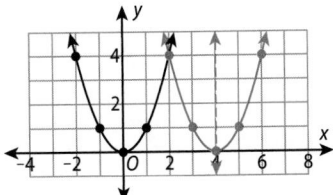

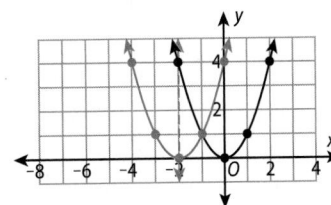

The graph and the line of symmetry are translated right 4 units.

The graph and the line of symmetry are translated left 2 units.

Watch Out !

The value of h in the function $y = (x - h)^2$ is being subtracted. So the minus sign in the function $y = (x - 4)^2$ indicates movement to the right because 4 is positive.

Think of the factor $x - 4$ as being associated with the root $+4$.

Combining Transformations

EXAMPLE 5

Graph each quadratic function along with the parent quadratic function $y = x^2$. Describe how the graph is transformed from the graph of the parent function.

a. $y = (x + 4)^2 + 1$

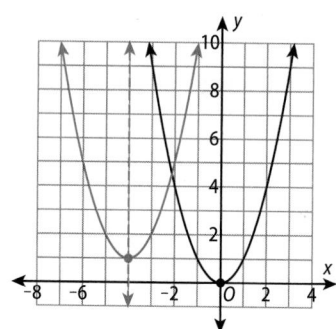

The graph is translated left 4 units and up 1 unit.

b. $y = -2x^2 + 9$

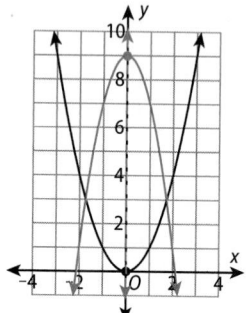

The graph is reflected across the x-axis, compressed by a factor of 2, and translated up 9 units.

c. $y = \frac{1}{4}(x - 3)^2$

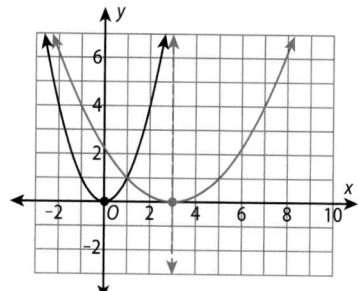

The graph is translated right 3 units and stretched by a factor of $\frac{1}{4}$.

d. $y = -(x + 2)^2 - 3$

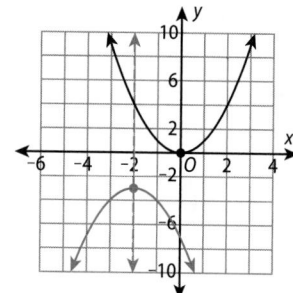

The graph is translated left 2 units, reflected across the x-axis, and translated down 3 units.

EXAMPLE 6

Translate the quadratic function $y = x^2$ so that the vertex is at $(2, -5)$. Then graph.

The vertex of $y = x^2$ is $(0, 0)$. To translate $y = x^2$ to the right 2 units, replace x with $x - 2$.

$y = (x - 2)^2 \rightarrow$ vertex $(2, 0)$

To translate 5 units down, subtract 5.

$y = (x - 2)^2 - 5 \rightarrow$ vertex $(2, -5)$

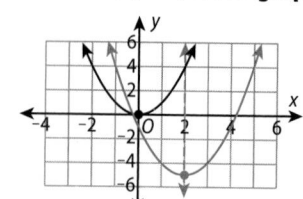

Need More
HELP?

After you find the vertex, use the line of symmetry to help you plot pairs of points.

One point is $(3, -4)$, so $(1, -4)$ is another point.

One point is $(4, -1)$, so $(0, -1)$ is another point.

One point is $(5, 4)$, so $(-1, 4)$ is another point.

EXAMPLE 7

The height of an object dropped from c feet above the surface of the earth or the moon is given by one of the functions below, where t is the time in seconds.

$$\text{Earth: } h(t) = -16t^2 + c \qquad \text{Moon: } h(t) = -2.7t^2 + c$$

a. One golf ball is dropped from 64 feet above the earth. Another is dropped from 16 feet above the earth. Use a graph to compare the heights of the balls t seconds after being dropped.

Graph $h(t) = -16t^2 + 64$ and $h(t) = -16t^2 + 16$ on the same graph. Only nonnegative values make sense in the problem.

The red curve represents the height of the ball dropped from a height of 64 feet.

The black curve represents the height of the ball dropped from a height of 16 feet.

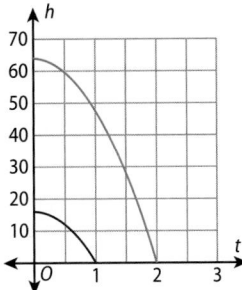

b. What does each y-intercept represent?

The y-intercept is the initial height of each ball.

c. How long does each ball take to hit the ground?

A golf ball hits the ground when the height is 0 feet. This is the x-intercept of each curve.

The ball dropped from a height of 64 feet hits the ground in 2 seconds. The ball dropped from a height of 16 feet hits the ground in 1 second.

d. About how long does a golf ball dropped from 68 feet above the moon take to hit the ground? Use a graph to answer the question.

Graph $h(t) = -2.7t^2 + 68$.

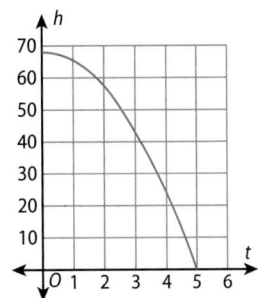

A ball dropped from a height of 68 feet above the moon hits the ground about 5 seconds later.

GOT TO KNOW!

Transforming Quadratic Functions

A transformation of the graph of the parent quadratic function $y = x^2$ is in the form $y = a(x - h)^2 + k$.

The vertex is translated from $(0, 0)$ to (h, k). The line of symmetry is translated from $x = 0$ to $x = h$.

When $|a| > 1$, the graph of $y = x^2$ is compressed by the factor a.

When $|a| < 1$, the graph of $y = x^2$ is stretched by the factor a.

When a is negative, the graph of $y = x^2$ is reflected across the y-axis.

Solving $ax^2 = b$

Solving $x^2 = b$

The equation $x^2 = b$ represents the value of x that has a square equal to b. So the solutions are the square roots of b. If b is positive, the equation $x^2 = b$ has two real square roots. If b equals 0, the equation has one real square root. If b is negative, the equation has no real square roots. The number of square roots is the number of solutions of $x^2 = b$.

$x^2 = 4$	$x^2 = 0$	$x^2 = -4$
2 solutions	1 solution	no solutions

SEARCH

To see step-by-step videos of these problems, enter the page number into the SWadvantage.com Search Bar.

EXAMPLE 1

Solve each quadratic equation.

a. $x^2 = 81$

This is in the form $x^2 = b$, where $b = 81$, a positive number. There are two solutions.

METHOD 1

Take the square root of both sides.
$$x^2 = 81$$
$$x = \pm 9$$

CHECK Substitute both roots into the equation.

$x^2 = 81$	$x^2 = 81$
$(-9)^2 \overset{?}{=} 81$	$(9)^2 \overset{?}{=} 81$
$81 = 81$ ✔	$81 = 81$ ✔

METHOD 2

Solve by factoring.

Subtract 81 from both sides to set one side equal to 0. $\qquad x^2 = 81$

This is a difference of two squares. $\qquad x^2 - 81 = 0$

Factor. $\qquad (x + 9)(x - 9) = 0$

Use the Zero-Product Property. $\qquad x = -9 \text{ or } x = 9$

METHOD 3

Solve by graphing the equation $x^2 = 81$ on a graphing calculator.

Graph Y1 $= x^2$ and Y2 $= 81$. $\qquad$ Find the x-values where the functions intersect.

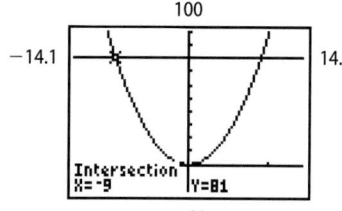 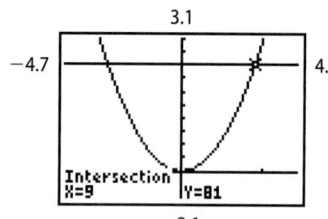

$$x = -9 \text{ or } x = 9$$

b. $x^2 = -2$

Because x^2 must be nonnegative and -2 has no real square roots, there is no solution.

Need More
HELP ?

Use 2nd CALC to access the intersect function on the graphing calculator.

For more help with using the intersect function, go to *Solving a System by Graphing* (p. 1564).

If a square root is not of a perfect square, you may be able to simplify it.

Need More

HELP ?

For more help with simplifying square roots, go to *Square Roots* (p. 1400).

EXAMPLE 2

Solve $x^2 = 45$.

$$x^2 = 45$$

45 is not a perfect square. $x = \pm\sqrt{45}$

Simplify the square root. $x = \pm\sqrt{3^2 \cdot 5}$

$$x = \pm 3\sqrt{5}$$

CHECK Substitute both roots into the equation.

$x^2 = 45$	$x^2 = 45$
$(-3\sqrt{5})^2 \overset{?}{=} 45$	$(3\sqrt{5})^2 \overset{?}{=} 45$
$(-3)^2 (\sqrt{5})^2 \overset{?}{=} 45$	$(3)^2 (\sqrt{5})^2 \overset{?}{=} 45$
$45 = 45$ ✔	$45 = 45$ ✔

Solving $ax^2 = b$

To solve $ax^2 = b$, first divide both sides by a. Then solve as for $x^2 = b$.

EXAMPLE 3

Solve each quadratic equation.

a. $-2x^2 = -50$

Divide both sides by -2. $\dfrac{-2x^2}{-2} = \dfrac{-50}{-2}$

$$x^2 = 25$$

$$x = \pm 5$$

CHECK Substitute both roots into the equation.

$-2x^2 = -50$	$-2x^2 = -50$
$-2(-5)^2 \overset{?}{=} -50$	$-2(5)^2 \overset{?}{=} -50$
$-50 = -50$ ✔	$-50 = -50$ ✔

b. $4x^2 = 48$

Divide both sides by 4. $\dfrac{4x^2}{4} = \dfrac{48}{4}$

$$x^2 = 12$$

12 is not a perfect square. $x = \pm\sqrt{12}$

Simplify the square root. $x = \pm\sqrt{2^2 \cdot 3}$

$$x = \pm 2\sqrt{3}$$

CHECK Substitute both roots into the equation.

$4x^2 = 48$	$4x^2 = 48$
$4(-2\sqrt{3})^2 \overset{?}{=} 48$	$4(2\sqrt{3})^2 \overset{?}{=} 48$
$4(-2)^2 (\sqrt{3})^2 \overset{?}{=} 48$	$4(2)^2 (\sqrt{3})^2 \overset{?}{=} 48$
$48 = 48$ ✔	$48 = 48$ ✔

GOT TO KNOW!

Solving $ax^2 = b$

1. Divide both sides by a.

2. Determine the number of solutions by the sign of the right side.

3. Find the square roots, or solve by factoring.

The Zero-Product Property

Multiplication by 0

When you multiply any real number by 0, the product is 0.

Numbers		Algebra	
$5 \cdot 0 = 0$	$0 \cdot 3 = 0$	$a \cdot 0 = 0$	$0 \cdot b = 0$
$3(0) = 0$	$0(-2) = 0$	If $a = 0$ or $b = 0$, then $ab = 0$.	
$\pi \times 0 = 0$	$0 \times \pi = 0$		

Because the product of two nonzero numbers cannot equal 0, it is also true that if the product of two numbers is 0, then at least one of the numbers must equal 0.

The Zero-Product Property

If a and b are real numbers and $ab = 0$, then $a = 0$ or $b = 0$.

If $a = 0$ or $b = 0$, then $ab = 0$. This is the converse of the property above.

Need More HELP?

Remember that the word *or* is used in a compound statement called a disjunction. A disjunction is true when one or both simple statements are true.

For more help with disjunctions, go to *Conditionals* in *Geometry* (Book 1, p. 612).

EXAMPLE 1

Solve.

a. $7x = 0$

> **METHOD 1**
>
> Divide both sides by 7. $\dfrac{7x}{7} = \dfrac{0}{7}$
>
> Simplify. $x = 0$

> **METHOD 2**
>
> Use the Zero-Product Property. $7 = 0$ ✗ or $x = 0$
>
> $7 = 0$ is a false statement. $x = 0$

b. $n \cdot 4 = 0$

> Use the Zero-Product Property. $n = 0$ or $4 = 0$ ✗
>
> $4 = 0$ is a false statement. $n = 0$

Because algebraic expressions represent numbers, the Zero-Product Property is true when factors of a product are algebraic expressions.

SEARCH

To see step-by-step videos of these problems, enter the page number into the SWadvantage.com Search Bar.

EXAMPLE 2

Use the Zero-Product Property to solve.

a. $4(x - 3) = 0$

> Use the Zero-Product Property. $4 = 0$ ✗ or $x - 3 = 0$
>
> Add 3 to both sides of $x - 3 = 0$. $x = 3$

b. $(r + 2)\pi = 0$

> Use the Zero-Product Property. $r + 2 = 0$ or $\pi = 0$ ✗
>
> Subtract 2 from both sides of $r + 2 = 0$. $r = -2$

EXAMPLE 3

Use the Zero-Product Property to solve.

a. $(x + 1)(x - 2) = 0$

Use the Zero-Product Property. $\qquad$ $x + 1 = 0$ or $x - 2 = 0$

Solve each equation separately. $\qquad$ $x = -1$ or $\quad x = 2$

CHECK Substitute each solution into the original equation.

$$(x + 1)(x - 2) = 0 \qquad (x + 1)(x - 2) = 0$$
$$(-1 + 1)(-1 - 2) \overset{?}{=} 0 \qquad (2 + 1)(2 - 2) \overset{?}{=} 0$$
$$0(-3) \overset{?}{=} 0 \qquad\qquad 3(0) \overset{?}{=} 0$$
$$0 = 0 ✔ \qquad\qquad\qquad 0 = 0 ✔$$

There are two solutions, $x = -1$ or $x = 2$. The solution set is $\{-1, 2\}$.

b. $3t(9 - t) = 0$

Use the Zero-Product Property. $\qquad$ $3t = 0$ or $9 - t = 0$

Solve each equation separately. $\qquad$ $t = 0$ or $\quad 9 = t$

The solution set is $\{0, 9\}$.

c. $(2x - 5)(4x + 3) = 0$

Use the Zero-Product Property. $\qquad$ $2x - 5 = 0$ or $4x + 3 = 0$

Solve each equation separately. $\qquad\qquad$ $2x = 5$ or $\quad 4x = -3$

$$x = \frac{5}{2} \text{ or} \quad x = -\frac{3}{4}$$

The solution set is $\left\{-\frac{3}{4}, \frac{5}{2}\right\}$.

The Zero-Product Property can be extended to products of more than two factors.

EXAMPLE 4

Use the Zero-Product Property to solve. $\qquad 2x\left(\frac{1}{2}x + 6\right)(3x - 1) = 0$

Use the Zero-Product Property. $\qquad$ $2x = 0$ or $\frac{1}{2}x + 6 = 0$ or $3x - 1 = 0$

Solve each equation separately. $\qquad$ $x = 0$ or $\qquad \frac{1}{2}x = -6$ or $\quad 3x = 1$

$$x = 0 \text{ or} \qquad x = -12 \text{ or} \quad x = \frac{1}{3}$$

The solution set is $\left\{-12, 0, \frac{1}{3}\right\}$.

GOT TO KNOW!

The Zero-Product Property

If a and b are real numbers and $ab = 0$, then $a = 0$ or $b = 0$.

Factoring to Solve Quadratics

Solving Quadratic Equations by Factoring

You know that if $(x - 2)(x - 1) = 0$, then $x - 2 = 0$ or $x - 1 = 0$ by the Zero-Product Property, so $x = 2$ or $x = 1$.

Equivalent equations have the same solutions.

Write a quadratic equation that is equivalent to $(x - 2)(x - 1) = 0$.

Use FOIL to multiply the factors. $x^2 - 1x - 2x + 2 = 0$

Combine like terms. $x^2 - 3x + 2 = 0$

Because $x^2 - 3x + 2 = 0$ and $(x - 2)(x - 1) = 0$ are equivalent equations, both equations have the same solution set, $\{1, 2\}$. So you can use factoring to solve some quadratic equations.

Need More HELP ?

Equivalent *expressions* have the same value for every value given to the variables.

So $2x + 4$ and $2(x + 2)$ are equivalent expressions.

Equivalent *equations* have the same solutions.

So $3x = 0$ and $x + 1 = 1$ are equivalent equations.

EXAMPLE 1

Solve $x^2 - 4 = 0$.

STEP 1 Factor the binomial. $x^2 - 4 = 0$

Use the difference of two squares. $(x + 2)(x - 2) = 0$

STEP 2 Solve.

Use the Zero-Product Property. $x + 2 = 0$ or $x - 2 = 0$

Solve each equation separately. $x = -2$ or $x = 2$

STEP 3 Check the solution set $\{-2, 2\}$ by substituting the values for x in the original equation.

CHECK $x^2 - 4 = 0$ $x^2 - 4 = 0$

$(-2)^2 - 4 \stackrel{?}{=} 0$ $2^2 - 4 \stackrel{?}{=} 0$

$4 - 4 \stackrel{?}{=} 0$ $4 - 4 \stackrel{?}{=} 0$

$0 = 0$ ✔ $0 = 0$ ✔

There are two solutions, $x = -2$ or $x = 2$. The solution set is $\{-2, 2\}$.

SEARCH

To see step-by-step videos of these problems, enter the page number into the SWadvantage.com Search Bar.

EXAMPLE 2

Solve $15t - t^2 = 0$.

STEP 1 Factor the binomial. $15t - t^2 = 0$

Use the Distributive Property. $t(15 - t) = 0$

STEP 2 Solve.

Use the Zero-Product Property. $t = 0$ or $15 - t = 0$

Solve the second equation. $t = 0$ or $t = 15$

STEP 3 Check the solution set $\{0, 15\}$ by substituting the values for t in the original quadratic equation.

CHECK $15t - t^2 = 0$ $15t - t^2 = 0$

$15(0) - (0)^2 \stackrel{?}{=} 0$ $15(15) - (15)^2 \stackrel{?}{=} 0$

$0 - 0 \stackrel{?}{=} 0$ $225 - 225 \stackrel{?}{=} 0$

$0 = 0$ ✔ $0 = 0$ ✔

There are two solutions, $t = 0$ or $t = 15$. The solution set is $\{0, 15\}$.

EXAMPLE 3

Solve $x^2 - 2x - 3 = 0$.

STEP 1 Factor the trinomial.

Find factors of -3 that have a sum of -2.

The factors are 1 and -3.

$$x^2 - 2x - 3 = 0$$

$$(x + 1)(x - 3) = 0$$

STEP 2 Solve.

Use the Zero-Product Property.

Solve each equation separately.

$$x + 1 = 0 \text{ or } x - 3 = 0$$

$$x = -1 \text{ or } x = 3$$

STEP 3 Check your solution.

METHOD 1

Substitute the values for x in the original quadratic equation.

CHECK

$$x^2 - 2x - 3 = 0 \qquad\qquad x^2 - 2x - 3 = 0$$

$$(-1)^2 - 2(-1) - 3 \overset{?}{=} 0 \qquad 3^2 - 2(3) - 3 \overset{?}{=} 0$$

$$1 + 2 - 3 \overset{?}{=} 0 \qquad\qquad 9 - 6 - 3 \overset{?}{=} 0$$

$$0 = 0 ✔ \qquad\qquad\qquad 0 = 0 ✔$$

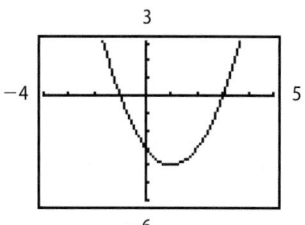

METHOD 2

Graph the related quadratic function and verify the solutions.

The x-intercepts are -1 and 3, so these are the solutions.

There are two solutions, $x = -1$ or $x = 3$. The solution set is $\{-1, 3\}$.

EXAMPLE 4

Solve $2x^2 + 7x - 4 = 0$.

STEP 1 Factor the trinomial. $2x^2 + 7x - 4 = 0$

Factors of 2: 1 and 2.   Factors of -4: -1 and 4, 1 and -4, 2 and -2.

Product   Coefficient of Middle Term

$(x + 1)(2x - 4)$ $-4 + 2 = -2$ ✘

$(x + 2)(2x - 2)$ $-2 + 4 = 2$ ✘

$(x + 4)(2x - 1)$ $-1 + 8 = 7$ ✔

The factored equation is $(x + 4)(2x - 1) = 0$.

STEP 2 Solve.

Use the Zero-Product Property. $x + 4 = 0 \text{ or } 2x - 1 = 0$

Solve each equation separately. $x = -4 \text{ or } x = \dfrac{1}{2}$

STEP 3 Check your solution by substitution.

CHECK

$$2x^2 + 7x - 4 = 0 \qquad\qquad 2x^2 + 7x - 4 = 0$$

$$2(-4)^2 + 7(-4) - 4 \overset{?}{=} 0 \qquad 2\left(\tfrac{1}{2}\right)^2 + 7\left(\tfrac{1}{2}\right) - 4 \overset{?}{=} 0$$

$$32 - 28 - 4 \overset{?}{=} 0 \qquad\qquad \tfrac{1}{2} + \tfrac{7}{2} - 4 \overset{?}{=} 0$$

$$0 = 0 ✔ \qquad\qquad\qquad 0 = 0 ✔$$

Need More

HELP ?

Remember, you only need to check factors until you find a set that works.

For more help with factoring, go to *Factoring $ax^2 + bx + c$* (p. 1666).

Writing the Quadratic in Standard Form Before Factoring

To use factoring to solve a quadratic equation, you may first need to write the equation in standard form, $ax^2 + bx + c = 0$.

EXAMPLE 5

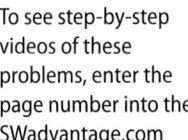

Watch Out !

Although you can factor the left side of the given equation in Example 5 to get $x(x + 3) = 18$, this won't help you to solve the equation.

Solve $x^2 + 3x = 18$.

STEP 1 Write the equation in standard form.

$$x^2 + 3x = 18$$

Subtract 18 from both sides. $x^2 + 3x - 18 = 0$

STEP 2 Factor the trinomial.

Find factors of -18 that have a sum of 3.

The factors are -3 and 6. $(x - 3)(x + 6) = 0$

STEP 3 Solve.

Use the Zero-Product Property. $x - 3 = 0$ or $x + 6 = 0$

Solve each equation separately. $x = 3$ or $x = -6$

Once the equation is in standard form, factor out the greatest common factor, if possible. If the GCF is a constant, you can divide both sides by the constant and simplify the equation.

EXAMPLE 6

SEARCH

To see step-by-step videos of these problems, enter the page number into the SWadvantage.com Search Bar.

Solve $-5x^2 + 40x = 80$.

STEP 1 Write the equation in standard form.

$$-5x^2 + 40x = 80$$

Subtract 80 from both sides. $-5x^2 + 40x - 80 = 0$

STEP 2 Factor the trinomial.

Divide both sides by the GCF, -5. $\dfrac{5x^2}{-5} + \dfrac{40x}{-5} - \dfrac{80}{-5} = \dfrac{0}{-5}$

Simplify. $x^2 - 8x + 16 = 0$

The trinomial is a perfect square. $(x - 4)^2 = 0$

STEP 3 Solve.

Use the Zero-Product Property. $x - 4 = 0$, so $x = 4$

STEP 4 Check by graphing the equation.

Enter $-5x^2 + 40x$ into Y1 and 80 into Y2.

Find the value of x where they intersect.

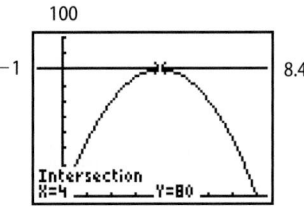

There is one solution, $x = 4$. The solution set is {4}.

Quadratic Functions and Equations   ALGEBRA

EXAMPLE 7

A tennis ball is launched upward from a height of 19.6 meters with an initial velocity of 14.7 meters per second. The height of the ball in meters is given by the equation $h = -4.9t^2 + 14.7t + 19.6$, where t is the number of seconds since the ball was launched. How long does it take for the ball to hit the ground?

Write the equation for the height. $h = -4.9t^2 + 14.7t + 19.6$

The ball hits the ground when $h = 0$. $0 = -4.9t^2 + 14.7t + 19.6$

Divide both sides by the GCF, -4.9. $\dfrac{0}{-4.9} = \dfrac{-4.9t^2}{-4.9} + \dfrac{14.7t}{-4.9} + \dfrac{19.6}{-4.9}$

Simplify. $0 = \quad t^2 \quad - \quad 3t \quad - \quad 4$

Factor the quadratic equation. $0 = (t - 4)(t + 1)$

Use the Zero-Product Property. $t - 4 = 0 \text{ or } t + 1 = 0$

Solve for t. $t = 4 \text{ or } t = -1$

Because time cannot be negative, $t = -1$ second does not make sense in the problem situation.

The tennis ball hits the ground in 4 seconds.

Check by graphing.

Find the positive zero.

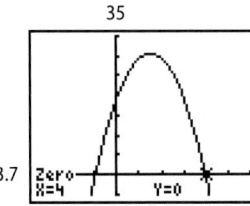

> **Need More HELP?**
>
> The reasonable domain of the height function $h = -4.9t^2 + 14.7t + 19.6$ is $\{t | t \geq 0\}$.
>
> Only points in the first quadrant or on the nonnegative t and h axes make sense in the problem situation.

EXAMPLE 8

The length of the rectangle shown is twice the width plus an additional 3 feet. What are the dimensions?

                                Area A = length $\ell \times$ width w

Substitute given values. $54 = (2x + 3)(x)$

Multiply. $54 = 2x^2 + 3x$

Write in standard form. $0 = 2x^2 + 3x - 54$

Factor the quadratic equation. $0 = (2x - 9)(x + 6)$

Use the Zero-Product Property to solve. $x = 4.5 \text{ or } x = -6$

The width x cannot be negative. So the width is 4.5 feet and the length is 2(4.5) + 3, or 12 feet.

CHECK Use substitution. $4.5(12) = 54 \text{ ft}^2 \checkmark$

GOT TO KNOW!

Solving Quadratic Equations by Factoring

1. Write the equation in standard form.

2. Factor out the GCF if possible, and divide both sides by the GCF if it is a constant.

3. Factor and use the Zero-Product Property to solve.

Completing the Square

Model Completing the Square

You know that you can solve an equation like $y = a^2$ by finding the square roots of a^2. **Completing the square** is a method for finding real solutions to a quadratic equation by forming an equivalent equation with a perfect trinomial square on one side. You can model this method by using algebra tiles.

SEARCH

To see step-by-step videos of these problems, enter the page number into the SWadvantage.com Search Bar.

EXAMPLE 1

Use algebra tiles to model $x^2 + 6x$. Then complete the square with unit tiles.

STEP 1 The tiles represent the expression $x^2 + 6x$. Arrange the tiles so that each side has a length of $x + 3$.

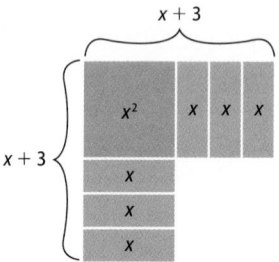

STEP 2 Complete the square with a 3×3 section of unit tiles.

The tiles represent the perfect trinomial square $x^2 + 6x + 9$.

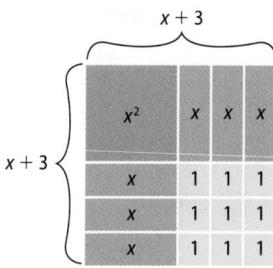

STEP 3 Write the area of the square in factored form.

$$x^2 + 6x + 9 = (x + 3)^2$$

EXAMPLE 2

Use algebra tiles to model $x^2 - 4x$. Then complete the square with unit tiles.

STEP 1 The tiles represent the expression $x^2 - 4x$. Arrange the tiles so that each side has a length of $x - 2$.

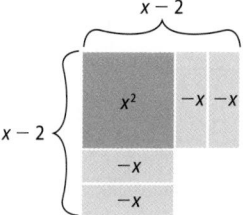

Need More

HELP

Remember that when you "multiply" negative tiles, the result is positive.

For more help with using algebra tiles to model binomial multiplication, go to *Multiplying Polynomials* (p. 1608).

STEP 2 Complete the square with a 2×2 section of positive unit tiles. The tiles in the square represent the perfect trinomial square $x^2 - 4x + 4$.

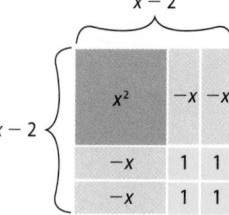

STEP 3 Write the area of the square in factored form.

$$x^2 - 4x + 4 = (x - 2)^2$$

Completing the Square for the Expression $x^2 + bx$

From Examples 1 and 2, you can generalize completing the square for $x^2 + bx$.

Original Terms	Constant to Complete the Square	Perfect Square Trinomial	Factored Form
$x^2 + 6x$	$\left(\frac{6}{2}\right)^2 = 3^2 = 9$	$x^2 + 6x + 9$	$(x + 3)^2$
$x^2 - 4x$	$\left(\frac{-4}{2}\right)^2 = (-2)^2 = 4$	$x^2 - 4x + 4$	$(x - 2)^2$
$x^2 + bx$	$\left(\frac{b}{2}\right)^2$	$x^2 + bx + \left(\frac{b}{2}\right)^2$	$\left(x + \frac{b}{2}\right)^2$

EXAMPLE 3

Complete the square to form a perfect trinomial square. Then write in factored form.

a. $x^2 + 8x$

> **METHOD 1**
>
> In $x^2 + bx$, $b = 8$.
>
> Substitute 8 for b in $\left(\frac{b}{2}\right)^2$. $x^2 + 8x + \left(\frac{8}{2}\right)^2$
>
> Simplify. $x^2 + 8x + 4^2$
>
> $x^2 + 8x + 16$
>
> Substitute 8 for b in $\left(x + \frac{b}{2}\right)^2$. $\left(x + \frac{8}{2}\right)^2$
>
> $(x + 4)^2$

Watch Out !

When you complete the square in this way, you are *not* creating an expression that is equivalent to the original expression.

$x^2 + 8x \neq (x + 4)^2$

b. $x^2 - 10x$

> **METHOD 2**
>
> Find the three key values first.
>
> Determine b, $\frac{b}{2}$, and $\left(\frac{b}{2}\right)^2$. $b = -10, \frac{b}{2} = -5, \left(\frac{b}{2}\right)^2 = 25$
>
> Substitute 25 for $\left(\frac{b}{2}\right)^2$ in $x^2 - 10x + \left(\frac{b}{2}\right)^2$. $x^2 - 10x + 25$
>
> Substitute -5 for $\frac{b}{2}$ in $\left(x + \frac{b}{2}\right)^2$. $(x - 5)^2$

c. $x^2 + 4.8x$

> Determine b, $\frac{b}{2}$, and $\left(\frac{b}{2}\right)^2$. $b = 4.8, \frac{b}{2} = 2.4, \left(\frac{b}{2}\right)^2 = 5.76$
>
> Substitute 5.76 for $\left(\frac{b}{2}\right)^2$ in $x^2 + 4.8x + \left(\frac{b}{2}\right)^2$. $x^2 + 4.8x + 5.76$
>
> Substitute 2.4 for $\frac{b}{2}$ in $\left(x + \frac{b}{2}\right)^2$. $(x + 2.4)^2$

Completing the Square to Solve an Equation

You can use the method of completing the square to solve a quadratic equation.

EXAMPLE 4

SEARCH

To see step-by-step videos of these problems, enter the page number into the SWadvantage.com Search Bar.

a. Solve $x^2 + 8x = 20$.

The equation is in the form $x^2 + bx = c$, where $b = 8$.	$x^2 + 8x = 20$
Complete the square. Add $\left(\frac{b}{2}\right)^2$, or 4^2, to both sides.	$x^2 + 8x + 16 = 20 + 16$
Simplify. Factor the perfect trinomial square.	$(x + 4)^2 = 36$
Take the square root of both sides.	$x + 4 = \pm 6$
Write the two equations.	$x + 4 = 6$ or $x + 4 = -6$
Solve for x.	$x = 2$ or $x = -10$

CHECK

$x^2 + 8x = 20$ $\qquad$ $x^2 + 8x = 20$

$2^2 + 8(2) \overset{?}{=} 20$ $\qquad$ $(-10)^2 + 8(-10) \overset{?}{=} 20$

$4 + 16 \overset{?}{=} 20$ $\qquad$ $100 - 80 \overset{?}{=} 20$

$20 = 20$ ✔ $\qquad$ $20 = 20$ ✔

The solution set is $\{-10, 2\}$.

b. Solve $x^2 - 6 = 2x$.

Write the equation in the form $x^2 + bx = c$ to see $b = -2$.	$x^2 - 2x = 6$
Complete the square. Add $\left(\frac{b}{2}\right)^2$, or $(-1)^2$, to both sides.	$x^2 - 2x + 1 = 6 + 1$
Simplify. Factor the perfect trinomial square.	$(x - 1)^2 = 7$
Take the square root of both sides.	$x - 1 = \pm\sqrt{7}$
Write the two equations.	$x - 1 = \sqrt{7}$ or $x - 1 = -\sqrt{7}$
Solve for x.	$x = 1 + \sqrt{7}$ or $x = 1 - \sqrt{7}$

CHECK Use a graphing calculator. Store one solution in X, and then evaluate both sides of $x^2 - 6 = 2x$. Repeat for the other solution.

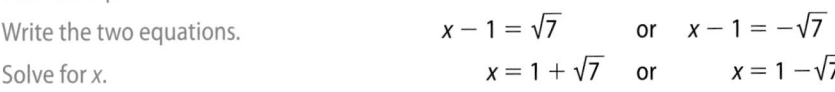

Need More

HELP

Remember, a quadratic equation can have two, one, or zero real solutions.

The solutions are $1 + \sqrt{7}$ and $1 - \sqrt{7}$.

c. Solve $x^2 - 3x + 8 = 0$.

Write the equation in the form $x^2 + bx = c$. Here $b = -3$.	$x^2 - 3x = -8$
Complete the square. Add $\left(\frac{b}{2}\right)^2$, or $\left(-\frac{3}{2}\right)^2$, to both sides.	$x^2 - 3x + \frac{9}{4} = -8 + \frac{9}{4}$
Simplify. Factor the perfect trinomial square.	$\left(x - \frac{3}{2}\right)^2 = -5\frac{3}{4}$

The right side of the equation is negative, so there is no real square root.

The equation has no solution.

EXAMPLE 5

Solve $4x^2 - 2x - 7 = 0$.

Add 7 to both sides.	$4x^2 - 2x = 7$
Divide each term by 4 so the coefficient of x^2 is 1.	$\dfrac{4x^2}{4} - \dfrac{2x}{4} = \dfrac{7}{4}$
The equation is in the form $x^2 + bx = c$, where $b = -0.5$.	$x^2 - 0.5x = 1.75$
Complete the square. Add $\left(\dfrac{b}{2}\right)^2$, or 0.25^2, to both sides.	$x^2 - 0.5x + 0.0625 = 1.75 + 0.0625$
Simplify. Factor the perfect trinomial square.	$(x - 0.25)^2 = 1.8125$
Take the square root of both sides.	$x - 0.25 = \pm\sqrt{1.8125}$
Write the two equations.	$x - 0.25 = \sqrt{1.8125}$ or $x - 0.25 = -\sqrt{1.8125}$
Solve for x.	$x = 0.25 + \sqrt{1.8125}$ or $x = 0.25 - \sqrt{1.8125}$

The solutions are $0.25 + \sqrt{1.8125}$ and $0.25 - \sqrt{1.8125}$, or approximately 1.6 and -1.1.

Need More
HELP ?

You can choose between decimal form and fraction form. Choose the form that you find easier to use.

EXAMPLE 6

The height of the triangle shown is equal to the base plus an additional 4 cm. What are the dimensions?

Write the formula for the area of a triangle.	Area $A = \dfrac{1}{2}$ base $b \times$ height h
Substitute the given values.	$82.5 = \dfrac{1}{2}x(x + 4)$
Multiply.	$82.5 = \dfrac{1}{2}x^2 + 2x$
Multiply both sides by 2.	$165 = x^2 + 4x$
Complete the square.	$165 + 4 = x^2 + 4x + 4$
Simplify and factor.	$169 = (x + 2)^2$
Take the square root of both sides.	$\pm\sqrt{169} = x + 2$
Write the two equations.	$13 = x + 2$ or $-13 = x + 2$
Solve for x.	$11 = x$ or $-15 = x$

$(x + 4)$ cm

$A = 82.5\ \text{cm}^2$

x cm

The length of the base must be positive. So the base is 11 centimeters and the height is $11 + 4$, or 15 cm.

CHECK Substitute the dimensions into the area equation. $\dfrac{1}{2}(11)(15) = 82.5\ \text{cm}^2$ ✓

Solving Quadratic Equations by Completing the Square

1. Write the equation in the form $x^2 + bx = c$.
2. Add $\left(\dfrac{b}{2}\right)^2$ to complete the square on the left side. Add the same quantity on the right side to keep the equation balanced.
3. Factor the perfect trinomial square on the left side of the equation.
4. Take the square roots of both sides, and then solve each equation.

The Quadratic Formula

Developing the Quadratic Formula

You can solve every quadratic equation of the form $ax^2 + bx + c = 0$ by completing the square. By solving the quadratic equation $ax^2 + bx + c = 0$ for x, you can develop a formula that you can use to solve any quadratic equation.

Subtract c from both sides.
$$ax^2 + bx = -c$$

Divide both sides by a.
$$\frac{ax^2}{a} + \frac{bx}{a} = \frac{-c}{a}$$

Simplify.
$$x^2 + \frac{b}{a}x = -\frac{c}{a}$$

Complete the square and balance the equation.
$$x^2 + \frac{b}{a}x + \left(\frac{b}{2a}\right)^2 = -\frac{c}{a} + \left(\frac{b}{2a}\right)^2$$

Simplify. Factor the perfect trinomial square.
$$\left(x + \frac{b}{2a}\right)^2 = -\frac{c}{a} + \frac{b^2}{4a^2}$$

Find a common denominator on the right side.
$$\left(x + \frac{b}{2a}\right)^2 = -\frac{4ac}{4a^2} + \frac{b^2}{4a^2}$$

Use the Commutative Property.
$$\left(x + \frac{b}{2a}\right)^2 = \frac{b^2}{4a^2} - \frac{4ac}{4a^2}$$

Simplify.
$$\left(x + \frac{b}{2a}\right)^2 = \frac{b^2 - 4ac}{4a^2}$$

Take the square roots of both sides.
$$x + \frac{b}{2a} = \pm\frac{\sqrt{b^2 - 4ac}}{2a}$$

Subtract $\frac{b}{2a}$ from both sides.
$$x = -\frac{b}{2a} \pm \frac{\sqrt{b^2 - 4ac}}{2a}$$

Simplify.
$$x = \frac{-b \pm \sqrt{b^2 - 4ac}}{2a}$$

To solve a quadratic equation by using the Quadratic Formula, write the equation in the form $ax^2 + bx + c = 0$.

Then find the value(s) of x by substituting the values of a, b, and c into $\frac{-b \pm \sqrt{b^2 - 4ac}}{2a}$.

Try It This Way

The next-to-last step in the development of the Quadratic Formula can be particularly useful when solving quadratic equations with a calculator.

Store $-\frac{b}{2a}$ in M. Then store $\frac{\sqrt{b^2 - 4ac}}{2a}$ in N. To find the two solutions, calculate the values for M + N and M − N.

GOT TO KNOW!

The Quadratic Formula

For $ax^2 + bx + c = 0$, where $a \neq 0$, the solutions are given by $x = \frac{-b \pm \sqrt{b^2 - 4ac}}{2a}$.

SEARCH 🔍

To see step-by-step videos of these problems, enter the page number into the SWadvantage.com Search Bar.

EXAMPLE 1

Solve $x^2 - 4x - 5 = 0$.

METHOD 1

Factor the trinomial.

STEP 1 Factor the trinomial. $x^2 - 4x - 5 = 0$

　　　　Find factors of -5 that have a sum of -4.
　　　　The factors are 1 and -5. $(x + 1)(x - 5) = 0$

STEP 2 Solve.

　　　　Use the Zero-Product Property. $x + 1 = 0$ or $x - 5 = 0$
　　　　Solve each equation separately. $x = -1$ or $x = 5$

METHOD 2

Use the Quadratic Formula.

The equation is in the form $ax^2 + bx + c = 0$.

Identify a, b, and c in $x^2 - 4x - 5 = 0$. $a = 1, b = -4, c = -5$

Substitute into $x = \dfrac{-b \pm \sqrt{b^2 - 4ac}}{2a}$. $x = \dfrac{-(-4) \pm \sqrt{(-4)^2 - 4(1)(-5)}}{2(1)}$

Simplify. $x = \dfrac{4 \pm \sqrt{16 + 20}}{2}$

Simplify. $x = \dfrac{4 \pm \sqrt{36}}{2}$

Simplify. $\sqrt{36} = 6$. $x = \dfrac{4 \pm 6}{2}$

Write as two equations. $x = \dfrac{10}{2}$ or $x = \dfrac{-2}{2}$

Simplify. $x = 5$ or $x = -1$

GOT TO KNOW!

The Five Quadratic Formula Substitutions

When solving $ax^2 + bx + c = 0$ by using the Quadratic Formula, you substitute 5 times in all:

a　two locations

b　two locations

c　one location

EXAMPLE 2

Solve $2x^2 + 5x + 3 = 0$.

The equation is in the form $ax^2 + bx + c = 0$.

Identify a, b, and c in $2x^2 + 5x + 3 = 0$. $a = 2, b = 5, c = 3$

Substitute into $x = \dfrac{-b \pm \sqrt{b^2 - 4ac}}{2a}$. $x = \dfrac{-(5) \pm \sqrt{(5)^2 - 4(2)(3)}}{2(2)}$

Simplify. $x = \dfrac{-5 \pm \sqrt{25 - 24}}{4}$

Simplify. $x = \dfrac{-5 \pm \sqrt{1}}{4}$

Simplify. $\sqrt{1} = 1$. $x = \dfrac{-5 \pm 1}{4}$

Write as two equations. $x = \dfrac{-4}{4}$ or $x = \dfrac{-6}{4}$

Simplify. $x = -1$ or $x = -\dfrac{3}{2}$

Using the Quadratic Formula

The quadratic formula gives exact solutions. A calculator can only give approximate solutions. But a calculator can be used to check exact solutions.

Remember to put a quadratic equation into standard form, $ax^2 + bx + c = 0$, before using the Quadratic Formula.

EXAMPLE 3

Solve $3(x - 2)(x - 4) = -1$. Find the exact solutions. Then approximate the solutions.

STEP 1 Write the equation in standard form.

$$3(x - 2)(x - 4) = -1$$

Multiply $(x - 2)(x - 4)$. $3(x^2 - 6x + 8) = -1$

Use the Distributive Property. $3x^2 - 18x + 24 = -1$

Write in standard form. $3x^2 - 18x + 25 = 0$

STEP 2 Use the Quadratic Formula.

Identify a, b, and c in $3x^2 - 18x + 25 = 0$. $a = 3, b = -18, c = 25$

Substitute into $x = \dfrac{-b \pm \sqrt{b^2 - 4ac}}{2a}$. $x = \dfrac{-(-18) \pm \sqrt{(-18)^2 - 4(3)(25)}}{2(3)}$

Simplify. $x = \dfrac{18 \pm \sqrt{324 - 300}}{6}$

Simplify. $x = \dfrac{18 \pm \sqrt{24}}{6}$

Simplify. $x = \dfrac{18 \pm 2\sqrt{6}}{6}$

Simplify. $x = 3 \pm \dfrac{\sqrt{6}}{3}$

Write as two equations. $x = 3 + \dfrac{\sqrt{6}}{3}$ or $x = 3 - \dfrac{\sqrt{6}}{3}$

STEP 3 Approximate the solutions.

$\sqrt{6} \approx 2.45$. Substitute. $x \approx 3 + \dfrac{2.45}{3}$ or $x \approx 3 - \dfrac{2.45}{3}$

Simplify. $x \approx 3.82$ or $x \approx 2.18$

STEP 4 **CHECK** by graphing.

Use a graphing calculator to graph the left and right sides of the original equation.

Graph the function $3(x - 2)(x - 4)$ in Y1 and -1 in Y2. For the two intersection points, Press **2nd** **CALC**, and use the calculator function **5:intersect** to find the value of x at each intersection point.

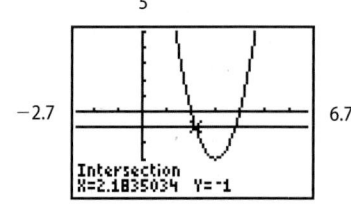

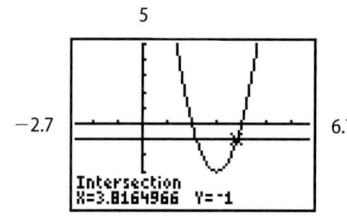

So, $x \approx 3.82$ or $x \approx 2.18$.

Watch Out !

Checking Equations

Although you may be tempted to check by using $3x^2 - 18x + 25 = 0$, you must always check by using the original equation.

EXAMPLE 4

A picture frame is 36 centimeters long and 24 centimeters wide. The picture area of the frame is 693 square centimeters.

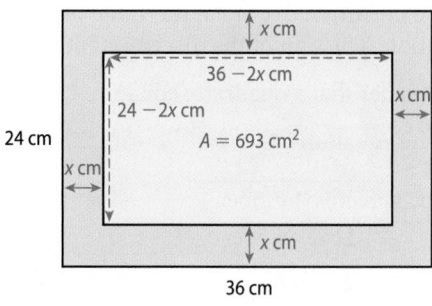

SEARCH 🔍

To see step-by-step videos of these problems, enter the page number into the SWadvantage.com Search Bar.

a. What is the width of the frame molding?

STEP 1 Find the equation for the width of the molding, and write it in standard form.

Let $x =$ the width of the molding.   Area $A =$ length $\ell \times$ width w

$$693 = (36 - 2x)(24 - 2x)$$
$$693 = 864 - 120x + 4x^2$$
$$0 = 171 - 120x + 4x^2$$
$$0 = 4x^2 - 120x + 171$$

STEP 2 Use the Quadratic Formula to find the solutions.

Identify a, b, and c in $4x^2 - 120x + 171 = 0$. $a = 4, b = -120, c = 171$

Substitute into $x = \dfrac{-b \pm \sqrt{b^2 - 4ac}}{2a}$. $x = \dfrac{-(-120) \pm \sqrt{(-120)^2 - 4(4)(171)}}{2(4)}$

Simplify. $x = \dfrac{120 \pm \sqrt{14{,}400 - 2{,}736}}{8}$

Simplify. $x = \dfrac{120 \pm \sqrt{11{,}664}}{8}$

Simplify. $x = \dfrac{120 \pm 108}{8}$

Simplify. $x = \dfrac{30 \pm 27}{2}$

Write as two equations. $x = 28.5$ or $x = 1.5$

STEP 3 CHECK Substitute each possible value for x into the area formula for the picture.

Find the length and width of the picture inside the frame.

Let $x = 28.5$.   Let $x = 1.5$.
$\quad A = \ell w$ $\quad A = \ell w$
$693 = [36 - 2(28.5)][24 - 2(28.5)]$ $693 = [36 - 2(1.5)][24 - 2(1.5)]$
$693 = (-21)(-33)$ ✗ $693 = (33)(21)$
                                          $693 = 693$ ✓

Because the dimensions must be positive, 28.5 centimeters is not a possible width for the molding. The width of the frame molding is 1.5 centimeters.

b. Is the ratio of length to width the same for the picture as for the frame?

The ratio of the length of the frame to its width is $\dfrac{36}{24} = 1.5$.

The ratio of the length of the picture to its width is $\dfrac{33}{21} \approx 1.57$. The ratios are not the same.

Using the Discriminant

The Discriminant

Need More

HELP ?

Remember, the Quadratic Formula is

$x = \dfrac{-b \pm \sqrt{b^2 - 4ac}}{2a}$,

and the values of a, b, and c come from the quadratic equation in standard form,

$ax^2 + bx + c = 0$.

In the Quadratic Formula, the value of $b^2 - 4ac$ is called the **discriminant** of the quadratic equation. The sign of the discriminant indicates the number of real solutions.

Remember that a quadratic equation can have two, one, or no real solutions.

For the equation $ax^2 + bx + c = 0$, the three possible cases are shown below.

$\dfrac{-b \pm \sqrt{\text{positive number}}}{2a}$	$\dfrac{-b \pm \sqrt{\text{zero}}}{2a}$	$\dfrac{-b \pm \sqrt{\text{negative number}}}{2a}$
$b^2 - 4ac > 0$	$b^2 - 4ac = 0$	$b^2 - 4ac < 0$
two real solutions	one real solution	no real solutions

Examples

$x^2 + x - 1 = 0$ $x^2 + 2x + 1 = 0$ $x^2 + x + 1 = 0$

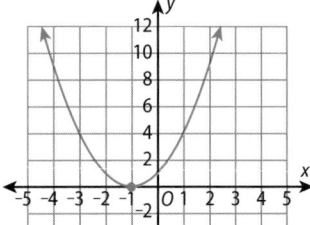

Discriminant   Discriminant   Discriminant

$1^2 - 4(1)(-1) = 5$ $2^2 - 4(1)(1) = 0$ $1^2 - 4(1)(1) = -3$

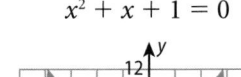

SEARCH 🔍

To see step-by-step videos of these problems, enter the page number into the SWadvantage.com Search Bar.

EXAMPLE 1

Find the value of the discriminant to determine the number of real solutions.

a. $2x^2 + 5x - 10 = 0$

Identify a, b, and c in $2x^2 + 5x - 10 = 0$. $a = 2, b = 5, c = -10$

                                         $b^2 - 4 \cdot a \cdot c$

Substitute values into $b^2 - 4ac$. $5^2 - 4(2)(-10)$

Simplify. $25 + 80 = 105$

Discriminant: 105

Since $b^2 - 4ac > 0$, the equation has two real solutions.

b. $3x^2 + 9x + 7 = 0$

Identify a, b, and c in $3x^2 + 9x + 7 = 0$. $a = 3, b = 9, c = 7$

                                         $b^2 - 4 \cdot a \cdot c$

Substitute values into $b^2 - 4ac$. $9^2 - 4(3)(7)$

Simplify. $81 - 84 = -3$

Discriminant: -3

Since $b^2 - 4ac < 0$, the equation has no real solutions.

You need to write the equation in standard form before you can find the discriminant.

EXAMPLE 2

Use the discriminant to determine the number of real solutions of $5(5x^2 - 2x) + 4 = 3$.

STEP 1 Write the equation in standard form $ax^2 + bx + c = 0$.

$$5(5x^2 - 2x) + 4 = 3$$

Subtract 3 from both sides. $\quad 5(5x^2 - 2x) + 1 = 0$

Multiply $(5x^2 - 2x)$ by 5. $\quad 25x^2 - 10x + 1 = 0$

STEP 2 Find the discriminant.

Identify a, b, and c in $25x^2 - 10x + 1 = 0$. $\quad a = 25, b = -10, c = 1$

$$b^2 - 4 \cdot a \cdot c$$

Substitute values into $b^2 - 4ac$. $\quad (-10)^2 - 4(25)(1)$

Simplify. $\quad 100 - 100 = 0$

$b^2 - 4ac = 0 \qquad$ The equation has one real solution.

GOT TO KNOW!

Perfect Trinomial Square

When $ax^2 + bx + c = 0$ is a perfect trinomial square, there is one real solution.

$25x^2 - 10x + 1 = 0$ is a perfect trinomial square. Its one (repeated) real solution is $x = \frac{1}{5}$.

EXAMPLE 3

Solve over the set of real numbers, if possible.

a. $-5x^2 + 4x - 2 = 0$

Identify a, b, and c in $-5x^2 + 4x - 2 = 0$. $\quad a = -5, b = 4, c = -2$

$$b^2 - 4 \cdot a \cdot c$$

Substitute values into $b^2 - 4ac$. $\quad 4^2 - 4(-5)(-2) = 16 - 40 = -24$

Discriminant: -24

$b^2 - 4ac < 0 \qquad$ The equation has no real solutions.

b. $-2x^2 + 9x - 7 = 0$

Identify a, b, and c in $-2x^2 + 9x - 7 = 0$. $\quad a = -2, b = 9, c = -7$

$$b^2 - 4 \cdot a \cdot c$$

Substitute into $b^2 - 4ac$. $\quad 9^2 - 4(-2)(-7) = 81 - 56 = 25$

Discriminant: 25

$b^2 - 4ac > 0 \qquad$ The equation has two real solutions.

Use the Quadratic Formula to solve. $\quad x = \dfrac{-b \pm \sqrt{b^2 - 4ac}}{2a}$

Substitute. Use $b^2 - 4ac = 25$. $\quad x = \dfrac{-9 \pm \sqrt{25}}{2(-2)}$

Simplify. $\quad x = \dfrac{-9 \pm 5}{-4}$

Write as two equations. $\quad x = \dfrac{-4}{-4}$ or $x = \dfrac{-14}{-4}$

Simplify. $\quad x = 1$ or $x = \dfrac{7}{2}$

Graphs, Intercepts, and the Discriminant

When $a > 0$ in $ax^2 + bx + c$, the discriminant gives this information.

If $b^2 - 4ac > 0$, the graph is a parabola that opens upward and has its vertex below the x-axis. There are two real solutions, at the x-intercepts.

If $b^2 - 4ac = 0$, the graph is a parabola that opens upward and has its vertex on the x-axis. There is one real solution, at the x-intercept (the vertex).

If $b^2 - 4ac < 0$, the graph is a parabola that opens upward and has its vertex above the x-axis. There are no real solutions, or x-intercepts.

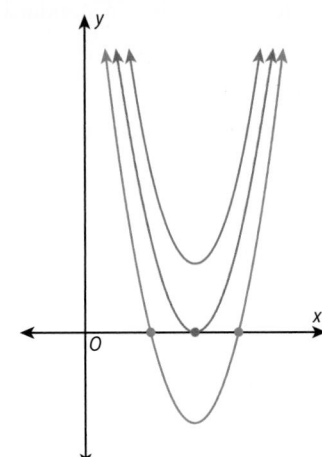

When $a < 0$ in $ax^2 + bx + c$, the discriminant gives this information.

If $b^2 - 4ac > 0$, the graph is a parabola that opens downward and has its vertex above the x-axis. There are two real solutions, at the x-intercepts.

If $b^2 - 4ac = 0$, the graph is a parabola that opens downward and has its vertex on the x-axis. There is one real solution, at the x-intercept (the vertex).

If $b^2 - 4ac < 0$, the graph is a parabola that opens downward and has its vertex below the x-axis. There are no real solutions, or x-intercepts.

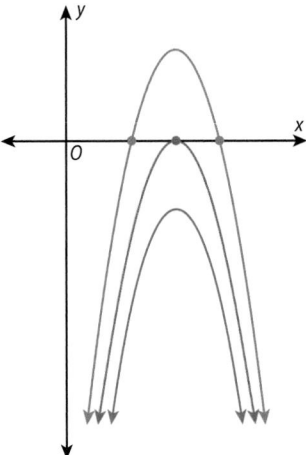

EXAMPLE 4

Need More

HELP?

When the negative sign appears only with the constant term c, the discriminant is always positive and the equation has two real solutions.

Without graphing, describe the graphs of $y = 2x^2 + 4x - 3$ and $y = -2x^2 - 4x - 7$.

The discriminant of $2x^2 + 4x - 3$ is $4^2 - 4(2)(-3) = 40$.

Since $a > 0$, the graph is a parabola that opens upward. Because the discriminant is positive, the graph has its vertex below the x-axis, and there are two solutions, at the x-intercepts.

The discriminant of $-2x^2 - 4x - 7$ is $(-4)^2 - 4(-2)(-7) = -40$.

Since $a < 0$, the graph is a parabola that opens downward. Because the discriminant is negative, the graph has its vertex below the x-axis, and there are no real solutions, or x-intercepts.

The graphs verify this information.

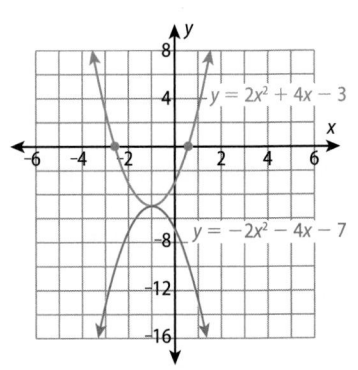

EXAMPLE 5

A model rocket is launched from a platform 3 feet above the ground with an initial velocity of 90 feet per second. Its height in feet is given by $h = -16t^2 + 90t + 3$, where t represents the number of seconds since the rocket was launched.

a. Does the rocket reach a height of 130 feet?

Determine whether real solutions exist for the equation $130 = -16t^2 + 90t + 3$.

STEP 1 Write the equation in standard form.

$$130 = -16t^2 + 90t + 3$$

Subtract 130 from each side. $0 = -16t^2 + 90t - 127$

STEP 2 Find the discriminant.

Identify a, b, and c in $-16t^2 + 90t - 127 = 0$. $a = -16, b = 90, c = -127$

Substitute values into $b^2 - 4ac$. $(90)^2 - 4(-16)(-127)$

Simplify. $8{,}100 - 8{,}128 = -28$

Discriminant: -28

The equation has no real solutions, so the rocket does not reach a height of 130 feet.

b. For how long is the rocket at or above a height of 102 feet?

Determine the solutions of the equation $102 = -16t^2 + 90t + 3$.

STEP 1 Write the equation in standard form.

$$102 = -16t^2 + 90t + 3.$$

Subtract 102 from each side. $0 = -16t^2 + 90t - 99.$

STEP 2 Use the Quadratic Formula to find the solutions.

Identify a, b, and c in $-16t^2 + 90t - 99 = 0$. $a = -16, b = 90, c = -99$

Substitute into $x = \dfrac{-b \pm \sqrt{b^2 - 4ac}}{2a}$. $x = \dfrac{-(90) \pm \sqrt{(90)^2 - 4(-16)(-99)}}{2(-16)}$

Simplify. $x = \dfrac{-90 \pm \sqrt{8{,}100 - 6{,}336}}{-32}$

Simplify. $x = \dfrac{-90 \pm 42}{-32}$

Write as two equations. $x = \dfrac{-48}{-32}$ or $x = \dfrac{-132}{-32}$

Simplify. $x = 1.5$ or $x = 4.125$

The rocket is 102 feet high at 1.5 seconds after launch and again at 4.125 seconds after launch.

STEP 3 Determine how long the rocket is at or above 102 feet.

Subtract. $4.125 - 1.5 = 2.625$

The rocket is at or above 102 feet for 2.625 seconds.

Try It This Way

For part (a), use a graphing calculator to graph the function and find the maximum.

For part (b), find the zeros and subtract one from the other.

SEARCH

To see step-by-step videos of these problems, enter the page number into the SWadvantage.com Search Bar.

GOT TO KNOW!

The Discriminant

For a quadratic equation in standard form, $ax^2 + bx + c = 0$, the discriminant gives this information.

- If $b^2 - 4ac > 0$, then the equation has two real solutions.

- If $b^2 - 4ac = 0$, then the equation has one real solution.

- If $b^2 - 4ac < 0$, then the equation has no real solutions.

Sum and Product of the Roots

Sum of Roots

When a quadratic equation in standard form $ax^2 + bx + c = 0$ has two real roots, the roots are mirror images of each other across the line of symmetry $x = -\frac{b}{2a}$.

The sum of the roots can be expressed as follows:

$$-\frac{b}{2a} + d + \left(-\frac{b}{2a} - d\right) = -\frac{2b}{2a}$$

$$= -\frac{b}{a}$$

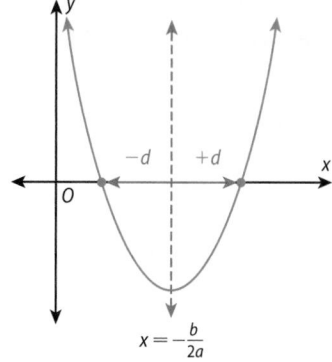

Product of Roots

The product of the roots of the equation $ax^2 + bx + c = 0$ can be expressed as $\frac{c}{a}$.

You can find the sum and product of the roots of a quadratic equation in standard form without solving the equation. Use the values of a, b, and c to calculate the sum and product.

GOT TO KNOW!

Sum and Product of Roots

If a quadratic equation is a perfect trinomial square, think of it as having two identical solutions. For example, for $x^2 - 6x + 9 = 0$, the factored form is $(x - 3)(x - 3) = 0$. So the sum of the solutions, or roots, is 6 and the product is 9.

Although the sum and product formulas work when there are no real roots and the discriminant $b^2 - 4ac$ is negative, checking the results is beyond the scope of Algebra.

SEARCH

To see step-by-step videos of these problems, enter the page number into the SWadvantage.com Search Bar.

EXAMPLE 1

Find the sum and product of the roots.

a. $2x^2 + 7x - 4 = 0$

Identify a, b, and c in $2x^2 + 7x - 4 = 0$. $a = 2, b = 7, c = -4$

The sum of the roots is $-\frac{b}{a}$. Substitute. $-\frac{b}{a} = -\frac{7}{2} = -3.5$

The product of the roots is $\frac{c}{a}$. Substitute. $\frac{c}{a} = \frac{-4}{2} = -2$

CHECK

Factor the quadratic equation. $(2x - 1)(x + 4) = 0$

$2x - 1 = 0$ or $x + 4 = 0$

$x = 0.5$ or $x = -4$

Sum of roots $= 0.5 + (-4) = -3.5$ ✔   Product of roots $= 0.5(-4) = -2$ ✔

b. $x^2 - 4x - 12 = 0$

Identify a, b, and c in $x^2 - 4x - 12 = 0$. $a = 1, b = -4, c = -12$

The sum of the roots is $-\frac{b}{a}$. Substitute. $-\frac{-4}{1} = 4$

The product of the roots is $\frac{c}{a}$. Substitute. $\frac{-12}{1} = -12$

CHECK

Factor the quadratic equation. $(x - 6)(x + 2) = 0$

$x - 6 = 0$ or $x + 2 = 0$

$x = 6$ or $x = -2$

Sum of roots $= 6 + (-2) = 4$ ✔   Product of roots $= 6(-2) = -12$ ✔

Writing Equations from Roots

The quadratic equation $ax^2 + bx + c = 0$ can be written with a leading coefficient of 1 by dividing each term by a.

$$\frac{ax^2}{a} + \frac{bx}{a} + \frac{c}{a} = 0$$

$$x^2 + \frac{b}{a}x + \frac{c}{a} = 0$$

The coefficient of the middle term is the *opposite* of the sum of the roots, $-\frac{b}{a}$.

The coefficient of the last term is the product of the roots, $\frac{c}{a}$.

EXAMPLE 2

Write a quadratic equation whose roots have a sum of $\frac{1}{2}$ and a product of -5.

Write the general equation above. $x^2 + \frac{b}{a}x + \frac{c}{a} = 0$

The sum $\frac{1}{2}$ is the opposite of the coefficient of the middle term, so $\frac{b}{a} = -\frac{1}{2}$.

The product -5 is equal to $\frac{c}{a}$.

Substitute for $\frac{b}{a}$ and $\frac{c}{a}$ in $x^2 + \frac{b}{a}x + \frac{c}{a} = 0$. $x^2 - \frac{1}{2}x - 5 = 0$

Multiply both sides by 2 to clear fractions. $2x^2 - x - 10 = 0$

CHECK

Factor the quadratic equation. $(2x - 5)(x + 2) = 0$

$$2x - 5 = 0 \text{ or } x + 2 = 0$$

$$x = \frac{5}{2} \quad \text{or} \quad x = -2$$

Sum of roots $= \frac{5}{2} + (-2) = \frac{1}{2}$ ✔ Product of roots $= \frac{5}{2}(-2) = -5$ ✔

The equation is $2x^2 - x - 10 = 0$.

Try It This Way

Check by using a graphing calculator to find the roots of the quadratic equation. Find the sum and product on the home screen.

Sum and Product of the Roots of a Quadratic Equation

For a quadratic equation in the standard form $ax^2 + bx + c = 0$, you can find the sum and product of the roots without finding the roots.

- The sum of the roots is $-\frac{b}{a}$.
- The product of the roots is $\frac{c}{a}$.

Solving Higher-Order Polynomial Equations

Solving Cubic and Quartic Equations

Higher-order equations are equations of degree 3 or greater. Solving such equations may involve separating out factors until a quadratic or linear equation remains to be factored.

EXAMPLE 1

Solve $2x^3 - 6x^2 - 8x = 0$.

Factor out the greatest common factor (GCF).

Factor the GCF, $2x$, from each term.	$2x^3 - 6x^2 - 8x = 0$
	$2x(x^2 - 3x - 4) = 0$
Factor the trinomial.	$2x(x - 4)(x + 1) = 0$
Use the Zero-Product Property.	$2x = 0$ or $x - 4 = 0$ or $x + 1 = 0$
	$x = 0$ or $x = 4$ or $x = -1$

EXAMPLE 2

Need More HELP?

If you see a proportion among the coefficients, try factoring by grouping.

In Example 2:
$$\frac{2}{1} = \frac{-18}{-9}$$

For more help factoring by grouping, go to *Factoring by Grouping* (p. 1672).

Solve $x^3 + 2x^2 - 9x - 18 = 0$.

Factor the cubic equation by grouping.

	$x^3 + 2x^2 - 9x - 18 = 0$
Factor each binomial pair.	$x^2(x + 2) - 9(x + 2) = 0$
Use the Distributive Property.	$(x^2 - 9)(x + 2) = 0$
Factor the difference of squares.	$(x + 3)(x - 3)(x + 2) = 0$
Use the Zero-Product Property.	$x + 3 = 0$ or $x - 3 = 0$ or $x + 2 = 0$
	$x = -3$ or $x = 3$ or $x = -2$

You can solve some higher-degree equations by a two-step process of factoring, using FOIL in reverse. Sometimes, before factoring, you can write the equation in quadratic form by using substitution.

EXAMPLE 3

Solve $x^4 - 13x^2 + 36 = 0$.

METHOD 1

Use FOIL in reverse to write two factors.	$x^4 - 13x^2 + 36 = 0$
STEP 1 Write the first term of each factor.	$(x^2\ \ )(x^2\ \ ) = 0$

STEP 2 Find factors of 36 that have a sum of -13.

The factors are -9 and -4.

Complete the factored equation.	$(x^2 - 9)(x^2 - 4) = 0$
Factor each difference of squares.	$(x + 3)(x - 3)(x + 2)(x - 2) = 0$
Use the Zero-Product Property.	$x + 3 = 0$ or $x - 3 = 0$ or $x + 2 = 0$ or $x - 2 = 0$
	$x = -3$ or $x = 3$ or $x = -2$ or $x = 2$

METHOD 2

Use substitution. $x^4 - 13x^2 + 36 = 0$

STEP 1 Substitute u for x^2. $u^2 - 13u + 36 = 0$

STEP 2 Factor the quadratic equation, and solve for u.

$$u^2 - 13x^2 + 36 = 0$$

Use FOIL in reverse to factor. $(u - 9)(u - 4) = 0$

Use the Zero-Product Property. $u = 9$ or $u = 4$

STEP 3 Substitute x^2 for u in the two solutions. $x^2 = 9$ or $x^2 = 4$

Take the square roots. $x = \pm 3$ or $x = \pm 2$

EXAMPLE 4

The inside of a glass tank has a volume of
40 cubic feet. The sides and bottom are
1 foot thick. The width and height are
equal, and the length is 3 times the width.
What are the outer dimensions of the tank?

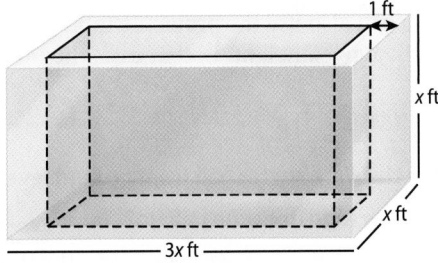

STEP 1 Write an equation in standard form for the volume of the inside of the tank.

Use the volume formula.   Volume $V = $ length $\ell \times$ width $w \times$ height h

Write the volume in terms of x. $40 = (3x - 2)(x - 2)(x - 1)$

Multiply. $40 = 3x^3 - 11x^2 + 12x - 4$

Subtract 40 from each side. $0 = 3x^3 - 11x^2 + 12x - 44$

STEP 2 Factor the cubic equation by grouping.

Notice that the coefficients form a proportion: $\frac{12}{3} = \frac{-44}{-11}$.

Use the Commutative Property. $0 = 3x^3 + 12x - 11x^2 - 44$

Factor each binomial pair. $0 = 3x(x^2 + 4) - 11(x^2 + 4)$

Use the Distributive Property. $0 = (3x - 11)(x^2 + 4)$

Use the Zero-Product Property. $3x - 11 = 0$ or $x^2 + 4 = 0$

Solve. $x = \frac{11}{3}$ or $x^2 = -4$ ✗

Only a real number for x makes sense in the problem.

$x = \frac{11}{3} = 3\frac{2}{3}$ ft

STEP 3 Solve the problem.

The outside of the glass tank is 11 feet long by $3\frac{2}{3}$ feet wide by $3\frac{2}{3}$ feet high.

CHECK Use the tank's inside volume. $40 = (3x - 2)(x - 2)(x - 1)$

Substitute $\frac{11}{3}$ for x. $40 \overset{?}{=} \left[3\left(\frac{11}{3}\right) - 2\right]\left(\frac{11}{3} - 2\right)\left(\frac{11}{3} - 1\right)$

$40 \overset{?}{=} 9 \cdot \frac{5}{3} \cdot \frac{8}{3}$

$40 = 40$ ✔

Need More

HELP ?

For more help
multiplying
polynomials, go to
Multiplying Polynomials
(p. 1608).

Projectile Motion Problems

Projectile Motion

A well-known, useful application of quadratic functions is modeling projectile motion. A projectile can be any object that is propelled by an external force.

The formula below models the height of a projectile over time after it is propelled straight up. Notice that the function is in the quadratic form $ax^2 + bx + c$.

$$s(t) = -\frac{1}{2}gt^2 + v_0 t + s_0$$

s = height at time t

g = acceleration due to gravity

v_0 = initial velocity

s_0 = initial height

Acceleration due to the gravity of Earth is about 32 feet per second per second, or 32 ft/s².

You can also use the projectile motion formula to describe the motion of an object dropped from a given height. In that case, the initial velocity is 0 feet per second.

EXAMPLE 1

Jim throws a soccer ball from ground level with a velocity of 48 ft/s straight up into the air.

a. How high does the ball go?

STEP 1 List the known information. Use the projectile motion formula to write a mathematical model.

$s_0 = 0$ ft $v_0 = 48$ ft/s $g = 32$ ft/s²

The independent variable t is unknown.

Write the projectile motion formula. $s(t) = -\frac{1}{2}gt^2 + v_0 t + s_0$

Substitute values to write the model. $s(t) = -\frac{1}{2}(32)t^2 + 48t + 0$

$$= -16t^2 + 48t$$

STEP 2 Graph the function.

The vertex (t, s) of the parabola represents the maximum height s, which occurs at time t.

STEP 3 Find the t-coordinate of the vertex, and interpret it in the context of the problem.

The t-coordinate of the vertex is $-\frac{b}{2a}$.

$$t = -\frac{b}{2a}$$

Substitute values from the model in Step 1.

$$= -\frac{48}{2(-16)}$$

$$= \frac{3}{2} = 1.5$$

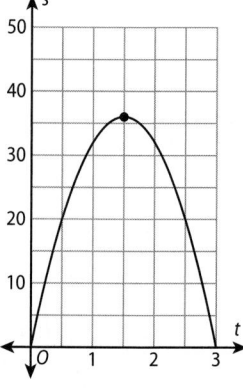

The ball reaches its maximum height 1.5 s after Jim tosses it into the air.

STEP 4 Find the s-coordinate of the vertex, and interpret it in the context of the problem.

$$s(t) = -16t^2 + 48t$$

$$= -16(1.5)^2 + 48(1.5)$$

$$= -36 + 72$$

$$= 36$$

The ball reaches a maximum height of 36 ft.

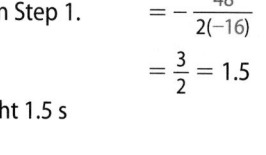

b. How long is the ball in the air?

The zeros of the function represent the times when the height of the ball is at ground level (0 ft).

$$s(t) = -16t^2 + 48t$$

Substitute 0 for $s(t)$. $0 = -16t^2 + 48t$

Divide both sides by -16. $0 = t^2 - 3t$

Factor. $0 = t(t - 3)$

Use the Zero-Product Property. $t = 0$ or $t - 3 = 0$

                                 $t = 0$ or $t = 3$

The ball is at ground level when $t = 0$ s, and then again when $t = 3$ s. So the ball is in the air for $3 - 0 = 3$ s. Use the graph on the previous page to verify this.

SEARCH

To see step-by-step videos of these problems, enter the page number into the SWadvantage.com Search Bar.

EXAMPLE 2

Sam drops a ball from a window 32 feet above ground level. To the nearest tenth of a second, how long does it take the ball to hit the ground?

STEP 1 List the known information and write the model.

$s_0 = 32$ ft

$v_0 = 0$ ft/s

$g = 32$ ft/s^2

Write the projectile motion formula. $s(t) = -\frac{1}{2}gt^2 + v_0t + s_0$

Substitute values to write the model. $s(t) = -\frac{1}{2}(32)t^2 + 0t + 32$

                                         $= -16t^2 + 32$

STEP 2 Graph the function.

The vertex of the parabola $(0, 32)$ represents the maximum height.

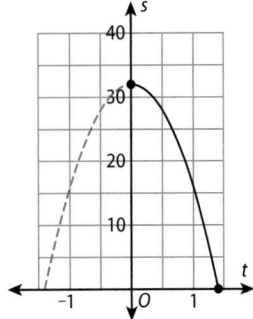

STEP 3 Find the zeros of the function to determine when the ball is at ground level (0 ft).

$$s(t) = -16t^2 + 32$$

Substitute 0 for $s(t)$. $0 = -16t^2 + 32$

Divide both sides by -16. $0 = t^2 - 2$

Add 2 to both sides. $2 = t^2$

Take the square root of both sides. $\pm\sqrt{2} = t$

Approximate the square roots. $\pm 1.4 \approx t$

A negative number does not make sense in the problem. To the nearest tenth of a second, the ball takes 1.4 s to hit the ground.

Need More

HELP ?

For examples of projectile motion for objects dropped on Earth and on the moon, go to *Transforming Quadratics* (p. 1694).

GOT TO KNOW!

Projectile Motion Formula

$s(t) = -\frac{1}{2}gt^2 + v_0t + s_0$

$s =$ height at time t

$g =$ acceleration due to gravity

$v_0 =$ initial velocity

$s_0 =$ initial height

Vertex Form

When a quadratic function is in the form $y = a(x - h)^2 + k$, the function is in vertex form. The vertex of the parabola is (h, k).

$$f(x) = 3(x - 5)^2 + 100 \qquad g(x) = -4(x + 2)^2 - 7 = -4[x - (-2)]^2 + (-7)$$

$$\text{Vertex: } (5, 100) \qquad\qquad \text{Vertex: } (-2, -7)$$

You can write a function in vertex form by completing the square.

EXAMPLE 3

SEARCH

To see step-by-step videos of these problems, enter the page number into the SWadvantage.com Search Bar.

Need More

HELP?

For more help, to go *Completing the Square* on page 1706.

Write the function $y = 2x^2 + 4x - 1$ in vertex form.

$$y = 2x^2 + 4x - 1$$

Add 1 to both sides.	$y + 1 = 2x^2 + 4x$
Factor the right side.	$y + 1 = 2(x^2 + 2x)$
Divide both sides by 2.	$\dfrac{y + 1}{2} = x^2 + 2x$
Complete the square.	$\dfrac{y + 1}{2} + 1 = x^2 + 2x + 1$
Factor the perfect trinomial square.	$\dfrac{y + 1}{2} + 1 = (x + 1)^2$
Subtract 1 from both sides.	$\dfrac{y + 1}{2} = (x + 1)^2 - 1$
Multiply both sides by 2.	$y + 1 = 2[(x + 1)^2 - 1]$
Simplify.	$y + 1 = 2(x + 1)^2 - 2$
Subtract 1 from both sides.	$y = 2(x + 1)^2 - 3$

The vertex is $(-1, -3)$.

EXAMPLE 4

A rocket is launched from a height of 3 ft with an initial velocity of 160 ft/s. Find the maximum height of the rocket.

Write the mathematical model.	$s = -16t^2 + 160t + 3$
Subtract 3 from both sides.	$s - 3 = -16t^2 + 160t$
Factor the right side.	$s - 3 = -16(t^2 - 10t)$
Divide both sides by -16.	$\dfrac{s - 3}{-16} = t^2 - 10t$
Complete the square.	$\dfrac{s - 3}{-16} + 25 = t^2 - 10t + 25$
Factor the perfect trinomial square.	$\dfrac{s - 3}{-16} + 25 = (t - 5)^2$
Subtract 25 from both sides.	$\dfrac{s - 3}{-16} = (t - 5)^2 - 25$
Multiply both sides by -16.	$s - 3 = -16[(t - 5)^2 - 25]$
Simplify.	$s - 3 = -16(t - 5)^2 + 400$
Add 3 to both sides.	$s = -16(t - 5)^2 + 403$

The vertex is (5, 403), so the maximum height of the rocket is 403 ft.

The acceleration due to the gravity of Earth is approximately 9.8 m/s².

EXAMPLE 5

A target is launched from a height of 2 m with an initial velocity of 14.7 m/s. Randi wants to hit the target at its maximum height. When will the target reach its maximum height, and what will the maximum height be?

METHOD 1

Write the function in vertex form.

Write the mathematical model.	$s = -4.9t^2 + 14.7t + 2$
Note: $-4.9 = -\left(\dfrac{1}{2}\right)(9.8)$	
Subtract 2 from both sides.	$s - 2 = -4.9t^2 + 14.7t$
Factor the right side.	$s - 2 = -4.9(t^2 - 3t)$
Divide both sides by -4.9.	$\dfrac{s-2}{-4.9} = t^2 - 3t$
Complete the square.	$\dfrac{s-2}{-4.9} + 2.25 = t^2 - 3t + 2.25$
Factor the perfect trinomial square.	$\dfrac{s-2}{-4.9} + 2.25 = (t - 1.5)^2$
Subtract 2.25 from both sides.	$\dfrac{s-2}{-4.9} = (t - 1.5)^2 - 2.25$
Multiply both sides by -4.9.	$s - 2 = -4.9[(t - 1.5)^2 - 2.25]$
Simplify.	$s - 2 = -4.9(t - 1.5)^2 + 11.025$
Add 2 to both sides.	$s = -4.9(t - 1.5)^2 + 13.025$

The vertex is (1.5, 13.025), so 1.5 s after launch, the target will reach its maximum height, 13.025 m.

METHOD 2

Find the line of symmetry.

The function is in $at^2 + bt + c$ form.	$s = -4.9t^2 + 14.7t + 2$
Find $t = -\dfrac{b}{2a}$.	$t = -\dfrac{14.7}{2(-4.9)} = 1.5$
Evaluate the function when $t = 1.5$.	$s = -4.9t^2 + 14.7t + 2$
Substitute.	$= -4.9(1.5)^2 + 14.7(1.5) + 2$
	$= -11.025 + 22.05 + 2$
	$= 13.025$

The vertex is (1.5, 13.025), so 1.5 s after launch, the target will reach its maximum height, 13.025 m.

Try It This Way

Use a graphing calculator to graph the function
$s = -4.9t^2 + 14.7t + 2$
as Y1 and
$s = -4.9(t - 1.5)^2 + 13.025$ as Y2.

Turn each function on and off for graphing so that you see only one function at a time. Both functions should have the same graph.

GOT TO KNOW!

Vertex Form of a Quadratic Function

$f(x) = a(x - h)^2 + k$

- vertex (h, k)

- k = maximum or minimum value

Systems of Quadratics

What Came Before?

- Systems of linear equations and linear inequalities
- Quadratic equations

What's This About?

- Solving and graphing systems with one linear equation and one quadratic equation
- Quadratic inequalities in one variable and in two variables
- Systems of quadratic inequalities

Practical Apps

- Agronomists and farmers can use quadratic systems to compare possible crop yields under various treatments.
- Circus trapeze artists can use quadratic systems to be certain that connections between swings are timed accurately.

just for FUN!

Q: Why was the quadratic function nice to the linear function?

A: It knew they might meet again.

You can find more practice problems online by visiting:
www.SWadvantage.com

Linear-Quadratic Systems

Linear-Quadratic Solutions

When a system of equations includes a quadratic equation and a linear equation, it is called a **linear-quadratic system**. Linear-quadratic systems can have two, one, or no real solutions. The points of intersection on the graph of the system represent the real solutions.

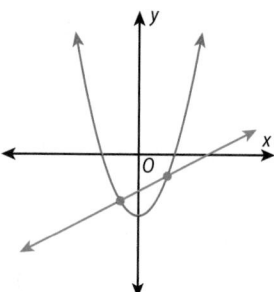

The graphs intersect at two points.

two real solutions

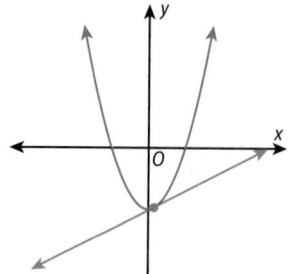

The graphs intersect at one point.

one real solution

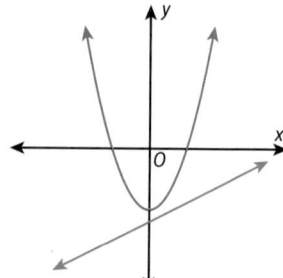

The graphs do not intersect.

no real solutions

EXAMPLE 1

Solve the system by graphing.

$$\begin{cases} y = 4x - 6 & \text{linear equation} \\ y = x^2 - 3 & \text{quadratic equation} \end{cases}$$

STEP 1 Graph the system.

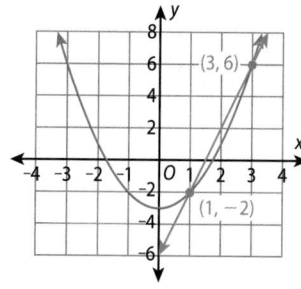

STEP 2 Look for any intersection points.

The graphs appear to intersect at $(1, -2)$ and $(3, 6)$.

STEP 3 Check the solutions in each equation.

CHECK $(1, -2)$.

$y = 4x - 6$	$y = x^2 - 3$
$-2 \overset{?}{=} 4(1) - 6$	$-2 \overset{?}{=} (1)^2 - 3$
$-2 \overset{?}{=} 4 - 6$	$-2 \overset{?}{=} 1 - 3$
$-2 = -2$ ✔	$-2 = -2$ ✔

CHECK $(3, 6)$.

$y = 4x - 6$	$y = x^2 - 3$
$6 \overset{?}{=} 4(3) - 6$	$6 \overset{?}{=} (3)^2 - 3$
$6 \overset{?}{=} 12 - 6$	$6 \overset{?}{=} 9 - 3$
$6 = 6$ ✔	$6 = 6$ ✔

SEARCH

To see step-by-step videos of these problems, enter the page number into the SWadvantage.com Search Bar.

Need More HELP?

Remember, the solution to a system of equations is an ordered pair or a set of ordered pairs.

For more help with solving systems of equations by graphing, go to *Solving a System by Graphing* (p. 1564).

EXAMPLE 2

Solve the system by graphing.

$$\begin{cases} y = 14 - 2x & \text{linear equation} \\ y = -x^2 + 6x - 2 & \text{quadratic equation} \end{cases}$$

STEP 1 Graph the system.

STEP 2 Look for any intersection points.

The graphs appear to intersect at (4, 6).

STEP 3 Check the solution in each equation.

CHECK (4, 6).

$y = 14 - 2x$	$y = -x^2 + 6x - 2$
$6 \overset{?}{=} 14 - 2(4)$	$6 \overset{?}{=} -(4)^2 + 6(4) - 2$
$6 \overset{?}{=} 14 - 8$	$6 \overset{?}{=} -16 + 24 - 2$
$6 = 6 ✔$	$6 = 6 ✔$

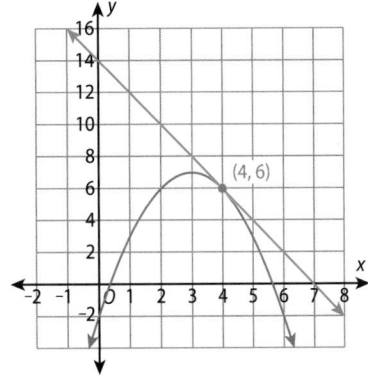

GOT TO KNOW!

Tangent Line

When a line touches a parabola at only one point, the line is said to be *tangent* to the parabola at that point.

EXAMPLE 3

Solve the system by graphing.

$$\begin{cases} 3x + 4y = 12 & \text{linear equation} \\ x^2 + 5x + y + 2 = 0 & \text{quadratic equation} \end{cases}$$

STEP 1 Solve each equation for y.

$3x + 4y = 12$ $x^2 + 5x + y + 2 = 0$

$\quad 4y = -3x + 12$ $y = -x^2 - 5x - 2$

$\quad\; y = -\frac{3}{4}x + 3$

STEP 2 Graph the system.

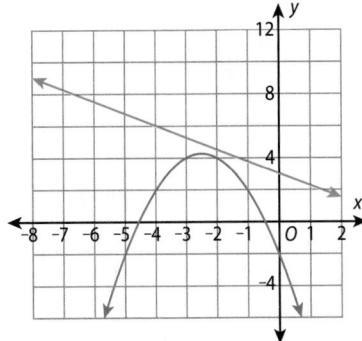

STEP 3 Look for any intersection points.

There are no intersection points, so there is no real solution.

Solving Nonlinear Systems Algebraically

For most nonlinear systems of equations, the points of intersection do not occur where grid lines of the graph intersect. So graphing is not the best method for solving when an exact answer is required. The substitution method usually works better.

EXAMPLE 4

SEARCH

To see step-by-step videos of these problems, enter the page number into the SWadvantage.com Search Bar.

Solve the system by substitution.

$$\begin{cases} x = y + 6 \\ y = x^2 - 18 \end{cases}$$

STEP 1 Solve the linear equation for y.

$$x = y + 6$$
$$x - 6 = y$$

STEP 2 Substitute the expression for y from the linear equation into the quadratic equation.

$$y = x^2 - 18$$

Substitute $x - 6$ for y in the quadratic equation. $x - 6 = x^2 - 18$

STEP 3 Simplify and solve for x.

Write in standard form. $0 = x^2 - x - 12$

Factor. $0 = (x - 4)(x + 3)$

Use the Zero-Product Property. $x = 4$ or $x = -3$

STEP 4 Find the corresponding y-values in one of the original equations.

Substitute 4 for x.   Substitute -3 for x.

$x = y + 6$ $x = y + 6$
$4 = y + 6$ $-3 = y + 6$
$-2 = y$ $-9 = y$
$(4, -2)$ Write the ordered pairs. $(-3, -9)$

STEP 5 Check the solutions in the other original equation.

CHECK $(4, -2)$.   **CHECK** $(-3, -9)$.

$y = x^2 - 18$ $y = x^2 - 18$
$-2 \overset{?}{=} (4)^2 - 18$ $-9 \overset{?}{=} (-3)^2 - 18$
$-2 \overset{?}{=} 16 - 18$ $-9 \overset{?}{=} 9 - 18$
$-2 = -2$ ✔ $-9 = -9$ ✔

You can also verify that the solution is reasonable by graphing.

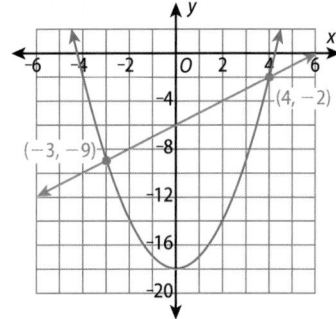

EXAMPLE 5

Solve the system by substitution.

$$\begin{cases} x = 2y + 4 \\ 2(y - 1) = x(4x - 9) \end{cases}$$

STEP 1 Solve each equation for y.

$x = 2y + 4$ $\longrightarrow$ $y = \frac{1}{2}x - 2$

$2(y - 1) = x(4x - 9)$ $\longrightarrow$ $y = 2x^2 - \frac{9}{2}x + 1$

STEP 2 Substitute the expression for y from the linear equation into the quadratic equation.

$$y = 2x^2 - \frac{9}{2}x + 1$$

Substitute $\frac{1}{2}x - 2$ for y in the quadratic equation. $\quad \frac{1}{2}x - 2 = 2x^2 - \frac{9}{2}x + 1$

STEP 3 Simplify and solve for x.

Write in standard form. $\qquad\qquad\qquad 0 = 2x^2 - 5x + 3$

Use the Quadratic Formula, $x = \frac{-b \pm \sqrt{b^2 - 4ac}}{2a}$. $\quad x = \frac{-(-5) \pm \sqrt{(-5)^2 - 4(2)(3)}}{2(2)}$

Simplify. $\qquad\qquad\qquad\qquad\qquad x = \frac{5 \pm \sqrt{25 - 24}}{4} = \frac{5 \pm 1}{4}$

$$x = \frac{3}{2} \text{ or } x = 1$$

STEP 4 Find the corresponding y-values in one of the original equations.

Substitute $\frac{3}{2}$ for x. $\qquad\qquad\qquad$ Substitute 1 for x.

$x = 2y + 4$ $\qquad\qquad\qquad\qquad x = 2y + 4$

$\frac{3}{2} = 2y + 4$ $\qquad\qquad\qquad\qquad 1 = 2y + 4$

$-\frac{5}{4} = y$ $\qquad\qquad\qquad\qquad\quad -\frac{3}{2} = y$

$\left(\frac{3}{2}, -\frac{5}{4} \right)$ $\qquad$ Write the ordered pairs. $\quad \left(1, -\frac{3}{2} \right)$

STEP 5 Check the solutions in the other original equation.

Because the fractions have simple decimal equivalents, check by using decimal equivalents.

CHECK $\left(\frac{3}{2}, -\frac{5}{4} \right)$. Use $(1.5, -1.25)$. $\qquad$ **CHECK** $\left(1, -\frac{3}{2} \right)$. Use $(1, -1.5)$.

$2(y - 1) = x(4x - 9)$ $\qquad\qquad\qquad 2(y - 1) = x(4x - 9)$

$2[(-1.25) - 1] \stackrel{?}{=} 1.5[4(1.5) - 9]$ $\qquad 2[(-1.5) - 1] \stackrel{?}{=} 1[4(1) - 9]$

$2(-2.25) \stackrel{?}{=} 1.5(6 - 9)$ $\qquad\qquad\quad 2(-2.5) \stackrel{?}{=} 1(4 - 9)$

$-4.5 = -4.5$ ✔ $\qquad\qquad\qquad\qquad -5 = -5$ ✔

Need More HELP?

To solve the quadratic equation for y in Step 1, use the Distributive Property first.

$2(y - 1) = x(4x - 9)$

$2y - 2 = 4x^2 - 9x$

$2y = 4x^2 - 9x + 2$

Then divide by 2.

$y = 2x^2 - \frac{9}{2}x + 1$

GOT TO KNOW!

To Solve a Linear-Quadratic System

1. Solve each equation for y.

2. Graph each equation, and find any intersection points. There are two, one, or none of them.

3. If intersection points are hard to identify, solve by a different method, such as substitution.

Quadratic-Quadratic Systems

Quadratic-Quadratic Solutions

Need More
HELP ?

For more examples of intersecting graphs of quadratic equations, look at the pairs of graphs in *Transforming Quadratics* (p. 1694).

When you solve a system of two quadratic equations, you are solving a **quadratic-quadratic system**. The solution is the intersection of two parabolas.

Quadratic-quadratic systems can have two, one, or no real solutions.

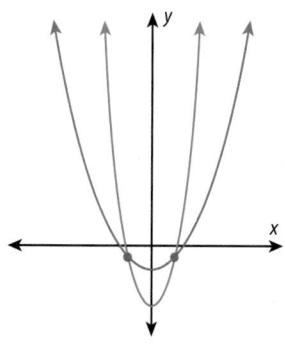

The graphs intersect in two locations.

two real solutions

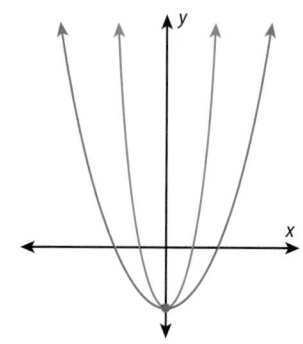

The graphs intersect in one location.

one real solution

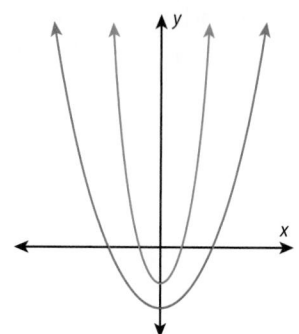

The graphs do not intersect.

no real solutions

SEARCH 🔍

To see step-by-step videos of these problems, enter the page number into the SWadvantage.com Search Bar.

EXAMPLE 1

Solve the system by graphing.

$$\begin{cases} y = x^2 \\ y = -2x^2 + 12x - 9 \end{cases}$$

STEP 1 Graph the system.

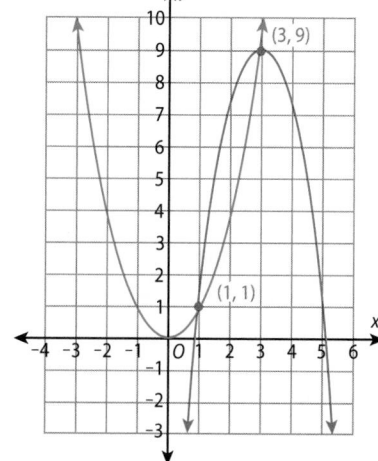

STEP 2 Look for any intersection points.

The graphs appear to intersect at (1, 1) and (3, 9).

STEP 3 Check the solutions in each equation.

Check (1, 1).

$y = x^2$	$y = -2x^2 + 12x - 9$
$1 \stackrel{?}{=} 1^2$	$1 \stackrel{?}{=} -2(1)^2 + 12(1) - 9$
$1 = 1 ✔$	$1 \stackrel{?}{=} -2 + 12 - 9$
	$1 = 1 ✔$

Check (3, 9).

$y = x^2$	$y = -2x^2 + 12x - 9$
$9 \stackrel{?}{=} 3^2$	$9 \stackrel{?}{=} -2(3)^2 + 12(3) - 9$
$9 = 9 ✔$	$9 \stackrel{?}{=} -18 + 36 - 9$
	$9 = 9 ✔$

Solving Quadratic-Quadratic Systems Algebraically

EXAMPLE 2

Solve the system by substitution.

$$\begin{cases} y = -x^2 + 6x - 8 \\ y = -2x^2 + 16x - 32 \end{cases}$$

STEP 1 Substitute the expression for y from one equation into the other equation.

Use the second original equation. $y = -2x^2 + 16x - 32$

Substitute $-x^2 + 6x - 8$ for y. $-x^2 + 6x - 8 = -2x^2 + 16x - 32$

STEP 2 Write in standard form.

Combine like terms on one side. $x^2 - 10x + 24 = 0$

Factor. $(x - 4)(x - 6) = 0$

Use the Zero-Product Property. $x = 4 \text{ or } x = 6$

STEP 3 Find the corresponding y-values by substituting into one of the original equations.

Substitute 4 for x.   Substitute 6 for x.

$y = -x^2 + 6x - 8$ $y = -x^2 + 6x - 8$

$y = -(4)^2 + 6(4) - 8$ $y = -(6)^2 + 6(6) - 8$

$y = -16 + 24 - 8$ $y = -36 + 6(6) - 8$

$y = 0$ $y = -8$

$(4, 0)$ Write the ordered pairs. $(6, -8)$

STEP 4 Check the solutions by substituting into the other equation.

Check $(4, 0)$.   Check $(6, -8)$.

$y = -2x^2 + 16x - 32$ $y = -2x^2 + 16x - 32$

$0 \overset{?}{=} -2(4)^2 + 16(4) - 32$ $-8 \overset{?}{=} -2(6)^2 + 16(6) - 32$

$0 \overset{?}{=} -32 + 64 - 32$ $-8 \overset{?}{=} -72 + 96 - 32$

$0 = 0 \checkmark$ $-8 = -8 \checkmark$

You can also verify the solution by graphing.

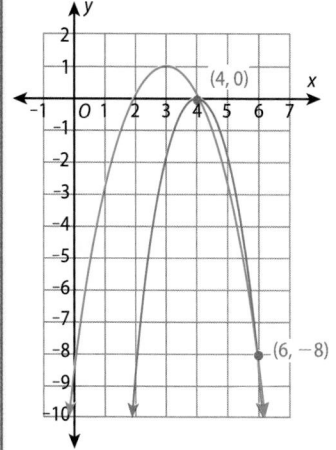

Quadratic Inequalities

Quadratic Inequalities in One Variable

The graph on a number line of an inequality in one variable consists of all solutions of the inequality.

EXAMPLE 1

Graph $x^2 - 3x - 10 > 0$.

STEP 1 Factor the related quadratic equation.

$$x^2 - 3x - 10 = 0$$
$$(x + 2)(x - 5) = 0$$

Use the Zero-Product Property.

$$x + 2 = 0 \text{ or } x - 5 = 0$$
$$x = -2 \text{ or } x = 5$$

STEP 2 Plot the solutions of the equation on the number line.

Use open circles for $>$.

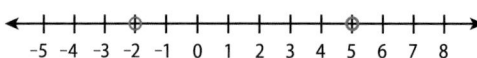

There are 3 intervals on the number line.

STEP 3 Test a value of x from each interval in the original inequality. Shade the interval if the value satisfies the inequality.

Test -3.
$(-3)^2 - 3(-3) - 10 > 0$
$9 + 9 - 10 > 0$ ✓

Test 0.
$(0)^2 - 3(0) - 10 > 0$
$0 + 0 - 10 > 0$ ✗

Test 6.
$(6)^2 - 3(6) - 10 > 0$
$36 - 18 - 10 > 0$ ✓

The solution is the disjunction $x < -2$ or $x > 5$.

EXAMPLE 2

Graph $-2x^2 + 21 \geq 3$.

STEP 1 Write an equivalent inequality with 0 on one side.

$$-2x^2 + 21 \geq 3$$
$$-2x^2 + 18 \geq 0$$

Divide both sides by -2, and reverse the inequality symbol.

$$x^2 - 9 \leq 0$$

STEP 2 Factor the related quadratic equation.

$$(x + 3)(x - 3) = 0$$

Use the Zero-Product Property.

$$x = -3 \text{ or } x = 3$$

STEP 3 Plot the solutions of the equation on the number line.

Use closed circles for $\geq$ or $\leq$.

STEP 4 Test a value of x from each interval in the original inequality. Shade the interval if the value satisfies the inequality.

Test -5.
$-2(-5)^2 + 21 \geq 3$
$-50 + 21 \geq 3$ ✗

Test 0.
$-2(0)^2 + 21 \geq 3$
$0 + 21 \geq 3$ ✓

Test 5.
$-2(5)^2 + 21 \geq 3$
$-50 + 21 \geq 3$ ✗

The solution is the conjunction $-2 \leq x \leq 3$.

Quadratic Inequalities in Two Variables

The graph on the coordinate plane of an inequality in two variables consists of all solutions (x, y) of the inequality.

The graph of a quadratic equation is a parabola. So the graph of a quadratic inequality consists of a parabola and all points above or below the parabola.

The parabola is like the boundary line in the graph of a linear inequality. The parabola is solid if it is a solution of the inequality. It is dashed if it is not a solution.

Need More

HELP

For more help with graphing inequalities in the coordinate plane, go to *Graphing a Linear Inequality* (p. 1558).

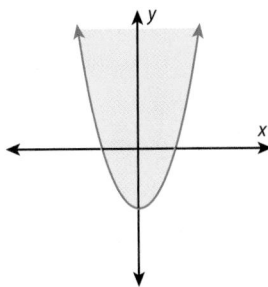

$y \geq ax^2 + bx + c$

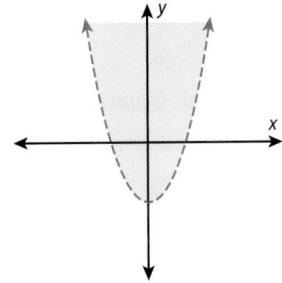

$y > ax^2 + bx + c$

$y \leq ax^2 + bx + c$

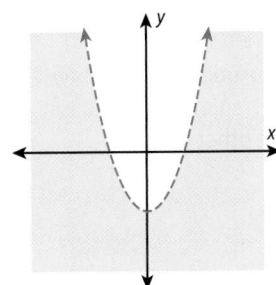

$y < ax^2 + bx + c$

EXAMPLE 3

Graph the quadratic inequality $y < -x^2 + 6x - 5$.

STEP 1 Graph the related quadratic equation.

Graph $y = -x^2 + 6x - 5$. Use a dashed line for $<$.

STEP 2 Shade the correct side of the curve.

The inequality is in the form $y < ax^2 + bx + c$, so shade below the curve.

CHECK Test $(0, 0)$ in the inequality to see whether the correct region is shaded.

Write the inequality. $y < -x^2 + 6x - 5$

Substitute $(0, 0)$. $0 \overset{?}{<} -(0)^2 + 6(0) - 5$

Point $(0, 0)$ is not in the shaded region. $0 < -5$ ✗

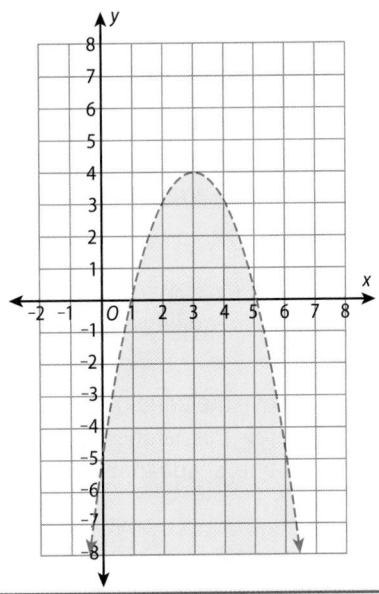

Watch Out !

Be sure that the inequality has the variable y alone on the left side of the inequality symbol before using the rule for shading above or below.

Solving Quadratic Inequalities in Two Variables

EXAMPLE 4

Graph the quadratic inequality $2(x - 5)^2 - 9 \leq y - 3$.

STEP 1 Solve the inequality for y.

Write the inequality.	$2(x - 5)^2 - 9 \leq y - 3$
Add 3 to both sides.	$2(x^2 - 10x + 25) - 6 \leq y$
Simplify.	$2x^2 - 20x + 44 \leq y$
Reverse the entire inequality.	$y \geq 2x^2 - 20x + 44$

STEP 2 Graph the related quadratic equation.

Graph $y = 2x^2 - 20x + 44$.

Use a solid line for $\geq$ or $\leq$.

STEP 3 Shade the correct side of the curve.

METHOD 1

The inequality is $\geq$, so shade above the curve.

METHOD 2

Test any point in the original inequality. If it is a solution, shade the region it is in. If it is not a solution, shade the other region.

Test (0, 0).

Write the inequality.	$2(x - 5)^2 - 9 \leq y - 3$
Substitute (0, 0).	$2(0 - 5)^2 - 9 \overset{?}{\leq} 0 - 3$
Simplify.	$2(25) - 9 \overset{?}{\leq} -3$
	$41 \leq -3$ ✗

Because (0, 0) is not a solution, shade the other region.

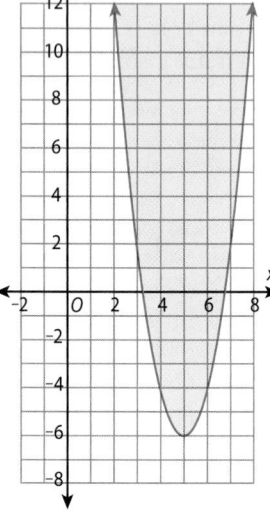

SEARCH

To see step-by-step videos of these problems, enter the page number into the SWadvantage.com Search Bar.

GOT TO KNOW!

Graphing a Quadratic Inequality in Two Variables

1. Solve the inequality for y.

2. Graph the related quadratic equation $y = ax^2 + bx + c$. Make the parabola solid if the equation is a solution of the inequality and dashed if it is not a solution.

3. For $y >$ and $y \geq$, shade the region above the parabola.
   For $y <$ and $y \leq$, shade the region below the parabola.
   You can also test a point. If it is a solution, shade that region. If not, shade the other region.

EXAMPLE 5

A farmer wants to use 60 meters of fencing to border a rectangular field. There is already a fence along one side, so the fencing will be used along three sides.

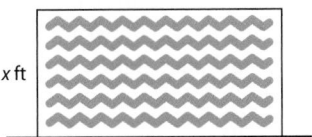
x ft

a. Write an expression for the area of the field.

Let x be the width, the dimension perpendicular to the existing fence. Then the length is $60 - 2x$. The area is $x(60 - 2x)$, or $-2x^2 + 60x$.

b. What widths will produce an area of at least 400 square meters?

METHOD 1

Write the inequality.	$-2x^2 + 60x \geq 400$
Subtract 400 from both sides.	$-2x^2 + 60x - 400 \geq 0$
Divide both sides by -2 and reverse the inequality symbol.	$x^2 - 30x + 200 \leq 0$
Factor.	$(x - 10)(x - 20) \leq 0$
Write the solutions of the related equation.	$x = 10$ or $x = 20$

Plot the solutions of the equation on a number line. Test a point in each interval.

Test 5.
$-2(5)^2 + 60\,(5) \geq 400$
$-50 + 300 \geq 400$ ✗

Test 15.
$-2(15)^2 + 60\,(15) \geq 400$
$-450 + 900 \geq 400$ ✓

Test 25.
$-2(25)^2 + 60\,(25) \geq 400$
$-1{,}250 + 1500 \geq 400$ ✗

0   5   10   15   20   25   30

Use closed circles for $\geq$ or $\leq$.

So, if $10 \leq x \leq 20$, then the area will be at least 400 m².

METHOD 2

Write the inequality. $-2x^2 + 60x \geq 400$

Graph the quadratic function for the area, $y = -2x^2 + 60x$. Find the x-values where the function value is greater than or equal to 400.

The area is at least 400 square meters for widths within the interval $10 \leq x \leq 20$.

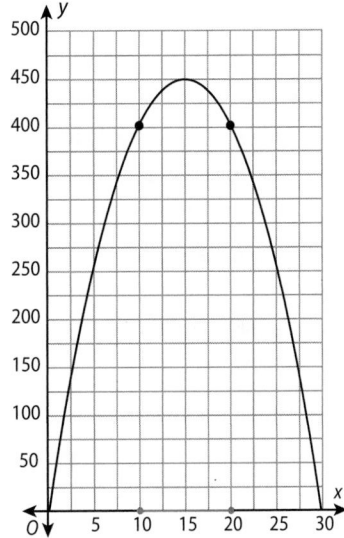

CHECK Test a solution in the problem situation.

If the width of the plot is 15 meters, the length is $60 - 2(15) = 30$ meters. The area is $30(15) = 450$ square meters, which is at least 400 square meters. ✔

Nonlinear Systems of Inequalities

Linear-Quadratic Systems of Inequalities

Graphing a system of inequalities with at least one quadratic inequality is similar to graphing a system of two linear inequalities. First, graph each inequality. Then identify the region of the coordinate plane where both inequalities are true.

EXAMPLE 1

Graph the system of inequalities.

$$\begin{cases} y < x + 3 & \text{linear inequality} \\ y \geq x^2 - 3 & \text{quadratic inequality} \end{cases}$$

Watch Out !

Remember, only the region where both inequalities are true is the solution region. So only the shading in that region represents the solution.

Lightly shading the solution for each inequality helps you identify the solution region for the entire system, that is, the region where the overlap occurs.

STEP 1 Graph the linear inequality $y < x + 3$.

Graph the dashed line $y = x + 3$, and shade below the line.

STEP 2 Graph the quadratic inequality $y \geq x^2 - 3$.

Graph the solid curve $y = x^2 - 3$, and shade above the curve.

STEP 3 Identify the solution region, where the graphs overlap.

STEP 4 Test a point in the solution region.

(0, 0) is a solution.

Substitute the ordered pair (0, 0) into each inequality.

$y < x + 3$		$y \geq x^2 - 3$
$0 \overset{?}{<} 0 + 3$	Substitute 0 for x and 0 for y.	$0 \overset{?}{\geq} (0)^2 - 3$
$0 < 3$ ✔		$0 \geq -3$ ✔

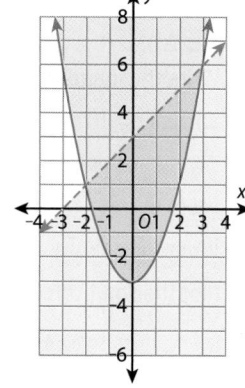

EXAMPLE 2

Graph the system of inequalities.

$$\begin{cases} 4x + y - 2 < x^2 & \text{quadratic inequality} \\ y - x > 1 & \text{linear inequality} \end{cases}$$

SEARCH

To see step-by-step videos of these problems, enter the page number into the SWadvantage.com Search Bar.

STEP 1 Solve each inequality for y.

$$4x + y - 2 < x^2 \longrightarrow y < x^2 - 4x + 2$$
$$y - x > 1 \longrightarrow y > x + 1$$

STEP 2 Graph the quadratic inequality $y < x^2 - 4x + 2$.

Graph the curve as dashed, and shade below the curve.

STEP 3 Graph the linear inequality $y > x + 1$.

Graph the line as dashed, and shade above the line.

STEP 4 Identify the solution region, where the graphs overlap. There are two solution regions.

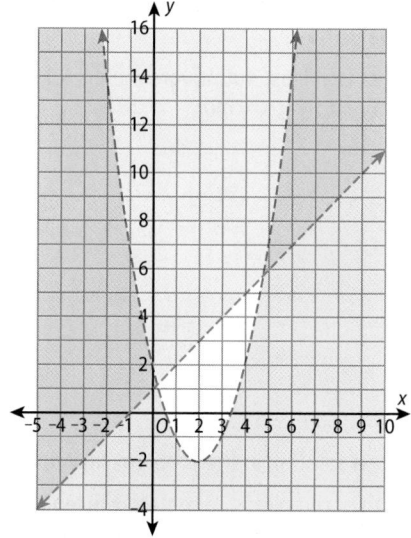

STEP 5 Test a point in each solution region.

(−3, 2) is a solution. (7, 10) is a solution.

4x + y − 2 < x²	**y − x > 1**	**4x + y − 2 < x²**	**y − x > 1**
$4(-3) + 2 - 2 \overset{?}{<} (-3)^2$	$(2) - (-3) \overset{?}{>} 1$	$4(7) + 10 - 2 \overset{?}{<} 7^2$	$10 - 7 \overset{?}{>} 1$
−12 < 9 ✔	5 > 1 ✔	36 < 49 ✔	3 > 1

Special Linear-Quadratic Systems

A linear-quadratic system may or may not have a solution.

EXAMPLE 3

Graph the system of inequalities.

$$\begin{cases} 3x + 4y \geq 28 \\ 2y \leq -x^2 + 8x - 10 \end{cases}$$

STEP 1 Solve each inequality for y.

$3x + 4y \geq 28 \longrightarrow y \geq -\dfrac{3}{4}x + 7$

$2y \leq -x^2 + 8x - 10 \longrightarrow y \leq -\dfrac{1}{2}x^2 + 4x - 5$

STEP 2 Graph the linear inequality $y \geq -\dfrac{3}{4}x + 7$.

Graph the line as solid, and shade above the line.

STEP 3 Graph the quadratic inequality $y \leq -\dfrac{1}{2}x^2 + 4x - 5$.

Graph the curve as solid, and shade below the curve.

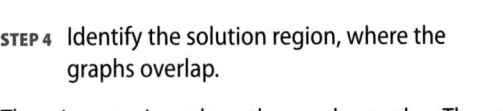

STEP 4 Identify the solution region, where the graphs overlap.

There is no region where the graphs overlap. The system has no solution.

Linear-Quadratic System Solutions

For a system of two linear inequalities, it is possible for the entire coordinate plane to be the solution region. This is not possible for a linear-quadratic system.

EXAMPLE 4

Graph the system of inequalities.

$$\begin{cases} y \geq 2x^2 - 7x + 6 \\ x < 1 \end{cases}$$

STEP 1 Graph the quadratic inequality $y \geq 2x^2 - 7x + 6$.

Graph the curve as solid, and shade above the curve.

STEP 2 Graph the vertical line $x = 1$.

Graph the line as dashed, and shade to the left of the line.

STEP 3 Identify the solution region, where the graphs overlap.

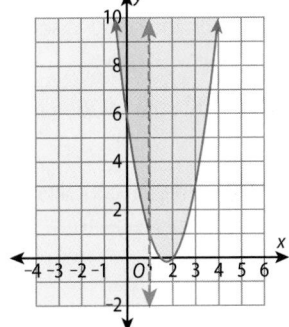

Need More HELP?

Remember that for a vertical line $x = a$, where a is a constant, shade the left side of the line for $x < a$ and shade the right side of the line for $x > a$.

Quadratic-Quadratic Systems of Inequalities

SEARCH

To see step-by-step videos of these problems, enter the page number into the SWadvantage.com Search Bar.

EXAMPLE 5

Graph the system of inequalities.

$$\begin{cases} y \le 7 - x^2 & \text{quadratic inequality} \\ y \ge x^2 + 2 & \text{quadratic inequality} \end{cases}$$

STEP 1 Graph the first inequality, $y \le 7 - x^2$.

Graph the solid curve $y = 7 - x^2$, and shade below the curve.

STEP 2 Graph the second inequality, $y \ge x^2 + 2$.

Graph the solid curve $y = x^2 + 2$, and shade above the curve.

STEP 3 Identify the solution region, where the graphs overlap.

STEP 4 Test a point in the solution region.

(0, 5) is a solution.

Substitute the ordered pair (0, 5) into each inequality.

$y \le 7 - x^2$		$y \ge x^2 + 2$
$5 \le 7 - 0$	Substitute 0 for x and 5 for y.	$5 \ge 0^2 + 2$
$5 \le 7$ ✔		$5 \ge 2$ ✔

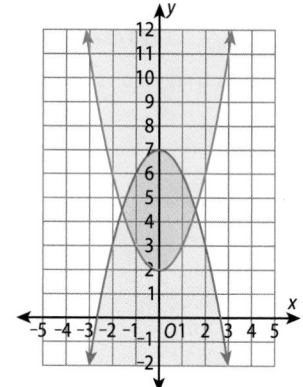

EXAMPLE 6

Need More

HELP ?

Both of the inequalities in Example 6 are in vertex form, $a(x - h)^2 + k$, where the vertex is (h, k).

For more help graphing and identifying parabolas in vertex form, go to *Transforming Quadratics* and *Projectile Motion Problems* (p. 1694 and p. 1722).

Graph the system of inequalities.

$$\begin{cases} y > -\frac{1}{2}(x - 5)^2 + 8 \\ y \ge (x - 3)^2 \end{cases}$$

STEP 1 Graph the first inequality,

$y > -\frac{1}{2}(x - 5)^2 + 8$.

Graph the curve as dashed, and shade above the curve.

STEP 2 Graph the second inequality, $y \ge (x - 3)^2$.

Graph the curve as solid, and shade above the curve.

STEP 3 Identify the solution region, where the graphs overlap.

The solution region contains (2, 6), but not (4, 6).

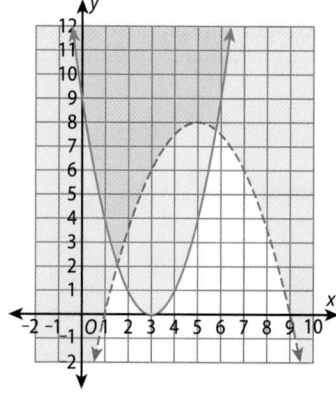

Special Quadratic-Quadratic Systems

A quadratic-quadratic system may or may not have a solution.

EXAMPLE 7

Graph the system of inequalities.

$$\begin{cases} y \geq 2x^2 - 20x + 51 \\ y < -x^2 + 2x + 8 \end{cases}$$

STEP 1 Graph the first inequality, $y \geq 2x^2 - 20x + 51$.

Graph the curve as solid, and shade above the curve.

STEP 2 Graph the second inequality, $y < -x^2 + 2x + 8$.

Graph the curve as dashed, and shade below the curve.

STEP 3 Identify the solution region, where the graphs overlap.

There is no region where the graphs overlap. The system has no solution.

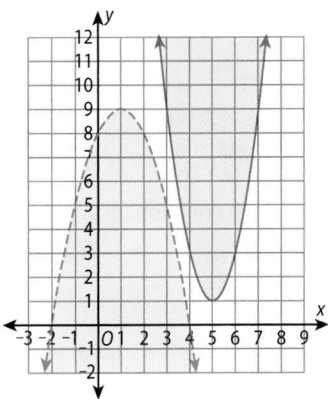

GOT TO KNOW!

Graphing a Nonlinear System of Inequalities

1. Solve each inequality for *y*.

2. Graph each inequality.

3. Identify any overlapping regions as the solution region.

EXAMPLE 8

Graph the system of inequalities.

$$\begin{cases} y < -(x + 3)^2 + x + 10 \\ y \leq -x^2 - 5x - 1 \end{cases}$$

STEP 1 Graph the quadratic inequality
$y < -(x + 3)^2 + x + 10$.

Graph the curve as dashed, and shade below the curve.

STEP 2 Graph the quadratic inequality
$y \leq -x^2 - 5x - 1$.

Graph the curve as solid, and shade below the curve.

STEP 3 Identify the solution region.
The second solution is entirely within the first.

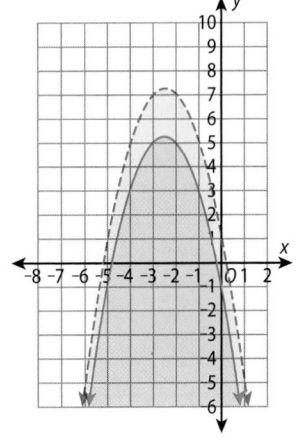

Need More HELP?

In Example 8, the first parabola simplifies to $y = -x^2 - 5x + 1$.

So the second parabola is a vertical translation of the first parabola 2 units down.

GOT TO KNOW!

Relating Systems of Quadratic Inequalities to Systems of Quadratic Equations

If the system of equations has a solution, the system of inequalities may still not have a solution.

For example, $\begin{cases} y > x^2 + 3 \\ y \leq x^2 + 3 \end{cases}$ has no solution, although the related equations are the same and so the boundaries coincide. So (0, 3) is a point on both boundaries and a solution to each related equation. However, the points on the boundary are not solutions of the system of inequalities.

Graphing Calculators

Nonlinear Systems of Equations

You can use a graphing calculator to solve linear-quadratic and quadratic-quadratic systems of equations. In some cases, the table function on the calculator may be useful.

SEARCH

To see step-by-step videos of these problems, enter the page number into the SWadvantage.com Search Bar.

EXAMPLE 1

Solve the system of equations.

$$\begin{cases} y - 6 = x(x - 2) \\ y - 3 = 2x \end{cases}$$

Solve each equation for y.

$y - 6 = x(x - 2) \longrightarrow y = x^2 - 2x + 6$

$y - 3 = 2x \longrightarrow y = 2x + 3$

METHOD 1 Use the subtraction method.

Subtract the second equation from the first: $\quad 0 = x^2 - 4x + 3$

Factor. $\quad 0 = (x - 1)(x - 3)$

Use the Zero-Product Property. $\quad x = 1 \text{ or } x = 3$

Find the corresponding y-values by substituting into one of the original equations.

When $x = 1$, $y - 3 = 2(1)$, so $(1, 5)$ is a solution.

When $x = 3$, $y - 3 = 2(3)$, so $(3, 9)$ is a solution.

METHOD 2 Use the graphing function on a graphing calculator.

GOT TO KNOW!

Friendly Windows

The TI-83 screen is 95 pixels wide. When you use TRACE to step across the window, it takes 94 steps. So if you set XMax − Xmin to 94, each step will be 1 unit. If you set it to 9.4, each step will be 0.1 unit.

For the window defined by XMax = 5.7 and XMin = −3.7, XMax − Xmin = 9.4.

STEP 1 Enter the solved equations in Y1 and Y2.

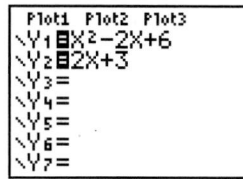

STEP 2 Graph in an appropriate viewing window.

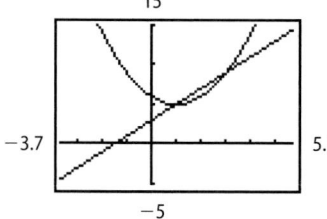

STEP 3 Find the first intersection point.

Press **2nd** **CALC**, and select 5:intersect.

Press **ENTER** twice to select each function.

Type 1 as the Guess, and press **ENTER**.

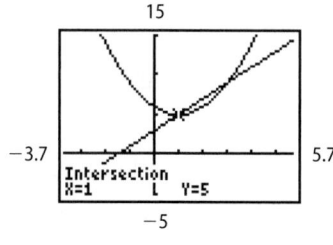

STEP 4 Find the second intersection point.

Press **2nd** **CALC**, and select 5:intersect.

Press **ENTER** twice to select each function.

Type 3 as the Guess, and press **ENTER**.

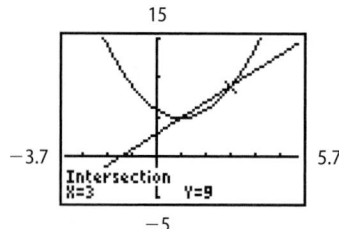

So, the solutions are $(1, 5)$ and $(3, 9)$.

METHOD 3

Use the table function on a graphing calculator.

Use **2nd** **TABLE** to make a table for each function.

Identify the values of x and y where Y1 = Y2.

(1, 5) and (3, 9) are the solutions.

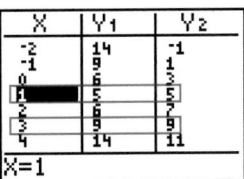

EXAMPLE 2

Solve the system of equations.

$$\begin{cases} y = 2x^2 - 14x + 27 \\ y = -4x + 14 \end{cases}$$

Enter the equations in Y1 and Y2, and graph in an appropriate viewing window.

There appears to be one intersection point.　　Use **ZOOM** 2:Zoom In at about (2.5, 4.5).

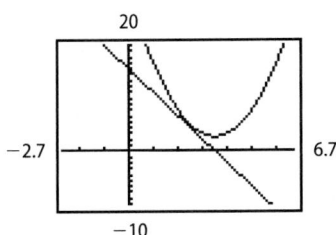 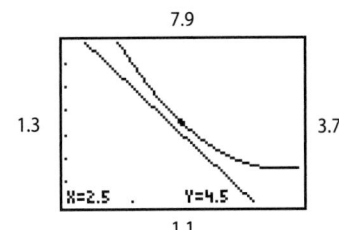

There is no intersection point, so the system has no solution.

Watch Out !

If you try to use the 5:intersect function with the system in Example 2, you will get the error

ERR:NO SIGN CHNG

1:Quit

This should alert you that the system has no solution.

EXAMPLE 3

During a circus performance, a performer on a trapeze is initially at a height of 30 feet. The trapeze begins rising at a rate of 2 feet per second at the same time that a ball is launched from the ground at a velocity of 48 feet per second straight up. The performer can catch the ball when it is above the height of her seat. When will the ball be above the performer's seat height?

STEP 1 Write a system of equations for the situation.

The trapeze is initially at 30 ft and rises at 2 ft/s.　　$y = 30 + 2x$

The ball is launched from 0 ft at a velocity of 48 ft/s.　　$y = -16x^2 + 48x$

STEP 2 Graph the system to find the solutions.

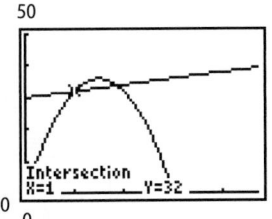 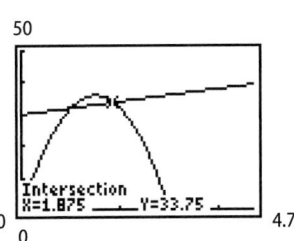

The ball is above her seat height between 1 second and 1.875 seconds.

Notice that the seat height and the ball height are the same at 32 ft (after 1 s) and 33.75 ft (after 1.875 s).

Try It This Way

Use the 2nd CALC 4:maximum function to find the maximum height of the ball.

Nonlinear Systems of Equations and Inequalities

SEARCH

To see step-by-step videos of these problems, enter the page number into the SWadvantage.com Search Bar.

EXAMPLE 4

Solve the system of equations.
$$\begin{cases} y = (x-1)^2 \\ y = 6 - 2(x-4)^2 \end{cases}$$

Use the graphing function on a graphing calculator.

Enter each equation, and use the intersect feature.

There is one solution, (3, 4).

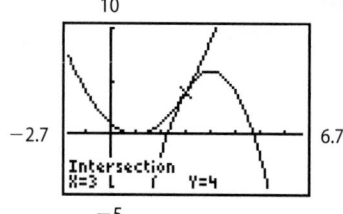

Graphing Inequalities on the TI-83 Calculator

To solve quadratic-quadratic systems of inequalities with a TI-83 graphing calculator, you can use the shading feature.

To graph the inequality $y > x^2 - 2$ or $y \geq x^2 - 2$, you can highlight the slanted line at the left of the function. Click several times to cycle through the choices. To shade above the parabola, stop when the icon shows shading above the slanted line. You can also shade below.

Shading icon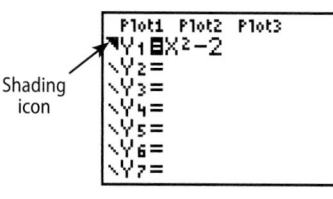

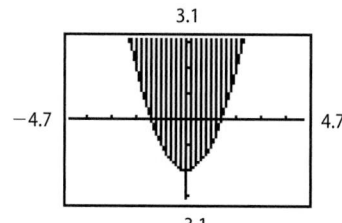

EXAMPLE 5

Graph the system of inequalities.
$$\begin{cases} y \leq 4 - 2x^2 \\ y \geq x^2 - 2x - 7 \end{cases}$$

Enter the inequalities in Y1 and Y2. Select the shade-below icon for the first inequality and the shade-above icon for the second inequality.

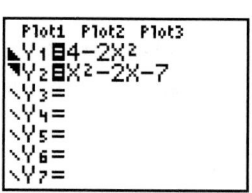

Graph in an appropriate viewing window. The overlapping region is the solution region.

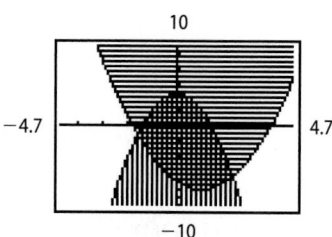

EXAMPLE 6

Each expression in the table shows the maximum crop yield in bushels per acre when one of two fertilizer brands, A or B, is used on a crop. The variable x represents the quantity of fertilizer used per acre.

Brand	Maximum Yield (bushels per acre)
Brand A	$-0.0048x^2 + 1.2x + 10$
Brand B	$-0.005x^2 + x + 10$

a. **Graph the system of inequalities that shows the difference in maximum yields per acre.**

Brand A has a higher curve. The system is as shown here.

$$\begin{cases} y \le -0.0048x^2 + 1.2x + 10 & \text{Brand A} \\ y \ge -0.005x^2 + x + 10 & \text{Brand B} \end{cases}$$

Enter the inequalities in Y1 and Y2. Select the shade-below icon for the Brand A inequality and the shade-above icon for the Brand B inequality.

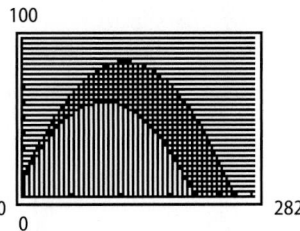

Graph in an appropriate viewing window. The overlapping region is the solution region.

b. **Give an example of a point inside the solution region that is not on either curve. What do the points in the solution region represent in the problem situation?**

Trace to an x-value on each curve. Then find a point between the y-values.

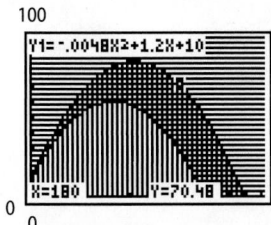 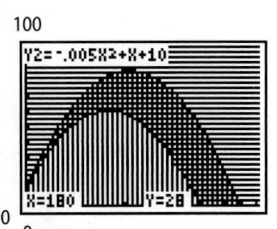

When $x = 180$, any y-value between 28 and 70.48 gives a point in the solution region, so (180, 50) is a point in the solution region. Points in the solution region represent possible yields when using Brand A that are not possible when using the same amount of Brand B.

Algebra

Properties of Equality

Addition	If $a = b$, then $a + c = b + c$.
Subtraction	If $a = b$, then $a - c = b - c$.
Multiplication	If $a = b$, then $a \cdot c = b \cdot c$.
Division	If $a = b$ and $c \neq 0$, then $\frac{a}{c} = \frac{b}{c}$.
Reflexive	$a = a$
Symmetric	If $a = b$, then $b = a$.
Transitive	If $a = b$ and $b = c$, then $a = c$.

Properties of Inequality

Addition	If $a < b$, then $a + c < b + c$.
Subtraction	If $a < b$, then $a - c < b - c$.
Multiplication	If $a < b$ and $c > 0$, then $a \cdot c < b \cdot c$.
	If $a < b$ and $c < 0$, then $a \cdot c > b \cdot c$.
Division	If $a < b$ and $c > 0$, then $\frac{a}{c} > \frac{b}{c}$.
	If $a < b$ and $c < 0$, then $\frac{a}{c} > \frac{b}{c}$.
Transitive	If $a < b$ and $b < c$, then $a < c$.

These properties are also true for $>$, $\leq$, and $\geq$.

Properties of Real Numbers

Commutative Property	$a + b = b + a$
	$a \cdot b = b \cdot a$
Associative Property	$(a + b) + c = a + (b + c)$
	$(a \cdot b) \cdot c = a \cdot (b \cdot c)$
Distributive Property	$a(b + c) = ab + ac$
	$a(b - c) = ab - ac$
Closure for Addition	$a + b$ is a real number.
Closure for Multiplication	$a \cdot b$ is a real number.
Identity Property	$a + 0 = a$
	$a \cdot 1 = a$
Inverse Property	$a + (-a) = 0$
	$a \cdot \frac{1}{a} = 1$
Multiplication by 0	$a \cdot 0 = 0$
Multiplication by -1	$a \cdot (-1) = -a$
Zero Product	If $ab = 0$, then $a = 0$, $b = 0$ or both a and $b = 0$.

Properties of Exponents

Zero exponent	$a^0 = 1$
Negative exponent	$a^{-1} = \frac{1}{a}$
Product of Powers	$a^m \times a^n = a^{m+n}$
Product to a Power	$(ab)^n = a^n \times b^n$
Power of a Power	$(a^m)^n = a^{m \cdot n}$
Quotient of Powers	$\frac{a^m}{a^n} = a^{m-n}$
Quotient to a Power	$\left(\frac{a}{b}\right)^n = \frac{a^n}{b^n}$

Translating Word Problems into Algebra

1. Read the problem carefully, and determine what number or numbers need to be found.
2. Represent this unknown number with a variable, for example, *x*.
3. Identify key words that show what operations are used with the numbers and variables in the problem.
4. Words like *equals* or *is* tell you to write an equation rather than just an expression.
5. Use numbers, variables, operation symbols, and a relationship stated in the problem to write any expression needed.
6. To write an equation, write two expressions and connect them with an equals sign.

Solving Word Problems

Step 1 Read the problem carefully and determine what number or numbers you need to find.

Step 2 Represent one unknown number with a variable.

Step 3 Use a condition stated in the problem to write an expression for a second number.

Step 4 Use a second condition to find two expressions that are equal. Then write these two expressions algebraically and connect them with an equals sign.

Step 5 Solve the equation.

Step 6 Check to make sure the result matches the conditions stated in the problem.

Operations with Signed Numbers

Adding

If the numbers have the same signs, add the absolute values and use the sign of the numbers.	$5 + 11 = 16$ $\qquad -5 + (-11) = -16$
If the numbers have different signs, subtract their absolute values and use the sign of the number with the greater absolute value.	$-7 + 11 = 4 \qquad -15 + 6 = -9$ $7 + (-11) = -4 \qquad 15 + (-6) = 9$

Subtracting

To subtract a number, add its opposite.	$8 - 6 = 8 + (-6) \qquad -1 - 7 = -1 + (-7)$

Multiplying or Dividing

If two numbers have the same sign, their product or quotient is positive.	$(+)(+) = (+)$ $\qquad (+) \div (+) = (+)$ $(-)(-) = (+)$ $\qquad (-) \div (-) = (+)$
If two numbers have different signs, their product or quotient is negative.	$(+)(-) = (-)$ $\qquad (+) \div (-) = (-)$ $(-)(+) = (-)$ $\qquad (-) \div (+) = (-)$

1747

Algebra

Graphing (x, y) on the Coordinate Plane

Value of x	Value of y	Location of Point
+	+	Quadrant I
−	+	Quadrant II
−	−	Quadrant III
+	−	Quadrant IV
0	+ or −	on the y-axis
+ or −	0	on the x-axis

Quadrant II (x negative, y positive) Quadrant I (x positive, y positive)

Quadrant III (x negative, y negative) Quadrant IV (x positive, y negative)

Formulas

Polynomials

Binomial squares	$(a + b)^2 = a^2 + 2ab + b^2$
	$(a − b)^2 = a^2 − 2ab + b^2$
Difference of squares	$a^2 − b^2 = (a + b)(a − b)$
Difference of cubes	$a^3 − b^3 = (a − b)(a^2 + ab + b^2)$
Sum of cubes	$a^3 + b^3 = (a + b)(a^2 − ab + b^2)$

Linear Equations

Slope	$m = \dfrac{y_2 − y_1}{x_2 − x_1}$
Slope-Intercept Form	$y = mx + b$
Point-Slope Form	$y − y_1 = m(x − x_1)$
Standard Form	$Ax + By = C$

Quadratic Equations and Functions

Standard Form	$ax^2 + bx + c = 0$
Quadratic Formula	$x = \dfrac{−b \pm \sqrt{b^2 − 4ac}}{2a}$
Discriminant	$b^2 − 4ac$
Vertex Form of a Function	$f(x) = a(x − h)^2 + k$
Line of Symmetry	$x = −\dfrac{b}{2a}$

Distance

horizontal distance between two points (x_1, y_1) and (x_2, y_2) on the coordinate plane	$|x_2 − x_1|$
vertical distance between two points (x_1, y_1) and (x_2, y_2) on the coordinate plane	$|y_2 − y_1|$

Theorems

Rational Zeros Theorem	If the polynomial function has integer coefficients, then every rational zero has this form. $\dfrac{p}{q}$ ← a factor of the constant term ← a factor of the leading coefficient
Rational Roots Theorem	If a polynomial equation $P(x) = 0$ has integer coefficients, then every rational root has this form. $\dfrac{p}{q}$ ← a factor of the constant term ← a factor of the leading coefficient
The Fundamental Theorem of Algebra and Its Corollary	*Theorem:* If $P(x)$ is a polynomial of degree n, then the equation $P(x) = 0$ has at least one root, which is complex. *Corollary:* If $P(x)$ is a polynomial of degree n, then the equation $P(x) = 0$ has exactly n roots when multiplicities are taken into account.
The Remainder Theorem	If a polynomial function $P(x)$ is divided by $x - a$, then the remainder r is equal to $P(a)$.
Descartes' Rule of Signs for Negative Real Zeros	The number of negative real zeros of the polynomial function $P(x)$ is either: • equal to the number of sign changes in $P(-x)$ or • less than the number of sign changes in $P(-x)$ by an even number.
Irrational Zeros Theorem	If $P(x)$ has a zero of the form $a + b\sqrt{c}$, it also has a zero of the form $a - b\sqrt{c}$.

Systems of Two Linear Equations

One Solution	No Solution	Infinitely Many Solutions
consistent system independent system	inconsistent system	consistent system dependent system
intersecting lines	parallel lines	same line
different slopes	same slope different y-intercepts	same slope same y-intercept

Advanced Algebra

The seeds of a sunflower grow in spirals in opposite directions. The numbers of spirals in each direction are consecutive numbers in the Fibonacci sequence.

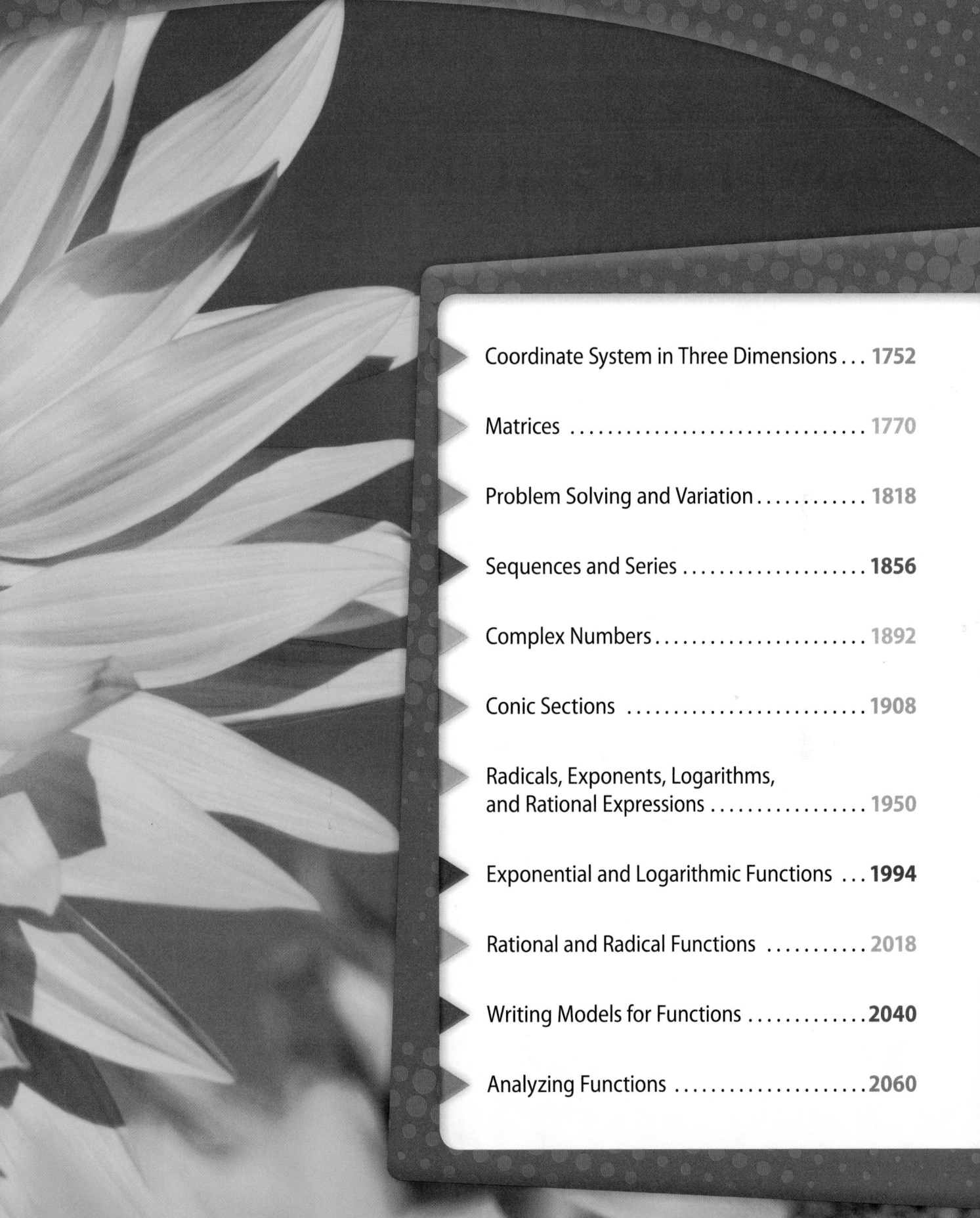

Coordinate System in Three Dimensions

What Came Before?
- Graphing in the x-y coordinate plane
- Solving systems of linear equations

What's This About?
- Plotting points in three dimensions using the x-, y- and z-axes
- Graphing planes in three dimensions
- Solving systems of three equations with three variables

Practical Apps
- 3D movie producers use three-dimensional graphing to project an image.
- When a manufacturer produces three different products, with three different costs, they utilize an equation with three variables.

just for FUN!

Q: How did the crime boss solve the system of three equations?

A: By elimination.

You can find more practice problems online by visiting:
www.SWadvantage.com

Plotting Points in Three Dimensions

Using a Three-Dimensional Coordinate System

A three-dimensional coordinate system has three axes: the *x*-axis, the *y*-axis, and the *z*-axis.

Need More HELP?

To review two-dimensional coordinate systems, go to *Four Quadrants* in *Algebra* (p. 1524).

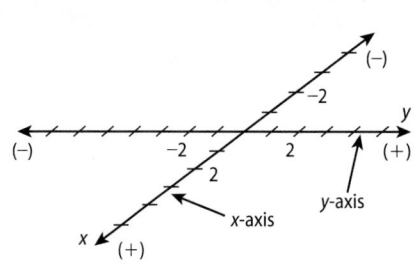

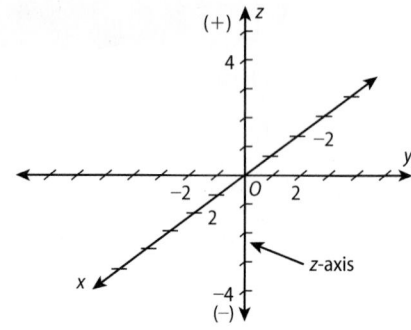

In three dimensions, the *x*-axis and the *y*-axis are drawn differently than they are drawn in two dimensions. In three dimensions, the *x*-axis is shown as coming toward you. The *y*-axis is shown as a horizontal line.

The *z*-axis is shown as a vertical line. Each axis is perpendicular to the other two axes. The three axes meet at the point $(0, 0, 0)$, which is the origin for a three-dimensional coordinate system.

The positive direction for the *x*-axis is toward you. For the *y*-axis, the positive direction is to the right. For the *z*-axis, the positive direction is up.

An **ordered triple** describes a point in a three-dimensional coordinate system. The numbers describe the *x*-, *y*-, and *z*-coordinates of the point in this order: (x, y, z).

EXAMPLE 1

SEARCH

To see step-by-step videos of these problems, enter the page number into the SWadvantage.com Search Bar.

Each ordered triple represents a point on one of the axes. For each ordered triple, tell which axis contains the point and whether the point is on the positive or negative part of that axis. Then, plot the point.

a. (4, 0, 0)

Comparing $(4, 0, 0)$ to (x, y, z) indicates that the point is on the *x*-axis. The value 4 is positive, so $(4, 0, 0)$ is on the positive *x*-axis.

Plot the point by counting 4 units on the *x*-axis in the positive direction.

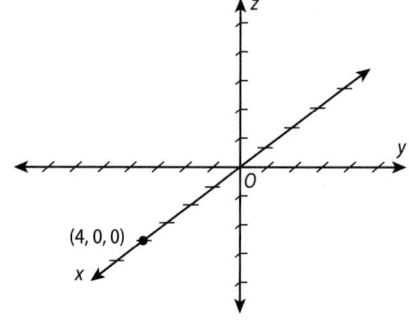

b. (0, 0, −2)

Comparing $(0, 0, -2)$ to (x, y, z) indicates the point is on the negative *z*-axis.

Count 2 units on the *z*-axis in the negative direction.

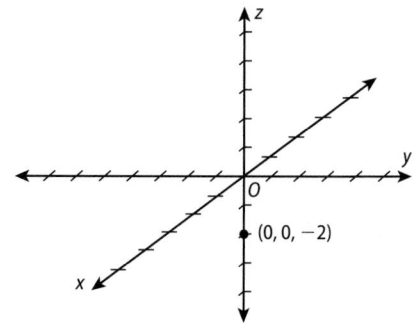

Example 1 showed how to plot an ordered triple if two of the numbers are zero. If just one number in an ordered triple is zero, plotting the point is similar to plotting points in a two-dimensional plane.

EXAMPLE 2

Plot the ordered triple (5, 3, 0).

STEP 1 Identify which of *x, y,* or *z* is zero. The *z*-value is zero, so the point lies on the plane determined by the *x*-axis and the *y*-axis.

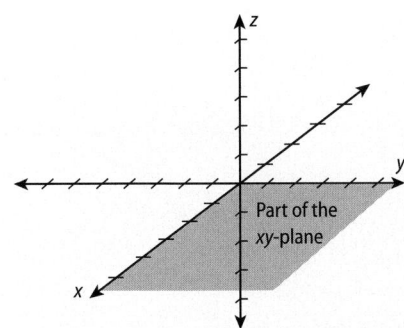 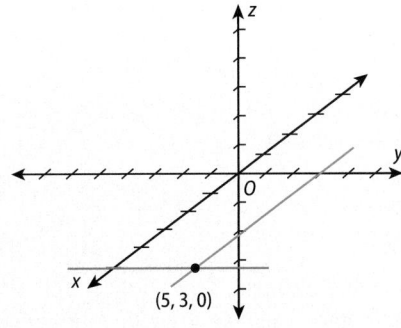

STEP 2 Count 5 units in the positive direction on the *x*-axis. Draw a line parallel to the *y*-axis at that point.

STEP 3 Count 3 units in the positive direction on the *y*-axis. Draw a line parallel to the *x*-axis at that point.

STEP 4 The two lines and the *x*- and *y*-axes form a parallelogram. Locate the vertex of the parallelogram that is opposite the origin. That point represents the ordered triple (5, 3, 0).

GOT TO KNOW!

The Axes and the Origin

Each axis is perpendicular to the other two axes. Each axis has a positive direction and a negative direction. The three axes meet at the origin.

x-axis	axis that comes toward you
y-axis	horizontal axis
z-axis	vertical axis
origin	(0, 0, 0)

EXAMPLE 3

In each of the following ordered triples, one of the numbers is zero. For each triple, tell whether the point is on the *xy*-plane, the *yz*-plane, or the *xz*-plane. Plot and label the point.

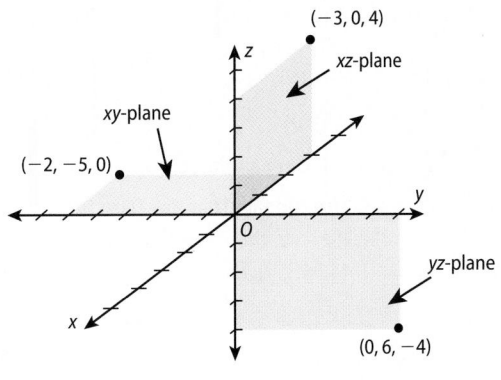

a. (−3, 0, 4)

The *y*-value is zero, so the point is on the *xz*-plane.

b. (−2, −5, 0)

The *z*-value is zero, so the point is on the *xy*-plane.

c. (0, 6, −4)

The *x*-value is zero, so the point is on the *yz*-plane.

Plotting Ordered Triples

To plot an ordered triple when no value is zero, it is important to be accurate and to label your diagram.

EXAMPLE 4

Plot the ordered triple (4, −3, 5).

METHOD 1

Start by finding related points on the axes.

STEP 1 Find the coordinates of the points on the axes that are related to (4, −3, 5). Plot those three points.

On the x-axis: (4, 0, 0)
On the y-axis: (0, −3, 0)
On the z-axis: (0, 0, 5)

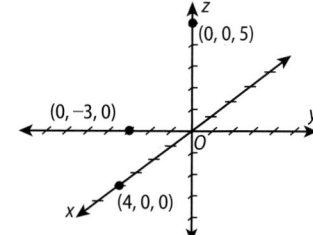

STEP 2 Through each point, draw lines parallel to the "other two" axes. For this example, draw lines through (4, 0, 0) parallel to the y- and z-axes; draw lines through (0, −3, 0) parallel to the x- and z-axes; and draw lines through (0, 0, 5) parallel to the x- and y-axes.

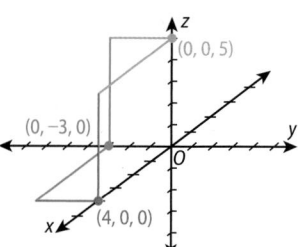

STEP 3 Those lines, along with the three axes, form part of a box. Complete the box to find the point (4, −3, 5).

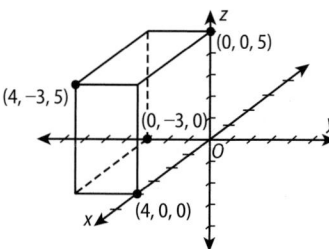

METHOD 2

Start by finding a related point on the xy-plane.

STEP 1 Use the fact that z = 0 on the xy-plane. If z = 0, the related ordered triple is (4, −3, 0). Plot the point (4, −3, 0).

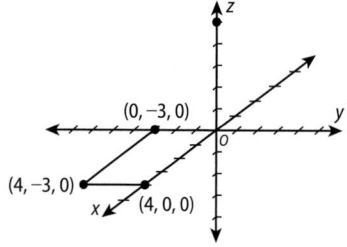

STEP 2 The z-value is 5, so go 5 units in the positive z direction from (4, −3, 0). Label that point (4, −3, 5).

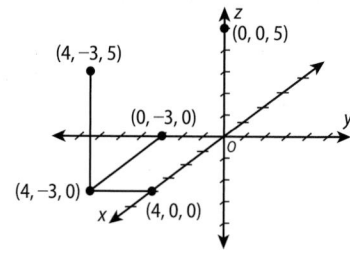

Try It This Way

You can make a physical model of a 3D coordinate grid to help see where a point is.

Use three straws, one for each axis. Set each straw perpendicular to the other two, and tie them together at the middle. Label each straw with axis numbers.

Then use your model and a marble (or other round object) to illustrate the position of the point (4, −3, 5).

Example 4 showed how to graph an ordered triple. Example 5 shows how to find the ordered triple for a point on a three-dimensional graph.

SEARCH 🔍

To see step-by-step videos of these problems, enter the page number into the SWadvantage.com Search Bar.

EXAMPLE 5

What are the coordinates of point A?

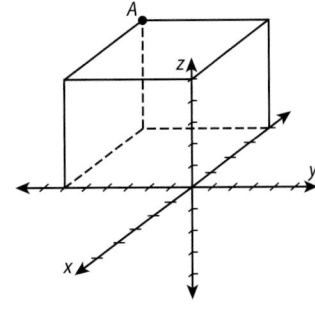

STEP 1 Label the other vertices of the box. Use the letter O to label the origin $(0, 0, 0)$.

STEP 2 Find the first number in the ordered triple for point A. Notice that a vertex on the x-axis is Q, and the coordinates for Q are $(-4, 0, 0)$. So the x-coordinate for point A is -4.

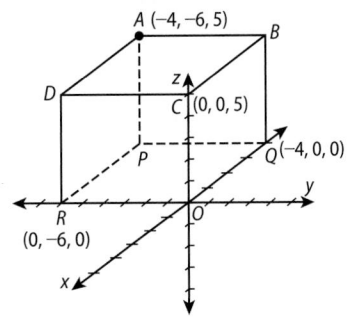

STEP 3 A vertex on the y-axis is R. Its coordinates are $(0, -6, 0)$. So the y-coordinate for point A is -6.

STEP 4 A vertex on the z-axis is C. Its coordinates are $(0, 0, 5)$. So the z-coordinate for point A is 5.

The coordinates for point A are $(-4, -6, 5)$.

GOT TO KNOW!

Coordinates of Points on Axes, on Planes, and in Space

Axes	Plane Formed	Coordinates of Points
x-axis	—	$(a, 0, 0)$
y-axis	—	$(0, b, 0)$
z-axis	—	$(0, 0, c)$
x-axis and y-axis	xy-plane	$(a, b, 0)$, with $z = 0$
y-axis and z-axis	yz-plane	$(0, b, c)$, with $x = 0$
x-axis and z-axis	xz-plane	$(a, 0, c)$, with $y = 0$
all three axes	none; points in 3D space	(a, b, c)

To plot the point (a, b, c), start by plotting and labeling the points $(a, 0, 0)$, $(0, b, 0)$, and $(0, 0, c)$. Draw a box using those three points. The vertex of the box that is opposite the origin has the coordinates (a, b, c).

Graphing in Three Dimensions

Linear Equations and Planes

In a three-dimensional coordinate system, the graph of every linear equation in two or three variables is a plane. You will first see how to graph a linear equation in two variables and then how to graph a linear equation in three variables.

Graphing a Linear Equation in Two Variables

EXAMPLE 1

Graph the equation $2x + y = 3$ on a three-dimensional coordinate system. Explain how the graph is related to the fact that the equation does not have a z-variable.

STEP 1 Find the x-intercept of the equation.

$$2x + y = 3$$

Set $y = 0$. $2x + (0) = 3$

Solve for x. $2x = 3$

$$x = 1.5$$

STEP 2 The x-intercept is 1.5, so plot the ordered triple $(1.5, 0, 0)$. The graph is to the right.

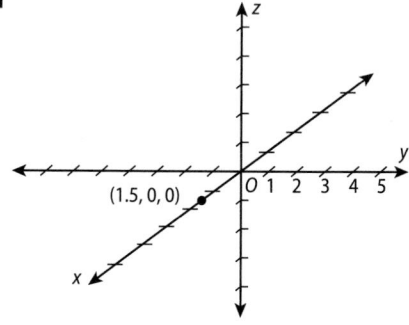

STEP 3 Find the y-intercept of the equation.

$$2x + y = 3$$

Set $x = 0$. $2(0) + y = 3$

Solve for y. $0 + y = 3$

$$y = 3$$

STEP 4 The y-intercept is 3, so plot the ordered triple $(0, 3, 0)$. Then draw a line through the two intercepts. This line represents $2x + y = 3$ in the xy-plane in the graph to the right. Another way to describe the line is that it represents $2x + y = 3$ when $z = 0$.

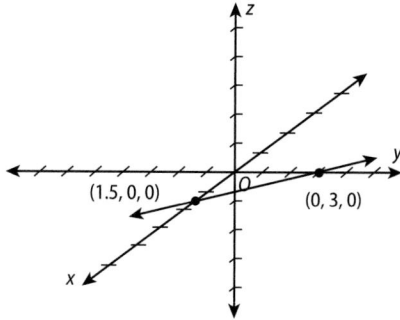

STEP 5 The plane for $2x + y = 3$ is related to three things:

- The line that connects the two intercepts

  The plane for $2x + y = 3$ intersects the xy-plane in the line $2x + y = 3$.

- The xy-plane

  The plane for $2x + y = 3$ is perpendicular to the xy-plane.

- The z-axis, whose variable is not included in the equation

  The plane for $2x + y = 3$ is parallel to the z-axis.

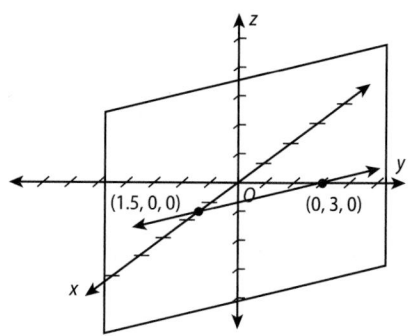

EXAMPLE 2

Graph each two-variable equation on a three-dimensional coordinate system. Identify the variable that is not in the equation, and describe the graph of the equation.

a. $2y - 3z = 12$

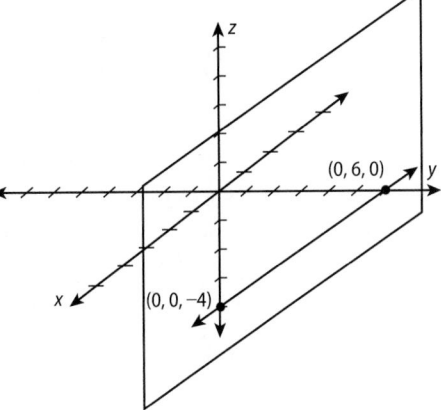

  STEP 1 Find the y-intercept and the z-intercept.

  For the y-intercept, $z = 0$: $2y - 3(0) = 12$

  $y = 6$

  For the z-intercept, $y = 0$: $2(0) - 3z = 12$

  $z = -4$

  The y-intercept is $(0, 6, 0)$. The z-intercept is $(0, 0, -4)$.

  STEP 2 Graph the y- and z-intercepts and connect them with a line. Then show a plane through that line that is perpendicular to the yz-plane and parallel to the x-axis.

  The graph of $2y - 3z = 12$ as shown above is a plane parallel to the x-axis and perpendicular to the yz-plane. It intersects the yz-plane in the line $2y - 3z = 12$.

b. $4x - 5z = -1$

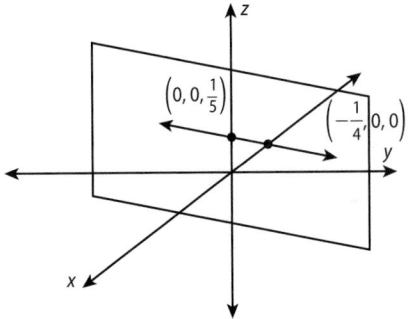

  STEP 1 Find the x-intercept and the z-intercept.

  For the x-intercept, $z = 0$: $4x - 5(0) = -1$

  $x = -\dfrac{1}{4}$

  For the z-intercept, $x = 0$: $4(0) - 5z = -1$

  $z = \dfrac{1}{5}$

  The x-intercept is $\left(-\dfrac{1}{4}, 0, 0\right)$. The z-intercept is $\left(0, 0, \dfrac{1}{5}\right)$.

  STEP 2 Graph the x- and z-intercepts and connect them with a line. Then show a plane through that line that is perpendicular to the xz-plane and parallel to the y-axis.

  The graph of $4x - 5z = -1$ as shown above is a plane parallel to the y-axis and perpendicular to the xz-plane. It intersects the xz-plane in the line $4x - 5z = -1$.

GOT TO KNOW!

Graphing a Linear Equation in Two Variables

Relationship	Example Equation: $2x - z = 4$
The plane contains the line determined by the two intercepts for the equation.	The plane contains the line containing the intercepts $(2, 0, 0)$ and $(0, 0, -4)$.
The plane is perpendicular to the plane determined by the axes for the two variables in the equation.	The plane is perpendicular to the xz-plane.
The plane is parallel to the axis for the variable that is NOT in the equation.	The plane is parallel to the y-axis.

Graphing a Linear Equation in Three Variables

To graph a linear equation in three variables, the first step is to find all three intercepts for the equation. Those intercepts determine three lines. You can use those lines to represent the plane for the equation.

EXAMPLE 3

SEARCH

To see step-by-step videos of these problems, enter the page number into the SWadvantage.com Search Bar.

Graph the plane that represents the equation $3x + 5y + 4z = 30$.

STEP 1 Find the three intercepts for the equation.

For the x-intercept, $y = 0$ and $z = 0$:

$$3x + 5y + 4z = 30$$
$$3x + 5(0) + 4(0) = 30$$
$$3x = 30$$
$$x = 10 \quad \text{The } x\text{-intercept is } (10, 0, 0).$$

For the y-intercept, $x = 0$ and $z = 0$:

$$3x + 5y + 4z = 30$$
$$3(0) + 5y + 4(0) = 30$$
$$5y = 30$$
$$y = 6 \quad \text{The } y\text{-intercept is } (0, 6, 0).$$

For the z-intercept, $x = 0$ and $y = 0$:

$$3x + 5y + 4z = 30$$
$$3(0) + 5(0) + 4z = 30$$
$$4z = 30$$
$$z = 7.5 \quad \text{The } z\text{-intercept is } (0, 0, 7.5).$$

STEP 2 Graph and label the three intercepts.

STEP 3 Draw line segments connecting pairs of intercepts and shade the triangle formed by the segments.

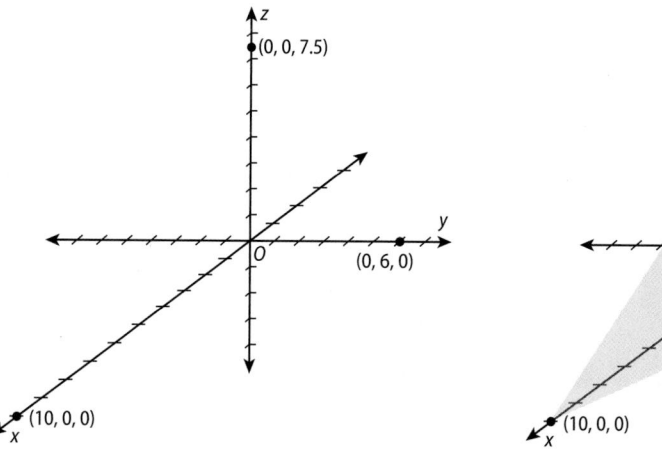

GOT TO KNOW!

Graphing a Three-Variable Linear Equation

1. Find the three intercepts.

2. Draw the triangle whose vertices are those intercepts.

3. Shade the triangle. That triangle is part of the plane that represents the graph of the equation.

The shaded triangle is part of the plane that represents $3x + 5y + 4z = 30$. Every point on that plane satisfies the equation and every ordered triple that satisfies the equation is on that plane.

The next two examples develop and use a property that can simplify the process of finding the intercepts for a three-variable linear equation.

EXAMPLE 4

Show that the following two equations have the same x-, y-, and z-intercepts.

$3x - 9y - 15z = 135$ $x - 3y - 5z = 45$

STEP 1   Find the intercepts for $3x - 9y - 15z = 135$.

x-intercept:	y-intercept:	z-intercept:
$3x - 9(0) - 15(0) = 135$	$3(0) - 9y - 15(0) = 135$	$3(0) - 9(0) - 15z = 135$
$3x = 135;\quad x = 45$	$-9y = 135;\quad y = -15$	$-15z = 135;\quad z = -9$
The x-intercept is $(45, 0, 0)$.	The y-intercept is $(0, -15, 0)$.	The z-intercept is $(0, 0, -9)$.

STEP 2   Find the intercepts for $x - 3y - 5z = 45$.

x-intercept:	y-intercept:	z-intercept:
$x - 3(0) - 5(0) = 45$	$(0) - 3y - 5(0) = 45$	$(0) - 3(0) - 5z = 45$
$x = 45$	$-3y = 45;\quad y = -15$	$-5z = 45;\quad z = -9$
The x-intercept is $(45, 0, 0)$.	The y-intercept is $(0, -15, 0)$.	The z-intercept is $(0, 0, -9)$.

Example 4 shows that the intercepts for $3x - 9y - 15z = 135$ are identical to the intercepts for $x - 3y - 5z = 45$. This example illustrates the following property:

If you multiply both sides of an equation by the same (nonzero) number, the two equations have the same intercepts.

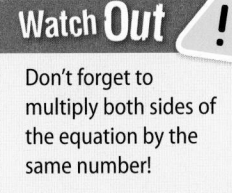

Watch Out !

Don't forget to multiply both sides of the equation by the same number!

EXAMPLE 5

Use the property described above to graph the plane that represents the following equation:
$0.3x - 1.2y + 0.8z = 24$

STEP 1   Multiply both sides of the equation by a number that will remove the decimals.
For this equation, multiply both sides of $0.3x - 1.2y + 0.8z = 24$ by 10. The result is:
$3x - 12y + 8z = 240$

STEP 2   Find the x-, y-, and z-intercepts for the new equation.
x-intercept: $3x - 12(0) + 8(0) = 240$, $3x = 240$, $x = 80$; the x-intercept is $(80, 0, 0)$.
y-intercept: $3(0) - 12y + 8(0) = 240$, $-12y = 240$, $y = -20$; the y-intercept is $(0, -20, 0)$.
z-intercept: $3(0) - 12(0) + 8z = 240$, $8z = 240$, $z = 30$; the z-intercept is $(0, 0, 30)$.

STEP 3   Graph the three intercepts, connect them with segments, and shade the triangle formed by the segments. The two equations $0.3x - 1.2y + 0.8z = 24$ and $3x - 12y + 8z = 240$ have the same intercepts, so the shaded triangle represents the plane for either equation.

The graph of the plane is shown to the right.

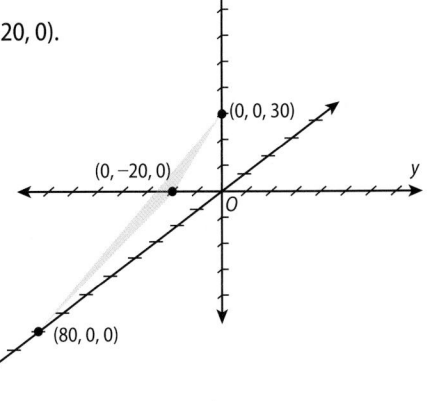

Solving Systems by Substitution

Need More

HELP ?

You can use many of the same strategies to solve systems of three equations with three variables that you used to solve systems of two equations with two variables. To review these strategies, go to *Solving a System by Substitution* in *Algebra* (p. 1568).

The Method of Substitution

A system of three equations involves three variables. The value of each variable can be determined by using one strategy or a combination of several strategies.

The solution to a system of three equations in three variables is an ordered triple. The ordered triple has to satisfy all three equations.

The method of substitution is one strategy that can be used to solve a system of three equations.

- In one of the three equations a variable is solved for or isolated.
- The value of that variable is then substituted into the other two equations. That process converts the original system of three equations in three variables into a new system of equations. The new system has two equations in two variables.
- The process is then repeated for the system of two equations in two variables.

In the examples below, the original equations of a system are labeled (1a), (2a), and (3a). When an equation such as (1a) is changed, the new equation is labeled (1b).

EXAMPLE 1

Use the method of substitution to find the solution (x, y, z) for the system below. Note that one of the equations has just one variable.

(1a) $3x + 5y - 2z = 5$
(2a) $4x - y + 3z = 16$
(3a) $x = 2$

STEP 1 Equation (3a) is already solved for x. Substitute that value of x into equations (1a) and (2a).

(1a) $3x + 5y - 2z = 5$ (2a) $4x - y + 3z = 16$
   $3(2) + 5y - 2z = 5$ $4(2) - y + 3z = 16$
(1b) $5y - 2z = -1$ (2b) $-y + 3z = 8$

STEP 2 Equations (1b) and (2b) form a system of two equations in two variables. One way to solve this system is to use substitution. Solve one of the equations for one of the variables. Then, substitute that value into the other equation. For equations (1b) and (2b), it is easier to solve equation (2b) for y.

(2b) $-y + 3z = 8$ (1b) $5y - 2z = -1$
   $y = 3z - 8$ $5(3z - 8) - 2z = -1$
   $15z - 40 - 2z = -1$
   $13z = 39$
   $z = 3$

STEP 3 It is now known that $x = 2$ and $z = 3$.
Substitute those values into either equation (1a) or equation (2a). The answer will be the same whichever equation you choose.

(1a) $3x + 5y - 2z = 5$
   $3(2) + 5y - 2(3) = 5$
  $6 + 5y - 6 = 5$
  $5y = 5$
  $y = 1$

The solution to the system is $(2, 1, 3)$.

STEP 4 Check the solution $(2, 1, 3)$ in all three *original* equations.

(1a) $3x + 5y - 2z = 5;$ (2a) $4x - y + 3z = 16$ (3a) $x = 2$
   $3(2) + 5(1) - 2(3) \stackrel{?}{=} 5$ $4(2) - (1) + 3(3) \stackrel{?}{=} 16$ $2 = 2$ ✔
  $6 + 5 - 6 = 5$ ✔ $8 - 1 + 9 = 16$ ✔

EXAMPLE 2

Use the method of substitution to find the solution (x, y, z) for the system below. Note that one of the equations has just two variables.

(1a) $2x - y + 4z = 2$
(2a) $3x + 2y + 3z = 9$
(3a) $2y + z = -2$

SEARCH

To see step-by-step videos of these problems, enter the page number into the SWadvantage.com Search Bar.

STEP 1 Solve one of the equations for one of the variables. In this example, let's solve equation (3a) for z.
(3a) $2y + z = -2$
$z = -2y - 2$

STEP 2 Then, substitute that value into the other two equations to form a system with two new equations in two variables.

(1a) $\quad 2x - y + 4z = 2$
$\quad 2x - y + 4(-2y - 2) = 2$
$\quad 2x - y - 8y - 8 = 2$
(1b) $\quad 2x - 9y = 10$

(2a) $\quad 3x + 2y + 3z = 9$
$\quad 3x + 2y + 3(-2y - 2) = 9$
$\quad 3x + 2y - 6y - 6 = 9$
(2b) $\quad 3x - 4y = 15$

STEP 3 The new system of (1b) and (2b) has two equations and two variables. Solve for either variable in either equation. Let's solve for x in (1b).
(1b) $2x - 9y = 10$
$2x = 10 + 9y$
$x = 5 + 4.5y$

STEP 4 Substitute this value into the other two-variable equation, and solve for the variable.
(2b) $\quad 3x - 4y = 15$
$\quad 3(5 + 4.5y) - 4y = 15$
$\quad 15 + 13.5y - 4y = 15$
$\quad 9.5y = 0$
$\quad y = 0$

STEP 5 Substitute $y = 0$ into either equation (1b) or (2b). Then, solve for x.
(1b) $\quad 2x - 9y = 10$
$\quad 2x - 9(0) = 10$
$\quad 2x = 10$
$\quad x = 5$

STEP 6 Substitute $y = 0$ and $x = 5$ into any of the original equations. Solve for z.
(1a) $\quad 2x - y + 4z = 2$
$\quad 2(5) - (0) + 4z = 2$
$\quad 4z = -8$
$\quad z = -2$
The solution is $(5, 0, -2)$.

STEP 7 Check the solution $(5, 0, -2)$ in all three *original* equations.
(1a) $\quad 2x - y + 4z = 2$
$\quad 2(5) - (0) + 4(-2) \stackrel{?}{=} 2$
$\quad 10 - 0 - 8 = 2 ✔$

(2a) $\quad 3x + 2y + 3z = 9$
$\quad 3(5) + 2(0) + 3(-2) \stackrel{?}{=} 9$
$\quad 15 + 0 - 6 = 9 ✔$

(3a) $\quad 2y + z = -2$
$\quad 2(0) + (-2) \stackrel{?}{=} -2$
$\quad 0 - 2 = -2 ✔$

1763

Three Equations with Three Variables

EXAMPLE 3

Use the method of substitution to find the solution (x, y, z) for the system shown below. Note that all three equations have three variables.

(1a) $x + 2y - z = 3$
(2a) $3x - y + 4z = 2$
(3a) $5x + 3y + 4z = 12$

STEP 1 Solve one of the equations for one of the variables. In this example, let's solve equation (1a) for z.
(1a) $x + 2y - z = 3$
$$z = x + 2y - 3$$

STEP 2 Then, substitute the expression for z into the other two equations. The result is a system with two equations in two variables.

(2a) $3x - y + 4z = 2$ (3a) $5x + 3y + 4z = 12$
$3x - y + 4(x + 2y - 3) = 2$ $5x + 3y + 4(x + 2y - 3) = 12$
$3x - y + 4x + 8y - 12 = 2$ $5x + 3y + 4x + 8y - 12 = 12$
$7x + 7y - 12 = 2$ $9x + 11y - 12 = 12$
$7x + 7y = 14$ (3b) $9x + 11y = 24$
(2b) $x + y = 2$

STEP 3 The new system of (2b) and (3b) has two equations and two variables. Solve for either variable in either equation. You might choose to solve equation (2b) for x.
(2b) $x + y = 2$
$$x = -y + 2$$

STEP 4 Substitute this value into the other two-variable equation, and solve for the variable.
(3b) $9x + 11y = 24$
$9(-y + 2) + 11y = 24$
$-9y + 18 + 11y = 24$
$2y = 6$
$y = 3$

STEP 5 Substitute y = 3 into either equation (2b) or (3b), and solve for x.
(2b) $x + y = 2$
$x + (3) = 2$
$x = -1$

STEP 6 Substitute x = -1 and y = 3 into one of the original equations. Solve for z.
(1a) $x + 2y - z = 3$
$(-1) + 2(3) - z = 3$
$-1 + 6 - z = 3$
$z = 2$
The solution is $(-1, 3, 2)$.

STEP 7 Check the solution $(-1, 3, 2)$ in all three original equations.
(1a) $x + 2y - z = 3$ (2a) $3x - y + 4z = 2$ (3a) $5x + 3y + 4z = 12$
$(-1) + 2(3) - (2) \overset{?}{=} 3$ $3(-1) - (3) + 4(2) \overset{?}{=} 2$ $5(-1) + 3(3) + 4(2) \overset{?}{=} 12$
$-1 + 6 - 2 = 3 ✔$ $-3 - 3 + 8 = 2 ✔$ $-5 + 9 + 8 = 12 ✔$

Exceptions to an Ordered Triple as a Solution

In the first three examples, the solution of the systems of equations is an ordered triple. However, sometimes there is no solution to a system of equations. And sometimes there is an infinite number of solutions.

EXAMPLE 4

Use the method of substitution to find the solution (x, y, z) for the system shown below.

(1a) $x + 3y - 2z = -1$
(2a) $2x - 4y + 6z = 5$
(3a) $x - 2y + 3z = 1$

STEP 1 Solve one of the equations for one of the variables. In this example, solve equation (3a) for x.
(3a) $x - 2y + 3z = 1$
$$x = 2y - 3z + 1$$

STEP 2 Then, substitute the expression for z into the other two equations to obtain a system with two equations in two variables.

(1a) $\quad\quad x + 3y - 2z = -1$
$\quad 2y - 3z + 1 + 3y - 2z = -1$
$\quad\quad\quad\quad 5y - 5z = -2$

(2a) $\quad\quad 2x - 4y + 6z = 5$
$\quad 2(2y - 3z + 1) - 4y + 6z = 5$
$\quad 4y - 6z + 2 - 4y + 6z = 5$
$\quad\quad\quad\quad\quad\quad 2 \neq 5$

The substitution into one of the equations, 2(a), resulted in a false statement, so there are no solutions to this system of equations.

EXAMPLE 5

Use the method of substitution to find the solution (x, y, z) for the system shown below.

(1a) $x + 3y - 2z = -1$
(2a) $4x + 12y - 8z = -4$
(3a) $2x + 6y - 4z = -2$

Solve one of the equations for one of the variables. In this example, solve equation (1a) for x.

(1a) $x + 3y - 2z = -1$, so $x = -3y + 2z - 1$

When this expression is substituted for x in the other two equations to obtain a system with two equations in two variables, the result is $0 = 0$.

(2a) $\quad\quad 4x + 12y - 8z = -4$
$\quad 4(-3y + 2z - 1) + 12y - 8z = -4$
$\quad -12y + 8z - 4 + 12y - 8z = -4$
$\quad -12y + 12y + 8z - 8z - 4 = -4$
$\quad\quad\quad\quad\quad\quad -4 = -4$
$\quad\quad\quad\quad\quad\quad\quad 0 = 0$

(3a) $\quad\quad 2x + 6y - 4z = -2$
$\quad 2(-3y + 2z - 1) + 6y - 4z = -2$
$\quad -6y + 4z - 2 + 6y - 4z = -2$
$\quad -6y + 6y + 4z - 4z - 2 = -2$
$\quad\quad\quad\quad\quad\quad -2 = -2$
$\quad\quad\quad\quad\quad\quad\quad 0 = 0$

This result means that for any value of x, there are values of y and z that are solutions to the system. There are an infinite number of solutions to this system.

GOT TO KNOW!

Using Substitution to Solve a System of Three Equations in Three Variables

1. Solve one of the equations for one variable.

2. Substitute for that variable in the other two equations. The result is a system of two equations in two variables.

3. Solve the two-variable system for another variable.

4. Substitute the two variables you know into an original equation, and solve for the third variable.

5. Check the ordered triple in all three original equations.

Solving Systems by Elimination

SEARCH

To see step-by-step videos of these problems, enter the page number into the SWadvantage.com Search Bar.

The Method of Elimination

The method of elimination is one strategy that can be used to solve a system of three equations. This method is called *elimination* because one of the three variables is eliminated by adding equations. The solution to a system of three equations in three variables is an ordered triple, (x, y, z). The ordered triple has to satisfy all three equations.

The examples show how to perform the two parts of the method of elimination.

- Add or subtract equations to produce a two-variable, two-equation system.
- Use the two-equation system to find the values for all three variables.

In the examples, the equations in the original system are labeled (1), (2), and (3) and the equations in the 2-equation system are usually labeled (4) and (5).

Ways to REMEMBER

This lesson uses labeled arrows such as $\xrightarrow{\times(-1)}$ to indicate that both sides of an equation are multiplied by -1 or $\xrightarrow{x=5, y=-3}$ to indicate substituting 5 for x and -3 for y. You should always write notes in your solutions so you will be able to explain your solution to a classmate or to remind yourself of what operations you performed for each step of the solution.

EXAMPLE 1

Use the method of elimination to find the solution (x, y, z) for the system shown at the right.

(1) $2x + 3y + 4z = 28$
(2) $x - 5y - 4z = -42$
(3) $5x + 4y = 6$

STEP 1 The first part of the process is to write a system of two equations in two variables. Equation (3) is already an equation using the two variables x and y. At the right, note what happens when we add equations (1) and (2).

(1) $2x + 3y + 4z = 28$
(2) $\underline{x - 5y - 4z = -42}$
(4) $3x - 2y \quad\quad = -14$

STEP 2 Equations (3) and (4) form a system of two equations in the same two variables x and y. In the equations, the y-coefficients are 4 and -2. Multiply equation (4) by 2 and add the result to equation (3).

(3) $5x + 4y = 6 \quad\longrightarrow$

(4) $3x - 2y = -14 \quad\xrightarrow{\times 2}$

$5x + 4y = \quad 6$
$\underline{6x - 4y = -28}$
$11x \quad\quad = -22, x = -2$

STEP 3 Now that we know $x = -2$, substitute that value into either equation (3) or equation (4) to find y.

(3) $5x + 4y = 6 \quad\xrightarrow{x=-2}\quad 5(-2) + 4y = 6$
$-10 + 4y = 6$
$4y = 16, y = 4$

STEP 4 To find the value of z, substitute $x = -2$ and $y = 4$ into equation (1) or equation (2).

(1) $2x + 3y + 4z = 28 \quad\xrightarrow{x=-2, y=4}\quad 2(-2) + 3(4) + 4z = 28$
$-4 + 12 + 4z = 28$
$4z = 20, z = 5$

The solution to the system is $(-2, 4, 5)$.

How to Eliminate a Variable

- If two equations have opposite coefficients for the same variable, adding the two equations produces another equation that does not contain that variable.

- You can multiply two equations by two different integers, resulting in equations that have opposite coefficients for the same variable.

As you study the following example, notice the flexibility in choosing equations to be used. There are several different ways to produce a system of two equations in two variables (Steps 1 and 2), in solving for the second variable to be found (Step 4), and in solving for the third variable (Step 5).

EXAMPLE 2

Use the method of elimination to find the solution (x, y, z) for the system shown at the right.

(1) $3x - y - 4z = 15$
(2) $2x + 2y + z = -1$
(3) $x + y + 3z = -8$

STEP 1 The first part of the process is to write a system of two equations in two variables. Produce one equation without y by adding equations (1) and (3).

(1) $3x - y - 4z = 15$
(3) $\underline{x + y + 3z = -8}$
(4) $4x \quad\quad - z = 7$

STEP 2 Produce another equation without y by using equations (1) and (2). The coefficients of y are -1 and 2. Multiply equation (1) by 2. Then add the new equations.

(1) $3x - y - 4z = 15$ $\xrightarrow{\times 2}$ $6x - 2y - 8z = 30$
(2) $2x + 2y + z = -1$ $\xrightarrow{}$ $\underline{2x + 2y + z = -1}$
(5) $8x \quad\quad - 7z = 29$

STEP 3 Equations (4) and (5) form a system of two equations in the same two variables x and z. The coefficients of z are -1 and -7. Multiply equation (4) by -7 and add the result to equation (5).

(4) $4x - z = 7$ $\xrightarrow{\times(-7)}$ $-28x + 7z = -49$
(5) $8x - 7z = 29$ $\xrightarrow{}$ $\underline{8x - 7z = 29}$
$-20x \quad\quad = -20, x = 1$

STEP 4 Use $x = 1$ to solve for z in equation (4) or (5). The value for z will be the same whichever equation you choose.

(5) $8x - 7z = 29$ $\xrightarrow{x=1}$ $8(1) - 7z = 29$
$8 - 7z = 29$
$-7z = 21, z = -3$

STEP 5 Use $x = 1$ and $z = -3$ to solve for y in any one of equations (1), (2), or (3).

(1) $3x - y - 4z = 15$ $\xrightarrow{x=1, z=-3}$ $3(1) - y - 4(-3) = 15$
$3 - y + 12 = 15$
$-y = 0, y = 0$

The solution to the original system is $(1, 0, -3)$.

STEP 6 Check the solution $(1, 0, -3)$ in all three original equations.

$3x - y - 4z = 15$	$2x + 2y + z = -1$	$x + y + 3z = -8$
$3(1) - (0) - 4(-3) \stackrel{?}{=} 15$	$2(1) + 2(0) + (-3) \stackrel{?}{=} -1$	$(1) + (0) + 3(-3) \stackrel{?}{=} -8$
$3 - 0 + 12 = 15$ ✔	$2 + 0 - 3 = -1$ ✔	$1 + 0 - 9 = -8$ ✔

Watch Out !

Solving a system of equations has many steps, and it is easy to make simple arithmetic errors or to make a mistake copying or changing an equation. That is why it is important to check the solution in the *original* equations.

GOT TO KNOW!

Method for Solving a System of Three Equations by Elimination

1. Use two combinations of the three-variable equations to produce two equations that use the same two variables.

2. Solve that two-variable, two-equation system to find the values of those two variables.

3. Substitute the values of those two variables into any of the original equations to find the value of the third variable.

4. Check the ordered triple in all three original equations.

SEARCH

To see step-by-step videos of these problems, enter the page number into the SWadvantage.com Search Bar.

Forming a Plan

Solving a system of three equations in three variables involves decisions. Which variable should I eliminate first? Which combinations of equations should I use? It also involves many calculations. To help organize the solution, it can be helpful to list all your decisions before doing any calculations.

Example 3 shows one plan to solve the system. Many other plans are possible.

EXAMPLE 3

Use the method of elimination to find the solution (x, y, z) for the system shown at the right. Before you start, show a plan for your solution.

(1) $5x - 2y + 3z = 15$
(2) $2x - 4y - 5z = 3$
(3) $3x + 5y - 4z = -3$

STEP 1 Make a plan for the solution.

It seems as if y is the easiest variable to eliminate, so the plan includes:

- Eliminate y using equations (1) and (2) (because the coefficients of y are multiples).
- Eliminate y using equations (1) and (3) (because the coefficients of y have opposite signs).
- Solve the resulting system of two equations in the two variables x and z.

STEP 2 To eliminate y using equations (1) and (2), multiply equation (1) by -2, then add the resulting equations.

(1) $5x - 2y + 3z = 15$ $\xrightarrow{\times(-2)}$ $\quad -10x + 4y - 6z = -30$
(2) $2x - 4y - 5z = 3$ $\xrightarrow{\quad\quad}$ $\quad \underline{2x - 4y - 5z = 3}$
$\quad\quad\quad\quad\quad\quad\quad\quad\quad\quad$ (4) $\;-8x \quad\quad -11z = -27$

STEP 3 To eliminate y using equations (1) and (3), multiply equation (1) by 5, multiply equation (3) by 2, and then add the resulting equations.

(1) $5x - 2y + 3z = 15$ $\xrightarrow{\times 5}$ $\quad 25x - 10y + 15z = 75$
(3) $3x + 5y - 4z = -3$ $\xrightarrow{\times 2}$ $\quad \underline{6x + 10y - 8z = -6}$
$\quad\quad\quad\quad\quad\quad\quad\quad\quad\quad$ (5) $\;31x \quad\quad\; + \;\;7z = 69$

STEP 4 Equations (4) and (5) form a system of two equations in two variables. The two z-coefficients are -11 and 7, so let's eliminate z by following these steps: multiply equation (4) by 7, multiply equation (5) by 11, and then add the resulting equations. Then, solve for x.

(4) $-8x - 11z = -27$ $\xrightarrow{\times 7}$ $\quad -56x - 77z = -189$
(5) $31x + 7z = 69$ $\xrightarrow{\times 11}$ $\quad \underline{341x + 77z = 759}$
$\quad\quad\quad\quad\quad\quad\quad\quad\quad\quad 285x \quad\quad\quad = 570, x = 2$

STEP 5 Substitute $x = 2$ into either equation (4) or equation (5) to find the value of z.

(4) $-8x - 11z = -27$ $\xrightarrow{x = 2}$ $\quad -8(2) - 11z = -27$
$\quad\quad\quad\quad\quad\quad\quad\quad\quad\quad\quad\quad -16 - 11z = -27$
$\quad\quad\quad\quad\quad\quad\quad\quad\quad\quad\quad\quad\quad -11z = -11, z = 1$

STEP 6 Substitute $x = 2$ and $z = 1$ into any of the original equations to find the value of y.

(1) $5x - 2y + 3z = 15$ $\xrightarrow{x = 2, z = 1}$ $\quad 5(2) - 2y + 3(1) = 15$
$\quad\quad\quad\quad\quad\quad\quad\quad\quad\quad\quad\quad\quad 10 - 2y + 3 = 15$
$\quad\quad\quad\quad\quad\quad\quad\quad\quad\quad\quad\quad\quad\quad -2y = 2, y = -1$

The solution to the system is $(2, -1, 1)$.

STEP 7 Check the solution $(2, -1, 1)$ in all three original equations.

$\quad\quad 5x - 2y + 3z = 15 \quad\quad\quad 2x - 4y - 5z = 3 \quad\quad\quad 3x + 5y - 4z = -3$
$\quad 5(2) - 2(-1) + 3(1) \overset{?}{=} 15 \quad 2(2) - 4(-1) - 5(1) \overset{?}{=} 3 \quad 3(2) + 5(-1) - 4(1) \overset{?}{=} -3$
$\quad\quad 10 + 2 + 3 = 15 ✔ \quad\quad\quad 4 + 4 - 5 = 3 ✔ \quad\quad\quad 6 - 5 - 4 = -3 ✔$

Keep in mind that the first step in solving a system of equations by elimination is to create a new system with one less variable and one less equation. Note that in Step 2 of Example 4, a new equation for the new system is created using all three initial equations instead of two of them.

EXAMPLE 4

Use the method of elimination to find the solution (x, y, z) for the system shown at the right. Analyze the system to identify the easiest way to solve it.

(1) $3x - 2y + 4z = -1$
(2) $-3x + y - 2z = -7$
(3) $2x + y + 4z = 0$

STEP 1 Analyze the system of equations, and make a plan.

It would be easy to produce one equation without the variable x by adding equations (1) and (2). But it is possible, and easy, to get two equations without the variable y, as shown in Steps 2 and 3 below.

STEP 2 Multiply equation (2) by -1, then add the result to equation (3).

(2) $-3x + y - 2z = -7$ $\xrightarrow{\times(-1)}$ $3x - y + 2z = 7$
(3) $2x + y + 4z = 0$ $\xrightarrow{}$ $2x + y + 4z = 0$
 (4) $5x + 6z = 7$

STEP 3 To get another equation without the variable y, add equations (1), (2), and (3):

(1) $3x - 2y + 4z = -1$
(2) $-3x + y - 2z = -7$
(3) $\underline{2x + y + 4z = 0}$
(5) $2x + 6z = -8$

STEP 4 Equations (4) and (5) form a system of two equations in two variables. Let's eliminate z by multiplying equation (4) by -1 and adding the result to equation (5).

(4) $5x + 6z = 7$ $\xrightarrow{\times(-1)}$ $-5x - 6z = -7$
(5) $2x + 6z = -8$ $\xrightarrow{}$ $\underline{2x + 6z = -8}$
 $-3x = -15, x = 5$

STEP 5 Substitute $x = 5$ into either of the two-variable equations, equation (4) or equation (5), to find the value of z.

(4) $5x + 6z = 7$ $\xrightarrow{x = 5}$ $5(5) + 6z = 7$
 $25 + 6z = 7$
 $6z = -18, z = -3$

STEP 6 Substitute $x = 5$ and $z = -3$ into any of the original equations to find the value of y.

(3) $2x + y + 4z = 0$ $\xrightarrow{x = 5, z = -3}$ $2(5) + y + 4(-3) = 0$
 $10 + y - 12 = 0$
 $y = 2$

The solution to the system is $(5, 2, -3)$.

STEP 7 Check the solution $(5, 2, -3)$ in all three original equations.

$3x - 2y + 4z = -1$ $-3x + y - 2z = -7$ $2x + y + 4z = 0$
$3(5) - 2(2) + 4(-3) \overset{?}{=} -1$ $-3(5) + (2) - 2(-3) \overset{?}{=} -7$ $2(5) + (2) + 4(-3) \overset{?}{=} 0$
$15 - 4 - 12 = -1$ ✔ $-15 + 2 + 6 = -7$ ✔ $10 + 2 - 12 = 0$ ✔

Watch Out !

In these examples, a true solution is found for each variable.

However, for some systems of equations, solving for a variable might result in a false equation, such as $1 = 0$. A false equation means that there is no solution to the system.

If solving for a variable results in a sentence that is always true, such as $1 = 1$, there are an infinite number of solutions to the system.

GOT TO KNOW !

Making a Plan to Solve a System of Three Equations

Examine the system of equations, and ask yourself these questions.

- Which variable is easiest to eliminate?
- Which two pairs of equations are best to use to eliminate the variable?
- What must be done to the pairs of equations in order to eliminate the variable?

Matrices

What Came Before?
- Solving systems of two and three linear equations
- Operations and properties of real numbers

What's This About?
- Characteristics of matrices
- Performing operations with matrices, both 2×2 and 3×3 matrices
- Using matrix operations and equations to solve systems of equations

Practical Apps
- Computer programmers use matrices to transform onscreen figures.
- Cryptographers can use matrices to encode and decode secret messages.

Just for FUN!

Someone stole $\begin{bmatrix} 1 & 0 \\ 0 & 1 \end{bmatrix}$. It was a clear-cut case of identity theft!

You can find more practice problems online by visiting:
www.SWadvantage.com

Rows and Columns

The Dimensions of a Matrix

A **matrix** is a rectangular arrangement of numbers or values. Each number or value in a matrix is called an **element** of the matrix. The elements are arranged in horizontal rows and vertical columns. A matrix is usually indicated using square brackets. The plural of matrix is *matrices*.

The **dimensions** of a matrix refer to the number of rows and columns that it has. The dimensions of a matrix are usually written $m \times n$, read "m by n," where the first letter indicates the number of rows and the second number indicates the number of columns.

$$\begin{bmatrix} 2 & 5 \\ 8 & -7 \\ 0.5 & 16 \\ 20 & -2 \\ 0 & 0 \\ 0 & 5 \end{bmatrix} \quad \begin{bmatrix} 5 & 7 & 3.5 & \frac{1}{2} \\ -1 & 0 & -2.3 & 6 \\ -\frac{3}{4} & -\frac{5}{2} & 8 & -10 \\ 1 & 2 & 3 & 4 \end{bmatrix} \quad \begin{bmatrix} 25 & -10 & -7 & 8.5 & -\frac{3}{10} \end{bmatrix}$$

SEARCH

To see step-by-step videos of these problems, enter the page number into the SWadvantage.com Search Bar.

EXAMPLE 1

Tell the dimensions of the three matrices shown above.

STEP 1 Count the number of rows and columns. Left matrix: 6 rows and 2 columns
Middle matrix: 4 rows and 4 columns
Right matrix: 1 row and 5 columns

STEP 2 Use the $m \times n$ format. Left matrix: 6×2
Middle matrix: 4×4
Right matrix: 1×5

EXAMPLE 2

Watch Out !

When a matrix is described as having dimensions $m \times n$, the first value *always* refers to the number of rows and the second value *always* refers to the number of columns.

Write a 5×3 matrix, where the elements in row m are $3m$, $5m$, and $10m$.

STEP 1 Set up a 5×3 matrix.

A 5×3 matrix has 5 rows and 3 columns. Prepare an outline for a 5×3 matrix, using $3m$, $5m$, and $10m$ to represent the elements in the matrix, as shown in the matrix to the right.

$$\begin{bmatrix} 3m & 5m & 10m \\ 3m & 5m & 10m \\ 3m & 5m & 10m \\ 3m & 5m & 10m \\ 3m & 5m & 10m \end{bmatrix}$$

STEP 2 Write the matrix.

The phrase "row m" means that $m = 1$ for row 1, $m = 2$ for row 2, and so on. Use the values of m to evaluate each element in the matrix.

$$\begin{bmatrix} 3(1) & 5(1) & 10(1) \\ 3(2) & 5(2) & 10(2) \\ 3(3) & 5(3) & 10(3) \\ 3(4) & 5(4) & 10(4) \\ 3(5) & 5(5) & 10(5) \end{bmatrix} \longrightarrow \begin{bmatrix} 3 & 5 & 10 \\ 6 & 10 & 20 \\ 9 & 15 & 30 \\ 12 & 20 & 40 \\ 15 & 25 & 50 \end{bmatrix}$$

Equal Matrices

Two matrices are **equal matrices** if they meet these conditions.
- The matrices have the same dimensions.
- Corresponding elements in the two matrices have the same value.

EXAMPLE 3

a. The two matrices below are equal. Use the definition of equal matrices to find the values of x, y, z, and w.

$$\begin{bmatrix} 3x - 8 & -35 \\ 7 & \dfrac{w + 8}{2} \end{bmatrix} = \begin{bmatrix} 1 & 3y - 5 \\ 10 - 2z & 4 \end{bmatrix}$$

STEP 1 Corresponding elements are equal, so set up four equations.

$$3x - 8 = 1 \qquad -35 = 3y - 5 \qquad 7 = 10 - 2z \qquad \frac{w + 8}{2} = 4$$

STEP 2 Solve each of the four equations.

$$3x - 8 = 1 \qquad -35 = 3y - 5 \qquad 7 = 10 - 2z \qquad \frac{w + 8}{2} = 4$$
$$3x = 9 \qquad -30 = 3y \qquad -3 = -2z \qquad w + 8 = 8$$
$$x = 3 \qquad y = -10 \qquad z = 1.5 \qquad w = 0$$

b. Use the results from part (a) to write all the elements in the following matrix as numbers, with no variables.

$$\begin{bmatrix} 2w - 7 & x \div 0.5 & 100z & y - 3 \\ x + 2y & x \div 2 & 8w & x + y + z + w \end{bmatrix}$$

STEP 1 Rewrite the matrix using the values of x, y, z, and w.

$$\begin{bmatrix} 2(0) - 7 & (3) \div 0.5 & 100(1.5) & (-10) - 3 \\ (3) + 2(-10) & (3) \div 2 & 8(0) & (3) + (-10) + (1.5) + (0) \end{bmatrix}$$

STEP 2 Evaluate each numerical expression in the matrix.

$$\begin{bmatrix} -7 & 6 & 150 & -13 \\ -17 & 1.5 & 0 & -5.5 \end{bmatrix}$$

> **Watch Out**
>
> When you identify corresponding elements in two matrices, be sure the elements are in the same row and in the same column in each matrix.

GOT TO KNOW!

Writing a Matrix

$$\begin{bmatrix} 3 & 5 & 10 \\ 6 & 10 & 20 \\ 9 & 15 & 30 \\ 12 & 20 & 40 \\ 15 & 25 & 50 \end{bmatrix} \text{row} \qquad \begin{bmatrix} 3 & 5 & 10 \\ 6 & 10 & 20 \\ 9 & 15 & 30 \\ 12 & 20 & 40 \\ 15 & 25 & 50 \end{bmatrix} \text{column} \qquad \begin{bmatrix} 3 & 5 & 10 \\ 6 & 10 & 20 \\ 9 & 15 & 30 \\ 12 & 20 & 40 \\ 15 & 25 & 50 \end{bmatrix} \text{element}$$

dimensions: 5 (rows) × 3 (columns)

The elements in a matrix can: be positive or negative numbers,
be zero, or
contain variables.

Adding or Subtracting Matrices

Sums and Differences of Corresponding Elements

If two matrices have the same dimensions, you can **add** the two matrices by finding the sums of pairs of corresponding elements. You can **subtract** them by finding the differences of corresponding elements.

For example, if Matrix $A = \begin{bmatrix} 3 & -2 & 5 \\ 0 & 2 & 6 \end{bmatrix}$ and Matrix $B = \begin{bmatrix} 4 & 10 & 0 \\ -5 & 0 & -2 \end{bmatrix}$,

then $A + B = \begin{bmatrix} 3+4 & -2+10 & 5+0 \\ 0+(-5) & 2+0 & 6+(-2) \end{bmatrix} = \begin{bmatrix} 7 & 8 & 5 \\ -5 & 2 & 4 \end{bmatrix}$

and $A - B = \begin{bmatrix} 3-4 & -2-10 & 5-0 \\ 0-(-5) & 2-0 & 6-(-2) \end{bmatrix} = \begin{bmatrix} -1 & -12 & 5 \\ 5 & 2 & 8 \end{bmatrix}$.

Watch Out !

When subtracting matrices, be sure to always subtract the element from the second matrix from the corresponding element in the first matrix, not the other way around.

For example, for $A - B$, every element in the resulting matrix is found by: element A − corresponding element B.

EXAMPLE 1

Using the matrices below, find $X + Z$, $Y - X$ and $X - (Z + Y)$.

$X = \begin{bmatrix} -3 & 2 \\ 4 & -3 \\ 8 & -1 \end{bmatrix}$, $Y = \begin{bmatrix} 7 & 10 \\ -3 & 0 \\ 5 & -2 \end{bmatrix}$, $Z = \begin{bmatrix} 8 & 0 \\ 0 & 0 \\ -1 & -1 \end{bmatrix}$

Write each expression, substitute the matrices, and evaluate.

$X + Z = \begin{bmatrix} -3 & 2 \\ 4 & -3 \\ 8 & -1 \end{bmatrix} + \begin{bmatrix} 8 & 0 \\ 0 & 0 \\ -1 & -1 \end{bmatrix} = \begin{bmatrix} -3+8 & 2+0 \\ 4+0 & -3+0 \\ 8+(-1) & -1+(-1) \end{bmatrix} = \begin{bmatrix} 5 & 2 \\ 4 & -3 \\ 7 & -2 \end{bmatrix}$

$Y - X = \begin{bmatrix} 7 & 10 \\ -3 & 0 \\ 5 & -2 \end{bmatrix} - \begin{bmatrix} -3 & 2 \\ 4 & -3 \\ 8 & -1 \end{bmatrix} = \begin{bmatrix} 7-(-3) & 10-2 \\ -3-4 & 0-(-3) \\ 5-8 & -2-(-1) \end{bmatrix} = \begin{bmatrix} 10 & 8 \\ -7 & 3 \\ -3 & -1 \end{bmatrix}$

$X - (Z + Y) = \begin{bmatrix} -3 & 2 \\ 4 & -3 \\ 8 & -1 \end{bmatrix} - \left(\begin{bmatrix} 8 & 0 \\ 0 & 0 \\ -1 & -1 \end{bmatrix} + \begin{bmatrix} 7 & 10 \\ -3 & 0 \\ 5 & -2 \end{bmatrix} \right)$

$= \begin{bmatrix} -3 & 2 \\ 4 & -3 \\ 8 & -1 \end{bmatrix} - \begin{bmatrix} 15 & 10 \\ -3 & 0 \\ 4 & -3 \end{bmatrix} = \begin{bmatrix} -18 & -8 \\ 7 & -3 \\ 4 & 2 \end{bmatrix}$

GOT TO KNOW!

Identifying Corresponding Elements in Two Matrices

1. Make sure that the two matrices have the same dimensions.

2. Check that for each pair of corresponding elements, the row number and column number exactly match.

Adding and Subtracting Matrices A and B

Operation	Procedure
Addition: $A + B$	Add each element in A to its corresponding element in B.
Subtraction: $A - B$	Subtract each element in B from its corresponding element in A.

Always check that two matrices have the same dimensions before you try to add or subtract them.

EXAMPLE 2

Here are several matrices.

$$A = \begin{bmatrix} 2 & 0 & 5 & -3 \end{bmatrix}, B = \begin{bmatrix} 6 & 8 \\ 1 & 3 \\ 2 & -2 \end{bmatrix}, C = \begin{bmatrix} 0 & 0 & 0 & 0 \end{bmatrix}, D = \begin{bmatrix} 2 \\ 5 \\ 2 \\ 8 \end{bmatrix}, E = \begin{bmatrix} -3 & -2 \\ -4 & 7 \\ 0 & 1 \end{bmatrix}$$

a. Determine whether it is possible to add or subtract matrices *B* and *E*. Explain. If it is possible, find the matrix for *B* + *E* and find the matrix for *B* − *E*.

Yes, matrices *B* and *E* are both 3 × 2 matrices. They have the same dimensions so you can find the sum or difference for each pair of corresponding elements.

$$B + E = \begin{bmatrix} 6 & 8 \\ 1 & 3 \\ 2 & -2 \end{bmatrix} + \begin{bmatrix} -3 & -2 \\ -4 & 7 \\ 0 & 1 \end{bmatrix} = \begin{bmatrix} 3 & 6 \\ -3 & 10 \\ 2 & -1 \end{bmatrix}, B - E = \begin{bmatrix} 6 & 8 \\ 1 & 3 \\ 2 & -2 \end{bmatrix} - \begin{bmatrix} -3 & -2 \\ -4 & 7 \\ 0 & 1 \end{bmatrix} = \begin{bmatrix} 9 & 10 \\ 5 & -4 \\ 2 & -3 \end{bmatrix}$$

b. Is it possible to add or subtract matrices *A* and *D*? Explain. If it is possible, find the matrix for *A* + *D* and find the matrix for *A* − *D*.

No, *A* is a 1 × 4 matrix and *D* is a 4 × 1 matrix. They do NOT have the same dimensions so you cannot identify pairs of corresponding elements to add or subtract.

c. Is it possible to add or subtract matrices *A* and *C*? Explain. If it is possible, find the matrix for *A* + *C* and find the matrix for *A* − *C*.

Yes, matrices *A* and *C* are both 1 × 4 matrices. They have the same dimensions so you can find the sum or difference of corresponding elements.

$$A + C = \begin{bmatrix} 2 & 0 & 5 & -3 \end{bmatrix} + \begin{bmatrix} 0 & 0 & 0 & 0 \end{bmatrix} = \begin{bmatrix} 2 & 0 & 5 & -3 \end{bmatrix}$$

$$A - C = \begin{bmatrix} 2 & 0 & 5 & -3 \end{bmatrix} - \begin{bmatrix} 0 & 0 & 0 & 0 \end{bmatrix} = \begin{bmatrix} 2 & 0 & 5 & -3 \end{bmatrix}$$

Watch Out !

A matrix with 1 row and 4 columns does NOT have the same dimensions as a matrix with 4 rows and 1 column.

Need More HELP ?

Remember: For the dimensions of a matrix, the first value always indicates the number of rows and the second number indicates the number of columns. So an *m* × *n* matrix has *m* rows and *n* columns.

EXAMPLE 3

Using the matrices in Example 2 above, find a matrix *X* so that *A* + *X* = *C*.

STEP 1 Write an equation. Use "?" symbols for the unknown elements in matrix *X*.

$$\begin{matrix} A & + & X & = & C \end{matrix}$$

$$\begin{bmatrix} 2 & 0 & 5 & -3 \end{bmatrix} + \begin{bmatrix} ? & ? & ? & ? \end{bmatrix} = \begin{bmatrix} 0 & 0 & 0 & 0 \end{bmatrix}$$

STEP 2 Find the values for the unknown elements. For example, find out what number needs to be added to 2 for the sum to be 0.

$$\begin{bmatrix} 2 & 0 & 5 & -3 \end{bmatrix} + \begin{bmatrix} -2 & 0 & -5 & 3 \end{bmatrix} = \begin{bmatrix} 0 & 0 & 0 & 0 \end{bmatrix}$$

$$\text{matrix } X = \begin{bmatrix} 2 & 0 & 5 & -3 \end{bmatrix}$$

SEARCH

To see step-by-step videos of these problems, enter the page number into the SWadvantage.com Search Bar.

Need More

HELP ?

For help, go to
*Commutative and
Associative Properties*
in *Algebra* (p. 1406).

SEARCH 🔍

To see step-by-step
videos of these
problems, enter the
page number into the
SWadvantage.com
Search Bar.

Some Algebraic Properties of Matrices

Many of the properties of algebra that apply to the real numbers also apply to operations involving matrices. Here are two algebraic properties that apply to real numbers.

Commutative Property of Addition
For all real numbers a and b, $a + b = b + a$.

Associative Property of Addition
For all real numbers a, b, and c, $(a + b) + c = a + (b + c)$.

EXAMPLE 4

a. **Show that $A + B = B + A$ and that $(A + B) + C = A + (B + C)$ for these matrices:**

$$A = \begin{bmatrix} 5 & 7 & -3 \\ -8 & 0 & 2 \end{bmatrix}, B = \begin{bmatrix} -2 & 5 & 1 \\ 3 & -1 & 4 \end{bmatrix}, \text{ and } C = \begin{bmatrix} -3 & -2 & -1 \\ 6 & 2 & 4 \end{bmatrix}$$

STEP 1 Find and compare the values of $A + B$ and $B + A$.

$$A + B = \begin{bmatrix} 5 & 7 & -3 \\ -8 & 0 & 2 \end{bmatrix} + \begin{bmatrix} -2 & 5 & 1 \\ 3 & -1 & 4 \end{bmatrix} = \begin{bmatrix} 5 + (-2) & 7 + 5 & -3 + 1 \\ -8 + 3 & 0 + (-1) & 2 + 4 \end{bmatrix} = \begin{bmatrix} 3 & 12 & -2 \\ -5 & -1 & 6 \end{bmatrix}$$

$$B + A = \begin{bmatrix} -2 & 5 & 1 \\ 3 & -1 & 4 \end{bmatrix} + \begin{bmatrix} 5 & 7 & -3 \\ -8 & 0 & 2 \end{bmatrix} = \begin{bmatrix} -2 + 5 & 5 + 7 & 1 + (-3) \\ 3 + (-8) & -1 + 0 & 4 + 2 \end{bmatrix} = \begin{bmatrix} 3 & 12 & -2 \\ -5 & -1 & 6 \end{bmatrix}$$

Therefore, $A + B = B + A$.

STEP 2 Find and compare the values of $(A + B) + C$ and $A + (B + C)$.

$$(A + B) + C = \left(\begin{bmatrix} 5 & 7 & -3 \\ -8 & 0 & 2 \end{bmatrix} + \begin{bmatrix} -2 & 5 & 1 \\ 3 & -1 & 4 \end{bmatrix} \right) + \begin{bmatrix} -3 & -2 & -1 \\ 6 & 2 & 4 \end{bmatrix}$$

$$= \begin{bmatrix} 3 & 12 & -2 \\ -5 & -1 & 6 \end{bmatrix} + \begin{bmatrix} -3 & -2 & -1 \\ 6 & 2 & 4 \end{bmatrix} = \begin{bmatrix} 0 & 10 & -3 \\ 1 & 1 & 10 \end{bmatrix}$$

$$A + (B + C) = \begin{bmatrix} 5 & 7 & -3 \\ -8 & 0 & 2 \end{bmatrix} + \left(\begin{bmatrix} -2 & 5 & 1 \\ 3 & -1 & 4 \end{bmatrix} + \begin{bmatrix} -3 & -2 & -1 \\ 6 & 2 & 4 \end{bmatrix} \right)$$

$$= \begin{bmatrix} 5 & 7 & -3 \\ -8 & 0 & 2 \end{bmatrix} + \begin{bmatrix} -5 & 3 & 0 \\ 9 & 1 & 8 \end{bmatrix} = \begin{bmatrix} 0 & 10 & -3 \\ 1 & 1 & 10 \end{bmatrix}$$

Therefore, $(A + B) + C = A + (B + C)$.

b. **Explain how the commutative and associative properties for addition with matrices depend on the commutative and associative properties for addition with real numbers.**

For each pair of corresponding elements, the commutative property of addition for real numbers means that the corresponding elements are equal. All pairs of corresponding elements are equal, which means that the matrices are equal.

$$A + B \quad \begin{bmatrix} 5 + (-2) & 7 + 5 & -3 + 1 \\ -8 + 3 & 0 + (-1) & 2 + 4 \end{bmatrix} = \begin{bmatrix} -2 + 5 & 5 + 7 & 1 + (-3) \\ 3 + (-8) & -1 + 0 & 4 + 2 \end{bmatrix} \quad B + A$$

So $A + B = B + A$. In general, the addition of matrices is commutative.

Similarly, in each element of $(A + B) + C$ and $A + (B + C)$, the addition of real numbers is associative, so $(A + B) + C = A + (B + C)$. In general, the addition of matrices is associative.

Ways to
REMEMBER

To remember
the meaning of
commutative, think
about a commuter
taking trip *a* and trip *b*
to and from work.
Both round trips are
the same distance,
so $a + b = b + a$. To
remember the meaning
of *associative*, think
of friends associating
together. If friends *a*
and *b* are with person *c*,
then person *a* is with
friends *b* and *c*.

Using the definition of equal matrices, we can combine matrices and the techniques of solving equations.

EXAMPLE 5

Find the values of x, y, z, and w in each matrix equation.

a. $\begin{bmatrix} 1.2 & 19 \\ 5x+1 & y-7 \end{bmatrix} - \begin{bmatrix} 2w & 3z+17 \\ -9 & -7 \end{bmatrix} = \begin{bmatrix} 1 & 2 \\ 3 & 4 \end{bmatrix}$

STEP 1 Write an equation for each set of corresponding elements.

$$1.2 - 2w = 1 \qquad 19 - (3z+17) = 2 \qquad (5x+1) - (-9) = 3 \qquad (y-7) - (-7) = 4$$

STEP 2 Solve each equation.

$$
\begin{array}{llll}
1.2 - 2w = 1 & 19 - (3z+17) = 2 & (5x+1) - (-9) = 3 & (y-7) - (-7) = 4 \\
-2w = -0.2 & 19 - 3z - 17 = 2 & 5x + 10 = 3 & y + 0 = 4 \\
w = 0.1 & -3z + 2 = 2 & 5x = -7 & y = 4 \\
& -3z = 0 & x = -1.4 & \\
& z = 0 & &
\end{array}
$$

For this matrix equation, $w = 0.1$, $x = -1.4$, $y = 4$, and $z = 0$.

b. $\begin{bmatrix} 17 & 2y & 20 & 5 \end{bmatrix} - \begin{bmatrix} 3x & y & 5 & 2w \end{bmatrix} = \begin{bmatrix} -1 & -2 & 3z & 3 \end{bmatrix}$

STEP 1 Write an equation for each set of corresponding elements.

$$17 - 3x = -1 \qquad 2y - y = -2 \qquad 20 - 5 = 3z \qquad 5 - 2w = 3$$

STEP 2 Solve each equation.

$$
\begin{array}{llll}
17 - 3x = -1 & 2y - y = -2 & 20 - 5 = 3z & 5 - 2w = 3 \\
-3x = -18 & y = -2 & 15 = 3z & -2w = -2 \\
x = 6 & & z = 5 & w = 1
\end{array}
$$

For this matrix equation, $w = 1$, $x = 6$, $y = -2$, and $z = 5$.

GOT TO KNOW!

Addition and Subtraction of Matrices

The elements in a matrix are indicated by terms such as a_1 and a_2 and are read "a-sub-one" and "a-sub-two."

Sum of two matrices $\qquad \begin{bmatrix} a_1 & b_1 & c_1 \\ d_1 & e_1 & f_1 \end{bmatrix} + \begin{bmatrix} a_2 & b_2 & c_2 \\ d_2 & e_2 & f_2 \end{bmatrix} = \begin{bmatrix} a_1 + a_2 & b_1 + b_2 & c_1 + c_2 \\ d_1 + d_2 & e_1 + e_2 & f_1 + f_2 \end{bmatrix}$

Difference of two matrices $\qquad \begin{bmatrix} p_1 & q_1 \\ r_1 & s_1 \\ t_1 & u_1 \end{bmatrix} - \begin{bmatrix} p_2 & q_2 \\ r_2 & s_2 \\ t_2 & u_2 \end{bmatrix} = \begin{bmatrix} p_1 - p_2 & q_1 - q_2 \\ r_1 - r_2 & s_1 - s_2 \\ t_1 - t_2 & u_1 - u_2 \end{bmatrix}$

Scalar Multiplication

Multiplying Each Matrix Element by the Same Number

The operation of multiplying a real number by every element in a matrix is called **scalar multiplication**.

- A matrix is a factor in scalar multiplication.

- For example, the expression $5 \cdot \begin{bmatrix} 2 & -3 & 5 \\ 7 & 0 & -8 \end{bmatrix}$ represents the matrix

  $\begin{bmatrix} 5 \cdot 2 & 5 \cdot (-3) & 5 \cdot 5 \\ 5 \cdot 7 & 5 \cdot 0 & 5 \cdot (-8) \end{bmatrix}$, where each element in the matrix is multiplied

  by the real-number factor. The simplified matrix is then $\begin{bmatrix} 10 & -15 & 25 \\ 35 & 0 & -40 \end{bmatrix}$.

- The scalar product of a real number p and a matrix M can be represented as $p \cdot M$ or as pM.

Need More

HELP ?

The term **scalar multiplication** comes from using matrices to represent ordered pairs for a geometric figure. For example, if

$\begin{bmatrix} 3 & -3 & 5 \\ 7 & 0 & -8 \end{bmatrix}$

represents the vertices $(3, 7)$, $(-3, 0)$, and $(5, -8)$ of a triangle, then the scalar product

$5 \cdot \begin{bmatrix} 3 & -3 & 5 \\ 7 & 0 & -8 \end{bmatrix}$

represents an enlargement of that triangle by a factor, or **scale**, of 5. You can see more uses of matrices in geometry in *Using Matrices in Geometry*.

EXAMPLE 1

Use scalar multiplication to find the product of each expression.

a. $12 \cdot \begin{bmatrix} 7 \\ -2 \\ 1 \end{bmatrix}$ b. $\dfrac{\begin{bmatrix} 6 & 0 \\ -4 & 5 \end{bmatrix}}{2}$ c. $0 \cdot \begin{bmatrix} a & b & c \\ d & e & f \end{bmatrix}$

a. Multiply 12 times each element in the matrix. Notice that the resulting matrix has the same dimensions as the original matrix:

$12 \cdot \begin{bmatrix} 7 \\ -2 \\ 1 \end{bmatrix} = \begin{bmatrix} 12 \cdot 7 \\ 12 \cdot (-2) \\ 12 \cdot 1 \end{bmatrix} = \begin{bmatrix} 84 \\ -24 \\ 12 \end{bmatrix}$.

b. Rewrite $\dfrac{\begin{bmatrix} 6 & 0 \\ -4 & 5 \end{bmatrix}}{2}$ as $\dfrac{1}{2} \cdot \begin{bmatrix} 6 & 0 \\ -4 & 5 \end{bmatrix}$ and use scalar multiplication:

$\dfrac{1}{2} \cdot \begin{bmatrix} 6 & 0 \\ -4 & 5 \end{bmatrix} = \begin{bmatrix} 3 & 0 \\ -2 & 2.5 \end{bmatrix}$

c. Multiply the scalar 0 by every element in the matrix.

$0 \cdot \begin{bmatrix} a & b & c \\ d & e & f \end{bmatrix} = \begin{bmatrix} 0 & 0 & 0 \\ 0 & 0 & 0 \end{bmatrix}$

Watch Out !

Scalar multiplication is not the same thing as *matrix multiplication*. Scalar multiplication is multiplying all the elements of a matrix by the same real number. Matrix multiplication is finding the product of two matrices.

As shown in Example 1(c), a matrix with 0 as every element is called a **zero matrix**.

The matrix $\begin{bmatrix} 0 & 0 & 0 \\ 0 & 0 & 0 \end{bmatrix}$ is the 2×3 zero matrix.

Scalar multiplication can be used to solve some matrix equations.

EXAMPLE 2

Find the value of each variable.

$$3 \cdot \begin{bmatrix} 3 & 0 & -10 & 5 \end{bmatrix} = 4 \cdot \begin{bmatrix} a & b^2 & c+3 & 0.5d \end{bmatrix}$$

STEP 1 Use scalar multiplication on each side of the equation.

$$\begin{bmatrix} 9 & 0 & -30 & 15 \end{bmatrix} = \begin{bmatrix} 4a & 4b^2 & 4c+12 & 2d \end{bmatrix}$$

STEP 2 Write an equation for each pair of corresponding elements. Then solve each equation.

$9 = 4a$	$0 = 4b^2$	$-30 = 4c + 12$	$15 = 2d$
$a = 2.25$	$b = 0$	$c = -10.5$	$d = 7.5$

> **Watch Out !**
> Check for a mistake if the product of scalar multiplication does not have the same dimensions as the original matrix.

Scalar multiplication also can be used to add or subtract multiples of the same matrix.

EXAMPLE 3

a. Show that $\begin{bmatrix} 12 & -28 \\ -4 & 0 \end{bmatrix}$ **can be written as** $4 \cdot \begin{bmatrix} 3 & -7 \\ -1 & 0 \end{bmatrix}$. **Relate this to factoring.**

Using the concepts of scalar multiplication, $\begin{bmatrix} 12 & -28 \\ -4 & 0 \end{bmatrix} = \begin{bmatrix} 4 \cdot 3 & 4 \cdot (-7) \\ 4 \cdot (-1) & 4 \cdot 0 \end{bmatrix} = 4 \cdot \begin{bmatrix} 3 & -7 \\ -1 & 0 \end{bmatrix}$.

In general, a matrix in which each element contains a common factor equals a scalar (the common factor) times a matrix with the common factor factored out.

> **Watch Out !**
> When you take a common factor out of a matrix, be sure you divide <u>every</u> element of the <u>matrix</u> by that factor.

b. Simplify $3 \cdot \begin{bmatrix} 2 & -3 \\ 5 & 9 \end{bmatrix} + 5 \cdot \begin{bmatrix} 2 & -3 \\ 5 & 9 \end{bmatrix}$. **Explain how this process relates to addition.**

$$3 \cdot \begin{bmatrix} 2 & -3 \\ 5 & 9 \end{bmatrix} + 5 \cdot \begin{bmatrix} 2 & -3 \\ 5 & 9 \end{bmatrix} = \begin{bmatrix} 6 & -9 \\ 15 & 27 \end{bmatrix} + \begin{bmatrix} 10 & -15 \\ 25 & 45 \end{bmatrix} = \begin{bmatrix} 16 & -24 \\ 40 & 72 \end{bmatrix}$$

$$\begin{bmatrix} 16 & -24 \\ 40 & 72 \end{bmatrix} = \begin{bmatrix} 8 \cdot 2 & 8 \cdot (-3) \\ 8 \cdot 5 & 8 \cdot 9 \end{bmatrix} = 8 \cdot \begin{bmatrix} 2 & -3 \\ 5 & 9 \end{bmatrix}$$

If a and b are real numbers and T is a matrix, then $aT + bT = (a + b)T$, and $aT - bT = (a - b)T$.

GOT TO KNOW !

Operations of Scalar Multiplication

When a, b, c, d, e, f, and g are real numbers:

$$a \begin{bmatrix} b & c \\ d & e \end{bmatrix} = \begin{bmatrix} ab & ac \\ ad & ae \end{bmatrix} \qquad f \begin{bmatrix} b & c \\ d & e \end{bmatrix} + g \begin{bmatrix} b & c \\ d & e \end{bmatrix} = (f + g) \begin{bmatrix} b & c \\ d & e \end{bmatrix}$$

Some Algebraic Properties of Scalar Multiplication

In scalar multiplication, a matrix is a factor, so the properties of scalar multiplication are the same properties that apply to other multiplication problems.

Ways to
REMEMBER

One way to distinguish between the associative property and the commutative property is to remember that *associates* stay in the same order [$(ab)c = a(bc)$] and that *commuters* switch order [$ab = ba$].

EXAMPLE 4

For real numbers $a = 10$ and $b = -7$ and for matrix $M = \begin{bmatrix} 2 & 5 & -2 \\ 1 & 8 & 0 \end{bmatrix}$, show that $(ab)M = a(bM)$.

What algebraic property does the example illustrate?

STEP 1 Find $(ab)M$ and $a(bM)$, and compare the products.

$$(ab)M = (10 \cdot (-7))\begin{bmatrix} 2 & 5 & -2 \\ 1 & 8 & 0 \end{bmatrix} = (-70) \cdot \begin{bmatrix} 2 & 5 & -2 \\ 1 & 8 & 0 \end{bmatrix} = \begin{bmatrix} -140 & -350 & 140 \\ -70 & -560 & 0 \end{bmatrix}$$

$$a(bM) = 10 \cdot \left(-7 \cdot \begin{bmatrix} 2 & 5 & -2 \\ 1 & 8 & 0 \end{bmatrix}\right) = 10 \cdot \begin{bmatrix} -14 & -35 & 14 \\ -7 & -56 & 0 \end{bmatrix} = \begin{bmatrix} -140 & -350 & 140 \\ -70 & -560 & 0 \end{bmatrix}$$

Therefore $(ab)M = a(bM)$.

STEP 2 Identify any properties that are used.

The factors in these expressions are in the same order; they are just grouped differently.

Because the grouping of factors in scalar multiplication does not change the results, scalar multiplication is associative according to the Associative Property of Multiplication.

Need More
HELP ?

For more on algebraic properties, go to *Commutative and Associative Properties* and *The Distributive Property* in *Algebra* (pp. 1406, 1410).

EXAMPLE 5

For the real number $q = 5$ and the two matrices $R = \begin{bmatrix} 5 & 3 & 2 \\ 1 & -7 & 8 \end{bmatrix}$ and $S = \begin{bmatrix} 0 & -2 & 5 \\ 4 & 0 & 3 \end{bmatrix}$, show that $q(R + S) = qR + qS$. What algebraic property does the example illustrate?

STEP 1 Find $q(R + S)$ and $qR + qS$.

$$q(R + S) = 5 \cdot \left(\begin{bmatrix} 5 & 3 & 2 \\ 1 & -7 & 8 \end{bmatrix} + \begin{bmatrix} 0 & -2 & 5 \\ 4 & 0 & 3 \end{bmatrix}\right) = 5 \cdot \begin{bmatrix} 5 & 1 & 7 \\ 5 & -7 & 11 \end{bmatrix} = \begin{bmatrix} 25 & 5 & 35 \\ 25 & -35 & 55 \end{bmatrix}$$

$$qR + qS = 5 \cdot \begin{bmatrix} 5 & 3 & 2 \\ 1 & -7 & 8 \end{bmatrix} + 5 \cdot \begin{bmatrix} 0 & -2 & 5 \\ 4 & 0 & 3 \end{bmatrix}$$

$$= \begin{bmatrix} 25 & 15 & 10 \\ 5 & -35 & 40 \end{bmatrix} + \begin{bmatrix} 0 & -10 & 25 \\ 20 & 0 & 15 \end{bmatrix} = \begin{bmatrix} 25 & 5 & 35 \\ 25 & -35 & 55 \end{bmatrix}$$

Therefore $q(R + S) = qR + qS$.

STEP 2 Identify any properties that were used.

The equation $q(R + S) = qR + qS$ is an example of the distributive property.

Scalar multiplication exhibits the Distributive Property over matrix addition.

Similarly, it can be shown that $pM = Mp$. In words, scalar multiplication is commutative according to the Commutative Property of Multiplication.

Part (c) of Example 1 introduced the term "zero matrix." The zero matrix plays the part of 0 in matrix algebra.

EXAMPLE 6

Suppose matrix Z is a 4 × 2 zero matrix and $A = \begin{bmatrix} 3 & -5 \\ 2 & 0 \\ -7 & 4 \\ 8 & 1 \end{bmatrix}$ **. Find matrix C so that the sum of matrices A and C is Z, the zero matrix. Then express matrix C as a scalar multiple of matrix A.**

STEP 1 For all 4 × 2 matrices, the zero matrix is $Z = \begin{bmatrix} 0 & 0 \\ 0 & 0 \\ 0 & 0 \\ 0 & 0 \end{bmatrix}$.

STEP 2 Write the equation using letters and matrices. To find each element in matrix C, multiply the corresponding element of matrix A by −1.

$$A \quad + \quad C \quad = \quad Z$$

$$\begin{bmatrix} 3 & -5 \\ 2 & 0 \\ -7 & 4 \\ 8 & 1 \end{bmatrix} + \begin{bmatrix} ? & ? \\ ? & ? \\ ? & ? \\ ? & ? \end{bmatrix} = \begin{bmatrix} 0 & 0 \\ 0 & 0 \\ 0 & 0 \\ 0 & 0 \end{bmatrix} \qquad \text{So matrix } C \text{ must be } \begin{bmatrix} -3 & 5 \\ -2 & 0 \\ 7 & -4 \\ -8 & -1 \end{bmatrix}.$$

STEP 3 Take out the common factor −1 from each element in matrix C:

$$C = \begin{bmatrix} -3 & 5 \\ -2 & 0 \\ 7 & -4 \\ -8 & -1 \end{bmatrix} = \begin{bmatrix} -1 \cdot 3 & -1 \cdot (-5) \\ -1 \cdot 2 & -1 \cdot 0 \\ -1 \cdot (-7) & -1 \cdot 4 \\ -1 \cdot 8 & -1 \cdot 1 \end{bmatrix} = -1 \cdot \begin{bmatrix} 3 & -5 \\ 2 & 0 \\ -7 & 4 \\ 8 & 1 \end{bmatrix} = -1 \cdot A$$

So $C = -1 \cdot A$. This is consistent with the statement that $A + C = Z$. If we replace Z, the zero matrix, with 0, then $A + C = 0$. Subtracting A from each side results in $C = -A$ or $C = -1 \cdot A$.

Need More HELP ?

A 4 × 2 matrix means that the matrix has 4 rows and 2 columns.

SEARCH

To see step-by-step videos of these problems, enter the page number into the SWadvantage.com Search Bar.

Properties of Scalar Multiplication

In each example, a and b are real numbers, and M is a matrix.

Property	Example
Associative Property of Multiplication	$(ab)M = a(bM)$
Commutative Property of Multiplication	$aM = Ma$
Distributive Property	$aM + bM = (a + b)M$
Multiplicative Identity Property	$1M = M$

Multiplying 2-By-2 Matrices

Need More

HELP

More applications for using *matrices in business* can be found in *Using Matrices for Inventory* on page 1810.

An Application: Combining Two Matrices

A clothing store has 4 sizes of sweatshirts: small, medium, large, and extra large. Each size has a different retail price. Information about the number of sweatshirts at each size and the cost for that size is shown in two matrices.

Numbers of Sweatshirts

$$\begin{array}{cccc} S & M & L & XL \end{array}$$
$$\begin{bmatrix} 11 & 9 & 13 & 7 \end{bmatrix}$$

Costs of Sweatshirts

$$\begin{bmatrix} 6 \\ 8 \\ 10 \\ 12 \end{bmatrix} \begin{array}{c} S \\ M \\ L \\ XL \end{array}$$

If the store managers want to know the wholesale value of all the sweatshirts, they can multiply pairs of corresponding elements in the two matrices and then add the products:

$$11 \times 6 + 9 \times 8 + 13 \times 10 + 7 \times 12 \qquad \text{(The total is } 66 + 72 + 130 + 84, \text{ or \$352.)}$$

This method of multiplying the pair of first terms, then multiplying the pair of second terms and so on, is the central idea for multiplying two matrices.

EXAMPLE 1

Watch Out

Be sure that the number of columns in the left factor equals the number of rows in the right factor. This is not an issue in multiplying 2-by-2 matrices, but it becomes more important when you multiply other matrices.

Use the method above for combining a row and a column in two matrices to find this product:

$$\begin{bmatrix} 3 & -5 \\ 2 & 8 \end{bmatrix} \cdot \begin{bmatrix} -4 & 0 \\ 1.5 & -1 \end{bmatrix}$$

STEP 1 In the product matrix, the element in the upper left corner is in row 1 and column 1. To find the value of that element, combine row 1 from the left factor and column 1 from the right factor.

Left Factor   Right Factor   Product

$$\begin{bmatrix} 3 & -5 \\ 2 & 8 \end{bmatrix} \cdot \begin{bmatrix} -4 & 0 \\ 1.5 & -1 \end{bmatrix} = \begin{bmatrix} 3(-4) + (-5)1.5 & \square \\ \square & \square \end{bmatrix} = \begin{bmatrix} -12 + (-7.5) & \square \\ \square & \square \end{bmatrix} = \begin{bmatrix} -19.5 & \square \\ \square & \square \end{bmatrix}$$

STEP 2 To find the element for row 1, column 2 for the product, combine row 1 from the left factor and use column 2 from the right factor.

Left Factor   Right Factor   Product

$$\begin{bmatrix} 3 & -5 \\ 2 & 8 \end{bmatrix} \cdot \begin{bmatrix} -4 & 0 \\ 1.5 & -1 \end{bmatrix} = \begin{bmatrix} 19.5 & 3(0) + (-5)(-1) \\ \square & \square \end{bmatrix} = \begin{bmatrix} 19.5 & 0 + 5 \\ \square & \square \end{bmatrix} = \begin{bmatrix} 19.5 & 5 \\ \square & \square \end{bmatrix}$$

STEP 3 Next, find the other two elements in the product.

Left Factor   Right Factor   Product

$$\begin{bmatrix} 3 & -5 \\ 2 & 8 \end{bmatrix} \cdot \begin{bmatrix} -4 & 0 \\ 1.5 & -1 \end{bmatrix} = \begin{bmatrix} 19.5 & 5 \\ 2(-4) + 8(1.5) & \square \end{bmatrix} = \begin{bmatrix} 19.5 & 5 \\ -8 + 12 & \square \end{bmatrix} = \begin{bmatrix} 19.5 & 5 \\ 4 & \square \end{bmatrix}$$

$$\begin{bmatrix} 3 & -5 \\ 2 & 8 \end{bmatrix} \cdot \begin{bmatrix} -4 & 0 \\ 1.5 & -1 \end{bmatrix} = \begin{bmatrix} 19.5 & 5 \\ 4 & 2(0) + 8(-1) \end{bmatrix} = \begin{bmatrix} 19.5 & 5 \\ 4 & 0 + (-8) \end{bmatrix} = \begin{bmatrix} 19.5 & 5 \\ 4 & -8 \end{bmatrix}$$

The product is $\begin{bmatrix} -19.5 & 5 \\ 4 & -8 \end{bmatrix}$, or $\begin{bmatrix} 3 & -5 \\ 2 & 8 \end{bmatrix} \cdot \begin{bmatrix} -4 & 0 \\ 1.5 & -1 \end{bmatrix} = \begin{bmatrix} -19.5 & 5 \\ 4 & -8 \end{bmatrix}$.

Labeling the Rows and Columns in a 2-By-2 Matrix

Each element in a product can be described in terms of its row number and column number.

Left Factor   **Right Factor**   **Product**

$$\begin{bmatrix} a & b \\ c & d \end{bmatrix} \cdot \begin{bmatrix} x & y \\ z & w \end{bmatrix} = \begin{bmatrix} \text{Row 1, Column 1} & \text{Row 1, Column 2} \\ \text{Row 2, Column 1} & \text{Row 2, Column 2} \end{bmatrix}$$

Need More

HELP ?

See the next page for examples on why it is necessary to refer to matrices as "the left factor" and "the right factor" when you multiply.

EXAMPLE 2

                       Matrix A   **Matrix B**

Find the matrix product $\begin{bmatrix} -2 & 4 \\ 6 & 8 \end{bmatrix} \cdot \begin{bmatrix} 3 & -7 \\ 0 & -1 \end{bmatrix}.$

STEP 1   Write the multiplication problem. For each element, list the row and column that are combined from the two factors.

$$\begin{bmatrix} -2 & 4 \\ 6 & 8 \end{bmatrix} \cdot \begin{bmatrix} 3 & -7 \\ 0 & -1 \end{bmatrix} = \begin{bmatrix} \text{Combine row 1A and column 1B.} & \text{Combine row 1A and column 2B.} \\ \text{Combine row 2A and column 1B.} & \text{Combine row 2A and column 2B.} \end{bmatrix}$$

STEP 2   Substitute the values from the left factor and the right factor.

$$\begin{bmatrix} -2 & 4 \\ 6 & 8 \end{bmatrix} \cdot \begin{bmatrix} 3 & -7 \\ 0 & -1 \end{bmatrix} = \begin{bmatrix} -2(3) + 4(0) & -2(-7) + 4(-1) \\ 6(3) + 8(0) & 6(-7) + 8(-1) \end{bmatrix}$$

STEP 3   Simplify the matrix to find the product.

$$\begin{bmatrix} -2(3) + 4(0) & -2(-7) + 4(-1) \\ 6(3) + 8(0) & 6(-7) + 8(-1) \end{bmatrix} = \begin{bmatrix} -6 + 0 & 14 - 4 \\ 18 + 0 & -42 - 8 \end{bmatrix} = \begin{bmatrix} -6 & 10 \\ 18 & -50 \end{bmatrix}$$

                Matrix A   **Matrix B**

The matrix product $\begin{bmatrix} -2 & 4 \\ 6 & 8 \end{bmatrix} \cdot \begin{bmatrix} 3 & -7 \\ 0 & -1 \end{bmatrix} = \begin{bmatrix} -6 & 10 \\ 18 & -50 \end{bmatrix}$

SEARCH 🔍

To see step-by-step videos of these problems, enter the page number into the SWadvantage.com Search Bar.

GOT TO KNOW!

Multiplying 2-By-2 Matrices

Left Factor   **Right Factor**   **Product**

$$\begin{bmatrix} a & b \\ c & d \end{bmatrix} \cdot \begin{bmatrix} x & y \\ z & w \end{bmatrix} = \begin{bmatrix} ax + bz & ay + bw \\ cx + dz & cy + dw \end{bmatrix}$$

Elements from Left Factor	Elements from Right Factor	Position of Element in the Product
Row 1	Column 1	Row 1, Column 1
Row 1	Column 2	Row 1, Column 2
Row 2	Column 1	Row 2, Column 1
Row 2	Column 2	Row 2, Column 2

Is Matrix Multiplication Commutative?

Example 3 shows why it is necessary to distinguish between "the left factor" and "the right factor" in matrix multiplication.

SEARCH

To see step-by-step videos of these problems, enter the page number into the SWadvantage.com Search Bar.

EXAMPLE 3

Find $\begin{bmatrix} -3 & -4 \\ 2 & 1 \end{bmatrix} \cdot \begin{bmatrix} 5 & -1 \\ 0 & 3 \end{bmatrix}$. Then find $\begin{bmatrix} 5 & -1 \\ 0 & 3 \end{bmatrix} \cdot \begin{bmatrix} -3 & -4 \\ 2 & 1 \end{bmatrix}$. What conclusion can be drawn about matrix multiplication and the algebraic Commutative Property of Multiplication?

STEP 1 $\begin{bmatrix} -3 & -4 \\ 2 & 1 \end{bmatrix} \cdot \begin{bmatrix} 5 & -1 \\ 0 & 3 \end{bmatrix} = \begin{bmatrix} -3(5) + (-4)(0) & -3(-1) + (-4)(3) \\ 2(5) + 1(0) & 2(-1) + 1(3) \end{bmatrix}$

$$= \begin{bmatrix} -15 + 0 & 3 + (-12) \\ 10 + 0 & -2 + 3 \end{bmatrix} = \begin{bmatrix} -15 & -9 \\ 10 & 1 \end{bmatrix}$$

STEP 2 $\begin{bmatrix} 5 & -1 \\ 0 & 3 \end{bmatrix} \cdot \begin{bmatrix} -3 & -4 \\ 2 & 1 \end{bmatrix} = \begin{bmatrix} 5(-3) + (-1)(2) & 5(-4) + (-1)(1) \\ 0(-3) + 3(2) & 0(-4) + 3(1) \end{bmatrix}$

$$= \begin{bmatrix} -15 - 2 & -20 - 1 \\ 0 + 6 & 0 + 3 \end{bmatrix} = \begin{bmatrix} -17 & -21 \\ 6 & 3 \end{bmatrix}$$

STEP 3 In general, if A and B are 2-by-2 matrices, then $A \cdot B \neq B \cdot A$. Matrix multiplication is **not** commutative.

A **square matrix** has an equal number of rows and columns. The **main diagonal** of a square matrix refers to the diagonal from the upper left corner to the lower right corner. Example 4 introduces a square matrix with all 1's on the main diagonal and all 0's everywhere else.

EXAMPLE 4

Find $\begin{bmatrix} a & b \\ c & d \end{bmatrix} \cdot \begin{bmatrix} 1 & 0 \\ 0 & 1 \end{bmatrix}$ and find $\begin{bmatrix} 1 & 0 \\ 0 & 1 \end{bmatrix} \cdot \begin{bmatrix} a & b \\ c & d \end{bmatrix}$. What does $\begin{bmatrix} 1 & 0 \\ 0 & 1 \end{bmatrix}$ act like?

Find each product.

$$\begin{bmatrix} a & b \\ c & d \end{bmatrix} \cdot \begin{bmatrix} 1 & 0 \\ 0 & 1 \end{bmatrix} = \begin{bmatrix} a \cdot 1 + b \cdot 0 & a \cdot 0 + b \cdot 1 \\ c \cdot 1 + d \cdot 0 & c \cdot 0 + d \cdot 1 \end{bmatrix} = \begin{bmatrix} a & b \\ c & d \end{bmatrix}$$

$$\begin{bmatrix} 1 & 0 \\ 0 & 1 \end{bmatrix} \cdot \begin{bmatrix} a & b \\ c & d \end{bmatrix} = \begin{bmatrix} 1 \cdot a + 0 \cdot c & 1 \cdot b + 0 \cdot d \\ 0 \cdot a + 1 \cdot c & 0 \cdot b + 1 \cdot d \end{bmatrix} = \begin{bmatrix} a & b \\ c & d \end{bmatrix}$$

Multiplying any 2-by-2 matrix by $\begin{bmatrix} 1 & 0 \\ 0 & 1 \end{bmatrix}$ does not change the matrix.

Watch Out !

For matrices in general, $A \cdot B \neq B \cdot A$. But if one of the factors in matrix multiplication is I, the identity matrix for multiplication, then $A \cdot I = I \cdot A$. So multiplication by the identity matrix IS commutative.

The matrix $\begin{bmatrix} 1 & 0 \\ 0 & 1 \end{bmatrix}$ is called the **identity matrix for multiplication**, and it acts like the number 1 in real-number multiplication. (The Multiplication Property of 1 for real numbers is that for any real number x, $x \cdot 1 = 1 \cdot x = x$.) An identity matrix is usually referred to using the letter I. So if A is any 2-by-2 matrix and I is the 2-by-2 identity matrix, then:

$$A \cdot I = I \cdot A = A$$

A Distributive Property for Matrices

EXAMPLE 5

Using $A = \begin{bmatrix} 4 & 2 \\ 1 & -3 \end{bmatrix}$, $B = \begin{bmatrix} -5 & 0 \\ 1.5 & -8 \end{bmatrix}$, and $C = \begin{bmatrix} 3 & -2 \\ 0 & 4 \end{bmatrix}$, test whether matrix multiplication might be distributive over matrix addition. That is, test whether $A(B + C) = AB + AC$ for the three given matrices.

STEP 1 Find $A(B + C)$ and $AB + AC$.

$$A(B + C) = \begin{bmatrix} 4 & 2 \\ 1 & -3 \end{bmatrix} \left(\begin{bmatrix} -5 & 0 \\ 1.5 & -8 \end{bmatrix} + \begin{bmatrix} 3 & -2 \\ 0 & 4 \end{bmatrix} \right)$$

$$= \begin{bmatrix} 4 & 2 \\ 1 & -3 \end{bmatrix} \cdot \begin{bmatrix} -2 & -2 \\ 1.5 & -4 \end{bmatrix} = \begin{bmatrix} -8 + 3 & -8 - 8 \\ -2 - 4.5 & -2 + 12 \end{bmatrix} = \begin{bmatrix} -5 & -16 \\ -6.5 & 10 \end{bmatrix}$$

$$AB + AC = \begin{bmatrix} 4 & 2 \\ 1 & -3 \end{bmatrix} \cdot \begin{bmatrix} -5 & 0 \\ 1.5 & -8 \end{bmatrix} + \begin{bmatrix} 4 & 2 \\ 1 & -3 \end{bmatrix} \cdot \begin{bmatrix} 3 & -2 \\ 0 & 4 \end{bmatrix}$$

$$= \begin{bmatrix} -20 + 3 & 0 - 16 \\ -5 - 4.5 & 0 + 24 \end{bmatrix} + \begin{bmatrix} 12 + 0 & -8 + 8 \\ 3 + 0 & -2 - 12 \end{bmatrix}$$

$$= \begin{bmatrix} -17 & -16 \\ -9.5 & 24 \end{bmatrix} + \begin{bmatrix} 12 & 0 \\ 3 & -14 \end{bmatrix}$$

$$= \begin{bmatrix} -5 & -16 \\ -6.5 & 10 \end{bmatrix}$$

STEP 2 Compare the values of $A(B + C)$ and $AB + AC$.

For these three specific matrices it is true that $A(B + C) = AB + AC$.

Need More
HELP ?
You can prove that a statement is NOT true by finding a specific *counterexample*. But specific, true examples are never enough to prove that a property is true.

Example 5 suggests that matrices have the property: matrix multiplication is distributive over matrix addition. You can prove that property to be true by multiplying matrices with variable terms. So, the distributive property applies to matrix multiplication.

Matrix Multiplication

Multiplying Matrices by Combining a Row and a Column

To multiply two matrices:

- the number of columns of the first matrix must equal the number of rows of the second matrix. If this is not true, the matrices cannot be multiplied.
- combine elements from one entire row in the first matrix and from one entire column in the second matrix.
- remember that matrix multiplication is not commutative.

EXAMPLE 1

Find the product $\begin{bmatrix} 4 & 3 & 5 & -2 \end{bmatrix} \cdot \begin{bmatrix} 0 & 2 \\ -1 & 4 \\ 6 & 0.5 \\ -1 & -2 \end{bmatrix}$.

STEP 1 To find the first column in the product, combine the entire row from the left factor with the first column from the right factor.

$$\begin{bmatrix} 4 & 3 & 5 & -2 \end{bmatrix} \cdot \begin{bmatrix} 0 & 2 \\ -1 & 4 \\ 6 & 0.5 \\ -1 & -2 \end{bmatrix} = \begin{bmatrix} (4)(0)+(3)(-1)+(5)(6)+(-2)(-1) \end{bmatrix} = \begin{bmatrix} 0-3+30+2 \end{bmatrix} = \begin{bmatrix} 29 \end{bmatrix}$$

STEP 2 To find the second column in the product, combine the entire row from the left factor with the second column from the right factor.

$$\begin{bmatrix} 4 & 3 & 5 & -2 \end{bmatrix} \cdot \begin{bmatrix} 0 & 2 \\ -1 & 4 \\ 6 & 0.5 \\ -1 & -2 \end{bmatrix} = \begin{bmatrix} 29 & (4)(2)+(3)(4)+(5)(0.5)+(-2)(-2) \end{bmatrix}$$

$$= \begin{bmatrix} 29 & 8+12+2.5+4 \end{bmatrix} = \begin{bmatrix} 29 & 26.5 \end{bmatrix}$$

Notice that the left factor has one row and the elements in that row are used in each column in the product. The right factor has two columns: the elements in the first column appear in the first column of the product and the elements in the second column appear in the second column of the product.

Need More HELP?

The steps for multiplying two 2-by-2 matrices are described in *Multiplying 2-by-2 Matrices* in *Matrices* on page 1782.

Need More HELP?

When a matrix is described as having dimensions "*r* by *s*," it has *r* rows and *s* columns.

GOT TO KNOW!

Multiplying Matrices

The product of a *C*-by-*D* matrix, *A*, and a *D*-by-*E* matrix, *B*, is the *C*-by-*E* matrix, *AB*.

*m*th column   *m*th column

*n*th row → $\begin{bmatrix} - & - & - & - \end{bmatrix} \cdot \begin{bmatrix} - \\ - \\ - \\ - \end{bmatrix} = \begin{bmatrix} \square \end{bmatrix}$ ← *n*th row

When Can You Find the Product of Two Matrices?

On the previous page, the number of columns in the left factor was an *exact match* for the number of rows in the right factor. Without that match, you cannot multiply two matrices.

EXAMPLE 2

An (*r* by *s*) matrix refers to a matrix with *r* rows and *s* columns. Explain whether or not you can multiply each pair of matrices.

a. (*a* by *b*) and (*b* by *c*)

Yes, the first matrix has *b* columns, and the second matrix has *b* rows. These numbers match, so you can multiply the matrices.

b. (*x* by *y*) and (*z* by *w*)

No, the first matrix has *y* columns, and the second matrix has *z* rows. These numbers do not match, so you cannot multiply the matrices.

> **GOT TO KNOW!**
>
> **When Can You Multiply Matrices?**
>
> You can multiply two matrices when:
>
> - the number of columns of the left factor = the number of rows of the right factor

EXAMPLE 3

Explain whether you can find each product. If you can, find the product. Use these matrices:

$$A = \begin{bmatrix} 3 & -1 & 2 \\ 0 & 5 & -4 \end{bmatrix}, B = \begin{bmatrix} 0 & 1 & -3 & 2 \\ 4 & -2 & 2 & 0 \end{bmatrix}, C = \begin{bmatrix} 5 \\ -2 \\ 6 \end{bmatrix}, D = \begin{bmatrix} 1 & 0 & 2 \\ 0 & -3 & 5 \\ -2 & 1 & 1 \end{bmatrix}, E = \begin{bmatrix} 5 & 0 \\ 2 & 5 \\ -3 & 6 \\ -1 & -2 \end{bmatrix}$$

> **SEARCH**
>
> To see step-by-step videos of these problems, enter the page number into the SWadvantage.com Search Bar.

a. *A* × *C*

A × *C* is (2 by 3) × (3 by 1), so you <u>can</u> find the product, because the 3's match.

$$\begin{bmatrix} 3 & -1 & 2 \\ 0 & 5 & -4 \end{bmatrix} \times \begin{bmatrix} 5 \\ -2 \\ 6 \end{bmatrix} = \begin{bmatrix} 15+2+12 \\ 0-10-24 \end{bmatrix} = \begin{bmatrix} 29 \\ -34 \end{bmatrix}$$

b. *C* × *A*

C × *A* is (3 by 1) × (2 by 3), so you <u>cannot</u> find the product, because the 1 and 2 do not match.

c. *E* × *B*

E × *B* is (4 by 2) × (2 by 4), so you <u>can</u> find the product, because the 2's match.

$$\begin{bmatrix} 5 & 0 \\ 2 & 5 \\ -3 & 6 \\ -1 & -2 \end{bmatrix}\begin{bmatrix} 0 & 1 & -3 & 2 \\ 4 & -2 & 2 & 0 \end{bmatrix} = \begin{bmatrix} 0+0 & 5+0 & -15+0 & 10+0 \\ 0+20 & 2-10 & -6+10 & 4+0 \\ 0+24 & -3-12 & 9+12 & -6+0 \\ 0-8 & -1+4 & 3-4 & -2+0 \end{bmatrix} = \begin{bmatrix} 0 & 5 & -15 & 10 \\ 20 & -8 & 4 & 4 \\ 24 & -15 & 21 & -6 \\ -8 & 3 & -1 & -2 \end{bmatrix}$$

Finding the Dimensions of a Matrix Product

When you multiply two matrices, the dimensions of the product are related to the dimensions of the left factor and the right factor. The example below shows that when the left factor is a 3-by-2 matrix and the right factor is a 2-by-4 matrix, the product is a 3-by-4 matrix.

Left Factor (3 by 2)   Right Factor (2 by 4)   Product (3 by 4)

$$\begin{bmatrix} 1 & 4 \\ 0 & -3 \\ -2 & 5 \end{bmatrix} \times \begin{bmatrix} 0 & 1 & -3 & 2 \\ 4 & -2 & 2 & 0 \end{bmatrix} = \begin{bmatrix} 0+16 & 1-8 & -3+8 & 2+0 \\ 0-12 & 0+6 & 0-6 & 0+0 \\ 0+20 & -2-10 & 6+10 & -4+0 \end{bmatrix} = \begin{bmatrix} 16 & -7 & 5 & 2 \\ -12 & 6 & -6 & 0 \\ 20 & -12 & 16 & -4 \end{bmatrix}$$

The left factor is a (3 by 2) matrix and the right factor is a (2 by 4) matrix.

The product is a (3 by 4) matrix.

The pattern is always the same: if the left factor is a (p by q) matrix and the right factor is a (q by r) matrix, then the product is a (p by r) matrix.

- The product has the same number of rows as the left factor.
- The product has the same number of columns as the right factor.

Dimensions of left factor: (p by q)

Dimensions of right factor: (q by r)

Dimensions of a Product: (p by r)

Summary:
(p by q) $\times$ (q by r) = (p by r)

EXAMPLE 4

For each pair of matrices, tell whether you can find the product. If you can, tell the dimensions of the product and then find the product. Use the following matrices:

$$A = \begin{bmatrix} 3 & -1 & 2 \\ 0 & 5 & -4 \end{bmatrix}, B = \begin{bmatrix} 0 & 1 & -3 & 2 \\ 4 & -2 & 2 & 0 \end{bmatrix}, C = \begin{bmatrix} 5 \\ -2 \\ 6 \end{bmatrix}, D = \begin{bmatrix} 1 & 0 & 2 \\ 0 & -3 & 5 \\ -2 & 1 & 1 \end{bmatrix}$$

a. $A \times D$

$A \times D$ is (2 by 3) $\times$ (3 by 3). The inner numbers, 3 and 3, *match,* so you can find the product. The outer numbers are 2 and 3, so the product will have 2 rows and 3 columns.

$$\begin{bmatrix} 3 & -1 & 2 \\ 0 & 5 & -4 \end{bmatrix} \times \begin{bmatrix} 1 & 0 & 2 \\ 0 & -3 & 5 \\ -2 & 1 & 1 \end{bmatrix} = \begin{bmatrix} 3+0-4 & 0+3+2 & 6-5+2 \\ 0+0+8 & 0-15-4 & 0+25-4 \end{bmatrix} = \begin{bmatrix} -1 & 5 & 3 \\ 8 & -19 & 21 \end{bmatrix}$$

b. $B \times B$

$B \times B$ is (2 by 4) $\times$ (2 by 4).

The inner numbers, 4 and 2, *do not match,* so you cannot find the product.

c. $C \times D$

$C \times D$ is (3 by 1) $\times$ (3 by 3).

The inner numbers, 1 and 3, *do not match,* so you cannot find the product.

Some Properties of Matrix Multiplication

The properties of real-number algebra include the associative, commutative, and distributive properties. Many of those properties, BUT NOT ALL of them, hold for matrix algebra.

EXAMPLE 5

Use the matrices $X = \begin{bmatrix} 1 & 2 & 3 \\ 4 & 5 & 6 \\ 7 & 8 & 9 \end{bmatrix}$, $Y = \begin{bmatrix} 1 & -2 & 3 \\ -4 & 5 & -6 \\ 7 & -8 & 9 \end{bmatrix}$, and $Z = \begin{bmatrix} 0 & 1 & 2 \\ 0 & 2 & 3 \\ 0 & 4 & 5 \end{bmatrix}$ to explore some

properties of matrix algebra.

a. Is $X(YZ) = (XY)Z$? What property does your result support?

$$X(YZ) = \begin{bmatrix} 1 & 2 & 3 \\ 4 & 5 & 6 \\ 7 & 8 & 9 \end{bmatrix} \left(\begin{bmatrix} 1 & -2 & 3 \\ -4 & 5 & -6 \\ 7 & -8 & 9 \end{bmatrix} \cdot \begin{bmatrix} 0 & 1 & 2 \\ 0 & 2 & 3 \\ 0 & 4 & 5 \end{bmatrix} \right) = \begin{bmatrix} 1 & 2 & 3 \\ 4 & 5 & 6 \\ 7 & 8 & 9 \end{bmatrix} \cdot \begin{bmatrix} 0 & 9 & 11 \\ 0 & -18 & -23 \\ 0 & 27 & 35 \end{bmatrix} = \begin{bmatrix} 0 & 54 & 70 \\ 0 & 108 & 139 \\ 0 & 162 & 208 \end{bmatrix}$$

$$(XY)Z = \left(\begin{bmatrix} 1 & 2 & 3 \\ 4 & 5 & 6 \\ 7 & 8 & 9 \end{bmatrix} \cdot \begin{bmatrix} 1 & -2 & 3 \\ -4 & 5 & -6 \\ 7 & -8 & 9 \end{bmatrix} \right) \cdot \begin{bmatrix} 0 & 1 & 2 \\ 0 & 2 & 3 \\ 0 & 4 & 5 \end{bmatrix} = \begin{bmatrix} 14 & -16 & 18 \\ 28 & -31 & 36 \\ 38 & -46 & 54 \end{bmatrix} \cdot \begin{bmatrix} 0 & 1 & 2 \\ 0 & 2 & 3 \\ 0 & 4 & 5 \end{bmatrix} = \begin{bmatrix} 0 & 54 & 70 \\ 0 & 108 & 139 \\ 0 & 162 & 208 \end{bmatrix}$$

The result that $X(YZ) = (XY)Z$ for these specific matrices is support that matrix multiplication is associative.

b. Is $XZ = ZX$? Interpret your result.

$$XZ = \begin{bmatrix} 1 & 2 & 3 \\ 4 & 5 & 6 \\ 7 & 8 & 9 \end{bmatrix} \cdot \begin{bmatrix} 0 & 1 & 2 \\ 0 & 2 & 3 \\ 0 & 4 & 5 \end{bmatrix} = \begin{bmatrix} 0 & 17 & 23 \\ 0 & 38 & 53 \\ 0 & 59 & 83 \end{bmatrix}, \quad ZX = \begin{bmatrix} 0 & 1 & 2 \\ 0 & 2 & 3 \\ 0 & 4 & 5 \end{bmatrix} \cdot \begin{bmatrix} 1 & 2 & 3 \\ 4 & 5 & 6 \\ 7 & 8 & 9 \end{bmatrix} = \begin{bmatrix} 18 & 21 & 24 \\ 29 & 34 & 39 \\ 51 & 60 & 69 \end{bmatrix}$$

One example that $XZ \neq ZX$ is enough to conclude that matrix multiplication is NOT commutative.

c. Show that $X(Y + Z) = XY + XZ$. What property does your result suggest?

$$X(Y + Z) = \begin{bmatrix} 1 & 2 & 3 \\ 4 & 5 & 6 \\ 7 & 8 & 9 \end{bmatrix} \left(\begin{bmatrix} 1 & -2 & 3 \\ -4 & 5 & -6 \\ 7 & -8 & 9 \end{bmatrix} + \begin{bmatrix} 0 & 1 & 2 \\ 0 & 2 & 3 \\ 0 & 4 & 5 \end{bmatrix} \right) = \begin{bmatrix} 1 & 2 & 3 \\ 4 & 5 & 6 \\ 7 & 8 & 9 \end{bmatrix} \left(\begin{bmatrix} 1 & -1 & 5 \\ -4 & 7 & -3 \\ 7 & -4 & 14 \end{bmatrix} \right) = \begin{bmatrix} 14 & 1 & 41 \\ 26 & 7 & 89 \\ 38 & 13 & 137 \end{bmatrix}$$

$$XY + XZ = \left(\begin{bmatrix} 1 & 2 & 3 \\ 4 & 5 & 6 \\ 7 & 8 & 9 \end{bmatrix} \cdot \begin{bmatrix} 1 & -2 & 3 \\ -4 & 5 & -6 \\ 7 & -8 & 9 \end{bmatrix} \right) + \left(\begin{bmatrix} 1 & 2 & 3 \\ 4 & 5 & 6 \\ 7 & 8 & 9 \end{bmatrix} \cdot \begin{bmatrix} 0 & 1 & 2 \\ 0 & 2 & 3 \\ 0 & 4 & 5 \end{bmatrix} \right)$$

$$= \begin{bmatrix} 14 & -16 & 18 \\ 26 & -31 & 36 \\ 38 & -46 & 54 \end{bmatrix} + \begin{bmatrix} 0 & 17 & 23 \\ 0 & 38 & 53 \\ 0 & 59 & 83 \end{bmatrix} = \begin{bmatrix} 14 & 1 & 41 \\ 26 & 7 & 89 \\ 38 & 13 & 137 \end{bmatrix}$$

The result that $X(Y + Z) = XY + XZ$ suggests that there IS a distributive property for matrix multiplication over matrix addition.

Watch Out !

Showing that a property holds for a specific example is not a proof that the property is always true. But showing that a property DOES NOT hold for a specific example is enough to disprove the property. An example that shows a property is not always true is called a *counterexample*.

GOT TO KNOW !

Algebraic Properties as Applied to Matrices

In general, matrices are:

- associative
- NOT commutative
- distributive for multiplication over addition

Organizing to Find a Matrix Product

Example 5 on the previous page shows that the steps of matrix multiplication involve several multiplications and additions and can sometimes need careful organization. The next example shows one way to organize the expressions for the elements of matrix multiplication.

EXAMPLE 6

Find the dimensions of the product $\begin{bmatrix} 3 & 4 & 2 & 3 \\ 1 & 3 & 7 & 7 \end{bmatrix} \cdot \begin{bmatrix} 5 & 0 & 6 \\ -2 & 3 & 2 \\ -8 & 7 & -1 \\ 2 & 0 & 1 \end{bmatrix}$ **and use those dimensions**

to organize the steps for finding the product.

STEP 1 Find the dimensions of the product matrix.

The multiplication is (2-by-4) × (4-by-3), so the product will be a 2-by-3 matrix.

STEP 2 Plan an organization of the elements of the product matrix.

A 2-by-3 matrix has six elements, so use ①, ②, ③, ④, ⑤, and ⑥ to label the six elements of the product matrix.

$$\begin{bmatrix} 3 & 4 & 2 & 3 \\ 1 & 3 & 7 & 7 \end{bmatrix} \cdot \begin{bmatrix} 5 & 0 & 6 \\ -2 & 3 & 2 \\ -8 & 7 & -1 \\ 2 & 0 & 1 \end{bmatrix} = \begin{bmatrix} ① & ② & ③ \\ ④ & ⑤ & ⑥ \end{bmatrix}$$

STEP 3 Write an expression for each of the six elements in the product.

① : $(3)(5) + (4)(-2) + (2)(-8) + (3)(2) = 15 - 8 - 16 + 6 = -3$

② : $(3)(0) + (4)(3) + (2)(7) + (3)(0) = 0 + 12 + 14 + 0 = 26$

③ : $(3)(6) + (4)(2) + (2)(-1) + (3)(1) = 18 + 8 - 2 + 3 = 27$

④ : $(1)(5) + (3)(-2) + (7)(-8) + (7)(2) = 5 - 6 - 56 + 14 = -43$

⑤ : $(1)(0) + (3)(3) + (7)(7) + (7)(0) = 0 + 9 + 49 + 0 = 58$

⑥ : $(1)(6) + (3)(2) + (7)(-1) + (7)(1) = 6 + 6 - 7 + 7 = 12$

STEP 4 Fill in the values for ① through ⑥.

$$\begin{bmatrix} 3 & 4 & 2 & 3 \\ 1 & 3 & 7 & 7 \end{bmatrix} \cdot \begin{bmatrix} 5 & 0 & 6 \\ -2 & 3 & 2 \\ -8 & 7 & -1 \\ 2 & 0 & 1 \end{bmatrix} = \begin{bmatrix} -3 & 26 & 27 \\ -43 & 58 & 12 \end{bmatrix}$$

Try It This Way

There are many free web sites that will let you keyboard in the elements of two matrices and then automatically show you the product. Many calculators also have the capability to perform operations with matrices.

GOT TO KNOW!

Identify the Dimensions of a Product Before Multiplying

Example	Matrix Factors	Product
1	2-by-3 × 3-by-5	2-by-5
2	3-by-2 × 2-by-4	3-by-4

Matrix Multiplication and Identity Properties

An *identity matrix* is a square matrix with 1's on the main diagonal and 0's everywhere else. The following examples explore identity matrices and 3 by 3 square matrices.

EXAMPLE 7

Let *I* be the 3-by-3 identity matrix. If *M* is the matrix $\begin{bmatrix} a & b & c \\ d & e & f \\ g & h & i \end{bmatrix}$, show that $M \cdot I = I \cdot M = M$.

STEP 1   Find $M \cdot I$ and $I \cdot M$.

$$M \cdot I = \begin{bmatrix} a & b & c \\ d & e & f \\ g & h & i \end{bmatrix} \cdot \begin{bmatrix} 1 & 0 & 0 \\ 0 & 1 & 0 \\ 0 & 0 & 1 \end{bmatrix} = \begin{bmatrix} a+0+0 & 0+b+0 & 0+0+c \\ d+0+0 & 0+e+0 & 0+0+f \\ g+0+0 & 0+h+0 & 0+0+i \end{bmatrix} = \begin{bmatrix} a & b & c \\ d & e & f \\ g & h & i \end{bmatrix}$$

$$I \cdot M = \begin{bmatrix} 1 & 0 & 0 \\ 0 & 1 & 0 \\ 0 & 0 & 1 \end{bmatrix} \cdot \begin{bmatrix} a & b & c \\ d & e & f \\ g & h & i \end{bmatrix} = \begin{bmatrix} a+0+0 & 0+b+0 & 0+0+c \\ d+0+0 & 0+e+0 & 0+0+f \\ g+0+0 & 0+h+0 & 0+0+i \end{bmatrix} = \begin{bmatrix} a & b & c \\ d & e & f \\ g & h & i \end{bmatrix}$$

STEP 2   The results in Step 1 show that $M \cdot I = I \cdot M = M$. Because *M* is any 3-by-3 matrix, the product of any square matrix and the identity matrix is the original matrix. In fact, the example shows why *I* is called the *identify element for multiplication*.

EXAMPLE 8

Find the two products that use $\begin{bmatrix} 2 & 0 & 4 \\ 0 & -2 & 0 \\ 2 & 4 & 2 \end{bmatrix}$ and $\begin{bmatrix} -0.5 & 2 & 1 \\ 0 & -0.5 & 0 \\ 0.5 & -1 & -0.5 \end{bmatrix}$ as factors.

Describe your result.

STEP 1   Find the two products of the matrices.

$$\begin{bmatrix} 2 & 0 & 4 \\ 0 & -2 & 0 \\ 2 & 4 & 2 \end{bmatrix} \cdot \begin{bmatrix} -0.5 & 2 & 1 \\ 0 & -0.5 & 0 \\ 0.5 & -1 & -0.5 \end{bmatrix} = \begin{bmatrix} -1+0+2 & 4+0-4 & 2+0-2 \\ 0+0+0 & 0+1+0 & 0+0+0 \\ -1+0+1 & 4-2-2 & 2+0-1 \end{bmatrix} = \begin{bmatrix} 1 & 0 & 0 \\ 0 & 1 & 0 \\ 0 & 0 & 1 \end{bmatrix}$$

$$\begin{bmatrix} -0.5 & 2 & 1 \\ 0 & -0.5 & 0 \\ 0.5 & -1 & -0.5 \end{bmatrix} \cdot \begin{bmatrix} 2 & 0 & 4 \\ 0 & -2 & 0 \\ 2 & 4 & 2 \end{bmatrix} = \begin{bmatrix} -1+0+2 & 4+0-4 & 2+0-2 \\ 0+0+0 & 0+1+0 & 0+0+0 \\ -1+0+1 & 4-2-2 & 2+0-1 \end{bmatrix} = \begin{bmatrix} 1 & 0 & 0 \\ 0 & 1 & 0 \\ 0 & 0 & 1 \end{bmatrix}$$

Using either matrix as the right factor or the left factor, the product is the identity matrix.

STEP 2   Describe the results.

From arithmetic and algebra, we know that the product of a number and its multiplicative inverse is 1. For example, $5 \times \frac{1}{5} = 1$, and $a \times \frac{1}{a} = 1$.

The product of the two matrices in this example is the identity matrix for multiplication. So the two matrices are inverses of each other.

The Identity Matrix

Square Matrices and Identities

A **square matrix** has the same number of rows and columns. The **main diagonal** of a square matrix refers to the elements in the diagonal that go from the upper left corner to the lower right corner.

EXAMPLE 1

To see step-by-step videos of these problems, enter the page number into the SWadvantage.com Search Bar.

Explain the difference between an *identity element for addition* and *an identity element for multiplication*. For square matrices, describe the matrix identity element for addition and describe the matrix identity element for multiplication.

STEP 1 Identify identity elements for addition and multiplication.

When you perform an operation on a number or expression using an identity element, you do not change that number or expression. In arithmetic and algebra, the number 0 is the identity element for addition (because for all a, $a + 0 = a$), and 1 is the identity element for multiplication (because for all a, $a \cdot 1 = a$).

STEP 2 Describe the identity matrix for addition.

We can use the idea that "an identity does not change a value" to find an identity element for

matrix addition: If $\begin{bmatrix} a & b \\ c & d \end{bmatrix} + \begin{bmatrix} ? & ? \\ ? & ? \end{bmatrix} = \begin{bmatrix} a & b \\ c & d \end{bmatrix}$, then $\begin{bmatrix} ? & ? \\ ? & ? \end{bmatrix}$ must be $\begin{bmatrix} 0 & 0 \\ 0 & 0 \end{bmatrix}$.

For any square matrix, the identity matrix for addition is a matrix, with the same dimensions, with 0 as every element.

STEP 3 Describe the identity matrix for multiplication.

HELP?

A demonstration of multiplying *any* 3-by-3 matrix by the identity matrix for multiplication is shown in Example 8 in *Matrix Multiplication* on page 1791.

The pattern for matrix multiplication combines entire rows from the left factor and entire columns from the right factor. Below, notice how a matrix with 1's in the main diagonal and 0's elsewhere does not change the elements in the other factor in matrix multiplication.

$$\begin{bmatrix} 5 & 2 & -1 \\ -2 & 7 & 8 \\ 0 & 5 & -2 \end{bmatrix} \cdot \begin{bmatrix} 1 & 0 & 0 \\ 0 & 1 & 0 \\ 0 & 0 & 1 \end{bmatrix} = \begin{bmatrix} 5+0+0 & 0+2+0 & 0+0-1 \\ -2+0+0 & 0+7+0 & 0+0+8 \\ 0+0+0 & 0+5+0 & 0+0-2 \end{bmatrix} = \begin{bmatrix} 5 & 2 & -1 \\ -2 & 7 & 8 \\ 0 & 5 & -2 \end{bmatrix}$$

$$\begin{bmatrix} 1 & 0 & 0 \\ 0 & 1 & 0 \\ 0 & 0 & 1 \end{bmatrix} \cdot \begin{bmatrix} 5 & 2 & -1 \\ -2 & 7 & 8 \\ 0 & 5 & -2 \end{bmatrix} = \begin{bmatrix} 5+0+0 & 0+2+0 & 0+0-1 \\ -2+0+0 & 0+7+0 & 0+0+8 \\ 0+0+0 & 0+5+0 & 0+0-2 \end{bmatrix} = \begin{bmatrix} 5 & 2 & -1 \\ -2 & 7 & 8 \\ 0 & 5 & -2 \end{bmatrix}$$

A square matrix with 1's in the main diagonal and 0's everywhere else is called an *identity matrix for multiplication*. The letter *I* is usually used to refer to an identity matrix for multiplication.

GOT TO KNOW!

Matrix Multiplication and the Commutative Property

Factors	Product	Commutative?
Any two matrices, *A* and *B*, with the exception of *I*	New matrix *AB*	No
I and another matrix, *M*	*M*	Yes

Identities and Non-square Matrices

Matrix addition adds two matrices with the same dimensions, so for any matrix A, the identity matrix for addition has the same dimensions as A and has 0's as every element.

$$\begin{bmatrix} a & b & c & d & e \\ f & g & h & i & j \end{bmatrix} + \begin{bmatrix} 0 & 0 & 0 & 0 & 0 \\ 0 & 0 & 0 & 0 & 0 \end{bmatrix} = \begin{bmatrix} a & b & c & d & e \\ f & g & h & i & j \end{bmatrix}.$$

Non-square matrices also have identity elements for multiplication. However, when you multiply two matrices the number of rows of the left factor must equal the number of columns of the right factor.

Need More
HELP

To use the expression $(p$ by $q) \times (q$ by $r)$, notice that the "inside" letters, q and q, match. Those letters indicate the number of columns for the left factor and the number of rows for the right factor. The "outside" letters, p and r, represent the number of rows of the left factor and the number of columns of the right factor; they also represent the numbers of rows and columns for the product.

EXAMPLE 2

Use matrix $B = \begin{bmatrix} 5 & -2 & 6 \\ 0 & 1 & -3 \end{bmatrix}$. What must be the dimensions of matrix I if $B \cdot I = B$? What must be the dimensions of matrix J if $J \cdot B = B$? Find matrices I and J so $B \cdot I = B$ and $J \cdot B = B$.

STEP 1 Find the dimensions of matrix I if $B \cdot I = B$.

In matrix multiplication, p-by-q × q-by-r = p-by-r, so the number of columns for the left factor must match the number of rows for the right factor (the "inside" numbers), and the product has the same number of rows as the left factor and the same number of columns as the right factor (the "outside" numbers).

The given matrix B is a 2 by 3 matrix, so:

$$\begin{array}{ccccc} B & \cdot & I & = & B \\ \text{2-by-3} & \times & \text{?-by-?} & = & \text{2-by-3} \end{array}$$

Therefore matrix I must be a 3-by-3 matrix.

STEP 2 The 3-by-3 identity matrix for multiplication is $\begin{bmatrix} 1 & 0 & 0 \\ 0 & 1 & 0 \\ 0 & 0 & 1 \end{bmatrix}$, so use that matrix for I.

$$B \cdot I = \begin{bmatrix} 5 & -2 & 6 \\ 0 & 1 & -3 \end{bmatrix} \cdot \begin{bmatrix} 1 & 0 & 0 \\ 0 & 1 & 0 \\ 0 & 0 & 1 \end{bmatrix} = \begin{bmatrix} 5+0+0 & 0-2+0 & 0+0+6 \\ 0+0+0 & 0+1+0 & 0+0-3 \end{bmatrix} = \begin{bmatrix} 5 & -2 & 6 \\ 0 & 1 & -3 \end{bmatrix} = B$$

STEP 3 Find J.

If matrix B appears as the factor on the right, an identity matrix for multiplication is different.

$$\begin{array}{ccccc} J & \cdot & B & = & B \\ \text{?-by-?} & \times & \text{2-by-3} & = & \text{2-by-3} \end{array}$$

Matrix J has to be a 2-by-2 matrix. Use $\begin{bmatrix} 1 & 0 \\ 0 & 1 \end{bmatrix}$ for J.

$$J \cdot B = \begin{bmatrix} 1 & 0 \\ 0 & 1 \end{bmatrix} \cdot \begin{bmatrix} 5 & -2 & 6 \\ 0 & 1 & -3 \end{bmatrix} = \begin{bmatrix} 5+0 & -2+0 & 6+0 \\ 0+0 & 0+1 & 0-3 \end{bmatrix} = \begin{bmatrix} 5 & -2 & 6 \\ 0 & 1 & -3 \end{bmatrix} = B$$

GOT TO KNOW!

Identity Matrices and Square Matrices

Identity matrices for multiplication are ALWAYS square matrices.

However, matrix addition is commutative, so the "right additive identity" is the same as the "left additive identity." Identity matrices for addition do not have to be square matrices.

For identity matrices for multiplication, Examples 1 and 2 illustrate an important difference:

- For square matrices, there is one I for each size matrix; you can multiply that matrix on the right or on the left by I, and the result will be the original matrix.
- For non-square matrices, use a different identity matrix, I_L or I_R, for multiplying on the right or for multiplying on the left. Identity matrices I_L and I_R are both square matrices.

Determinants

Determinants and Square Matrices

Associated with every square matrix is a unique number called the *determinant* of that matrix. The examples in this section show how to find a determinant.

For a square matrix M, vertical lines (similar to absolute value symbols) or the abbreviation "det (M)" can be used to indicate the determinant. The value of a **determinant** for a 2-by-2 matrix is the product of elements in the main diagonal minus the product of the elements in the other diagonal.

SEARCH

To see step-by-step videos of these problems, enter the page number into the SWadvantage.com Search Bar.

EXAMPLE 1

Find the value of the determinant for each matrix.

a. **Find det (A) if $A = \begin{bmatrix} 5 & -2 \\ 3 & -1 \end{bmatrix}$.**

Use the pattern $\begin{vmatrix} a & b \\ c & d \end{vmatrix} = ad - bc$. Then det $(A) = \begin{vmatrix} 5 & -2 \\ 3 & -1 \end{vmatrix} = (5)(-1) - (-2)(3) = -5 - (-6) = 1$.

b. **Find det (B) if $B = \begin{bmatrix} 4 & 12 \\ -2 & -6 \end{bmatrix}$.**

det $(B) = \begin{vmatrix} 4 & 12 \\ -2 & -6 \end{vmatrix} = (4)(-6) - (12)(-2) = -24 - (-24) = -24 + 24 = 0$

c. **Find det (C) if $C = \begin{bmatrix} a & 1 \\ b & 0 \end{bmatrix}$.**

det $(C) = \begin{vmatrix} a & 1 \\ b & 0 \end{vmatrix} = (a)(0) - (1)(b) = 0 - b = -b$

Watch Out !

To find a determinant, use the pattern "main diagonal minus other diagonal." Don't be confused by the elements that appear in those positions.

GOT TO KNOW !

Finding a 2-by-2 Determinant

If $M = \begin{bmatrix} a & b \\ c & d \end{bmatrix}$, then

det $(M) = \begin{vmatrix} a & b \\ c & d \end{vmatrix}$

$= ad - bc$.

Switching Rows or Columns in a Matrix

$\begin{vmatrix} a & b \\ c & d \end{vmatrix}$

$= (-1) \begin{vmatrix} c & d \\ a & b \end{vmatrix}$

$= (-1) \begin{vmatrix} b & a \\ d & c \end{vmatrix}$

EXAMPLE 2

Show that if you switch two rows or two columns of a 2-by-2 matrix, the determinant of the new matrix is -1 times the determinant of the original matrix.

STEP 1 Start with the general 2-by-2 matrix $M = \begin{bmatrix} a & b \\ c & d \end{bmatrix}$. Then det $(M) = \begin{vmatrix} a & b \\ c & d \end{vmatrix} = ad - bc$.

STEP 2 Let matrix R be the result of switching the rows and let matrix C be the result of switching the columns. Find det (R) and det (C).

det $(R) = \begin{vmatrix} c & d \\ a & b \end{vmatrix} = cb - da = -1 \cdot (ad - bc)$ det $(C) = \begin{vmatrix} b & a \\ d & c \end{vmatrix} = bc - ad = -1 \cdot (ad - bc)$

Steps 1 and 2 show that det $(R) = -1 \cdot$ det (M) and det $(C) = -1 \cdot$ det (M); that is, if you switch the rows or switch the columns of a 2-by-2 matrix, you multiply the determinant of the matrix by negative one.

The Determinant of a 3-by-3 Matrix

To find a determinant for a 3-by-3 matrix, begin with the general matrix $M = \begin{bmatrix} a & b & c \\ d & e & f \\ g & h & i \end{bmatrix}$.

Rewrite the three columns, and repeat the first two columns. Then, identify two kinds of diagonals:

Upper Left to Lower Right Diagonals   Upper Right to Lower Left Diagonals

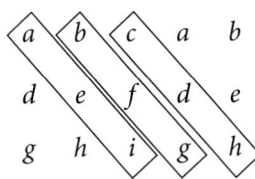   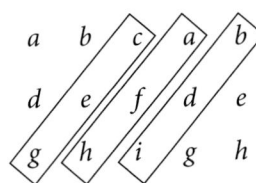

Look at the three "upper left to lower right" diagonals. Write the three products and add them:
$aei + bfg + cdh$

Look at the three "upper right to lower left" diagonals. Write the three products and add them:
$ceg + afh + bdi$

The determinant of a 3-by-3 matrix is the first sum minus the second sum:

$$\det (M) = aei + bfg + cdh - (ceg + afh + bdi)$$

The name *determinant* refers to systems of equations. You can write the coefficients of the equations as a matrix, and the value of the determinant *determines* whether or not that system has a solution. Matrices and systems are covered in *Cramer's Rule* on page 1814.

Need More HELP?

EXAMPLE 3

Find the determinant of P **if** $P = \begin{bmatrix} 2 & -3 & 5 \\ 1 & 6 & 0 \\ -3 & -1 & 4 \end{bmatrix}$.

STEP 1 Write the columns of the matrix and repeat the first two columns. Then identify the upper left to lower right diagonals and the upper right to lower left diagonals.

Upper Left to Lower Right Diagonals   Upper Right to Lower Left Diagonals

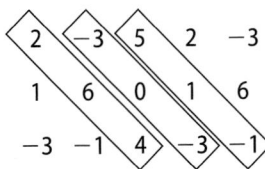

STEP 2 Find the sum of the three products formed from the upper left to lower right diagonals. Then subtract the sum of the three products formed by working from upper right to lower left.

$\det (P) = (2)(6)(4) + (-3)(0)(-3) + (5)(1)(-1) - [(5)(6)(-3) + (2)(0)(-1) + (-3)(1)(4)]$

$= 48 + 0 - 5 - [-90 + 0 - 12]$

$= 43 - (-102)$

$= 145$

Watch Out!

When you calculate a 3-by-3 determinant by hand, be especially careful when you copy numbers, when you find products, and when you write "+" and "−" signs.

GOT TO KNOW!

Finding a 3-by-3 Determinant

det (M) = (sum of the products on the ↘ diagonals) − (sum of the products on the ↗ diagonals)

Some Properties of Determinants

For two square matrices with the same dimensions:

- the product of the determinants is equal to the determinant of the product of the matrices.

Another property involves *transposing* a matrix:

- If M is a square matrix, then the *transpose* of M, denoted M^T, is formed by keeping the elements on the main diagonal and reflecting all the other elements across that diagonal:

If $M = \begin{bmatrix} a & b \\ c & d \end{bmatrix}$ and $N = \begin{bmatrix} a & b & c \\ d & e & f \\ g & h & i \end{bmatrix}$, then $M^T = \begin{bmatrix} a & c \\ b & d \end{bmatrix}$ and $N^T = \begin{bmatrix} a & d & g \\ b & e & h \\ c & f & i \end{bmatrix}$.

EXAMPLE 4

SEARCH

To see step-by-step videos of these problems, enter the page number into the SWadvantage.com Search Bar.

Use matrices $Q = \begin{bmatrix} 2 & 3 \\ -1 & 5 \end{bmatrix}$, $R = \begin{bmatrix} -7 & 0 \\ 4 & 2 \end{bmatrix}$, and $S = \begin{bmatrix} 1 & 3 & 2 \\ 5 & -1 & 6 \\ 4 & 2 & 7 \end{bmatrix}$.

a. Verify that det (Q) · det (R) = det $(Q \cdot R)$.

$\det (Q) = \begin{vmatrix} 2 & 3 \\ -1 & 5 \end{vmatrix} = 10 - (-3) = 13$ and $\det (R) = \begin{vmatrix} -7 & 0 \\ 4 & 2 \end{vmatrix} = -14 - 0 = -14$

$\det (Q) \cdot \det (R) = (13)(-14) = -182$

$Q \cdot R = \begin{bmatrix} 2 & 3 \\ -1 & 5 \end{bmatrix} \cdot \begin{bmatrix} -7 & 0 \\ 4 & 2 \end{bmatrix} = \begin{bmatrix} -14+12 & 0+6 \\ 7+20 & 0+10 \end{bmatrix} = \begin{bmatrix} -2 & 6 \\ 27 & 10 \end{bmatrix}$

$\det (Q \cdot R) = \begin{vmatrix} -2 & 6 \\ 27 & 10 \end{vmatrix} = -20 - 162 = -182$ Thus, det (Q) · det (R) = det $(Q \cdot R)$.

b. Verify that $Q \cdot R \neq R \cdot Q$, but that det $(Q \cdot R)$ = det $(R \cdot Q)$.

$Q \cdot R = \begin{bmatrix} -2 & 6 \\ 27 & 10 \end{bmatrix}$ and det $(Q \cdot R) = -182$ were found in part (a).

$R \cdot Q = \begin{bmatrix} -7 & 0 \\ 4 & 2 \end{bmatrix} \cdot \begin{bmatrix} 2 & 3 \\ -1 & 5 \end{bmatrix} = \begin{bmatrix} -14+0 & -21+0 \\ 8-2 & 12+10 \end{bmatrix} = \begin{bmatrix} -14 & -21 \\ 6 & 22 \end{bmatrix}$

$\det (R \cdot Q) = \begin{vmatrix} -14 & -21 \\ 6 & 22 \end{vmatrix} = (-14)(22) - (-21)(6) = -308 - (-126) = -182$

Finding these matrices and determinants shows that $Q \cdot R \neq R \cdot Q$ and det $(Q \cdot R)$ = det $(R \cdot Q)$.

GOT TO KNOW!

Properties of Determinants

det (Q) · det (R)
$= $ det $(Q \cdot R)$
det $(Q \cdot R)$
$= $ det $(R \cdot Q)$
det (S) = det (S^T)

c. Verify that det (S) = det (S^T).

Use $\begin{vmatrix} 1 & 3 & 2 & 1 & 3 \\ 5 & -1 & 6 & 5 & -1 \\ 4 & 2 & 7 & 4 & 2 \end{vmatrix}$ for det (S). $S^T = \begin{bmatrix} 1 & 5 & 4 \\ 3 & -1 & 2 \\ 2 & 6 & 7 \end{bmatrix}$, so use $\begin{vmatrix} 1 & 5 & 4 & 1 & 5 \\ 3 & -1 & 2 & 3 & -1 \\ 2 & 6 & 7 & 2 & 6 \end{vmatrix}$ for det (S^T).

$\det (S) = -7 + 72 + 20 - (-8 + 12 + 105) = 85 - (109) = -24$

$\det (S^T) = -7 + 20 + 72 - (-8 + 12 + 105) = 85 - (109) = -24$

So, det (S) = det (S^T).

A General Way to Find a Determinant

If you identify one element in a determinant and then form a determinant by deleting the rest of the row and column for that element, the new, smaller determinant is called a **minor** for the original determinant.

To find the determinant for a 4-by-4 matrix, identify one row (or column) in the determinant. Then, for each element in that row, multiply that element by its minor. Alternate between addition and subtraction symbols after each product. In symbols:

$$\text{If } M = \begin{bmatrix} a & b & c & d \\ e & f & g & h \\ i & j & k & l \\ m & n & o & p \end{bmatrix}, \text{ then det } (M) = \begin{vmatrix} a & b & c & d \\ e & f & g & h \\ i & j & k & l \\ m & n & o & p \end{vmatrix}$$

$$= a \cdot \begin{vmatrix} f & g & h \\ j & k & l \\ n & o & p \end{vmatrix} - b \cdot \begin{vmatrix} e & g & h \\ i & k & l \\ m & o & p \end{vmatrix} + c \cdot \begin{vmatrix} e & f & h \\ i & j & l \\ m & n & p \end{vmatrix} - d \cdot \begin{vmatrix} e & f & g \\ i & j & k \\ m & n & o \end{vmatrix}$$

Then you can use a row in each 3-by-3 determinant to write the 2-by-2 minors for that row. One more *iteration*, or repetition, of this process replaces the 2-by-2 determinants with 1-by-1 determinants. The next Example illustrates how to use minors to find a determinant.

Watch Out !
Be sure to alternate between addition and subtraction symbols when you use minors.

EXAMPLE 5

Use minors to find the determinant of a 2-by-2 matrix and a 3-by-3 matrix. Explain whether or not those determinants agree with the other expressions for determinants.

STEP 1 Using minors, find the determinant of a 2-by-2 matrix.

Use $P = \begin{bmatrix} a & b \\ c & d \end{bmatrix}$, the general 2-by-2 matrix.

Using minors for the top row of P, det $(P) = \begin{vmatrix} a & b \\ c & d \end{vmatrix} = a \cdot |d| - b \cdot |c|$. Since $|d|$ and $|c|$ are 1-by-1 determinants, their values are d and c, respectively.

So det $(P) = a \cdot d - b \cdot c$, which is the same as the earlier expression for the determinant of a 2-by-2 matrix.

STEP 2 Using minors, find the determinant of a 3-by-3 matrix.

Use $Q = \begin{bmatrix} a & b & c \\ d & e & f \\ g & h & i \end{bmatrix}$, the general 3-by-3 matrix. Using minors for the top row of det (Q),

$$\det (Q) = a \cdot \begin{vmatrix} e & f \\ h & i \end{vmatrix} - b \cdot \begin{vmatrix} d & f \\ g & i \end{vmatrix} + c \cdot \begin{vmatrix} d & e \\ g & h \end{vmatrix}$$

$$= a \cdot [e \cdot |i| - f \cdot |h|] - b \cdot [d \cdot |i| - f \cdot |g|] + c \cdot [d \cdot |h| - e \cdot |g|]$$

$$= aei - afh - bdi + bfg + cdh - ceg$$

$$= aei + bfg + cdh - (ceg + afh + bdi)$$

That expression agrees with the earlier expression for the determinant of a 3-by-3 matrix.

Watch Out !
Symbols such as $|d|$ and $|c|$ mean determinants in this context, not absolute value. Unlike absolute value, a determinant can be negative.

GOT TO KNOW !
1-by-1 Determinants
The value of a 1-by-1 determinant is the value of its single element.

The Inverse of a Matrix

Matrix Multiplication and the Identity Matrix

Need More HELP ?

The determinant for a 2-by-2 matrix

$$\begin{bmatrix} a & b \\ c & d \end{bmatrix}$$ is $ad - bc$.

The determinant can be indicated by

$$\begin{vmatrix} a & b \\ c & d \end{vmatrix}, |A|,$$ or $\det(A)$.

For more on determinants, go to *Determinants* on page 1794.

When the product of two square matrices is the identity matrix, then each matrix is the **inverse** of the other. Here is a pair of inverse matrices:

$$\begin{bmatrix} -5 & -2 \\ 3 & 1 \end{bmatrix} \cdot \begin{bmatrix} 1 & 2 \\ -3 & -5 \end{bmatrix} = \begin{bmatrix} -5+6 & -10+10 \\ 3-3 & 6-5 \end{bmatrix} = \begin{bmatrix} 1 & 0 \\ 0 & 1 \end{bmatrix}$$

$$\begin{bmatrix} 1 & 2 \\ -3 & -5 \end{bmatrix} \cdot \begin{bmatrix} -5 & -2 \\ 3 & 1 \end{bmatrix} = \begin{bmatrix} -5+6 & -2+2 \\ 15-15 & 6-5 \end{bmatrix} = \begin{bmatrix} 1 & 0 \\ 0 & 1 \end{bmatrix}$$

So, $\begin{bmatrix} -5 & -2 \\ 3 & 1 \end{bmatrix}$ and $\begin{bmatrix} 1 & 2 \\ -3 & -5 \end{bmatrix}$ are inverses of each other.

The 2-by-2 identity matrix is $\begin{bmatrix} 1 & 0 \\ 0 & 1 \end{bmatrix}$. Matrix multiplication is NOT commutative. To show that two matrices A and B are inverses, you must show that $A \cdot B = I$ and that $B \cdot A = I$.

To find the inverse for a matrix, first find the determinant of that matrix. Then use the determinant to find the inverse.

SEARCH

To see step-by-step videos of these problems, enter the page number into the SWadvantage.com Search Bar.

EXAMPLE 1

Find the inverse of each matrix.

$$C = \begin{bmatrix} 7 & 5 \\ 3 & 2 \end{bmatrix}$$

STEP 1 Find $\det(C)$. $\det(C) = 7 \cdot 2 - 5 \cdot 3 = 14 - 15 = -1.$

STEP 2 Use the pattern $C^{-1} = \dfrac{1}{\det(C)} \cdot \begin{bmatrix} d & -b \\ -c & a \end{bmatrix}$. $C^{-1} = \dfrac{1}{-1} \cdot \begin{bmatrix} 2 & -5 \\ -3 & 7 \end{bmatrix} = \begin{bmatrix} -2 & 5 \\ 3 & -7 \end{bmatrix}$

STEP 3 Test your result. $\begin{bmatrix} 7 & 5 \\ 3 & 2 \end{bmatrix} \cdot \begin{bmatrix} -2 & 5 \\ 3 & -7 \end{bmatrix} = \begin{bmatrix} -14+15 & 35-35 \\ -6+6 & 15-14 \end{bmatrix} = \begin{bmatrix} 1 & 0 \\ 0 & 1 \end{bmatrix}$

$$\begin{bmatrix} -2 & 5 \\ 3 & -7 \end{bmatrix} \cdot \begin{bmatrix} 7 & 5 \\ 3 & 2 \end{bmatrix} = \begin{bmatrix} -14+15 & -10+10 \\ 21-21 & 15-14 \end{bmatrix} = \begin{bmatrix} 1 & 0 \\ 0 & 1 \end{bmatrix}$$

Both products are the identity matrix, so the two matrices are inverses of each other.

GOT TO KNOW!

Finding the Inverse of a Matrix

The **inverse** of a matrix A is represented by the symbol A^{-1} (read "A-inverse").

For a 2-by-2 matrix $A = \begin{bmatrix} a & b \\ c & d \end{bmatrix}$, find the inverse using these steps.

1. Find the determinant of the matrix. $\det(A) = ad - bc$

2. Use the formula for the inverse. $A^{-1} = \dfrac{1}{\det(A)} \cdot \begin{bmatrix} d & -b \\ -c & a \end{bmatrix}$

Inverses and Products

One property of inverses relates to the fact that matrix multiplication is NOT commutative. In symbols, the property is $(A \cdot B)^{-1} = B^{-1} \cdot A^{-1}$. In other words, the property states that the inverse of a product is the product of the inverses, but with the order of the matrices reversed on the two sides of the equation.

Need More
HELP ?
You can review matrix multiplication for 2-by-2 matrices in *Multiplying 2-by-2 Matrices* on page 1782.

EXAMPLE 2

Using $A = \begin{bmatrix} 2 & 1 \\ -3 & 4 \end{bmatrix}$ and $B = \begin{bmatrix} 1 & 0 \\ 4 & -2 \end{bmatrix}$, verify that $(A \cdot B)^{-1} = B^{-1} \cdot A^{-1}$.

STEP 1 Find $A \cdot B$. $A \cdot B = \begin{bmatrix} 2 & 1 \\ -3 & 4 \end{bmatrix} \cdot \begin{bmatrix} 1 & 0 \\ 4 & -2 \end{bmatrix} = \begin{bmatrix} 2+4 & 0-2 \\ -3+16 & 0-8 \end{bmatrix} = \begin{bmatrix} 6 & -2 \\ 13 & -8 \end{bmatrix}$

STEP 2 Find $(A \cdot B)^{-1}$.

$$(A \cdot B)^{-1} = \frac{1}{\det(A \cdot B)} \cdot \begin{bmatrix} d & -b \\ -c & a \end{bmatrix} = \frac{1}{-48-(-26)} \cdot \begin{bmatrix} -8 & 2 \\ -13 & 6 \end{bmatrix} = \frac{1}{-22} \cdot \begin{bmatrix} -8 & 2 \\ -13 & 6 \end{bmatrix} = \begin{bmatrix} \frac{4}{11} & -\frac{1}{11} \\ \frac{13}{22} & -\frac{3}{11} \end{bmatrix}$$

STEP 3 Find B^{-1} and A^{-1}.

$$B^{-1} = \frac{1}{\det(B)} \cdot \begin{bmatrix} d & -b \\ -c & a \end{bmatrix} = \frac{1}{-2-0} \cdot \begin{bmatrix} -2 & 0 \\ -4 & 1 \end{bmatrix} = -\frac{1}{2} \cdot \begin{bmatrix} -2 & 0 \\ -4 & 1 \end{bmatrix} = \begin{bmatrix} 1 & 0 \\ 2 & -\frac{1}{2} \end{bmatrix}$$

$$A^{-1} = \frac{1}{\det(A)} \cdot \begin{bmatrix} d & -b \\ -c & a \end{bmatrix} = \frac{1}{8-(-3)} \cdot \begin{bmatrix} 4 & -1 \\ 3 & 2 \end{bmatrix} = \frac{1}{11} \cdot \begin{bmatrix} 4 & -1 \\ 3 & 2 \end{bmatrix} = \begin{bmatrix} \frac{4}{11} & -\frac{1}{11} \\ \frac{3}{11} & \frac{2}{11} \end{bmatrix}$$

STEP 4 Find $B^{-1} \cdot A^{-1}$.

$$B^{-1} \cdot A^{-1} = \begin{bmatrix} 1 & 0 \\ 2 & -\frac{1}{2} \end{bmatrix} \cdot \begin{bmatrix} \frac{4}{11} & -\frac{1}{11} \\ \frac{3}{11} & \frac{2}{11} \end{bmatrix} = \begin{bmatrix} \frac{4}{11}+0 & -\frac{1}{11}+0 \\ \frac{8}{11}-\frac{3}{22} & -\frac{2}{11}-\frac{1}{11} \end{bmatrix} = \begin{bmatrix} \frac{4}{11} & -\frac{1}{11} \\ \frac{13}{22} & -\frac{3}{11} \end{bmatrix}$$

$(A \cdot B)^{-1} = B^{-1} \cdot A^{-1}$, so the results verify the following property: the inverse of a product of two matrices is the product of the inverses of those two matrices, if the order is switched.

EXAMPLE 3

Show that for any square matrix M, $(M^2)^{-1} = (M^{-1})^2$. In words, show that for a square matrix, the inverse of the square of the matrix is equal to the square of the inverse of that matrix.

STEP 1 Write the property used in Example 3, substituting M for matrix A and also for matrix B.

$(A \cdot B)^{-1} = B^{-1} \cdot A^{-1}$ becomes $(M \cdot M)^{-1} = M^{-1} \cdot M^{-1}$.

STEP 2 Use the exponent 2 to indicate that an expression is multiplied by itself.

$(M \cdot M)^{-1} = M^{-1} \cdot M^{-1}$ becomes $(M^2)^{-1} = (M^{-1})^2$.

Watch Out !
Example 4 uses "square" to mean two different things: a matrix with the same number of rows and columns, and an expression multiplied by itself.

Inverses, Transposed Matrices, and Scalar Multiplication

Two other properties of inverses involve transposed matrices and scalar multiplication. See the *Got To Know!* box for how these matrices relate to each other.

To form the transpose of a square matrix, keep the elements on the main diagonal. For all the other elements, reflect them over the main diagonal. (The *main diagonal* goes from the upper left corner to the lower right corner.)

EXAMPLE 4

Using $A = \begin{bmatrix} 2 & 1 \\ -3 & 4 \end{bmatrix}$, show that $(A^T)^{-1} = (A^{-1})^T$.

STEP 1 To find A^T, rewrite the main diagonal and reflect the other elements over the main diagonal.

$$A = \begin{bmatrix} 2 & 1 \\ -3 & 4 \end{bmatrix} \text{ so } A^T = \begin{bmatrix} 2 & -3 \\ 1 & 4 \end{bmatrix}.$$

STEP 2 Find the inverse of A^T.

$$(A^T)^{-1} = \frac{1}{\det(A^T)} \cdot \begin{bmatrix} d & -b \\ -c & a \end{bmatrix} = \frac{1}{8-(-3)} \cdot \begin{bmatrix} 4 & 3 \\ -1 & 2 \end{bmatrix} = \frac{1}{11} \cdot \begin{bmatrix} 4 & 3 \\ -1 & 2 \end{bmatrix} = \begin{bmatrix} \frac{4}{11} & \frac{3}{11} \\ -\frac{1}{11} & \frac{2}{11} \end{bmatrix}$$

STEP 3 Find $= (A^{-1})^T$.   From Example 3, $A^{-1} = \begin{bmatrix} \frac{4}{11} & -\frac{1}{11} \\ \frac{3}{11} & \frac{2}{11} \end{bmatrix}$ so $(A^{-1})^T = \begin{bmatrix} \frac{4}{11} & \frac{3}{11} \\ -\frac{1}{11} & \frac{2}{11} \end{bmatrix}$.

It is verified that $(A^T)^{-1} = (A^{-1})^T$.

EXAMPLE 5

Using $k = 8$ and $M = \begin{bmatrix} 3 & -4 \\ 2 & -3 \end{bmatrix}$, show that $(k \cdot M)^{-1} = k^{-1} \cdot M^{-1}$.

STEP 1 Find $8 \cdot M$ and then find $(8 \cdot M)^{-1}$. $8 \cdot M = 8 \cdot \begin{bmatrix} 3 & -4 \\ 2 & -3 \end{bmatrix} = \begin{bmatrix} 24 & -32 \\ 16 & -24 \end{bmatrix}$

$$(8 \cdot M)^{-1} = \frac{1}{\det(8 \cdot M)} \cdot \begin{bmatrix} d & -b \\ -c & a \end{bmatrix} = \frac{1}{-576+512} \begin{bmatrix} -24 & 32 \\ -16 & 24 \end{bmatrix} = -\frac{1}{64} \cdot \begin{bmatrix} -24 & 32 \\ -16 & 24 \end{bmatrix} = \begin{bmatrix} \frac{3}{8} & -\frac{1}{2} \\ \frac{1}{4} & -\frac{3}{8} \end{bmatrix}$$

STEP 2 Find the inverse of 8, the inverse of M, and multiply those two results.

$$8^{-1} = \frac{1}{8}; M^{-1} = \frac{1}{\det(M)} \cdot \begin{bmatrix} d & -b \\ -c & a \end{bmatrix} = \frac{1}{-9-(-8)} \cdot \begin{bmatrix} -3 & 4 \\ -2 & 3 \end{bmatrix} = \frac{1}{-1} \cdot \begin{bmatrix} -3 & 4 \\ -2 & 3 \end{bmatrix} = \begin{bmatrix} 3 & -4 \\ 2 & -3 \end{bmatrix}$$

So $8^{-1} \cdot M^{-1} = \frac{1}{8} \cdot \begin{bmatrix} 3 & -4 \\ 2 & -3 \end{bmatrix} = \begin{bmatrix} \frac{3}{8} & -\frac{1}{2} \\ \frac{1}{4} & -\frac{3}{8} \end{bmatrix}$, and the property is verified.

The Inverse of a 3-by-3 Matrix

Finding the inverse of a 3-by-3 matrix (or a higher square matrix) involves many steps and many calculations. Expressions for an inverse involve determinants, minors, transposed matrices, and many, many calculations, so finding the inverse for a 3-by-3 matrix is almost always done by a graphing calculator or computer program. The next two examples refer to, but do not find, inverses of 3-by-3 matrices.

EXAMPLE 6

Show that $N = \begin{bmatrix} 1 & 5 & -2 \\ 4 & 0 & 1 \\ -3 & -15 & 6 \end{bmatrix}$ **does not have an inverse.** *Hint:* **Refer to Example 1(b).**

The first step in finding the inverse is to find det(N). Use $\begin{bmatrix} 1 & 5 & -2 & 1 & 5 \\ 4 & 0 & 1 & 4 & 0 \\ -3 & -15 & 6 & -3 & -15 \end{bmatrix}$ to find det(N).

det(N) = (1)(0)(6) + (5)(1)(−3) + (−2)(4)(−15) − [(−2)(0)(−3) + (1)(1)(−15) + (5)(4)(6)]

$\qquad$ = 0 − 15 + 120 − [0 − 15 + 120]

$\qquad$ = 105 − 105 = 0

The determinant is 0 so matrix N does not have an inverse.

EXAMPLE 7

If $A = \begin{bmatrix} 1 & 2 & 0 \\ -1 & 1 & 1 \\ 0 & 2 & 1 \end{bmatrix}$ **and** $B = \begin{bmatrix} -1 & -2 & 1 \\ 1 & 1 & -1 \\ -2 & -2 & 3 \end{bmatrix}$, **show that** $A = B^{-1}$.

STEP 1 Two matrices are inverses if their product is the identity element. First find the product $A \cdot B$.

$$A \cdot B = \begin{bmatrix} 1 & 2 & 0 \\ -1 & 1 & 1 \\ 0 & 2 & 1 \end{bmatrix} \cdot \begin{bmatrix} -1 & -2 & 2 \\ 1 & 1 & -1 \\ -2 & -2 & 3 \end{bmatrix} = \begin{bmatrix} -1+2+0 & -2+2+0 & 2-2+0 \\ 1+1-2 & 2+1-2 & -2-1+3 \\ 0+2-2 & 0+2-2 & 0-2+3 \end{bmatrix} = \begin{bmatrix} 1 & 0 & 0 \\ 0 & 1 & 0 \\ 0 & 0 & 1 \end{bmatrix}$$

STEP 2 Next find the product $B \cdot A$.

$$B \cdot A = \begin{bmatrix} -1 & -2 & 2 \\ 1 & 1 & -1 \\ -2 & -2 & 3 \end{bmatrix} \cdot \begin{bmatrix} 1 & 2 & 0 \\ -1 & 1 & 1 \\ 0 & 2 & 1 \end{bmatrix} = \begin{bmatrix} -1+2+0 & -2-2+4 & 0-2+2 \\ 1-1+0 & 2+1-2 & 0+1-1 \\ -2+2+0 & -4-2+6 & 0-2+3 \end{bmatrix} = \begin{bmatrix} 1 & 0 & 0 \\ 0 & 1 & 0 \\ 0 & 0 & 1 \end{bmatrix}$$

Because $A \cdot B = I$ and $B \cdot A = I$, A is the inverse matrix for B. That result, stated in symbols, is $A = B^{-1}$.

Need More HELP

The identity element for 3-by-3 matrices is

$$\begin{bmatrix} 1 & 0 & 0 \\ 0 & 1 & 0 \\ 0 & 0 & 1 \end{bmatrix}.$$

GOT TO KNOW!

Inverses of Transposed Matrices and Scalar Multiples

- The inverse of a transposed matrix is the transpose of the inverse of the original matrix. $(M^T)^{-1} = (M^{-1})^T$
- The inverse of a scalar multiple is the inverse of the scalar times the inverse of the matrix. $(k \cdot M)^{-1} = k^{-1} \cdot M^{-1}$

Solving Matrix Equations

Solve an Equation, Write a Matrix

For some matrix equations, you add or subtract matrices and use scalar multiplication. The key idea is that if two matrices are equal, then corresponding elements are equal.

Need More HELP ?

To review matrix addition, go to *Adding or Subtracting Matrices* on page 1774. To review scalar multiplication, see *Scalar Multiplication* on page 1778.

EXAMPLE 1

Find matrix P if $P + \begin{bmatrix} -1 & 3 \\ -2 & -5 \end{bmatrix} = \begin{bmatrix} 4 & 6 \\ -7 & 5 \end{bmatrix}$.

Add the same matrix to each side of the equation so one side becomes P plus the zero matrix.

$$P + \begin{bmatrix} -1 & 3 \\ -2 & -5 \end{bmatrix} + \begin{bmatrix} 1 & -3 \\ 2 & 5 \end{bmatrix} = \begin{bmatrix} 4 & 6 \\ -7 & 5 \end{bmatrix} + \begin{bmatrix} 1 & -3 \\ 2 & 5 \end{bmatrix}$$

$$P + \begin{bmatrix} 0 & 0 \\ 0 & 0 \end{bmatrix} = \begin{bmatrix} 5 & 3 \\ -5 & 10 \end{bmatrix}$$

P must be $\begin{bmatrix} 5 & 3 \\ -5 & 10 \end{bmatrix}$.

EXAMPLE 2

Find matrix Q if $\begin{bmatrix} 1 & -2 \\ 4 & 5 \end{bmatrix} - 3Q = \begin{bmatrix} 4 & 10 \\ 1 & -1 \end{bmatrix}$.

STEP 1 Subtract $\begin{bmatrix} 1 & -2 \\ 4 & 5 \end{bmatrix}$ from each side.

$$\begin{bmatrix} 1 & -2 \\ 4 & 5 \end{bmatrix} - \begin{bmatrix} 1 & -2 \\ 4 & 5 \end{bmatrix} - 3Q = \begin{bmatrix} 4 & 10 \\ 1 & -1 \end{bmatrix} - \begin{bmatrix} 1 & -2 \\ 4 & 5 \end{bmatrix}$$

$$\begin{bmatrix} 0 & 0 \\ 0 & 0 \end{bmatrix} - 3Q = \begin{bmatrix} 3 & 12 \\ -3 & -6 \end{bmatrix}$$

STEP 2 Multiply both sides by $-\frac{1}{3}$.

$$\left(-\frac{1}{3}\right)(-3Q) = -\frac{1}{3} \cdot \begin{bmatrix} 3 & 12 \\ -3 & -6 \end{bmatrix} = \begin{bmatrix} -1 & -4 \\ 1 & 2 \end{bmatrix}$$

Q must be $\begin{bmatrix} -1 & -4 \\ 1 & 2 \end{bmatrix}$.

Need More HELP ?

Remember—scalar multiplication of the zero matrix is still the zero matrix. Thus, the zero matrix can be ignored in Step 2.

GOT TO KNOW!

The Zero Matrix

A "zero matrix" is any matrix with a zero as every element.

$$\begin{bmatrix} a & b \\ c & d \end{bmatrix} + \begin{bmatrix} -a & -b \\ -c & -d \end{bmatrix} = \begin{bmatrix} 0 & 0 \\ 0 & 0 \end{bmatrix}$$

Matrix Equations and Systems of Equations

Another kind of matrix equation begins with a system of equations. The two examples on this page are related. The first one shows how to write a system of equations and the second one shows how to solve the matrix equation.

EXAMPLE 3

Write this system of equations so it uses three matrices:

$$2x - 3y = 13$$
$$x + 4y = -10$$

STEP 1 Write the system as two equal matrices.

$$\begin{bmatrix} 2x-3y \\ x+4y \end{bmatrix} = \begin{bmatrix} 13 \\ -10 \end{bmatrix}$$

Then write the left matrix as a product.

$$\begin{bmatrix} 2x-3y \\ x+4y \end{bmatrix} = \begin{bmatrix} 2 & -3 \\ 1 & 4 \end{bmatrix} \cdot \begin{bmatrix} x \\ y \end{bmatrix}$$

STEP 2 Substitute the product into the first matrix equation.

$$\begin{bmatrix} 2 & -3 \\ 1 & 4 \end{bmatrix} \cdot \begin{bmatrix} x \\ y \end{bmatrix} = \begin{bmatrix} 13 \\ -10 \end{bmatrix}.$$

SEARCH

To see step-by-step videos of these problems, enter the page number into the SWadvantage.com Search Bar.

The steps of solving the matrix equation in Example 3 are shown in Example 4.

EXAMPLE 4

Solve $\begin{bmatrix} 2 & -3 \\ 1 & 4 \end{bmatrix} \cdot \begin{bmatrix} x \\ y \end{bmatrix} = \begin{bmatrix} 13 \\ -10 \end{bmatrix}$ **for x and y.**

STEP 1 Find the inverse of $\begin{bmatrix} 2 & -3 \\ 1 & 4 \end{bmatrix}$.

The determinant is $(2)(4) - (-3)(1) = 8 + 3 = 11$.

So the inverse is:

$$\frac{1}{11} \cdot \begin{bmatrix} 4 & 3 \\ -1 & 2 \end{bmatrix} = \begin{bmatrix} \frac{4}{11} & \frac{3}{11} \\ -\frac{1}{11} & \frac{2}{11} \end{bmatrix}.$$

Need More HELP?

Remember that if $M = \begin{bmatrix} a & b \\ c & d \end{bmatrix}$, then the determinant of M is $ad - bc$ and that $M^{-1} = \frac{1}{\det(M)} \cdot \begin{bmatrix} d & -b \\ -c & a \end{bmatrix}$.

STEP 2 Multiply both sides of the original equation <u>on the left</u> by the inverse.

$$\begin{bmatrix} \frac{4}{11} & \frac{3}{11} \\ -\frac{1}{11} & \frac{2}{11} \end{bmatrix} \cdot \begin{bmatrix} 2 & -3 \\ 1 & 4 \end{bmatrix} \cdot \begin{bmatrix} x \\ y \end{bmatrix} = \begin{bmatrix} \frac{4}{11} & \frac{3}{11} \\ -\frac{1}{11} & \frac{2}{11} \end{bmatrix} \cdot \begin{bmatrix} 13 \\ -10 \end{bmatrix}$$

$$\begin{bmatrix} \frac{8}{11}+\frac{3}{11} & -\frac{12}{11}+\frac{12}{11} \\ -\frac{2}{11}+\frac{2}{11} & \frac{3}{11}+\frac{8}{11} \end{bmatrix} \cdot \begin{bmatrix} x \\ y \end{bmatrix} = \begin{bmatrix} \frac{52}{11}-\frac{30}{11} \\ -\frac{13}{11}-\frac{20}{11} \end{bmatrix}$$

STEP 3 Simplify the two sides of the equation.

$$\begin{bmatrix} 1 & 0 \\ 0 & 1 \end{bmatrix} \cdot \begin{bmatrix} x \\ y \end{bmatrix} = \begin{bmatrix} \frac{22}{11} \\ -\frac{33}{11} \end{bmatrix}, \text{ so } \begin{bmatrix} x \\ y \end{bmatrix} = \begin{bmatrix} 2 \\ -3 \end{bmatrix}, \text{ and } x = 2 \text{ and } y = -3.$$

Need More HELP?

Matrix multiplication is not commutative. So, if you multiply one side of an equation by a matrix <u>on the left</u>, you have to multiply <u>on the left</u> for the other side of the equation.

Need More
HELP ?

To review different methods to solve systems, see *Systems of Linear Equations and Inequalities* in *Algebra* (p. 1562).

Using a Matrix Equation to Solve a System of Equations

The next example combines the steps of Examples 3 and 4 into a single process. It starts with a system of equations and writes it as a matrix equation. The last steps are to find an inverse matrix and solve for the variables.

EXAMPLE 5

Write the system of equations on the right as a matrix equation. Then, solve the matrix equation.

$$a - 2b = -8$$
$$4a + 3b = 1$$

STEP 1 Rewrite the left side of the two equations as $\begin{bmatrix} 1 & -2 \\ 4 & 3 \end{bmatrix} \cdot \begin{bmatrix} a \\ b \end{bmatrix}$.

Then write the system as a matrix equation: $\begin{bmatrix} 1 & -2 \\ 4 & 3 \end{bmatrix} \cdot \begin{bmatrix} a \\ b \end{bmatrix} = \begin{bmatrix} -8 \\ 1 \end{bmatrix}$.

STEP 2 Find the inverse of $\begin{bmatrix} 1 & -2 \\ 4 & 3 \end{bmatrix}$.

The determinant is $(1)(3) - (-2)(4) = 3 - (-8) = 11$, so the inverse is:

$$\frac{1}{11} \cdot \begin{bmatrix} 3 & 2 \\ -4 & 1 \end{bmatrix} = \begin{bmatrix} \frac{3}{11} & \frac{2}{11} \\ -\frac{4}{11} & \frac{1}{11} \end{bmatrix}.$$

STEP 3 On both sides of the original equation, multiply on the left by $\begin{bmatrix} \frac{3}{11} & \frac{2}{11} \\ -\frac{4}{11} & \frac{1}{11} \end{bmatrix}$.

$$\begin{bmatrix} \frac{3}{11} & \frac{2}{11} \\ -\frac{4}{11} & \frac{1}{11} \end{bmatrix} \cdot \begin{bmatrix} 1 & -2 \\ 4 & 3 \end{bmatrix} \cdot \begin{bmatrix} a \\ b \end{bmatrix} = \begin{bmatrix} \frac{3}{11} & \frac{2}{11} \\ -\frac{4}{11} & \frac{1}{11} \end{bmatrix} \cdot \begin{bmatrix} -8 \\ 1 \end{bmatrix}$$

$$\begin{bmatrix} \frac{3}{11}+\frac{8}{11} & -\frac{6}{11}+\frac{6}{11} \\ -\frac{4}{11}+\frac{4}{11} & \frac{8}{11}+\frac{3}{11} \end{bmatrix} \cdot \begin{bmatrix} a \\ b \end{bmatrix} = \begin{bmatrix} -\frac{24}{11}+\frac{2}{11} \\ \frac{32}{11}+\frac{1}{11} \end{bmatrix} \rightarrow \begin{bmatrix} 1 & 0 \\ 0 & 1 \end{bmatrix} \cdot \begin{bmatrix} a \\ b \end{bmatrix} = \begin{bmatrix} -\frac{22}{11} \\ \frac{33}{11} \end{bmatrix}$$

STEP 4 Simplifying, $\begin{bmatrix} a \\ b \end{bmatrix} = \begin{bmatrix} -2 \\ 3 \end{bmatrix}$. Corresponding elements are equal, so $a = -2$ and $b = 3$.

Watch Out !

In the multiplications in Step 3, be sure that the product of two 2-by-2 matrices is another 2-by-2 matrix and that the product of a 2-by-2 matrix and a 2-by-1 matrix is a 2-by-1 matrix.

In general, $(a\text{-by-}b) \times (b\text{-by-}c)$ produces an a-by-c matrix. The "inner" values must match; the "outer" values give you the dimensions of the product.

GOT TO KNOW!

Representing a System of Equations as a Matrix Equation

Matrix multiplication and matrix equality provide a shortcut for showing a system of equations.

$\begin{matrix} ax + by \\ dx + ey \end{matrix}$ can be shown as $\begin{bmatrix} a & b \\ d & e \end{bmatrix} \cdot \begin{bmatrix} x \\ y \end{bmatrix}$, so $\begin{matrix} ax + by = c \\ dx + ey = f \end{matrix} \rightarrow \begin{bmatrix} a & b \\ d & e \end{bmatrix} \cdot \begin{bmatrix} x \\ y \end{bmatrix} = \begin{bmatrix} c \\ f \end{bmatrix}$.

Using a 3-by-3 Matrix to Solve a System of Equations

The steps to solve a system of equations by writing and using a 3-by-3 matrix equation are similar to the steps for using a 2-by-2 matrix.

Need More
HELP

Inverses of 3-by-3 matrices are discussed on page 1801.

EXAMPLE 6

Use a matrix equation to solve the following system of equations:

$$2x - y - z = -1$$
$$x + y - z = 2$$
$$-x + y + z = 2$$

In the solution, use the fact that the inverse of $\begin{bmatrix} 2 & -1 & -1 \\ 1 & 1 & -1 \\ -1 & 1 & 1 \end{bmatrix}$ **is** $\begin{bmatrix} 1 & 0 & 1 \\ 0 & \frac{1}{2} & \frac{1}{2} \\ 1 & -\frac{1}{2} & \frac{3}{2} \end{bmatrix}$.

STEP 1 Rewrite the system as a matrix equation: $\begin{bmatrix} 2 & -1 & -1 \\ 1 & 1 & -1 \\ -1 & 1 & 1 \end{bmatrix} \cdot \begin{bmatrix} x \\ y \\ z \end{bmatrix} = \begin{bmatrix} -1 \\ 2 \\ 2 \end{bmatrix}$

STEP 2 Multiply both sides of the equation, on the left, by the inverse matrix.

$$\begin{bmatrix} 1 & 0 & 1 \\ 0 & \frac{1}{2} & \frac{1}{2} \\ 1 & -\frac{1}{2} & \frac{3}{2} \end{bmatrix} \cdot \begin{bmatrix} 2 & -1 & -1 \\ 1 & 1 & -1 \\ -1 & 1 & 1 \end{bmatrix} \begin{bmatrix} x \\ y \\ z \end{bmatrix} = \begin{bmatrix} 1 & 0 & 1 \\ 0 & \frac{1}{2} & \frac{1}{2} \\ 1 & -\frac{1}{2} & \frac{3}{2} \end{bmatrix} \cdot \begin{bmatrix} -1 \\ 2 \\ 2 \end{bmatrix}$$

$$\begin{bmatrix} 2+0-1 & -1+0+1 & -1+0+1 \\ 0+\frac{1}{2}-\frac{1}{2} & 0+\frac{1}{2}+\frac{1}{2} & 0-\frac{1}{2}+\frac{1}{2} \\ 2-\frac{1}{2}-\frac{3}{2} & -1-\frac{1}{2}+\frac{3}{2} & -1+\frac{1}{2}+\frac{3}{2} \end{bmatrix} \cdot \begin{bmatrix} x \\ y \\ z \end{bmatrix} = \begin{bmatrix} -1+0+2 \\ 0+1+1 \\ -1-1+3 \end{bmatrix}$$

$$\begin{bmatrix} 1 & 0 & 0 \\ 0 & 1 & 0 \\ 0 & 0 & 1 \end{bmatrix} \cdot \begin{bmatrix} x \\ y \\ z \end{bmatrix} = \begin{bmatrix} 1 \\ 2 \\ 1 \end{bmatrix}$$

STEP 3 Simplifying results in $\begin{bmatrix} x \\ y \\ z \end{bmatrix} = \begin{bmatrix} 1 \\ 2 \\ 1 \end{bmatrix}$, so $x = 1$, $y = 2$, and $z = 1$.

GOT TO KNOW!

Verifying Inverse Matrices

Step 2 contains *part of* a verification that two matrices are inverses by showing that their product is the identity matrix.

To completely verify that any two matrices *A* and *B* are inverses, you would have to show that $A \cdot B = I$ and also that $B \cdot A = I$.

GOT TO KNOW!

Solving Systems of Equations Using Matrices

Write the system of equations as a matrix equation using three matrices. → Find the inverse of the matrix containing the equation coefficients. → Multiply both sides of the equation, on the left, by the inverse matrix. → Simplify.

Augmented Matrices

Matrices and Systems of Equations

Need More

HELP ?

Using matrices to represent systems of equations is covered in *Solving Matrix Equations* (p. 1803).

One of the important uses of matrices is to represent a system of equations. For example, here is a system of equations and a matrix equation representing that system.

$$3x + 4y = -6 \\ 2x - y = 7 \rightarrow \begin{bmatrix} 3 & 4 \\ 2 & -1 \end{bmatrix} \cdot \begin{bmatrix} x \\ y \end{bmatrix} = \begin{bmatrix} -6 \\ 7 \end{bmatrix}$$

Another use of matrices involves writing, and working with, an **augmented matrix**, which consists of the coefficients and constant from a system of equations. For example, here is the same system as above and an augmented matrix for the system. Note that a vertical line separates the coefficients and the constants.

$$3x + 4y = -6 \\ 2x - y = 7 \rightarrow \left[\begin{array}{cc|c} 3 & 4 & -6 \\ 2 & -1 & 7 \end{array} \right]$$

Row Operations for an Augmented Matrix

Augmented matrices can be used to solve systems of equations. The following are three operations that when applied to an augmented matrix, result in a matrix that *is row-equivalent* to the original matrix. (The usefulness of *row-equivalent augmented matrices* is explained on the next page.)

1. You can switch any two rows.

2. You can multiply all the elements in a row by any (non-zero) number.

3. You can find a multiple of any row, and add the result to another row.

EXAMPLE 1

Using the operations above, show that $\left[\begin{array}{cc|c} 3 & 4 & -6 \\ 2 & -1 & 7 \end{array} \right]$ **is row-equivalent to** $\left[\begin{array}{cc|c} 1 & 5 & -13 \\ 0 & 1 & -3 \end{array} \right]$.

STEP 1 Beginning with $\left[\begin{array}{cc|c} 3 & 4 & -6 \\ 2 & -1 & 7 \end{array} \right]$, subtract Row 2 from Row 1. The result is $\left[\begin{array}{cc|c} 1 & 5 & -13 \\ 2 & -1 & 7 \end{array} \right]$.

STEP 2 Multiply the new Row 1 by 2 and subtract it from Row 2. The result is $\left[\begin{array}{cc|c} 1 & 5 & -13 \\ 0 & -11 & 33 \end{array} \right]$.

STEP 3 Divide Row 2 by -11. The result is $\left[\begin{array}{cc|c} 1 & 5 & -13 \\ 0 & 1 & -3 \end{array} \right]$.

As Example 2 explains, an augmented matrix in which the first row begins "1" and the second row begins with "0 1" is especially useful.

Watch Out !

To multiply a row by a number, multiply every element in the row by that number. And when you add two rows, always add corresponding pairs of elements.

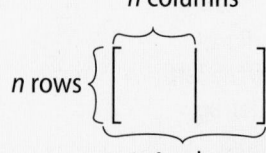
GOT TO KNOW !

The Size of an Augmented Matrix

n columns

n rows $\left\{ \begin{bmatrix} \end{bmatrix} \right.$

n + 1 columns

Using an Augmented Matrix to Solve a System

On the previous page, we represented a system with an augmented matrix and found a row-equivalent matrix:

$$3x + 4y = -6 \atop 2x - y = 7 \rightarrow \begin{bmatrix} 3 & 4 & | & -6 \\ 2 & -1 & | & 7 \end{bmatrix} \rightarrow \begin{bmatrix} 1 & 5 & | & -13 \\ 0 & 1 & | & -3 \end{bmatrix}$$

The augmented matrix at the far right contains the solution to the system! The second row represents the equation $0x + 1y = -3$, or $y = -3$. Using $y = -3$ in the first row, $1x + 5y = -13$, or $x + 5(-3) = -13$, so $x - 15 = -13$ and $x = 2$. The solution, $(2, -3)$, satisfies both equations in the original system so it is the solution to the system.

The key is to rewrite the augmented matrix so it is in the form $\begin{bmatrix} 1 & \cdot & | & \cdot \\ 0 & 1 & | & \cdot \end{bmatrix}$.

- The second row gives the value of y (in this case, $y = -3$).
- Substituting that value of y into the first-row equation (in which x has a coefficient of 1) lets you solve for x.

EXAMPLE 2

Use an augmented matrix to solve the system $2x + 4y = 10 \atop 4x + y = -1$.

STEP 1 Write the augmented matrix. $\begin{bmatrix} 2 & 4 & | & 10 \\ 4 & 1 & | & -1 \end{bmatrix}$

STEP 2 Divide Row 1 by 2. $\begin{bmatrix} 1 & 2 & | & 5 \\ 4 & 1 & | & -1 \end{bmatrix}$

STEP 3 Multiply Row 1 by -4 and add the result to Row 2. $\begin{bmatrix} 1 & 2 & | & 5 \\ 0 & -7 & | & -21 \end{bmatrix}$

STEP 4 Divide Row 2 by -7. $\begin{bmatrix} 1 & 2 & | & 5 \\ 0 & 1 & | & 3 \end{bmatrix}$

STEP 5 Solve for x and y.

The second row in Step 4 means $y = 3$. Using that result in the first row, $x + 2(3) = 5$, $x = -1$. The solution to the original system is $(-1, 3)$.

Need More HELP?

The purpose of Step 2 is to change the augmented matrix so its first row begins with "1". The purpose for Steps 3 and 4 is so its second row begins with "0 1".

As Example 2 illustrates, when two augmented matrices are row equivalent they represent systems of equations that have the same solution. So, a solution to the final augmented matrix is also a solution to the original system of equations.

EXAMPLE 3

Use an augmented matrix to solve the system $3a - 5b = 29 \atop 4a + b = 8$.

STEP 1 Write the augmented matrix. $\begin{bmatrix} 3 & -5 & | & 29 \\ 4 & 1 & | & 8 \end{bmatrix}$

STEP 2 Switch Row 1 and Row 2. $\begin{bmatrix} 4 & 1 & | & 8 \\ 3 & -5 & | & 29 \end{bmatrix}$

STEP 3 Subtract Row 2 from Row 1. $\begin{bmatrix} 1 & 6 & | & -21 \\ 3 & -5 & | & 29 \end{bmatrix}$

STEP 4 Multiply Row 1 by -3 and add the result to Row 2. $\begin{bmatrix} 1 & 6 & | & -21 \\ 0 & -23 & | & 92 \end{bmatrix}$

STEP 5 Divide Row 2 by -23. $\begin{bmatrix} 1 & 6 & | & -21 \\ 0 & 1 & | & -4 \end{bmatrix}$

STEP 6 The last line in Step 5 means $b = -4$. Using that result in the first row, $a = 3$.

SEARCH

To see step-by-step videos of these problems, enter the page number into the SWadvantage.com Search Bar.

Augmented Matrices and Systems of Three Equations

If you have a system of three equations in three variables, the same rules for finding row-equivalent matrices can be applied to an augmented matrix for that system.

EXAMPLE 4

A system of equations is $\begin{array}{l} 2x - y + 3z = -10 \\ x + 2y - z = 5 \\ x - 3y + 2z = -13 \end{array}$. Use an augmented matrix to solve the system.

STEP 1 Write the augmented matrix for the system.

$$\begin{bmatrix} 2 & -1 & 3 & | & -10 \\ 1 & 2 & -1 & | & 5 \\ 1 & -3 & 2 & | & -13 \end{bmatrix}$$

Use the square matrix of coefficients on the left of the vertical line and use the constants on the right of the line.

STEP 2 Switch Row 1 and Row 2.

$$\begin{bmatrix} 1 & 2 & -1 & | & 5 \\ 2 & -1 & 3 & | & -10 \\ 1 & -3 & 2 & | & -13 \end{bmatrix}$$

The first goal is to get 1 as the first element in Row 1. Use the rule about switching rows, and switch Row 1 with Row 2 or Row 3.

STEP 3 Multiply Row 1 by -2, then add the result to Row 2.

$$\begin{bmatrix} 1 & 2 & -1 & | & 5 \\ 0 & -5 & 5 & | & -20 \\ 1 & -3 & 2 & | & -13 \end{bmatrix}$$

The next goal is to change the first element in Row 2 from 2 to 0. Look at Row 1: $(-2) \times$ Row 1 = "$-2 \ -4 \ 2 \ | \ -10$". The first element is -2, so adding that to Row 2 will give 0 as the first element of Row 2.

STEP 4 Divide Row 2 by -5.

$$\begin{bmatrix} 1 & 2 & -1 & | & 5 \\ 0 & 1 & -1 & | & 4 \\ 1 & -3 & 2 & | & -13 \end{bmatrix}$$

In Row 2, the second element was -5. Be sure to divide all the elements in Row 2 by -5.

STEP 5 Multiply Row 1 by -1, then add the result to Row 3.

$$\begin{bmatrix} 1 & 2 & -1 & | & 5 \\ 0 & 1 & -1 & | & 4 \\ 0 & -5 & 3 & | & -18 \end{bmatrix}$$

The first goal for Row 3 is to change the first element to 0. The first element was 1, and multiplying Row 1 by -1 results in "$-1 \ -2 \ 1 \ | \ -5$". Adding that to Row 3 will give 0 as the first element of Row 3.

STEP 6 Multiply Row 2 by 5, then add the result to Row 3.

$$\begin{bmatrix} 1 & 2 & -1 & | & 5 \\ 0 & 1 & -1 & | & 4 \\ 0 & 0 & -2 & | & 2 \end{bmatrix}$$

In Row 3, the next goal is to change the second element to 0. The second element in Row 2 is 1, so multiplying Row 2 by 5 results in "0 5 -5 | 20". Adding that to Row 3 will give 0 as the second element in Row 3.

STEP 7 Divide Row 3 by -2.

$$\begin{bmatrix} 1 & 2 & -1 & | & 5 \\ 0 & 1 & -1 & | & 4 \\ 0 & 0 & 1 & | & -1 \end{bmatrix}$$

Be sure to divide all the elements by -2. Notice that the augmented matrix now has the form

$$\begin{bmatrix} 1 & \cdot & \cdot & | & \cdot \\ 0 & 1 & \cdot & | & \cdot \\ 0 & 0 & 1 & | & \cdot \end{bmatrix}.$$

STEP 8 The augmented matrix is done. Use it to solve for the variables. Row 3 indicates that $z = -1$. Row 2 means $y - z = 4$; substituting $z = -1$ into that equation gives $y - (-1) = 4$ so $y = 3$. Row 1 indicates $x + 2y - z = 5$; substituting the known values $y = 3$ and $z = -1$ gives $x + 2(3) - (-1) = 5$, so $x + 6 + 1 = 5$ and $x = -2$. The solution is $(-2, 3, -1)$.

Why Row Operations Don't Change a Solution

We have been using three rules to change augmented matrices: switching rows, multiplying a row by a (nonzero) number, and adding a multiple of one row to another row. This section explores why applying those rules to a system of equations produces another system that has the same solution.

The justification for the first rule, switching rows, is simple. In the two systems below, equations (1) and (2) are switched.

$$2x + 3y - z = 4$$
$$x - 4y + 2z = -3$$ and $$x - 4y + 2z = -3$$
$$3x + y - 2z = 7$$ $$2x + 3y - z = 4$$
$$3x + y - 2z = 7$$

The systems have the same three equations, so switching equations (or switching rows in an augmented matrix) doesn't change the solution. The next example deals with the other two rules.

EXAMPLE 5

a. Show that the second rule, "You can multiply all the elements in a row by a (nonzero) number," does not change the solution to a system.

STEP 1 Start with a system of equations such as $\begin{matrix} 2x + 3y - z = 4 \\ x - 4y + 2z = -3. \\ 3x + y - 2z = 7 \end{matrix}$

STEP 2 Multiply any equation by a nonzero number. For example, multiply the second equation by -2. $\begin{matrix} 2x + 3y - z = 4 \\ -2x + 8y - 4z = 6 \\ 3x + y - 2z = 7 \end{matrix}$

STEP 3 The Multiplication Property of Equality states that if we multiply an equation by a nonzero number, the new equation is equivalent to the old equation; that is, the values of the variables that satisfy the equation do not change. Because the two forms of the second equation are equivalent, the two systems have the same solution.

As a check, $(1, 0, -2)$ is the solution to the first system; it is also the solution to the second system.

b. Show that the third rule, "You can add a multiple of any row to another row," does not change the solution to a system.

STEP 1 This time let's use a system with two equations: $\begin{matrix} 2x - 3y = 7 \\ -5x + y = -11 \end{matrix}$.
The solution to the system is $(2, -1)$.

STEP 2 Multiply Equation (1) by a number, say -3, to get $-6x + 9y = -21$. Adding that to Equation (2), the new system is $\begin{matrix} 2x - 3y = 7 \\ -11x + 10y = -32 \end{matrix}$.

STEP 3 Confirm that both systems of equations have the same solutions.

We know that the first system of equations is satisfied by $(2, -1)$. Use substitution to show that $(2, -1)$ satisfies the second equation in the new system. Because the new system has the same solution as the original system, the two systems are equivalent. So, adding a multiple of one equation to another (or, in an augmented matrix, adding a multiple of one row to another row) does not change the solution of the system.

GOT TO KNOW!

Using an Augmented Matrix to Solve a System of Equations

1. Use the coefficients and constants to write an augmented matrix.

2. Use row operations to rewrite the augmented matrix. The final matrix should be in this form:

$$\begin{bmatrix} 1 & \cdot & \cdot & | & \cdot \\ 0 & 1 & \cdot & | & \cdot \\ 0 & 0 & 1 & | & \cdot \end{bmatrix}$$

3. Use the last row of the augmented matrix to find the last variable. Then work up, one row at a time, to find the other variables.

Need More HELP?

Remember: in addition to using a matrix, there are many ways to solve a system of equations. See *Graphing* (p. 1564), *Substitution* (p. 1568), *Addition or Subtraction* (p. 1572), and *Elimination* (p. 1576) in *Algebra*.

Using Matrices for Inventory

 SOUTHWESTERN

Matrices for Sales and Inventory

When similar inventory items are organized into different categories, matrices can be a useful way to record the inventory.

EXAMPLE 1

A student has an after-school business selling ink cartridges. She organizes her inventory as a matrix, as shown at the right.

$$\begin{array}{c} \text{Refilled New} \\ \begin{array}{c} \text{Colors} \\ \text{Black} \end{array} \begin{bmatrix} \square & \square \\ \square & \square \end{bmatrix} \end{array}$$

She records her sales at the end of every month. Here are her sales figures:

January	February	March	April	May	June
$\begin{bmatrix} 21 & 7 \\ 3 & 8 \end{bmatrix}$	$\begin{bmatrix} 9 & 6 \\ 5 & 6 \end{bmatrix}$	$\begin{bmatrix} 15 & 9 \\ 2 & 5 \end{bmatrix}$	$\begin{bmatrix} 10 & 10 \\ 6 & 7 \end{bmatrix}$	$\begin{bmatrix} 12 & 10 \\ 6 & 6 \end{bmatrix}$	$\begin{bmatrix} 10 & 6 \\ 2 & 6 \end{bmatrix}$

July	August	September	October	November	December
$\begin{bmatrix} 14 & 10 \\ 3 & 6 \end{bmatrix}$	$\begin{bmatrix} 11 & 8 \\ 5 & 5 \end{bmatrix}$	$\begin{bmatrix} 10 & 8 \\ 4 & 7 \end{bmatrix}$	$\begin{bmatrix} 12 & 10 \\ 6 & 5 \end{bmatrix}$	$\begin{bmatrix} 15 & 9 \\ 5 & 8 \end{bmatrix}$	$\begin{bmatrix} 10 & 6 \\ 4 & 5 \end{bmatrix}$

She purchases cartridges every three months. Here are her purchases for the year.

March	June	September	December
$\begin{bmatrix} 40 & 25 \\ 20 & 25 \end{bmatrix}$	$\begin{bmatrix} 30 & 30 \\ 20 & 20 \end{bmatrix}$	$\begin{bmatrix} 35 & 35 \\ 15 & 5 \end{bmatrix}$	$\begin{bmatrix} 20 & 0 \\ 0 & 10 \end{bmatrix}$

a. How many of each type of cartridge did she sell each quarter? (The quarters end on the last days of March, June, September, and December.)

Add the three sales matrices for each quarter. For the first quarter, the sum is

$$\begin{bmatrix} 21 & 7 \\ 3 & 8 \end{bmatrix} + \begin{bmatrix} 9 & 6 \\ 5 & 6 \end{bmatrix} + \begin{bmatrix} 15 & 9 \\ 2 & 5 \end{bmatrix} = \begin{bmatrix} 45 & 22 \\ 10 & 19 \end{bmatrix}.$$

For the other quarters the sums are $\begin{bmatrix} 32 & 26 \\ 14 & 19 \end{bmatrix}$, $\begin{bmatrix} 35 & 26 \\ 12 & 18 \end{bmatrix}$, and $\begin{bmatrix} 37 & 25 \\ 15 & 18 \end{bmatrix}$.

b. How many more of each cartridge did she sell in November than she sold in December? $\begin{bmatrix} 15 & 9 \\ 5 & 8 \end{bmatrix} - \begin{bmatrix} 10 & 6 \\ 4 & 5 \end{bmatrix} = \begin{bmatrix} 5 & 3 \\ 1 & 3 \end{bmatrix}$

c. How many cartridges of each type did she sell during the year? How many more cartridges did she sell during the year than she bought to replenish her inventory?

To find her total sales, add the four matrices from part (a); that sum is $\begin{bmatrix} 149 & 99 \\ 51 & 74 \end{bmatrix}$.

For her total purchases, the sum of the four "purchases" matrices is $\begin{bmatrix} 125 & 90 \\ 55 & 60 \end{bmatrix}$.

The difference is Sales $-$ Purchases $= \begin{bmatrix} 149 & 99 \\ 51 & 74 \end{bmatrix} - \begin{bmatrix} 125 & 90 \\ 55 & 60 \end{bmatrix} = \begin{bmatrix} 24 & 9 \\ -4 & 14 \end{bmatrix}.$

The -4 means that she sold more than she purchased this year. So, she may have had inventory left over from last year that she sold this year.

Need More
HELP ?

Remember—to add or subtract matrices, first check that the matrices have the same dimensions. Then add or subtract pairs of corresponding elements.

SEARCH

To see step-by-step videos of these problems, enter the page number into the SWadvantage.com Search Bar.

Using Matrices to Multiply Prices and Items Sold

Example 1 used matrix addition and subtraction to record information about inventory. The next example uses matrix multiplication to combine cost and numbers of items sold to generate information on income.

EXAMPLE 2

The matrices at the right show the costs for buying and selling ink cartridges. She pays $6 for any refilled cartridge and $8 for any new cartridge, and she charges $10 for any refilled cartridge and $15 for any new cartridge.

What She Pays to Buy Cartridges ($)	What Customers Pay Her ($)
$\begin{bmatrix} 6 \\ 8 \end{bmatrix}$	$\begin{bmatrix} 10 \\ 15 \end{bmatrix}$

a. **What income did she get from her sales in February?**

Refer to the February sales from Example 1. Multiply the matrix of her February sales times the matrix of what her customers pay.

$$\begin{bmatrix} 9 & 6 \\ 5 & 6 \end{bmatrix} \cdot \begin{bmatrix} 10 \\ 15 \end{bmatrix} = \begin{bmatrix} 9 \cdot 10 + 6 \cdot 15 \\ 5 \cdot 10 + 6 \cdot 15 \end{bmatrix} = \begin{bmatrix} 90 + 90 \\ 50 + 90 \end{bmatrix} = \begin{bmatrix} 180 \\ 140 \end{bmatrix}$$

Remember that the matrices for numbers of cartridges looks like this:
$\begin{array}{cc} & \text{Refilled New} \\ \text{Colors} & \begin{bmatrix} \square & \square \\ \square & \square \end{bmatrix} \\ \text{Black} & \end{array}$.

We want to be sure the multiplication shows that customers pay her the same amount for any refilled cartridge ($10) and they pay her the same amount for any new cartridge ($15). The matrix multiplication does that: the numbers of refilled cartridges are multiplied by $10 and the numbers of new cartridges are multiplied by $15.

b. **What was the total income from her sales for the year?**

Her total sales for the year were found in part (c) of Example 1. Multiply that total times the matrix of what her customers pay for ink cartridges.

$$\begin{bmatrix} 149 & 99 \\ 51 & 74 \end{bmatrix} \cdot \begin{bmatrix} 10 \\ 15 \end{bmatrix} = \begin{bmatrix} 1,490 + 1,485 \\ 510 + 1,110 \end{bmatrix} = \begin{bmatrix} 2,975 \\ 1,620 \end{bmatrix}$$

c. **What was the difference between her total sales and her total purchases for the year?**

Her total purchases for the year were found in part (c) of Example 1. Multiply that total times what she paid for ink cartridges: $\begin{bmatrix} 125 & 90 \\ 55 & 50 \end{bmatrix} \cdot \begin{bmatrix} 6 \\ 8 \end{bmatrix} = \begin{bmatrix} 750 + 720 \\ 330 + 400 \end{bmatrix} = \begin{bmatrix} 1,470 \\ 730 \end{bmatrix}$. Then subtract the

result from the result from part (b) of this example. $\begin{bmatrix} 2,975 \\ 1,620 \end{bmatrix} - \begin{bmatrix} 1,470 \\ 730 \end{bmatrix} = \begin{bmatrix} 1,505 \\ 890 \end{bmatrix}$.

Need More HELP?

For review in multiplying matrices, see *Matrix Multiplication* in *Advanced Algebra* (p. 1786).

Watch Out!

When you use matrices to represent real-world objects, be sure you are consistent in how you interpret what is represented by the rows and by the columns in the matrix.

GOT TO KNOW!

Matrix Multiplication

- The number of columns in the left factor must be the same as the number of rows in the right factor: (a-by-b) × (b-by-c) = (a-by-c).

- Matrix multiplication is not commutative.

Using Matrices in Geometry

Scalar Multiplication and Size Changes

Need More HELP ?
To review scalar multiplication and determinants, go to *Scalar Multiplication* (p. 1778) and *Determinants* (p. 1794).

Suppose in $\triangle ABC$, vertex A has coordinates $(2, 3)$, B is $(3, -1)$, and $C(-2, -1)$. The vertices of $\triangle ABC$ can be written as the matrix $\begin{bmatrix} 2 & 3 & -2 \\ 3 & -1 & -1 \end{bmatrix}$. Scalar multiplication of that matrix results in a size change for the triangle.

EXAMPLE 1

Start with $\triangle ABC$ as described above and shown to the right.

a. **Multiply the matrix of vertices by the scalar value 3. Draw the new figure and label its vertices as A', B', and C'.**

$$3 \cdot \begin{bmatrix} 2 & 3 & -2 \\ 3 & -1 & -1 \end{bmatrix} = \begin{bmatrix} 6 & 9 & -6 \\ 9 & -3 & -3 \end{bmatrix}.$$

The vertices of the new triangle are $A'(6, 9)$, $B'(9, -3)$, and $C'(-6, -3)$.

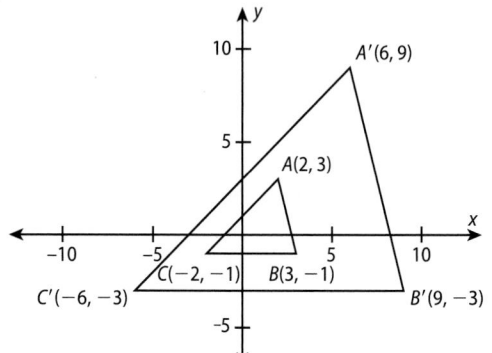

b. **Describe some of the relationships between $\triangle ABC$ and $\triangle A'B'C'$.**

To show that corresponding sides are proportional, find ratios of corresponding sides:

$$\frac{AC}{A'C'} = \frac{\sqrt{32}}{\sqrt{288}} = \frac{1}{3}; \frac{AB}{A'B'} = \frac{\sqrt{17}}{\sqrt{153}} = \frac{1}{3}; \frac{BC}{B'C'} = \frac{5}{15} = \frac{1}{3}$$

Because the three pairs of corresponding sides are proportional, the two triangles are similar. The scale factor is 3, so the area of $\triangle A'B'C'$ is 3^2 or 9 times the area of $\triangle ABC$.

Determinants and the Area of a Parallelogram

If a parallelogram has one vertex at the origin, the area of the parallelogram can be calculated using a determinant.

$$Area\ of\ \square = \pm \begin{vmatrix} x_1 & x_2 \\ y_1 & y_2 \end{vmatrix} = x_1 y_2 - x_2 y_1$$

Area is always nonnegative. For this property, the "$\pm$" symbol in $= \pm \begin{vmatrix} x_1 & x_2 \\ y_1 & y_2 \end{vmatrix}$ means that if the value of the determinant is negative, then take the absolute value of the result.

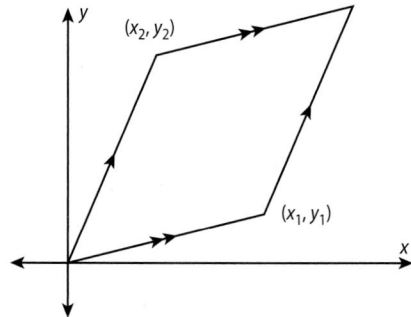

EXAMPLE 2

Three of the vertices of a parallelogram are (5, 2), (0, 0), and (4, 6). Find the area of the parallelogram.

Write a determinant using the ordered pairs and then find its value: $\begin{vmatrix} 5 & 4 \\ 2 & 6 \end{vmatrix} = 30 - 8 = 22.$

The area of the parallelogram is 22 square units.

Determinants and an Equation of a Line

If (x_1, y_1) and (x_2, y_2) are two points on a line, one way to find the equation of the line

through the points is to use this property: $\begin{vmatrix} x & x_1 & x_2 \\ y & y_1 & y_2 \\ 1 & 1 & 1 \end{vmatrix} = 0.$

EXAMPLE 3

a. Find an equation of the line through the points (2, −1) and (−3, −11).

STEP 1 Use $(2, -1)$ and $(-3, -11)$ as (x_1, y_1) and (x_2, y_2): $\begin{vmatrix} x & x_1 & x_2 \\ y & y_1 & y_2 \\ 1 & 1 & 1 \end{vmatrix} = 0 \rightarrow \begin{vmatrix} x & 2 & -3 \\ y & -1 & -11 \\ 1 & 1 & 1 \end{vmatrix} = 0$

STEP 2 Using $\begin{vmatrix} x & 2 & -3 \\ y & -1 & -11 \\ 1 & 1 & 1 \end{vmatrix} \begin{matrix} x & 2 \\ y & -1 \\ 1 & 1 \end{matrix}$ to find the value of the determinant, the equation becomes

$$-x - 22 - 3y - (3 - 11x + 2y) = 0$$

STEP 3 Rewrite the equation in $y = mx + b$ form.

$$-x - 22 - 3y - 3 + 11x - 2y = 0$$
$$10x - 5y - 25 = 0$$
$$10x - 5y = 25$$
$$y = 2x - 5$$

STEP 4 Check that the ordered pairs $(2, -1)$ and $(-3, -11)$ satisfy $y = 2x - 5$.

$$-1 = 2(2) - 5 ✔ \qquad -11 = 2(-3) - 5 ✔$$

SEARCH

To see step-by-step videos of these problems, enter the page number into the SWadvantage.com Search Bar.

EXAMPLE 4

Show that $\begin{vmatrix} x & x_1 & x_2 \\ y & y_1 & y_2 \\ 1 & 1 & 1 \end{vmatrix} = 0$ **is equivalent to the point-slope formula,** $\dfrac{y - y_1}{x - x_1} = \dfrac{y_2 - y_1}{x_2 - x_1}.$

STEP 1 Use $\begin{vmatrix} x & x_1 & x_2 \\ y & y_1 & y_2 \\ 1 & 1 & 1 \end{vmatrix} \begin{matrix} x & x_1 \\ y & y_1 \\ 1 & 1 \end{matrix}$ to find the value of the determinant.

$$xy_1 + x_1y_2 + x_2y - (x_2y_1 + xy_2 + x_1y) = 0$$
$$xy_1 + x_1y_2 + x_2y - x_2y_1 - xy_2 - x_1y = 0$$

STEP 2 Rewrite $\dfrac{y - y_1}{x - x_1} = \dfrac{y_2 - y_1}{x_2 - x_1}$ by finding the cross products.

$$(y - y_1)(x_2 - x_1) = (x - x_1)(y_2 - y_1)$$
$$x_2y - x_1y - x_2y_1 + x_1y_1 = xy_2 - xy_1 - x_1y_2 + x_1y_1$$
$$x_2y + xy_1 + x_1y_2 - x_1y - x_2y_1 - xy_2 = 0$$

Therefore $\begin{vmatrix} x & x_1 & x_2 \\ y & y_1 & y_2 \\ 1 & 1 & 1 \end{vmatrix} = 0$ is equivalent to the point-slope formula $\dfrac{y - y_1}{x - x_1} = \dfrac{y_2 - y_1}{x_2 - x_1}.$

Cramer's Rule

Cramer's Rule and a System of 2 Equations in 2 Variables

To solve the system of equations $\begin{array}{l} ax + by = c \\ dx + ey = f \end{array}$, the first step is to identify three matrices.s

Need More

HELP

The expressions M_c, M_x, and M_y are read "M-sub-c," "M-sub-x," and "M-sub-y."

- One matrix uses the x- and y-coefficients.

    We can label the matrix of coefficients as M_c, so $M_c = \begin{bmatrix} a & b \\ d & e \end{bmatrix}$.

- Another matrix replaces the x-coefficients with the column of constants.

    If we label this matrix as M_x, then $M_x = \begin{bmatrix} c & b \\ f & e \end{bmatrix}$.

- The third matrix replaces the y-coefficients with the column of constants.

    Label this matrix as M_y, so $M_y = \begin{bmatrix} a & c \\ d & f \end{bmatrix}$.

Watch Out !

To solve a system of equations, the equations must be written in the form $ax + by = c$.

Cramer's Rule

The solution of a system of 2 equations in 2 variables is:

$$x = \frac{\det(M_x)}{\det(M_c)} = \frac{\begin{vmatrix} c & b \\ f & e \end{vmatrix}}{\begin{vmatrix} a & b \\ d & e \end{vmatrix}} \text{ and } y = \frac{\det(M_y)}{\det(M_c)} = \frac{\begin{vmatrix} a & c \\ d & f \end{vmatrix}}{\begin{vmatrix} a & b \\ d & e \end{vmatrix}}$$

EXAMPLE 1

Use Cramer's Rule to solve this system: $\begin{array}{l} 2x - 5y = 26 \\ 3x + 2y = 1 \end{array}$.

STEP 1 Write the three matrices M_c, M_x, and M_y:

$$M_c = \begin{bmatrix} 2 & -5 \\ 3 & 2 \end{bmatrix}, M_x = \begin{bmatrix} 26 & -5 \\ 1 & 2 \end{bmatrix}, M_y = \begin{bmatrix} 2 & 26 \\ 3 & 1 \end{bmatrix}$$

STEP 2 Use Cramer's Rule: $x = \dfrac{\det(M_x)}{\det(M_c)}$ and $y = \dfrac{\det(M_y)}{\det(M_c)}$.

Need More

HELP

To review determinants, go to *Determinants* on page 1794.

$$x = \frac{\det(M_x)}{\det(M_c)} = \frac{\begin{vmatrix} 26 & -5 \\ 1 & 2 \end{vmatrix}}{\begin{vmatrix} 2 & -5 \\ 3 & 2 \end{vmatrix}} = \frac{(26)(2)-(-5)(1)}{(2)(2)-(-5)(3)} = \frac{52-(-5)}{4-(-15)} = \frac{57}{19} = 3$$

$$y = \frac{\det(M_y)}{\det(M_c)} = \frac{\begin{vmatrix} 2 & 26 \\ 3 & 1 \end{vmatrix}}{\begin{vmatrix} 2 & -5 \\ 3 & 2 \end{vmatrix}} = \frac{(2)(1)-(26)(3)}{(2)(2)-(-5)(3)} = \frac{2-78}{4-(-15)} = \frac{-76}{19} = -4$$

STEP 3 Check $x = 3$ and $y = -4$ in each equation.

$2x - 5y = 26$	$3x + 2y = 1$
$2(3) - 5(-4) \overset{?}{=} 26$	$3(3) + 2(-4) \overset{?}{=} 1$
$6 - (-20) \overset{?}{=} 26$	$9 + (-8) \overset{?}{=} 1$
$26 = 26 \checkmark$	$1 = 1 \checkmark$

The solution is $(3, -4)$.

Cramer's Rule and Inconsistent or Dependent Systems

If two equations represent parallel lines, then the system has *no* solution and is called *inconsistent*. If two equations represent the same line, then the system has *many* solutions and is called *dependent*. The next two examples illustrate how Cramer's Rule identifies inconsistent or dependent systems.

EXAMPLE 2

SEARCH

To see step-by-step videos of these problems, enter the page number into the SWadvantage.com Search Bar.

The equations $y = 2x + 3$ and $y = 2x - 4$ represent parallel lines. Describe what happens when Cramer's Rule is applied to an inconsistent system.

STEP 1 Write the equations as a system. Each equation should be in $ax + by = c$ form.

$$2x - y = -3$$
$$2x - y = 4$$

STEP 2 Find M_c, M_x, and M_y for the system.

$$M_c = \begin{bmatrix} 2 & -1 \\ 2 & -1 \end{bmatrix}, M_x = \begin{bmatrix} -3 & -1 \\ 4 & -1 \end{bmatrix}, M_y = \begin{bmatrix} 2 & -3 \\ 2 & 4 \end{bmatrix}$$

STEP 3 Find expressions for x and y.

$$x = \frac{\begin{vmatrix} -3 & -1 \\ 4 & -1 \end{vmatrix}}{\begin{vmatrix} 2 & -1 \\ 2 & -1 \end{vmatrix}} = \frac{3-(-4)}{-2-(-2)} = \frac{7}{0}; y = \frac{\begin{vmatrix} 2 & -3 \\ 2 & 4 \end{vmatrix}}{\begin{vmatrix} 2 & -1 \\ 2 & -1 \end{vmatrix}} = \frac{8-(-6)}{-2-(-2)} = \frac{14}{0}$$

Division by 0 is **undefined**. When Cramer's Rule results in an undefined expression, the system is inconsistent and has no solution.

EXAMPLE 3

GOT TO KNOW!

Undefined vs. Indeterminate

There is an important difference between **undefined** and **indeterminate**.

For example, if we could say that $\frac{5}{0} = p$, then $0 \cdot p = 5$. That statement is not true for *any* possible value of p. The expression $\frac{5}{0}$ is *undefined*.

If we could say that $\frac{0}{0} = q$, then $0 \cdot q = 0$. That statement is true for *any* value of q.

The expression $\frac{0}{0}$ is *indeterminate*.

The equations $y = 3x - 2$ and $2y = 6x - 4$ represent the same line. Explain what happens when Cramer's Rule is applied to a dependent system.

STEP 1 Write the equations as a system, with each equation in $ax + by = c$ form.

$$3x - y = 2$$
$$6x - 2y = 4$$

STEP 2 Find M_c, M_x, and M_y for the system.

$$M_c = \begin{bmatrix} 3 & -1 \\ 6 & -2 \end{bmatrix}, M_x = \begin{bmatrix} 2 & -1 \\ 4 & -2 \end{bmatrix}, M_y = \begin{bmatrix} 3 & 2 \\ 6 & 4 \end{bmatrix}$$

STEP 3 Find expressions for x and y.

$$x = \frac{\begin{vmatrix} 2 & -1 \\ 4 & -2 \end{vmatrix}}{\begin{vmatrix} 3 & -1 \\ 6 & -2 \end{vmatrix}} = \frac{-4-(-4)}{-6-(-6)} = \frac{0}{0}; y = \frac{\begin{vmatrix} 3 & 2 \\ 6 & 4 \end{vmatrix}}{\begin{vmatrix} 3 & -1 \\ 6 & -2 \end{vmatrix}} = \frac{12-12}{-6-(-6)} = \frac{0}{0}$$

The expression $\frac{0}{0}$ is called **indeterminate**. When Cramer's Rule results in an indeterminate expression, the system is dependent and has many solutions.

SOUTHWESTERN

Need More
HELP ?

The steps of finding a determinant for a 3-by-3 matrix are discussed in *Determinants* on page 1795.

Cramer's Rule for a System of 3 Equations in 3 Variables

Cramer's Rule for three equations is quite similar to the rule for a two-equation system.

$$ax + by + cz = d$$

For the system of three equations $ex + fy + gz = h$, you can write four matrices:

$$ix + jy + kz = l$$

$$M_c = \begin{bmatrix} a & b & c \\ e & f & g \\ i & j & k \end{bmatrix}, M_x = \begin{bmatrix} d & b & c \\ h & f & g \\ l & j & k \end{bmatrix}, M_y = \begin{bmatrix} a & d & c \\ e & h & g \\ i & l & k \end{bmatrix}, \text{ and } M_z = \begin{bmatrix} a & b & d \\ e & f & h \\ i & j & l \end{bmatrix}.$$

Cramer's Rule

The solution of a system of 3 equations in 3 variables is: $x = \dfrac{\det(M_x)}{\det(M_c)}, y = \dfrac{\det(M_y)}{\det(M_c)}, z = \dfrac{\det(M_z)}{\det(M_c)}$

Note that M_c is the matrix of coefficients, and in M_x, M_y, and M_z the column of constants replaces the column of coefficients for x, y, or z.

EXAMPLE 4

Use Cramer's Rule to solve this system:

$$2x - 3y + z = 10$$
$$x + 2y + 2z = 6$$
$$-x - y + 2z = 5$$

STEP 1 Write the matrices M_c, M_x, M_y, and M_z:

$$M_c = \begin{bmatrix} 2 & -3 & 1 \\ 1 & 2 & 2 \\ -1 & -1 & 2 \end{bmatrix}, M_x = \begin{bmatrix} 10 & -3 & 1 \\ 6 & 2 & 2 \\ 5 & -1 & 2 \end{bmatrix}, M_y = \begin{bmatrix} 2 & 10 & 1 \\ 1 & 6 & 2 \\ -1 & 5 & 2 \end{bmatrix}, M_z = \begin{bmatrix} 2 & -3 & 10 \\ 1 & 2 & 6 \\ -1 & -1 & 5 \end{bmatrix}$$

GOT TO KNOW!

Using Cramer's Rule for Higher Order Systems

• You can use Cramer's Rule for any system of *n* equations in *n* variables.

• You might have to use a graphing calculator or computer to find the values of the determinants.

STEP 2 Find the determinant for each matrix. Use these arrays: For M_c:
$$\begin{vmatrix} 2 & -3 & 1 & 2 & -3 \\ 1 & 2 & 2 & 1 & 2 \\ -1 & -1 & 2 & -1 & -1 \end{vmatrix}$$

For M_x:
$$\begin{vmatrix} 10 & -3 & 1 & 10 & -3 \\ 6 & 2 & 2 & 6 & 2 \\ 5 & -1 & 2 & 5 & -1 \end{vmatrix}$$
For M_y:
$$\begin{vmatrix} 2 & 10 & 1 & 2 & 10 \\ 1 & 6 & 2 & 1 & 6 \\ -1 & 5 & 2 & -1 & 5 \end{vmatrix}$$
For M_z:
$$\begin{vmatrix} 2 & -3 & 10 & 2 & -3 \\ 1 & 2 & 6 & 1 & 2 \\ -1 & -1 & 5 & -1 & -1 \end{vmatrix}$$

Then det $(M_c) = 8 + 6 + (-1) - [(-2) + (-4) + (-6)] = 13 - (-12) = 25$

det $(M_x) = 40 + (-30) + (-6) - [10 + (-20) + (-36)] = 4 - (-46) = 50$

det $(M_y) = 24 + (-20) + 5 - [(-6) + 20 + 20] = 9 - (34) = -25$

det $(M_z) = 20 + 18 + (-10) - [(-20) + (-12) + (-15)] = 28 - (-47) = 75$

STEP 3 Use Cramer's Rule:

$$x = \frac{\det(M_x)}{\det(M_c)} = \frac{50}{25} = 2; y = \frac{\det(M_y)}{\det(M_c)} = \frac{-25}{25} = -1; z = \frac{\det(M_z)}{\det(M_c)} = \frac{75}{25} = 3$$

The solution is $(2, -1, -3)$.

Deriving Cramer's Rule for a Two-Equation System

One way to show that Cramer's Rule works for a system of two equations in two variables is to solve the general system of equations $\begin{matrix} ax + by = c \\ dx + ey = f \end{matrix}$ for x and y.

EXAMPLE 5

Solve the system $\begin{matrix} ax + by = c \\ dx + ey = f \end{matrix}$ **for x and y. Relate the solution to matrices and their determinants.**

STEP 1 Rewrite the system as a matrix equation.
$$\begin{bmatrix} a & b \\ d & e \end{bmatrix} \cdot \begin{bmatrix} x \\ y \end{bmatrix} = \begin{bmatrix} c \\ f \end{bmatrix}$$

STEP 2 Find the inverse of $\begin{bmatrix} a & b \\ d & e \end{bmatrix}$.

Because $\begin{vmatrix} a & b \\ d & e \end{vmatrix} = ae - bd$, the inverse of $\begin{bmatrix} a & b \\ d & e \end{bmatrix}$ is $\dfrac{1}{ae - bd} \cdot \begin{bmatrix} e & -b \\ -d & a \end{bmatrix}$.

STEP 3 Multiply both sides of the original equation by the inverse, on the left.

$$\frac{1}{ae - bd} \cdot \begin{bmatrix} e & -b \\ -d & a \end{bmatrix} \cdot \begin{bmatrix} a & b \\ d & e \end{bmatrix} \cdot \begin{bmatrix} x \\ y \end{bmatrix} = \frac{1}{ae - bd} \cdot \begin{bmatrix} e & -b \\ -d & a \end{bmatrix} \cdot \begin{bmatrix} c \\ f \end{bmatrix}$$

The left side is the identity matrix times $\begin{bmatrix} x \\ y \end{bmatrix}$.

The right side is $\dfrac{1}{ae - bd} \cdot \begin{bmatrix} ec - bf \\ -cd + af \end{bmatrix}$, so $\begin{bmatrix} x \\ y \end{bmatrix} = \begin{bmatrix} \dfrac{ce - bf}{ae - bd} \\ \dfrac{af - cd}{ae - bd} \end{bmatrix}$.

STEP 4 Corresponding elements are equal, so $x = \dfrac{ce - bf}{ae - bd}$ and $y = \dfrac{af - cd}{ae - bd}$.

STEP 5 Analyze these results.

The expressions for x and y have the same denominator, $ae - bd$, which is the determinant $\begin{vmatrix} a & b \\ d & e \end{vmatrix}$; notice that the determinant uses the coefficients for x and y in the system of equations. The numerator for x is $ce - bf$, which is $\begin{vmatrix} c & b \\ f & e \end{vmatrix}$, the determinant for the matrix that begins as the matrix of coefficients for the system, but replaces the x-coefficients with the column of constants. Similarly, the numerator for y is $af - cd$. That is $\begin{vmatrix} a & c \\ d & f \end{vmatrix}$, which begins as the matrix for the coefficients but replaces the y-coefficients with the column of constants.

The solution to the system $\begin{matrix} ax + by = c \\ dx + ey = f \end{matrix}$ is $x = \dfrac{\begin{vmatrix} c & b \\ f & e \end{vmatrix}}{\begin{vmatrix} a & b \\ d & e \end{vmatrix}}$ and $y = \dfrac{\begin{vmatrix} a & c \\ d & f \end{vmatrix}}{\begin{vmatrix} a & b \\ d & e \end{vmatrix}}$.

This pattern is called **Cramer's Rule**.

SEARCH

To see step-by-step videos of these problems, enter the page number into the SWadvantage.com Search Bar.

Watch Out

In Step 3, the product on the right side of an equation,

$$\frac{1}{ae - bd} \cdot \begin{bmatrix} ec - bf \\ -cd + af \end{bmatrix}$$

simplifies to the matrix

$$\begin{bmatrix} \dfrac{ce - bf}{ae - bd} \\ \dfrac{af - cd}{ae - bd} \end{bmatrix}.$$

Notice that each term in the matrix is multiplied by $\dfrac{1}{ae - bd}$.

Problem Solving and Variation

What Came Before?

- Translating a problem situation into an equation
- Systems of two and three linear equations

What's This About?

- Solving a variety of types of real world problems
- Transforming literal equations and formulas
- Solving variation equations and problems involving variation

Practical Apps

- Chemists use formulas, such as Boyle's Law, to find the volume of gases.
- Banks and loan agents use compound interest formulas when lending money.

Just for FUN!

Q: If I'm 5 years older than my sister, and 5 years ago I was twice her age, how old am I?

A: You really don't know how old you are? That's sad.

You can find more practice problems online by visiting:
www.SWadvantage.com

Modeling Word Problems

Diagrams and Word Problems

People often say that word problems are difficult or confusing. In fact, word problems are no more difficult than the mathematics used in them. The real problem often is that people do not know how take information from word problems and put it in a form that is useful for solving math problems.

One method that is useful for pulling information from word problems is diagramming. Diagramming is making a visual representation of information in a problem. A diagram can be a table, a simple geometric shape, a more complex drawing, or any other representation that makes it easier to visualize the information contained in the word problem.

EXAMPLE 1

Draw a diagram to display the information presented in the following word problem.

Before she leaves for vacation, Michaela needs to take her puppy, kitten, and goldfish to her parents' house. Michaela can only transport one pet at a time, and her parents aren't home right now. Michaela cannot leave the puppy and kitten alone together because they tend to fight, and she cannot leave the kitten and goldfish together because the kitten might eat the fish. How can Michaela get all three pets safely to her parents' house?

Because Michaela can transport only one animal at a time, she needs to make multiple trips. To solve the problem, draw a diagram that shows which pets are at Michaela's house, which pet she takes on each trip, and which pets are at her parents' house.

Michaela's House	Traveling	Parents' House	Explanation
Michaela, puppy, kitten, fish			Start
puppy, fish	Michaela, kitten →	Michaela, kitten	Michaela takes the kitten to her parents' house and returns home alone.
Michaela, puppy, fish	← Michaela	kitten	
puppy	Michaela, fish →	Michaela, kitten, fish	Michaela takes the fish to her parents' house and returns home with the kitten.
Michaela, puppy, kitten	← Michaela, kitten	fish	
kitten	Michaela, puppy →	Michaela, puppy, fish	Michaela takes the puppy to her parents' house and returns home alone.
Michaela, kitten	← Michaela	puppy, fish	
	Michaela, kitten →	Michaela, puppy, kitten, fish	Michaela takes the kitten to her parents' house.

It takes Michaela 3 round trips and 1 one-way trip to safely transport the pets.

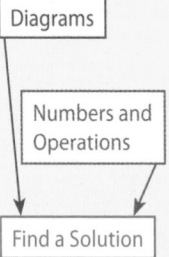

Words to Numbers

To solve word problems algebraically, first change words and phrases into mathematical expressions. The table shows common English phrases and their algebraic translations.

English		Algebra
• the sum of 2 and a number • a number increased by 2	• a number plus 2 • 2 more than a number	$x + 2$
• a number minus 2 • a number decreased by 2 • the difference between a number and 2	• a number less 2 • 2 less than a number	$x - 2$
• a number multiplied by 2 • the product of 2 and a number	• 2 times a number • 2 of a number	$2x$
• a number divided by 2 • the quotient of a number and 2	• one-half of a number	$\frac{x}{2}$
• a number is 2		$x = 2$
• a number is more than 2		$x > 2$
• a number is less than 2		$x < 2$
• a number is at least 2		$x \geq 2$
• a number is at most 2		$x \leq 2$

Need More HELP?

For more on algebraic expressions, see *Variables and Algebraic Expressions* in *Algebra* (p. 1422).

EXAMPLE 2

Translate each English sentence into an algebraic expression.

a. 13 is the sum of a number and 7.

STEP 1 Identify the English phrases.   13 is the sum of a number and 7.

STEP 2 Write the corresponding algebra translations. $13 =$ $x + 7$

The algebraic expression is $13 = x + 7$.

b. A number divided by 11 is at least 10 of another number.

STEP 1 Identify the English phrases.   A number divided by 11 is at least 10 of another number.

STEP 2 Write the corresponding algebra translations. $\frac{x}{11}$ $\geq$ $10y$

The algebraic expression is $\frac{x}{11} \geq 10y$.

Watch Out !

Several different English phrases might translate into the same algebraic expression. Any English phrase that shows the correct numbers, variables, operations, and relationships in the algebraic expression is acceptable.

EXAMPLE 3

Translate each algebraic expression into an English sentence.

a. $x - 22 = 3x$

STEP 1 Identify the algebraic expressions and operations. $x - 22$ $=$ $3x$

STEP 2 Write the corresponding English sentence.   22 less than a number is 3 times the number.

b. $x + 14 < y \div 10$

STEP 1 Identify the algebraic expressions and operations. $x + 14$ $<$ $y \div 10$

STEP 2 Write the sentence.   A number increased by 14 is less than one-tenth of another number.

SEARCH

To see step-by-step videos of these problems, enter the page number into the SWadvantage.com Search Bar.

Solving Word Problems

As with any task, it is helpful to have a plan, or an orderly list of steps, to follow when solving word problems. The following steps provide such a problem-solving plan.

STEP 1 Read the problem carefully. Determine what number or numbers need to be found.

STEP 2 Represent one unknown number with a suitable variable.

STEP 3 Use conditions stated in the problem to write expressions for other numbers.

STEP 4 Use additional conditions to find the relationship between expressions. Write the expressions algebraically. Connect them with the appropriate sign ($=$, $<$, $>$, $\leq$, or $\geq$.)

STEP 5 Solve the equation or inequality.

STEP 6 Check to see if the resulting solution matches the conditions stated in the problem.

EXAMPLE 4

SEARCH

To see step-by-step videos of these problems, enter the page number into the SWadvantage.com Search Bar.

In the 7th grade, $\frac{3}{4}$ of the students play soccer. If a total of 36 students play soccer, how many students are in the 7th grade? Use the 6-step problem-solving plan to solve.

STEP 1 Read the problem carefully and determine what number or numbers need to be found.
You need to find the total number of 7th graders.

STEP 2 Represent one unknown number with a suitable variable.
The only unknown is the number of students in 7th grade. Represent this with the variable s.

STEP 3 Use conditions stated in the problem to write expressions for other numbers.
The problem states that $\frac{3}{4}$ of the 7th graders play soccer. The word *of* signals multiplication, so use a multiplication expression to represent the number of soccer players.
$$\frac{3}{4}s$$

STEP 4 Use additional conditions to find the relationship between expressions. Write the expressions algebraically. Connect them with the appropriate sign.
The problem also states that 36 students play soccer, so this number is equal to the expression in Step 3. $\qquad 36 = \frac{3}{4}s$

STEP 5 Solve the equation.

Write the equation.	$36 = \frac{3}{4}s$
Divide both sides by $\frac{3}{4}$.	$36 \div \frac{3}{4} = \frac{3}{4}s \div \frac{3}{4}$
Multiply both sides by the multiplicative inverse of $\frac{3}{4}$.	$36\left(\frac{4}{3}\right) = \frac{3}{4}s\left(\frac{4}{3}\right)$
Simplify.	$48 = s$

STEP 6 Check to see if the resulting solution matches the conditions stated in the problem.
Because a fraction of the students in 7th grade play soccer, we know that the total number of students is greater than the number of soccer players, and $48 > 36$. Because that fraction is greater than $\frac{1}{2}$, we also know that more than half of the total students play soccer, and $36 > 24$. This is a reasonable answer.

There are 48 students in 7th grade.

EXAMPLE 5

The sum of two integers is 42. One of the numbers is 12 less than the other. What are the numbers? Use the 6-step problem-solving plan to solve.

STEP 1 Read the problem carefully and determine what number or numbers need to be found. There are two numbers that need to be found—the two integers mentioned in the first sentence of the problem.

STEP 2 Represent one unknown number with a suitable variable. Use n to represent one of the integers.

STEP 3 Use conditions stated in the problem to write expressions for other numbers. The problem states that "one of the numbers is 12 less than the other." Because we assigned n to represent one of the numbers, the second one can be represented by the subtraction expression $n - 12$.

STEP 4 Use additional conditions to find the relationship between expressions. Write the expressions algebraically. Connect them with the appropriate sign. The sum of the two numbers is given, so set the sum of the expressions that have been assigned to the two numbers equal to 42.
$$n + (n - 12) = 42$$

STEP 5 Solve the equation.

Write the equation.	$n + (n - 12) = 42$
Combine like terms.	$2n - 12 = 42$
Add 12 to both sides.	$2n - 12 + 12 = 42 + 12$
Simplify.	$2n = 54$
Divide both sides by 2.	$n = 27$

To find the other number, use the expression $n - 12$.

Write the expression and substitute 27 for n.　　$n - 12 = 27 - 12 = 15$

STEP 6 Check to see if the resulting solution matches the conditions stated in the problem. The two integers have a sum of 42 and a difference of 12. We already know that their difference is 12, because we used that condition to find the second integer.

Write the equation.	$27 + 15 \overset{?}{=} 42$
Simplify.	$42 = 42$

The two integers are 27 and 15.

> **Watch Out !**
>
> Be careful to remember how you represent each variable. For example, the variables in Example 5 could be expressed as n and $n + 12$, with n being the smaller number instead of the larger number. Either representation is valid. Just keep track of what each representation stands for.

EXAMPLE 6

The perimeter of a rectangle is 40 cm. Find the length and the width if the length is three times the width.

Identify the variables.	width $= w$; length $= 3w$
Write the equation for the perimeter.	$2(w) + 2(3w) = 40$
Simplify to solve for the width.	$8w = 40$
	$w = 5$
Find the length.	$3w = 3 \cdot 5 = 15$

Number and Integer Problems

Solving Problems with Integers

The six-step problem solving plan was introduced in the last lesson. This plan applies to several different sets of numbers, including integers.

Need More HELP ?

For more on sets of numbers, see *Rational Numbers and Number Sets* in *Numbers and Operations* (Book 1, p. 268).

The six-step problem-solving plan can be found in *Modeling Word Problems* (p. 1820).

Watch Out !

Realize that there is usually more than one way to represent numbers in a problem. For example, you could have chosen the expressions mentioned in Example 1 for the three integers, or you could have chosen $n - 1$, n, and $n + 1$, or $n - 2$, $n - 1$, and n.

EXAMPLE 1

The sum of 3 consecutive integers is −84. What are the integers?

STEP 1 Read the problem carefully and determine what number or numbers need to be found.
The numbers that need to be found are the 3 consecutive integers whose sum is −84.

STEP 2 Represent one unknown number with a suitable variable.
Represent the first of the integers with the variable n.

STEP 3 Use conditions stated in the problem to write expressions for other numbers.
Because the integers are consecutive, we can say that the second integer is 1 more than the first, and the third integer is 2 more than the first.

2nd integer: $n + 1$
3rd integer: $n + 2$

STEP 4 Use additional conditions to find expressions that are equal. Then write these expressions algebraically and connect them with an equal sign.
The sum of the 3 integers is −84, so write the sum of the expressions on one side of the equal sign, and −84 on the other.

$n + (n + 1) + (n + 2) = -84$

STEP 5 Solve the equation.

Write the equation.	$n + (n + 1) + (n + 2) = -84$
Remove parentheses and combine like terms.	$3n + 3 = -84$
Simplify.	$3n = -87$
Divide both sides of the equation by 3.	$\dfrac{3n}{3} = \dfrac{-87}{3}$
Simplify.	$n = -29$
Find the 2nd and 3rd integers.	2nd integer: $-29 + 1 = -28$
	3rd integer: $-29 + 2 = -27$

STEP 6 Check to see if the resulting solution matches the conditions stated in the problem.
The two conditions in the problem are 1) the integers are consecutive; and 2) the sum of the integers is −84.

1) −27, −28, and −29 are consecutive integers
2) $-27 + (-28) + (-29) \overset{?}{=} -84$
   $-84 = -84$

The three integers are −27, −28, and −29.

Solving Problems with Rational Numbers

Recall that, in addition to the set of integers, rational numbers include fractions, decimals, and percents.

EXAMPLE 2

During marching band auditions, 75% of the students who auditioned for the percussion section were selected. If the percussion section has 15 members, how many students auditioned?

SEARCH

To see step-by-step videos of these problems, enter the page number into the SWadvantage.com Search Bar.

STEP 1 Read the problem carefully and determine what number or numbers need to be found.
The number of students who auditioned for the percussion section needs to be found.

STEP 2 Represent one unknown number with a suitable variable.
Represent the number of auditioning students with s.

STEP 3 Use conditions stated in the problem to write expressions for other numbers.

Because 75% of the students who auditioned were selected, multiply the number of students who auditioned by 0.75.

$0.75s$

STEP 4 Use additional conditions to find expressions that are equal. Then write these expressions algebraically and connect them with an equal sign.

Use two expressions to show how many students were selected for the percussion section.

$0.75s = 15$

STEP 5 Solve the equation.

Write the equation.	$0.75s = 15$
Divide both sides of the equation by 0.75.	$\dfrac{0.75s}{0.75} = \dfrac{15}{0.75}$
Simplify.	$s = 20$

STEP 6 Check to see if the resulting solution matches the conditions stated in the problem.

Because 75% < 100%, fewer students were selected than auditioned. Because 15 < 20, this answer is reasonable.

The number of students who auditioned was 20.

EXAMPLE 3

Sofia earns 1.6 times her normal hourly rate for every hour she works over 35 hours per week. Last week, she was paid $525.80 for working 43 hours. What is Sofia's normal hourly pay rate?

Let Sofia's normal rate of pay equal p. Her total pay is the sum of the amounts she earned for the first 35 hours she worked, and the remaining 8 hours.

Write the equation.	$35p + 8(1.6p) = 525.80$
Simplify.	$35p + 12.8p = 525.8$
Combine like terms.	$47.8p = 525.8$
Divide both sides of the equation by 47.8.	$\dfrac{47.8p}{47.8} = \dfrac{525.8}{47.8}$
Simplify.	$p = 11$

Sofia's normal hourly rate of pay is $11.00.

Age Problems

Solving Problems about Age

Problems dealing with the ages of subjects are common. This is because, while the difference between two ages is always the same, ratios of those ages change each year.

EXAMPLE 1

Naomi is 6 years older than Amy. Five years ago, Naomi's age was 3 times Amy's. How old is each girl now?

STEP 1 Read the problem carefully and determine what number or numbers need to be found. The problem asks for Amy's and Naomi's ages.

STEP 2 Represent one unknown number with a suitable variable.
Represent Amy's age with the variable a.

STEP 3 Use conditions stated in the problem to write expressions for other numbers.

The problem discusses Amy's and Naomi's ages now, and their ages 5 years ago. All of these can be written as expressions based on Amy's current age (a).

Naomi's current age: $6 + a$
Amy's age 5 years ago: $a - 5$
Naomi's age 5 years ago: $3(a - 5)$

STEP 4 Use additional conditions to find expressions that are equal. Then write these expressions algebraically and connect them with an equal sign.

There are two different ways to write Naomi's age 5 years ago. The first is given in Step 3. The second is her current age minus 5 years.

$$3(a - 5) = (6 + a) - 5$$

STEP 5 Solve the equation.

Write the equation.	$3(a - 5) = (6 + a) - 5$
Clear parentheses and combine like terms on each side.	$3a - 15 = 1 + a$
Subtract a from both sides of the equation.	$3a - 15 - a = 1 + a - a$
Combine like terms.	$2a - 15 = 1$
Add 15 to both sides of the equation.	$2a - 15 + 15 = 1 + 15$
Combine like terms.	$2a = 16$
Divide both sides of the equation by 2.	$\frac{2a}{2} = \frac{16}{2}$
Simplify. This is Amy's age.	$a = 8$
Add 6 to find Naomi's age.	$6 + a = 14$

STEP 6 Check to see if the resulting solution matches the conditions stated in the problem.
Condition 1: Naomi is 6 years older than Amy. We know this is true because we added 6 to Amy's age to find Naomi's age.

Condition 2: Five years ago, Naomi's age was 3 times Amy's

$$14 - 5 \overset{?}{=} 3(8 - 5)$$
$$9 \overset{?}{=} 3(3)$$
$$9 = 9 \checkmark$$

Amy is 8 years old and Naomi is 14 years old.

GOT TO KNOW!

Step 3 of the 6-Step Problem Solving Plan

Write expressions to cover every value in the problem. Even though you might not use them all in the equation you use to solve the problem, they can help you come up other expressions that are useful.

In Example 1, writing an expression for Amy's age 5 years ago leads to one of the expressions for Naomi's age 5 years ago.

EXAMPLE 2

Chung is 13 and Javonn is 11. How long ago was Chung twice as old as Javonn?

STEP 1 Read the problem carefully and determine what number or numbers need to be found.
The problem asks for the number of years in the past that Chung was twice as old as Javonn.

STEP 2 Represent one unknown number with a suitable variable.
Represent the number of years with the variable y.

STEP 3 Use conditions stated in the problem to write expressions for other numbers.
The problem gives the boys' current ages. Use y to express the boys' ages in the past.
Chung's past age: $13 - y$ Javonn's past age: $11 - y$

STEP 4 Use additional conditions to find expressions that are equal. Then write these expressions algebraically and connect them with an equal sign.
We are trying to find a time when Chung's past age was twice Javonn's past age.
$13 - y = 2(11 - y)$

STEP 5 Solve the equation.

Write the equation.	$13 - y = 2(11 - y)$
Use the Distributive Property.	$13 - y = 22 - 2y$
Add $2y$ to both sides of the equation.	$13 - y + 2y = 22 - 2y + 2y$
Combine like terms.	$13 + y = 22$
Subtract 13 from both sides of the equation.	$13 + y - 13 = 22 - 13$
Simplify.	$y = 9$

STEP 6 Check to see if Chung was twice as old.
$$13 - 9 \stackrel{?}{=} 2(11 - 9)$$
$$4 = 4 \checkmark$$

Chung was twice as old as Javonn 9 years ago.

SEARCH

To see step-by-step videos of these problems, enter the page number into the SWadvantage.com Search Bar.

Need More

HELP ?

For more on the Distributive Property, see *The Distributive Property* in *Algebra* (p. 1410).

EXAMPLE 3

Tanya is twice as old as Mary. Fourteen years ago, Tanya was 4 times as old as Mary. How old is Tanya?

Mary's current age $= m$; Tanya's current age $= 2m$; Mary's age 14 years ago $= m - 14$; Tanya's age 14 years ago $= 4(m - 14)$

Write an equation using 2 expressions for Tanya's past age.	$4(m - 14) = 2m - 14$
Use the Distributive Property.	$4m - 56 = 2m - 14$
Subtract $2m$ from both sides of the equation.	$4m - 56 - 2m = 2m - 14 - 2m$
Combine like terms.	$2m - 56 = -14$
Add 56 to both sides of the equation.	$2m - 56 + 56 = -14 + 56$
Simplify. This is Tanya's age.	$2m = 42$
Divide both sides by 2. Simplify. This is Mary's age.	$m = 21$
Check whether Tanya's age 14 years ago was 4 times Mary's.	$42 - 14 \stackrel{?}{=} 4(21 - 14)$
	$28 = 28 \checkmark$

Tanya is 42 years old.

Coin Problems

Solving Problems about Coins

Another popular category of word problems is those dealing with coins. Coin problems are popular because of the different values of the coins.

EXAMPLE 1

Jose has a total of 26 coins that are quarters and dollars in his pocket. If the total value of the coins is $17.00, how many of each type of coin does Jose have?

STEP 1 The problem asks for the number of quarters and the number of dollar coins that Jose has in his pocket.

STEP 2 Represent the number of quarters with the variable q.

STEP 3 You also need to find the number of dollar coins.
$$26 - q$$

STEP 4 You know that each quarter is worth $0.25, and each dollar coin is worth $1.00, and that the total value of the coins is $17.00.
$$0.25q + (26 - q) = 17$$

STEP 5 Solve the equation.

Write the equation.	$0.25q + (26 - q) = 17$
Remove parentheses and combine like terms.	$-0.75q + 26 = 17$
Subtract 26 from both sides of the equation.	$-0.75q + 26 - 26 = 17 - 26$
Simplify.	$-0.75q = -9$
Divide both sides of the equation by -0.75.	$q = 12$
Subtract 12 from 26 to find the number of dollar coins.	$26 - 12 = 14$

STEP 6 Check that the total value of these numbers of quarters and dollar coins is $17.00.
$$0.25(12) + 14 \stackrel{?}{=} 17$$
$$3 + 14 \stackrel{?}{=} 17$$
$$17 = 17$$

Jose has 12 quarters and 14 dollar coins.

> **Watch Out !**
>
> Since these problems deal with coins, decimal values should be used for both the individual coin values and the total values.

EXAMPLE 2

Maria has a total of 100 nickels and dimes. The total value of the coins is $7.65. How many nickels does Maria have?

Let n = number of nickels.

Write the equation for the value of the coins.	$0.05n + 0.1(100 - n) = 7.65$
Multiply.	$0.05n + 10 - 0.1n = 7.65$
Combine like terms.	$-0.05n + 10 = 7.65$
Subtract 10 from both sides of the equation.	$-0.05n + 10 - 10 = 7.65 - 10$
Simplify.	$-0.05n = -2.35$
Divide both sides of the equation by -0.05.	$n = 47$

Maria has 47 nickels.

EXAMPLE 3

James has twice as many nickels as pennies, twice as many dimes as nickels, twice as many quarters as dimes, and twice as many dollar coins as quarters. If the total value of these coins is \$92.55, how many of each coin does James have?

SEARCH

To see step-by-step videos of these problems, enter the page number into the SWadvantage.com Search Bar.

METHOD 1   Use dollar values. These show the portion of 1 dollar for each coin.

STEP 1 The problem asks for the numbers of pennies, nickels, dimes, quarters, and dollar coins that James has.

STEP 2 Represent the number of pennies with the variable p.

STEP 3 For each increasing denomination of coin, there are twice as many coins as the next lower denomination. You can express all of these by relating them to the number of pennies.
nickels: $2p$
dimes: $2(2p) = 4p$
quarters: $2(4p) = 8p$
dollar coins: $2(8p) = 16p$

STEP 4 Since the total value of the coins is \$92.55, you can use the values of each denomination to write an equation.
$0.01p + 0.05(2p) + 0.1(4p) + 0.25(8p) + 16p = 92.55$

STEP 5 Solve the equation.

Write the equation.	$0.01p + 0.05(2p) + 0.1(4p) + 0.25(8p) + 16p = 92.55$
Multiply.	$0.01p + 0.1p + 0.4p + 2p + 16p = 92.55$
Combine like terms.	$18.51p = 92.55$
Divide both sides by 18.51.	$p = 5$
Find the number of nickels.	$2p = 10$
Find the number of dimes.	$4p = 20$
Find the number of quarters.	$8p = 40$
Find the number of dollar coins.	$16p = 80$

STEP 6 Check whether the total value of these numbers of coins is \$92.55.
$5(0.01) + 10(0.05) + 20(0.1) + 40(0.25) + 80(1) \overset{?}{=} 92.55$
$0.05 + 0.5 + 2 + 10 + 80 \overset{?}{=} 92.55$
$92.55 = 92.55$

METHOD 2   Use cent values. These show how many cents each value equals.

Write the equation.	$p + 5(2p) + 10(4p) + 25(8p) + 100(16p) = 9255$
Multiply.	$p + 10p + 40p + 200p + 1600p = 9255$
Combine like terms.	$1851p = 9255$
Divide both sides by 1851.	$p = 5$
Find the number of nickels.	$2p = 10$
Find the number of dimes.	$4p = 20$
Find the number of quarters.	$8p = 40$
Find the number of dollar coins.	$16p = 80$

Distance Problems

Distance, Rate, and Time

Movies and television shows often use distance problems to show how difficult math is. The classic example is the kind of problem that begins "A train leaves New York at 10:00. . . ". Using the Distance Formula, or Distance = Rate × Time, these and other problems involving distance are easy to solve.

EXAMPLE 1

Train A leaves City A for City B at 10:00 A.M., traveling at a rate of 70 mph. At the same time, Train B leaves City B for City A, traveling at a rate of 60 mph. If City A and City B are 455 miles apart by rail, how long will it take the two trains to pass one another?

STEP 1 Read the problem carefully and determine what number or numbers need to be found.

The problem asks for the amount of time it will take for the two trains to pass one another.

STEP 2 Represent one unknown number with a suitable variable.

Represent the amount of time with the variable t.

STEP 3 Use conditions stated in the problem to write expressions for other numbers.

We can use the formula $d = rt$ to show the distance each train travels over time t.

Train A: $d = 70t$ Train B: $d = 60t$

STEP 4 Use additional conditions to find expressions that are equal. Then write these expressions algebraically and connect them with an equal sign.

We want to know how long it will take both trains to be the same distance from one of the two cities. We can set one of the distances equal to 455 minus the other distance.

Distance A = 455 − Distance B

$70t = 455 − 60t$

STEP 5 Solve the equation.

Write the equation.	$70t = 455 − 60t$
Add $60t$ to both sides of the equation.	$70t + 60t = 455 − 60t + 60t$
Combine like terms.	$130t = 455$
Divide both sides of the equation by 130.	$\dfrac{130t}{130} = \dfrac{455}{130}$
Simplify.	$t = 3.5$

STEP 6 Check to see if the resulting solution matches the conditions stated in the problem.

Find the distance that each train travels in 3.5 hours. This is the distance of each train from its originating city.

Train A: $d = rt$ Train B: $d = rt$

$\quad\quad\ = 70(3.5)$ $\quad\quad\ = 60(3.5)$

$\quad\quad\ = 245$ $\quad\quad\ = 210$

Find the distance of Train A from City B after 3.5 hours by subtracting its distance traveled from 455 miles.

$455 − 245 = 210$

This is the same distance that Train B has traveled from City B.

The trains will pass one another after traveling for 3.5 hours.

Try It This Way

If you are a visual learner, distance, rate, and time problems are often easier to solve if you sketch the information in the problem.

In Example 1, sketch the cities, labeling the distance between them and the location of the trains, although the sketch is not part of the actual solution.

GOT TO KNOW!

Units of Measurement

Use clues from the context of the problem to determine what units of measurement to use. In Example 1, we knew that the time was measured in hours because the rates were given in miles per hour.

EXAMPLE 2

It took Kyra 14.2 hours to drive 975 miles. During the trip, the highway speed limits change back and forth several times between 65 mph and 75 mph. If Kyra drove at the speed limit for the entire trip, how long was she traveling at each speed?

SEARCH

To see step-by-step videos of these problems, enter the page number into the SWadvantage.com Search Bar.

STEP 1 Read the problem carefully and determine what number or numbers need to be found.

The problem asks for the amount of time Kyra drove at 65 mph and the amount of time she drove at 75 mph.

STEP 2 Represent one unknown number with a suitable variable.

Represent the time driven at 65 mph with the variable t.

STEP 3 Use conditions stated in the problem to write expressions for other numbers.

Distance at 65 mph: $d = 65t$
Time at 75 mph: $14.2 - t$
Distance at 75 mph: $d = 75(14.2 - t)$

STEP 4 Use additional conditions to find expressions that are equal. Then write these expressions algebraically and connect them with an equal sign.

The total traveled was 975 miles, so this is the sum of the two distances.

$$65t + 75(14.2 - t) = 975$$

STEP 5 Solve the equation.

Write the equation.	$65t + 75(14.2 - t) = 975$
Apply the Distributive Property.	$65t + 1065 - 75t = 975$
Combine like terms.	$-10t + 1065 = 975$
Subtract 1065 from both sides of the equation.	$-10t + 1065 - 1065 = 975 - 1065$
Simplify.	$-10t = -90$
Divide both sides of the equation by -10.	$\dfrac{-10t}{-10} = \dfrac{-90}{-10}$
Simplify. This is the time traveled at 65 mph.	$t = 9$
Find the time traveled at 75 mph.	$14.2 - 9 = 5.2$

STEP 6 Check to see if the resulting solution matches the conditions stated in the problem.

Find the distance traveled at each speed.

65 mph: $d = rt$ 75 mph: $d = rt$
      $= 65(9)$ $= 75(5.2)$
      $= 585$ $= 390$

Add the distances to check whether the sum is the same as Kyra's total distance traveled.

$$585 + 390 \stackrel{?}{=} 975$$
$$975 = 975$$

Kyra drove at 65 mph for 9 hours and at 75 mph for 5.2 hours.

Need More

HELP?

For more on dimensional analysis, see *Dimensional Analysis* in *Measurement* (Book 1, p. 492).

Using Reflections to Find Distances

Finding distances does not always involve solving equations. There are times when a graphical representation can be used to determine the closest point to two other points.

EXAMPLE 3

Metroville and Patrickton are working together to build a regional airport. They want to choose a location that is along a nearby river, as that minimizes the amount of new road that needs to be built to the site. Where should the airport be built?

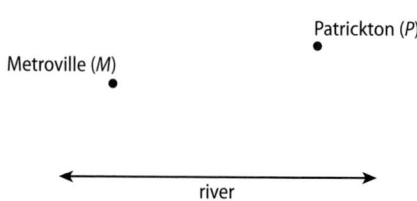

The problem is asking for the location of the airport (A), so that $MA + PA$ is the least possible value.

Need More
HELP ?
For more on the Triangle Inequality Theorem, see *Triangle Inequalities* in *Geometry* (Book 1, p. 664).

STEP 1 Draw Point P' so that it is the reflection of Point P across the river. Now, for any Point A that lies on the river, $PA = P'A$, and $MA + PA = MA + P'A$.

STEP 2 By the Triangle Inequality Theorem, $MA + P'A$ is the least possible distance when M, A, and P' are collinear, so draw a line connecting M and P', and label the point where this line crosses the river as A.

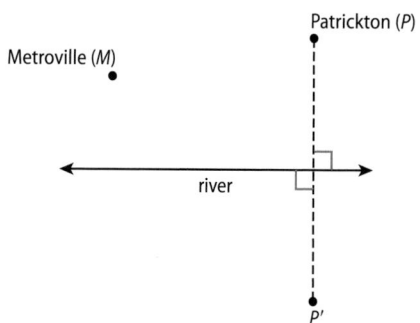

STEP 3 Draw lines connecting Points M and A and points P and A. These lines show the distances from the two cities to the new airport location.

STEP 4 Check the reasonableness of this answer. Point A is much closer to Point M than to Point P, so this location may not seem like the correct answer. To test it, draw a few more points along the river, and find the sums of their distances from the two cities.

$MA + PA = 0.81 + 1.17 = 1.98$
$MA' + PA' = 0.58 + 1.58 = 2.16$
$MA'' + PA'' = 1.12 + 0.93 = 2.05$
$MA''' + PA''' = 1.5 + 0.83 = 2.33$

Try It
This Way
In problems such as the one featured in Example 3, it is possible to use actual distances by using right triangles and the Pythagorean Theorem rather than just diagramming a physical location.

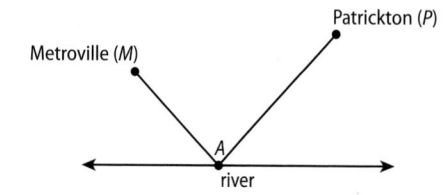

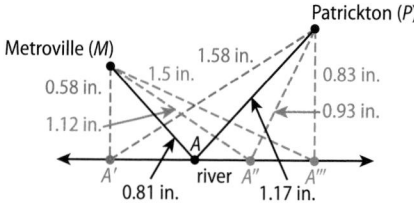

Geometry can be useful in other ways when solving distance problems.

SEARCH

To see step-by-step videos of these problems, enter the page number into the SWadvantage.com Search Bar.

EXAMPLE 4

The towns of Diretown, River City, and Markville do not lie in a straight line. The distance from Diretown to River City is 244 miles, and the distance from River City to Markville is 307 miles. A friend told you that he thinks the distance from Markville to Diretown is 613 miles. Can your friend be correct? Explain your answer.

Draw a diagram using the information from the problem. Use dots to represent the three towns, and label the known distances. Any three points in a plane can serve as the vertices of a triangle, so the three towns form a triangle.

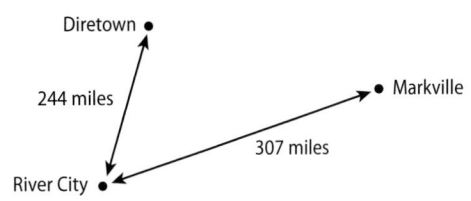

By the Triangle Inequality Theorem, the sum of any two sides of a triangle must be greater than the third side. Test whether this is true for the three distances in the problem.

Write the inequality. $244 + 307 \overset{?}{>} 613$
Add. $551 \ngtr 613$

It is not possible that the distance from Markville to Diretown is 613 miles. By the Triangle Inequality Theorem, the distance must be less than 551 miles.

EXAMPLE 5

The diagram at the right shows the relative positions of Cities X, Y, and Z. How far apart can Cities Z and X be?

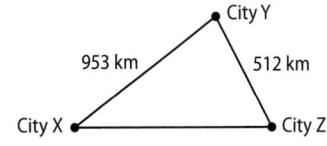

Use the Triangle Inequality Theorem to set up an inequality to solve this problem.
$953 + 512 > d$
$1465 \quad > d$

Cities Z and X must be fewer than 1465 miles apart.

EXAMPLE 6

Eric wanted to build a bridge across a stream on his property. He drew the diagram at the right to determine the distance across the stream. What is the distance across?

Eric's diagram shows similar right triangles. One of the legs of the larger triangle is the distance across the stream. Use the fact that corresponding sides of similar triangles are proportional to find the answer.

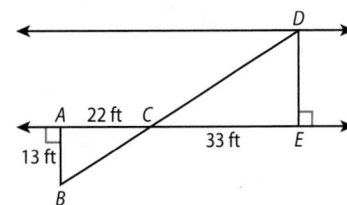

Set up the proportion. $\dfrac{AB}{ED} = \dfrac{AC}{EC}$

Substitute values from the figure. $\dfrac{13}{DE} = \dfrac{22}{33}$

Find the cross products. $22DE = 13(33)$

Simplify. $22DE = 429$

Divide both sides by 22. $\dfrac{22DE}{22} = \dfrac{429}{22}$

Simplify. $DE = 19.5$

The distance across the stream is 19.5 feet.

Mixture Problems

Using Diagrams to Solve Mixture Problems

Mixture problems involve mixing quantities of different values to create a quantity with another value. One method to solve mixture problems is to draw a diagram.

SEARCH

To see step-by-step videos of these problems, enter the page number into the SWadvantage.com Search Bar.

EXAMPLE 1

A doctor has 5 milliliters (mL) of a 60% antibiotic solution. How much water must she add to make a 25% antibiotic solution?

STEP 1 Draw a diagram to represent the starting solution.
There are 5 mL of solution, so start by drawing 5 containers, each representing 1 mL of solution. Because each mL is 60% antibiotic, divide each container into 5 equal sections. Shade 2 sections in each container blue to indicate water, and leave 3 in each white to indicate antibiotic.

STEP 2 Add 0.4 mL of water to each container. Because each section equals 0.2 mL, add 2 blue sections to the bottom of each container. This makes each container 3 parts antibiotic and 4 parts water; 3 of the 7 parts are antibiotic. Find this percentage.
$\frac{3}{7} \approx 42.9\%$, so more water is needed.

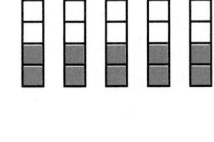

STEP 3 Add another 0.4 mL of water to each container.
Add 2 blue sections to the bottom of each container. This makes each container 3 parts antibiotic and 6 parts water; 3 of the 9 parts are antibiotic. Find this percentage.
$\frac{3}{9} \approx 33.3\%$, so more water is needed.

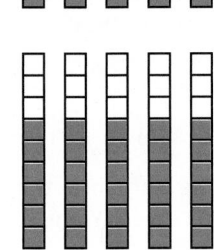

Need More HELP?

For more on writing fractions as percents, see *Decimals, Fractions, and Percents* in *Numbers and Operations* (Book 1, p. 272).

STEP 4 Add another 0.4 mL of water to each container. Add 2 blue sections to the bottom of each container. Each container is 3 parts antibiotic and 8 parts water; 3 of the 11 parts are antibiotic. Find this percentage.
$\frac{3}{11} \approx 27.3\%$, so more water is needed, but not much.

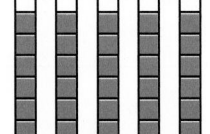

STEP 5 Add 0.2 mL of water to each container. Add 1 blue section to the bottom of each container. This makes each container 3 parts antibiotic and 9 parts water; 3 of the 12 parts are antibiotic. Find this percentage.
$\frac{3}{12} = 25\%$

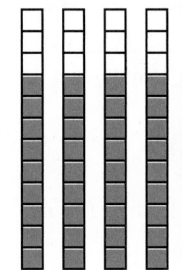

STEP 6 Find the total amount of water added.
Each of the 5 containers got an additional 1.4 mL of water. Multiply to find the total added.
$5 \times 1.4 = 7$

The doctor needs to add 7 mL of water to get a 25% antibiotic solution.

EXAMPLE 2

Isabel has 7 kiloliters (kL) of a 75% alcohol solution. How many kiloliters of water must she add to have a 25% alcohol solution?

STEP 1 Draw a diagram to represent the starting solution.
There are 7 kL of solution, so start by drawing 7 containers, each representing 1 kL of solution. Because each kL is 75% alcohol, divide each container into 4 equal sections. Shade 3 sections in each container yellow to indicate alcohol, and shade 1 section in each container blue to indicate water.

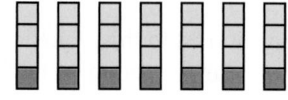

STEP 2 Add 0.5 kL of water to each container. Because each section represents 0.25 kL of solution, add 2 blue sections to the bottom of each container. This makes each container 3 parts alcohol and 3 parts water; 3 of the 6 parts are alcohol. Find this percentage.

$$\frac{3}{6} = \frac{1}{2} = 50\%$$

More water is needed.

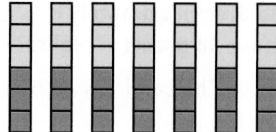

STEP 3 Add 0.5 kL more water to each container.
Add 2 blue sections to the bottom of each container. This makes each container 3 parts alcohol and 5 parts water; 3 of the 8 parts are alcohol. Find this percentage.

$$\frac{3}{8} = 37.5\%$$

More water is needed.

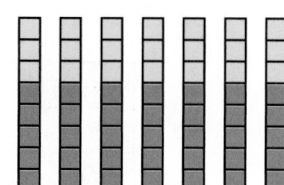

STEP 4 Add yet 0.5 kL more water to each container.

Add 2 blue sections to the bottom of each container. This makes each container 3 parts alcohol and 7 parts water; 3 of the 10 parts are alcohol. Find this percentage.

$$\frac{3}{10} = 30\%$$

More water is needed.

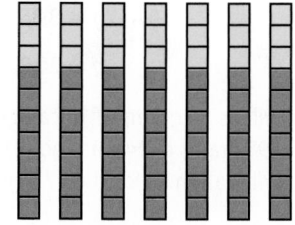

STEP 5 Again, add 0.5 kL water to each container.

Add 2 blue sections to the bottom of each container. This makes each container 3 parts alcohol and 9 parts water; 3 of the 12 parts are alcohol. Find this percentage.

$$\frac{3}{12} = \frac{1}{4} = 25\%$$

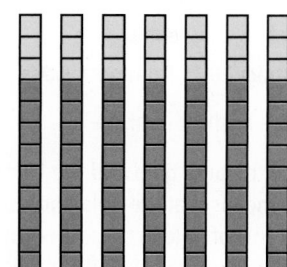

STEP 6 Find the total amount of water added.
Initially, each container contained 1 kiloliter. It now contains three times as much.
So, 2 kiloliters of water were added to each container. Seven containers were used, so:

$$7 \times 2 \text{ kL of water} = 14 \text{ kL of water were added.}$$

Isabel needs to add 14 kiloliters of water to get a 25% alcohol solution.

Using Tables and Equations to Solve Mixture Problems

As you saw, pictures provide a trial-and-error method for solving mixture problems. This method becomes more difficult to use as the percents in the solutions become more complicated to display graphically.

In contrast to this, equations work easily for any percent. The equations can sometimes be confusing to set up, so tables help to organize the information given in the problem.

EXAMPLE 3

Fourteen carat gold is approximately 58.3% pure gold, while eighteen carat gold is 75% pure gold. Approximately how much pure gold must a goldsmith mix with fourteen carat gold to make 50 grams of eighteen carat gold?

STEP 1 The problem asks for the amount of pure gold the goldsmith needs.

STEP 2 Represent one unknown number with a suitable variable.

Represent the amount of pure gold with the variable g.

STEP 3 Use a table to show the different relationships. Multiply across each row to find the values for the last column.

	Grams	Percent Gold	Total Grams Gold
14 carat gold	$50 - g$	58.3%	$0.583(50 - g)$
pure gold	g	100%	g
18 carat gold	50	75%	$50(0.75) = 37.5$

Need More
HELP ?

For more on writing decimals as percents, see *Decimals, Fractions, and Percents* in *Numbers and Operations* (Book 1, p. 272).

STEP 4 When the goldsmith mixes the 14 carat gold and the pure gold to get 50 grams of 18 carat gold, the weight of the gold in the final mixture will be 37.5 grams. Add the grams of 14 carat gold to the grams of pure gold, and set it equal to 37.5.

$0.583(50 - g) + g = 37.5$

STEP 5 Solve the equation.

Write the equation.	$0.583(50 - g) + g = 37.5$
Apply the Distributive Property.	$29.15 - 0.583g + g = 37.5$
Combine like terms.	$29.15 + 0.417g = 37.5$
Subtract 29.15 from both sides of the equation.	$0.417g = 8.35$
Divide both sides of the equation by 0.417.	$g \approx 20.02$

STEP 6 Once the pure gold and the 14 carat gold are mixed, there will be 50 grams of 18 carat gold. This means that the goldsmith starts with $50 - 20.02 = 29.98$ grams of 14 carat gold. Use the percents of gold in these amounts to check whether the combination yields the 37.5 grams of gold in 50 grams of 18 carat gold.

$20.02 + 0.583(29.98) \overset{?}{=} 37.5$

$37.49834 \approx 37.5$ ✓

The goldsmith needs to use approximately 20.02 grams of pure gold.

EXAMPLE 4

Aaliyah needs 150 liters of a 45% sulfuric acid solution. The laboratory only has 20% and 60% sulfuric acid solutions. How much of each will Aaliyah need to mix to get what she needs?

SEARCH

To see step-by-step videos of these problems, enter the page number into the SWadvantage.com Search Bar.

STEP 1 The problem asks for the amounts of the 20% and 60% solutions that Aaliyah needs.

STEP 2 Represent the amount of 20% solution with the variable a.

STEP 3 Use a table to show relationships. Multiply across each row to find values for the last column.

	Liters	Percent Acid	Total Liters Acid
20% Solution	a	20%	$0.2a$
60% Solution	$150 - a$	60%	$0.6(150 - a)$
45% Solution	150	45%	$0.45(150) = 67.5$

STEP 4 When Aaliyah mixes the 20% and 60% solutions to get 150 liters of 45% solution, the volume of acid in the final solution will be 67.5 liters. Add the liters acid in the 20% solution to the liters of acid in the 60% solution, and set it equal to 67.5.

$0.2a + 0.6(150 - a) = 67.5$

STEP 5 Solve the equation.

Write the equation.	$0.2a + 0.6(150 - a) = 67.5$
Apply the Distributive Property.	$0.2a + 90 - 0.6a = 67.5$
Combine like terms.	$90 - 0.4a = 67.5$
Subtract 90 from both sides of the equation.	$-0.4a = -22.5$
Divide both sides by -0.4. This is the volume of the 20% solution.	$a = 56.25$
Find the volume of the 60% solution.	$150 - 56.25 = 93.75$

STEP 6 Use the percent of acid in each solution to check whether the combination yields the 67.5 liters of acid in 150 liters of the 45% solution.

$0.2(56.25) + 0.6(93.75) \stackrel{?}{=} 67.5$

$67.50 = 67.5 ✓$

Aaliyah needs to mix 56.25 liters of 20% sulfuric acid solution with 93.75 liters of 60% sulfuric acid solution to obtain 150 liters of 45% sulfuric acid solution.

Tables and Mixture Problems

Concentration	Volume	Percent Substance	Total Volume Substance
1	V	$a\%$	$0.01(a)(V)$
2	Total $- V$	$b\%$	$0.01(b)(\text{Total} - V)$
Final	Total	$c\%$	$0.01(c)(\text{Total})$

Interest Problems

Simple Interest

Interest is the fee paid for the use of money. When you borrow money from a bank, you pay interest; when you deposit money in a savings account, the bank pays you interest. Interest is a percentage of the **principal**, which is the amount of money borrowed or deposited.

There are two types of interest, the first of which is *simple interest*. **Simple interest** is the amount of interest paid only on the principal. When solving problems involving simple interest, use the formula

$$I = Prt$$

where I = the amount of interest, P = the principal, r = the interest rate per time period (stated as a decimal), and t = the number of time periods.

SEARCH

To see step-by-step videos of these problems, enter the page number into the SWadvantage.com Search Bar.

EXAMPLE 1

Diego's parents are saving money for his college education. This year, they deposited $1750 in a savings account that pays 8.2% simple interest annually. How much interest will they earn in 4 years?

This is a simple interest problem, so we can use the formula $I = Prt$.

First, write the value of each variable.

I = unknown

P = $1750

r = 8.2% = 0.082

t = 4 years

Write the formula. $I = Prt$

Substitute the values from the problem. = (1750)(0.082)(4)

Multiply. = 574

Diego's parents will earn $574 in interest over 4 years.

EXAMPLE 2

Eleven years ago, Zalika deposited $9300 in a savings account that paid an annual simple interest rate. Yesterday, she withdrew all the money from the account, which was $17,279.40. What was the interest rate the account paid?

This is a simple interest problem, so we can use the formula $I = Prt$.

First, write the value of each variable.

I = 17,279.40 − 9300 = 7979.40

P = 9300

r = unknown

t = 11

Write the formula. $I = Prt$

Substitute the values from the problem. 7979.40 = 9300(r)(11)

Multiply. 7979.40 = 102,300r

Divide both sides of the equation by 102,300. $\dfrac{7979.40}{102,300} = \dfrac{102,300r}{102,300}$

Simplify. 0.078 = r

Zalika's savings account paid 7.8% simple interest annually.

Compound Interest

A second type of interest is compound interest. **Compound interest** is the interest paid both on the principal and any previously earned interest. When solving problems involving compound interest, use the formula

$$A = P\left(1 + \frac{r}{n}\right)^{nt}$$

where A = the final balance, P = the principal, r = the annual interest rate (expressed as a decimal), n = the number of times interest is compounded per year, and t = time in years.

Need More
HELP ❓

For more on exponents, see *Exponents* in *Numbers and Operations* (Book 1, p. 294).

EXAMPLE 3

Carlos borrowed $3000 at an interest rate of 5%, compounded quarterly. If he waits 4 years before beginning to pay the loan, how much will he owe?

This is a compound interest problem, so use the formula $A = P\left(1 + \frac{r}{n}\right)^{nt}$.

First, write the value of each variable. A = Unknown; P = 3000; r = 5% = 0.05; n = 4; t = 4

Write the formula. $A = P\left(1 + \frac{r}{n}\right)^{nt}$

Substitute the values from the problem. $= 3000\left(1 + \frac{0.05}{4}\right)^{(4)(4)}$

Multiply the exponents. $= 3000\left(1 + \frac{0.05}{4}\right)^{16}$

Simplify the power. $= 3000(1 + 0.0125)^{16} = 3000(1.0125)^{16} = 3000(1.21989)$

Multiply. $= 3659.67$

Carlos will owe $3659.67.

EXAMPLE 4

Thomas has $2015.87 in his savings account. The account pays 6% interest, compounded semi-annually. Thomas has not deposited or withdrawn any money from the account for 5 years. What was the account balance 5 years ago?

This is a compound interest problem, so use the formula $A = P\left(1 + \frac{r}{n}\right)^{nt}$.

First, write the value of each variable. A = 2015.87; P = Unknown; r = 6% = 0.06; n = 2; t = 5

Substitute the values from the problem into the formula. $A = P\left(1 + \frac{r}{n}\right)^{nt} = P\left(1 + \frac{0.06}{2}\right)^{(2)(5)}$

Multiply the exponents. $2015.87 = P\left(1 + \frac{0.06}{2}\right)^{10}$

Simplify the power. $2015.87 = P(1 + 0.03)^{10} = P(1.03)^{10} = P(1.343916)$

Divide both sides of the equation by 1.343916. $\frac{2015.87}{1.343916} = \frac{P(1.343916)}{1.343916}$

Simplify. $1499.997 \approx P$

The account had $1500 five years ago.

GOT TO KNOW!

Interest Formulas

Simple Interest:

$I = Prt$, where I = the amount of interest, P = the principal, r = the interest rate per time period (expressed as a decimal), and t = the number of time periods.

Compound Interest:

$A = P\left(1 + \frac{r}{n}\right)^{nt}$, where A = the final balance, P = the principal, r = the annual interest rate (expressed as a decimal), n = the number of times interest is compounded per year, and t = time in years.

Formulas and Literal Equations

Solving Literal Equations

In most of the instances in which you have dealt with formulas, you have substituted numbers from word problems into the formulas, and then solved for a single variable.

Another option would be to solve a formula for one of the variables other than the one that is already isolated, using the same rules for equations that you have used with numbers. This method is known as **solving literal equations**.

SEARCH 🔍

To see step-by-step videos of these problems, enter the page number into the SWadvantage.com Search Bar.

EXAMPLE 1

Solve the formula for the area of a triangle for h, the height of the triangle.

The formula for the area of a triangle is $A = \frac{1}{2}bh$.

Write the formula. $A = \frac{1}{2}bh$

Divide both sides of the equation by $\frac{1}{2}$. $\dfrac{A}{\frac{1}{2}} = \dfrac{\frac{1}{2}bh}{\frac{1}{2}}$

Rewrite using multiplication. $2(A) = 2\left(\frac{1}{2}bh\right)$

Simplify. $2A = bh$

Divide both sides of the equation by b. $\dfrac{2A}{b} = \dfrac{bh}{b}$

Simplify. $\dfrac{2A}{b} = h$

The formula for the height of a triangle, when the area and base length are known, is $h = \frac{2A}{b}$.

EXAMPLE 2

The formula for converting a temperature measured in degrees Fahrenheit to a temperature measured in degrees Celsius is $C = \frac{5}{9}(F - 32)$. Solve this formula for F.

Write the formula. $C = \frac{5}{9}(F - 32)$

Divide both sides of the equation by $\frac{5}{9}$. $\dfrac{C}{\frac{5}{9}} = \dfrac{\frac{5}{9}(F - 32)}{\frac{5}{9}}$

Rewrite using multiplication. $\frac{9}{5}(C) = \frac{9}{5}\left[\frac{5}{9}(F - 32)\right]$

Simplify. $\frac{9}{5}C = F - 32$

Add 32 to both sides of the equation. $\frac{9}{5}C + 32 = F - 32 + 32$

Simplify. $\frac{9}{5}C + 32 = F$

The formula for converting a temperature measured in degrees Celsius to a temperature measured in degrees Fahrenheit is $F = \frac{9}{5}C + 32$.

EXAMPLE 3

Manuel drove a distance of 221 miles in 3 hours and 24 minutes. Solve the distance formula for *r*, and then use it to determine Manuel's speed.

STEP 1 Solve for *r*.

Write the formula. $\qquad\qquad\qquad\qquad\qquad D = rt$

Divide both sides of the equation by *t*. $\qquad \dfrac{D}{t} = \dfrac{rt}{t}$

Simplify. $\qquad\qquad\qquad\qquad\qquad\qquad \dfrac{D}{t} = r$

The formula for the rate of speed, when the distance and time are known, is $r = \dfrac{D}{t}$.

STEP 2 Find Manuel's rate of speed.

Divide 24 by 60 to find the decimal portion of an hour. $\qquad \dfrac{24}{60} = 0.4$

Write the formula. $\qquad\qquad\qquad\qquad\qquad\qquad r = \dfrac{D}{t}$

Substitute values from the problem. $\qquad\qquad\qquad r = \dfrac{221}{3.4}$

Simplify. $\qquad\qquad\qquad\qquad\qquad\qquad\qquad r = 65$

Manuel's speed was 65 miles per hour.

EXAMPLE 4

A cylinder with surface area 3102.32 ft² has a radius of 13 ft. Solve the formula for the surface area of a cylinder for *h*, the height. Then, calculate the height of the cylinder. Use 3.14 for π.

STEP 1 Solve for *h*.

Write the formula. $\qquad\qquad\qquad\qquad\qquad SA = 2\pi r(r + h)$

Divide both sides of the equation by $2\pi r$. $\qquad \dfrac{SA}{2\pi r} = \dfrac{2\pi r(r + h)}{2\pi r}$

Simplify. $\qquad\qquad\qquad\qquad\qquad\qquad \dfrac{SA}{2\pi r} = r + h$

Subtract *r* from both sides of the equation. $\qquad \dfrac{SA}{2\pi r} - r = r + h - r$

Simplify. $\qquad\qquad\qquad\qquad\qquad\qquad \dfrac{SA}{2\pi r} - r = h$

The formula for the height of a cylinder, when the surface area and radius are known, is $h = \dfrac{SA}{2\pi r} - r$.

STEP 2 Find the height of the cylinder.

Write the formula. $\qquad\qquad\qquad\qquad h = \dfrac{SA}{2\pi r} - r$

Substitute values from the problem. $\qquad = \dfrac{3102.32}{(2)(3.14)(13)} - 13$

Multiply. $\qquad\qquad\qquad\qquad\qquad\qquad = \dfrac{3102.32}{81.64} - 13$

Simplify. $\qquad\qquad\qquad\qquad\qquad\qquad = 38 - 13$

Simplify. $\qquad\qquad\qquad\qquad\qquad\qquad = 25$

The height of the cylinder is 25 ft.

Need More

HELP ?

For more on the surface area of cylinders, see *Surface Area of Cylinders* in *Measurement* (Book 1, p. 562).

Direct Variation

Determining Direct Variation

A certain car can travel for 22 miles on 1 gallon of gasoline. The same car travels 44 miles on 2 gallons of gas, 66 miles on 3 gallons, and so on.

Notice in this example that the ratio of gallons of gasoline to distance traveled is constant: $\frac{\text{miles}}{\text{gallon}} = \frac{22}{1} = \frac{44}{2} = \frac{66}{3}$, or 1 gallon for every 22 miles. This relationship is called a **direct variation**. In a direct variation, two variable quantities are related proportionally by a constant positive ratio. This ratio is called the **constant of proportionality**. All direct variations can be written in the form $y = kx$, or $k = \frac{y}{x}$, where x and y are the variable quantities, and k is the constant of proportionality. The graph of a direct variation will always be a straight line.

EXAMPLE 1

Determine whether the data shows a direct variation.

Movie Ticket Prices

Number of Tickets	1	5	10	20	40
Total Cost	$9	$45	$80	$140	$240

METHOD 1

Make a graph of the data.

Draw a Quadrant I graph of the data from the table. These are discrete data points, so there is no line connecting them. Notice, however, that if a line were to be drawn to connect the points, it would not be straight. Therefore, the data in the table does not represent a direct variation.

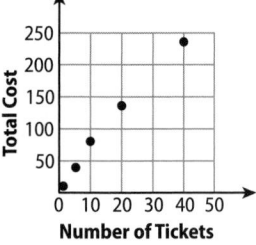

METHOD 2

Use proportions to test for direct variation.

Remember that the variable quantities in a direct variation are related proportionally. This means that each individual ratio of $\frac{\text{Number of Tickets}}{\text{Total Cost}}$ will be proportional to all of the other ratios, if the relationship is a direct variation. Test all of the ratios given. If they are all proportional, then the relationship is a direct variation. If there is even one case where ratios are not proportional, then the relationship is not a direct variation.

Write the proportion.	$\frac{1}{9} \overset{?}{=} \frac{5}{45}$	$\frac{5}{45} \overset{?}{=} \frac{10}{80}$
Find the cross products.	$9(5) \overset{?}{=} 1(45)$	$45(10) \overset{?}{=} 5(80)$
Simplify.	$45 = 45$	$450 \neq 400$

Because not all of the ratios are proportional, the variation is not a direct variation.

GOT TO KNOW!

Graphs of Direct Variations

- The graphs of direct variations are always straight lines.
- The graphs of direct variations always pass through the origin.

EXAMPLE 2

Determine whether the data shows a direct variation.

Gas Mileage

Gallons of Gas	5	15	20	30	35
Miles Traveled	100	300	400	600	700

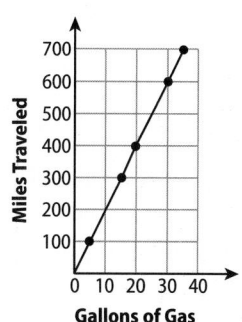

METHOD 1 Make a graph of the data.

Draw a Quadrant I graph of the data from the table. While there are discrete data points given in the table, the graph can be a line because it is possible to have a number of gallons between the whole gallons. Notice that the line for this graph is straight, and that it passes through the origin. The data does show a direct variation.

METHOD 2 Use proportions to test for direct variation.

Each individual ratio of $\frac{\text{Gallons of Gas}}{\text{Miles Traveled}}$ will be proportional to all of the other ratios, if the relationship is a direct variation. Test all of the ratios given. If they are all proportional, then the relationship is a direct variation. If there is even one case where ratios are not proportional, then the relationship is not a direct variation.

Write the proportion.	$\frac{5}{100} \overset{?}{=} \frac{15}{300}$	$\frac{15}{300} \overset{?}{=} \frac{20}{400}$	$\frac{20}{400} \overset{?}{=} \frac{30}{600}$
Find the cross products.	$100(15) \overset{?}{=} 5(300)$	$300(20) \overset{?}{=} 15(400)$	$400(30) \overset{?}{=} 20(600)$
Simplify.	$1500 = 1500$	$6000 = 6000$	$12{,}000 = 12{,}000$
Write the proportion.	$\frac{30}{600} \overset{?}{=} \frac{35}{700}$	$\frac{35}{700} \overset{?}{=} \frac{5}{100}$	
Find the cross products.	$600(35) \overset{?}{=} 30(700)$	$700(5) \overset{?}{=} 35(100)$	
Simplify.	$21{,}000 = 21{,}000$	$3500 = 3500$	

By the Transitive Property, all of the ratios are proportional. Therefore, the data shows a direct variation.

SEARCH

To see step-by-step videos of these problems, enter the page number into the SWadvantage.com Search Bar.

Need More HELP?

For more on solving proportions, see *Solving Proportions* in *Numbers and Operations* (Book 1, p. 370).

EXAMPLE 3

Marcus went for a 6-mile walk. It took him 15 minutes to walk the first mile, a total of 45 minutes to complete half of his walk, and 1.5 hours to complete the entire walk. Use proportions to determine whether this data shows a direct variation.

STEP 1 Write all the times so that they use the same measure.

Because two of the given times are in minutes, write the third time in minutes.

1.5 hours = 90 minutes

STEP 2 Test the proportions.

Write the proportion.	$\frac{15}{1} \overset{?}{=} \frac{45}{3}$	$\frac{45}{3} \overset{?}{=} \frac{90}{6}$	$\frac{90}{6} \overset{?}{=} \frac{15}{1}$
Find the cross products.	$1(45) \overset{?}{=} 15(3)$	$3(90) \overset{?}{=} 45(6)$	$6(15) \overset{?}{=} 90(1)$
Simplify.	$45 = 45$	$270 = 270$	$90 = 90$

By the Transitive Property, all of the ratios are proportional. The data shows a direct variation.

Using Direct Variation

Once it has been established that a relationship is a direct variation, the next step is to find k, the constant of proportionality. There are 2 ways to accomplish this.

- **Present the relationship as an equation or number sentence.**

  The equation form of a direct variation, $y = kx$, can also be written as $k = \frac{y}{x}$.

- **Present the relationship as a graph or as discrete data points.**

  Use one of the ratios and write it in simplest form.

EXAMPLE 4

Find the constant of proportionality in each relationship. Then, write the equation of direct variation.

a. *y* and *x* vary directly; *y* is 41.3 when *x* is 13

  STEP 1 It is given that the relationship is a direct variation.

  STEP 2 Find the constant of proportionality.

  Set up the formula for direct variation, and then solve for k.

Write the formula.	$y = kx$
Substitute for x and y.	$41.3 = k(13)$
Divide both sides of the equation by 13.	$3.2 = k$

  STEP 3 Write the equation of direct variation.

Write the formula for direct variation.	$y = kx$
Substitute the constant of proportionality.	$y = 3.2x$

  The constant of proportionality is 3.2, and the equation of direct variation is $y = 3.2x$.

b. $y = \frac{7}{9}x + 11$

  STEP 1 Determine whether the relationship is a direct variation.

  This relationship is not a direct variation. Remember that graphs of direct variations are always straight lines that pass through the origin. While the graph of the equation $y = \frac{7}{9}x + 11$ is a straight line, it has a y-intercept of 11, so it does not pass through the origin. There is no need to complete the final 2 steps.

c. Marcus went for a 6-mile walk. It took him 15 minutes to walk the first mile, a total of 45 minutes to complete half of his walk, and 1.5 hours to complete the entire walk. Use proportions to determine whether this data shows a direct variation.

  STEP 1 It was shown in Example 3 that this relationship is a direct variation.

  STEP 2 Find the constant of proportionality.

  Use the ratio for the time and distance for Marcus's entire walk, and write it in simplest form. $\frac{90}{6} = 15$

  STEP 3 Write the equation of direct variation.

Write the formula for direct variation.	$y = kx$
Substitute the constant of proportionality.	$y = 15x$

  The equation of direct variation is $y = 15x$.

Need More

HELP ?

For more on the slope-intercept form of the equation of a line, see *Slope-Intercept Form of Linear Equations* in *Algebra* (p. 1540).

Once the constant of proportionality for a direct variation is known, it can be used to find any value of one of the variable quantities when a value of the other is known.

EXAMPLE 5

Find the constant of proportionality for the following direct variation. Then, find the value of y when x = 273.
y is 379.5 when x is 33

SEARCH 🔍

To see step-by-step videos of these problems, enter the page number into the SWadvantage.com Search Bar.

STEP 1 Find the constant of proportionality.

Write the direct variation formula.	$y = kx$
Substitute for x and y.	$379.5 = k(33)$
Divide both sides of the equation by 33.	$11.5 = k$

STEP 2 Find y when x is 273.

Write the equation of direct variation.	$y = k(273)$
Substitute the constant of proportionality.	$= 11.5(273)$
Multiply.	$= 3139.5$

The constant of proportionality is 11.5, and y is 3139.5 when x is 273.

EXAMPLE 6

In a recipe for blueberry muffins, the number of muffins produced varies directly with the amount of sugar used. The table to the right shows the number of muffins produced for various amounts of sugar used. Find the constant of proportionality for this relationship, and then find the amount of sugar needed for 100 muffins.

Sugar in Blueberry Muffins

Muffins	8	16	24
Cups of Sugar	$\frac{3}{4}$	$1\frac{1}{2}$	$2\frac{1}{4}$

STEP 1 Find the constant of proportionality.

Write the first ratio from the table.

$$k = \frac{8}{\frac{3}{4}}$$

Rewrite using multiplication, then multiply.

$$= \frac{8}{1} \times \frac{4}{3} = \frac{32}{3}$$

STEP 2 Find the amount of sugar needed for 100 muffins.

Write the equation of direct variation.

$$y = kx$$

Substitute for y and the constant of proportionality.

$$100 = \frac{32}{3}x$$

Divide both sides by $\frac{32}{3}$.

$$\frac{100}{\frac{32}{3}} = \frac{\frac{32}{3}x}{\frac{32}{3}}$$

Rewrite using multiplication.

$$\frac{100}{1} \times \frac{3}{32} = \frac{32}{3}x \times \frac{3}{32}$$

Multiply.

$$\frac{300}{32} = x$$

Simplify.

$$9\frac{3}{8} = x$$

The constant of proportionality is $\frac{32}{3}$, and $9\frac{3}{8}$ cups of sugar are needed for 100 muffins.

Inverse Variation

Determining Inverse Variation

Consider a large block of ice. The amount of time it takes for the ice to melt decreases as the temperature of the room containing the ice increases. A relationship like this is known as an *inverse variation*.

An **inverse variation** is a relationship in which one variable quantity increases as the other variable quantity decreases. The product of the values of the variable quantities in an inverse variation is always the same constant. All inverse variations can be written in the form $y = \frac{k}{x}$ or $xy = k$, where x and y are the variable quantities and k is the constant. For an inverse variation, $k \neq 0$ and $x \neq 0$.

EXAMPLE 1

SEARCH

To see step-by-step videos of these problems, enter the page number into the SWadvantage.com Search Bar.

Determine whether each relationship is an inverse variation.

a.

x	18	36	72
y	100	50	25

STEP 1 Determine whether one value is increasing while the other value is decreasing.
As x increases, y decreases.

STEP 2 Determine whether the products of the variable quantities are constant.
Find the product of each set of variable quantities.
$18 \times 100 = 1800$
$36 \times 50 = 1800$
$72 \times 25 = 1800$

The product of each pair of numbers is the same. Therefore, the relationship is an inverse variation.

b. The table shows the number of hours it takes to clean a local park based on the number of volunteers.

Volunteers	10	20	30
Hours	8	4	$2\frac{2}{3}$

STEP 1 Determine whether one value is increasing while the other value is decreasing. As the number of volunteers increases, the number of hours needed to clean the park decreases.

STEP 2 Determine whether the products of the variable quantities are constant.
Find the product of each set of variable quantities.
$10 \times 8 = 80$
$20 \times 4 = 80$
$30 \times 2\frac{2}{3} = 80$

The product of each pair of numbers is the same. Therefore, the relationship is an inverse variation.

c. The table shows the number of sandwiches needed to feed a volunteer cleanup crew based on the number of volunteers.

Volunteers	10	20	40
Sandwiches	30	40	80

STEP 1 Determine whether one value is increasing while the other value is decreasing.

Both values are increasing, so this is not an inverse variation. In fact, this is a direct variation. It is not necessary to continue with the remaining steps.

EXAMPLE 2

Determine whether each relationship is an inverse variation.

a.

x	2	3	4	5
y	17	16	15	14

STEP 1   Determine whether one value is increasing while the other value is decreasing.
As x increases, y decreases.

STEP 2   Determine whether the products of the variable quantities are constant.
Find the product of each set of variable quantities.
$2 \times 17 = 34$
$3 \times 16 = 48$
$4 \times 15 = 60$
$5 \times 14 = 70$

The products are all different. Therefore, the relationship is not an inverse variation.

b. **The table shows the number of hours it takes a large block of ice to melt, based on the temperature of the room containing the ice.**

Temperature (°F)	80	100	60	40
Hours	15	12	20	30

Watch Out

Pay close attention to the order in which information is presented in a table.

STEP 1   Determine whether one value is increasing while the other value is decreasing.
As the temperature increases, the amount of time it takes the ice to melt decreases.

STEP 2   Determine whether the products of the variable quantities are constant.
Find the product of each set of variable quantities.
$80 \times 15 = 1200$
$100 \times 12 = 1200$
$60 \times 20 = 1200$
$40 \times 30 = 1200$

The product of each pair of numbers is 1200. Therefore, the relationship is an inverse variation.

GOT TO KNOW!

Comparing Direct Variation and Inverse Variation

Property	Direct Variation	Inverse Variation
It shows relationships between two variable quantities.	X	X
It uses a constant.	X	X
Both quantities increase at the same time.	X	
One quantity increases as the other decreases.		X

SOUTHWESTERN

Using Inverse Variation

Just as with direct variation, once it has been established that a relationship is an inverse variation, the next step is to find k, the constant. There are two ways to accomplish this.

- **Present the relationship as an equation or number sentence.**
  The equation form of an inverse variation, $y = \frac{k}{x}$, can also be written as $k = xy$.
- **Present the relationship as a graph or as discrete data points.**
  In this instance, simply use the common product of the data points.

EXAMPLE 3

SEARCH

To see step-by-step videos of these problems, enter the page number into the SWadvantage.com Search Bar.

Find the constant, k, in each relationship. Then, write the equation of inverse variation.

a. y and x vary inversely; y is 30 when x is 12

STEP 1 Determine whether the relationship is an inverse variation.
It is given that y and x vary inversely.

STEP 2 Find the constant.
Set up the formula for inverse variation, and then solve for k.

Write the formula. $\qquad y = \frac{k}{x}$

Substitute for x and y. $\qquad 30 = \frac{k}{12}$

Multiply both sides of the equation by 12. $\qquad 30(12) = \frac{k}{12}(12)$

Simplify. $\qquad 360 = k$

STEP 3 Write the equation of inverse variation.

Write the formula for inverse variation. $\qquad y = \frac{k}{x}$

Substitute for k. $\qquad y = \frac{360}{x}$

The constant is 360, and the equation of inverse variation is $y = \frac{360}{x}$.

b. The table shows the number of hours it takes a large block of ice to melt, based on the temperature of the room containing the ice.

Temperature (°F)	80	100	60	40
Hours	15	12	20	30

STEP 1 Determine whether the relationship is an inverse variation.
It was shown in Example 2 that this relationship is an inverse variation.

STEP 2 Find the constant.
The constant is the common product.
Multiply the values in the first pair. $\qquad 80 \times 15 = 1200$

STEP 3 Write the equation of inverse variation.
Write the formula for inverse variation. $\qquad y = \frac{k}{x}$

Substitute for k. $\qquad y = \frac{1200}{x}$

The constant is 1200, and the equation of inverse variation is $y = \frac{1200}{x}$.

Once the constant for an inverse variation is known, it can be used to find any value of one of the variable quantities when a value of the other is known.

EXAMPLE 4

Find the constant for the following inverse variation. Then, find the value of y when $x = 2$.
y is 20 when x is 30

STEP 1 Find the constant.

Write the inverse variation formula.	$y = \dfrac{k}{x}$
Substitute for x and y.	$20 = \dfrac{k}{30}$
Multiply both sides of the equation by 30.	$20(30) = \dfrac{k}{30}(30)$
Simplify.	$600 = k$

The constant is 600.

STEP 2 Find y when x is 2.

Write the equation of direct variation.	$y = \dfrac{k}{x}$
Substitute for k and x.	$= \dfrac{600}{2}$
Divide.	$= 300$

y is 300 when x is 2.

> **Watch Out !**
>
> Since the value for x that is being used to find the new value of y is so much less than the value of x in the stated relation, you may be expecting y to also be smaller. Remember that this is an inverse variation, and the value of y will increase and the value of x decreases.

EXAMPLE 5

The amount of laundry detergent in a container varies inversely with the number of loads that have been washed. The table below shows the amount of detergent left in a container and the number of loads that have been washed. Find the constant for this relationship, and then find the amount of detergent left after 40 loads have been washed.

Laundry Detergent Use			
Detergent Remaining (oz)	125	100	50
Loads Washed	20	25	50

STEP 1 Find the constant.

Because it is given that this is an inverse relationship, choose any pair of values and find their product.

Multiply the first pair in the table. $125 \times 20 = 2500$

The constant is 2500.

STEP 2 Find the amount of detergent left after 40 loads have been washed.

Write the equation of inverse variation.	$y = \dfrac{k}{x}$
Substitute for x and the constant.	$y = \dfrac{2500}{40}$
Divide.	$y = 62.5$

There will be 62.5 oz of detergent left after 40 loads of laundry are washed.

Joint Variation

Using Joint Variation

A third type of variation is called *joint variation*. In **joint variation**, three variable quantities are related. Joint variations can be written in the form $y = kxz$ or $\frac{y}{xz} = k$, where k is the constant of variation. In the formula $y = kxz$, y is said to vary jointly with x and z.

Notice that joint variation is very similar to direct variation, with the only real difference being that a third variable quantity has been added. Because of that third variable, the test for joint variation has an extra step. If the ratios of y-values to the products of the x- and z-values are proportional, then a relation is a joint variation.

EXAMPLE 1

Determine whether the relationship below is a joint variation. If it is, find the constant of proportionality, and then write the equation of joint variation.

x	22	33	44
y	2	6	12
z	1	2	3

STEP 1 Determine whether the relationship is a joint variation.

Test whether the ratio $\frac{y}{xz}$ is proportional for all of the sets of numbers.

Set up the proportion.
$$\frac{2}{(22)(1)} \stackrel{?}{=} \frac{6}{33(2)} \qquad \frac{6}{33(2)} \stackrel{?}{=} \frac{12}{44(3)} \qquad \frac{12}{44(3)} \stackrel{?}{=} \frac{2}{(22)(1)}$$

Multiply.
$$\frac{2}{22} \stackrel{?}{=} \frac{6}{66} \qquad \frac{6}{66} \stackrel{?}{=} \frac{12}{132} \qquad \frac{12}{132} \stackrel{?}{=} \frac{2}{22}$$

Find the cross products. $22(6) \stackrel{?}{=} 2(66) \qquad 66(12) \stackrel{?}{=} 6(132) \qquad 132(2) \stackrel{?}{=} 12(22)$

Multiply. $132 = 132 \qquad\qquad 792 = 792 \qquad\qquad 264 = 264$

The ratios are all proportional, so this is a joint variation.

STEP 2 Find the constant of proportionality.

Choose one of the sets of numbers, and write the ratio $\frac{y}{xz}$. Simplify the ratio, if possible.

Set up the ratio. $\frac{y}{xz} = \frac{2}{(22)(1)}$

Multiply. $= \frac{2}{22}$

Simplify. $= \frac{1}{11}$

The constant of proportionality is $\frac{1}{11}$.

STEP 3 Write the equation of joint variation.

Write the formula for a joint variation. $y = kxz$

Substitute for k. $y = \frac{1}{11}xz$

The equation of joint variation is $y = \frac{1}{11}xz$, or $y = \frac{xz}{11}$.

Once the constant of proportionality is known for a joint variation, it can be used to find the value of any one of the variable quantities, when the other two are known.

EXAMPLE 2

Find the constant of proportionality for the following joint variation. Then, use it to find the value of z when y is 58 and x is 29.

y is 18 when x is 20 and z is 1.8.

STEP 1 Find the constant of proportionality.

Substitute for x, y, and z and simplify.

$y = kxz \rightarrow 18 = k(20)(1.8) = k(36)$

Divide both sides of the equation by 36.

$\frac{18}{36} = \frac{k(36)}{36}$

Simplify.

$\frac{1}{2} = k$

The constant of proportionality is $\frac{1}{2}$.

STEP 2 Find z when x is 29 and y is 58.

Substitute for x, y, and z and simplify.

$y = kxz \rightarrow 58 = \frac{1}{2}(29)z = \frac{29}{2}z$

Multiply both sides by $\frac{2}{29}$.

$58\left(\frac{2}{29}\right) = \frac{29}{2}z\left(\frac{2}{29}\right).$

Simplify.

$4 = z$

z is 4 when x is 29 and y is 58.

Need More HELP?

To review division of fractions, see *Dividing Fractions and Fractions* in *Numbers and Operations* (Book 1, p. 346).

EXAMPLE 3

The area of any triangle varies jointly with the height of the triangle and the length of the triangle's base. A triangle with area 88 cm² has height 11 cm and base length of 16 cm. Find the constant of proportionality for this joint variation, and then find the height of a triangle with area 104 mm² and base length 13 mm.

STEP 1 Find the constant.

Substitute for x, y, and z and simplify.

$y = kxz \rightarrow 88 = k(11)(16) = k(176)$

Divide both sides of the equation by 176.

$\frac{88}{176} = \frac{k(176)}{176}$

Simplify.

$\frac{1}{2} = k$

The constant of proportionality is $\frac{1}{2}$.

STEP 2 Find the height of a triangle with area 104 mm² and base length 13 mm.

Substitute for x, y, and z and simplify.

$y = kxz \rightarrow 104 = \frac{1}{2}x(13) = \frac{13}{2}x$

Multiply both sides by $\frac{2}{13}$.

$104\left(\frac{2}{13}\right) = \frac{13}{2}x\left(\frac{2}{13}\right)$

Multiply.

$16 = x$

A triangle with area 104 mm² and base length 13 mm has a height of 16 mm.

Need More HELP?

For more on the area of a triangle, see *Areas of Triangles* in *Measurement* (Book 1, p. 536).

Mixed Variation Problems

Determining Variation

The previous three lessons dealt with three different kinds of variation.

- direct variation
- inverse variation
- joint variation

The flowchart below will help you to distinguish among the three kinds of variation.

The flowchart gives all of the decision points you will encounter, and then directs you how to proceed for each answer you give. For instance, start by asking the question, "Are there 2 or 3 variables?" If the answer is "2," the next question is, "Does x increase as y increases?" If the answer is "3," the next question is, "Is $\frac{y}{xz}$ proportional?"

This process continues until a conclusion is reached.

GOT TO KNOW!

Flowchart to Determine Variability

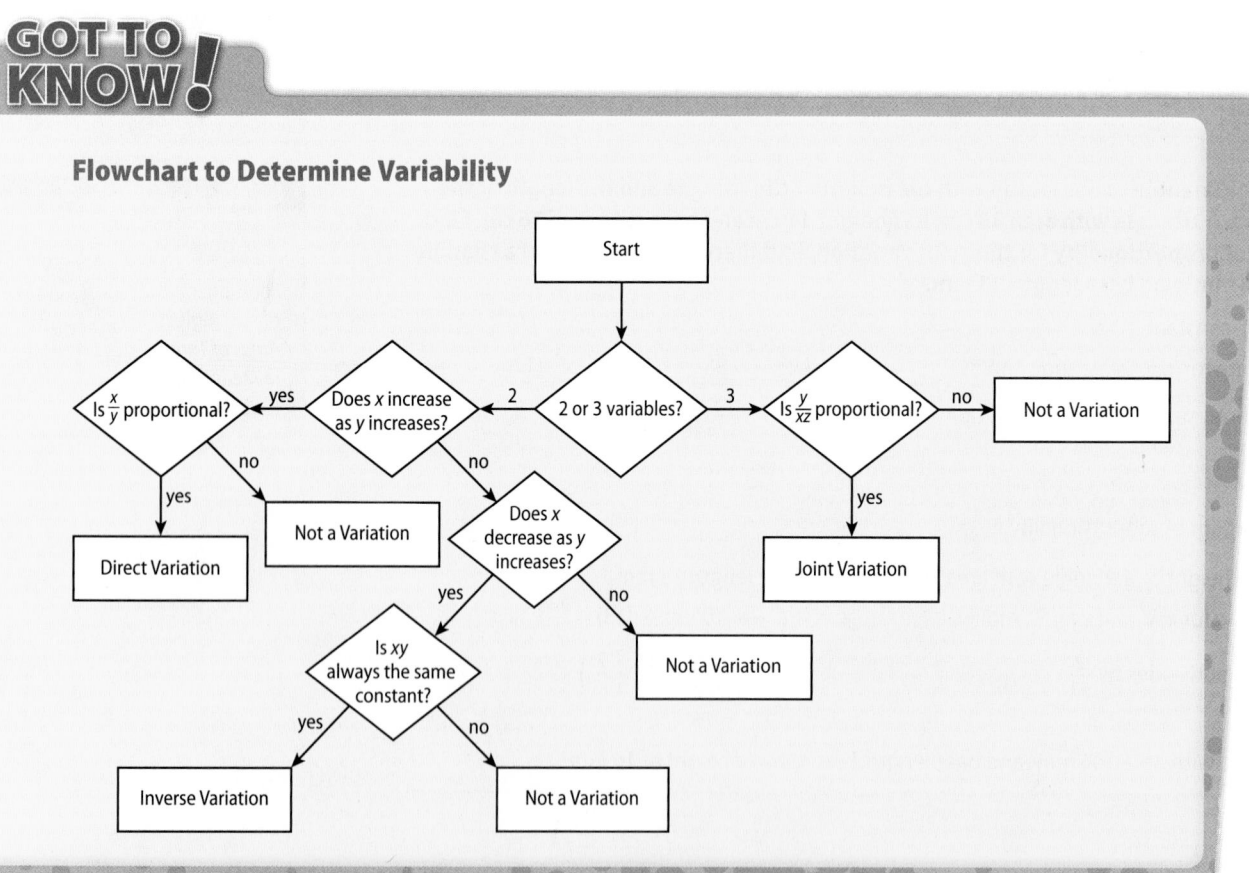

EXAMPLE 1

Determine what kind of variation, if any, is shown in each relationship.

a.

x	12	48	192
y	10	20	30
z	5	2.5	0.9375

Follow the flowchart to reach a conclusion about the kind of variation.

STEP 1 Are there 2 or 3 variables?   There are 3 variables, x, y, and z.

STEP 2 Is $\frac{y}{xz}$ proportional?

Set up the proportion. $\frac{10}{60} \overset{?}{=} \frac{20}{120}$ $\frac{20}{120} \overset{?}{=} \frac{30}{180}$ $\frac{30}{180} \overset{?}{=} \frac{10}{60}$

Find the cross products. $60(20) \overset{?}{=} 10(120)$ $120(30) \overset{?}{=} 20(180)$ $180(10) \overset{?}{=} 30(60)$

Multiply. $1200 = 1200$ $3600 = 3600$ $1800 = 1800$

$\frac{y}{xz}$ is proportional for each of the data sets, so the relationship is a joint variation.

b.

x	3	15	75
y	8	40	200

Follow the flowchart to reach a conclusion about the kind of variation.

STEP 1 Are there 2 or 3 variables?   There are 2 variables, x and y.

STEP 2 Does x increase as y increases?   Yes. x goes from 3 to 15 to 75. y goes from 8 to 40 to 200.

STEP 3 Is $\frac{x}{y}$ proportional?

Test the ratios to determine whether they are proportional.

Write the proportion. $\frac{3}{8} \overset{?}{=} \frac{15}{40}$ $\frac{15}{40} \overset{?}{=} \frac{75}{200}$ $\frac{75}{200} \overset{?}{=} \frac{3}{8}$

Find the cross products. $8(15) \overset{?}{=} 3(40)$ $40(75) \overset{?}{=} 15(200)$ $200(3) \overset{?}{=} 75(8)$

Multiply. $120 = 120$ $3000 = 3000$ $600 = 600$

Yes, $\frac{x}{y}$ is proportional, so the relationship is a direct variation.

c.

x	26	52	65
y	10	5	4

Follow the flowchart to reach a conclusion about the kind of variation.

STEP 1 Are there 2 or 3 variables?   There are 2 variables, x and y.

STEP 2 Does x increase as y increases?   No. x goes from 26 to 52 to 65. y goes from 10 to 5 to 4.

STEP 3 Does x decrease as y increases?

Yes. As y increases from 4 to 5 to 10, x decreases from 65 to 52 to 26.

STEP 4 Is xy always the same constant?

Find each product xy. $26 \times 10 = 260$ $52 \times 5 = 260$ $65 \times 4 = 260$

Yes, xy is always 260, so the relationship is an inverse variation.

Need More
HELP ?
For more on proportions, see *Solving Proportions* in *Numbers and Operations* (Book 1, p. 370).

Watch Out !
Do not stop following the flowchart until you reach one of the conclusions. There is always the possibility that a relationship is not a variation at all.

SEARCH
To see step-by-step videos of these problems, enter the page number into the SWadvantage.com Search Bar.

Using Variations

Remember from the three previous lessons, determining whether a relationship is a variation is only half of the battle. The real usefulness of variations is that the constants of proportionality can be used to find other values of the variable quantities.

SEARCH

To see step-by-step videos of these problems, enter the page number into the SWadvantage.com Search Bar.

EXAMPLE 2

The table below shows a relationship.

x	4	15	21	30
y	525	140	100	70

a. Determine what kind of variation, if any, is shown in the table.

STEP 1 Are there 2 or 3 variables?

The relationship shows 2 variables, x and y.

STEP 2 Does x increase as y increases?

No. As x increases from 4 to 15 to 21 to 30, y decreases from 525 to 140 to 100 to 70.

STEP 3 Does x decrease as y increases?

Yes. As y increases from 70 to 100 to 140 to 525, x decreases from 30 to 21 to15 to 4.

STEP 4 Is xy always the same constant?

Find each product xy.

$4 \times 525 = 2100$

$15 \times 140 = 2100$

$21 \times 100 = 2100$

$30 \times 70 = 2100$

The relationship is an inverse variation.

b. Find the constant.

Write the formula for inverse variation. $y = \frac{k}{x}$

Substitute for x and y. $525 = \frac{k}{4}$

Multiply both sides of the equation by 4. $525(4) = \frac{k}{4}(4)$

Simplify. $2100 = k$

The constant is 2100.

c. Find x when y is 600.

Write the formula for inverse variation. $y = \frac{k}{x}$

Substitute for k and y. $600 = \frac{2100}{x}$

Multiply both sides of the equation by x. $600x = \frac{2100}{x}(x)$

Simplify. $600x = 2100$

Divide both sides of the equation by 600. $x = 3.5$

When y is 600, x is 3.5.

EXAMPLE 3

The table below shows the number of teaspoons of ground coffee needed to brew various numbers of cups of coffee.

Ground Coffee (tsp)	6	12	24
Brewed Coffee (cups)	2	4	8

a. Determine what kind of variation, if any, is shown in the table.

STEP 1 Are there 2 or 3 variables?

There are 2 variables, ground coffee and brewed coffee.

STEP 2 Does x increase as y increases?

Yes. As y (brewed coffee) increases from 2 to 4 to 8, x (ground coffee) increases from 6 to 12 to 24.

STEP 3 Is $\frac{x}{y}$ proportional?

Test the ratios $\frac{\text{Ground Coffee}}{\text{Brewed Coffee}}$ to determine whether they are proportional.

Write the proportion.

$$\frac{6}{2} \overset{?}{=} \frac{12}{4} \qquad \frac{12}{4} \overset{?}{=} \frac{24}{8} \qquad \frac{24}{8} \overset{?}{=} \frac{6}{2}$$

Find the cross products.

$$2(12) \overset{?}{=} 6(4) \qquad 4(24) \overset{?}{=} 12(8) \qquad 8(6) \overset{?}{=} 24(2)$$

Multiply.

$$24 = 24 \qquad\qquad 96 = 96 \qquad\qquad 48 = 48$$

Yes, the ratios are proportional.

The relationship is a direct variation.

b. Find the constant of proportionality.

Write the direct variation formula. $y = kx$

Substitute for x and y. $2 = k(6)$

Divide both sides of the equation by 6. $\frac{2}{6} = \frac{k(6)}{6}$

Simplify. $\frac{1}{3} = k$

The constant of proportionality is $\frac{1}{3}$.

Need More HELP ?

For more on solving equations, see *One-Variable Linear Equations* in *Algebra* (p. 1456).

c. Find the number of teaspoons of ground coffee needed to brew 21 cups of coffee.

Write the direct variation formula. $y = kx$

Substitute for y and k. $21 = \frac{1}{3}x$

Divide both sides of the equation by $\frac{1}{3}$. $\dfrac{21}{\frac{1}{3}} = \dfrac{\frac{1}{3}x}{\frac{1}{3}}$

Rewrite using multiplication. $21\left(\frac{3}{1}\right) = \frac{1}{3}x\left(\frac{3}{1}\right)$

Simplify. $63 = x$

63 teaspoons of ground coffee are needed to brew 21 cups of coffee.

Sequences and Series

What Came Before?
- Common differences and ratios
- Inductive and deductive reasoning

What's This About?
- Finding terms and sums of arithmetic and geometric sequences
- General rules of sequences, including the Fibonacci Sequence
- Evaluating and finding the partial sums of arithmetic and geometric series

Practical Apps
- Rates of depreciation of automobiles can be found using a geometric sequence.
- The Parthenon was built with dimensions based on terms of the Fibonacci Sequence.

just for FUN!

CUSTOMER: "How much is a large order of Fibonachos?"

CASHIER: "It's the price of a small order plus the price of a medium order."

You can find more practice problems online by visiting:
www.SWadvantage.com

Arithmetic Sequences

SOUTHWESTERN

Sequences

A **sequence** is a function whose domain is a set of ordered numbers.

- The numbers in a sequence are called **terms**.
- The terms in a sequence can be any ordered numbers, not just integers.
- The nth term of a sequence is called the **general term**. Instead of using function notation such as $a(n)$, the notation a_n is used for the general term. The general term is the rule that determines the numbers in a sequence and their order.
- A sequence can be written by listing its terms in braces, such as $\{1, 3, 5, \ldots\}$ or by describing its general term, such as $\{a_1, a_2, \ldots, a_n, \ldots\}$, where $a_n = 2n - 1$. Notice that these two examples describe the same sequence.
- A sequence that has a specific number of terms is called a **finite sequence**. A sequence that has an infinite number of terms is called an **infinite sequence**.

EXAMPLE 1

Write the first five terms of the sequence whose general term is $a_n = 5n^2 - 3$.

Substitute ordered values for n, then simplify.

Substitute 1 for n.	$a_1 = 5(1)^2 - 3 = 2$
Substitute 2 for n.	$a_2 = 5(2)^2 - 3 = 17$
Substitute 3 for n.	$a_3 = 5(3)^2 - 3 = 42$
Substitute 4 for n.	$a_4 = 5(4)^2 - 3 = 77$
Substitute 5 for n.	$a_5 = 5(5)^2 - 3 = 122$

The first five terms are 2, 17, 42, 77, and 122.

EXAMPLE 2

Find the 50th term of the sequence whose general term is $a_n = \dfrac{n + 2}{2n - 1}$.

Substitute 50 for n. $\qquad a_{50} = \dfrac{50 + 2}{2(50) - 1} = \dfrac{52}{99}$

The 50th term is $\dfrac{52}{99}$.

Given the first few terms of a sequence, you can find the general term of the sequence.

EXAMPLE 3

a. Write a rule for the sequence $\{2, 6, 12, 20, \ldots\}$.

Identify the pattern. The terms can be written as $1(2), 2(3), 3(4), 4(5) \ldots$

Therefore, $a_n = n(n + 1)$.

b. Find the tenth term.

Substitute 10 for n. $\qquad a_{10} = 10(10 + 1) = 110$

The tenth term is 110.

Arithmetic Sequences

An **arithmetic sequence** is a sequence in which consecutive terms differ by a constant amount d. The constant amount is referred to as the **common difference**.

General Pattern of an Arithmetic Sequence

$a_2 = a_1 + d$

$a_3 = a_2 + d$
$\quad = (a_1 + d) + d$
$\quad = a_1 + 2d$

$a_4 = a_3 + d$
$\quad = (a_1 + 2d) + d$
$\quad = a_1 + 3d$

$a_5 = a_4 + d$
$\quad = (a_1 + 3d) + d$
$\quad = a_1 + 4d$

In general, a_n
$\quad = a_1 + (n - 1)d.$

EXAMPLE 4

Write the first five terms of the arithmetic sequence whose first term is 4 and whose common difference is 7.

The first term is given. To find the second term, add 7 to the first term. To find the third term, add 7 to the second term, and so on.

$a_1 = 4 \qquad a_2 = 4 + 7 = 11 \qquad a_3 = 11 + 7 = 18 \qquad a_4 = 18 + 7 = 25 \qquad a_5 = 25 + 7 = 32$

The first five terms are 4, 11, 18, 25, and 32.

The nth term of an arithmetic sequence with a_1 as the first term and d as the common difference is written as $a_n = a_1 + (n - 1)d$.

EXAMPLE 5

Find the formula for the nth term of the arithmetic sequence whose first term is -2 and whose common difference is 3.

Use the formula. $\qquad\qquad a_n = a_1 + (n - 1)d$

Substitute -2 for a_1 and 3 for d. $\qquad a_n = -2 + (n - 1)3$

Distribute. $\qquad\qquad = -2 + 3n - 3$

Add like terms. $\qquad\qquad = 3n - 5$

The nth term of this arithmetic sequence is $a_n = 3n - 5$.

EXAMPLE 6

What is the common difference of an arithmetic sequence whose fifth term is 6.5 and whose first term is 4.5?

Use the formula. $\qquad\qquad a_n = a_1 + (n - 1)d$

Substitute 4.5 for a_1, 6.5 for a_n, and 5 for n. $\qquad 6.5 = 4.5 + (5 - 1)d$

Simplify. $\qquad\qquad 2 = 4d,\text{ so } d = 0.5$

The common difference for this arithmetic sequence is 0.5.

Using Arithmetic Sequences

EXAMPLE 7

a. Find the general term of the sequence $\{-11, -2, 7, 16, 25, \ldots\}$.

STEP 1 Find d.

Choose two consecutive terms. $-11, -2$

Use the terms to calculate d. $-11 + d = -2$

$d = 11 - 2 = 9$

STEP 2 Use given information to find the general term.

Use the equation for an arithmetic sequence. $a_n = a_1 + (n - 1)d$

Substitute -11 for a_1 and 9 for d. $= -11 + (n - 1)9$

Distribute. $= -11 + 9n - 9$

Add like terms. $= 9n - 20$

The general term of the sequence is $a_n = 9n - 20$.

b. Use a different term of the sequence to check the accuracy of the general term.

Choose a term.   7 is the third term.

Substitute and simplify. $a_n = 9n - 20$

$7 = 9(3) - 20$

The general term is accurate. $7 = 7$

c. Find a_{15}.

Use the general term for the sequence. $a_n = 9n - 20$

Substitute 15 for n. $a_{15} = 9(15) - 20$

Simplify. $= 135 - 20 = 115$

The fifteenth term of the sequence is 115.

Need More
HELP?

You can find d by subtracting any two consecutive terms.

$7 - (-2) = 9$

$16 - 7 = 9$

$25 - 16 = 9$

EXAMPLE 8

Find the fifth term of the arithmetic sequence whose first term is 8 and whose common difference is -6.

STEP 1 Find the formula for the general term a_n. $a_n = a_1 + (n - 1)d$

Substitute 8 for a_1 and -6 for d. $= 8 + (n - 1)(-6)$

Distribute. $= 8 - 6n + 6$

Add like terms. $= -6n + 14$

The general term for this sequence is $a_n = -6n + 14$.

STEP 2 Substitute 5 for n. $a_5 = -6(5) + 14$

$= -30 + 14$

$= -16$

The fifth term of the sequence is -16.

SEARCH

To see step-by-step videos of these problems, enter the page number into the SWadvantage.com Search Bar.

Given any two terms of a sequence, the general term can be found by using a system of equations. Other terms can also be found.

EXAMPLE

Find the seventh term of the arithmetic sequence if $a_3 = 13$ and $a_{10} = 48$.

STEP 1 Write a system of equations.

Substitute 3 for n. $a_3 = a_1 + (3 - 1)d$ Substitute 10 for n. $a_{10} = a_1 + (10 - 1)d$

Substitute 13 for a_3. $13 = a_1 + 2d$ Substitute 48 for a_{10}. $48 = a_1 + 9d$

The equations $13 = a_1 + 2d$ and $48 = a_1 + 9d$ form a system that expresses the sequence.

STEP 2 Use the system of equations $\begin{array}{l} 13 = a_1 + 2d \\ 48 = a_1 + 9d \end{array}$ to find the values of a_1 and d.

Multiply the second equation by -1.

$$\begin{array}{r} 13 = a_1 + 2d \\ -48 = -a_1 - 9d \\ \hline -35 = -7d \end{array}$$

Add the equations.

Divide. $5 = d$

STEP 3 Solve for a_1.

Substitute 5 for d in either equation in Step 1. $13 = a_1 + 2(5)$

Simplify. $13 = a_1 + 10$

$a_1 = 3$

STEP 4 Find the general term for the sequence. $a_n = a_1 + (n - 1)d$

Substitute $a_1 = 3$ and $d = 5$. $a_n = 3 + (n - 1)5$

Simplify. $= 5n - 2$

The general term for this sequence is $a_n = 5n - 2$.

STEP 5 Find the seventh term of the sequence. $a_n = 5n - 2$

Substitute 7 for n in the general term. $a_7 = 5(7) - 2 = 33$

The seventh term of the arithmetic sequence is 33.

Need More HELP ?

For help in solving systems of equations by graphing, substitution, addition, subtraction or elimination, see *Systems of Linear Equations and Inequalities* in *Algebra* (p. 1574).

EXAMPLE 10

Jose eats 2 ounces of cereal each morning. After he ate cereal the first morning, there were 20 ounces of cereal remaining in the box. How many ounces are left after 5 mornings?

STEP 1 Find the general term of the sequence. $a_n = a_1 + (n - 1)d$

Substitute 20 for a_1 and -2 for d. $a_n = 20 + (n - 1)(-2)$

Simplify. $= 20 - 2n + 2$

$= -2n + 22$

The general term for this sequence is $a_n = -2n + 22$.

STEP 2 Calculate a_5 from the general term. $a_n = -2n + 22$

Substitute 5 for n. $a_5 = -2(5) + 22$

Simplify. $= 12$

There are 12 ounces left after 5 mornings.

Arithmetic Series

SOUTHWESTERN

Series

The sum of the terms of a sequence is called a **series**. If the sequence is an arithmetic sequence, then the sum of the terms is called an **arithmetic series**.

- A series can be finite or infinite. A **finite series** is the sum of a finite number of terms. An **infinite series** is the sum of an infinite number of terms.
- The Greek symbol sigma, Σ, is used for summation notation, also called sigma notation.
- An **index of summation** is used to indicate the lower and upper limit of the summation. For example, the notation $\sum_{n=1}^{3}(n+1)$ indicates the sum of the terms of the sequence $\{2, 3, 4\}$. This example is read as "the sum from n equals 1 to n equals 3 of $n + 1$." Any variable can be used as the index of summation. The variables i and n are the most commonly used.

EXAMPLE 1

a. Evaluate $\sum_{n=1}^{4}(2n + 7)$.

$$\sum_{n=1}^{4}(2n + 7) = (2 \cdot 1 + 7) + (2 \cdot 2 + 7) + (2 \cdot 3 + 7) + (2 \cdot 4 + 7)$$
$$= 9 + 11 + 13 + 15$$
$$= 48$$

b. Evaluate $\sum_{i=3}^{6}(5i - 4)$.

$$\sum_{i=3}^{6}(5i - 4) = (5 \cdot 3 - 4) + (5 \cdot 4 - 4) + (5 \cdot 5 - 4) + (5 \cdot 6 - 4)$$
$$= 11 + 16 + 21 + 26$$
$$= 74$$

EXAMPLE 2

Need More

HELP?

To review arithmetic sequences, go to *Arithmetic Sequences* on page 1858.

Write the series $-5 + 2 + 9 + 16 + 23$ using summation notation.

STEP 1 Find d.

Use any two consecutive terms to calculate d. $2 + d = 9$
$$d = 9 - 2 = 7$$

STEP 2 Use the equation for an arithmetic sequence, $a_n = a_1 + d(n - 1)$, to find the general term.

Substitute -5 for a_1 and 7 for d. $a_n = -5 + 7(n - 1)$
Simplify. $= -5 + 7n - 7 = 7n - 12$

STEP 3 Use summation notation to write the sum.

Because there are 5 terms in the series, the lower limit is 1 and the upper limit is 5.

$$\sum_{n=1}^{5}(7n - 12)$$

Partial Sums

The sum of the first n terms of a sequence is called a **partial sum** and is denoted S_n. Because a partial sum has a finite number of terms, it is an example of a finite series.

A formula can be used to find a partial sum of an arithmetic series. The partial sum S_n of the arithmetic sequence $\{a_1, a_2, a_3, \ldots, a_n\}$, with common difference d, can be written as follows:

$$S_n = a_1 + a_2 + a_3 + \ldots + a_n$$
$$= a_1 + (a_1 + d) + (a_1 + 2d) + (a_1 + 3d) + \ldots + [a_1 + (n-1)d]$$

This sum can also be written in reverse as shown below.

$$S_n = a_n + (a_n - d) + (a_n - 2d) + (a_n - 3d) + \ldots + a_1$$

Aligning like terms and adding these two equations for S_n gives:

$$S_n = a_1 \qquad + (a_1 + d) + (a_1 + 2d) + (a_1 + 3d) + \ldots + a_n$$
$$\underline{S_n = a_n \qquad + (a_n - d) + (a_n - 2d) + (a_n - 3d) + \ldots + a_1}$$
$$2S_n = (a_1 + a_n) + (a_1 + a_n) + (a_1 + a_n) + (a_1 + a_n) + \ldots + (a_1 + a_n) = n(a_1 + a_n)$$

$$S_n = \frac{n(a_1 + a_n)}{2}$$

So, the partial sum of the first n terms of a sequence, S_n, equals n times the average of a_1 and a_n.

EXAMPLE 3

Find the partial sum S_n of the first 20 terms of the arithmetic sequence whose general term is $a_n = 5 - 3n$.

STEP 1 Find a_1. $a_n = 5 - 3n$

  Substitute 1 for n. $a_1 = 5 - 3(1)$

  Simplify. $= 2$

STEP 2 Find a_{20}. $a_n = 5 - 3n$

  Substitute 20 for n. $a_{20} = 5 - 3(20)$

  Simplify. $= -55$

STEP 3 Find the partial sum.

  Use the formula for the partial sum. $S_n = \frac{n(a_1 + a_n)}{2}$.

  Substitute $a_1 = 2$ and $a_{20} = -55$. $S_{20} = \frac{20[2 + (-55)]}{2}$

  Simplify. $= -530$

The partial sum, S_{20}, equals -530.

SEARCH

To see step-by-step videos of these problems, enter the page number into the SWadvantage.com Search Bar.

GOT TO KNOW!

Partial Sum of an Arithmetic Sequence

The sum of the first n terms of an arithmetic sequence $\{a_1, a_2, a_3, \ldots, a_n\}$ is $S_n = \frac{n(a_1 + a_n)}{2}$.

Alternate Formula for S_n

Sometimes it is useful to write the formula for the partial sum of an arithmetic series in terms of the first term, a_1, and the common difference, d. Substituting $a_1 + (n-1)d$ for a_n in $S_n = \dfrac{n(a_1 + a_n)}{2}$ gives this alternate formula for S_n.

$$S_n = \frac{n(a_1 + a_n)}{2} = \frac{n(a_1 + [a_1 + (n-1)d])}{2}$$

$$S_n = \frac{n[2a_1 + (n-1)d]}{2}$$

SEARCH 🔍

To see step-by-step videos of these problems, enter the page number into the SWadvantage.com Search Bar.

EXAMPLE 4

Find the sum of the first 16 terms of the arithmetic sequence whose first term is 12 and whose common difference is 4.

Choose the appropriate formula for S_n. $S_n = \dfrac{n[2a_1 + (n-1)d]}{2}$

Substitute 16 for n, 12 for a_1, and 4 for d. $S_{16} = \dfrac{16[2 \cdot 12 + (16-1)4]}{2}$

Simplify. $= \dfrac{16(24 + 60)}{2}$

$= 672$

The partial sum of this series, S_{16}, equals 672.

EXAMPLE 5

A theater has 20 rows of seats in one section. The first row of seating in a section has 6 seats and each successive row has two additional seats. How many seats are in one section?

Choose the appropriate formula for S_n. $S_n = \dfrac{n[2a_1 + (n-1)d]}{2}$

Find a_1, n, and d. $a_1 = 6, n = 20,$ and $d = 2$

Substitute 20 for n, 6 for a_1, and 2 for d. $S_{20} = \dfrac{20[2 \cdot 6 + (20-1)2]}{2}$

Simplify. $= \dfrac{20(12 + 38)}{2}$

$= 500$

There are 500 seats in one section.

GOT TO KNOW!

Partial Sum of an Arithmetic Sequence

Known	a_1, a_n, n	a_1, d, n
Equation	$S_n = \dfrac{n(a_1 + a_n)}{2}$	$S_n = \dfrac{n[2a_1 + (n-1)d]}{2}$

EXAMPLE 6

Find the sum of the first 50 terms of the arithmetic sequence $\{-8, 5, 18, 31, 43, \ldots\}$.

METHOD 1

STEP 1 Choose the best formula to use.
For this sequence, d is easier to find than a_n. $S_n = \dfrac{n[2a_1 + (n-1)d]}{2}$.

STEP 2 Find the common difference. $d = 5 - (-8) = 13$

STEP 3 Substitute 50 for n, -8 for a_1, and 13 for d. $S_{50} = \dfrac{50[2(-8) + (50-1)13]}{2}$

STEP 4 Simplify. $S_{50} = \dfrac{50(-16 + 637)}{2} = 15{,}525$

METHOD 2

STEP 1 Find the common difference. $d = 5 - (-8) = 13$

STEP 2 Use $a_n = a_1 + (n-1)d$ to find a_{50}. $a_{50} = -8 + (50-1)13$
$= -8 + 49(13) = 629$

STEP 3 Calculate S_{50}.
Choose the best equation to use. $S_n = \dfrac{n(a_1 + a_n)}{2}$

Substitute $n = 50$, $a_1 = -8$, and $a_n = 629$ into the equation. $S_{50} = \dfrac{50(-8 + 629)}{2}$

Simplify. $= 15{,}525$

The partial sum of the sequence is 15,525.

EXAMPLE 7

For the arithmetic sequence $\{a_1, a_2, \ldots, a_n\}$ whose general term is $a_n = -5n + 15$, the sum of the first n terms is -35. Find n.

STEP 1 Find a_1 and a_2. $a_1 = -5(1) + 15 = 10;\ a_2 = -5(2) + 15 = 5$

STEP 2 Find d. $d = a_2 - a_1 = 5 - 10 = -5$

STEP 3 Choose the best formula to use. $S_n = \dfrac{n[2a_1 + (n-1)d]}{2}$

STEP 4 Substitute -35 for S_n, 10 for a_1, and -5 for d. $-35 = \dfrac{n[2 \cdot 10 + (n-1)(-5)]}{2}$

STEP 5 Solve for n.
Simplify. $-35 = \dfrac{n(20 - 5n + 5)}{2} = \dfrac{n(-5n + 25)}{2}$
$= \dfrac{-5n^2 + 25n}{2}$

Multiply both sides of the equation by 2. $-70 = -5n^2 + 25n$
Add 70 to both sides of the equation. $0 = -5n^2 + 25n + 70$
Divide both sides of the equation by -5. $0 = n^2 - 5n - 14$
Factor. $0 = (n - 7)(n + 2)$
Solve for n. $n = 7, n = -2$

Because n must be a natural number, $n = 7$.

Need More
HELP ?

Notice that the common difference, d, is equal to the coefficient of n, -5.

Geometric Sequences

Geometric Sequences

A sequence in which the ratio of consecutive terms is a non-zero constant is called a **geometric sequence**. The constant ratio, denoted r, is called the **common ratio**. For example, the sequence $\{2, 4, 8, 16, \ldots\}$ is a geometric sequence with a common ratio of 2.

In general, r can be found by calculating the ratio $\dfrac{a_n}{a_{n-1}}$, and each successive term of a geometric sequence can be found by multiplying the preceding term by r.

SEARCH

To see step-by-step videos of these problems, enter the page number into the SWadvantage.com Search Bar.

EXAMPLE 1

Write the first four terms of the geometric sequence whose first term is 6 and whose common ratio is 0.3.

STEP 1	Identify the first term.	$a_1 = 6$
STEP 2	Multiply the first term by r.	$a_2 = 6(0.3) = 1.8$
STEP 3	Multiply the second term by r.	$a_3 = 1.8(0.3) = 0.54$
STEP 4	Multiply the third term by r.	$a_4 = 0.54(0.3) = 0.162$

The first four terms of the geometric sequence are 6, 1.8, 0.54, and 0.162.

EXAMPLE 2

Determine if the given sequence is geometric. If it is geometric, find r.

a. $\{3, 12, 48, 192, 768, \ldots\}$

Calculate the ratio of consecutive terms. $\quad \dfrac{12}{3} = 4, \dfrac{48}{12} = 4, \dfrac{192}{48} = 4, \dfrac{768}{192} = 4$

The ratios are constant, so it is a geometric sequence with a common ratio of $r = 4$.

b. $\{3, 6, 10, 15, 21, \ldots\}$

Calculate the ratio of consecutive terms. $\quad \dfrac{6}{3} = 2, \dfrac{10}{6} = \dfrac{5}{3}, \dfrac{15}{10} = \dfrac{3}{2}, \dfrac{21}{15} = \dfrac{7}{5}$

The ratios are not constant, so the sequence is not geometric.

EXAMPLE 3

Determine if the sequence $\{a_n\} = \{2^n\}$ is geometric. If it is geometric, find r.

The sequence is geometric if the ratio $\dfrac{a_n}{a_{n-1}}$ is constant.

Need More HELP?

For help with exponent rules, see *Exponents* in *Algebra* (p. 1396).

STEP 1	Substitute 2^n for a_n.	$\dfrac{a_n}{a_{n-1}} = \dfrac{2^n}{2^{n-1}}$
STEP 2	Use the exponent rule $\dfrac{a^m}{a^n} = a^{m-n}$.	$= 2^{n-(n-1)}$
STEP 3	Simplify.	$= 2^{n-n+1}$
		$= 2^1 = 2$

The ratio of consecutive terms is 2, so the sequence is geometric with a common ratio of $r = 2$.

General Term of a Geometric Sequence

Notice the general pattern for each successive term of a geometric sequence.

$$a_2 = a_1 r$$
$$a_3 = a_2 r = (a_1 r)r = a_1 r^2$$
$$a_4 = a_3 r = (a_1 r^2)r = a_1 r^3$$
$$a_5 = a_4 r = (a_1 r^3)r = a_1 r^4$$

In general, $a_n = a_1 r^{n-1}$.

EXAMPLE 4

Find the third term of a geometric sequence. Its first term is 2, and its common ratio is 5.

STEP 1 Identify the formula for the general term a_n. $a_n = a_1 r^{n-1}$

STEP 2 Substitute 2 for a_1, 5 for r, and 3 for n. $a_3 = 2(5^{3-1})$

STEP 3 Simplify. $= 2(5^2) = 2(25) = 50$

The third term of this geometric sequence is 50.

EXAMPLE 5

Find the fourth term of a geometric sequence. Its first term is 9, and its common ratio is $\frac{2}{5}$.

STEP 1 Identify the formula for the general term a_n. $a_n = a_1 r^{n-1}$

STEP 2 Substitute 9 for a_1 and $\frac{2}{5}$ for r. $a_n = 9\left(\frac{2}{5}\right)^{n-1}$

STEP 3 Substitute 4 for n. $a_4 = 9\left(\frac{2}{5}\right)^{4-1}$

STEP 4 Simplify. $= 9\left(\frac{2}{5}\right)^3$

STEP 5 Use the exponent rule $\left(\frac{a}{b}\right)^m = \frac{a^m}{b^m}$. $= 9\left(\frac{8}{125}\right)$

STEP 6 Simplify. $= \frac{72}{125}$

The fourth term of this geometric sequence is $\frac{72}{125}$.

GOT TO KNOW!

General Term of a Geometric Sequence

$$a_n = a_1 r^{n-1}, r \neq 0$$

n = number of the term a_1 = first term r = common ratio

Using Geometric Sequences

Sometimes the first term of a geometric sequence is not known.

- If the values of two consecutive terms are known, r is easily calculated by dividing the term by the term preceding it.
- If the value of two terms and r are known, the value of a_1, a_n, or n can be determined using the equation $a_n = a_1 r^{n-1}$.

SEARCH 🔍

To see step-by-step videos of these problems, enter the page number into the SWadvantage.com Search Bar.

EXAMPLE 6

Find the seventh term of the geometric sequence {3, 15, 75, 375, . . .}.

STEP 1 Find r.

Choose any two consecutive terms.　　3 and 15

Find r, the ratio of the terms.　　$r = \dfrac{15}{3} = 5$

STEP 2 Substitute 3 for a_1 and 5 for r into the formula $a_n = a_1 r^{n-1}$.

$a_n = 3(5^{n-1})$

STEP 3 Using $a_n = 3(5^{n-1})$, find a_7.

Substitute 7 for n.　　$a_7 = 3(5^{7-1})$

Simplify.　　$= 3(5^6) = 46{,}875$

The seventh term of the sequence is 46,875.

EXAMPLE 7

Find the first term a_1 and the common ratio r of the geometric sequence whose second term is 12 and whose third term is 36.

STEP 1 Find r.

The sequence is geometric, and the terms are consecutive, so $r = \dfrac{a_3}{a_2} = \dfrac{36}{12} = 3$.

STEP 2 Using $a_n = a_1 r^{n-1}$, find a_1.

Try It This Way

You can work backward to find the previous term. Because each successive term is multiplied by r, each previous term is divided by r. So,
$a_1 = \dfrac{a_2}{r}$.
In this example,
$a_1 = \dfrac{12}{3} = 4$.

METHOD 1

Substitute 2 for n.　　　　$a_2 = a_1 r^{2-1}$

Substitute 12 for a_2 and 3 for r.　　$12 = a_1(3)^{2-1}$

Simplify.　　　　　　$12 = a_1(3)$

　　　　　　　　　$4 = a_1$

METHOD 2

Substitute 3 for n.　　　　$a_3 = a_1 r^{3-1}$

Substitute 36 for a_3 and 3 for r.　　$36 = a_1(3)^{3-1}$

Simplify.　　　　　　$36 = a_1(9)$

　　　　　　　　　$4 = a_1$

The first term is 4 and the common ratio is 3.

Using a System of Equations to Find a Geometric Sequence

If two non-consecutive terms of a geometric sequence are given, the first term and common ratio of the sequence can be found using a system of equations. Once a_1 and r are known, you can write a formula for the general term and find the value of any term.

EXAMPLE 8

Find the first term a_1 and the common ratio r of the geometric sequence whose third term is 20 and whose sixth term is -160.

Need More
HELP
For help with solving systems, see *Solving a System by Substitution* in *Algebra* (p. 1568).

STEP 1 Write a system of equations from the given information and $a_n = a_1 r^{n-1}$.

| Substitute 3 for n. | $a_3 = a_1 r^{3-1}$ | Substitute 6 for n. | $a_6 = a_1 r^{6-1}$ |
| Substitute 20 for a_3. | $20 = a_1 r^{3-1}$ | Substitute -160 for a_6. | $-160 = a_1 r^{6-1}$ |

STEP 2 Solve both equations for a_1.

$$20 = a_1 r^{3-1} \qquad -160 = a_1 r^{6-1}$$

$$a_1 = \frac{20}{r^2} \qquad a_1 = \frac{-160}{r^5}$$

STEP 3 Find r.

Substitute one expression equal to a_1 into the other equation. $\quad \dfrac{20}{r^2} = \dfrac{-160}{r^5}$

Rearrange the equation. $\quad \dfrac{r^5}{r^2} = \dfrac{-160}{20}$

Simplify. $\quad r^3 = -8$

$$r = -2$$

STEP 4 Solve for a_1.

Substitute -2 for r into either equation in Step 1. $\quad 20 = a_1 r^2 = a_1(-2)^2$

Simplify. $\quad 20 = 4a_1$

$$a_1 = 5$$

The first term is 5 and the common ratio is -2.

EXAMPLE 9

Michael has worked for his current employer for the past 5 years. Each year, the only raise he received was a cost-of-living raise of 3%. His current salary is \$56,000. Find Michael's starting salary to the nearest dollar.

STEP 1 Find r.

Because Michael's salary increases by 3% each year, his salary each year is a term of the geometric sequence with $r = 1 + 0.03 = 1.03$.

STEP 2 Using $a_n = a_1 r^{n-1}$, find Michael's starting salary. $\quad a_n = a_1 r^{n-1}$

Substitute 5 for n, 1.03 for r, and 56,000 for a_5. $\quad 56{,}000 = a_1(1.03)^{5-1}$

Simplify. $\quad a_1 \approx 49{,}755$

Michael's starting salary was about \$49,755.

Geometric Series

Geometric Series

The sum of the terms of a geometric sequence is called a **geometric series**. Recall that the sum of the first n terms of a sequence is called a partial sum and is denoted S_n.

A formula for the partial sum S_n of the geometric sequence with first term a_1 and common ratio r can be derived as follows:

1. Write the sum of the first n terms of a geometric series.

$$S_n = a_1 + a_1 r + a_1 r^2 + a_1 r^3 + \ldots + a_1 r^{n-1}$$

2. Multiply both sides of the equation by r.

$$rS_n = a_1 r + a_1 r^2 + a_1 r^3 + \ldots + a_1 r^{n-1} + a_n r^n$$

3. Subtract the second equation from the first.

$$S_n = a_1 + a_1 r + a_1 r^2 + a_1 r^3 + \ldots + a_1 r^{n-1}$$
$$-\left(rS_n = \qquad a_1 r + a_1 r^2 + a_1 r^3 + \ldots + a_1 r^{n-1} + a_1 r^n \right)$$
$$\overline{S_n - rS_n = a_1 + 0 \quad + 0 \quad + 0 \quad + \ldots + 0 \quad - a_1 r^n}$$

> **Watch Out** !
>
> Remember that $1 - r^n \neq (1 - r)^n$. An exponent applies to what is directly before it. In $1 - r^n$, the exponent applies to r only. In $(1 - r)^n$, the exponent applies to everything inside the parentheses.

4. Factor out a common factor of S_n from the left-hand side of the equation, and factor out a common factor of a_1 from the right-hand side of the equation.

$$S_n(1 - r) = a_1(1 - r^n)$$

5. Divide both sides of the equation by $(1 - r)$, $r \neq 1$, to solve for S_n.

$$S_n = \frac{a_1(1 - r^n)}{(1 - r)}$$

Note that if $r = 1$, the formula does not hold. If $r = 1$, the denominator of this formula is 0.

EXAMPLE 1

Find the sum of the first ten terms of the geometric sequence $\{7, 21, 63, 189, 567, \ldots\}$.

STEP 1 Find r.

The sequence is geometric, so r is the ratio of consecutive terms.

$r = \frac{21}{7} = 3$

STEP 2 Use the formula for the partial sum of a geometric series.

$$S_n = \frac{a_1(1 - r^n)}{(1 - r)}$$

Substitute 7 for a_1, 3 for r, and 10 for n.

$$S_{10} = \frac{7(1 - 3^{10})}{(1 - 3)}$$

Simplify.

$$= \frac{7(1 - 59{,}049)}{(1 - 3)}$$

$$= \frac{-413{,}336}{-2}$$

$$= 206{,}668$$

The sum of the first 10 terms of the sequence is 206,668.

EXAMPLE 2

Find the sum of the first six terms of the geometric sequence whose first term is 5 and whose common ratio is 3.

Use the formula for the partial sum of a geometric series.

$$S_n = \frac{a_1(1 - r^n)}{(1 - r)}$$

Substitute 6 for n, 5 for a_1, and 3 for r.

$$S_6 = \frac{5(1 - 3^6)}{(1 - 3)}$$

Simplify.

$$= \frac{5(1 - 729)}{-2} = \frac{5(-728)}{-2}$$

$$= \frac{3640}{2} = 1820$$

The sum of the first six terms of the geometric series is 1820.

SEARCH

To see step-by-step videos of these problems, enter the page number into the SWadvantage.com Search Bar.

EXAMPLE 3

Find the sum of the first four terms of the geometric sequence whose first term is 12 and whose common ratio is $\frac{3}{2}$.

Use the formula for the partial sum of a geometric series.

$$S_n = \frac{a_1(1 - r^n)}{(1 - r)}$$

Substitute 4 for n, 12 for a_1, and $\frac{3}{2}$ for r.

$$S_4 = \frac{12\left[1 - \left(\frac{3}{2}\right)^4\right]}{\left(1 - \frac{3}{2}\right)}$$

Simplify.

$$= \frac{12\left(1 - \frac{81}{16}\right)}{\left(1 - \frac{3}{2}\right)} = \frac{12\left(-\frac{65}{16}\right)}{-\frac{1}{2}} = \frac{195}{2} = 97\frac{1}{2}$$

The sum of the first four terms of the geometric series is $97\frac{1}{2}$.

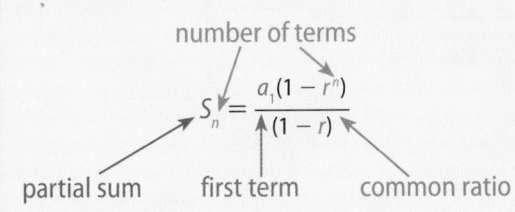

GOT TO KNOW!

Partial Sum of a Geometric Series

number of terms

$$S_n = \frac{a_1(1 - r^n)}{(1 - r)}$$

partial sum   first term   common ratio

Evaluating Geometric Series

Recall that sums can be written using summation, or sigma, notation. If the given sequence is geometric and the lower limit of the sum is one, the formula for the partial sum of a geometric sequence can be used.

EXAMPLE 4

Evaluate $\sum_{n=1}^{6} -5\left(\frac{1}{2}\right)^{n-1}$.

STEP 1 Find the general term of the sequence.

The general term of the given sequence is $a_n = -5\left(\frac{1}{2}\right)^{n-1}$, which is of the form $a_n = a_1 r^{n-1}$.

STEP 2 Identify a_1 and r.

$a_1 = -5$ and $r = \frac{1}{2}$

STEP 3 Determine the formula for the partial sum of the series.

Because the sequence is geometric and the lower limit of the sum is one, the formula for the partial sum of a geometric series applies: $S_n = \frac{a_1(1 - r^n)}{(1 - r)}$.

STEP 4 Find the partial sum of the series.

Substitute -5 for a_1, $\frac{1}{2}$ for r, and 6 for n.

$$S_6 = \frac{-5\left[1 - \left(\frac{1}{2}\right)^6\right]}{\left(1 - \frac{1}{2}\right)}$$

Simplify.

$$= \frac{-5\left(1 - \frac{1}{64}\right)}{\left(1 - \frac{1}{2}\right)} = \frac{-5\left(\frac{63}{64}\right)}{\frac{1}{2}} = -\frac{315}{32} = -9\frac{27}{32}$$

The partial sum of the geometric series $\sum_{n=1}^{6} -5\left(\frac{1}{2}\right)^{n-1}$ is $-9\frac{27}{32}$.

EXAMPLE 5

Evaluate $\sum_{n=1}^{4} (9 - 2n)^{n-1}$.

STEP 1 Find the general term of the sequence.

The general term of the given sequence is $a_n = (9 - 2n)^{n-1}$, which is **not** of the form $a_n = a_1 r^{n-1}$, and the sequence is not geometric.

STEP 2 Find the sum by substituting 1, 2, 3, and 4, respectively, for n, and adding the results.

$$\sum_{n=1}^{4} (9 - 2n)^{n-1} = (9 - 2 \cdot 1)^{1-1} + (9 - 2 \cdot 2)^{2-1} + (9 - 2 \cdot 3)^{3-1} + (9 - 2 \cdot 4)^{4-1}$$

$$= 1 + 5 + 9 + 1 = 16$$

EXAMPLE

According to an ancient tale, the inventor of the game of chess impressed his ruler so much that he was allowed to choose his own reward. The inventor, who was also a mathematician, asked for one grain of rice to be placed on the first square of the chessboard, two grains of rice on the second square, four grains of rice on the third square, eight grains of rice on the fourth square, and so on until all 64 squares of the chessboard were filled with the appropriate number of grains of rice.

a. How many grains of rice were to be placed on the 64th square of the chessboard?

STEP 1   Find r.

Twice as many grains of rice are placed on each successive square of the chessboard, so the number of grains of rice on each square forms a geometric sequence with a common ratio of 2.

STEP 2   Use the formula for the general term, $a_n = a_1 r^{n-1}$, to find a_{64}.

Substitute 64 for n, 1 for a_1, and 2 for r. $a_{64} = 1(2)^{64-1}$

Simplify. $= 2^{63} \approx 9{,}223{,}372{,}037{,}000{,}000{,}000$

The sixty-fourth square of the chessboard contains approximately 9,223,372,037,000,000,000 grains of rice.

b. Use summation notation to write an expression for the total number of grains of rice on the chessboard.

STEP 1   Write an expression for the general term.

Write the equation for the general term. $a_n = a_1 r^{n-1}$

Substitute 1 for a_1 and 2 for r. $= 1(2)^{n-1}$

Simplify. $= 2^{n-1}$

STEP 2   Find the limits of the summation.

The summation starts at the first square, 1.

There are a total of 64 squares on a chessboard, so the upper limit of the summation is 64.

STEP 3   Write the summation notation.

The total number of grains of rice can be written as $\displaystyle\sum_{n=1}^{64} 2^{n-1}$.

c. How many total grains of rice did the inventor ask to be paid?

Write the formula for the partial sum of a geometric series used to evaluate $\displaystyle\sum_{n=1}^{64} 2^{n-1}$.

$$S_n = \frac{a_1(1 - r^n)}{(1 - r)}$$

Substitute 64 for n, 1 for a_1, and 2 for r. $S_{64} = \dfrac{1(1 - 2^{64})}{(1 - 2)}$

Simplify. $= \dfrac{1 - 2^{64}}{-1} = 2^{64} - 1$

$\approx 18{,}446{,}744{,}070{,}000{,}000{,}000$

The inventor asked to be paid approximately 18,446,744,070,000,000,000 grains of rice.

Infinite Geometric Series

Need More HELP

For help with partial sums of a geometric sequence, go to *Geometric Series* (p. 1870).

Infinite Geometric Series

Recall that a geometric sequence with an infinite number of terms is an infinite geometric sequence. The sum of the terms of an infinite geometric sequence is called an **infinite geometric series**.

A formula for the sum of an infinite geometric series can be developed by examining the partial sums of an infinite geometric sequence.

EXAMPLE 1

Develop the formula for the sum of an infinite geometric series by examining partial sums.

STEP 1 Choose an infinite geometric series, and identify a_1 and r.

$\frac{1}{2} + \frac{1}{4} + \frac{1}{8} + \frac{1}{16} + \frac{1}{32} + \ldots$ is an infinite geometric series with $a_1 = \frac{1}{2}$ and $r = \frac{1}{2}$.

STEP 2 Write and examine the first several partial sums of the series.

Its first five partial sums are:

$S_1 = a_1 = \frac{1}{2}$

$S_2 = a_1 + a_2 = \frac{1}{2} + \frac{1}{4} = \frac{3}{4} = 0.75$

$S_3 = a_1 + a_2 + a_3 = \frac{1}{2} + \frac{1}{4} + \frac{1}{8} = \frac{7}{8} = 0.875$

$S_4 = a_1 + a_2 + a_3 + a_4 = \frac{1}{2} + \frac{1}{4} + \frac{1}{8} + \frac{1}{16} = \frac{15}{16} = 0.9375$

$S_5 = a_1 + a_2 + a_3 + a_4 + a_5 = \frac{1}{2} + \frac{1}{4} + \frac{1}{8} + \frac{1}{16} + \frac{1}{32} = \frac{31}{32} = 0.96875$

While the value of each successive term gets smaller, the value of each successive partial sum gets closer and closer to 1. In other words, as n gets larger, a_n approaches 0 and S_n approaches 1.

This relationship can also be seen using the formula for the partial sum of a geometric series, $S_n = \frac{a_1(1 - r^n)}{1 - r}$. Substituting $\frac{1}{2}$ for a_1 and $\frac{1}{2}$ for r gives $S_n = \frac{\frac{1}{2}\left[1 - \left(\frac{1}{2}\right)^n\right]}{\left(1 - \frac{1}{2}\right)} = 1 - \left(\frac{1}{2}\right)^n$.

As n increases, $\left(\frac{1}{2}\right)^n$ approaches 0, so S_n approaches $1 - 0$, or 1, which is said to be the **limit** of S_n. The sum of an infinite geometric series is the limit of S_n as n approaches infinity.

GOT TO KNOW!

Sum of an Infinite Geometric Series

For $|r| < 1$	• r^n approaches 0 as n approaches infinity. • As n approaches infinity, $S_n = \frac{a_1(1 - r^n)}{1 - r}$ approaches $\frac{a_1}{1 - r}$.
For $|r| \geq 1$	• S_n also increases as n increases. • The sum S_n does not exist.

EXAMPLE 2

Find the sum of the infinite geometric sequence whose first term is 2 and whose common ratio is $-\frac{1}{4}$.

Use the formula for the sum of an infinite geometric series.

$$S = \frac{a_1}{1 - r}$$

Substitute 2 for a_1 and $-\frac{1}{4}$ for r.

$$= \frac{2}{1 - \left(-\frac{1}{4}\right)}$$

Simplify.

$$= \frac{2}{\frac{5}{4}} = \frac{8}{5} = 1\frac{3}{5}$$

The sum equals $1\frac{3}{5}$.

Try It This Way

Decimal values can also be used to solve Example 2. Writing $-\frac{1}{4}$ as -0.25 gives:

$$S = \frac{2}{1 - (-0.25)}$$

$$= \frac{2}{1.25}$$

$$= 1.6$$

EXAMPLE 3

Find the sum of the infinite geometric sequence $\left\{\frac{4}{9}, \frac{8}{27}, \frac{16}{81}, \frac{32}{243}, \cdots\right\}$.

STEP 1   Find r.

The sequence is geometric, so r is the ratio of consecutive terms.

$$r = \frac{\frac{8}{27}}{\frac{4}{9}} = \frac{8}{27} \cdot \frac{9}{4} = \frac{2}{3}$$

STEP 2   Find the sum of the series.

Because r is less than 1, use the formula for the sum of an infinite geometric series.

$$S = \frac{a_1}{1 - r}$$

Substitute $\frac{4}{9}$ for a_1 and $\frac{2}{3}$ for r.

$$= \frac{\frac{4}{9}}{1 - \frac{2}{3}}$$

Simplify.

$$= \frac{4}{9} \cdot \frac{3}{1} = \frac{4}{3} = 1\frac{1}{3}$$

The sum of the series is $1\frac{1}{3}$.

SEARCH

To see step-by-step videos of these problems, enter the page number into the SWadvantage.com Search Bar.

GOT TO KNOW!

Sum of an Infinite Geometric Series

first term of the series

sum of an infinite geometric series $\longrightarrow S = \frac{a_1}{(1 - r)} \longleftarrow$ common ratio, if $|r| < 1$.

If $|r| \geq 1$, the sum does not exist.

Using Summation Notation

Any sum can be written using summation notation. In general, an infinite geometric series can be written as:
$$\sum_{n=1}^{\infty} a_1 r^{n-1}$$

For example, the sum in Example 3 can be written as $\sum_{n=1}^{\infty} \frac{4}{9}\left(\frac{2}{3}\right)^{n-1}$.

EXAMPLE 4

Evaluate $\sum_{n=1}^{\infty} \frac{3}{4}\left(\frac{2}{5}\right)^{n-1}$.

STEP 1 Find the formula to use.

The general term of the given sequence is $a_n = \frac{3}{4}\left(\frac{2}{5}\right)^{n-1}$. This is of the form $a_n = a_1 r^{n-1}$, so the sequence is geometric with $a_1 = \frac{3}{4}$ and $r = \frac{2}{5}$. Because $|r| < 1$, the formula for the sum of an infinite geometric series applies.

$$S = \frac{a_1}{1-r}$$

STEP 2 Substitute $\frac{3}{4}$ for a_1 and $\frac{2}{5}$ for r.

$$= \frac{\frac{3}{4}}{1-\frac{2}{5}}$$

STEP 3 Simplify.

$$= \frac{3}{4} \cdot \frac{5}{3} = \frac{5}{4} = 1\frac{1}{4}$$

The sum of the geometric sequence is $1\frac{1}{4}$.

EXAMPLE 5

Evaluate $\sum_{n=1}^{\infty} \frac{1}{3}(-3)^{n-1}$.

STEP 1 Find the formula to use.

The general term of the given sequence is $a_n = \frac{1}{3}(-3)^{n-1}$.

This is of the form $a_n = a_1 r^{n-1}$, so the sequence is geometric with $a_1 = \frac{1}{3}$ and $r = -3$.

STEP 2 Evaluate the known information.

$|r| = |-3| = 3$, so $r > 1$.

The sum of the series does not exist.

Writing Repeating Decimals as Fractions

Repeating decimals can be written as infinite geometric series. For example, $0.33\overline{3}$ can be written as $0.3 + 0.03 + 0.003 + \ldots$ or $0.3 + 0.3(0.1) + 0.3(0.1)^2 + 0.3(0.1)^3 + \ldots$. Notice that $r = 0.1$ is less than 1, so you can use the formula for the sum of an infinite geometric series to write the repeating decimal as a fraction.

EXAMPLE 6

Write $0.\overline{12}$ as a fraction in lowest terms.

STEP 1   Write the repeating decimal as an infinite geometric series.

$0.\overline{12} = 0.12 + 0.12(0.01) + 0.12(0.01)^2 + 0.12(0.01)^3 + \ldots$

STEP 2   Find the formula to use.

For this infinite geometric series, $a_1 = 0.12$ and $r = 0.01$. Because $|r| < 1$, the formula for the sum of an infinite geometric series applies.

$$S = \frac{a_1}{1 - r}$$

STEP 3   Substitute 0.12 for a_1 and 0.01 for r.

$$= \frac{0.12}{1 - 0.01}$$

STEP 4   Simplify.

$$= \frac{0.12}{0.99} = \frac{12}{99} = \frac{4}{33}$$

As a fraction in lowest terms, $0.\overline{12} = \frac{4}{33}$.

SEARCH

To see step-by-step videos of these problems, enter the page number into the SWadvantage.com Search Bar.

EXAMPLE 7

A ball is dropped from a height of 10 feet. Each time the ball hits the ground, it bounces to a height 75% of the previous bounce.

a. Write an expression for the total distance the ball bounces.

The height of the ball after each bounce forms an infinite geometric sequence with a common ratio of 75%, or 0.75, and an initial height of 10 feet. The total distance the ball bounces can be written using summation notation.

$$\text{Total distance} = \sum_{n=1}^{\infty} 10(0.75)^{n-1}$$

b. What is the total distance the ball bounces?

Because $|r| < 1$, the formula for the sum of an infinite geometric series can be used to find the total distance the ball bounces.

$$S = \frac{a_1}{1 - r}$$

Substitute 10 for a_1 and 0.75 for r.

$$= \frac{10}{1 - 0.75}$$

Simplify.

$$= \frac{10}{0.25} = 40$$

The ball bounces a total distance of 40 feet.

The Fibonacci Sequence

The Fibonacci Sequence

The **Fibonacci sequence** is a special sequence named after the Italian mathematician Leonardo of Pisa, also known as Fibonacci. The first two terms of the sequence are 1, and each successive term is the sum of the previous two terms. The terms of the sequence are called **Fibonacci numbers**. The general term of the Fibonacci sequence is given by:

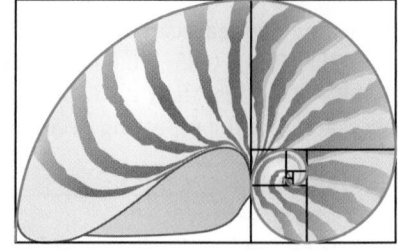

$$a_n = \frac{(1 + \sqrt{5})^n - (1 - \sqrt{5})^n}{2^n \sqrt{5}}$$

EXAMPLE 1

Use the formula for the general term to find the first five terms of the Fibonacci sequence.

Substitute 1 for n.
$$a_1 = \frac{(1 + \sqrt{5}) - (1 - \sqrt{5})}{2\sqrt{5}}$$
$$= \frac{2\sqrt{5}}{2\sqrt{5}} = 1$$

Need More

HELP?

When evaluating the formula for values of $n \geq 2$, treat $(1 + \sqrt{5})^n$ and $(1 - \sqrt{5})^n$ like polynomials. For more help with multiplying polynomials, go to *Multiplying Polynomials* in *Algebra* (p. 1608).

Substitute 2 for n.
$$a_2 = \frac{(1 + \sqrt{5})^2 - (1 - \sqrt{5})^2}{2^2 \sqrt{5}}$$
$$= \frac{6 + 2\sqrt{5} - (6 - 2\sqrt{5})}{4\sqrt{5}}$$
$$= \frac{4\sqrt{5}}{4\sqrt{5}} = 1$$

Substitute 3 for n.
$$a_3 = \frac{(1 + \sqrt{5})^3 - (1 - \sqrt{5})^3}{(2^3)\sqrt{5}}$$
$$= \frac{16 + 8\sqrt{5} - (16 - 8\sqrt{5})}{8\sqrt{5}}$$
$$= \frac{16\sqrt{5}}{8\sqrt{5}} = 2$$

Substitute 4 for n.
$$a_4 = \frac{(1 + \sqrt{5})^4 - (1 - \sqrt{5})^4}{(2^4)\sqrt{5}}$$
$$= \frac{56 + 24\sqrt{5} - (56 - 24\sqrt{5})}{16\sqrt{5}}$$
$$= \frac{48\sqrt{5}}{16\sqrt{5}} = 3$$

Substitute 5 for n.
$$a_5 = \frac{(1 + \sqrt{5})^5 - (1 - \sqrt{5})^5}{2^5 \sqrt{5}}$$
$$= \frac{176 + 80\sqrt{5} - (176 - 80\sqrt{5})}{32\sqrt{5}}$$
$$= \frac{160\sqrt{5}}{32\sqrt{5}} = 5$$

The first five terms of the Fibonacci sequence are 1, 1, 2, 3, 5.

EXAMPLE 2

Terms a_6 through a_{11} of the Fibonacci sequence are 8, 13, 21, 34, 55, 89. Calculate the ratio $\dfrac{a_{n+1}}{a_n}$ for these terms. Round to the nearest thousandth if necessary.

$$\frac{a_7}{a_6} = \frac{13}{8} = 1.625$$

$$\frac{a_8}{a_7} = \frac{21}{13} \approx 1.615$$

$$\frac{a_9}{a_8} = \frac{34}{21} \approx 1.619$$

$$\frac{a_{10}}{a_9} = \frac{55}{34} \approx 1.618$$

$$\frac{a_{11}}{a_{10}} = \frac{89}{55} \approx 1.618$$

SEARCH

To see step-by-step videos of these problems, enter the page number into the SWadvantage.com Search Bar.

As n gets larger and larger, the ratio in Example 2 approaches the irrational number $\dfrac{1 + \sqrt{5}}{2}$, or approximately 1.6180339887. This number is known as the **golden ratio**.

It is thought that items built or drawn using the golden ratio are naturally pleasing to the eye. For example, a golden rectangle, or a rectangle in which the ratio of the longer side to the shorter side is equal to the golden ratio, is often used in art and architecture. Fibonacci numbers and the golden ratio can also be found in nature.

Need More

HELP ?

Where have golden rectangles been used? The façade of the Parthenon appears to have been built using a golden rectangle. The face of Mona Lisa was painted to fit inside a vertical golden rectangle.

EXAMPLE 3

Female honeybees hatch from a fertilized egg, while male honeybees hatch from an unfertilized egg. This means that female honeybees have two parents, and male honeybees have just one parent.

a. **Draw a family tree for five generations of a male honeybee.**

   Start with a male honeybee, M.

   The male honeybee has one parent, a female F.

   That female has two parents, male M and female F.

   Continue drawing parents to get the tree diagram at right.

b. **How many honeybees are in each of the five generations of a male honeybee?**

   Use the family tree to count the number of honeybees in each generation. The first five generations have 1, 1, 2, 3, and 5 honeybees.

c. **How many honeybees will be in the eighth generation?**

   The number of honeybees in each generation forms the Fibonacci sequence. Continue the sequence to the eighth term.

   1, 1, 2, 3, 5, 8, 13, 21

   The eighth generation will have 21 honeybees.

Recursive Rules

Recursive Rules

A rule for each term of a sequence written in terms of one or more of the preceding terms is called a **recursive rule**. For example, $a_n = a_{n-1} + 2$ where $a_1 = 3$ forms the sequence $\{3, 5, 7, 9, \ldots\}$. Notice that a recursive rule requires both an equation and at least one initial value.

SEARCH

To see step-by-step videos of these problems, enter the page number into the SWadvantage.com Search Bar.

EXAMPLE 1

Find the first five terms of the sequence formed by the recursive rule $a_n = \frac{1}{2}a_{n-1} + 6$, $a_1 = 4$.

METHOD 1

Use the rule to calculate the value of the first five terms.

The value of a_1 is given. $\quad a_1 = 4$

Substitute 2 for n. $\quad a_2 = \frac{1}{2}a_1 + 6$

$$= \frac{1}{2}(4) + 6 = 8$$

Substitute 3 for n. $\quad a_3 = \frac{1}{2}a_2 + 6$

$$= \frac{1}{2}(8) + 6 = 10$$

Substitute 4 for n. $\quad a_4 = \frac{1}{2}a_3 + 6$

$$= \frac{1}{2}(10) + 6 = 11$$

Substitute 5 for n. $\quad a_5 = \frac{1}{2}a_4 + 6$

$$= \frac{1}{2}(11) + 6 = 11.5$$

METHOD 2

Use a graphing calculator to generate a table of values for a_n.

Press MODE and select SEQ. Then press Y= and enter the following equations.

nMin $= 1$

$u(n) = (1/2)u(n - 1) + 6$

$u(n$Min$) = 4$

Press TBLSET and enter the following settings.

TblStart $= 1$ Indpnt: Auto

$\triangle$Tbl $= 1$ Depend: Auto

Press TABLE to display the values of n and the corresponding terms of the sequence.

n	$u(n)$
1	4
2	8
3	10
4	11
5	11.5
6	11.75
7	11.875

$u(n)=11.5$

EXAMPLE 2

Use the sequence {7, 2, −3, −8, −13, . . .} to answer the following.

a. Write a recursive rule for the sequence.

Each successive term is five less than the previous term and the first term is 7. So, the recursive rule is $a_n = a_{n-1} - 5, a_1 = 7$.

b. Is the sequence arithmetic, geometric, or neither?

Consecutive terms differ by a constant amount, so the sequence is arithmetic.

Each successive term of any arithmetic sequence is found by adding the common difference d to the previous term. So, in general, a recursive equation for the nth term of any arithmetic sequence is $a_n = a_{n-1} + d$.

EXAMPLE 3

Write a recursive rule for the sequence {15, 24, 33, 42, 51, . . .}.

Consecutive terms differ by a constant amount, so the sequence is arithmetic with $a_1 = 15$ and $d = 9$. Use the general recursive equation for an arithmetic sequence.

$$a_n = a_{n-1} + d$$

Substitute 9 for d. $a_n = a_{n-1} + 9$

So, a recursive rule for the sequence is $a_n = a_{n-1} + 9, a_1 = 15$.

> **Watch Out !**
>
> It is important to note that in addition to the recursive equation, an initial value is needed to complete the recursive rule.

EXAMPLE 4

Use the sequence {8, 2, $\frac{1}{2}, \frac{1}{8}, \frac{1}{32}$, . . .} to answer the following.

a. Write a recursive rule for the sequence.

Each successive term is one-fourth of the previous term and the first term is 8. So, the recursive rule is $a_n = \frac{a_{n-1}}{4}, a_1 = 8$.

b. Is the sequence arithmetic, geometric, or neither?

The ratio of consecutive terms is constant, so the sequence is geometric.

Each successive term of any geometric sequence is found by multiplying the previous term by the common ratio r. So in general, a recursive equation for the nth term of any geometric sequence is $a_n = r \cdot a_{n-1}$.

EXAMPLE 5

Write a recursive rule for the sequence {5, 15, 45, 135, 405, . . .}.

The ratio of consecutive terms is constant, so the sequence is geometric with $a_1 = 5$ and $r = 3$. Use the general recursive equation for a geometric sequence.

$$a_n = r \cdot a_{n-1}$$

Substitute 3 for r. $a_n = 3a_{n-1}$

Sequences that Are Neither Arithmetic nor Geometric

Some sequences are neither arithmetic nor geometric but can still be described by a recursive rule.

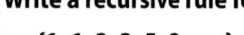

EXAMPLE 6

Need More

HELP?

For help with the Fibonacci sequence, see *The Fibonacci Sequence* in *Advanced Algebra* (p. 1878).

Write a recursive rule for each sequence.

a. {1, 1, 2, 3, 5, 8, ...}

Notice that this is the Fibonacci sequence in which the first two terms are 1 and then each successive term is the sum of the previous two terms. So, the recursive rule is $a_n = a_{n-2} + a_{n-1}, a_1 = 1, a_2 = 1$.

b. {3, 11, 27, 59, 123, ...}

Notice the following pattern.

$a_1 = 3$

$a_2 = 11$
$= 2 \cdot 3 + 5 = 2a_1 + 5$

$a_3 = 27$
$= 2 \cdot 11 + 5 = 2a_2 + 5$

$a_4 = 59$
$= 2 \cdot 27 + 5 = 2a_3 + 5$

$a_5 = 123$
$= 2 \cdot 59 + 5 = 2a_4 + 5$

Beginning with the second term, each term is the sum of twice the preceding term and 5. The initial term is 3, so the recursive rule is $a_n = 2a_{n-1} + 5, a_1 = 3$.

c. {4, 5, 9, 18, 34, ...}

Notice the following pattern.

$a_1 = 4$

$a_2 = 5$
$= 4 + 1 = a_1 + 1^2$

$a_3 = 9$
$= 5 + 4 = a_2 + 2^2$

$a_4 = 18$
$= 9 + 9 = a_3 + 3^2$

$a_5 = 34$
$= 18 + 16 = a_4 + 4^2$

Beginning with the second term, each term is the sum of the preceding term and the value of $(n - 1)^2$. The initial term is 4, so the recursive rule is $a_n = a_{n-1} + (n - 1)^2, a_1 = 4$.

Triangular numbers are numbers that form a triangle when represented by dots as shown below. Write a recursive rule for the triangular numbers.

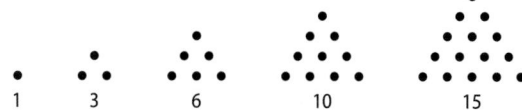

Examine the pattern.

$a_1 = 1$

$a_2 = 3$

$\quad = 1 + 2 = a_1 + 2$

$a_3 = 6$

$\quad = 3 + 3 = a_2 + 3$

$a_4 = 10$

$\quad = 6 + 4 = a_3 + 4$

$a_5 = 15$

$\quad = 10 + 5 = a_4 + 5$

Beginning with the second term, each term is the sum of the preceding term and the value of n. The initial term is 1, so the recursive rule for triangular numbers is $a_n = a_{n-1} + n, a_1 = 1$.

EXAMPLE 8

Jack has lived in the same apartment for five years. When he first moved in, the rent cost $800 per month. Each year, the monthly cost of rent increased 2%.

a. Write a recursive rule for the cost of rent n years after Jack moved into his apartment.

The initial cost of rent is $800 and each successive year's monthly rent is 2% greater than the previous year's monthly rent. So, the recursive rule is $a_n = 1.02a_{n-1}, a_1 = 800$.

b. Find the monthly cost of Jack's current rent. Round to the nearest cent.

Jack has lived in the apartment for five years, so find the value of a_5.

METHOD 1

Use the formula to calculate each year's monthly rent.

First year's monthly rent $\qquad a_1 = 800$

Second year's monthly rent $\qquad a_2 = 1.02(800) = 816$

Third year's monthly rent $\qquad a_3 = 1.02(816) = 832.32$

Fourth year's monthly rent $\qquad a_4 = 1.02(832.32) \approx 848.97$

Fifth year's monthly rent $\qquad a_5 = 1.02(848.97) \approx 865.95$

The monthly cost of Jack's current rent is $865.95.

METHOD 2

Use a graphing calculator. Enter the initial value, [8][0][0].
Then enter the formula, [1][.][0][2][×][ANS].
Press [ENTER] to find a_2. Press [ENTER] again to find a_3.
Press [ENTER] twice more to find a_5.

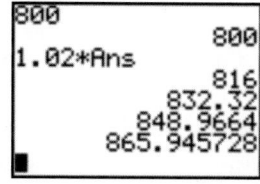

The monthly cost of Jack's current rent is $865.95.

SEARCH

To see step-by-step videos of these problems, enter the page number into the SWadvantage.com Search Bar.

Explicit and Recursive Rules

SOUTHWESTERN

Explicit and Recursive Rules

A sequence can be represented by both explicit and recursive rules.

- An **explicit rule** gives the value of the general term a_n in terms of n.
- A recursive rule gives the value of the general term a_n in terms of one or more of the preceding terms and includes at least one initial value.

Recursive rules are useful when examining the values of terms close to the given term. For example, given the recursive rule $a_n = a_{n-1} + 17$, $a_1 = 8$, a_2 can be calculated in one step. However, it would take many steps to calculate $a_{1,000}$. In this case, it would be more helpful to use an explicit rule for a_n.

EXAMPLE 1

Write an explicit and a recursive rule for the arithmetic sequence whose first term is 10 and whose common difference is −12.

STEP 1 Use the explicit rule for an arithmetic sequence, $a_n = a_1 + (n-1)d$.

Substitute 10 for n and −12 for d.	$= 10 + (n-1)(-12)$
Use the Distributive Property.	$= 10 - 12n + 12$
Simplify.	$= -12n + 22$

An explicit rule is $a_n = -12n + 22$.

STEP 2 Use the recursive equation for an arithmetic sequence.

$$a_n = a_{n-1} + d$$

Substitute −12 for d. $= a_{n-1} + (-12)$

A recursive rule is $a_n = a_{n-1} - 12$, $a_1 = 10$.

Explicit and Recursive Rules

Type of Rule	Equation for Rule		Determine a Rule		Calculate the Value of a_n
	Arithmetic Sequence	Geometric Sequence	Arithmetic Sequence	Geometric Sequence	
Explicit	$a_n = a_1 + (n-1)d$	$a_n = a_1 r^{n-1}$	Substitute the value of a_1 and d into the equation and simplify the result.	Substitute the value of a_1 and r into the equation and simplify the result.	Given a rule, substitute the value of n into the equation and simplify the result.
Recursive	$a_n = a_{n-1} + d$	$a_n = r \cdot a_{n-1}$	Substitute the value of d into the equation and simplify the result. State the value of a_1.	Substitute the value of r into the equation and simplify the result. State the value of a_1.	Find the value of each of the preceding terms.

EXAMPLE 2

Write an explicit and a recursive rule for the geometric sequence whose first term is 4 and whose common ratio is $\frac{5}{8}$. Then find a_2.

STEP 1 Use the explicit rule for a geometric sequence.

$$a_n = a_1 r^{n-1}$$

Substitute 4 for a_1 and $\frac{5}{8}$ for r.
$$= 4\left(\frac{5}{8}\right)^{n-1}$$

An explicit rule is $a_n = 4\left(\frac{5}{8}\right)^{n-1}$.

STEP 2 Use the recursive equation for a geometric sequence.

$$a_n = r \cdot a_{n-1}$$

Substitute $\frac{5}{8}$ for r.
$$= \frac{5}{8} a_{n-1}$$

A recursive rule is $a_n = \frac{5}{8} a_{n-1}, a_1 = 4$.

STEP 3 Because a_2 is close to the given term, it is reasonable to use either rule to find its value.

METHOD 1

Use the explicit rule, $a_n = 4\left(\frac{5}{8}\right)^{n-1}$.

Substitute 2 for n. $\quad a_2 = 4\left(\frac{5}{8}\right)^{2-1}$

Simplify. $\quad = 4\left(\frac{5}{8}\right)$

$\quad = \frac{5}{2}$

METHOD 2

Use the recursive rule, $a_n = \frac{5}{8} a_{n-1}, a_1 = 4$.

Substitute 2 for n. $\quad a_2 = \frac{5}{8} a_{2-1}$

Simplify. $\quad = \left(\frac{5}{8}\right)4$

$\quad = \frac{5}{2}$

SEARCH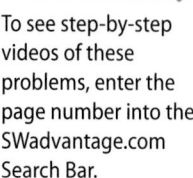

To see step-by-step videos of these problems, enter the page number into the SWadvantage.com Search Bar.

EXAMPLE 3

Write an explicit rule for the sequence described by the recursive rule $a_n = a_{n-1} + 17, a_1 = 8$. Then find $a_{1,000}$.

STEP 1 The recursive equation is in the form $a_n = a_1 + (n-1)d$, so it defines an arithmetic sequence whose common difference is $d = 17$.

$$a_n = a_1 + (n-1)d$$

Substitute 8 for a_1 and 17 for d. $\quad = 8 + (n-1)17$

Distribute. $\quad = 8 + 17n - 17$

Simplify. $\quad = 17n - 9$

An explicit rule is $a_n = 17n - 9$.

STEP 2 Use the explicit rule to find $a_{1,000}$.

$$a_n = 17n - 9$$

Substitute 1,000 for n. $\quad = 17(1{,}000) - 9$

$\quad = 16{,}991$

Try It

This Way

Use your graphing calculator to make a table of values for a_n. Use the table to find a_n when $n = 1{,}000$.

Writing Explicit and Recursive Rules

Need More

HELP ?

For help with recursive rules, go to *Recursive Rules* (p. 1880).

EXAMPLE 4

Determine whether the sequence {77, 70, 63, 56, . . .} is arithmetic, geometric, or neither. Then find an explicit rule and a recursive rule for the sequence.

STEP 1 Examine the consecutive terms.

The terms have a common difference but no common ratio.

$70 - 77 = -7$ $63 - 70 = -7$ $56 - 63 = -7$

$\frac{70}{77} = 0.91$ $\frac{63}{70} = 0.90$ $\frac{56}{63} = 0.89$

The sequence is arithmetic with $a_1 = 77$ and $d = -7$.

STEP 2 The sequence is arithmetic, so use the rule $a_n = a_1 + (n-1)d$ to find an explicit rule.

$$a_n = a_1 + (n-1)d$$

Substitute 77 for a_1 and -7 for d. $= 77 + (n-1)(-7)$

Distribute. $= 77 - 7n + 7$

Simplify. $= -7n + 84$

An explicit rule is $a_n = -7n + 84$.

STEP 3 To find a recursive rule, use the recursive equation for an arithmetic sequence, $a_n = a_{n-1} + d$.

$$a_n = a_{n-1} + d$$

Substitute -7 for d. $= a_{n-1} + (-7)$

A recursive rule is $a_n = a_{n-1} - 7, a_1 = 77$.

EXAMPLE 5

Determine whether the sequence {20, 120, 720, 4320, . . .} is arithmetic, geometric, or neither. Then find an explicit and recursive rule for the sequence.

STEP 1 Examine the consecutive terms.

The terms have a common ratio but no common difference.

$120 - 20 = 100$ $720 - 120 = 600$ $4320 - 720 = 3600$

$\frac{120}{20} = 6$ $\frac{720}{120} = 6$ $\frac{4320}{720} = 6$

The sequence is geometric with $a_1 = 20$ and $r = 6$.

STEP 2 The sequence is geometric, so use the rule $a_n = a_1 r^{n-1}$ to find an explicit rule.

$$a_n = a_1 r^{n-1}$$

Substitute 20 for a_1 and 6 for r. $= 20 \cdot 6^{n-1}$

An explicit rule is $a_n = 20 \cdot 6^{n-1}$.

STEP 3 To find a recursive rule, use the recursive equation for a geometric sequence, $a_n = r \cdot a_{n-1}$.

$$a_n = r \cdot a_{n-1}$$

Substitute 6 for r. $= 6a_{n-1}$

A recursive rule is $a_n = 6a_{n-1}, a_1 = 20$.

Explicit and recursive rules can be used to solve practical problems that involve arithmetic or geometric sequences.

EXAMPLE 6

Andrea recently opened a savings account. After one month, the account has a balance of $1,250. She plans to deposit $420 each month for the next three years.

a. Find an explicit rule for the balance of Andrea's savings account after n months.

STEP 1 Determine the type of sequence.

The balance of Andrea's account changes by a constant amount each month, so the monthly balance forms an arithmetic sequence with $a_1 = 1,250$ and $d = 420$.

STEP 2 Write an explicit rule for the sequence.

Use the equation for an explicit rule for an arithmetic sequence.

$$a_n = a_1 + (n - 1)d$$

Substitute 1,250 for a_1 and 420 for d. $= 1,250 + (n - 1)420$

Distribute. $= 1,250 + 420n - 420$

Simplify. $= 420n + 830$

An explicit rule for the balance of Andrea's savings account after n months is $a_n = 420n + 830$.

b. Find a recursive rule for the balance of Andrea's savings account after n months.

The balance forms an arithmetic sequence, so use the recursive equation $a_n = a_{n-1} + d$.

$$a_n = a_{n-1} + d$$

Substitute 420 for d. $= a_{n-1} + 420$

A recursive rule for the balance of Andrea's savings account after n months is $a_n = a_{n-1} + 420$, $a_1 = 1,250$.

c. Find Andrea's balance after 12 months. Would it be easier for her to use the explicit rule or the recursive rule?

Using the explicit rule, she can find the balance after 12 months in just a few steps. If she used the recursive rule, she would have to find the balance after each month until she got to 12 months. This would take much longer than using the explicit rule.

Use the explicit rule.

$$a_n = 420n + 830$$

Substitute 12 for n. $a_{12} = 420(12) + 830 = 5870$

Andrea's balance after 12 months is $5,870.

SEARCH

To see step-by-step videos of these problems, enter the page number into the SWadvantage.com Search Bar.

Understand that either the explicit rule or the recursive rule can be used to solve the problem. However, one method is usually easier to use than the other method. For example, in Example 6, $a_1 = 1,250$ is used as a_{n-1} to calculate a_2. This result is then used as a_{n-1} to calculate a_3, and so on. It takes much more time to calculate the results using the recursive rule.

Mathematical Induction

Mathematical Induction

Some mathematical statements are true for all natural numbers. For example, $1 + 2 + 3 + \cdots + n = \frac{n(n + 1)}{2}$ is true for all natural numbers n. Consider the first four values of n.

$n = 1$ $\qquad 1 \stackrel{?}{=} \frac{1(1 + 1)}{2}$

$\qquad\qquad 1 = 1 ✔$

$n = 2$ $\qquad 1 + 2 \stackrel{?}{=} \frac{2(2 + 1)}{2}$

$\qquad\qquad 3 = 3 ✔$

$n = 3$ $\qquad 1 + 2 + 3 \stackrel{?}{=} \frac{3(3 + 1)}{2}$

$\qquad\qquad 6 = 6 ✔$

$n = 4$ $\qquad 1 + 2 + 3 + 4 \stackrel{?}{=} \frac{4(4 + 1)}{2}$

$\qquad\qquad 10 = 10 ✔$

While the equation is true for these four cases, there are an infinite number of natural numbers, so it is impossible to check this equation for all possible values of n. Instead, a proof is used to show that the equation is true for all natural numbers. The method of proving that a statement is true for all natural numbers is called **mathematical induction**.

There are two parts to mathematical induction.

- The base case shows that the statement is true for $n = 1$.
- The inductive step assumes that the statement is true when $n = k$ and then shows that the statement is true when $n = k + 1$.

The domino effect illustrates mathematical induction. Suppose an infinite number of dominoes are lined up similar to those shown at the right. If the first domino is knocked over, it knocks over the second domino, which knocks over the third domino, etc. By induction, it can be concluded that all the dominoes will be knocked over.

GOT TO KNOW!

Mathematical Induction

To prove a statement is true for all natural numbers, the following two parts must be shown.

1. The statement is true for $n = 1$.

2. If the statement is true when $n = k$, where k is any natural number, then it is true when $n = k + 1$.

EXAMPLE 1

Use mathematical induction to prove that $1 + 2 + 3 + \cdots + n = \dfrac{n(n+1)}{2}$ for all natural numbers n.

STEP 1 Show that $1 + 2 + 3 + \cdots + n = \dfrac{n(n+1)}{2}$ is true for $n = 1$.

$$1 \overset{?}{=} \frac{1(1+1)}{2}$$

$$1 = 1 \; \checkmark$$

STEP 2 Assume that $1 + 2 + 3 + \cdots + k = \dfrac{k(k+1)}{2}$ is true for some natural number k. Show that

$1 + 2 + 3 + \cdots + k + (k+1) = \dfrac{(k+1)[(k+1)+1]}{2}$.

Assumed statement	$1 + 2 + 3 + \cdots + k = \dfrac{k(k+1)}{2}$
Add $(k+1)$ to both sides.	$1 + 2 + 3 + \cdots + k + (k+1) = \dfrac{k(k+1)}{2} + k + 1$
Add.	$= \dfrac{k(k+1) + 2(k+1)}{2}$
Factor out $k + 1$.	$= \dfrac{(k+1)(k+2)}{2}$
Rewrite $k + 2$ as $(k+1) + 1$.	$= \dfrac{(k+1)[(k+1)+1]}{2}$

Both parts of mathematical induction have been shown to be true, so $1 + 2 + 3 + \cdots + n = \dfrac{n(n+1)}{2}$ for all natural numbers n.

EXAMPLE 2

Use mathematical induction to prove that $1 + 3 + 5 + \cdots + (2n - 1) = n^2$ for all natural numbers n.

STEP 1 Show that $1 + 3 + 5 + \cdots + (2n - 1) = n^2$ is true for $n = 1$.

$$1 \overset{?}{=} 1^2$$

$$1 = 1 \; \checkmark$$

STEP 2 Assume that $1 + 3 + 5 + \cdots + (2k - 1) = k^2$ is true for some natural number k. Show that

$1 + 3 + 5 + \cdots + (2k - 1) + [2(k+1) - 1] = (k+1)^2$.

Find the sum of the first $(k+1)$ terms.	$1 + 3 + 5 + \cdots + (2k - 1) + [2(k+1) - 1]$
Substitute k^2 for $1 + 3 + 5 + \cdots + (2k - 1)$.	$= k^2 + [2(k+1) - 1]$
Simplify.	$= k^2 + 2k + 1$
Factor.	$= (k+1)(k+1)$
Simplify.	$= (k+1)^2$

Both parts of mathematical induction have been shown to be true, so $1 + 3 + 5 + \cdots + (2n - 1) = n^2$ is true for all natural numbers n.

SEARCH

To see step-by-step videos of these problems, enter the page number into the SWadvantage.com Search Bar.

Using Mathematical Induction

EXAMPLE 3

Use mathematical induction to prove that $1 + 2 + 4 + 8 + \cdots + 2^{n-1} = 2^n - 1$ for all natural numbers n.

STEP 1 Show that $1 + 2 + 4 + 8 + \cdots + 2^{n-1} = 2^n - 1$ is true for $n = 1$.

$$1 \overset{?}{=} 2^1 - 1$$
$$1 = 1 \checkmark$$

STEP 2 Assume that $1 + 2 + 4 + 8 + \cdots + 2^{k-1} = 2^k - 1$ is true for some natural number k. Show that $1 + 2 + 4 + 8 + \cdots + 2^{k-1} + 2^{(k+1)-1} = 2^{k+1} - 1$.

Write the sum of the first $(k + 1)$ terms.	$1 + 2 + 4 + 8 + \cdots + 2^{k-1} + 2^{(k+1)-1}$
Simplify the exponent.	$= 1 + 2 + 4 + 8 + \cdots + 2^{k-1} + 2^k$
Substitute $2^k - 1$ for the sum of the first k terms.	$= 2^k - 1 + 2^k$
Simplify.	$= 2 \cdot 2^k - 1$
Use the multiplication property of exponents.	$= 2^{k+1} - 1$

Both parts of mathematical induction have been shown to be true, so $1 + 2 + 4 + 8 + \cdots + 2^{n-1} = 2^n - 1$ is true for all natural numbers n.

Need More

HELP ?

For help with exponent rules, see *Monomials* in *Algebra* (p. 1600).

EXAMPLE 4

Use mathematical induction to prove that $1 + 5 + 9 + \cdots + (4n - 3) = n(2n - 1)$ for all natural numbers n.

STEP 1 Show that $1 + 5 + 9 + \cdots + (4n - 3) = n(2n - 1)$ is true for $n = 1$.

$$1 \overset{?}{=} 1(2 \cdot 1 - 1)$$
$$1 = 1 \checkmark$$

STEP 2 Assume that $1 + 5 + 9 + \cdots + (4k - 3) = k(2k - 1)$ is true for some natural number k. Show that $1 + 5 + 9 + \cdots + (4k - 3) + [4(k + 1) - 3] = (k + 1)[2(k + 1) - 1]$.

Write the sum of the first $(k + 1)$ terms.	$1 + 5 + 9 + \cdots + (4k - 3) + [4(k + 1) - 3]$
Substitute $k(2k - 1)$ for the sum of the first k terms.	$= k(2k - 1) + [4(k + 1) - 3]$
Use the Distributive Property.	$= 2k^2 - k + (4k + 4 - 3)$
Simplify.	$= 2k^2 + 3k + 1$
Factor.	$= (k + 1)(2k + 1)$
Rewrite $(2k + 1)$ as $[2(k + 1) - 1]$.	$= (k + 1)[2(k + 1) - 1]$

Both parts of mathematical induction have been shown to be true, so $1 + 5 + 9 + \cdots + (4n - 3) = n(2n - 1)$ is true for all natural numbers n.

To show that the function is true for a specific value of k, substitute it into the original relationship. Suppose you want to prove that $1 + 5 + 9 + \cdots + (4n - 3) = n(2n - 1)$ is true for $k = 5$, substitute 5 for n in the equation. Supply any missing numbers in the sequence.

$$1 + 5 + 9 + 13 + 17 \overset{?}{=} 5[2(5) - 1]$$

$$45 = 45$$

EXAMPLE 5

Use mathematical induction to prove that $1^2 + 2^2 + 3^3 + \cdots + n^2 = \dfrac{n(n + 1)(2n + 1)}{6}$
for all natural numbers n.

STEP 1   Show that $1^2 + 2^2 + 3^2 + \cdots + n^2 = \dfrac{n(n + 1)(2n + 1)}{6}$ is true for $n = 1$.

$$1^2 \stackrel{?}{=} \frac{1(1 + 1)(2 \cdot 1 + 1)}{6}$$

$$1 \stackrel{?}{=} \frac{1(2)(3)}{6}$$

$$1 = 1 \checkmark$$

SEARCH

To see step-by-step videos of these problems, enter the page number into the SWadvantage.com Search Bar.

STEP 2   Assume that $1^2 + 2^2 + 3^2 + \cdots + k^2 = \dfrac{k(k + 1)(2k + 1)}{6}$ is true for some natural number k. Show

that $1^2 + 2^2 + 3^2 + \cdots + k^2 + (k + 1)^2 = \dfrac{(k + 1)[(k + 1) + 1][2(k + 1) + 1]}{6}$.

Write the sum of the first $(k + 1)$ terms.	$1^2 + 2^2 + 3^2 + \cdots + k^2 + (k + 1)^2$
Substitute $\dfrac{k(k + 1)(2k + 1)}{6}$ for the sum of the first k terms.	$= \dfrac{k(k + 1)(2k + 1)}{6} + (k + 1)^2$
Add.	$= \dfrac{k(k + 1)(2k + 1) + 6(k + 1)^2}{6}$
Factor out $(k + 1)$.	$= \dfrac{(k + 1)[k(2k + 1) + 6(k + 1)]}{6}$
Use the Distributive Property.	$= \dfrac{(k + 1)(2k^2 + k + 6k + 6)}{6}$
Simplify.	$= \dfrac{(k + 1)(2k^2 + 7k + 6)}{6}$
Factor the trinomial.	$= \dfrac{(k + 1)(k + 2)(2k + 3)}{6}$
Rewrite $(k + 2)$ as $[(k + 1) + 1]$ and $(2k + 3)$ as $[2(k + 1) + 1]$.	$= \dfrac{(k + 1)[(k + 1) + 1][2(k + 1) + 1]}{6}$

Both parts of mathematical induction have been shown to be true, so $1^2 + 2^2 + 3^2 + \cdots + n^2 = \dfrac{n(n + 1)(2n + 1)}{6}$ is true for all natural numbers n.

You can show that the function is true for a specific value of k. Choose a value for k, then substitute it into the original relationship. Suppose you want to prove that $1^2 + 2^2 + 3^2 + \cdots + n^2 = \dfrac{n(n + 1)(2n + 1)}{6}$ is true for $k = 4$, substitute 4 for n in the equation. Supply any missing numbers in the sequence.

$$1^2 + 2^2 + 3^2 + 4^2 \stackrel{?}{=} \frac{4(4 + 1)[2(4) + 1]}{6}$$

$$1 + 4 + 9 + 16 \stackrel{?}{=} \frac{4 \cdot 5 \cdot 9}{6}$$

$$30 = 30$$

Complex Numbers

What Came Before?
- Solving quadratic equations
- Simplifying radicals

What's This About?
- Simplifying radicals with negative numbers under the radical sign
- Operations with complex numbers
- Absolute value of complex numbers

Practical Apps
- Complex numbers can be used when describing the strength of electromagnetic fields.
- Electrical engineers use complex numbers to find their solutions to differential equations.

Just for **FUN!**

Be rational.

i

Get real.

$\sqrt{2}$

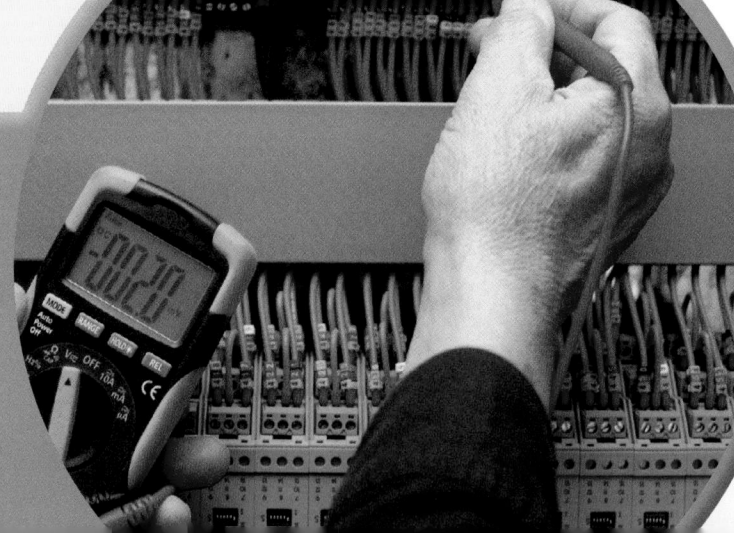

CONTENTS UPLOAD DOWNLOAD *Advanced Algebra*

You can find more practice problems online by visiting:
www.SWadvantage.com

The Symbol *i*

The Symbol *i*

Some equations do not have a solution in the real number system. For example, $x^2 = -1$ does not have a real number solution. However, $x^2 = -1$ does have an imaginary solution called the **imaginary unit *i***. The symbol *i* is defined as $i = \sqrt{-1}$. So, $i^2 = -1$.

The definition of *i* can be used to simplify square roots of negative numbers. In general, if *a* is a positive number, then $\sqrt{-a} = i\sqrt{a}$.

Watch Out !

$3i\sqrt{2}$ can also be written $3\sqrt{2}\,i$. If written this way, be careful to write the *i* clearly outside of the square root symbol.

EXAMPLE 1

Simplify.

a. $\sqrt{-25}$

STEP 1 Rewrite $\sqrt{-25}$ as the product of a positive number and -1. $\sqrt{-25} = \sqrt{-1 \cdot 25}$

STEP 2 Write the radical as the product of two radicals. $= \sqrt{-1} \cdot \sqrt{25}$

STEP 3 Write the product in terms of *i*. $= 5i$

b. $\sqrt{-18}$

STEP 1 Rewrite $\sqrt{-18}$ as the product of a positive number, a perfect square and -1. $\sqrt{-18} = \sqrt{-1 \cdot 9 \cdot 2}$

STEP 2 Write the radical as the product of three radicals. $= \sqrt{-1} \cdot \sqrt{9} \cdot \sqrt{2}$

STEP 3 Write the product in terms of *i*. $= 3i\sqrt{2}$

Need More HELP ?

The Product Rule for Radicals is explained more completely in *Multiplying Radical Expressions* (p. 1956).

Powers of *i*

The definition of *i* can be used to calculate powers of *i*. The first four powers of *i* are shown below.

$i^1 = i$ $i^3 = i^2 \cdot i = -1 \cdot i = -i$

$i^2 = -1$ $i^4 = i^2 \cdot i^2 = -1(-1) = 1$

These values can be used to find the next four powers of *i*.

$i^5 = i^4 \cdot i = 1 \cdot i = i$ $i^7 = i^4 \cdot i^3 = 1 \cdot -i = -i$

$i^6 = i^4 \cdot i^2 = 1(-1) = -1$ $i^8 = i^4 \cdot i^4 = 1(1) = 1$

Notice that the values i, -1, $-i$, 1 repeat every four powers of *i*. This pattern continues for higher powers of *i*.

$i^9 = i$ $i^{13} = i$

$i^{10} = -1$ $i^{14} = -1$

$i^{11} = -i$ $i^{15} = -i$

$i^{12} = 1$ $i^{16} = 1$

Any power of *i* can be simplified to i, -1, $-i$, or 1 by rewriting the power in terms of i^4.

Need More HELP ?

The Product of Powers Property is explained more completely in *Properties of Exponents* (p. 1970).

EXAMPLE 2

Simplify.

a. i^{32}

STEP 1 Write i^{32} in terms of i^4. $= (i^4)^8$

STEP 2 Substitute 1 for i^4. $= 1^8$

STEP 3 Simplify. $= 1$

b. i^{25}

STEP 1 Write i^{25} in terms of i^4. $= (i^4)^6 \cdot i$

STEP 2 Substitute 1 for i^4. $= 1^6 \cdot i$

STEP 3 Simplify. $= 1 \cdot i = i$

c. i^{38}

STEP 1 Write i^{38} in terms of i^4. $= (i^4)^9 \cdot i^2$

STEP 2 Substitute 1 for i^4. $= 1^9 \cdot i^2$

STEP 3 Simplify. $= 1(-1) = -1$

d. i^{55}

STEP 1 Write i^{55} in terms of i^4. $= (i^4)^{13} \cdot i^3$

STEP 2 Substitute 1 for i^4. $= 1^{13} \cdot i^3$

STEP 3 Simplify. $= 1(-i) = -i$

SEARCH

To see step-by-step videos of these problems, enter the page number into the SWadvantage.com Search Bar.

Notice that the pattern for the powers of i can also be thought of in terms of the remainder of the exponent divided by 4.

EXAMPLE 3

Simplify.

a. i^{27}

27 divided by 4 is 6 with a remainder of 3, so $i^{27} = i^3 = -i$.

b. i^{42}

42 divided by 4 is 10 with a remainder of 2, so $i^{42} = i^2 = -1$.

c. i^{56}

56 divided by 4 is 14 with no remainder, so $i^{56} = i^0 = 1$.

d. i^{21}

21 divided by 4 is 5 with a remainder of 1, so $i^{21} = i^1 = i$.

GOT TO KNOW!

Pattern of the Remainder of $\frac{n}{4}$

To quickly determine the value of a power of i, divide the exponent by 4, and use the value of the remainder to determine the value of i^n.

Remainder of $\frac{n}{4}$	i^n
0	$i^0 = 1$
1	$i^1 = i$
2	$i^2 = -1$
3	$i^3 = -i$

Complex Numbers

A **complex number** is a number of the form $a + bi$ where a and b are real numbers. The form $a + bi$ is considered **standard form** of a complex number.

- There are two parts to a complex number, the real part a, and the imaginary part bi.
- If $a = 0$ and $b \neq 0$, then $a + bi = 0 + bi = bi$, and $a + bi$ is called a **pure imaginary number**. For example, $5i$, $1.4i$, and $\frac{4}{5}i$ are pure imaginary numbers.
- If $b = 0$, then $a + bi = a + 0i = a$, and $a + bi$ is a real number. For example, if $a = 7$ and $b = 0$, then $a + bi = 7 + 0i = 7$.

Pure imaginary numbers and the real numbers are both subsets of the complex numbers, as illustrated in the diagram below.

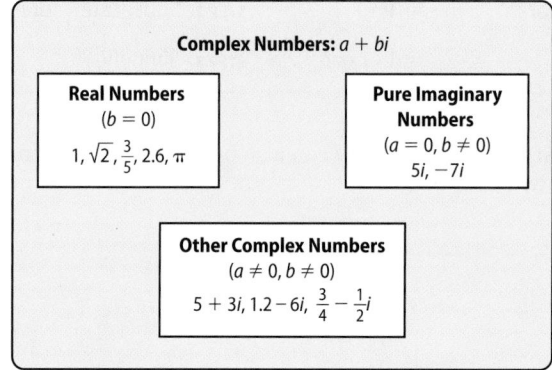

Two complex numbers are equal if and only if both the imaginary parts are equal and the real parts are equal. For example, the two complex numbers $a + bi$ and $c + di$ are equal if and only if $a = c$ and $b = d$.

Adding and Subtracting Complex Numbers

To add or subtract complex numbers, add or subtract their real parts and add or subtract their imaginary parts. Complex numbers can be added and subtracted using either a horizontal or vertical format.

SEARCH

To see step-by-step videos of these problems, enter the page number into the SWadvantage.com Search Bar.

EXAMPLE 1

Add $(5 + 2i) + (7 + 10i)$. Write the sum in standard form.

METHOD 1

$$(5 + 2i) + (7 + 10i) = (5 + 7) + (2 + 10)i$$
$$= 12 + 12i$$

METHOD 2

$$5 + 2i$$
$$\underline{+ \ 7 + 10i}$$
$$12 + 12i$$

The sum of $(5 + 2i) + (7 + 10i)$ is $12 + 12i$.

EXAMPLE 2

Add. Write the sum in standard form.

a. $(-13 + 4i) + (3 - 8i)$

STEP 1 Group real parts and imaginary parts.

STEP 2 Add real parts together and imaginary parts together.

$$(-13 + 4i) + (3 - 8i) = (-13 + 3) + [4 + (-8)]i$$
$$= -10 - 4i$$

b. $9 + (6 + 11i)$

STEP 1 Group real parts and imaginary parts.

STEP 2 Add real parts together and imaginary parts together.

$$9 + (6 + 11i) = (9 + 6) + 11i$$
$$= 15 + 11i$$

c. $-21 + (18 - 5i) + 7i$

STEP 1 Group real parts and imaginary parts.

STEP 2 Add real parts together and imaginary parts together.

$$-21 + (18 - 5i) + 7i = (-21 + 18) + (-5 + 7)i$$
$$= -3 + 2i$$

> **Try It This Way**
>
> To add or subtract complex numbers on a graphing calculator, set the Mode to $a + bi$. Then enter the sum or difference on the home screen. Press [2nd] [.] to enter i, and remember to use parentheses as needed.

EXAMPLE 3

Subtract. Write the difference in standard form.

a. $(17 + 4i) - (10 - 6i)$

METHOD 1

$$(17 + 4i) - (10 - 6i) = (17 - 10) + [4 - (-6)]i$$
$$= 7 + 10i$$

METHOD 2

$$\begin{array}{r} 17 + 4i \\ - (10 - 6i) \\ \hline 7 + 10i \end{array}$$

b. $(1 + 2i) - 7$

METHOD 1

$$(1 + 2i) - 7 = (1 - 7) + (2 - 0)i$$
$$= -6 + 2i$$

METHOD 2

$$\begin{array}{r} 1 + 2i \\ - 7 \\ \hline -6 + 2i \end{array}$$

c. $9i - (6 + 3i)$

METHOD 1

$$9i - (6 + 3i) = (0 - 6) + (9 - 3)i$$
$$= -6 + 6i$$

METHOD 2

$$\begin{array}{r} 9i \\ - (6 + 3i) \\ \hline -6 + 6i \end{array}$$

> **GOT TO KNOW!**
>
> **Adding and Subtracting Complex Numbers**
>
> *Addition:*
> $(a + bi) + (c + di) =$
> $(a + c) + (b + d)i$
>
> *Subtraction:*
> $(a + bi) - (c + di) =$
> $(a - c) + (b - d)i$

Multiplying Complex Numbers

SOUTHWESTERN

Multiplying Imaginary Numbers

Multiplication in the complex number system is very similar to multiplication in the real number system. To multiply pure imaginary numbers:

- Use the Commutative Property of Multiplication.
- Substitute -1 for i^2 whenever possible.

SEARCH 🔍

To see step-by-step videos of these problems, enter the page number into the SWadvantage.com Search Bar.

EXAMPLE 1

Multiply.

a. $4i \cdot 5i$

Use the Commutative Property.	$4i \cdot 5i = 4 \cdot 5 \cdot i \cdot i$
Multiply.	$= 20i^2$
Substitute -1 for i^2.	$= 20(-1)$
Simplify.	$= -20$

The product $4i \cdot 5i$ equals -20.

b. $-11i \cdot 7i$

Use the Commutative Property.	$-11i \cdot 7i = -11 \cdot 7 \cdot i \cdot i$
Multiply.	$= -77i^2$
Substitute -1 for i^2.	$= -77(-1)$
Simplify.	$= 77$

The product $-11i \cdot 7i$ equals 77.

GOT TO KNOW!

Multiplying Pure Imaginary and Complex Numbers

Multiplying

Pure Imaginary Number Times a Pure Imaginary Number

Use the Commutative Property of Multiplication.

Substitute -1 for i^2 whenever possible.

Pure Imaginary Number Times a Complex Number

Use the Distributive property.
a, b, and c are real numbers.

$$ci(a + bi) = aci + bci^2$$
$$= aci - bc$$
$$= -bc + aci$$

Complex Number Times a Complex Number

Use the Distributive property.
a, b, c, and d are real numbers.

$$(a + bi)(c + di) = ac + adi + bci + bdi^2$$
$$= ac + i(ad + bc) - bd$$
$$= (ac - bd) + (ad + bc)i$$

Multiplying Complex Numbers

The Distributive Property also extends to the complex number system. It can be used to multiply two complex numbers just as it was used to multiply real numbers and algebraic expressions.

EXAMPLE 2

Multiply $2i(9 + 3i)$. Write the product in standard form.

METHOD 1

Use a horizontal format.

Use the Distributive Property.	$2i(9 + 3i) = 2i \cdot 9 + 2i \cdot 3i$
Multiply.	$= 18i + 6i^2$
Substitute -1 for i^2.	$= 18i + 6(-1)$
Write in standard form.	$= -6 + 18i$

METHOD 2

Use a vertical format.

$$
\begin{array}{r}
9 + 3i \\
\times \quad 2i \\
\hline
18i + 6i^2
\end{array}
$$

Substitute -1 for i^2.	$18i + 6i^2 = 18i + 6(-1)$
Write in standard form.	$= -6 + 18i$

EXAMPLE 3

Multiply $(3 + 4i)(2 + 6i)$. Write the product in standard form.

METHOD 1

Use the Distributive Property.

Use the Distributive Property.	$(3 + 4i)(2 + 6i) = 6 + 18i + 8i + 24i^2$
Add like terms.	$= 6 + 26i + 24i^2$
Substitute -1 for i^2.	$= 6 + 26i + 24(-1)$
Simplify.	$= 6 + 26i - 24$
Add like terms and write in standard form.	$= -18 + 26i$

METHOD 2

Use a graphing calculator.

Press **MODE** and select 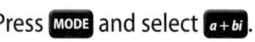.

On the home screen, enter $(3 + 4i)(2 + 6i)$.

Remember to press  to enter i.

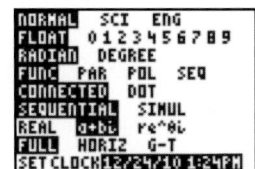

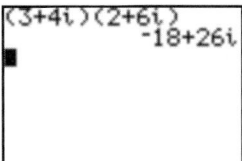

Need More
HELP ❓

For more help multiplying binomials and the FOIL method, see *Multiplying Polynomials* in *Algebra* (p. 1608).

SEARCH 🔍

To see step-by-step videos of these problems, enter the page number into the SWadvantage.com Search Bar.

Using FOIL to Multiply Complex Numbers

Multiplying two complex numbers is like multiplying two binomials, so the FOIL method can be used to apply the Distributive Property.

EXAMPLE 4

Multiply $(-7 + 3i)(8 + 2i)$. Write the product in standard form.

Use FOIL.

First: $-7 \cdot 8 = -56$ Outer: $-7 \cdot 2i = -14i$ Inner: $3i \cdot 8 = 24i$ Last: $3i \cdot 2i = 6i^2$

Use the FOIL method.	$(-7 + 3i)(8 + 2i) = -56 - 14i + 24i + 6i^2$
Add like terms.	$= -56 + 10i + 6i^2$
Substitute -1 for i^2.	$= -56 + 10i + 6(-1)$
Simplify.	$= -56 + 10i - 6$
Add like terms and write in standard form.	$= -62 + 10i$

The product $(-7 + 3i)(8 + 2i)$ equals $-62 + 10i$.

EXAMPLE 5

Multiply. Write the product in standard form.

a. $(4 - 5i)^2$

Write the problem in expanded form.	$(4 - 5i)^2 = (4 - 5i)(4 - 5i)$
Use the Distributive Property or FOIL method.	$= 16 - 20i - 20i + 25i^2$
Add like terms and substitute -1 for i^2.	$= 16 - 40i + 25(-1)$
Simplify.	$= 16 - 40i - 25$
Add like terms and write in standard form.	$= -9 - 40i$

The product $(4 - 5i)^2$ equals $-9 - 40i$.

b. $(3 + 5i)(6 - 2i)(2 + i)$

STEP 1 Find the product of the first two factors.

Use the Distributive Property or FOIL method.	$(3 + 5i)(6 - 2i) = 18 - 6i + 30i - 10i^2$
Add like terms and substitute -1 for i^2.	$= 18 + 24i - 10(-1)$
Simplify.	$= 18 + 24i + 10$
Add like terms and write in standard form.	$= 28 + 24i$

STEP 2 Multiply the result by the third factor.

Use the Distributive Property or FOIL method.	$(28 + 24i)(2 + i) = 56 + 28i + 48i + 24i^2$
Add like terms and substitute -1 for i^2.	$= 56 + 76i + 24(-1)$
Simplify.	$= 56 + 76i - 24$
Add like terms and write in standard form.	$= 32 + 76i$

The product $(3 + 5i)(6 - 2i)(2 + i)$ equals $32 + 76i$.

Multiplying Square Roots of Negative Numbers

When multiplying complex numbers that contain square roots of negative numbers, it is important to write the square roots as expressions in terms of i before multiplying.

Correct	Incorrect
$\sqrt{-4} \cdot \sqrt{-25} = 2i \cdot 5i$	$\sqrt{-4} \cdot \sqrt{-25} = \sqrt{-4(-25)}$
$= 10i^2$	$= \sqrt{100}$
$= 10(-1)$	$= 10$
$= -10$	

EXAMPLE 6

Multiply. Write the product in standard form.

a. $\sqrt{-36} \cdot \sqrt{-64}$

Write square roots in terms of i.　　$\sqrt{-36} \cdot \sqrt{-64} = 6i \cdot 8i$

Multiply.　　$= 48i^2$

Substitute -1 for i^2, and simplify.　　$= 48(-1) = -48$

The product $\sqrt{-36} \cdot \sqrt{-64}$ equals -48.

b. $-5\sqrt{-9} \cdot 2\sqrt{-49}$

Write square roots in terms of i.　　$-5\sqrt{-9} \cdot 2\sqrt{-49} = -5 \cdot 3i \cdot 2 \cdot 7i$

Multiply.　　$= -210i^2$

Substitute -1 for i^2, and simplify.　　$= -210(-1) = 210$

The product $-5\sqrt{-9} \cdot 2\sqrt{-49}$ equals 210.

c. $\left(1 + \sqrt{-25}\right)\left(3 + \sqrt{-4}\right)$

Write square roots in terms of i.　　$\left(1 + \sqrt{-25}\right)\left(3 + \sqrt{-4}\right) = (1 + 5i)(3 + 2i)$

Use the Distributive Property or FOIL method.　　$= 3 + 2i + 15i + 10i^2$

Add like terms and substitute -1 for i^2.　　$= 3 + 17i + 10(-1)$

Simplify.　　$= 3 + 17i - 10$

Add like terms and write in standard form.　　$= -7 + 17i$

The product $\left(1 + \sqrt{-25}\right)\left(3 + \sqrt{-4}\right)$ equals $-7 + 17i$.

d. $\left(6 + \sqrt{-81}\right)\left(6 - \sqrt{-81}\right)$

Write square roots in terms of i.　　$\left(6 + \sqrt{-81}\right)\left(6 - \sqrt{-81}\right) = (6 + 9i)(6 - 9i)$

Use the Distributive Property or FOIL method.　　$= 36 - 54i + 54i - 81i^2$

Add like terms.　　$= 36 - 81i^2$

Substitute -1 for i^2.　　$= 36 - 81(-1)$

Simplify.　　$= 36 + 81 = 117$

The product $\left(6 + \sqrt{-81}\right)\left(6 - \sqrt{-81}\right)$ equals 117.

Division and Complex Conjugates

Complex Conjugates

The complex numbers $a + bi$ and $a - bi$ are called **complex conjugates** of each other. Every complex number has a conjugate.

To find the conjugate of a complex number, change the sign between the real part, a, and the imaginary part, b, to its opposite.

- If the sign between a and b is a plus sign, change it to a minus sign.
- If the sign between a and b is a minus sign, change it to a plus sign.

SEARCH

To see step-by-step videos of these problems, enter the page number into the SWadvantage.com Search Bar.

EXAMPLE 1

Find the complex conjugate.

a. 5 + 4i

Change the plus sign between 5 and 4i to a minus sign.

The complex conjugate of 5 + 4i is 5 − 4i.

b. 12 − 8i

Change the minus sign between 12 and 8i to a plus sign.

The complex conjugate of 12 − 8i is 12 + 8i.

c. −6 − 7i

Change the minus sign between −6 and 7i to a plus sign.

The complex conjugate of −6 − 7i is −6 + 7i.

d. i

i can be written as 0 + i. Changing the plus sign between 0 and i to a minus sign results in 0 − i, or −i.

The complex conjugate of i is −i.

e. −9i

−9i can be written as 0 − 9i. Changing the minus sign between 0 and −9i to a plus sign gives 0 + 9i, or 9i.

The complex conjugate of −9i is 9i.

GOT TO KNOW!

Complex Conjugates

Complex numbers of the form $a + bi$ and $a - bi$ are complex conjugates of each other.

Complex Conjugates

$$a + bi \Longleftrightarrow a - bi$$

Product of Complex Conjugates

Complex conjugates have a special relationship because their product is always a real number.

Recall that when multiplying $(a + b)$ and $(a - b)$, the product is $(a^2 - b^2)$.

$$(a + b)(a - b) = a^2 - b^2$$

The multiplication of complex conjugates that are binomials is similar:

$$(a + bi)(a - bi) = a^2 - b^2i^2$$

Because $i^2 = -1$:

$$(a + bi)(a - bi) = a^2 - b^2i^2$$
$$= a^2 - b^2(-1)$$
$$= a^2 + b^2$$

Need More

HELP ?

For more help with multiplying complex numbers, see *Multiplying Complex Numbers* (p. 1898).

EXAMPLE 2

Multiply the complex conjugates. Write the product in standard form.

a. (5 + 4*i*)(5 − 4*i*)

Multiply the complex conjugates.	$(5 + 4i)(5 - 4i) = (25 + 20i - 20i - 16i^2)$
Simplify.	$= 25 - 16i^2$
Substitute −1 for i^2.	$= 25 - 16(-1)$
Multiply.	$= 25 + 16$
Add.	$= 41$

b. (12 − 8*i*)(12 + 8*i*)

Multiply the complex conjugates.	$(12 - 8i)(12 + 8i) = (144 + 96i - 96i + 64i^2)$
Simplify.	$= 144 - 64i^2$
Substitute −1 for i^2.	$= 144 - 64(-1)$
Multiply.	$= 144 + 64$
Add.	$= 208$

c. −9*i* • 9*i*

Multiply.	$-9i \cdot 9i = -81i^2$
Substitute −1 for i^2.	$= -81(-1)$
Simplify.	$= 81$

GOT TO KNOW!

The Product of Complex Conjugates
$$(a + bi)(a - bi) = a^2 - b^2i^2 \longrightarrow i^2 = -1$$
$$= a^2 - b^2(-1)$$
$$= a^2 + b^2$$

SOUTHWESTERN

Dividing Complex Numbers

Because the product of complex conjugates is a real number, multiplying the numerator and denominator of a fraction by the conjugate of the denominator will result in a real number in the denominator. For example, to find $\frac{5 + 2i}{3 + i}$, multiplying the numerator and denominator by the complex conjugate of $3 + i$ will result in a denominator of $(3 + i)(3 - i)$, or 10. After multiplying the numerator and denominator by the conjugate of the denominator, the quotient can be simplified and written in standard form.

EXAMPLE 3

SEARCH

To see step-by-step videos of these problems, enter the page number into the SWadvantage.com Search Bar.

Divide. Write the answer in standard form.

a. $\dfrac{3 - 5i}{7i}$

Multiply the numerator and denominator by the conjugate of $7i$.

Simplify.

Write in standard form, and simplify.

$$\frac{3 - 5i}{7i} = \frac{3 - 5i}{7i} \cdot \frac{-7i}{-7i} = \frac{-21i + 35i^2}{-49i^2}$$

$$= \frac{-21i + 35(-1)}{-49(-1)} = \frac{-21i - 35}{49}$$

$$= \frac{-35}{49} - \frac{21i}{49} = -\frac{5}{7} - \frac{3}{7}i$$

b. $\dfrac{12}{6 + 4i}$

Multiply the numerator and denominator by the conjugate of $6 + 4i$.

Simplify.

Write in standard form, and simplify.

$$\frac{12}{6 + 4i} = \frac{12}{6 + 4i} \cdot \frac{6 - 4i}{6 - 4i} = \frac{72 - 48i}{36 - 16i^2}$$

$$= \frac{72 - 48i}{36 - 16(-1)} = \frac{72 - 48i}{52}$$

$$= \frac{72}{52} - \frac{48i}{52} = \frac{18}{13} - \frac{12}{13}i$$

c. $\dfrac{-9i}{1 - 3i}$

Multiply the numerator and denominator by the conjugate of $1 - 3i$.

Simplify.

Write in standard form.

$$\frac{-9i}{1 - 3i} = \frac{-9i}{1 - 3i} \cdot \frac{1 + 3i}{1 + 3i} = \frac{-9i - 27i^2}{1 - 9i^2}$$

$$= \frac{-9i - 27(-1)}{1 - 9(-1)} = \frac{-9i + 27}{10}$$

$$= \frac{27}{10} - \frac{9}{10}i$$

GOT TO KNOW!

Dividing Complex Numbers

1. Write the numerator and denominator in standard form.

2. Multiply the numerator and denominator by the complex conjugate of the denominator.

3. Write the quotient in standard form.

EXAMPLE 4

Divide. Write the answer in standard form.

a. $\dfrac{2 + 5i}{-4 - i}$

Multiply the numerator and denominator by the conjugate of $-4 - i$.

$$\dfrac{2 + 5i}{-4 - i} = \dfrac{2 + 5i}{-4 - i} \cdot \dfrac{-4 + i}{-4 + i}$$

Multiply.

$$= \dfrac{-8 + 2i - 20i + 5i^2}{16 - i^2}$$

Simplify and substitute -1 for i^2.

$$= \dfrac{-8 - 18i + 5(-1)}{16 - (-1)}$$

Simplify.

$$= \dfrac{-13 - 18i}{17}$$

Write in standard form.

$$= -\dfrac{13}{17} - \dfrac{18}{17}i$$

b. $\dfrac{-2 - 9i}{-7 - 3i}$

Multiply the numerator and denominator by the conjugate of $-7 - 3i$.

$$\dfrac{-2 - 9i}{-7 - 3i} = \dfrac{-2 - 9i}{-7 - 3i} \cdot \dfrac{-7 + 3i}{-7 + 3i}$$

Multiply.

$$= \dfrac{14 - 6i + 63i - 27i^2}{49 - 9i^2}$$

Simplify and substitute -1 for i^2.

$$= \dfrac{14 + 57i - 27(-1)}{49 - 9(-1)}$$

Simplify.

$$= \dfrac{41 + 57i}{58}$$

Simplify and write in standard form.

$$= \dfrac{41}{58} + \dfrac{57}{58}i$$

EXAMPLE 5

Divide. Write the answer in standard form.

$$\dfrac{(9 + 6i) - (8 + i)}{(-12 - 4i) + (10 + 7i)}$$

Write the numerator and denominator in standard form.

$$\dfrac{(9 + 6i) - (8 + i)}{(-12 - 4i) + (10 + 7i)} = \dfrac{1 + 5i}{-2 + 3i}$$

Multiply the numerator and denominator by the conjugate of $-2 + 3i$.

$$= \dfrac{1 + 5i}{-2 + 3i} \cdot \dfrac{-2 - 3i}{-2 - 3i}$$

Multiply.

$$= \dfrac{-2 - 3i - 10i - 15i^2}{4 - 9i^2}$$

Simplify and substitute -1 for i^2.

$$= \dfrac{-2 - 13i - 15(-1)}{4 - 9(-1)}$$

Simplify.

$$= \dfrac{13 - 13i}{13}$$

Write in standard form.

$$= 1 - i$$

Need More

HELP?

For help with adding and subtracting complex numbers, see *Adding and Subtracting Complex Numbers* (p. 1896).

The Complex Plane

Just as every coordinate pair corresponds to exactly one point in the rectangular coordinate plane, every complex number corresponds to exactly one point in the **complex plane**.

- The horizontal axis of the complex plane is the real axis.
- The vertical axis of the complex plane is the imaginary axis.

To plot a complex number in the complex plane, identify the real and imaginary parts of the number.

- The real part indicates how many units from the origin to move left or right along the horizontal axis.
- The imaginary part indicates how many units from the origin to move up or down along the vertical axis.

Need More
HELP?

For more on the complex number system, go to *Complex Roots of Equations* in *Trigonometry* (Book 1, p. 1110).

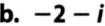

EXAMPLE 1

Plot the complex numbers.

a. 1 + 3i

Start at the origin and move 1 unit to the right and 3 units up.

b. −2 − i

Start at the origin and move 2 units to the left and 1 unit down.

c. −3i

Start at the origin and move 3 units down.

d. 4 + 2i

Start at the origin and move 4 units to the right and 2 units up.

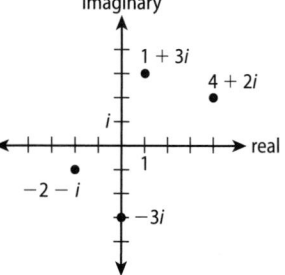

Absolute Value of a Complex Number

The absolute value of a complex number $z = a + bi$ is the distance between the origin and z in the complex plane.

- The absolute value of z is written $|z|$.
- Using the Pythagorean theorem, $|z| = \sqrt{a^2 + b^2}$.
- Because $|z| = \sqrt{a^2 + b^2}$ where a and b are real numbers, $|z|$ is a non-negative real number.

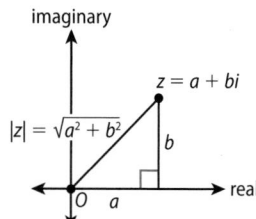

EXAMPLE 2

Find the absolute value of the complex number. Write the answer in simplest form.

SEARCH

To see step-by-step videos of these problems, enter the page number into the SWadvantage.com Search Bar.

a. 2 + 4i

Substitute 2 for a and 4 for b in $|z| = \sqrt{a^2 + b^2}$. $\qquad |2 + 4i| = \sqrt{2^2 + 4^2}$

Simplify the powers. $= \sqrt{4 + 16}$

Add. $= \sqrt{20}$

Write the radical as the product of two square roots. $= \sqrt{4} \cdot \sqrt{5}$

Find the square root of the perfect square. $= 2\sqrt{5}$

b. −5i

Substitute 0 for a and -5 for b in $|z| = \sqrt{a^2 + b^2}$. $\quad |-5i| = \sqrt{0^2 + (-5)^2}$

Simplify the powers. $= \sqrt{25}$

Find the square root of the perfect square. $= 5$

c. $\sqrt{7} + i$

Substitute $\sqrt{7}$ for a and 1 for b in $|z| = \sqrt{a^2 + b^2}$. $\quad |\sqrt{7} + i| = \sqrt{(\sqrt{7^2}) + 1^2}$

Simplify the powers. $= \sqrt{7 + 1}$

Add. $= \sqrt{8}$

Write the radical as the product of two square roots. $= \sqrt{4} \cdot \sqrt{2}$

Find the square root of the perfect square. $= 2\sqrt{2}$

EXAMPLE 3

Simplify. Write the answer in simplest form.

a. $|12 - 5i| \cdot |3 - 4i|$

Substitute for a and b in $z = \sqrt{a^2 + b^2}$. $|12 - 5i| \cdot |-3 - 4i| = \sqrt{12^2 + (-5)^2} \cdot \sqrt{(-3)^2 + (-4)^2}$

Simplify the powers. $= \sqrt{144 + 25} \cdot \sqrt{9 + 16}$

Add. $= \sqrt{169} \cdot \sqrt{25}$

Find the square roots. $= 13 \cdot 5$

Multiply. $= 65$

b. $\dfrac{|-8 + 15i|}{|9 + 12i|}$

Substitute for a and b in $|z| = \sqrt{a^2 + b^2}$. $\dfrac{-8 + 15i}{9 + 12} = \dfrac{\sqrt{(-8)^2 + 15^2}}{\sqrt{9^2 + 12^2}}$

Simplify the powers. $= \dfrac{\sqrt{64 + 225}}{\sqrt{81 + 144}}$

Add. $= \dfrac{\sqrt{289}}{\sqrt{225}}$

Find the square roots. $= \dfrac{17}{15}$

Conic Sections

What Came Before?
- Writing the equations of circles
- Graphing quadratic equations in standard form

What's This About?
- Understanding and using their equations to graph the conic sections
- Finding the eccentricity of conic sections
- Translating the graphs of conic sections

Practical Apps
- Planetary orbits are ellipses, while paths of other objects in space are hyperbolas.
- Physicists use equations of parabolas to describe the path of projectiles.

just for FUN!

The hyperbolic pilot announced that the flight was on final approach to the asymptote.

You can find more practice problems online by visiting:
www.SWadvantage.com

Graphing Parabolas

Parabolas

A parabola is the set of points equidistant from a fixed point, called the **focus**, and a fixed line, called the **directrix**. The **axis of symmetry** is the line that is perpendicular to the directrix and passes through the focus. The **vertex** of a parabola is the point on the parabola where it intersects the axis of symmetry. The **latus rectum (LR)** is the segment through the focus parallel to the directrix. The endpoints of the latus rectum are on the parabola.

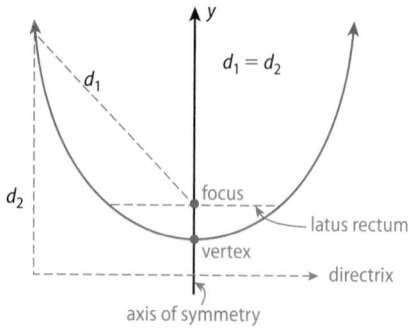

The equation of a parabola whose vertex is at the origin is either $y^2 = 4px$ or $x^2 = 4py$.

- The constant p is the distance between the vertex and the focus and the vertex and the directrix. To solve for p in either equation, set $4p$ equal to the coefficient of the linear term x or y in the equation.

- To find the endpoints of the latus rectum (LR), substitute the value of p for x in the equation $y^2 = 4px$ and solve for y, or substitute the value of p for y in the equation $x^2 = 4py$ and solve for x.

Need More

HELP ?

Remember that a quadratic equation can have two roots that are opposites of each other. For more review of quadratic equations, go to pages 1702–1713. On these pages, various methods of solving quadratic equations are explained.

EXAMPLE 1

Find the focus and the directrix of the parabola $y^2 = 8x$. Then graph the parabola.

STEP 1 The vertex of this parabola is at the origin $(0, 0)$. The squared term is y^2, so the axis of symmetry is the x-axis.

STEP 2 Solve for p by setting $4p$ equal to 8, the coefficient of x. $4p = 8$, so $p = 2$

STEP 3 The constant $p > 0$, so the parabola opens to the right. The focus lies 2 units to the right of the vertex, and its coordinates are $(2, 0)$.

STEP 4 The directrix is the vertical line p units from the vertex. Its equation is $x = -2$.

STEP 5 The LR is a vertical segment through the focus. To find the coordinates of its endpoints, substitute 2 for x into the equation and solve for y.

$$y^2 = 8(2) \longrightarrow y = \pm\sqrt{16} = \pm 4$$

The focus is at $(2, 0)$. The directrix has the equation $x = -2$. The graph of the parabola $y^2 = 8x$ is shown to the right.

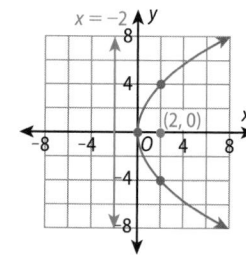

GOT TO KNOW!

Forms of the Equations of Parabolas with Vertex (0, 0)

Equation	Vertex	Axis of Symmetry	Directrix	Direction of Parabola
$y^2 = 4px$	$(0, 0)$	x-axis	Vertical	$p > 0$: opens to the right $p < 0$: opens to the left
$x^2 = 4py$	$(0, 0)$	y-axis	Horizontal	$p > 0$: opens up $p < 0$: opens down

EXAMPLE 2

Find the focus and directrix of the parabola $x^2 = -4y$. Then graph the parabola.

SEARCH

To see step-by-step videos of these problems, enter the page number into the SWadvantage.com Search Bar.

METHOD 1

STEP 1 The vertex of this parabola is at the origin (0, 0). The squared term is x^2, so the axis of symmetry is the y-axis.

STEP 2 Solve for p by setting $4p$ equal to -4.

$$4p = -4$$
$$p = -1$$

STEP 3 The constant $p < 0$, so the parabola opens down. The focus lies 1 unit below the vertex, and its coordinates are (0, −1).

STEP 4 The directrix is the horizontal line p units above the vertex. Its equation is $y = 1$.

STEP 5 The LR is a vertical segment through the focus. To find the coordinates of its endpoints, substitute −1 for y into the equation and solve for x.

$$x^2 = -4(-1)$$
$$x = \pm\sqrt{4} = \pm 2$$

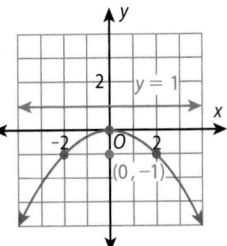

The focus is at (0, −1). The equation of the directrix is $y = 1$. The graph of the parabola $x^2 = -4y$ showing its focus and directrix appears to the right.

METHOD 2

You can use a table of values to graph parabolas whose equations are in this form.

Rewrite the equation $x^2 = -4y$ solved for y.

$$x^2 = -4y$$
$$y = -\frac{1}{4}x^2$$

Set up a table of x and y values. Substitute at least three values of x into the equation and solve for y.

x	$-\frac{1}{4}x^2$	y
0	$-\frac{1}{4}(0)^2$	0
2	$-\frac{1}{4}(2)^2$	−1
−2	$-\frac{1}{4}(-2)^2$	−1

Plot the points and draw the parabola.

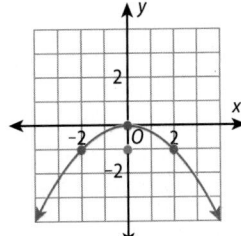

The coordinates of the focus are (0, −1). The directrix is 1 unit above the vertex, and its equation is $y = 1$. The vertex of the graph is on (0, 0), and the parabola opens down.

Equations of Parabolas in Standard Form

Watch Out !

It's easy to make a mistake with the signs in these formulas. Remember that subtracting a negative number is the same thing as adding a positive number.

For example, if h is negative, then the expression is written as $x + h$.

If k is negative, then the expression is written as $y + k$.

Not all parabolas have a vertex located at $(0, 0)$. The standard form of the equation of all parabolas can be written as $(x - h)^2 = 4p(y - k)$ or $(y - k)^2 = 4p(x - h)$. The point (h, k) is the vertex of the parabola, and p is the distance between the vertex and the focus and the vertex and the directrix.

- If the axis of symmetry is horizontal, the directrix is vertical and its equation is $x = h - p$. The graphs of these parabolas are not functions.
  - If $p > 0$, then the focus lies to the right of the vertex along the axis of symmetry.
  - If $p < 0$, the focus lies to the left of the vertex along the axis of symmetry.
- If the axis of symmetry is vertical, the directrix is horizontal and its equation is $y = k - p$. The graphs of these parabolas are functions.
  - If $p > 0$, then the focus lies above the vertex along the axis of symmetry.
  - If $p < 0$, the focus lies below the vertex along the axis of symmetry.
- If the vertex is located at the origin, then both h and k are 0, and the equations simplify to either $x^2 = 4py$ or $y^2 = 4px$.

EXAMPLE 3

Find the vertex, the focus, and the directrix of the parabola $(x + 3)^2 = -8(y - 1)$. Graph the parabola.

STEP 1 Find the vertex.

Rewrite the equation in standard form.
$$(x - h)^2 = 4p(y - k)$$
$$(x - (-3))^2 = -8(y - 1)$$

Use the equation to find the vertex.
$$(h, k) = (-3, 1)$$

STEP 2 Find the coordinates of the focus.

Solve for p.
$$4p = -8$$
$$p = -2$$

The x-term is squared, so the axis of symmetry is vertical and contains the focus.

Because $p = -2$, which is < 0, the focus lies 2 units below the vertex at $(-3, -1)$.

STEP 3 Find the directrix.

Because the axis of symmetry is vertical, the directrix is horizontal.

Substitute into the equation for a horizontal directrix; solve.
$$y = k - p$$
$$= 1 - (-2) = 3$$

The equation for the directrix is $y = 3$.

STEP 4 Use the LR and the vertex to graph the parabola. The y-coordinate of the LR is -1. To find the x-coordinates, substitute -1 for y into the equation of the parabola and solve the resulting quadratic equation for the two x-coordinates.
$$(x + 3)^2 = -8(-1 - 1) = 16$$
$$(x + 3) = \pm\sqrt{16} = \pm4$$
$$x = +4 - 3 = 1$$
$$x = -4 - 3 = -7$$

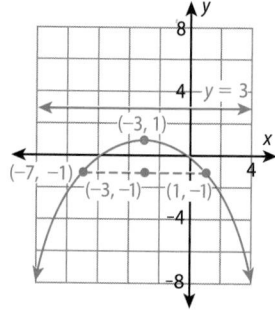

EXAMPLE 4

Find the vertex, the focus, and the directrix of the parabola $(y + 1)^2 = -16(x - 1)$. Graph the parabola.

SEARCH

To see step-by-step videos of these problems, enter the page number into the SWadvantage.com Search Bar.

STEP 1 Find the vertex.

Rewrite the equation in standard form.
$$(y - k)^2 = 4p(x - h)$$
$$(y - (-1))^2 = -16(x - 1)$$

Use the equation to find the vertex.
$$(h, k) = (1, -1)$$

STEP 2 Find the coordinates of the focus.

Solve for p.
$$4p = -16$$
$$p = -4$$

The y-term is squared, so the axis of symmetry is horizontal and contains the focus.

Because $p = -4$, which is < 0, the focus lies 4 units to the left of the vertex at $(-3, -1)$.

STEP 3 Find the directrix.

Because the axis of symmetry is horizontal, the directrix is vertical.

Substitute into the equation for a horizontal directrix; solve.
$$x = h - p$$
$$= 1 - (-4) = 5$$

The equation for the directrix is $x = 5$.

STEP 4 Use the LR and the vertex to graph the parabola. The x-coordinate of the LR is -3. To find the y-coordinates, substitute -3 for x into the equation of the parabola and solve the resulting quadratic equation for the two y-coordinates.

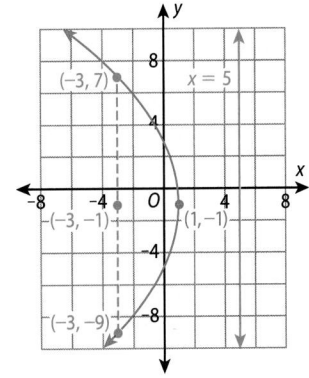

$$(y + 1)^2 = -16(-3 - 1) = 64$$
$$y + 1 = \pm\sqrt{64}$$
$$y = 8 - 1 \text{ and } y = -8 - 1$$
$$y = 7 \text{ and } y = -9$$

The graph of the parabola is shown to the right.

GOT TO KNOW!

Standard Forms of the Equations of Parabolas with Vertex (h, k) and Their Properties

Equation	Vertex	Axis of Symmetry	Focus	Directrix	Length of the LR	Direction of Parabola
$(y - k)^2 = 4p(x - h)$	(h, k)	Horizontal	$(h + p, k)$	$x = h - p$	$|4p|$	$p > 0$: opens to the right $p < 0$: opens to the left
$(x - h)^2 = 4p(y - k)$	(h, k)	Vertical	$(h, k + p)$	$y = k - p$	$|4p|$	$p > 0$: opens up $p < 0$: opens down

Using Intercepts to Graph a Parabola

You now know how to graph a parabola using an equation from which you can find information about the vertex, the directrix, the latus rectum, and the focus of the parabola. You can also graph a parabola by using the vertex and information on where the parabola intersects at least one axis of the graph. No matter where the graph of the parabola is on the coordinate plane, the parabola will eventually cross either the x-axis, the y-axis, or both.

- A parabola intersects the x-axis at the point where $y = 0$. To find an x-intercept, substitute the value of 0 for y in the equation for the parabola. When you solve for x, the solution is the x coordinate where the parabola crosses the x-axis.

- A parabola intersects the y-axis at the point where $x = 0$. To find a y-intercept, substitute the value of 0 for x in the equation for the parabola. When you solve for y, the solution is the y coordinate where the parabola crosses the y-axis.

All parabolas will intersect one time with at least one axis. You might find two intercepts, or even three. You need at least three points to draw a graph of a parabola.

- If you find three intercepts, use those three points to graph the parabola.

- If you find two intercepts, use those two points and another point to graph the parabola. That other point might be the vertex, or it might be a point obtained by substituting a value for x or y into the equation, then simplifying to find another point.

- If you find only one intercept, find two other points on the parabola to use in graphing it.

EXAMPLE 5

Some quadratic equations are not easily factored and other solution methods must be used. For review on solving quadratic equations, see pages 1702–1713 in this volume.

Using intercepts, graph the parabola given by the equation $(y - 1)^2 = x + 16$.

STEP 1 Find any x-intercepts.

Substitute $y = 0$ into the equation.

$(y - 1)^2 = x + 16$
$(0 - 1)^2 = x + 16$

Solve the equation for x.

$(-1)^2 = x + 16$
$x = -16 + 1$
$x = -15$

The x-intercept is $(-15, 0)$.

STEP 2 Find any y-intercepts.

Substitute $x = 0$ into the equation.

$(y - 1)^2 = x + 16$
$(y - 1)^2 = 0 + 16$

Solve the equation for y.

$y^2 - 2y + 1 = 16$
$y^2 - 2y - 15 = 0$
$(y - 5)(y + 3) = 0$
$y = 5, -3$

The y-intercepts are $(0, 5)$ and $(0, -3)$.

STEP 3 Plot the three intercept points.
Use the points to graph the parabola.

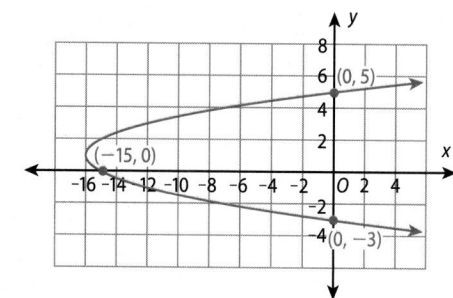

EXAMPLE 6

Using intercepts, graph the parabola given by the equation $(x + 3)^2 = 4(y + 6)$.

STEP 1 Find any y-intercepts.

Substitute $x = 0$ into the equation.

$(x + 3)^2 = 4(y + 6)$

$(0 + 3)^2 = 4y + 24$

Solve the equation for y.

$(3)^2 = 4y + 24$

$4y = -24 + 9$

$4y = -15$

$y = -3.75$

The y-intercept is $(0, -3.75)$.

STEP 2 Find any x-intercepts.

Substitute $y = 0$ into the equation.

$(x + 3)^2 = 4(y + 6)$

$(x + 3)^2 = 4(0 + 6)$

$x^2 + 6x + 9 = 24$

$x^2 + 6x - 15 = 0$

This quadratic equation will not factor. The other choices for solving the quadratic equation are completing the square or using the quadratic formula. For this example, completing the square is used. The same results would be obtained by using the quadratic formula.

STEP 3 Write the equation as a square. $(x + 3)^2 = 24$

STEP 4 Find the square root of both sides. $(x + 3) = \sqrt{24}$

Simplify.

$x + 3 = \sqrt{4 \times 6}$

$x + 3 = 2\sqrt{6}$

STEP 5 Solve for x.

Use a calculator to find the square root of 6. $\sqrt{6} = \pm 2.45$

Substitute ± 2.45 into the equation. $x + 3 = 2(2.45)$ and $x + 3 = 2(-2.45)$

Simplify. $x = 4.90 - 3$ and $x = -4.90 - 3$

$x = 1.90$ and $x = -7.90$

The x-intercepts are $(1.9, 0)$ and $(-7.9, 0)$.

STEP 6 Plot the three intercept points. Use the points to graph the parabola.

The graph of the parabola is shown below.

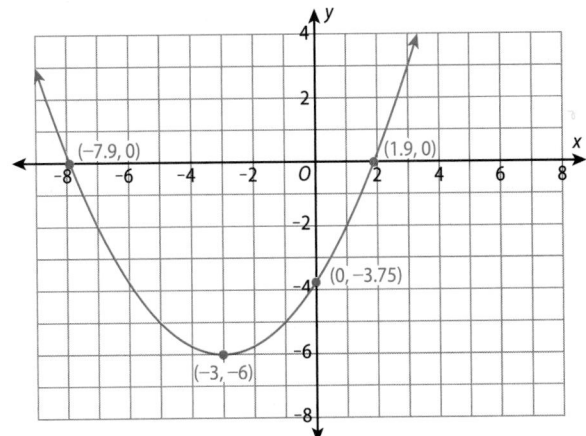

Equations for Parabolas

Writing Equations Using Focus and Vertex

Just as a parabola can be graphed if you know its equation, the equation of a parabola can be written if you know certain properties about its graph.

The standard forms of the equations of parabolas are $(x - h)^2 = 4p(y - k)$ or $(y - k)^2 = 4p(x - h)$, where (h, k) are the coordinates of the vertex, and $|p|$ is the distance between the vertex and focus. Both the vertex and the focus lie on the axis of symmetry.

You can write the standard form of an equation of a parabola if you know the coordinates of its vertex and the coordinates of its focus.

Try It This Way

Try sketching the location of the given points or lines on graph paper. Be sure to label each point or line. From this graph, you can easily determine the axis of symmetry and in what direction the parabola opens.

EXAMPLE 1

Write the standard form of the equation of a parabola whose vertex is (0, 2) and whose focus is (0, 5).

STEP 1 Determine the axis of symmetry.

The x-coordinates of the vertex and the focus are both 0, so these points lie on the y-axis. The y-axis is the axis of symmetry for this parabola.

STEP 2 Determine which equation for a parabola to use.

The y-axis is a vertical axis of symmetry. The squared term in a parabola that has a vertical axis of symmetry is x. So, the equation has the form $(x - h)^2 = 4p(y - k)$.

STEP 3 Use the general equation to find a specific equation for this parabola.

$(x - h)^2 = 4p(y - k)$

Substitute the coordinates of the vertex into the equation. $(x - 0)^2 = 4p(y - 2)$

Simplify. $x^2 = 4p(y - 2)$

STEP 4 Determine the sign of p.

The y-coordinate of the focus is greater than the y-coordinate of the vertex, so the focus lies above the vertex and the parabola opens up. Therefore, $p > 0$.

STEP 5 Find the value of p.

The distance between the y-coordinates of the vertex and the focus is 3. So, $p = 3$.

STEP 6 Write the equation for the parabola. $x^2 = 4p(y - 2)$

Substitute the value of p into the equation for the parabola. $= 4(3)(y - 2)$

Simplify. $= 12(y - 2)$

The equation of this parabola is $x^2 = 12(y - 2)$.

GOT TO KNOW!

Standard Forms of the Equations of Parabolas

Equation	Vertex	Axis of Symmetry
$(y - k)^2 = 4p(x - h)$	(h, k)	Horizontal
$(x - h)^2 = 4p(y - k)$	(h, k)	Vertical

The constant p is a *directed distance* from the vertex to the focus. This means that p can be either positive or negative.

- If $p > 0$, the focus lies to the right of the vertex or above the vertex.
- If $p < 0$, the focus lies to the left of the vertex or below the vertex.

EXAMPLE 2

What is the equation of the parabola whose focus is $(-6, 0)$ and whose vertex is $(-2, 0)$?

STEP 1 Determine the axis of symmetry.

The y-coordinates of the vertex and the focus are both 0, so these points lie on the x-axis. The x-axis is the axis of symmetry for this parabola.

STEP 2 Determine which equation for a parabola to use.

The x-axis is a horizontal axis of symmetry. The squared term in a parabola that has a horizontal axis of symmetry is y. So, the equation has the form $(y - k)^2 = 4p(x - h)$.

STEP 3 Use the general equation to find a specific equation for this parabola.

$(y - k)^2 = 4p(x - h)$

Substitute the coordinates of the vertex into the equation. $(y - 0)^2 = 4p(x - (-2))$

Simplify. $y^2 = 4p(x + 2)$

STEP 4 Determine the sign of p.

The x-coordinate of the focus is less than the x-coordinate of the vertex, so the focus lies to the left of the vertex, and the parabola opens to the left. Therefore, $p < 0$.

STEP 5 Find the value of p.

The distance between the x-coordinates of the vertex and the focus is 4 and $p < 0$. So, $p = -4$.

STEP 6 Write the equation for the parabola.

$y^2 = 4p(x + 2)$

Substitute the value of p into the equation for the parabola. $= 4(-4)(x + 2)$

Simplify. $= -16(x + 2)$

The equation of this parabola is $y^2 = -16(x + 2)$.

SEARCH

To see step-by-step videos of these problems, enter the page number into the SWadvantage.com Search Bar.

GOT TO KNOW!

Writing Equations for Parabolas from the Focus and the Vertex

1. Determine the axis of symmetry from common coordinates of the focus and the vertex.
2. Based on the axis of symmetry, determine which equation for a parabola to use.
3. Use the general equation and the coordinates of the vertex to find a specific equation for this parabola.
4. Determine the sign of p from the relative locations of the focus and the vertex.
5. Find the value of p from the distance between the focus and the vertex.
6. Write the equation for the parabola from the specific equation for the parabola and the value of p.

Writing Equations When the Vertex Is Not the Origin

SEARCH 🔍

To see step-by-step videos of these problems, enter the page number into the SWadvantage.com Search Bar.

EXAMPLE 3

What is the equation of the parabola whose focus is (2, 3) and whose vertex is (2, −5)?

STEP 1 Determine the axis of symmetry.

The x-coordinates of the vertex and the focus are the same, so these points lie on the line $x = 2$. Thus, the axis of symmetry for this parabola is vertical.

STEP 2 Determine which equation for a parabola to use.

Because the x-values of the focus and vertex are the same, the axis of symmetry is vertical. The squared term in a parabola that has a vertical axis of symmetry is x. So, the equation has the form $(x - h)^2 = 4p(y - k)$.

STEP 3 Use the general equation. $(x - h)^2 = 4p(y - k)$

Substitute the coordinates of the vertex into the equation. $(x - 2)^2 = 4p(y - (-5))$

Simplify. $(x - 2)^2 = 4p(y + 5)$

STEP 4 Determine the sign and value of p.

The y-coordinate of the focus is greater than the y-coordinate of the vertex, so the focus lies above the vertex along the axis of symmetry, and the parabola opens up. Therefore, $p > 0$.

The distance between the y-coordinates of the vertex and the focus is 8 and $p > 0$. So, $p = 8$.

STEP 5 Write the equation for the parabola. $(x - 2)^2 = 4p(y + 5)$

Substitute the value of p into the equation for the parabola. $(x - 2)^2 = 4(8)(y + 5)$

Simplify. $= 32(y + 5)$

The equation of this parabola is $(x - 2)^2 = 32(y + 5)$.

Writing Equations Using Focus and Directrix

EXAMPLE 4

What is the equation of the parabola whose focus is (0, 15) and whose directrix is $y = -15$?

STEP 1 Determine the axis of symmetry.

The directrix is horizontal, so the axis of symmetry is vertical.

STEP 2 Determine which equation for a parabola to use.

The squared term in a parabola that has a vertical axis of symmetry is x. So, the equation has the form $(x - h)^2 = 4p(y - k)$.

STEP 3 Find the coordinates of the vertex.

The vertex is halfway between the focus, (0, 15), and the point on the directrix that intersects the axis of symmetry, (0, −15). The vertex is at (0, 0).

STEP 4 Find a specific equation for this parabola. Find the sign and value of p, which is 15. Substitute p, h, and k into the general equation for the parabola, and simplify.

The equation of this parabola is $(x - 0)^2 = 4(15)(y - 0)$, which simplifies to $x^2 = 60y$.

Need More
HELP ?

For more about calculating the distance between points, go to *Distance Formula* in *Geometry* (Book 1, p. 818).

EXAMPLE 5

What is the equation of the parabola whose focus is (2, 0) and directrix is $x = -2$?

STEP 1 Determine the axis of symmetry.

The directrix is vertical, so the axis of symmetry is horizontal.

STEP 2 Determine which equation for a parabola to use.

The squared term in a parabola that has a horizontal axis of symmetry is y. So, the equation has the form $(y - k)^2 = 4p(x - h)$.

STEP 3 Find the coordinates of the vertex.

The vertex is halfway between the focus, (2, 0), and the point on the directrix that intersects the axis of symmetry, $(-2, 0)$. The vertex is at (0, 0).

STEP 4 Find the sign and value of p.

The x-coordinate of the focus is greater than the x-coordinate of the vertex. So, the parabola opens to the right, and $p > 0$. The focus is at a distance of $(2 - 0) = 2$ units from the vertex, so $p = 2$.

STEP 5 Use the general equation.

Substitute p, h, and k into the general equation for the parabola.

Simplify.

$$(y - k)^2 = 4p(x - h)$$
$$(y - 0)^2 = 4(2)(x - 0)$$
$$y^2 = 8x$$

The equation of this parabola is $y^2 = 8x$.

EXAMPLE 6

What is the equation of the parabola whose focus is (5, −1) and whose directrix is $x = -6$?

STEP 1 Determine the axis of symmetry.

The directrix is vertical, so the axis of symmetry is horizontal.

STEP 2 Determine which equation for a parabola to use.

The squared term in a parabola that has a horizontal axis of symmetry is y. So, the equation has the form $(y - k)^2 = 4p(x - h)$.

STEP 3 Find the coordinates of the vertex.

The vertex is halfway between the focus, (5, −1), and the point on the directrix that intersects the axis of symmetry, $(-6, -1)$. There are 11 units between the two points.

So the coordinates of the vertex are $(-0.5, -1)$.

STEP 4 Find the sign and value of p.

The x-coordinate of the focus is greater than the x-coordinate of the vertex. So, the parabola opens to the right, and $p > 0$. The focus is at a distance of 5.5 units from the vertex.

So $p = 5.5$.

STEP 5 Use the general equation.

Substitute p, h, and k into the general equation.

Simplify.

$$(y - k)^2 = 4p(x - h)$$
$$(y - (-1))^2 = 4(5.5)(x - (-0.5))$$
$$(y + 1)^2 = 22(x + 0.5)$$

The equation of this parabola is $(y + 1)^2 = 22(x + 0.5)$.

Graphing Circles

Graphing Circles Using the Center and a Radius

A **circle** is the set of all points in a plane that are equidistant from a fixed point called the center. The fixed distance from the center of the circle to any point on the circle is called the **radius**. The radius r of a circle is a positive number that is the length of a segment from the center to a point on the circle.

One way to graph a circle in the coordinate plane is to know the coordinates of its center (h, k) and its radius r.

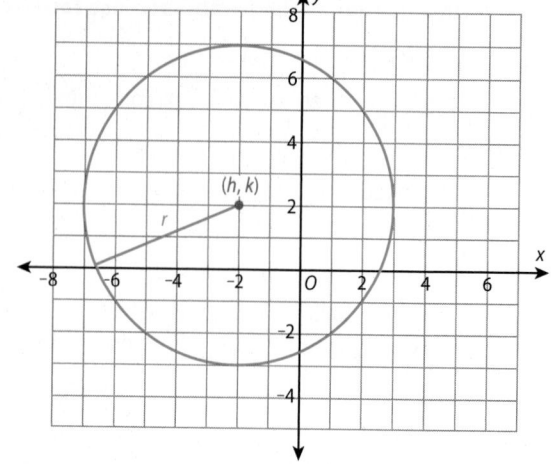

SEARCH

To see step-by-step videos of these problems, enter the page number into the SWadvantage.com Search Bar.

EXAMPLE 1

Graph the circle whose center is at (0, 0) and whose radius is 2.5.

STEP 1 Plot the point that is the center at the origin.

STEP 2 The radius is 2.5, so plot several points 2.5 units from the origin. Easy points to plot are (2.5, 0), (0, 2.5), (-2.5, 0), and (0, -2.5), which are on the x- and y-axes. Draw the circle through the four points.

The graph of the circle whose center is at (0, 0) and whose radius is 2.5 is shown at the right.

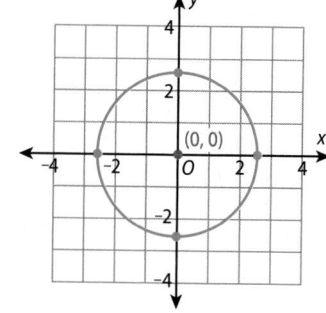

EXAMPLE 2

Graph the circle whose center is at (4, 5) and whose radius is 5.

STEP 1 Plot the center of the circle at (4, 5).

STEP 2 Starting at the center, plot several points that are 5 units from the center. You might move 5 units along the line $y = 5$ to the right and left of the center to the points (9, 5), and (-1, 5), and 5 units up and down along the line $x = 4$, to the points (4, 10) and (4, 0).

The graph of the circle whose center is at (4, 5) and whose radius is 5 is shown at the right.

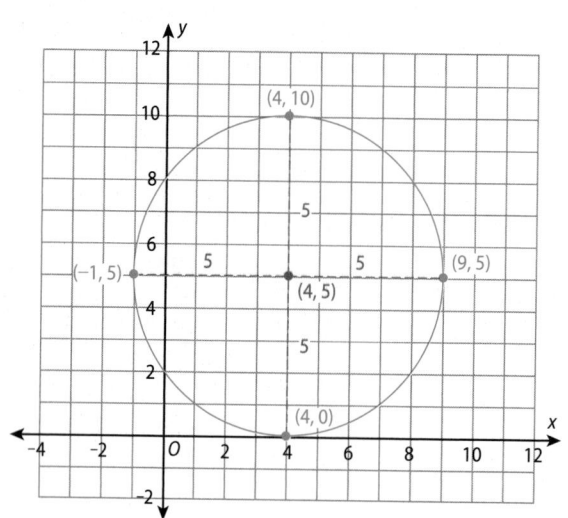

Using the Center and a Point on the Circle

The Distance Formula can be used to find the distance d between the points (x_1, y_1) and (x_2, y_2): $d = \sqrt{(x_2 - x_1)^2 + (y_2 - y_1)^2}$. So, to graph a circle given the coordinates of its center and a point on the circle, find the radius by letting $d = r$ and solving for r, a positive number.

Need More
HELP

For more help, go to *Distance Formula* in *Geometry* (Book 1, p. 818).

EXAMPLE 3

Graph the circle whose center is $(-1, 0)$ and that contains the point $(-4, -4)$.

STEP 1 Let $d = r$ and use the Distance Formula to calculate the distance between $(-1, 0)$ and $(-4, -4)$. Substitute the x- and y-coordinates of each point into the formula, and simplify the expression under the radical sign.

$$d = \sqrt{(x_2 - x_1)^2 + (y_2 - y_1)^2}$$
$$r = \sqrt{(-1 - (-4))^2 + (0 - (-4))^2}$$
$$= \sqrt{3^2 + 4^2} = \sqrt{9 + 16} = \sqrt{25} = 5$$

STEP 2 Plot the center. Draw the vertical line $x = -1$ through the center.

STEP 3 Plot several points that are 5 units from the center. Points easy to plot are those 5 units from $(-1, 0)$ along the x-axis and those 5 units above and below $(-1, 0)$ on the line $x = -1$.

STEP 4 Draw the circle through the points.

The graph of the circle is shown at the right.

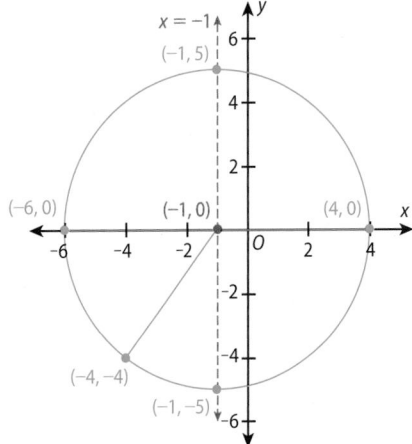

EXAMPLE 4

Graph the circle whose center is $(-3, -6)$ and that contains the point $(9, -1)$.

STEP 1 Let $r = d$ and use the Distance Formula to calculate the distance between $(-3, -6)$ and $(9, -1)$. Substitute the x- and y-coordinates of the two points into the formula and simplify the radical expression.

$$d = \sqrt{(x_2 - x_1)^2 + (y_2 - y_1)^2}$$
$$r = \sqrt{(9 - (-3))^2 + (-1 - (-6))^2}$$
$$= \sqrt{12^2 + 5^2} = \sqrt{144 + 25}$$
$$= \sqrt{169} = 13$$

STEP 2 Plot the center. Draw the vertical line $x = -3$ and the horizontal line $y = -6$.

STEP 3 Plot several points that are 13 units from the center. Points easy to plot are those along the lines $x = -3$ and $y = -6$: $(10, -6)$, $(-3, 7)$, $(-16, -6)$ and $(-3, -19)$.

STEP 4 Draw the circle through the points.

The graph of the circle is shown at the right.

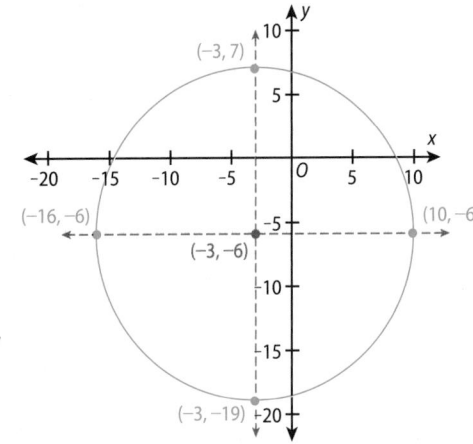

Using the Endpoints of a Diameter

You can also graph a circle if you know the endpoints of a diameter of the circle.

- The radius of a circle equals half its diameter, so you can find the radius of a circle by finding half the distance of the diameter.
- Given the coordinates of the endpoints of a diameter, you can find the center of the circle by finding the midpoint of the diameter.
- Using this information, you can then draw the graph of the circle.

EXAMPLE 5

Graph the circle with a diameter whose endpoints are $(-9, 3)$ and $(-1, 3)$.

The horizontal line $y = 3$ contains the diameter. Draw this line, and plot the points $(-9, 3)$ and $(-1, 3)$.

METHOD 1

STEP 1 Find the length of the diameter d.

$$d = \sqrt{(x_2 - x_1)^2 + (y_2 - y_1)^2}$$
$$= \sqrt{(-9 - (-1))^2 + (3 - 3)^2}$$
$$= \sqrt{(-8)^2 + (0)^2} = \sqrt{64} = 8$$

STEP 2 From the length of the diameter, find the length of the radius.

$$r = d \div 2$$
$$= 8 \div 2 = 4$$

STEP 3 The center of the circle is halfway between the endpoints of a diameter. So, plot the point 4 units between the endpoints $(-9, 3)$ and $(-1, 3)$. The center coordinates are $(-5, 3)$.

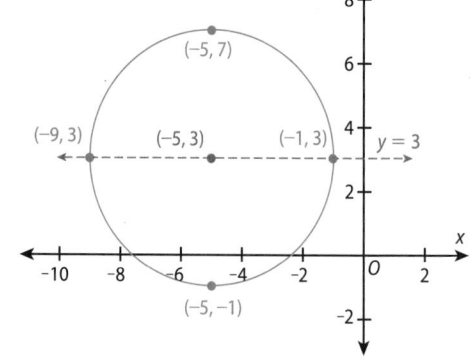

STEP 4 Use the center $(-5, 3)$ and $r = 4$ to draw the circle.

METHOD 2

STEP 1 The center of a circle is the midpoint of a diameter. The coordinates of the midpoint of a segment whose endpoints are (x_1, y_1) and (x_2, y_2) are $\left(\dfrac{x_1 + x_2}{2}, \dfrac{y_1 + y_2}{2}\right)$.

Its midpoint coordinates are $\left(\dfrac{-9 + (-1)}{2}, 3\right) = (-5, 3)$.

STEP 2 The radius of the circle is the distance between the midpoint $(-5, 3)$ and either of its endpoints, $(-9, 3)$ or $(-1, 3)$. This distance is 4, so $r = 4$.

STEP 3 Use the center $(-5, 3)$ and $r = 4$ to draw the circle.

The graph of the circle is shown above.

Need More

HELP ?

For more help, go to *Midpoint Formula* in *Geometry* (Book 1, p. 820).

EXAMPLE 6

Graph the circle with a diameter whose endpoint coordinates are (5, 3) and (5, −5).

STEP 1 Draw the vertical line $x = 5$, which contains the diameter.

STEP 2 Find the length of the diameter.

$$d = \sqrt{(x_2 - x_1)^2 + (y_2 - y_1)^2}$$
$$= \sqrt{(5 - 5)^2 + (3 - (-5))^2} = \sqrt{0^2 + 8^2} = \sqrt{64} = 8$$

STEP 3 Find the length of the radius.

$$r = d \div 2$$
$$= 8 \div 2 = 4$$

STEP 3 Find the center of the circle.

The center of the circle is the midpoint of the diameter, so plot the point that is 4 units from either (5, 3) or (5, −5). The center coordinates are (5, −1).

STEP 4 Use the center (5, −1) and a radius of 4 to draw the circle.

The graph of the circle is shown above.

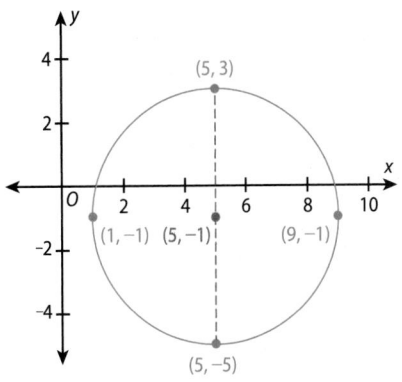

EXAMPLE 7

Graph the circle with a diameter whose endpoint coordinates are (2, 6) and (0, −4).

STEP 1 Plot the points that are the endpoints of the diameter. The diameter is neither horizontal nor vertical.

STEP 2 Use the Distance Formula to find the length of d, the diameter. Use estimation or a calculator for a better approximation.

$$d = \sqrt{(2 - 0)^2 + (6 - (-4))^2}$$
$$= \sqrt{2^2 + 10^2}$$
$$= \sqrt{104} \approx 10.2$$

STEP 3 Find the radius.

The radius is half the diameter, so $r \approx 5.1$.

STEP 4 Find the center of the circle.

Use the midpoint formula to find the midpoint coordinates of the diameter.

$$\left(\frac{2 + 0}{2}, \frac{6 + (-4)}{2}\right) = (1, 1)$$

STEP 5 Use the center (1, 1) and a radius of about 5.1 and draw the circle.

The graph of the circle is shown to the right.

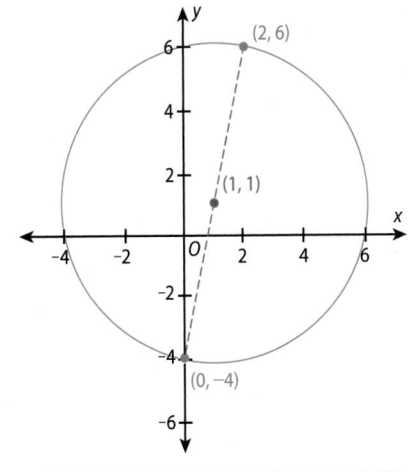

SEARCH

To see step-by-step videos of these problems, enter the page number into the SWadvantage.com Search Bar.

Equations for Circles

The Standard Form of the Equation of a Circle

The standard form of the equation of a circle is $(x - h)^2 + (y - k)^2 = r^2$, where (h, k) are the coordinates of the center of the circle, and r is the radius of the circle. You can write the equation of a circle if you know the coordinates of its center and its radius.

EXAMPLE 1

Write the standard form of the equation of a circle whose center is at the origin and whose radius is 5.

STEP 1 Identify h and k.

The center of this circle is at the origin, so $h = 0$ and $k = 0$.

STEP 2 Write the equation of the circle.

Substitute values of h, k, and r into the equation for a circle.

$$(x - h)^2 + (y - k)^2 = r^2$$
$$(x - 0)^2 + (y - 0)^2 = 5^2$$

Simplify.

$$x^2 + y^2 = 25$$

The equation of the circle is $x^2 + y^2 = 25$.

EXAMPLE 2

Write the standard form of the equation of a circle whose center is at (1, −5) and whose diameter is 2.

STEP 1 Identify h, k and r.

The center of this circle is at $(1, -5)$, so $h = 1$ and $k = -5$.
The diameter is $2r$, so $2 = 2r$, and $r = 1$.

STEP 2 Write the equation of the circle.

Substitute values of h, k, and r into the equation for a circle.

$$(x - h)^2 + (y - k)^2 = r^2$$
$$(x - 1)^2 + (y - (-5))^2 = 1^2$$

Simplify.

$$(x - 1)^2 + (y + 5)^2 = 1$$

The standard form of the equation of the circle is $(x - 1)^2 + (y + 5)^2 = 1$.

> **Watch Out !**
>
> Remember that subtracting a negative number is the same as adding the positive number with the same absolute value as the negative number.
>
> So, if $h < 0$, then $x - h = x + |h|$.
>
> If $k < 0$, then $y - k = y + |k|$.

EXAMPLE 3

Write the equation of a circle whose center is at (−2, −6) and whose radius is $\sqrt{6}$.

STEP 1 Identify h and k.

The center of this circle is at $(-2, -6)$, so $h = -2$ and $k = -6$.

STEP 2 Write the equation of the circle.

Substitute values of h, k, and r into the equation for a circle.

$$(x - h)^2 + (y - k)^2 = r^2$$
$$(x - (-2))^2 + (y - (-6))^2 = (\sqrt{6})^2$$

Simplify.

$$(x + 2)^2 + (y + 6)^2 = 6$$

The equation of the circle is $(x + 2)^2 + (y + 6)^2 = 6$.

EXAMPLE 4

What is the standard form of the equation of a circle whose diameter has endpoint coordinates of (5, 8) and (−3, −6)?

STEP 1 Find the center of the circle.

The midpoint of the diameter is the center of the circle. Use the coordinates of the endpoints of the diameter and the Midpoint Formula $\left(\frac{x_2 + x_1}{2}, \frac{y_2 + y_1}{2}\right)$ to find the coordinates of the center: $\left(\frac{5 + (-3)}{2}, \frac{8 + (-6)}{2}\right) = (1, 1)$

METHOD 1 **(for step 2)**

STEP 2 Find r.

Use the Distance Formula $d = \sqrt{(x_2 - x_1)^2 + (y_2 - y_1)^2}$ to find the length of the segment between one of the endpoints and the center of the circle. For this segment, $d = r$.
$$r = \sqrt{(5 - 1)^2 + (8 - 1)^2} = \sqrt{16 + 49} = \sqrt{65}$$

METHOD 2 **(for step 2)**

STEP 2 Find the length of the diameter and the radius.

Use the Distance Formula $d = \sqrt{(x_2 - x_1)^2 + (y_2 - y_1)^2}$ to find the length of the diameter:
$$d = \sqrt{(5 - (-3))^2 + (8 - (-6))^2}$$
$$= \sqrt{64 + 196} = \sqrt{260} = \sqrt{4 \times 65} = 2\sqrt{65}$$

The radius is half the diameter, so $r = \frac{2\sqrt{65}}{2} = \sqrt{65}$

STEP 3 Write the equation of the circle.

Substitute values of h, k, and r into the equation for a circle.
$(x - h)^2 + (y - k)^2 = r^2$
$(x - 1)^2 + (y - 1)^2 = (\sqrt{65})^2$

Simplify.
$(x - 1)^2 + (y - 1)^2 = 65$

The equation of the circle is $(x - 1)^2 + (y - 1)^2 = 65$.

SEARCH
To see step-by-step videos of these problems, enter the page number into the SWadvantage.com Search Bar.

GOT TO KNOW!

Writing the Standard Form of the Equation of a Circle

$$(\boldsymbol{x - h})^2 + (\boldsymbol{y - k})^2 = \boldsymbol{r}^2$$

x-coordinate of the center of the circle

y-coordinate of the center of the circle

radius of the circle

Writing the General Form from the Standard Form

The general form of the equation of a circle is $x^2 + y^2 + Dx + Ey + F = 0$, where D, E, and F are real numbers. The standard form of the equation of a circle $(x - h)^2 + (y - k)^2 = r^2$ can be expanded into its general form using algebra.

EXAMPLE

Rewrite the equation $(x + 4)^2 + y^2 = 3$ in general form.

STEP 1 Expand the binomial in x. $(x^2 + 8x + 16) + y^2 = 3$

STEP 2 Set the equation equal to 0.

Subtract 3 from both sides. $x^2 + 8x + 16 + y^2 - 3 = 0$

Simplify. $x^2 + 8x + y^2 + 13 = 0$

STEP 3 Rewrite the equation in general form, starting with the second degree terms, x^2 and y^2, followed by the linear terms, x and y, and then the constant.

Apply the Commutative Property of Addition. $x^2 + y^2 + 8x + 13 = 0$

The general form of the equation of this circle is $x^2 + y^2 + 8x + 13 = 0$.

Need More

HELP ?

The Commutative Property of Addition states that the order of terms being added can be switched:

$a + b = b + a$

To review, go to *Properties* in *Algebra* (pp. 1406–1409).

SEARCH

To see step-by-step videos of these problems, enter the page number into the SWadvantage.com Search Bar.

EXAMPLE 6

Rewrite the equation $(x - 6)^2 + (y^2 + 2)^2 = 15$ in general form.

STEP 1 Expand the binomials in x and y. $(x^2 - 12x + 36) + (y^2 + 4y + 4) = 15$

STEP 2 Set the equation to 0.

Subtract 15 from both sides. $x^2 - 12x + 36 + y^2 + 4y + 4 - 15 = 0$

Simplify. $x^2 - 12x + y^2 + 4y + 25 = 0$

STEP 3 Rewrite the equation in general form, starting with the second degree terms, x^2 and y^2, followed by the linear terms, x and y, and then the constant.

Apply the Commutative Property of Addition $x^2 + y^2 - 12x + 4y + 25 = 0$

The general form of the equation of this circle is $x^2 + y^2 - 12x + 4y + 25 = 0$.

GOT TO KNOW!

Changing from Standard Form to General Form for the Equation of a Circle

Standard Form: $$(x - h)^2 + (y - k)^2 = r^2$$

$$\downarrow$$

$$x^2 - 2hx + h^2 + y^2 - 2ky + k^2 = r^2$$

$$\downarrow$$

$$x^2 - 2hx + h^2 + y^2 - 2ky + k^2 - r^2 = 0$$

$$\downarrow$$

$$x^2 + y^2 - 2hx - 2ky + h^2 + k^2 - r^2 = 0$$

$$\downarrow$$

General Form: $x^2 + y^2 + Dx + Ey + F = 0$, where $D = -2h$, $E = -2k$, and $F = (h^2 + k^2 - r^2)$

Writing the Standard Form from the General Form

The general form of the equation of a circle $x^2 + y^2 + Dx + Ey + F = 0$ can be converted into the standard form $(x - h)^2 + (y - k)^2 = r^2$ using a method known as completing the square.

Completing the square is based on factoring a quadratic trinomial expression $a^2 + 2ab + b^2$ into the square of a binomial $(a + b)^2$, such that $a^2 + 2ab + b^2 = (a + b)^2$. To convert a quadratic binomial into a perfect square trinomial, each of the following must be true.

- The coefficient of the quadratic term must equal 1.
- A perfect square equal to the square of half the coefficient of the linear term must be added to the expression.

If the general equation is written as $(x^2 + Dx) + (y^2 + Ey) + F = 0$, then the quadratic expressions are $(x^2 + Dx)$ and $(y^2 + Ey)$. To convert each of these binomials into perfect square trinomials, the squares to be added are equal to $\frac{1}{2}$ the coefficients of x and y; namely $\left(\frac{1}{2}D\right)^2$ and $\left(\frac{1}{2}E\right)^2$, respectively.

> **Need More**
> **HELP** ❓
>
> To review the method of completing the square, go to *Completing the Square* in *Algebra* (p. 1706).

EXAMPLE 7

The general equation of a circle is $x^2 + y^2 + 6x + 2y + 6 = 0$.

a. What is the standard form of the equation of this circle?

STEP 1 Rewrite the equation arranging the like x and y terms together in descending order.

Use the Commutative Property of Addition. $x^2 + 6x + y^2 + 2y + 6 = 0$

Subtract 6 from both sides. $x^2 + 6x + y^2 + 2y = -6$

STEP 2 Use the Associative Property of Addition to separate the x and y expressions.

$$(x^2 + 6x) + (y^2 + 2y) = -6$$

STEP 3 Complete the square in both x and y expressions.

Calculate $\left(\frac{1}{2}D\right)^2$ and $\left(\frac{1}{2}E\right)^2$. $\left(\frac{1}{2}\cdot 6\right)^2 = 9$ and $\left(\frac{1}{2}\cdot 2\right)^2 = 1$

Add these values to both sides of the equation. $(x^2 + 6x + 9) + (y^2 + 2y + 1) = -6 + 9 + 1$

Simplify. $(x^2 + 6x + 9) + (y^2 + 2y + 1) = 4$

STEP 4 Factor each perfect square trinomial into two binomials. $(x + 3)^2 + (y + 1)^2 = 4$

The standard form of the equation is $(x + 3)^2 + (y + 1)^2 = 4$.

> **Need More**
> **HELP** ❓
>
> The Associate Property of Addition is the grouping property:
> $(a + b) + c = a + (b + c)$.
>
> To review, go to *Properties* in *Algebra* (pp. 1406–1409).

b. What are the coordinates of the center of the circle?

Find the coordinates of the center of the circle. $(x - h)^2 + (y - k)^2 = r^2$

$$(x - (-3))^2 + (y - (-1))^2 = 4$$

The coordinates of the center of the circle, (h, k), are $(-3, -1)$.

c. What is the radius of the circle?

Find the radius of the circle. $r^2 = 4$, so $r = 2$

The radius is 2.

Graphing Ellipses

Graphing an Ellipse with Center at (0, 0)

An **ellipse** is the set of all points in a plane whose distances from two fixed points called the **foci** total a positive constant. The midpoint of the segment connecting the foci is the center of the ellipse.

An ellipse can be oriented horizontally or vertically. The perpendicular segments through the center of an ellipse are its **major axis** and its **minor axis**. The longer axis is the major axis.

There are two equations for an ellipse whose center is at the origin.

- If the major axis is horizontal, the equation is $\frac{x^2}{a^2} + \frac{y^2}{b^2} = 1$. If the major axis is vertical, the equation is $\frac{x^2}{b^2} + \frac{y^2}{a^2} = 1$. In each equation, $a^2 > b^2$.
- The length of the major axis is $2a$, and the length of the minor axis is $2b$, where a and b are positive numbers.
- The vertices of an ellipse are on its major axis, a units from the center.
- The foci of an ellipse are always located on the major axis, c units from the center, where $c^2 = a^2 - b^2$ and $\pm\sqrt{a^2 - b^2}$.

Watch Out !

When finding the square root of a number in a problem such as this example, the sign of the root depends on whether the answer is a location or a distance. A location can be either positive or negative, but a length is always positive. For example, if $c^2 = 16$, the foci are located at $+4$ and -4 units from the center. Both foci are at a distance of 4 units from the center.

EXAMPLE 1

Locate the foci and graph the ellipse whose equation is $\frac{x^2}{25} - \frac{y^2}{9} = 1$.

STEP 1 In this equation, the denominator of the x^2 term is greater than the denominator of the y^2 term, so the major axis is horizontal, and $a^2 = 25$.

STEP 2 Because $a^2 = 25$, $a = \pm 5$. The coordinates of the vertices are 5 units to the left and right of the center at (5, 0) and (–5, 0).

Because $b^2 = 9$, $b = \pm 3$. The endpoints of the minor axis are 3 units above and below the center at (0, 3) and (0, –3).

STEP 3 To locate the foci of the ellipse, solve the equation $c^2 = a^2 - b^2$ for c.

$c^2 = 25 - 9 = 16; c = \pm 4$

The foci are 4 units to the left and right of the center, at (4, 0) and (–4, 0).

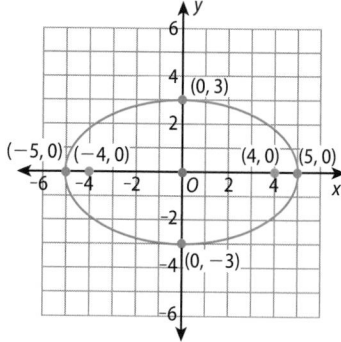

GOT TO KNOW!

Parts of an Ellipse

Major axis length = $2a$
Minor axis length = $2b$
Focus: c units from the center
Vertex: a units from the center

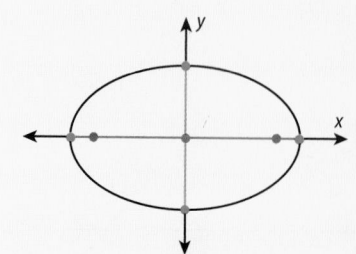

Graphing an Ellipse with Center at (*h, k*)

The center of an ellipse can be any point (h, k) in the coordinate plane.

Equation: $\dfrac{(x-h)^2}{a^2} + \dfrac{(y-k)^2}{b^2} = 1$ $\dfrac{(x-h)^2}{b^2} + \dfrac{(y-k)^2}{a^2} = 1$ In both equations, $a^2 > b^2$.

Major axis: horizontal   vertical

EXAMPLE 2

Locate the foci and graph the ellipse whose equation is $\dfrac{(x+2)^2}{16} + \dfrac{(y-6)^2}{36} = 1$.

STEP 1 Find the center of the ellipse. $h = -2$ and $k = 6$, so $(h, k) = (-2, 6)$

STEP 2 Find the information needed to graph the ellipse: orientation, vertices, and minor axis.

Orientation: The denominator of the y^2-term is greater than the denominator of the x^2-term, so the major axis is vertical, and $a^2 = 36$.

Vertices: $a^2 = 36$, so the vertices are 6 units above and below the center at $(-2, 6+6)$ and $(-2, 6-6)$, or $(-2, 12)$ and $(-2, 0)$.

Minor axis: $b^2 = 16$, so the endpoints of the horizontal minor axis are 4 units to the left and right of the center at $(-2-4, 6)$ and $(-2+4, 6)$, or $(-6, 6)$ and $(2, 6)$.

STEP 3 Find the focus.
$c^2 = a^2 - b^2 = 36 - 16 = 20; c = \sqrt{20} \approx \pm 4.5$

The foci are about 4.5 units above and below the center.

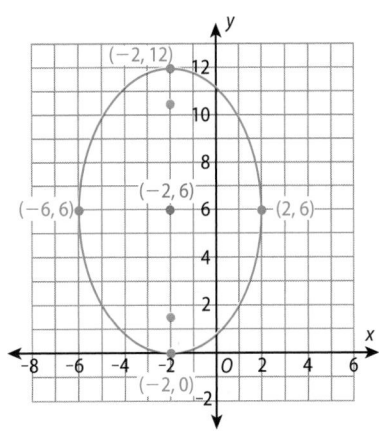

SEARCH

To see step-by-step videos of these problems, enter the page number into the SWadvantage.com Search Bar.

EXAMPLE 3

Locate the foci and graph the ellipse whose equation is $\dfrac{(x-1)^2}{64} + \dfrac{(y+3)^2}{49} = 1$.

STEP 1 Find the center of the ellipse. $h = 1$ and $k = -3$, so $(h, k) = (1, -3)$.

STEP 2 Find the information needed to graph the ellipse: orientation, vertices, and minor axis.

Orientation: The denominator of the x^2-term is greater than the denominator of the y^2-term, so the major axis is horizontal and $a^2 = 64$.

Vertices: $a^2 = 64$, so the vertices are 8 units along the major axis, to the right and left of the center at $(1-8, -3)$ and $(1+8, -3)$, or $(-7, -3)$ and $(9, -3)$.

Minor axis: $b^2 = 49$, so the endpoints of the minor axis are 7 units above and below the center at $(1, -3+7)$ and $(1, -3-7)$, or $(1, 4)$ and $(1, -10)$.

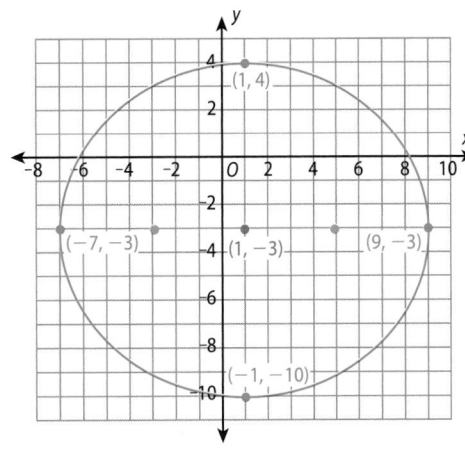

STEP 3 Find the focus.
$c^2 = 64 - 49 = 15; c = \sqrt{15} \approx \pm 3.9$

The foci are about 3.9 units to the left of the center.

Equations for Ellipses

Equations for Ellipses with Center at (0, 0)

There are two standard forms for an equation for an ellipse whose center is at the origin.

- If the major axis is horizontal, $\frac{x^2}{a^2} + \frac{y^2}{b^2} = 1$. If the major axis is vertical, $\frac{x^2}{b^2} + \frac{y^2}{a^2} = 1$. For both equations, $a^2 > b^2$, and a and b are positive numbers.
- The length of the major axis is $2a$, and the length of the minor axis is $2b$.
- The vertices of an ellipse are on its major axis, a units from the center.
- In both equations, the foci of an ellipse are located on the major axis, c units from the center, where $c^2 = a^2 - b^2$.

EXAMPLE 1

The foci of an ellipse are $(-3, 0)$ and $(3, 0)$. Its vertices are $(-8, 0)$ and $(8, 0)$. What is its equation?

STEP 1 Find the orientation of the ellipse and the resulting equation.

The y-coordinates of the foci are both 0, so the foci lie on the x-axis where $y = 0$. This means that the major axis is horizontal and the standard form of the equation is $\frac{x^2}{a^2} + \frac{y^2}{b^2} = 1$.

STEP 2 Find a^2.

The distance between the vertices is $|8 - (-8)| = 16$, which is the length of the major axis, $2a$. If $2a = 16$, then $a = 8$ and $a^2 = 64$.

STEP 3 Find b^2.

Both foci are 3 units from the origin, so $c = 3$. To find b^2, use the equation $c^2 = a^2 - b^2$.

$3^2 = 8^2 - b^2 \rightarrow 9 = 64 - b^2 \rightarrow 55 = b^2$

The equation of the ellipse is $\frac{x^2}{64} + \frac{y^2}{55} = 1$.

EXAMPLE 2

The foci of an ellipse are $(0, -2)$ and $(0, 2)$. Its x-intercepts are -2 and 2. What is the equation?

STEP 1 Find the orientation of the ellipse and the resulting equation.

The x-coordinates of the foci are 0, so the foci lie on the y-axis, whose equation is $x = 0$.

Therefore, the major axis is vertical and the standard form of the equation is $\frac{x^2}{b^2} + \frac{y^2}{a^2} = 1$.

STEP 2 Find b^2.

The distance between the x-intercepts is $|-2 - 2| = 4$, which is the length of the minor axis, $2b$. So, if $2b = 4$, then $b = 2$ and $b^2 = 4$.

STEP 3 Find a^2.

Both foci are 2 units from the origin, so $c = 2$. To find a^2, use the equation $c^2 = a^2 - b^2$.

$2^2 = a^2 - 2^2 \rightarrow 4 = a^2 - 4 \rightarrow 8 = a^2$

The equation of the ellipse is $\frac{x^2}{4} + \frac{y^2}{8} = 1$.

Equations for Ellipses with Centers at (*h, k*)

The standard forms of an equation for an ellipse with center at (*h, k*) are:

$$\frac{(x-h)^2}{a^2} + \frac{(y-k)^2}{b^2} = 1 \text{ if horizontal major axis} \qquad \frac{(x-h)^2}{b^2} + \frac{(y-k)^2}{a^2} = 1 \text{ if vertical major axis}$$

In both equations, $a^2 > b^2$, and *a* and *b* are positive numbers.

EXAMPLE 3

What are the vertices and the equation of the ellipse that has a vertical major axis of length 14, a minor axis of length 4, and center at (−4, −4)?

STEP 1 Determine the general equation of the ellipse.

The equation for an ellipse with a vertical major axis is $\frac{(x-h)^2}{b^2} + \frac{(y-k)^2}{a^2} = 1$.

STEP 2 Find *h* and *k*.

The center of the ellipse is (*h, k*) = (−4, −4), so *h* = −4 and *k* = −4.

STEP 3 Find a^2.

The length of the major axis is 2*a*, which equals 14. So, *a* = 7 and a^2 = 49.

STEP 4 Find b^2.

The length of the minor axis is 2*b*, which equals 4. So, *b* = 2 and b^2 = 4.

STEP 5 Determine the vertices.

The center of the ellipse is on the vertical line *x* = −4, and is 7 units from each vertex. So, the coordinates of the vertices are (−4, −4 + 7) and (−4, −4 − 7), which equal (−4, 3) and (−4, −11).

The vertices of the ellipse are (−4, 3) and (−4, −11), and its equation is $\frac{(x+4)^2}{4} + \frac{(y+4)^2}{49} = 1$.

SEARCH

To see step-by-step videos of these problems, enter the page number into the SWadvantage.com Search Bar.

EXAMPLE 4

What is the equation of the ellipse if the coordinates of the endpoints of its major axis are (7, 9) and (7, 3), and the endpoints of its minor axis are (5, 6) and (9, 6)?

STEP 1 Find the orientation of the ellipse and the resulting general equation.

The vertices of the ellipse are on the line *x* = 7, so the ellipse is vertical. The equation for an ellipse with a vertical major axis is $\frac{(x-h)^2}{b^2} + \frac{(y-k)^2}{a^2} = 1$.

STEP 2 Find a^2.

The length of the major axis is 2*a*, which equals |9 − 3| = 6. So, *a* = 3 and a^2 = 9.

STEP 3 Find b^2.

The length of the minor axis is 2*b*, which equals |9 − 5| = 4. So, *b* = 2 and b^2 = 4.

STEP 4 Find *h* and *k*.

The center of the ellipse, (*h, k*), is where the major (*x* = 7) and minor (*y* = 6) axes intersect. They intersect at (7, 6), so *h* = 7 and *k* = 6.

The equation of the ellipse is $\frac{(x-7)^2}{4} + \frac{(y-6)^2}{9} = 1$.

Graphing Hyperbolas

Hyperbolas with Center at (0, 0)

A hyperbola is the set of points in a plane the difference of whose distances from two fixed points, called the **foci**, is a constant. The line through the foci intersects the hyperbola at two points called **vertices**. The line that passes through both vertices is the **transverse axis**. The vertices are a units from the center of the hyperbola—the midpoint of the transverse axis. Each hyperbola also has **asymptotes**, which are lines that pass through the center of the hyperbola and approach intersecting the hyperbola near infinity.

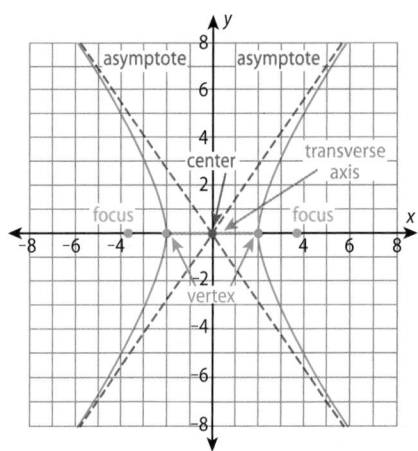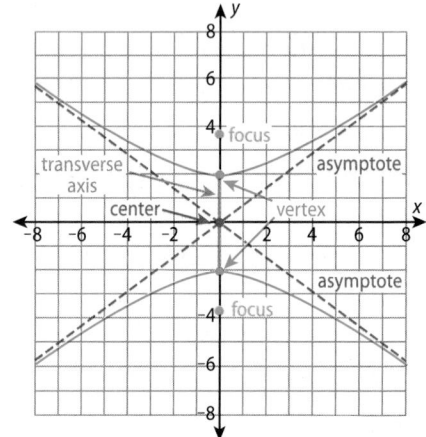

If the center of the hyperbola is at the origin, and the transverse axis is on the x-axis, the standard form of the equation for the hyperbola is $\frac{x^2}{a^2} - \frac{y^2}{b^2} = 1$. If the transverse axis is on the y-axis, the standard form of the equation is $\frac{y^2}{a^2} - \frac{x^2}{b^2} = 1$.

SEARCH 🔍

To see step-by-step videos of these problems, enter the page number into the SWadvantage.com Search Bar.

EXAMPLE 1

Graph the hyperbola whose equation in standard form is $\frac{x^2}{36} - \frac{y^2}{25} = 1$.

STEP 1 Find the orientation of the hyperbola.

The x^2-term occurs first in the equation, so the transverse axis of the hyperbola is on the x-axis.

STEP 2 Locate and plot the vertices of the hyperbola.

The denominator of the x^2-term is a^2. Because $a^2 = 36$, $a = \pm 6$, and the vertices on the transverse axis are a units from the center at $(6, 0)$ and $(-6, 0)$. Plot these points on the graph.

STEP 3 Draw the asymptotes of the hyperbola.

Use dashed lines and draw the rectangle centered at the origin whose vertices are $(\pm a, 0)$ and $(0, \pm b)$. The coordinates of the vertices are $(\pm 6, 0)$ and $(0, \pm 5)$. Draw and extend the diagonals of the rectangle. These lines are the asymptotes of the hyperbola.

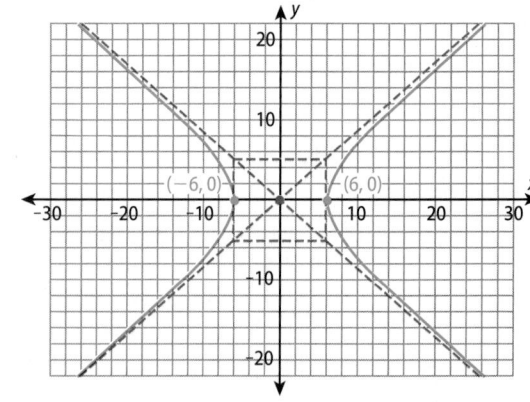

STEP 4 Start at the vertices of each hyperbola and draw the two branches of the hyperbola so that they approach the asymptotes but do not intersect them.

Hyperbolas with Centers at (h, k)

The standard form of the equations for a hyperbola with center at (h, k) is
$\dfrac{(x-h)^2}{a^2} - \dfrac{(y-k)^2}{b^2} = 1$, if the transverse axis is horizontal, and $\dfrac{(y-k)^2}{a^2} - \dfrac{(x-h)^2}{b^2} = 1$,
if the transverse axis is vertical.

If the transverse axis is horizontal, the coordinates of the vertices are ($h - a$, k) and ($h + a$, k). If the transverse axis is vertical, the vertices are (h, $k - a$) and (h, $k + a$).

EXAMPLE 2

Graph the hyperbola whose equation in standard form is $\dfrac{(y-2)^2}{81} - \dfrac{(x-3)^2}{49} = 1$.

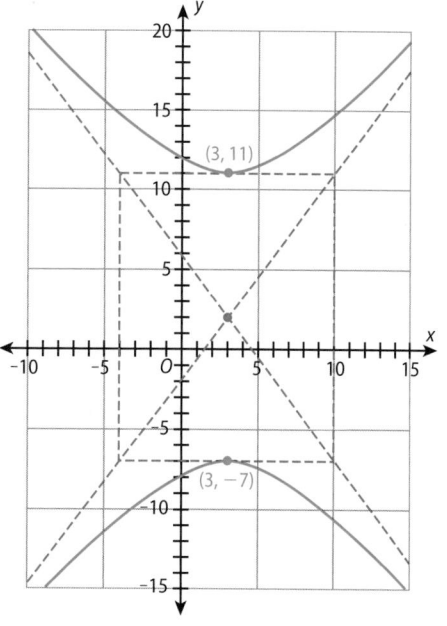

STEP 1 Find and plot the center of the hyperbola.

The center (h, k) of this hyperbola is (3, 2). Plot this point on the graph.

STEP 2 Find the values of a and b.

The constant $a^2 = 81$, so $a = \pm9$, and $b^2 = 49$, so $b = \pm7$.

STEP 3 Determine the orientation of the hyperbola.

The y^2-term comes first in the equation, so the transverse axis of the hyperbola is vertical and passes through the center. Its equation is $x = 3$.

STEP 4 Find and plot the vertices.

Because the transverse axis is vertical, the vertices are located a units from the center at (h, $k + a$) and (h, $k - a$). Because $a = \pm9$, the vertices are (3, 2 + 9) and (3, 2 − 9), or (3, 11) and (3, −7). Plot these points on the graph.

STEP 5 Draw the asymptotes of the hyperbola.

Use dashed lines and draw the rectangle that passes through points that are $a = 9$ units above and below the center and $b = 7$ units to the right and left of the center. The rectangle is defined by the points (−4, −7), (−4, 11), (10, 11), and (10, −7). Draw the diagonals of the rectangle using dashed lines and extend them to form the asymptotes of the hyperbola.

STEP 6 Start at the vertices of each hyperbola, and draw the two branches of the hyperbola so that they approach the asymptotes but do not intersect them.

Try It This Way

If you have difficulty drawing the rectangle that determines the asymptotes based on its vertices, draw it based on the distance of each side from the center. Draw the center first. Then locate the midpoints of each side of the rectangle. Draw the rectangle based on these midpoints.

GOT TO KNOW!

Graphing Hyperbolas

Transverse Axis	Center is (0, 0)		Center is (h, k)	
	Equation	**Vertices**	**Equation**	**Vertices**
Horizontal	$\dfrac{x^2}{a^2} - \dfrac{y^2}{b^2} = 1$	($\pm a$, 0)	$\dfrac{(x-h)^2}{a^2} - \dfrac{(y-k)^2}{b^2} = 1$	($h \pm a$, k)
Vertical	$\dfrac{y^2}{a^2} - \dfrac{x^2}{b^2} = 1$	(0, $\pm a$)	$\dfrac{(y-k)^2}{a^2} - \dfrac{(x-h)^2}{b^2} = 1$	(h, $k \pm a$)

Equations for Hyperbolas

Equations for Hyperbolas with Center at (0, 0)

There are two standard forms for an equation for a hyperbola whose center is at the origin.

- $\frac{x^2}{a^2} - \frac{y^2}{b^2} = 1$ if horizontal transverse axis

- $\frac{y^2}{a^2} - \frac{x^2}{b^2} = 1$ if vertical transverse axis

- The length of the transverse axis is $2a$, where a is a positive number.
- The vertices of a hyperbola are on the transverse axis, a units from the center.
- The foci of a hyperbola are located on the transverse axis, c units from the center, where c is a positive number and $c^2 = a^2 + b^2$.

Watch Out !

In the standard form of the equations for hyperbolas, there can be three possible relationships between a and b:
$a > b$, $a < b$, or $a = b$.

EXAMPLE 1

What is the standard form of the equation of a hyperbola whose foci are $(-5, 0)$ and $(5, 0)$ and whose vertices are $(-1, 0)$ and $(1, 0)$?

STEP 1 Find the general formula of the hyperbola from the orientation of the transverse axis.

The y-coordinates of the foci are both 0, so the foci lie on the x-axis. This means that the transverse axis is horizontal, and the standard form of the equation is $\frac{x^2}{a^2} - \frac{y^2}{b^2} = 1$.

STEP 2 Determine the values of a.

The coordinates of the vertices are $(\pm a, 0)$. The vertices are $(-1, 0)$ and $(1, 0)$, so $a = 1$.

STEP 3 Find the value of c.

The distance from the center to a focus is c. The foci are $(-5, 0)$ and $(5, 0)$, so $c = 5$.

STEP 4 Calculate b^2.

$c^2 = a^2 + b^2$, so $b^2 = c^2 - a^2 = 5^2 - 1^2 = 25 - 1 = 24$

The standard form of the equation of the hyperbola is $\frac{x^2}{1} - \frac{y^2}{24} = 1$, or $x^2 - \frac{y^2}{24} = 1$.

SEARCH

To see step-by-step videos of these problems, enter the page number into the SWadvantage.com Search Bar.

EXAMPLE 2

What is the standard form of the equation of a hyperbola whose foci are $(0, -4)$ and $(0, 4)$ and whose vertices are $(0, -2)$ and $(0, 2)$?

STEP 1 Find the general formula of the hyperbola from the orientation of the transverse axis.

The x-coordinates of the foci are both 0, so the foci lie on the y-axis. Therefore, the transverse axis is vertical and the standard form of the equation is $\frac{y^2}{a^2} - \frac{x^2}{b^2} = 1$.

STEP 2 Determine the value of a.

The coordinates of the vertices are $(0, \pm a)$. The vertices are $(0, -2)$ and $(0, 2)$, so $a = 2$.

STEP 3 Find the value of c.

The distance from the center to a focus is c. The foci are $(0, -4)$ and $(0, 4)$, so $c = 4$.

STEP 4 Calculate b^2.

$c^2 = a^2 + b^2$, so $b^2 = c^2 - a^2 = 4^2 - 2^2 = 16 - 4 = 12$

The standard form of the equation of the hyperbola is $\frac{y^2}{4} - \frac{x^2}{12} = 1$.

Equations for Hyperbolas with Centers at (h, k)

If the transverse axis of a hyperbola is horizontal, the standard form of its equation is $\frac{(x-h)^2}{a^2} - \frac{(y-k)^2}{b^2} = 1$. Its vertices are $(h-a, k)$ and $(h+a, k)$. If the transverse axis is vertical, its standard form is $\frac{(y-k)^2}{a^2} - \frac{(x-h)^2}{b^2} = 1$. Its vertices are $(h, k-a)$ and $(h, k+a)$.

EXAMPLE 3

What is the standard form of the equation of the hyperbola that has center at (4, −2), one focus at (7, −2), and one vertex at (6, −2)?

STEP 1 Find the values of h and k.

The center of the hyperbola (h, k) is $(4, -2)$, so $h = 4$, and $k = -2$.

STEP 2 Find the general formula of the hyperbola from the orientation of the transverse axis.

Both the center and the vertex lie on the line $y = -2$, so the transverse axis is horizontal. The equation has the form $\frac{(x-h)^2}{a^2} - \frac{(y-k)^2}{b^2} = 1$.

STEP 3 Find a.

The distance from the center and a vertex is a, so $a = |6 - 4| = 2$.

STEP 4 Calculate c.

The distance between a focus and the center is c. So, $c = |7 - 4| = 3$.

STEP 5 Find b^2.

$c^2 = a^2 + b^2$, so $b^2 = c^2 - a^2 = 3^2 - 2^2 = 9 - 4 = 5$

The standard form of the equation of the hyperbola is $\frac{(x-4)^2}{4} - \frac{(y+2)^2}{5} = 1$.

Watch Out!

Distance is never negative. So, to find a distance, calculate the absolute value of a difference between coordinates.

EXAMPLE 4

What is the standard form of the equation of the hyperbola that has one focus at (5, −11) and vertices at (5, 3) and (5, −9)?

STEP 1 Find the general formula of the hyperbola from the orientation of the transverse axis.

The x-coordinates of the vertices are both 5, so the transverse axis lies on the vertical line $x = 5$, and the standard form of the equation of the hyperbola is $\frac{(y-k)^2}{a^2} - \frac{(x-h)^2}{b^2} = 1$.

STEP 2 Find a.

The distance between the vertices is $2a$. So, $2a = |-9 - 3| = 12$, and $a = 6$.

STEP 3 Find (h, k), the center of the hyperbola.

The center of the hyperbola lies 6 units from each vertex. So, 6 units below $(5, 3)$ is $(5, 3 - 6)$ and (h, k) is $(5, -3)$.

STEP 4 Calculate c.

Each focus is c units from the center. So, c is the absolute value of the difference between the y-coordinates of the focus and the center: $c = |-11 - (-3)| = 8$

STEP 5 Find b^2.

$c^2 = a^2 + b^2$, so $b^2 = c^2 - a^2 = 8^2 - 6^2 = 64 - 36 = 28$

The standard form of the equation of the hyperbola is $\frac{(y+3)^2}{36} - \frac{(x-5)^2}{28} = 1$.

Graphing Conic Inequalities

Inequalities Involving Parabolas

A parabola divides the coordinate plane into three regions: points on the parabola, a **half-plane** that lies in the interior of the parabola, and a half plane that lies in its exterior of the parabola.

- If the inequality sign is $\leq$ or $\geq$, points on the parabola are part of the graph. When you draw the graph, use a solid curve.
- If the inequality sign is $<$ or $>$, points on the parabola are not part of the graph. When you draw the graph, use a dashed curve.

To graph the half-plane, choose a point in the coordinate plane that is not on the parabola and substitute it into the inequality. A good point to choose is (0, 0).

- If the resulting inequality is true, shade the half-plane that contains the point.
- If the resulting inequality is false, shade the other half-plane.

Need More

HELP

For help, go to *Graphing a Linear Inequality* in *Algebra* (p. 1558). To review terms and standard equations for parabolas, circles, ellipses, and hyperbolas, refer to *earlier topics* in *Conic Sections* (pp. 1910–1935).

EXAMPLE 1

Graph the inequality $x^2 \leq 8(y - 2)$.

STEP 1 Find the vertex of the parabola.

The equation of the parabola has the form $(x - h)^2 = 4p(y - k)$, where (h, k) is the vertex. In this parabola, the vertex is (0, 2) and lies on the y-axis.

STEP 2 Determine the orientation and focus of the parabola.

The coefficient of the y-term is positive, so the parabola turns up.

The term $4p = 8$, so $p = 2$. The focus is 2 units above the vertex at (0, 4).

STEP 3 Find the endpoints of the latus rectum.

The latus rectum (LR) is the horizontal segment through the focus. Its endpoints are on the parabola. To find their coordinates, let $y = 4$ and solve the resulting quadratic equation for x: $x^2 = 8(4 - 2)$ and $x = \pm 4$.

The endpoints are $(-4, 4)$ and $(4, 4)$.

STEP 4 Draw the parabola.

The inequality sign includes points on the parabola. Therefore, use a solid line to draw the parabola.

STEP 5 Determine which half-plane should be shaded.

Choose a point not on the parabola. The point (0, 0) does not lie on the parabola.

Substitute (0, 0) into the inequality.
$$0^2 \leq 8(0 - 2)$$

Solve the inequality.
$$0^2 \leq -16$$

The statement is false.

The half-plane that contains (0, 0) is not correct, so shade the other half-plane, the interior of the parabola.

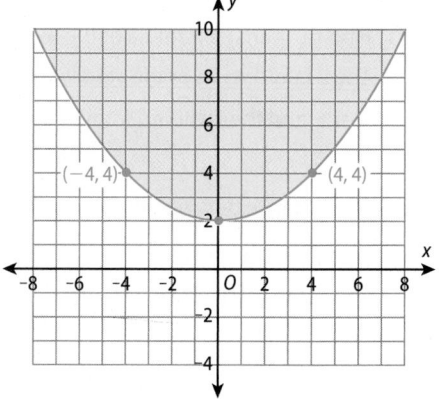

Try It

This Way

This parabola is a function, so you can rewrite the equation solved for y, and use a graphing calculator to enter Y1 = X²/8 + 2.

```
Plot1  Plot2  Plot3
\Y1◻X²/8+2
\Y2=
\Y3=
\Y4=
\Y5=
\Y6=
\Y7=
```

Inequalities Involving Circles

A circle divides the coordinate plane into three regions: points on the circle, points in the interior of the circle, and points in the exterior of the circle. The $\geq$ and $\leq$ signs include the circle; the $>$ and $<$ signs do not include the circle.

EXAMPLE 2

Graph the inequality $\frac{x^2}{9} + \frac{y^2}{9} < 1$.

STEP 1 Analyze the circle.

The center is at the origin, (0, 0). The denominators both equal 9, so $r^2 = 9$, and $|r| = 3$.

STEP 2 Graph the circle with an origin of (0, 0) and a radius of 3.

Because of the inequality sign ($<$), draw the circle using a dashed line.

STEP 3 Decide which region to shade.

Choose a point that is not on the circle.   (0, 0)

Substitute into the inequality, and solve. $\frac{0^2}{9} + \frac{0^2}{9} < 1$, so $0 < 1$.

The resulting inequality is true, so shade the interior of the circle.

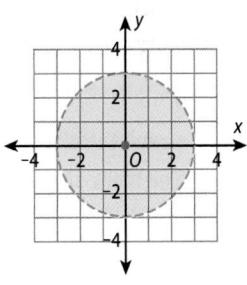

> **Watch Out !**
> The radius of a circle is always a positive number.

EXAMPLE 3

Graph the inequality $(x - 4)^2 + (y - 1)^2 > 8$.

STEP 1 Write the inequality of the circle in standard form. $\frac{(x-4)^2}{8} + \frac{(y-1)^2}{8} > 1$

STEP 2 Analyze the circle.   The center of the circle is $(h, k) = (4, 1)$.

$r^2 = 8$, so $|r| = \sqrt{8}$, or about 2.8.

STEP 3 Graph the circle with an origin of (4, 1) and a radius of 2.8.

Because of the inequality sign ($>$), draw the circle using a dashed line.

STEP 4 Decide which region to shade.

Choose a point that is not on the circle.   (0, 0)

Substitute into the inequality, and solve.

$\frac{(0-4)^2}{8} + \frac{(0-1)^2}{8} > 1$, so $\frac{17}{8} > 1$

The resulting inequality is true, so shade the exterior of the circle.

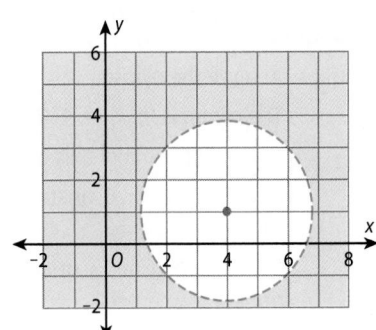

> **SEARCH**
> To see step-by-step videos of these problems, enter the page number into the SWadvantage.com Search Bar.

GOT TO KNOW !

Standard Equations for Parabolas and Circles

Parabola $(x - h)^2 = 4p(y - k)$ and $(y - k)^2 = 4p(x - h)$

Circle $(x - h)^2 + (y - k)^2 = r^2$ or $\frac{(x-h)^2}{r^2} + \frac{(y-k)^2}{r^2} = 1$, where $r > 0$.

Inequalities Involving Ellipses

An ellipse divides the coordinate plane into three regions: points on the ellipse, and points in the interior of the ellipse, and points in the exterior of the ellipse. The $\geq$ and $\leq$ signs include the ellipse; the $>$ and $<$ signs do not include the ellipse.

EXAMPLE 4

Graph the inequality $\dfrac{(x+3)^2}{9} + \dfrac{y^2}{4} \leq 1$.

STEP 1 Analyze the ellipse.

The center is $(h, k) = (-3, 0)$.

$9 > 4$, so the major axis of the ellipse is horizontal.

$a^2 = 9$, so $|a| = 3$, and the ends of the major axis are 3 units left and right of the center.

$b^2 = 9$, so $|b| = 2$, and the ends of the minor axis are 2 units above and below the center.

STEP 2 Graph the ellipse.

The inequality sign includes the equality, so draw the graph of the ellipse with a solid line.

STEP 3 Decide which region of the plane to shade.

Choose a point that is not on the ellipse. $(-3, 0)$

Substitute into the inequality, and solve.

$\dfrac{(-3+3)^2}{9} + \dfrac{0^2}{4} \leq 1$, so $0 \leq 1$

The resulting inequality is true, so shade the region that contains $(-3, 0)$.

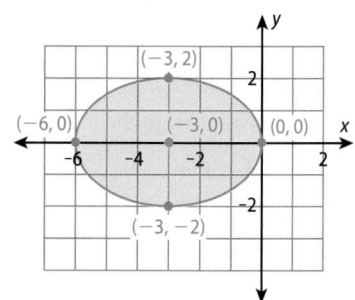

Try It This Way

To use a graphing calculator to graph this ellipse, solve the equation for y, and enter

$Y1 = \dfrac{2}{3}\sqrt{-x^2 - 6x}$

and

$Y2 = -\dfrac{2}{3}\sqrt{-x^2 - 6x}$.

Watch Out !

The point $(0, 0)$ lies on the ellipse, so it is not a point to be used to decide which region to shade.

SEARCH

To see step-by-step videos of these problems, enter the page number into the SWadvantage.com Search Bar.

EXAMPLE 5

Graph the inequality $\dfrac{(y-2)^2}{6} + \dfrac{(x+2)^2}{3} < 1$.

STEP 1 Analyze the ellipse.

The center is $(h, k) = (-2, 2)$.

$6 > 3$, so the major axis of the ellipse is vertical.

$a^2 = 6$, so $|a| = \sqrt{6}$ or about 2.4, and the ends of the major axis are 2.4 units above and below the center.

$b^2 = 3$, and $|b| = \sqrt{3}$ or about 1.7, and the ends of the minor axis are 1.7 units to the left and right of the center.

STEP 2 Graph the ellipse.

The inequality sign is $<$, so draw the ellipse with a dashed line.

STEP 3 Decide which region to shade.

Choose a point that is not on the ellipse. $(0, 0)$

Substitute into the inequality, and solve.

$\dfrac{(0-2)^2}{6} + \dfrac{(0+2)^2}{3} < 1$, so $2 < 1$

The resulting inequality is false, so shade the interior region that does not contain $(0, 0)$.

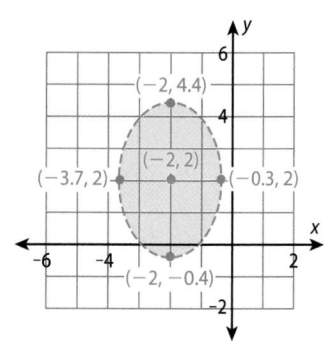

Inequalities Involving Hyperbolas

A hyperbola consists of two branches that separate the points in the coordinate plane into three regions: points on the hyperbola, points between the branches of the hyperbola, and points in the interior of the hyperbola. The $\geq$ and $\leq$ signs include the branches of the hyperbola; the $>$ and $<$ signs do not include the branches of the hyperbola.

EXAMPLE 6

Graph the inequality $\dfrac{(y-2)^2}{16} - \dfrac{(x+2)^2}{25} > 1.$

Watch Out !

The constant a^2 in a hyperbola is always the denominator of the positive term.

STEP 1 Analyze the hyperbola.

The center of the hyperbola is $(h, k) = (-2, 2)$.

$25 > 16$, so the transverse (major) axis of the hyperbola is vertical. Its equation is $x = -2$.

STEP 2 Find the vertices.

The vertices are on the transverse axis and located a units from the center at $(h, k + a)$ and $(h, k - a)$. Because $a^2 = 16$, $a = \pm 4$, and the vertices are $(-2, 2 + 4)$ and $(-2, 2 - 4)$, which equal $(-2, 6)$ and $(-2, -2)$.

STEP 3 Draw the asymptotes of the hyperbola.

The denominator of the x^2-term is $b^2 = 25$ and $b = \pm 5$. Use a and b to draw the rectangle that passes through points that are $a = 4$ units above and below the center and $b = 5$ units to the right and left of the center. The vertices of the rectangle are at $(-7, 6)$, $(3, 6)$, $(3, -2)$, and $(-7, -2)$. Draw the diagonals of the rectangle using dashed lines and extend them to form the asymptotes of the hyperbola.

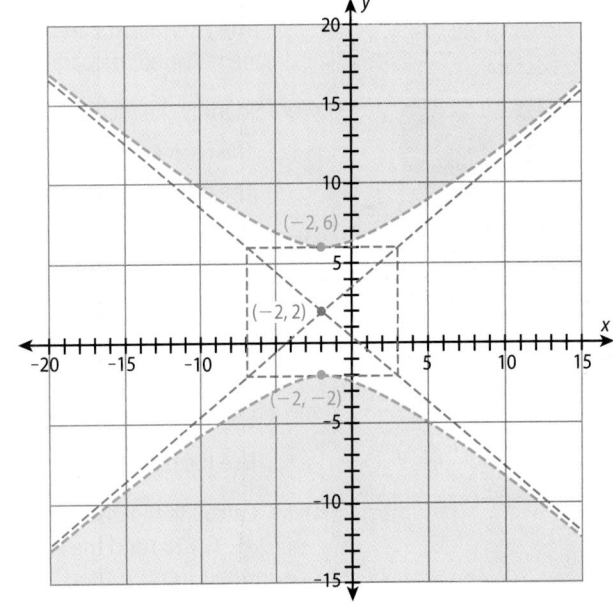

STEP 4 Using the asymptotes, graph the hyperbola.

The sign of the inequality, $>$, does not include points on the hyperbola. Start at the vertices of each hyperbola, and use a dashed line to draw the two branches of the hyperbola.

STEP 5 Decide what region to shade.

Choose a point not on the hyperbola. $(-2, 2)$

Substitute it into the inequality, and solve. Substituting the center coordinates results

in the inequality $\dfrac{(2-2)^2}{16} - \dfrac{(-2+2)^2}{25} > 1$, so $0 > 1$.

This inequality is false, so the region to be shaded is within the two branches of the hyperbola.

GOT TO KNOW !

Equations of Ellipses and Hyperbolas

Ellipse $\dfrac{(x-h)^2}{a^2} + \dfrac{(y-k)^2}{b^2} = 1$ and $\dfrac{(y-k)^2}{a^2} + \dfrac{(x-h)^2}{b^2} = 1$ where a and $b > 0$, and $a > b$.

Hyperbola $\dfrac{(x-h)^2}{a^2} - \dfrac{(y-k)^2}{b^2} = 1$ and $\dfrac{(y-k)^2}{a^2} - \dfrac{(x-h)^2}{b^2} = 1$ where a and $b > 0$.

Eccentricity and Conic Sections

The Eccentricity of a Parabola

The conic sections are the parabola, the circle, the ellipse, and the hyperbola. The **eccentricity** of a conic section is called e, a number that describes the "roundness" of a conic section. Values of e are positive numbers or 0, depending on the conic section.

The eccentricity of a parabola is the ratio of the distance (d_1) between any point P on the parabola and the focus and the distance (d_2) between the point P and the directrix. In a parabola, the distances d_1 and d_2 are equal. So, the eccentricity of a parabola is always equal to $\dfrac{d_1}{d_2} = 1$.

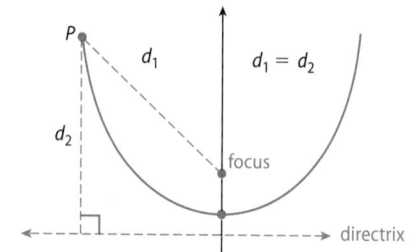

EXAMPLE 1

Show that the eccentricity of the parabola $y^2 = -28x$ is 1.

STEP 1 Identify the vertex and the orientation of the parabola.

The equation of this parabola has the form $(y - k)^2 = 4p(x - h)$, where (h, k) is the vertex. In this parabola, the vertex is $(0, 0)$.

The y-term is squared, so the axis of symmetry is the x-axis. The coefficient of the x-term is negative, so the parabola opens to the left.

STEP 2 Identify the focus and directrix of the parabola.

The term $4p = -28$, so $p = -7$. Therefore, the focus is 7 units to the left of the vertex at $(-7, 0)$.

The directrix is 7 units to the right of the vertex and its equation is $x = 7$.

STEP 3 Identify the coordinates of a point on the parabola.

Choose a negative value of x and substitute it into the equation of the parabola.

Let $x = -1$. $\qquad\qquad y^2 = -28(-1)$

Solve the equation for y. $\qquad y = \pm\sqrt{28}$

STEP 4 Calculate the distance d_1 between the point $(-1, \sqrt{28})$ and the focus $(-7, 0)$.

Use the distance formula: $d_1 = \sqrt{(-1 - (-7))^2 + \left(\sqrt{28} - 0\right)^2} = \sqrt{64} = 8$

STEP 5 Calculate the distance d_2 between the point $(-1, \sqrt{28})$ and the line $x = 7$.

The distance from the point to the directrix is the length of the horizontal segment between the point and the line. Therefore, the distance is

$$d_2 = \sqrt{(-1 - 7)^2 + \left(\sqrt{28} - \sqrt{28}\right)^2}$$
$$= \sqrt{64} = 8.$$

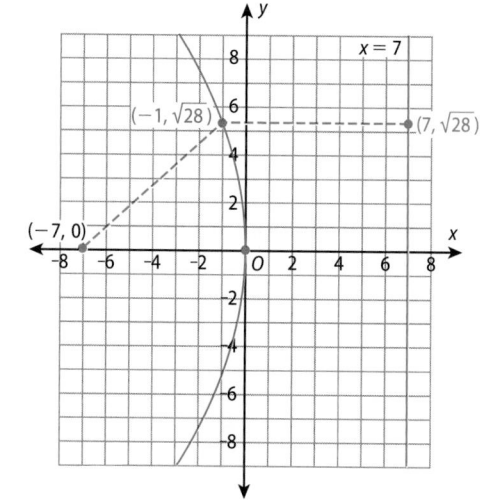

STEP 6 Calculate the eccentricity of the parabola.

Form the ratio of the distance between the focus and the point and the distance between the directrix and the point.

$\dfrac{d_1}{d_2} = \dfrac{8}{8} = 1$. So, $e = 1$.

The Eccentricity of an Ellipse

An **ellipse** is the set of all points in a plane the sum of whose distances from two fixed points, called the **foci**, is a positive constant. An ellipse has a major and a minor axis, with two vertices on each axis. The foci are located on the major (longer) axis.

- The equations of an ellipse are and $\dfrac{(x-h)^2}{a^2} + \dfrac{(y-k)^2}{b^2} = 1$ and $\dfrac{(x-h)^2}{b^2} + \dfrac{(y-k)^2}{a^2} = 1$.

- For an ellipse, $a^2 > b^2$, where a is the distance from the center to a vertex along the major axis, and b is the distance from the center to a vertex along the minor axis.

- The distance from a focus to the center of the ellipse is $c = \sqrt{a^2 - b^2}$.

- The eccentricity e of an ellipse is the ratio $\dfrac{c}{a}$. The foci are always in the interior of the ellipse, so $a > c$, and the eccentricity, $\dfrac{c}{a} < 1$.

EXAMPLE 2

What is the eccentricity to the nearest hundredth of an ellipse whose major axis is 12 and whose minor axis is 4?

STEP 1 Calculate a and b.

The length of the major axis of an ellipse is $2a$, so $2a = 12$ and $a = 6$.

The length of the minor axis is $2b$, so $2b = 4$ and $b = 2$.

STEP 2 Calculate c. $c = \sqrt{a^2 - b^2} = \sqrt{6^2 - 2^2} = \sqrt{32}$.

STEP 3 Find e. $e = \dfrac{c}{a} = \dfrac{\sqrt{32}}{6} \approx 0.94$

The eccentricity of this ellipse is 0.94.

EXAMPLE 3

Find the eccentricity to the nearest hundredth of the ellipse $\dfrac{x^2}{16} + \dfrac{y^2}{9} = 1$.

STEP 1 Identify the center and orientation of the ellipse.

The center of the ellipse is $(h, k) = (0, 0)$. The denominator of the x^2-term is greater than the denominator of the y^2-term, so the major axis is horizontal.

STEP 2 Find the vertices of the ellipse.

$a^2 = 16$, so $a = \pm 4$. The vertices along the major axis are $(-4, 0)$ and $(4, 0)$.

$b^2 = 9$, so $b = \pm 3$. The vertices along the minor axis are $(0, 3)$ and $(0, -3)$.

STEP 3 Calculate c. $c = \sqrt{a^2 - b^2} = \sqrt{4^2 - 3^2}$
$= \sqrt{7}$.

STEP 4 Find e. $e = \dfrac{c}{a} = \dfrac{\sqrt{7}}{4} \approx 0.66$

The eccentricity of this ellipse is 0.66. The graph of the ellipse is shown to the right.

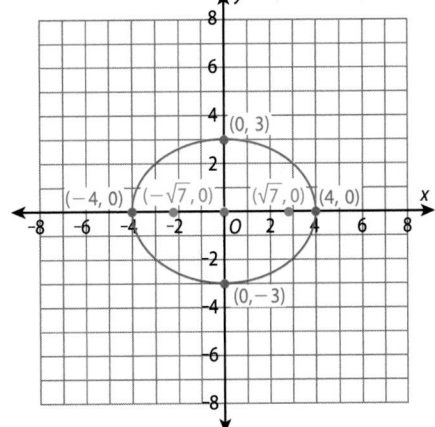

The Eccentricity of a Hyperbola

A hyperbola is the set of points in a plane the difference of whose distances from two fixed points, called the **foci**, is a constant.

- The standard forms of the equations for a hyperbola with center at (h, k) are
$\frac{(x-h)^2}{a^2} - \frac{(y-k)^2}{b^2} = 1$, if the major axis is horizontal, and $\frac{(y-k)^2}{a^2} - \frac{(x-h)^2}{b^2} = 1$, if the major axis is vertical.

- The eccentricity e of a hyperbola, like the ellipse, is the ratio $\frac{c}{a}$, where $c = \sqrt{a^2 + b^2}$.

- c is the distance from the center of the hyperbola to a focus, and a is the distance from the center to a vertex. In a hyperbola, $c > a$. Therefore, $\frac{c}{a} > 1$.

EXAMPLE 4

What is the eccentricity to the nearest hundredth of the hyperbola $\frac{x^2}{18} - \frac{y^2}{6} = 1$?

STEP 1 Identify a^2 and b^2.　　$a^2 = 18$ and $b^2 = 6$.

STEP 2 Calculate c.
$$c = \sqrt{a^2 + b^2}$$
$$= \sqrt{18 + 6}$$
$$= \sqrt{24}$$

STEP 3 Find e.
$$e = \frac{c}{a} = \frac{\sqrt{24}}{\sqrt{18}}$$
$$= \sqrt{\frac{24}{18}}$$
$$= \sqrt{\frac{4}{3}}$$
$$\approx 1.15$$

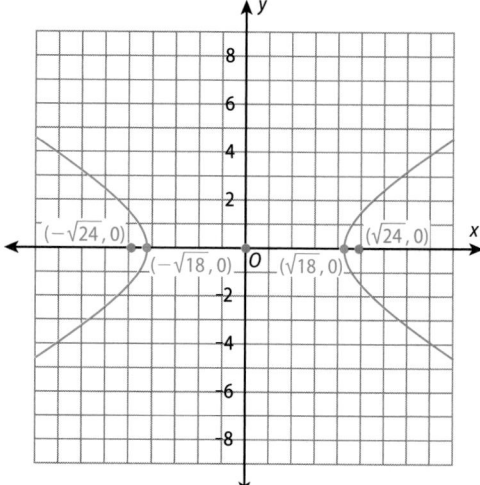

The eccentricity of this hyperbola is 1.15.

Its graph is shown to the right.

EXAMPLE 5

What is the eccentricity to the nearest hundredth of the hyperbola $8y^2 - 4x^2 = 8$?

STEP 1 Rewrite the given equation in standard form.

Divide each term by 8.
$$\frac{8}{8}y^2 - \frac{4}{8}x^2 = \frac{8}{8}$$
$$\frac{y^2}{1} - \frac{x^2}{2} = 1$$

STEP 2 Identify a^2 and b^2.　　$a^2 = 1$ and $b^2 = 2$

STEP 3 Calculate c.
$$c = \sqrt{a^2 + b^2}$$
$$= \sqrt{1 + 2} = \sqrt{3}$$

STEP 4 Calculate e.
$$e = \frac{c}{a} = \frac{\sqrt{3}}{1} = \sqrt{3}$$
$$\approx 1.73$$

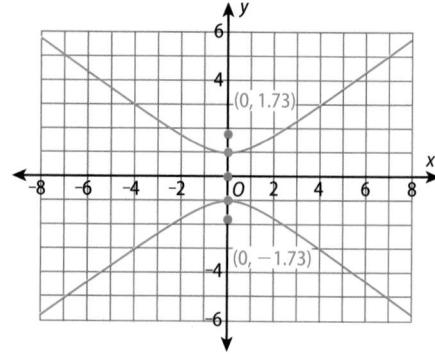

The eccentricity of this hyperbola is 1.73. Its graph is shown above.

EXAMPLE 6

Without graphing, tell which hyperbola is more eccentric: $\frac{x^2}{9} - \frac{y^2}{25} = 1$ **or** $\frac{x^2}{25} - \frac{y^2}{9} = 1$.

STEP 1 Identify a and b for each hyperbola.

In $\frac{x^2}{9} - \frac{y^2}{25} = 1$, $a = 3$ and $b = 5$.

In $\frac{x^2}{25} - \frac{y^2}{9} = 1$, $a = 5$ and $b = 3$.

STEP 2 Calculate e for both hyperbolas where $e = \frac{\sqrt{a^2 + b^2}}{a}$.

For $\frac{x^2}{9} - \frac{y^2}{25} = 1$, $e_1 = \frac{\sqrt{3^2 + 5^2}}{3} = \frac{\sqrt{34}}{3}$.

For $\frac{x^2}{25} - \frac{y^2}{9} = 1$, $e_2 = \frac{\sqrt{5^2 + 3^2}}{5} = \frac{\sqrt{34}}{5}$.

STEP 3 Compare the values of e_1 and e_2.

$\frac{\sqrt{34}}{3} \approx 1.9$ and $\frac{\sqrt{34}}{5} \approx 1.17$, so $e_1 > e_2$.

$\frac{x^2}{9} - \frac{y^2}{25} = 1$ is more eccentric than $\frac{x^2}{25} - \frac{y^2}{9} = 1$.

SEARCH

To see step-by-step videos of these problems, enter the page number into the SWadvantage.com Search Bar.

The Eccentricity of a Circle

A circle is the set of points in a plane that are equidistant from a given point called the center. The radius of a circle is the distance between the center and any point on the circle.

- The standard form of the equation for a circle with center at (h, k) is
$\frac{(x - h)^2}{r^2} + \frac{(y - k)^2}{r^2} = 1$, where r is the radius of the circle.

- The equation of a circle resembles the equation of an ellipse except that the denominators of the variable terms are equal, and a and b equal r, the radius. This means that the foci coincide with the center of the circle and $c = \sqrt{a^2 - b^2} = 0$.

- Thus, the eccentricity $\frac{c}{a}$ of a circle equals 0.

Eccentricities of the Conics

Conic	Eccentricity
Circle	$e = 0$
Ellipse	$0 < e < 1$ and $e = \frac{c}{a} = \frac{\sqrt{a^2 - b^2}}{a}$
Parabola	$e = 1$
Hyperbola	$e > 1$ and $e = \frac{c}{a} = \frac{\sqrt{a^2 + b^2}}{a}$

Translated Conics

Translating Parabolas

The equation in standard form of a parabola that is not centered at the origin is either $(x - h)^2 = 4p(y - k)$ or $(y - k)^2 = 4p(x - h)$. The values of h and k represent the amount and direction of a horizontal translation (h) and a vertical translation (k). These values can be positive, negative, or 0. The constant p is the distance from the vertex to the focus.

EXAMPLE 1

Find the vertex, focus, and directrix of the parabola $(x - 2)^2 = 8(y + 3)$. Then graph the parabola.

STEP 1 Identify the vertex.

The constants h and k equal 2 and -3, respectively. They represent translating the parabola 2 units in a positive direction (to the right) and 3 units in a negative direction (down) from $(0, 0)$. The vertex is $(2, -3)$.

STEP 2 Find the axis of symmetry.

The x-term in the equation is squared, so the axis of symmetry is vertical. Its equation is $x = 2$.

STEP 3 Find p and the focus.

The coefficient of the y-term is $4p$ and equals 8. Therefore, $p = 2$. The focus lies on the axis of symmetry 2 units from the vertex. The focus is $(2, -3 + 2)$, which equals $(2, -1)$.

STEP 4 Find the directrix.

The directrix is horizontal and its equation is $y = k - p$. The directrix is $y = -3 - 2 = -5$.

STEP 5 Calculate the coordinates of two points on the parabola.

The latus rectum (LR) is a segment through the focus with endpoints on the parabola at $(x_1, -1)$ and $(x_2, -1)$. Substitute -1 into the equation for y and find the corresponding values of x.

Let $y = -1$ $(x - 2)^2 = 8(-1 + 3)$
$$= 16$$
$$x - 2 = \pm 4$$

$x_1 = -2$ and $x_2 = 6$, and the points to plot are $(-2, -1)$ and $(6, -1)$.

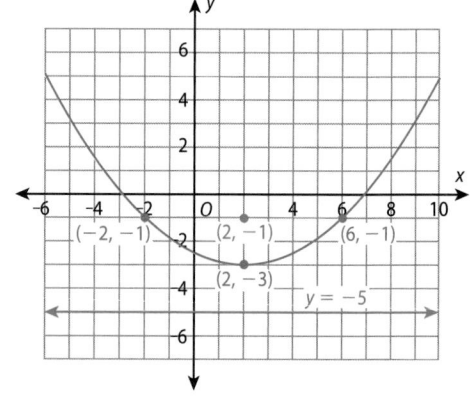

STEP 6 Plot the vertex, the focus, and the directrix. Then, graph the parabola.

The graph is shown to the right.

Properties of Translated Parabolas

Equation	Axis of symmetry	Vertex	Focus	Directrix
$(x - h)^2 = 4p(y - k)$	Vertical	(h, k)	$(h, k + p)$	$y = k - p$
$(y - k)^2 = 4p(x - k)$	Horizontal	(h, k)	$(h + p, k)$	$x = h - p$

Translating Circles

The standard form of an equation of a circle that has been translated in the coordinate plane has the form $\frac{(x-h)^2}{r^2} + \frac{(y-k)^2}{r^2} = 1$, where h is the horizontal translation of the center from the origin and k is the vertical translation. The center of the translated circle is (h, k).

> **Watch Out** ⚠️
>
> Remember that the length of the radius of a circle is always a positive number.

EXAMPLE 2

Describe the translation of a circle whose equation is $\frac{(x-5)^2}{4} + \frac{(y+5)^2}{4} = 1$.

STEP 1 Identify h and k, the horizontal and vertical translations, and the center of the circle.

$h = 5$, so the center is translated 5 units to the right of the origin. $k = -5$, so the center is translated 5 units below the origin. The center of the translated circle is $(5, -5)$.

STEP 2 Identify the coordinates of four points on the translated circle.

The denominator of the fractions is r^2, which equals 4. Therefore, $r = 2$. Four points on the circle are two units on either side of the center at $(3, -5)$ and $(7, -5)$, and two units above and below the center at $(5, -3)$ and $(5, -7)$.

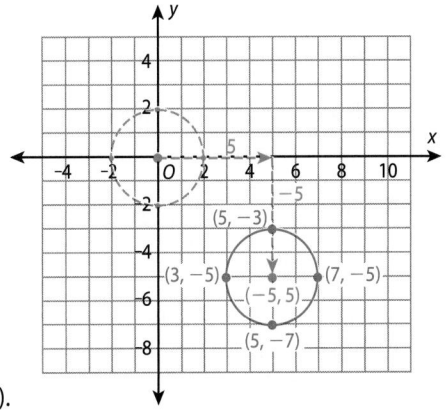

The graph at the right shows the translation of the circle centered from the origin to its new center at $(5, -5)$.

EXAMPLE 3

Find the center and radius of the circle $\frac{(x+1)^2}{9} + \frac{(y-4)^2}{9} = 1$. Then graph the circle. Explain how this graph shows a translation of the circle.

SEARCH 🔍

To see step-by-step videos of these problems, enter the page number into the SWadvantage.com Search Bar.

STEP 1 Identify the center of the circle.

The center of the circle is (h, k), which in this equation is $(-1, 4)$.

STEP 2 Find the radius of the circle.

The denominator of the fractions is r^2, which equals 9. Therefore, the radius $r = 3$.

STEP 3 Graph the circle.

Plot the center $(-1, 4)$. Then draw horizontal and vertical lines through the center.

On each line, plot two points three units to the right and left of the center, and plot two points 3 units above and below the center.

Draw the circle through the four points: $(-4, 4)$, $(-1, 7)$, $(2, 4)$, and $(-1, 1)$.

The circle is shown to the right.

STEP 4 The graph shows a circle translated 1 unit to the left and 4 units up from a circle with center $(0, 0)$.

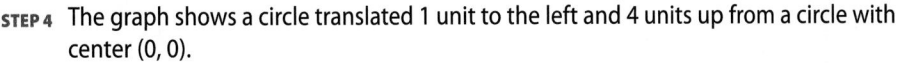

Translating Ellipses

The standard form of an equation of an ellipse that has been translated in the coordinate plane is $\dfrac{(x-h)^2}{a^2} + \dfrac{(y-k)^2}{b^2} = 1$ or $\dfrac{(y-k)^2}{a^2} + \dfrac{(x-h)^2}{b^2} = 1$, where h and k are the horizontal and vertical transformations from $(0, 0)$ and the coordinates of the center of the ellipse.

The lengths of the major and minor axes are $2a$ and $2b$, respectively, where a and b are positive numbers, and $a > b$. The foci of the ellipse lie at a distance c from the center, where $c = \sqrt{a^2 - b^2}$.

SEARCH 🔍

To see step-by-step videos of these problems, enter the page number into the SWadvantage.com Search Bar.

EXAMPLE 4

Find the center, vertices, and foci of the ellipse $\dfrac{(y-3)^2}{16} + \dfrac{(x-6)^2}{8} = 1$. **Then graph the ellipse.**

STEP 1 Identify the center of the ellipse.

The ellipse was translated 3 units up and 6 units to the right of the origin, so $(h, k) = (6, 3)$.

STEP 2 Identify the vertices of the ellipse.

The y-squared term has the greater denominator, so the major axis of the ellipse is vertical: $a^2 = 16$ and $a = \pm 4$. The vertices along the major axis are 4 units above and below the center at $(6, 3 + 4) = (6, 7)$ and $(6, 3 - 4) = (6, -1)$.

The minor axis of the ellipse is horizontal: $b^2 = 8$ and $b = \pm\sqrt{8}$. The vertices along the minor axis are $\sqrt{8}$ units to the right and left of the center at $(6 + \sqrt{8}, 3)$ and $(6 - \sqrt{8}, 3)$ or about $(8.8, 3)$ and $(3.2, 3)$.

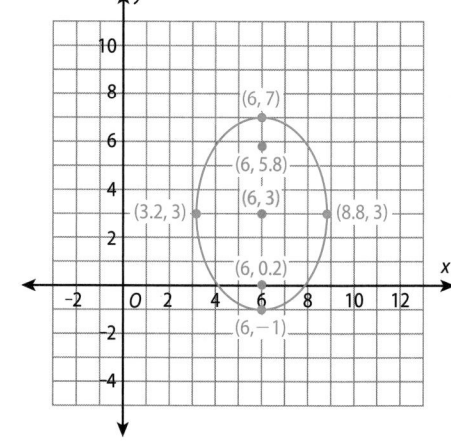

STEP 3 Find c.

The constant c is the distance between the foci and the center of the ellipse:
$c = \sqrt{a^2 - b^2} = \sqrt{16 - 8} = \sqrt{8}$

The foci are $(6, 3 + \sqrt{8})$ and $(6, 3 - \sqrt{8})$ or about $(6, 5.8)$ and $(6, 0.2)$.

STEP 4 Graph the ellipse.

GOT TO KNOW!

Properties of Translated Ellipses

Equation	Major axis	Center	Foci	Vertices	Endpoints of minor axis
$\dfrac{(y-k)^2}{a^2} + \dfrac{(x-h)^2}{b^2} = 1$, $a^2 > b^2$ and $c = \sqrt{a^2 - b^2}$	Vertical	(h, k)	$(h, k + c)$ $(h, k - c)$	$(h, k + a)$ $(h, k - a)$	$(h + b, k)$ $(h - b, k)$
$\dfrac{(x-h)^2}{a^2} + \dfrac{(y-k)^2}{b^2} = 1$, $a^2 > b^2$ and $c = \sqrt{a^2 - b^2}$	Horizontal	(h, k)	$(h + c, k)$ $(h - c, k)$	$(h + a, k)$ $(h - a, k)$	$(h + b, k)$ $(h - b, k)$

Translating Hyperbolas

The equations of hyperbolas are $\dfrac{(x - h)^2}{a^2} - \dfrac{(y - k)^2}{b^2} = 1$ or $\dfrac{(y - k)^2}{a^2} - \dfrac{(x - h)^2}{b^2} = 1$, where (h, k) is the center of a hyperbola translated from the origin. The lengths of the transverse (major) and minor axes are $2a$ and $2b$, respectively, where a and b are positive numbers. The foci of the hyperbola lie at a distance of c from the center, and $c = \sqrt{a^2 + b^2}$.

Watch Out

Be careful when finding the center of a hyperbola whose equation is of the form $\dfrac{(y - k)^2}{a^2} - \dfrac{(x - h)^2}{b^2} = 1$.

Do *not* read the equation from left to right to find (h, k). The center is *not* (k, h).

EXAMPLE 5

Find the center, vertices, and foci of the hyperbola $\dfrac{(y + 2)^2}{4} - \dfrac{(x + 5)^2}{9} = 1$. Then graph the hyperbola.

STEP 1   Identify the center of the hyperbola.

The center of the hyperbola has been translated 5 units to the left and 2 units below the origin. The new center is $(-5, -2)$.

STEP 2   Identify the vertices of the hyperbola.

The transverse axis is vertical. The denominator $a^2 = 4$, so $a = \pm 2$. The vertices are 2 units above and below the center at $(-5, -2 + 2) = (-5, 0)$ and $(-5, -2 - 2) = (-5, -4)$.

STEP 3   Identify the foci.

The foci are at a distance c from the center.
$c = \sqrt{a^2 + b^2} = \sqrt{4 + 9} = \sqrt{13}$
The foci are $(-5, 0 + \sqrt{13})$ and $(-5, -2 - \sqrt{13})$, or about $(-5, 1.6)$ and $(-5, -5.6)$.

STEP 4   Draw the asymptotes and graph the branches of the hyperbola.

Draw the rectangle that passes through points that are 2 units above and below the center of the hyperbola and 3 units to the right and left of the center. The vertices of the rectangle are at $(-8, -4)$, $(-8, 0)$, $(-2, -4)$, and $(-2, 0)$.

Draw the diagonals of the rectangle using dashed lines and extend them to form the asymptotes of the hyperbola.

To the right is the graph of the hyperbola and its asymptotes.

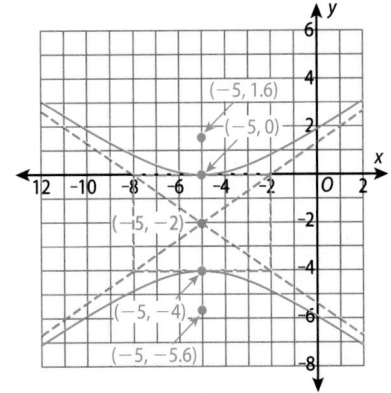

Need More HELP?

Remember: The graph of a hyperbola does not include its asymptotes.

GOT TO KNOW!

Properties of Translated Hyperbolas

Equation	Major axis	Center	Foci	Vertices
$\dfrac{(y - k)^2}{a^2} - \dfrac{(x - h)^2}{b^2} = 1$, $c = \sqrt{a^2 + b^2}$	Vertical	(h, k)	$(h, k + c)$ $(h, k - c)$	$(h, k + a)$ $(h, k - a)$
$\dfrac{(x - h)^2}{a^2} - \dfrac{(y - k)^2}{b^2} = 1$, $c = \sqrt{a^2 + b^2}$	Horizontal	(h, k)	$(h + c, k)$ $(h - c, k)$	$(h + a, k)$ $(h - a, k)$

Equations of Translated Parabolas

The equations in standard form of a parabola are $(x - h)^2 = 4p(y - k)$ or $(y - k)^2 = 4p(x - h)$, where (h, k) is the vertex, and p is the directed distance between the vertex and the focus.

EXAMPLE 6

A parabola that turns up has its vertex at the origin. The parabola is translated 3 units to the left and 1 unit below the origin. If the distance between the vertex of the parabola and its focus is 5, what is the equation of the parabola in standard form?

STEP 1 Identify which standard form of the equation to use.

The parabola has a vertical axis of symmetry. Its equation is of the form $(x - h)^2 = 4p(y - k)$.

STEP 2 Identify the vertex.

The horizontal translation (h) is -3, and the vertical translation (k) is -1. The vertex is $(-3, -1)$.

STEP 3 Find $4p$.

The distance between the vertex and the focus is $p = 5$. $\quad$ $4p = 4(5) = 20$.

STEP 4 Write the equation.

Substitute h, k, and $4p$ into the standard form of the equation. $(x - (-3))^2 = 20(y - (-1))$

The equation of this parabola is $(x + 3)^2 = 20(y + 1)$.

Equations of Translated Ellipses

The equation of an ellipse is $\dfrac{(x - h)^2}{a^2} + \dfrac{(y - k)^2}{b^2} = 1$ or $\dfrac{(y - k)^2}{a^2} + \dfrac{(x - h)^2}{b^2} = 1$, where $a > b$.

EXAMPLE 7

The major axis of an ellipse centered at the origin is vertical and its length is 10. The length of its minor axis is 6. From the origin, the center of the ellipse is translated $\frac{1}{2}$ unit to the left and $\frac{1}{4}$ unit below the origin. What is the equation in standard form of the ellipse?

STEP 1 Identify which standard form of the equation to use.

The orientation of the ellipse is vertical, so the standard form to use is $\dfrac{(y - k)^2}{a^2} + \dfrac{(x - h)^2}{b^2} = 1$.

STEP 2 Find a and b.

The length of the major axis is $2a = 10$, so $a = 5$. The length of its minor axis is $2b = 6$, so $b = 3$.

STEP 3 Identify the center and write the equation of the ellipse.

The horizontal translation (h) is $-\frac{1}{2}$. The vertical translation (k) is $-\frac{1}{4}$. So, $(h, k) = \left(-\frac{1}{2}, -\frac{1}{4}\right)$.

The equation of the ellipse is $\dfrac{\left(y + \frac{1}{4}\right)^2}{5^2} + \dfrac{\left(x + \frac{1}{2}\right)^2}{3^2} = 1$ or $\dfrac{\left(y + \frac{1}{4}\right)^2}{25} + \dfrac{\left(x + \frac{1}{2}\right)^2}{9} = 1$

Equations of Translated Circles

The standard form of the equation of a circle is $\dfrac{(x - h)^2}{r^2} + \dfrac{(y - k)^2}{r^2} = 1$, where h and k are the horizontal and vertical transformations of the circle, and r is the radius.

EXAMPLE 8

A circle whose center is at the origin is translated 6 units to the right and 7 units above the origin. What is the equation of the circle if its radius is 8?

STEP 1 Identify the center of the translated circle.

The horizontal translation is 6, and the vertical translation is 7. Therefore, the center is $(6, 7)$.

STEP 2 Use substitution to write the equation.

Substitute the values of h, k, and r into the equation: $\dfrac{(x - 6)^2}{8^2} + \dfrac{(y - 7)^2}{8^2} = 1$.

The equation of the circle is : $\dfrac{(x - 6)^2}{64} + \dfrac{(y - 7)^2}{64} = 1$.

Watch **Out**

Remember to square the radius when writing the equation of the circle.

Equations of Translated Hyperbolas

The standard form of the equation of a hyperbola is either $\dfrac{(x - h)^2}{a^2} - \dfrac{(y - k)^2}{b^2} = 1$ or $\dfrac{(y - k)^2}{a^2} - \dfrac{(x - h)^2}{b^2} = 1$ depending on its orientation. The center is (h, k) and the lengths of the transverse (major) and minor axes are $2a$ and $2b$, respectively.

EXAMPLE 9

The major axis of a hyperbola is vertical and its length is 5. The length of the minor axis is 12. The hyperbola is translated 5 units to the right and 5 units below the origin. What is the standard form of the equation of this hyperbola?

STEP 1 Identify which standard form of the equation of this hyperbola to use.

The transverse axis is vertical and its length is $2a$. Therefore, $2a = 5$ and $a = \dfrac{5}{2}$. The length of the minor axis is $2b$, where $2b = 12$ and $b = 6$. Because the orientation of the hyperbola is vertical, the standard form of the equation to use is is $\dfrac{(y - k)^2}{a^2} - \dfrac{(x - h)^2}{b^2} = 1$.

STEP 2 Identify the center and write the equation of the hyperbola.

The horizontal translation is positive and the vertical translation is negative. So, $h = 5$ and $k = -5$. Substitute these values and the values of a and b into the equation above.

The equation of this hyperbola: $\dfrac{(y + 5)^2}{\left(\dfrac{25}{4}\right)} - \dfrac{(x - 5)^2}{36} = 1$.

Radicals, Exponents, Logarithms, and Rational Expressions

What Came Before?
- Properties of exponents
- Simplifying radicals

What's This About?
- Operations with radical and rational expressions
- Properties of logarithms
- Converting between exponential equations and logarithmic equations

Practical Apps
- Circuit designers use rational equations to predict the amount of current that flows through a circuit.
- The Richter Scale, a logarithmic scale used by geologists, measures the intensity of earthquakes.

Just for FUN!

Her real name was Natural Log, but most people knew her as Ellen.

You can find more practice
problems online by visiting:
www.SWadvantage.com

Square Roots

The Principal Square Root of a Number

Any non-negative real number a has a unique non-negative square root r, called the **principal square root**. The number r can be written as $\sqrt{a}$, where $a > 0$.

The $\sqrt{\ }$ symbol is called a **radical sign**, and the number under the sign is called the **radicand**. Together, these two parts are called a **radical**.

EXAMPLE 1

What is $\sqrt{81}$?

There are two numbers that when squared equal 81: 9^2 and $(-9)^2$.

The symbol $\sqrt{81}$ denotes the principal square root of 81, which is a non-negative number.

So, $\sqrt{81} = 9$.

A number that is the square of a rational number is called a **perfect square**. The square root of a perfect square can be represented as $\sqrt{a^2} = |a|$.

For example, $\sqrt{5^2} = |5| = 5$ and $\sqrt{(-5)^2} = |-5| = 5$. The principal square root of a perfect square is a rational number.

EXAMPLE 2

Simplify $\sqrt{\left(\frac{1}{2}\right)^2}$.

The radicand is the square of the rational number $\frac{1}{2}$. Use the rule $\sqrt{a^2} = |a|$ to simplify it.

$$\sqrt{\left(\frac{1}{2}\right)^2} = \left|\frac{1}{2}\right| = \frac{1}{2}.$$

EXAMPLE 3

Simplify $\sqrt{(-4)^2}$.

METHOD 1

The expression $(-4)^2$ is a perfect square where $\sqrt{a^2} = |a|$. In this example, $a = -4$, so $\sqrt{(-4)^2} = |-4| = 4$.

METHOD 2

STEP 1 Calculate $(-4)^2$ by squaring the factors. $(-4)^2 = (-4) \times (-4) = 16$

STEP 2 Evaluate the square root of a perfect square. $\sqrt{16} = 4$

Product and Quotient Rules

Rules for radicals are similar to rules for exponents.

To simplify radicals using the product rule, find the greatest factor of the radicand that is a perfect square greater than 1. A simplified radical can be a rational number or an irrational number.

EXAMPLE 4

Use the Product Rule to simplify $\sqrt{96}$.

STEP 1 Write 96 as a product where one factor is the greatest perfect square in the 96.

$$\sqrt{96} = \sqrt{16 \cdot 6}$$

STEP 2 Write the square root of the product as the product of the square roots.

$$\sqrt{16 \cdot 6} = \sqrt{16} \cdot \sqrt{6}$$

STEP 3 Replace $\sqrt{16}$ with its principal square root.

$$\sqrt{16} \cdot \sqrt{6} = \sqrt{4^2} \cdot \sqrt{6}$$
$$= 4\sqrt{6}$$

SEARCH

To see step-by-step videos of these problems, enter the page number into the SWadvantage.com Search Bar.

EXAMPLE 5

Simplify $\sqrt{\dfrac{108}{9}}$.

METHOD 1

STEP 1 Write the square root of the quotient as the quotient of the square roots.

$$\sqrt{\frac{108}{9}} = \frac{\sqrt{108}}{\sqrt{9}}$$

STEP 2 Express 108 as a product where one factor is the greatest perfect square in 108. Express 9 as the perfect square of 3.

$$\frac{\sqrt{108}}{\sqrt{9}} = \frac{\sqrt{36 \cdot 3}}{\sqrt{3^2}}$$

STEP 3 Apply the Product Rule to the numerator and simplify the resulting fraction.

$$\frac{\sqrt{36 \cdot 3}}{\sqrt{3^2}} = \frac{\sqrt{36} \cdot \sqrt{3}}{\sqrt{3^2}}$$
$$= \frac{6\sqrt{3}}{3}$$
$$= 2\sqrt{3}$$

METHOD 2

STEP 1 Use division to simplify the radicand.

$$\sqrt{\frac{108}{9}} = \sqrt{12}$$

STEP 2 Simplify $\sqrt{12}$ using the Product Rule.

$$\sqrt{12} = \sqrt{4} \cdot \sqrt{3} = 2\sqrt{3}$$

Product and Quotient Rules for Radicals

If a and b are non-negative numbers, then:

Product Rule

$$\sqrt{a \cdot b} = \sqrt{a} \cdot \sqrt{b} \qquad \sqrt{a} \cdot \sqrt{b} = \sqrt{a \cdot b}$$

Quotient Rule $(b \neq 0)$

$$\sqrt{\frac{a}{b}} = \frac{\sqrt{a}}{\sqrt{b}} \qquad \frac{\sqrt{a}}{\sqrt{b}} = \sqrt{\frac{a}{b}}$$

Other Roots

Principal Roots of a Number

The radical expression $\sqrt[n]{a}$ represents the principal nth root of a real number a. As with square roots, the $\sqrt{}$ symbol is called a **radical sign**, and the number under the sign is called the **radicand**.

By definition, $\sqrt[n]{a} = b$ means that $b^n = a$. For example, $\sqrt[3]{8} = 2$ means $2^3 = 8$.

The number n is called the **index** of the radical and is an integer such that $n \geq 2$. The index n for the square root of a number $a \geq 0$ is understood to be 2.

- If n is even, then $a \geq 0$ and $b \geq 0$. That is, a and b are never negative.
- If n is odd, then a and b can be any real number.

The radical expression $\sqrt[n]{a} = b$ is read as "the nth root of a is b." For example, $\sqrt[3]{8} = 2$ is read as "the cube root of 8 is 2," and $\sqrt[5]{-32} = -2$ is read as "the fifth root of -32 is -2."

Finding nth Roots of Perfect nth Powers

If the index of the radical is equal to the exponent of a radicand, then there are two possible roots depending on whether n is even or odd.

- If n is even, then $\sqrt[n]{a^n} = |a|$.
- If n is odd, then $\sqrt[n]{a^n} = a$.

EXAMPLE 1

Simplify $\sqrt[3]{(-5)^3}$.

Determine whether n is even or odd.	$n = 3$, which is an odd number.
Identify a.	$a = -5$
Apply the rule $\sqrt[n]{a^n} = a$.	$\sqrt[3]{(-5)^3} = -5$

Simplified, $\sqrt[3]{(-5)^3} = -5$.

You can read that as "the third root of negative five to the third is negative five."

Watch Out !

Remember that raising a negative number to an even power is not equal to the opposite of the number raised to an even power.

$(-a)^n \neq -a^n, a > 0$

For example, if $a = -1$ and $n = 4$, $(-1)^4 = 1$, but $-1^4 = -1$.

EXAMPLE 2

Simplify $\sqrt[4]{(-2)^4}$.

Determine whether n is even or odd.	$n = 4$, which is an even number.
Identify a.	$a = -2$
Apply the rule $\sqrt[n]{a^n} = |a|$.	$\sqrt[4]{(-2)^4} = |-2| = 2$

Simplified, $\sqrt[4]{(-2)^4} = 2$.

You can read that as "the fourth root of negative two to the fourth is two."

The Product and Quotient Rules of *n*th Roots

If a and b are real numbers and n is an integer > 1, the Product and Quotient Rules are

$$\sqrt[n]{a \cdot b} = \sqrt[n]{a} \cdot \sqrt[n]{b} \text{ and } \sqrt[n]{\frac{a}{b}} = \frac{\sqrt[n]{a}}{\sqrt[n]{b}}.$$

To simplify *n*th roots, find the greatest factor of the radicand that is a perfect *n*th power.

EXAMPLE 3

Use the Product Rule to simplify $\sqrt[3]{24}$.

STEP 1 Write 24 as a product where one factor is the greatest perfect cube in 24.

$$\sqrt[3]{24} = \sqrt[3]{8 \cdot 3}$$

STEP 2 Write the cube root of the product as the product of the cube roots.

$$\sqrt[3]{8 \cdot 3} = \sqrt[3]{8} \cdot \sqrt[3]{3}$$

STEP 3 Simplify $\sqrt[3]{8}$ in the expression.

$$\sqrt[3]{8} \cdot \sqrt[3]{3} = 2\sqrt[3]{3}$$

GOT TO KNOW!

Common Perfect *n*th Roots

$\sqrt[3]{8} = 2$

$\sqrt[3]{27} = 3$

$\sqrt[3]{64} = 4$

$\sqrt[3]{125} = 5$

$\sqrt[4]{16} = 2$

$\sqrt[4]{81} = 3$

$\sqrt[4]{256} = 4$

$\sqrt[4]{625} = 5$

$\sqrt[5]{32} = 2$

$\sqrt[5]{243} = 3$

EXAMPLE 4

Use the Quotient Rule to simplify $\sqrt[4]{\frac{162}{48}}$.

STEP 1 Write the fourth root of the quotient as the quotient of the fourth roots.

$$\sqrt[4]{\frac{162}{48}} = \frac{\sqrt[4]{162}}{\sqrt[4]{48}}$$

STEP 2 Express the radicands 162 and 48 as products where the greatest perfect power of 4 is a factor in each number.

$$\frac{\sqrt[4]{162}}{\sqrt[4]{48}} = \frac{\sqrt[4]{81 \cdot 2}}{\sqrt[4]{16 \cdot 3}}$$

STEP 3 Apply the Product Rule to the numerator and denominator of the fraction.

$$\frac{\sqrt[4]{81 \cdot 2}}{\sqrt[4]{16 \cdot 3}} = \frac{\sqrt[4]{81} \cdot \sqrt[4]{2}}{\sqrt[4]{16} \cdot \sqrt[4]{3}}$$

STEP 4 Simplify the resulting fraction.

$$= \frac{3\sqrt[4]{2}}{2\sqrt[4]{3}}$$

EXAMPLE 5

Use the Quotient Rule to simplify $\sqrt[3]{\frac{-32}{125}}$.

STEP 1 Write the cube root of the quotient as the quotient of the cube roots.

$$\sqrt[3]{\frac{-32}{125}} = \frac{\sqrt[3]{-32}}{\sqrt[3]{125}}$$

STEP 2 Apply the Product Rule in the numerator and rewrite the denominator 125 as the cube of 5.

$$\frac{\sqrt[3]{-32}}{\sqrt[3]{125}} = \frac{\sqrt[3]{-8 \cdot 4}}{\sqrt[3]{125}}$$

$$= \frac{\sqrt[3]{-8} \cdot \sqrt[3]{4}}{\sqrt[3]{5^3}}$$

STEP 3 Simplify the resulting fraction.

$$\frac{\sqrt[3]{-8} \cdot \sqrt[3]{4}}{\sqrt[3]{5^3}} = \frac{-2\sqrt[3]{4}}{5}$$

SEARCH

To see step-by-step videos of these problems, enter the page number into the SWadvantage.com Search Bar.

Multiplying Radical Expressions

Multiplying Radicals

Radicals that have the same index can be multiplied. The Product Rule for multiplying radicals states that if a and b are real numbers, then $\sqrt[n]{a} \cdot \sqrt[n]{b} = \sqrt[n]{ab}$.

EXAMPLE 1

Multiply $\sqrt{6} \cdot \sqrt{2}$.

STEP 1 Use the Product Rule to write the product of the square roots as the square root of the product.	$\sqrt{6} \cdot \sqrt{2} = \sqrt{6 \cdot 2}$
STEP 2 Find the product of 6 and 2.	$= \sqrt{12}$
STEP 3 Write 12 as a product where one factor is a perfect square.	$= \sqrt{4 \cdot 3}$
STEP 4 Apply the Product Rule and write the square root of the product as the product of the square roots.	$= \sqrt{4} \cdot \sqrt{3}$
STEP 5 Simplify the square root of the perfect square.	$= 2\sqrt{3}$

The product of $\sqrt{6} \cdot \sqrt{2}$ is $2\sqrt{3}$.

EXAMPLE 2

Multiply $\sqrt[3]{-18} \cdot \sqrt[3]{6}$.

STEP 1 The index n of both radicals is 3, so use the Product Rule to find the product.	$\sqrt[3]{-18} \cdot \sqrt[3]{6} = \sqrt[3]{(-18) \cdot 6}$
	$= \sqrt[3]{-108}$
STEP 2 Find the greatest perfect cube that is a factor of -108.	$= \sqrt[3]{-27 \cdot 4}$
STEP 3 Apply the Product Rule to separate the cube roots of each factor.	$= \sqrt[3]{-27} \cdot \sqrt[3]{4}$
STEP 4 Express $\sqrt[3]{-27}$ as an integer.	$= \sqrt[3]{(-3)^3} \cdot \sqrt[3]{4}$
STEP 5 Simplify.	$= -3\sqrt[3]{4}$

The product of $\sqrt[3]{-18} \cdot \sqrt[3]{6}$ is $-3\sqrt[3]{4}$.

EXAMPLE 3

Multiply $\sqrt[4]{4x^3} \cdot \sqrt[4]{8x}$, where $x \geq 0$.

STEP 1 The factors have the same index, 4, so use the Product Rule to write the product of the 4th roots as the 4th root of the product.	$\sqrt[4]{4x^3} \cdot \sqrt[4]{8x}$
	$= \sqrt[4]{(4x^3) \cdot (8x)}$
	$= \sqrt[4]{32x^4}$
STEP 2 Find the factor of 32 that is a perfect fourth.	$= \sqrt[4]{2^4 \cdot 2 \cdot x^4}$
STEP 3 Rewrite the root of the product as the product of the roots.	$= \sqrt[4]{2^4} \cdot \sqrt[4]{2} \cdot \sqrt[4]{x^4}$
STEP 4 Simplify the fourth roots of 2^4 and x^4.	$= 2x\sqrt[4]{2}$

The product of $\sqrt[4]{4x^3} \cdot \sqrt[4]{8x}$ is $2x\sqrt[4]{2}$.

SEARCH

To see step-by-step videos of these problems, enter the page number into the SWadvantage.com Search Bar.

Multiplying Radicals Using the Distributive Property

The Distributive Property of Multiplication over Addition states that if a, b, and c are real numbers, then $a(b + c) = ab + ac$.

Need More

HELP ❓

To learn more about the Distributive Property of Multiplication over Addition, see *The Distributive Property* in *Algebra* (p. 1410).

EXAMPLE

Simplify $\sqrt[3]{6} \cdot \left(\sqrt[3]{4} + \sqrt[3]{36}\right)$.

STEP 1 Apply the Distributive Property.

$$\sqrt[3]{6} \cdot \left(\sqrt[3]{4} + \sqrt[3]{36}\right) = \sqrt[3]{6} \cdot \sqrt[3]{4} + \sqrt[3]{6} \cdot \sqrt[3]{36}$$

STEP 2 Apply the Product Rule to each term.

$$= \sqrt[3]{6 \cdot 4} + \sqrt[3]{6 \cdot 36}$$

STEP 3 Multiply the factors in each radicand.

$$= \sqrt[3]{24} + \sqrt[3]{216}$$

STEP 4 Apply the Product Rule and identify each perfect cube.

$$= \sqrt[3]{8 \cdot 3} + \sqrt[3]{216}$$
$$= \sqrt[3]{8} \cdot \sqrt[3]{3} + \sqrt[3]{216}$$
$$= \sqrt[3]{2^3} \cdot \sqrt[3]{3} + \sqrt[3]{6^3}$$

STEP 5 Simplify.

$$= 2\sqrt[3]{3} + 6$$

The solution to $\sqrt[3]{6} \cdot \left(\sqrt[3]{4} + \sqrt[3]{36}\right)$ is $2\sqrt[3]{3} + 6$.

EXAMPLE 5

Multiply $\left(\sqrt{5} + \sqrt{2}\right)\left(\sqrt{5} - \sqrt{2}\right)$.

STEP 1 Apply the Distributive Property.

$$\left(\sqrt{5} + \sqrt{2}\right)\left(\sqrt{5} - \sqrt{2}\right)$$
$$= \left(\sqrt{5} + \sqrt{2}\right) \cdot \sqrt{5} - \left(\sqrt{5} + \sqrt{2}\right) \cdot \sqrt{2}$$

STEP 2 Apply the Distributive Property $a(b + c) = ab + ac$ to each pair of terms.

$$= \left(\sqrt{5} \cdot \sqrt{5} + \sqrt{2} \cdot \sqrt{5}\right) - \left(\sqrt{5} \cdot \sqrt{2} + \sqrt{2} \cdot \sqrt{2}\right)$$

STEP 3 Apply the Product Rule and express the product of each square root as the square root of the product.

$$= \sqrt{5 \cdot 5} + \sqrt{5 \cdot 2} - \sqrt{2 \cdot 5} - \sqrt{2 \cdot 2}$$

STEP 4 Multiply the factors in each radicand, and simplify.

$$= \sqrt{25} + \sqrt{10} - \sqrt{10} - \sqrt{4} = 5 - 2 = 3$$

The solution to $\left(\sqrt{5} + \sqrt{2}\right)\left(\sqrt{5} - \sqrt{2}\right)$ is 3.

GOT TO KNOW!

Multiplying Radicals

If a, b, and c are real numbers:

Product Rule for Radicals

$$\sqrt[n]{a} \cdot \sqrt[n]{b} = \sqrt[n]{ab}$$

Distributive Property of Multiplication over Addition

$$a(b + c) = ab + ac$$

Adding and Subtracting Square Roots

Like radicals are radicals that have the same index and the same radicand.

All like radicals can be added or subtracted using the Distributive Property of Multiplication over Addition: $a \cdot b + a \cdot c = a(b + c)$, where a is a radical, and b and c are real numbers.

EXAMPLE 1

Add $3\sqrt{2} + 5\sqrt{2}$.

STEP 1 To add the square roots, apply the Distributive Property. $\quad 3\sqrt{2} + 5\sqrt{2} = (3 + 5)\sqrt{2}$

STEP 2 Combine like terms. $\qquad\qquad\qquad\qquad\qquad\qquad\qquad = 8\sqrt{2}$

The sum of $3\sqrt{2} + 5\sqrt{2}$ is $8\sqrt{2}$.

EXAMPLE 2

Subtract $5\sqrt{6} - 12\sqrt{6}$.

STEP 1 To subtract the square roots, apply the Distributive Property. $\quad 5\sqrt{6} - 12\sqrt{6} = (5 - 12)\sqrt{6}$

STEP 2 Combine like terms. $\qquad\qquad\qquad\qquad\qquad\qquad\qquad = -7\sqrt{6}$

The difference of $5\sqrt{6} - 12\sqrt{6}$ is $-7\sqrt{6}$.

In some cases, radicals must be simplified into like radicals before they can be added or subtracted. Use the Product Rule, $\sqrt{ab} = \sqrt{a} \cdot \sqrt{b}$, to extract the square roots that are perfect square factors of one or more radicands.

Simplifying Before Adding Square Roots

EXAMPLE 3

Add $6\sqrt{8} + 4\sqrt{2}$.

STEP 1 Simplify the radical $6\sqrt{8}$ using the Product Rule.

$$6\sqrt{8} = 6\sqrt{4 \cdot 2}$$
$$= 6\sqrt{4} \cdot \sqrt{2}$$
$$= 6 \cdot 2\sqrt{2}$$
$$= 12\sqrt{2}$$

STEP 2 To add the like radicals, apply the Distributive Property.

$$6\sqrt{8} + 4\sqrt{2} = 12\sqrt{2} + 4\sqrt{2}$$
$$= (12 + 4)\sqrt{2}$$
$$= 16\sqrt{2}$$

STEP 3 Combine like terms.

The sum of $6\sqrt{8} + 4\sqrt{2}$ is $16\sqrt{2}$.

Simplifying Before Subtracting Square Roots

EXAMPLE 4

Subtract $4\sqrt{27} - 3\sqrt{75}$.

STEP 1 Use the Product Rule to simplify each radicand.

$$4\sqrt{27} = 4\sqrt{9 \cdot 3} \qquad 3\sqrt{75} = 3\sqrt{25 \cdot 3}$$
$$= 4 \cdot \sqrt{9} \cdot \sqrt{3} \qquad = 3 \cdot \sqrt{25} \cdot \sqrt{3}$$
$$= 4 \cdot 3 \cdot \sqrt{3} \qquad = 3 \cdot 5 \cdot \sqrt{3}$$
$$= 12\sqrt{3} \qquad = 15\sqrt{3}$$

STEP 2 Subtract the like radicals.

$$4\sqrt{27} - 3\sqrt{75} = 12\sqrt{3} - 15\sqrt{3} = -3\sqrt{3}$$

The difference of $4\sqrt{27} - 3\sqrt{75}$ is $-3\sqrt{3}$.

Need More HELP?

To simplify large radicands, find the prime factors of the radicand and group like factors together to find the perfect nth root in the number.

Adding and Subtracting *n*th Roots

As with square roots, simplify *n*th radicals and use the Distributive Property to add and subtract like radicals.

EXAMPLE 5

Add $7\sqrt[3]{16} + \sqrt[3]{2}$.

STEP 1 Find the greatest perfect cube in $7\sqrt[3]{16}$ and simplify first.

$$7\sqrt[3]{16} = 7\sqrt[3]{8 \cdot 2}$$
$$= 7 \cdot \sqrt[3]{8} \cdot \sqrt[3]{2}$$
$$= 7 \cdot 2 \cdot \sqrt[3]{2} = 14\sqrt[3]{2}$$

STEP 2 The two radicals are alike, so add using the Distributive Property.

$$7\sqrt[3]{16} + \sqrt[3]{2} = 14\sqrt[3]{2} + \sqrt[3]{2}$$
$$= (14 + 1) \cdot \sqrt[3]{2}$$
$$= 15\sqrt[3]{2}$$

The sum of $7\sqrt[3]{16} + \sqrt[3]{2}$ is $15\sqrt[3]{2}$.

EXAMPLE 6

Subtract $2\sqrt[4]{32} - \sqrt[4]{162}$.

STEP 1 Simplify each term using the Product Rule.

$$2\sqrt[4]{32} = 2\sqrt[4]{16 \cdot 2} \qquad \sqrt[4]{162} = \sqrt[4]{81 \cdot 2}$$
$$= 2\sqrt[4]{16} \cdot \sqrt[4]{2} \qquad = \sqrt[4]{81} \cdot \sqrt[4]{2} = 3\sqrt[4]{2}$$
$$= 2 \cdot 2 \cdot \sqrt[4]{2} = 4\sqrt[4]{2}$$

STEP 2 Apply the Distributive Property and subtract.

$$2\sqrt[4]{32} - \sqrt[4]{162} = 4\sqrt[4]{2} - 3\sqrt[4]{2}$$
$$= (4 - 3) \cdot \sqrt[4]{2}$$
$$= \sqrt[4]{2}$$

The difference of $2\sqrt[4]{32} - \sqrt[4]{162}$ is $\sqrt[4]{2}$.

Multiplying Sums and Differences of Square Roots

The product of two binomial expressions that involve radicals can be found using the Distributive Property $ab + ac = a(b + c)$, the Commutative Property of Addition $a + b = b + a$, and the rules for simplifying, multiplying, and adding or subtracting radicals.

The results can be either rational or irrational numbers.

EXAMPLE 7

Find the product of $(\sqrt{2} + 3)(3\sqrt{2} - 5)$.

STEP 1 Apply the Distributive Property to multiply the two binomials.

$(\sqrt{2} + 3)(3\sqrt{2} - 5)$
$= \sqrt{2} \cdot 3\sqrt{2} + \sqrt{2} \cdot (-5) + 3 \cdot 3\sqrt{2} + 3 \cdot (-5)$
$= 3 \cdot \sqrt{2} \cdot \sqrt{2} - 5\sqrt{2} + 9\sqrt{2} - 15$

STEP 2 Simplify the first term using the Product Rule for multiplying radicals.

$= 3 \cdot \sqrt{4} - 5\sqrt{2} + 9\sqrt{2} - 15$
$= 3 \cdot 2 - 5\sqrt{2} + 9\sqrt{2} - 15$
$= 6 - 5\sqrt{2} + 9\sqrt{2} - 15$

STEP 3 Apply the Commutative Property of Addition.

$= 6 - 15 - 5\sqrt{2} + 9\sqrt{2}$

STEP 4 Use the Distributive Property to add like radicals and simplify.

$= 6 - 15 - (5 - 9)\sqrt{2}$
$= -9 + 4\sqrt{2}$

The product of $(\sqrt{2} + 3)(3\sqrt{2} - 5)$ is $-9 + 4\sqrt{2}$.

Squaring Binomial Radical Expressions

As in the Example above, you can use the Distributive Property to square a radical binomial, or you can use the algebraic identity $(a + b)^2 = a^2 + 2ab + b^2$.

EXAMPLE 8

Expand $(2\sqrt{3} + 5)^2$.

STEP 1 Use the pattern $(a + b)^2 = a^2 + 2ab + b^2$.

$(2\sqrt{3} + 5)^2 = (2\sqrt{3})^2 + 2(2\sqrt{3})(5) + 5^2$

STEP 2 Simplify the terms.

$= 2^2 \cdot (\sqrt{3})^2 + 2 \cdot 2 \cdot 5\sqrt{3} + 25$
$= 4 \cdot 3 + 20\sqrt{3} + 25$
$= 12 + 20\sqrt{3} + 25$

STEP 3 Combine like terms.

$= 37 + 20\sqrt{3}$

The result of simplifying $(2\sqrt{3} + 5)^2$ is $37 + 20\sqrt{3}$.

Radical Conjugates

In the algebraic identity $(a + b)(a - b) = a^2 - b^2$, the binomial factors are called **conjugates** of each other. The product is the difference of two squares. If a or b, or both, are irrational square roots, then multiplying the conjugates produces a rational number.

Ways to
REMEMBER

The word *rational* contains the word *ratio*. Therefore, a rational number is the ratio of two integers $\frac{p}{q}$, where $q \neq 0$. An irrational number is not rational. The prefix *ir-* means *not*.

EXAMPLE 9

Multiply the conjugates $\left(\sqrt{5} - 8\right)\left(\sqrt{5} + 8\right)$.

METHOD 1

STEP 1 Use the Distributive Property to multiply.

$$\left(\sqrt{5} - 8\right)\left(\sqrt{5} + 8\right)$$
$$= \left(\sqrt{5}\right)^2 + 8 \cdot \sqrt{5} - 8 \cdot \sqrt{5} - 8^2$$

STEP 2 Use the Product Rule, the Distributive Property, and addition of like terms, including like radicals, to simplify the expression.

$$= \sqrt{5^2} + (8 - 8)\sqrt{5} - 64$$
$$= 5 + 0 \cdot \sqrt{5} - 64 = -59$$

METHOD 2

STEP 1 The binomial factors are conjugates of each other. Their product is the difference of two squares a^2 and b^2, where $a = \sqrt{5}$ and $b = 8$.

$$\left(\sqrt{5} - 8\right)\left(\sqrt{5} + 8\right)$$
$$= \left(\sqrt{5}\right)^2 - 8^2$$

STEP 2 Simplify.

$$= 5 - 64 = -59$$

The product $\left(\sqrt{5} - 8\right)\left(\sqrt{5} + 8\right)$ is -59.

EXAMPLE 10

Multiply the conjugates $\left(2\sqrt{3} - \sqrt{2}\right)\left(2\sqrt{3} + \sqrt{2}\right)$.

STEP 1 The product of two conjugates is the difference of two squares.

$$\left(2\sqrt{3} - \sqrt{2}\right)\left(2\sqrt{3} + \sqrt{2}\right)$$
$$= \left(2\sqrt{3}\right)^2 - \left(\sqrt{2}\right)^2$$

STEP 2 Use the Product Rule to square each irrational number.

$$= 2^2 \cdot \left(\sqrt{3}\right)^2 - \left(\sqrt{2}\right)^2$$

STEP 3 Simplify.

$$= 4 \cdot 3 - 2 = 12 - 2 = 10$$

The product $\left(2\sqrt{3} - \sqrt{2}\right)\left(2\sqrt{3} + \sqrt{2}\right)$ is 10.

GOT TO KNOW!

Algebraic Identities

If a and b are real numbers, then

- $(a + b)^2 = a^2 + 2ab + b^2$ and $(a - b)^2 = a^2 - 2ab + b^2$.
- $(a + b)(a - b) = a^2 - b^2$, where the product is the difference of two squares.

Dividing Radical Expressions

Quotients of Square Roots

Radicals that have the same index can be expressed as quotients.

Need More
HELP **?**
Remember that when there is no index number for a radical, it is understood to be 2.

EXAMPLE 1

Simplify $\sqrt{\dfrac{100}{9}}$.

METHOD 1

STEP 1 Apply the Quotient Rule. $\qquad\qquad\qquad\sqrt{\dfrac{100}{9}} = \dfrac{\sqrt{100}}{\sqrt{9}}$

STEP 2 Write each radicand as a perfect square. $\qquad\qquad = \dfrac{\sqrt{10^2}}{\sqrt{3^2}}$

STEP 3 Simplify. $\qquad\qquad\qquad\qquad\qquad\qquad = \dfrac{10}{3}$

METHOD 2

STEP 1 Rewrite the numerator and the denominator of the given quotient as perfect squares. $\qquad\sqrt{\dfrac{100}{9}} = \sqrt{\dfrac{10^2}{3^2}}$

STEP 2 Use the Quotient Rule to write the square root of the quotient as the quotient of the square roots. $\qquad = \dfrac{\sqrt{10^2}}{\sqrt{3^2}}$

STEP 3 Simplify. $\qquad\qquad\qquad\qquad\qquad\qquad = \dfrac{10}{3}$

The radical $\sqrt{\dfrac{100}{9}}$ simplifies to $\dfrac{10}{3}$.

SEARCH
To see step-by-step videos of these problems, enter the page number into the SWadvantage.com Search Bar.

EXAMPLE 2

Simplify $\dfrac{\sqrt{150}}{\sqrt{2}}$.

METHOD 1

STEP 1 Use the Quotient Rule to write the quotient of the square roots as the square root of the quotient. $\qquad\dfrac{\sqrt{150}}{\sqrt{2}} = \sqrt{\dfrac{150}{2}}$

STEP 2 Divide to simplify the radicand. $\qquad\qquad = \sqrt{75}$

STEP 3 Use the Product Rule to separate the radicand into a perfect square and another factor. $\qquad = \sqrt{25 \cdot 3}$

$\qquad\qquad\qquad\qquad\qquad\qquad\qquad\qquad\qquad = \sqrt{25} \cdot \sqrt{3}$

STEP 4 Simplify. $\qquad\qquad\qquad\qquad\qquad\qquad = 5\sqrt{3}$

METHOD 2

STEP 1 Use the Product Rule to separate the radicand into a perfect square and another factor.

STEP 2 Cancel like factors in the numerator and denominator of the fraction to reduce the fraction to lowest terms.

STEP 3 Use the Product Rule again to simplify the radicand.

STEP 4 Simplify.

$$\frac{\sqrt{150}}{\sqrt{2}} = \frac{\sqrt{75 \cdot 2}}{\sqrt{2}}$$

$$= \frac{\sqrt{75} \cdot \sqrt{2}}{\sqrt{2}}$$

$$= \frac{\sqrt{75} \cdot \cancel{\sqrt{2}}}{\cancel{\sqrt{2}}}$$

$$= \sqrt{75}$$

$$= \sqrt{25 \cdot 3}$$

$$= \sqrt{25} \cdot \sqrt{3}$$

$$= \sqrt{5^2} \cdot \sqrt{3}$$

$$= 5\sqrt{3}$$

The quotient of $\frac{\sqrt{150}}{\sqrt{2}}$ is $5\sqrt{3}$.

Need More

HELP ?

To simplify large radicands, find the prime factors of the radicand and group like factors together to find the perfect nth root in the number.

Quotients of *n*th Roots

EXAMPLE 3

Simplify $\sqrt[4]{\frac{81}{16}}$.

STEP 1 Use the Quotient Rule to rewrite the 4th root of the quotient as the quotient of the 4th roots.

STEP 2 Simplify the numerator and denominator by writing each radicand as the perfect 4th power of a prime number.

STEP 3 Simplify.

$$\sqrt[4]{\frac{81}{16}} = \frac{\sqrt[4]{81}}{\sqrt[4]{16}}$$

$$= \frac{\sqrt[4]{3^4}}{\sqrt[4]{2^4}}$$

$$= \frac{3}{2}$$

The radical $\sqrt[4]{\frac{81}{16}}$ simplifies to $\frac{3}{2}$.

GOT TO KNOW!

Quotient Rules for Radicals

If a and b are non-negative numbers and $b \neq 0$, then:

Quotient Rule for Square Roots

$$\sqrt{\frac{a}{b}} = \frac{\sqrt{a}}{\sqrt{b}} \qquad \frac{\sqrt{a}}{\sqrt{b}} = \sqrt{\frac{a}{b}}$$

Quotient Rule for *n*th Roots

$$\sqrt[n]{\frac{a}{b}} = \frac{\sqrt[n]{a}}{\sqrt[n]{b}} \qquad \frac{\sqrt[n]{a}}{\sqrt[n]{b}} = \sqrt[n]{\frac{a}{b}}$$

Dividing *n*th Roots

EXAMPLE 4

Simplify $\dfrac{\sqrt[3]{32}}{\sqrt[3]{8}}$.

STEP 1 Use the Quotient Rule to rewrite the quotient of the cubic roots as the cube root of the quotient.

$$\frac{\sqrt[3]{32}}{\sqrt[3]{8}} = \sqrt[3]{\frac{32}{8}}$$

STEP 2 Use division to simplify the radicand.

$$= \sqrt[3]{4}$$

The quotient $\dfrac{\sqrt[3]{32}}{\sqrt[3]{8}}$ simplifies to $\sqrt[3]{4}$.

Watch Out !

Although 4 is a perfect square, it is not a perfect cube, and $\sqrt[3]{4}$ cannot be simplified further.

Rationalizing Denominators

When a quotient has a radical in the denominator that cannot be simplified further, the process known as **rationalizing the denominator** is used to rewrite it. To rationalize a denominator when it is an irrational square root, multiply the quotient by 1 in the form of a fraction that produces the square root of the least perfect square in the denominator.

EXAMPLE 5

Rationalize the denominator in $\dfrac{1}{\sqrt{6}}$.

The nearest perfect square to 6 that contains 6 as a factor is 36.

So, multiply the fraction by 1 in the form of $\dfrac{\sqrt{6}}{\sqrt{6}}$ and simplify the denominator.

$$\frac{1}{\sqrt{6}} \cdot \frac{\sqrt{6}}{\sqrt{6}} = \frac{\sqrt{6}}{\sqrt{6^2}} = \frac{\sqrt{6}}{6}$$

When rationalized, $\dfrac{1}{\sqrt{6}}$ is $\dfrac{\sqrt{6}}{6}$.

Try It This Way

You can use a calculator to verify that $\dfrac{1}{\sqrt{6}}$ and $\dfrac{\sqrt{6}}{6}$ are equivalent. First, divide 1 by $\sqrt{6}$. To get the radical sign, press the 2nd key, then the radical sign. Then, divide $\sqrt{6}$ by 6, and compare the results.

EXAMPLE 6

Rationalize the denominator in $\dfrac{2}{\sqrt{8}}$.

STEP 1 16 is a perfect square that contains 8 as a factor. Multiply by $\dfrac{\sqrt{2}}{\sqrt{2}}$ to make the denominator a perfect square.

$$\frac{2}{\sqrt{8}} \cdot \frac{\sqrt{2}}{\sqrt{2}} = \frac{2\sqrt{2}}{\sqrt{16}}$$

STEP 2 Simplify.

$$\frac{2\sqrt{2}}{4} = \frac{\sqrt{2}}{2}$$

When rationalized, $\dfrac{2}{\sqrt{8}}$ is $\dfrac{\sqrt{2}}{2}$.

SEARCH

To see step-by-step videos of these problems, enter the page number into the SWadvantage.com Search Bar.

Rationalizing Binomial Denominators

The binomials $(a + b)$ and $(a - b)$ are *conjugates*, where a and b are real numbers, and $a \neq b$. Their product is $a^2 - b^2$. To rationalize the binomial denominator of a quotient that contains a radical, multiply the quotient by 1 in the form of either $\frac{a - b}{a - b}$ or $\frac{a + b}{a + b}$.

Need More

HELP ?

Using FOIL,
$(a + b)(a - b)$ equals
$a^2 + ab - ab + b^2$,
which simplifies to
$a^2 - b^2$. This expression
is known as the
difference of two
squares.

EXAMPLE 7

Rationalize the denominator of $\dfrac{3}{\sqrt{5} + 3}$.

STEP 1 Multiply the fraction by 1 in the form of $\dfrac{\sqrt{5} - 3}{\sqrt{5} - 3}$ because $\sqrt{5} - 3$ is the conjugate of the denominator.

$$\frac{3}{\sqrt{5} + 3} \cdot \frac{\sqrt{5} - 3}{\sqrt{5} - 3} = \frac{3(\sqrt{5} - 3)}{(\sqrt{5} + 3)(\sqrt{5} - 3)}$$

STEP 2 Rewrite the denominator of the fraction as the difference of two squares.

$$= \frac{3(\sqrt{5} - 3)}{(\sqrt{5})^2 - 3^2} = \frac{3(\sqrt{5} - 3)}{\sqrt{25} - 9}$$

STEP 3 Apply the Distributive Property in the numerator, and simplify the denominator.

$$= \frac{3(\sqrt{5} - 3)}{5 - 9} = -\frac{3\sqrt{5} - 9}{4}$$

When rationalized, $\dfrac{3}{\sqrt{5} + 3}$ is $-\dfrac{3\sqrt{5} - 9}{4}$.

Watch Out !

You do not rationalize
a numerator that
contains a radical. In
fact, in most cases,
rationalizing the
denominator of a
quotient results
in a radical in the
numerator.

EXAMPLE 8

Rationalize the denominator of $\dfrac{6}{10 - \sqrt{2}}$.

STEP 1 The conjugate of the denominator is $\sqrt{10} + 2$. So, multiply the fraction by 1 in the form of $\dfrac{\sqrt{10} + 2}{\sqrt{10} + 2}$.

$$\frac{6}{10 - \sqrt{2}} \cdot \frac{10 + \sqrt{2}}{10 + \sqrt{2}} = \frac{6 \cdot (10 + \sqrt{2})}{(10 - \sqrt{2})(10 + \sqrt{2})}$$

STEP 2 Rewrite the denominator of the fraction as the difference of two squares.

$$= \frac{6 \cdot (10 + \sqrt{2})}{10^2 - (\sqrt{2})^2}$$

STEP 3 Apply the Distributive Property in the numerator, and simplify the denominator.

$$= \frac{60 + 6\sqrt{2}}{100 - 2} = \frac{60 + 6\sqrt{2}}{98} = \frac{(30 + 3\sqrt{2})}{49}$$

GOT TO KNOW!

Conjugate Pairs and Their Product

The two pairs of binomial factors in the identity below are **conjugates**, where a and b are real numbers, and $a \neq b$. Their product is the difference of two squares.

$$(a + b)(a - b) = (a - b)(a + b) = a^2 - b^2$$

Integer and Rational Exponents

Integer Exponents

An integer is an element of the set $\{\ldots, -3, -2, -3, 0, 1, 2, 3, \ldots\}$. If n is an integer and a is a real number, then the meaning of a^n depends on whether $n > 0$, $n = 0$, or $n < 0$.

- If $n > 0$, then $a^n = \underbrace{a \cdot a \cdot a \cdot \ldots \cdot a}_{n \text{ times}}$.

- If $n = 0$, then $a^0 = 1$, where $a \neq 0$. This is called the Zero Exponent Property.

- If $n < 0$, then, $a^n = \dfrac{1}{a^{-n}}$, where $a \neq 0$.

Use one or more of these definitions to simplify exponential expressions of the form a^n, where n is an integer.

EXAMPLE 1

Simplify the expression $(3^4)(5^0)$.

In the first factor, $n > 0$. In the second factor, $n = 0$. So, simplify each factor using the first two definitions above.

$(3^4)(5^0) = (3 \cdot 3 \cdot 3 \cdot 3)(1)$
$= 81$

EXAMPLE 2

Simplify 2^{-5}.

When $n < 0$, use the definition, $a^n = \dfrac{1}{a^{-n}}$.

$2^{-5} = \dfrac{1}{2^5} = \dfrac{1}{32}$

EXAMPLE 3

Simplify -3^4.

STEP 1 Rewrite -3^4 as the product of -1 and 3^4.

$-3^4 = -1 \cdot 3^4$

STEP 2 Apply the first property where $n > 0$ and $a^n = a_1 \cdot a_2 \cdot a_3 \cdot \ldots \cdot a_n$.

$= -1 \cdot 3 \cdot 3 \cdot 3 \cdot 3$

STEP 3 Simplify the product.

$= -81$

EXAMPLE 4

Simplify $\dfrac{2}{3^{-2}}$.

STEP 1 Rewrite the expression as a product.

$\dfrac{2}{3^{-2}} = 2 \cdot \dfrac{1}{3^{-2}}$

STEP 2 Use the definition, $a^n = \dfrac{1}{a^{-n}}$ where $n = -2$, to rewrite the expression.

$\dfrac{2}{3^{-2}} = 2 \cdot \dfrac{1}{3^{-2}}$

Then simplify.

$= 2 \cdot \dfrac{3^2}{1}$

$= 18$

Rational Exponents of the Form $\frac{1}{n}$

A rational number is defined as $\frac{m}{n}$, where m and n are integers, and $n \neq 0$. When $m = 1$, then $\frac{m}{n} = \frac{1}{n}$, and $a^{\frac{1}{n}} = \sqrt[n]{a}$, where $n \geq 2$.

Need More
HELP ?

Remember that for all these examples, if n is an even integer, $\sqrt[n]{a} = |a|$.

If n is an odd integer, $\sqrt[n]{a} = a$.

EXAMPLE 5

Simplify $64^{\frac{1}{2}}$.

Use the property $a^{\frac{1}{n}} = \sqrt[n]{a}$, where $n = 2$. Rewrite the expression and simplify. $\qquad 64^{\frac{1}{2}} = \sqrt{64} = 8$

EXAMPLE 6

Simplify $-8^{\frac{1}{3}}$.

Use the property $a^{\frac{1}{n}} = \sqrt[n]{a}$, where $a = -8$ and $n = 3$. Rewrite the expression and simplify.

$$-8^{\frac{1}{3}} = \sqrt[3]{-8}$$
$$= -2$$

Watch Out !

The radical symbol $\sqrt{}$ stands for the **principal** (non-negative) **square root** of a number.

EXAMPLE 7

Simplify $32^{\frac{1}{4}}$.

STEP 1 Apply the property $a^{\frac{1}{n}} = \sqrt[n]{a}$, where $n = 4$. $\qquad 32^{\frac{1}{4}} = \sqrt[4]{32}$

STEP 2 Rewrite the radicand, using the Product Rule, $\sqrt[n]{ab} = \sqrt[n]{a} \cdot \sqrt[n]{b}$, to identify the largest factor that is an integer to the fourth power.

$$= \sqrt[4]{16 \cdot 2} = \sqrt[4]{16} \cdot \sqrt[4]{2}$$
$$= \sqrt[4]{2^4} \cdot \sqrt[4]{2}$$

STEP 3 Simplify. $\qquad\qquad\qquad\qquad\qquad\qquad = 2\sqrt[4]{2}$

EXAMPLE 8

Simplify $27^{-\frac{1}{3}}$.

STEP 1 Apply the property $a^n = \frac{1}{a^{-n}}$, where $n = -\frac{1}{3}$. $\qquad 27^{-\frac{1}{3}} = \frac{1}{27^{\frac{1}{3}}}$

STEP 2 Apply the property $a^{\frac{1}{n}} = \sqrt[n]{a}$, where $n = 3$. $\qquad\qquad = \frac{1}{\sqrt[3]{27}}$

STEP 3 Find the cube root of the radicand 27. $\qquad\qquad = \frac{1}{3}$

SEARCH 🔍

To see step-by-step videos of these problems, enter the page number into the SWadvantage.com Search Bar.

Rational Exponents of the Form $\frac{m}{n}$

Exponents of the form $\frac{m}{n}$ are fractions in which $\frac{m}{n}$ is in lowest terms, and m and n are integers with $n \geq 2$. For the real number a, the following properties are true.

- $a^{\frac{m}{n}} = \left(\sqrt[n]{a}\right)^m = \sqrt[n]{a^m}$, where m is the exponent and n is the root (index).
- $a^{-\frac{m}{n}} = \frac{1}{a^{\frac{m}{n}}}$, where $m > 0$.

Need More

HELP ?

For a fraction to be in lowest terms means that the numerator and denominator share no common factor other than 1.

EXAMPLE 9

Write $\sqrt[4]{(-2)^3}$ as an exponential expression.

The radicand is $(-2)^3$, so $a = -2$. Use $\sqrt[n]{a^m} = a^{\frac{m}{n}}$ to rewrite the expression. $\qquad \sqrt[4]{(-2)^3} = (-2)^{\frac{3}{4}}$

EXAMPLE 10

Simplify $27^{\frac{2}{3}}$.

METHOD 1

STEP 1 Use the property $a^{\frac{m}{n}} = \left(\sqrt[n]{a}\right)^m$ to rewrite the expression, where the exponent is $m = 2$ and the root is $n = 3$. $\qquad 27^{\frac{2}{3}} = \left(\sqrt[3]{27}\right)^2$

STEP 2 Express the perfect cube 27 as the cube of 3. $\qquad = \left(\sqrt[3]{3^3}\right)^2$

STEP 3 Simplify the cube root of 3^3. $\qquad = (3)^2$

STEP 4 Square the result. $\qquad = 9$

METHOD 2

STEP 1 Use the property $a^{\frac{m}{n}} = \sqrt[n]{a^m}$ to rewrite the expression. $\qquad 27^{\frac{2}{3}} = \sqrt[3]{27^2}$

STEP 2 Express the square of the 27 as the square of 3^3 and rewrite the radicand as the product of the two cubes. $\qquad = \sqrt[3]{(3^3)^2}$

$\qquad = \sqrt[3]{3^3 \cdot 3^3}$

STEP 3 Use the Product Rule $\sqrt[n]{ab} = \sqrt[n]{a} \cdot \sqrt[n]{b}$ to write the cube root of the product of two cubes as the product of two cube roots. $\qquad = \sqrt[3]{3^3} \cdot \sqrt[3]{3^3}$

STEP 4 Simplify each radical. $\qquad = 3 \cdot 3$

STEP 5 Multiply the roots. $\qquad = 9$

$27^{\frac{2}{3}} = 9$

GOT TO KNOW!

Forms of a Rational Exponent

To rewrite the exponential expression $a^{\frac{m}{n}}$, you can use either radical equivalent:

$a^{\frac{m}{n}} = \left(\sqrt[n]{a}\right)^m$ or
$a^{\frac{m}{n}} = \sqrt[n]{a^m}$

SEARCH 🔍

To see step-by-step videos of these problems, enter the page number into the SWadvantage.com Search Bar.

EXAMPLE 11

Simplify $25^{-\frac{3}{2}}$.

STEP 1 The rational exponent is a negative number. So, use the property $a^{-\frac{m}{n}} = \frac{1}{a^{\frac{m}{n}}}$ to rewrite the expression, where $m = 3$ and $n = 2$.

$$25^{-\frac{3}{2}} = \frac{1}{25^{\frac{3}{2}}}$$

STEP 2 Use the property $a^{\frac{m}{n}} = \left(\sqrt[n]{a}\right)^m$ to rewrite the denominator as the cube of the square root of 25.

$$\frac{1}{25^{\frac{3}{2}}} = \frac{1}{\left(\sqrt{25}\right)^3}$$

STEP 3 Simplify the square root of 25.

$$= \frac{1}{5^3}$$

STEP 4 Cube the principal square root of 25.

$$= \frac{1}{125}$$

Reducing the Index of a Radical

If the rational exponent of a radical expression is not in lowest terms, you can reduce the exponent to lowest terms by removing a common factor greater than 1. This results in reducing the index n of the radical.

EXAMPLE 12

Simplify $\sqrt[6]{27^2}$.

STEP 1 Use the property $\sqrt[n]{a^m} = a^{\frac{m}{n}}$ to rewrite the expression, where $m = 2$ and $n = 6$. The fraction $\frac{m}{n}$ is not in lowest terms.

$$\sqrt[6]{27^2} = 27^{\frac{2}{6}}$$

STEP 2 Reduce the rational exponent by removing the common factor of 3 and rewriting the expression as a radical.

$$= 27^{\frac{1}{3}} = \sqrt[3]{27}$$

STEP 3 Simplify the cube root of 27.

$$= 3$$

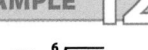

GOT TO KNOW!

Rational Exponents

For n, an integer such that $n \geq 2$; m, an integer; and real number a:

$$a^{\frac{1}{n}} = \sqrt[n]{a}$$

$$a^{\frac{m}{n}} = \left(\sqrt[n]{a}\right)^m = \sqrt[n]{a^m}, \text{ where } \frac{m}{n} \text{ is in lowest terms.}$$

$$a^{-\frac{m}{n}} = \frac{1}{a^{\frac{m}{n}}}, \text{ where } m > 0.$$

Properties of Exponents

Properties of Negative, Zero, and Rational Powers

A non-zero real number a can be raised to any rational power, including 0. By definition, a **rational number** is of the form $\frac{p}{q}$, where p and q are integers, and $q \neq 0$.

- The Negative Exponent Property states that $a^{-n} = \frac{1}{a^n}$ and $\frac{1}{a^{-n}} = a^n$.
- The Zero Exponent Property states that if $a \neq 0$, $a^0 = 1$.
- $a^{\frac{1}{n}} = \sqrt[n]{a}$, $n \geq 2$
- $a^{\frac{m}{n}} = (\sqrt[n]{a})^m = \sqrt[n]{a^m}$, where m and n are integers, $\frac{m}{n}$ is in lowest terms, and $n \geq 2$.

Need More HELP?

Remember that 0^0 is undefined.

EXAMPLE 1

Simplify $\frac{1}{3^{-2}}$.

STEP 1 Apply the Negative Exponent Property, $\frac{1}{a^{-n}} = a^n$, where $a = 3$ and $n = -2$. $\frac{1}{3^{-2}} = 3^2$

STEP 2 Simplify the result. $= 9$

$\frac{1}{3^{-2}} = 9$

Watch Out!

When working with radicals, be sure that the radicand is not negative when the index is even.

EXAMPLE 2

Simplify -6^0.

STEP 1 Apply the Zero Exponent Property $a^0 = 1$, where $a = 6$. $-6^0 = -1 \cdot 6^0 = -1 \cdot 1$

STEP 2 Simplify the result. $= -1$

$-6^0 = -1$

Product of Powers Property

The product of like bases raised to a power equals the base raised to the sum of the powers.

$$a^m \cdot a^n = a^{m+n}$$

Watch Out!

Be sure that the bases are the same when using the Product of Powers Property.

For example,

$2^3 \cdot 3^2 \neq 6^{3+2}$

$\downarrow \qquad \downarrow$

$8 \times 9 \neq 6^5$

$\downarrow \qquad \downarrow$

$72 \neq 7{,}776$

EXAMPLE 3

Simplify $(2^{-5})(2^3)$.

STEP 1 Apply the Product of Powers Property where $a = 2$, $m = -5$, and $n = 3$. $(2^{-5})(2^3) = 2^{-5+3}$

STEP 2 Add the exponents. $= 2^{-2}$

STEP 3 Apply the Negative Exponent Property $a^{-n} = \frac{1}{a^n}$, where $n = -2$. $= \frac{1}{2^2} = \frac{1}{4}$

$(2^{-5})(2^3) = \frac{1}{4}$

EXAMPLE 4

Simplify $\left(5^{\frac{1}{2}}\right) \cdot \left(5^{\frac{3}{4}}\right)$ and express the result as a radical expression in its simplest form.

STEP 1 Use the Power of a Product Property $a^m \cdot a^n = a^{m+n}$ to rewrite
the expression, where $a = 5$, $m = \frac{1}{2}$, and $n = \frac{3}{4}$.

$$\left(5^{\frac{1}{2}}\right) \cdot \left(5^{\frac{3}{4}}\right) = 5^{\frac{1}{2}+\frac{3}{4}}$$

STEP 2 Add the fractional exponents.

$$= 5^{\frac{5}{4}}$$

STEP 3 Use the Rational Exponents Property $a^{\frac{m}{n}} = \sqrt[n]{a^m}$ and write
the expression as a radical expression.

$$= \sqrt[4]{5^5}$$

STEP 4 Rewrite the radicand as the product of two powers.

$$= \sqrt[4]{5^4 \cdot 5^1}$$

STEP 5 Simplify.

$$= 5\sqrt[4]{5}$$

$$\left(5^{\frac{1}{2}}\right) \cdot \left(5^{\frac{3}{4}}\right) = 5\sqrt[4]{5}$$

> **Need More HELP?**
>
> Remember that to add two fractions with different denominators, find the lowest common denominator of the two numbers.

Power of a Product Property

The power of a product is equal to the product of the powers of each base.

$$(a \cdot b)^n = a^n \cdot b^n$$

EXAMPLE 5

Simplify $(5 \cdot 3)^2$.

STEP 1 Use the Property $(a \cdot b)^n = a^n \cdot b^n$ and rewrite the expression,
where $a = 5$, $b = 3$, and $n = 2$.

$$(5 \cdot 3)^2 = 5^2 \cdot 3^2$$

STEP 2 Square each factor and multiply the results.

$$= 25 \cdot 9$$
$$= 225$$

$$(5 \cdot 3)^2 = 225$$

> **Watch Out!**
>
> In the Power of a Product Property, the bases a and b do not have to be equal.

EXAMPLE 6

Simplify $(4 \cdot 3)^{\frac{1}{2}}$.

STEP 1 Use the Property $(a \cdot b)^n = a^n \cdot b^n$ and rewrite the expression,
where $a = 4$, $b = 3$, and $n = \frac{1}{2}$.

$$(4 \cdot 3)^{\frac{1}{2}} = 4^{\frac{1}{2}} \cdot 3^{\frac{1}{2}}$$

STEP 2 Use the Rational Exponents Property $a^{\frac{1}{n}} = \sqrt[n]{a}$ and rewrite
each factor as an equivalent radical expression.

$$= \sqrt{4} \cdot \sqrt{3}$$

STEP 3 Simplify the first factor, then multiply.

$$= \sqrt{2^2} \cdot \sqrt{3} = 2\sqrt{3}$$

$$(4 \cdot 3)^{\frac{1}{2}} = 2\sqrt{3}$$

> **SEARCH**
>
> To see step-by-step videos of these problems, enter the page number into the SWadvantage.com Search Bar.

Power of a Power Property

The power of a base raised to a power equals the base raised to the product of the powers.

$$(a^m)^n = a^{m \cdot n}$$

EXAMPLE 7

Simplify $(2^3)^2$.

STEP 1 Use the Power of a Power property $(a^m)^n = a^{m \cdot n}$, where $a = 2$, $m = 3$ and $n = 2$, and rewrite the expression.

$(2^3)^2 = 2^{3 \cdot 2}$

STEP 2 Multiply the exponents, and simplify the result.

$= 2^6 = 64$

$(2^3)^2 = 64$

SEARCH

To see step-by-step videos of these problems, enter the page number into the SWadvantage.com Search Bar.

EXAMPLE 8

Simplify $\left(5^{-\frac{1}{2}}\right)^{\frac{2}{3}}$.

STEP 1 Use the Power of a Power Property $(a^m)^n = a^{m \cdot n}$, where $a = 5$, $m = -\frac{1}{2}$, and $n = \frac{2}{3}$, to rewrite the expression. Then multiply.

$\left(5^{-\frac{1}{2}}\right)^{\frac{2}{3}} = 5^{-\frac{1}{2} \times \frac{2}{3}} = 5^{-\frac{1}{3}}$

STEP 2 Use the Rational Exponents Property $a^{-n} = \frac{1}{a^n}$ and rewrite the exponential expression as an equivalent radical expression.

$= \frac{1}{5^{\frac{1}{3}}} = \frac{1}{\sqrt[3]{5}}$

STEP 3 Multiply the fraction by a form of 1 that will rationalize the denominator of the fraction.

$= \frac{1}{\sqrt[3]{5}} \times \frac{\sqrt[3]{5^2}}{\sqrt[3]{5^2}} = \frac{\sqrt[3]{5^2}}{\sqrt[3]{5^3}}$

STEP 4 Simplify.

$= \frac{\sqrt[3]{5^2}}{5}$

Need More
HELP?

Remember that radicals are not left in the denominator of a fraction. For more information on rationalizing denominators, see *Dividing Radical Expressions* on page 754.

Quotient of Powers Property

The quotient of like bases each raised to a power equals the base a raised to the difference between the powers.

$$\frac{a^m}{a^n} = a^{m-n}$$

EXAMPLE 9

Simplify $\frac{3^5}{3^2}$.

STEP 1 Use the Quotient of Powers Property $\frac{a^m}{a^n} = a^{m-n}$, where $a = 3$, $m = 5$, and $n = 2$ and rewrite the expression.

$\frac{3^5}{3^2} = 3^{5-2}$

STEP 2 Subtract the exponents, and simplify the result.

$= 3^3 = 27$

Watch Out!

The difference between the exponents equals the exponent of the numerator minus the exponent of the denominator. The order of numerators is important.

EXAMPLE 10

Simplify $\dfrac{3^{\frac{1}{2}}}{3^{\frac{2}{5}}}$.

STEP 1 Use the Quotient of Powers Property $\dfrac{a^m}{a^n} = a^{m-n}$ to rewrite the expression, where $a = 3$, $m = \dfrac{1}{2}$, and $n = \dfrac{2}{5}$.

$$\dfrac{3^{\frac{1}{2}}}{3^{\frac{2}{5}}} = 3^{\frac{1}{2}-\frac{2}{5}}$$

STEP 2 Find a lowest common denominator and subtract the exponents.

$$= 3^{\frac{5}{10}-\frac{4}{10}}$$
$$= 3^{\frac{1}{10}}$$

STEP 3 Use the Rational Exponents Property $a^{\frac{1}{n}} = \sqrt[n]{a}$ and write the expression as an equivalent radical expression.

$$= \sqrt[10]{3}$$

Need More
HELP ?

Remember that when adding two fractions with different denominators, find the lowest common denominator of the two numbers.

Power of a Quotient Property

The power of a quotient is equal to the quotient of the powers of each base: $\left(\dfrac{a}{b}\right)^n = \dfrac{a^n}{b^n}$.

EXAMPLE 11

Simplify $\left(\dfrac{3}{5}\right)^3$.

STEP 1 Use the Power of a Quotient Property $\left(\dfrac{a}{b}\right)^n = \dfrac{a^n}{b^n}$ to rewrite the expression, where $a = 3$, $b = 5$, and $n = 3$.

$$\left(\dfrac{3}{5}\right)^3 = \dfrac{3^3}{5^3}$$

STEP 2 Cube the numerator and the denominator.

$$= \dfrac{27}{125}$$

Watch Out !

In this property, the bases a and b do not have to be equal.

GOT TO KNOW!

Properties of Exponents

If m and n are integers, and a and b are real numbers, the following properties hold.

Zero Exponent	$a^0 = 1, a \neq 0$	**Power of a Product**	$a^n \cdot b^n = (a \cdot b)^n, a \neq 0$ and $b \neq 0$
Negative Exponent	$a^{-n} = \dfrac{1}{a^n}, a \neq 0$	**Power of a Power**	$(a^m)^n = a^{m \cdot n}, a \neq 0$
Rational Exponents	$a^{\frac{1}{n}} = \sqrt[n]{a}, n \geq 2$ $a^{\frac{m}{n}} = \left(\sqrt[n]{a}\right)^m = \sqrt[n]{a^m}, n \geq 2$	**Quotient of Powers**	$\dfrac{a^m}{a^n} = a^{m-n}, a \neq 0$
Product of Powers	$a^m \cdot a^n = a^{m+n}$	**Power of a Quotient**	$\left(\dfrac{a}{b}\right)^n = \dfrac{a^n}{b^n}, b \neq 0$

Logarithms

Common Logarithms

Need More HELP?

Remember that the ↔ symbol in the definition $a = b^n \leftrightarrow \log_b a = n$ means that the statement is symmetric. That is, it can be read from left to right, or from right to left.

The logarithmic expression $\log_b a = n$ is the inverse of the exponential expression $a = b^n$. You can use this definition to write an exponential expression as a logarithmic expression, and vice versa.

$$a = b^n \leftrightarrow \log_b a = n$$

Three properties that apply to all logarithms depend on the value of a, where $a > 0$.

- If $a < 1$, then $\log a < 0$.
- If $a = 1$, then $\log a = 0$.
- If $a > 1$, then $\log a > 0$.

If the base in a log expression is 10, the logarithm is known as a **common logarithm**. Common logs are usually written without the base.

$$a = 10^n \leftrightarrow \log a = n.$$

EXAMPLE 1

Write $3^4 = 243$ as an equivalent logarithmic expression.

STEP 1 Identify the values of a, b, and n in $a = b^n$. $\qquad a = 243, b = 3, n = 4$

STEP 2 Substitute these values into the logarithmic expression $\log_b a = n$. $\qquad \log_3 243 = 4$

The equivalent logarithmic expression for $3^4 = 243$ is $\log_3 243 = 4$.

EXAMPLE 2

Write $\log_4 64 = 3$ as an equivalent exponential expression.

STEP 1 Identify the values of a, b, and n in $\log_b a = n$. $\qquad a = 64, b = 4, n = 3$

STEP 2 Substitute these values into the exponential expression $a = b^n$. $\qquad 4^3 = 64$

The equivalent exponential expression for $\log_4 64 = 3$ is $4^3 = 64$.

Need More HELP?

The common logarithms of positive multiples of 10 are positive integers:
$\log 10 = 1$
$\log 100 = 2$
$\log 1000 = 3$, etc.

The common logarithms of reciprocals of the positive multiples of 10 are negative integers:
$\log 0.1 = -1$
$\log 0.01 = -2$
$\log 0.001 = -3$, etc.

EXAMPLE 3

Write $10^5 = 10,000$ as an equivalent logarithmic expression.

STEP 1 Identify the values of a, b, and n in $a = b^n$. $\qquad a = 10,000, b = 10, n = 5$

STEP 2 Substitute these values into $\log_b a = n$. $\qquad \log 10,000 = 5$

The expression $\log 10,000 = 5$ is written without an identified base because the base is 10.

EXAMPLE 4

Write $\log 0.01 = -2$ as an equivalent exponential expression.

STEP 1 Identify the values of a, b, and n in $\log_b a = n$. $\qquad a = 0.01, b = 10, n = -2$

STEP 2 Substitute these values into the exponential expression $a = b^n$. $\qquad 10^{-2} = 0.01$

The equivalent exponential expression for $\log 0.01 = -2$ is $10^{-2} = 0.01$.

Natural Logarithms

The **natural logarithm** is the logarithm to the base e, where e is called the Euler number, and is the irrational constant $2.718\dots$. The abbreviation "ln" is used to indicate the natural log: the base e is not included when writing the logarithmic expression

$$a = e^n \leftrightarrow \ln a = n$$

EXAMPLE 5

Write ln 1 = 0 as an equivalent exponential expression.

STEP 1 Identify the values of a and n in $\ln a = n$. $a = 1, n = 0$

STEP 2 Substitute these values into the exponential expression $a = e^n$. $e^0 = 1$

The equivalent exponential expression for $\ln 1 = 0$ is $e^0 = 1$.

EXAMPLE 6

Write $e^3 \approx 1.1$ as an equivalent logarithmic expression.

STEP 1 Identify the values of a and n in $a = e^n$. $a \approx 1.1, n = 3$

STEP 2 Substitute these values into the logarithmic expression $\ln a = n$. $\ln 1.1 \approx 3$

The equivalent logarithmic expression for $e^3 \approx 1.1$ is $\ln 1.1 \approx 3$.

Need More HELP?

For more information on e and natural logarithms, see *Base* e in *Exponential and Logarithmic Functions* on page 2004.

Watch Out!

Because e is an irrational number, any non-zero power of e is also irrational, and its value must be approximated.

The Product Rule for Logarithms

Rules for working with logarithms are derived from rules for working with exponents. When multiplying powers of like bases, you add exponents. Because logarithms are exponents, the logarithm of a product is equal to the sum of the logarithms to the same base.

Exponential form	**Common logarithmic form**
$(b^x) \cdot (b^y) = b^{x+y}$	$\log_b(xy) = \log_b x + \log_b y$

For common logarithms: $\log(xy) = \log x + \log y$.

For natural logarithms, $\ln(xy) = \ln x + \ln y$.

EXAMPLE 7

a. Use the product rule to expand $\log_2(3 \cdot 5)$.

STEP 1 Identify the values of b, x, and y in $\log_b(xy)$. $b = 2, x = 3, y = 5$

STEP 2 Substitute these values into $\log_b x + \log_b y$. $\log_2(3 \cdot 5) = \log_2 3 + \log_2 5$

b. Use the product rule to expand $\ln(2 \cdot 7)$.

STEP 1 Identify the values of x and y in $\ln(xy)$. $x = 2, y = 7$

STEP 2 Substitute these values into $\ln x + \ln y$. $\ln(2 \cdot 7) = \ln 2 + \ln 7$

SEARCH

To see step-by-step videos of these problems, enter the page number into the SWadvantage.com Search Bar.

The Quotient Rule for Logarithms

When dividing powers of like bases, you subtract the exponents. So, when working with logarithms, the logarithm of a quotient is equal to the difference of the logarithms to the same base.

Exponential form	**Common logarithmic form**
$\left(\dfrac{b^x}{b^y}\right) = b^{x-y}$	$\log_b\left(\dfrac{x}{y}\right) = \log_b x - \log_b y$
$\left(\dfrac{1}{b^y}\right) = b^{-y}$	$\log_b\left(\dfrac{1}{y}\right) = -\log_b y$

If $x \neq 1$, then $\log \dfrac{x}{y} = \log x - \log y$ and $\ln \dfrac{x}{y} = \ln x - \ln y$.

If $x = 1$, then $\log \dfrac{1}{y} = -\log y$ and $\ln \dfrac{1}{y} = -\ln y$; $y \neq 0$.

EXAMPLE 8

Use the Quotient Rule to expand $\log_2\left(\dfrac{1}{4}\right)$.

STEP 1 Identify the values of b, x, and y in $\log_b \dfrac{x}{y}$. $\quad b = 2, x = 1, y = 4$

STEP 2 Because $x = 1$, substitute these values into $-\log_b y$. $\quad \log_2\left(\dfrac{1}{4}\right) = -\log_2 4$

EXAMPLE 9

Use the Quotient Rule to expand $\log_3\left(\dfrac{4}{7}\right)$.

STEP 1 Identify the values of b, x, and y in $\log_b \dfrac{x}{y}$. $\quad b = 3, x = 4, y = 7$

STEP 2 Substitute these values into $\log_b x - \log_b y$. $\quad \log_3\left(\dfrac{4}{7}\right) = \log_3 4 - \log_3 7$

EXAMPLE 10

Use the Quotient Rule to expand $\ln \dfrac{9}{2}$.

STEP 1 Identify the values of x and y in $\ln \dfrac{x}{y}$. $\quad x = 9, y = 2$

STEP 2 Substitute these values into $\ln x - \ln y$. $\quad \ln\left(\dfrac{9}{2}\right) = \ln 9 - \ln 2$

The Power Rule for Logarithms

When raising the power of a base to a power, multiply the exponents. Therefore, the logarithm of the power of a power is the product of the power and the logarithm of the number to the same base.

Exponential form	**Common logarithmic form**
$(b^x)^y = b^{xy}$	$\log_b x^y = y \log_b x$

For common logarithms, $\log x^y = y \log x$.

For natural logarithms, $\ln x^y = y \ln x$.

EXAMPLE 11

Use the Power Rule to expand log 8³.

STEP 1 Identify the values of x and y in $\log x^y$. $x = 8, y = 3$

STEP 2 Use the Power Rule, and substitute these values into $y \log x$. $\log 8^3 = 3 \log 8$

EXAMPLE 12

Use the Power Rule to expand $\ln \sqrt{6}$.

STEP 1 Use the definition $a^{\frac{1}{n}} = \sqrt[n]{a}$, where n is a positive integer not equal to 1, to write $\ln \sqrt{6}$ in exponential form. $\ln \sqrt{6} = \ln 6^{\frac{1}{2}}$

STEP 2 Apply the Power Rule, $\ln x^y = y \ln x$, where $x = 6$ and $y = \frac{1}{2}$. $= \frac{1}{2} \ln 6$

Watch Out !

It is important to pay attention to the proper domains of numbers when specifying values for b, x, and y in exponential and logarithmic expressions.

GOT TO KNOW !

Properties of Logarithms

For real numbers x and y, and b a positive number other than 1:

Exponential form	**For all b**	**Common logs**	**Natural logs**
$b^0 = 1, b \neq 0$	$\log_b 1 = 0$	$\log 1 = 0$	$\ln 1 = 0$
$b^1 = b$	$\log_b b = 1$	$\log 10 = 1$	$\ln e = 1$
$b^x \cdot b^y = b^{x+y}$	$\log_b(xy) = \log_b x + \log_b y$	$\log(xy) = \log x + \log y$	$\ln(xy) = \ln x + \ln y$
$\left(\dfrac{b^x}{b^y}\right) = b^{x-y}$	$\log_b\left(\dfrac{x}{y}\right) = \log_b x - \log_b y$	$\log\left(\dfrac{x}{y}\right) = \log x - \log y$	$\ln\left(\dfrac{x}{y}\right) = \ln x - \ln y$
$b^{\frac{1}{y}} = b^{-y}, y \neq 0$	$\log_b\left(\dfrac{1}{y}\right) = -\log_b y$	$\log\left(\dfrac{1}{y}\right) = -\log y$	$\ln\left(\dfrac{1}{y}\right) = -\ln y$
$(b^x)^y = b^{xy}$	$\log_b x^y = y \log_b x$	$\log x^y = y \log x$	$\ln x^y = y \ln x$

Common Logarithms and Natural Logarithms

Solving Equations Using Common Logs

A logarithm is an exponent and is the inverse of an exponential expression. The base of a common logarithm is 10 and is usually not written.

$$y = \log x \leftrightarrow 10^y = x$$

The graph of the function $y = \log x$ appears to the right. Its **domain** is all positive numbers. Its **range** is all real numbers.

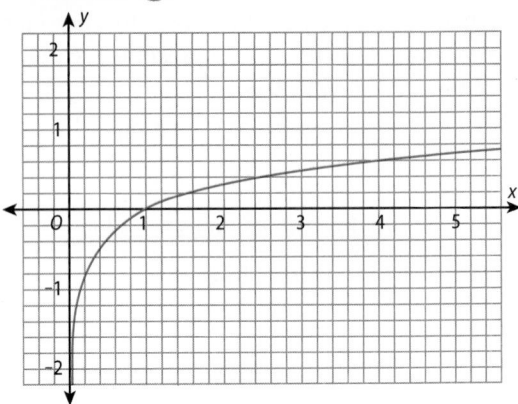

Logarithms are useful in solving **exponential equations**—equations that contain a variable in an exponent.

You can use these steps to solve an exponential equation.

1. Isolate the exponential expression.
2. Take the log of both sides of the equation.
3. Simplify, and solve for the variable.

Need More

HELP ?

To review the domain and range of functions, go to *Functions* in *Algebra* (p. 1438). To learn more about properties of logarithms, go to *Logarithms* (p. 1974).

Need More

HELP ?

The following properties are useful when solving exponential and logarithmic equations:

- $\log 1 = 0$
- $\log 10 = 1$
- $\log 10^x = x$
- $10^{\log x} = x$

EXAMPLE 1

Solve the equation $10^{\log 12} = x$ for x without using a calculator.

Apply the property $10^{\log x} = x$, where $x = 12$. By substitution, $x = 12$.

CHECK

STEP 1 Take the log of both sides of the equation. $\qquad\qquad \log(10^{\log 12}) \stackrel{?}{=} \log(12)$

STEP 2 Apply the Power Rule for Logarithms, $\log x^y = y \log x$, to expand the left side of the equation, where $x = 10$ and $y = \log 12$. $\qquad \log 12 \cdot \log 10 \stackrel{?}{=} \log 12$

STEP 3 Because $\log 10 = 1$, substitute 1 for $\log 10$. $\qquad\qquad \log 12 \cdot 1 = \log 12$ ✔

EXAMPLE 2

Solve the equation $8^x = 36$ for x.

STEP 1 Take the log of both sides of the equation. $\qquad\qquad\qquad \log 8^x = \log 36$

STEP 2 Apply the Power Rule for Logarithms, $\log x^y = y \log x$ to rewrite $\log 8^x$. $\qquad x \log 8 = \log 36$

STEP 3 To solve for x, divide both sides of the equation by $\log 8$. $\qquad\qquad x = \dfrac{\log 36}{\log 8}$

STEP 4 Use a calculator or a table to find the log of the numerator and denominator. Then, divide the numerator by the denominator.
$$x = \dfrac{\log 36}{\log 8}$$
$$\approx \dfrac{1.556}{0.9031}$$
$$\approx 1.72$$

CHECK

Substitute 1.72 for x and use a calculator to verify that $8^{1.72} \approx 36$. $\qquad 8^{1.72} \stackrel{?}{\approx} 36$

[8] [^] [1] [.] [7] [2] [ENTER] $\qquad\qquad\qquad\qquad 35.8 \approx 36$ ✔

Try It
This Way

To use a calculator to find the log of a number, press **LOG**, enter the number, and press **ENTER**.

Solving Equations Using Natural Logs

The symbol for the natural log of a number x is ln x, where the base is e, the irrational constant 2.7182… . The equation ln $x = y$ is equivalent to its inverse exponential equation.

$$y = \ln x \leftrightarrow e^y = x$$

The graph of the function $y = \ln x$ appears to the right. Its domain is all positive numbers, and its range is all real numbers.

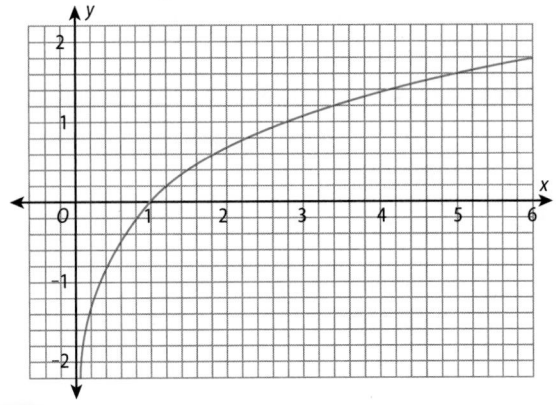

Need More

HELP ?

Remember—The following properties are true for the natural log function.

- ln $1 = 0$
- ln $e = 1$
- ln $e^x = x$

EXAMPLE 3

Solve. $3^x = 21$

STEP 1 Take the natural log of both sides of the equation.

$\ln(3^x) = \ln(21)$

STEP 2 Apply the Power Rule for Logarithms, $\ln x^y = y \ln x$, to expand the left side of the equation, where $x = 10$ and $y = \ln 12$.

$x \cdot \ln 3 = \ln 21$

STEP 3 Divide both sides of the equation by ln 3.

$x = \dfrac{\ln 21}{\ln 3}$

STEP 4 Use a calculator to approximate ln 21 and ln 3. Then divide.

$x \approx \dfrac{3.045}{1.099} \approx 2.78$

CHECK

STEP 1 Substitute $x = 2.78$ into the original exponential equation.

$3^{2.78} \stackrel{?}{\approx} 21$

STEP 2 Use a calculator to raise 3 to the 2.78, power. Enter ⟨ 3 ⟩, press the ⟨ ^ ⟩ key, press ⟨ 2 ⟩⟨ . ⟩⟨ 7 ⟩⟨ 8 ⟩ and then press ⟨ENTER⟩.

$21.02 \approx 21$ ✔

Watch Out !

$\dfrac{\ln 21}{\ln 3} \neq \ln \dfrac{21}{3}$

$\dfrac{\ln 21}{\ln 3} \approx 2.78$ and

$\ln \dfrac{21}{3} = \ln 7 \approx 1.9$.

Expanding Logarithmic Expressions

Use the Properties of Logarithms to expand logarithmic expressions.

Property	Common logs	Natural logs
Product Rule	$\log(xy) = \log x + \log y$	$\ln(xy) = \ln x + \ln y$
Quotient Rule	$\log\left(\frac{x}{y}\right) = \log x - \log y$	$\log\left(\frac{x}{y}\right) = \ln x - \ln y$
Power Rule	$\log x^y = y \log x$	$\ln x^y = y \ln x$

EXAMPLE 4

Expand $\log(x^2y)$ as much as possible.

STEP 1 Apply the Product Rule and write the product as a sum.

$\log(x^2y) = \log x^2 + \log y$

STEP 2 Apply the Power Rule, writing 2 as the coefficient of the first term.

$= 2 \log x + \log y$

SEARCH

To see step-by-step videos of these problems, enter the page number into the SWadvantage.com Search Bar.

EXAMPLE 5

Expand $\ln\left(\dfrac{\sqrt[3]{x + 1}}{25y^2}\right)$ as much as possible.

STEP 1 Apply the Quotient Rule to the expression.

$$\ln\left(\dfrac{\sqrt[3]{x + 1}}{25y^2}\right) = \ln\sqrt[3]{x + 1} - \ln(25y^2)$$

STEP 2 Rewrite $\sqrt[3]{x + 1}$ as an exponential expression.

$$= \ln(x + 1)^{\frac{1}{3}} - \ln(25y^2)$$

STEP 3 Apply the Power Rule.

$$= \frac{1}{3}\ln(x + 1) - \ln(25y^2)$$

STEP 4 Use the Product Rule to expand the logarithm of the product $25y^2$.

$$= \frac{1}{3}\ln(x + 1) - (\ln 25 + \ln y^2)$$

STEP 5 Clear the parentheses from the second term.

$$= \frac{1}{3}\ln(x + 1) - \ln 25 - \ln y^2$$

STEP 6 Apply the Power Rule.

$$= \frac{1}{3}\ln(x + 1) - \ln 25 - 2\ln y$$

Condensing Logarithmic Expressions

You can use the Properties of Logarithms to condense logarithmic expressions.

EXAMPLE 6

Write the expression $2\log x - 3\log y$ as a single logarithm.

STEP 1 Apply the Product Rule to rewrite each term with coefficients of 1.

$$2\log x - 3\log y = \log x^2 - \log y^3$$

STEP 2 Apply the Quotient Rule.

$$= \log\frac{x^2}{y^3}$$

EXAMPLE 7

Write the expression $3\ln(x + 2) + \ln 5$ as a single logarithm.

STEP 1 Apply the Product Rule to the first term.

$$3\ln(x + 2) + \ln 5 = \ln(x + 2)^3 + \ln 5$$

STEP 2 Apply the Product Rule to the addends.

$$= \ln[(x + 2)^3 \cdot 5]$$

STEP 3 Use the Commutative Property to simplify the expression.

$$= \ln 5(x + 2)^3$$

The Properties of Logarithms apply to logarithms of like bases. It is unlikely that a problem contains both log and ln functions. It will contain either log or ln. If a problem should contain both log and ln functions, the properties of logarithms do not apply to a combination of log and ln functions because the bases differ.

Change-of-Base Formula

To evaluate the logarithm of a number whose base is not 10 or e, you can use the Change of Base Formula, $\log_b x = \dfrac{\log x}{\log b} = \dfrac{\ln x}{\ln b}$, where b is a positive number other than 1.

EXAMPLE 8

Evaluate $\log_5 75$ to three decimal places using common logarithms.

STEP 1 Apply the Change of Base Formula, where $b = 5$ and $x = 75$. $\log_5 75 = \dfrac{\log 75}{\log 5}$

STEP 2 Use a calculator to evaluate the common logs of the numerator and denominator. $\approx \dfrac{1.875}{0.699}$

STEP 3 Divide. ≈ 2.683

CHECK

Because $\dfrac{\log x}{\log b} = \dfrac{\ln x}{\ln b}$, you can use natural logarithms to check. $\dfrac{\log 75}{\log 5} = \dfrac{\ln 75}{\ln 5} \approx \dfrac{4.317}{1.609} \approx 2.683 \checkmark$

SEARCH

To see step-by-step videos of these problems, enter the page number into the SWadvantage.com Search Bar.

EXAMPLE 9

Evaluate $\log_\pi 100$ to three decimal places using common logarithms.

STEP 1 Apply the Change of Base Formula, where $b = \pi$ and $x = 100$. $\log_\pi 100 = \dfrac{\log 100}{\log \pi}$

STEP 2 Use a calculator and evaluate the logs of the numerator and denominator. $\approx \dfrac{2}{0.497}$

STEP 3 Divide. ≈ 4.023

CHECK

Because $\dfrac{\log x}{\log b} = \dfrac{\ln x}{\ln b}$, you can use natural logarithms to check. $\dfrac{\log 100}{\log \pi} = \dfrac{\ln 100}{\ln \pi} \approx \dfrac{4.605}{1.145} \approx 4.022 \checkmark$

Try It This Way

You don't need a calculator to evaluate $\log 100 = 2$. By inspection, $10^2 = 100$.

Working with Common and Natural Logarithms

- To solve an exponential equation:
  1. Isolate the term with the variable in the exponent.
  2. Take the common or natural logarithm of both sides.
  3. Use a calculator to evaluate the logs.
  4. Simplify as necessary.

- To expand or condense a logarithmic expression, use the Properties of Logarithms.

- To evaluate the log of a number whose base is neither 10 (the common log) nor e (the natural log), use the Change of Base Formula,
$$\log_b x = \dfrac{\log x}{\log b} = \dfrac{\ln x}{\ln b}.$$

Need More
HELP ?

To review the algebra of polynomials, go to the section on *Polynomials* in *Algebra* (p. 1598).

Multiplying Rational Expressions

The quotient of two polynomials $\frac{a}{b}$, with $b \neq 0$, is called a **rational expression**. A **polynomial** can consist of one term (a **monomial**) or a finite sum of terms whose variables have exponents that are positive integers or zero. To multiply two rational expressions, apply the rule $\frac{a}{b} \cdot \frac{c}{d} = \frac{a \cdot c}{b \cdot d}$, where b and d do not equal zero.

EXAMPLE 1

Multiply $\frac{16x^2}{5y} \cdot \frac{15y}{8x}$**, where x and $y \neq 0$.**

METHOD 1

STEP 1 Apply the rule for multiplying two rational expressions, $\frac{a}{b} \cdot \frac{c}{d} = \frac{a \cdot c}{b \cdot d}$, where the numerators and denominators are monomials and where $a = 16x^2$, $b = 5y$, $c = 15y$, and $d = 8x$, and x and $y \neq 0$.

$$\frac{16x^2}{5y} \cdot \frac{15y}{8x} = \frac{16x^2 \cdot 15y}{5y \cdot 8x}$$

STEP 2 Rewrite the numerator and denominator showing like factors.

$$= \frac{2 \cdot 8 \cdot x \cdot x \cdot 3 \cdot 5 \cdot y}{5 \cdot y \cdot 8 \cdot x}$$

STEP 3 Apply the Commutative Property of Multiplication to reorder the factors in the numerator and denominator. Then cancel like factors.

$$= \frac{2 \cdot \overset{1}{\cancel{8}} \cdot 3 \cdot \overset{1}{\cancel{5}} \cdot \overset{1}{\cancel{y}} \cdot x \cdot \overset{1}{\cancel{y}}}{\underset{1}{\cancel{5}} \cdot \underset{1}{\cancel{8}} \cdot \underset{1}{\cancel{y}} \cdot \underset{1}{\cancel{x}}}$$

STEP 4 Write the product in lowest terms.

$$= \frac{2 \cdot 3 \cdot x}{1} = 6x$$

The product is $6x$.

METHOD 2

STEP 1 Rewrite the two rational expressions in factored form before multiplying.

$$\frac{16x^2}{5y} \cdot \frac{15y}{8x} = \frac{2 \cdot 8 \cdot x^2}{5 \cdot y} \cdot \frac{3 \cdot 5 \cdot y}{8 \cdot x}$$

STEP 2 Cancel like factors in the numerators and the denominators.

$$= \frac{2 \cdot \overset{1}{\cancel{8}} \cdot x^2}{\underset{1}{\cancel{5}} \cdot \underset{1}{\cancel{y}}} \cdot \frac{3 \cdot \overset{1}{\cancel{5}} \cdot \overset{1}{\cancel{y}}}{\underset{1}{\cancel{8}} \cdot x}$$

$$= \frac{2 \cdot x^2}{1} \cdot \frac{3}{x}$$

STEP 3 Apply the Property of Negative exponents to rewrite $\frac{1}{x}$ as x^{-1}.

$$= \frac{2 \cdot x^2}{1} \cdot 3 \cdot \frac{1}{x}$$

$$= 2 \cdot x^2 \cdot 3 \cdot x^{-1}$$

STEP 4 Apply the Product Rule for multiplying like bases, $a^n \cdot a^m = a^{n+m}$, and simplify the result.

$$= 2 \cdot 3 \cdot x^{2+(-1)}$$

$$= 6x$$

The product is $6x$.

Watch Out !

When simplifying a rational expression, only like factors can be canceled. Do not cancel part of a sum.
$$\frac{\cancel{a}+c}{\cancel{a} \cdot d} \neq \frac{c}{d}$$

Need More
HELP ?

A rational expression is in lowest terms if the numerator and denominator share no common factor other than 1.

EXAMPLE 2

Multiply. $\dfrac{a+4}{2a-10} \cdot \dfrac{a^2-25}{a^2-16}$

STEP 1 Multiply the numerators and denominators to form one fraction.

$$\frac{a+4}{2a-10} \cdot \frac{a^2-25}{a^2-16} = \frac{(a+4) \cdot (a^2-25)}{(2a-10) \cdot (a^2-16)}$$

STEP 2 Factor the numerator and denominator, and cancel like factors.

$$= \frac{{}^1(a+4) \cdot (a+5) \cdot (a-5)^1}{2 \cdot (a-5)_1 \cdot (a+4)_1 \cdot (a-4)}$$

STEP 3 Write the product in lowest terms.

$$= \frac{(a+5)}{2(a-4)}$$

CHECK

Let $a = 0$ and substitute 0 into the original expression and the product to see if they are equal.

$$\frac{(0)+4}{2 \cdot (0)-10} \cdot \frac{(0)^2-25}{(0)^2-16} = \frac{4(-25)}{(-10)(-16)} = \frac{-100}{160} = \frac{-5}{8}$$

$$\frac{(0)+5}{2(0-4)} = \frac{5}{-8} \; \checkmark$$

The two expressions are equal, so the product is correct.

> **Need More HELP ?**
>
> Recall that the difference of two squares can be factored into two binomial factors:
>
> $a^2 - b^2 = (a+b)(a-b)$

EXAMPLE 3

Multiply. $\dfrac{x^2+2x-15}{x^2+11x+30} \cdot \dfrac{x^2+2x-24}{x^2-8x+15}$

STEP 1 Factor the numerators and denominators in each rational expression.

$$\frac{x^2+2x-15}{x^2+11x+30} \cdot \frac{x^2+2x-24}{x^2-8x+15}$$

$$= \frac{(x+5)(x-3)}{(x+6)(x+5)} \cdot \frac{(x+6)(x-4)}{(x-3)(x-5)}$$

STEP 2 Cancel like factors in the numerators and denominators of the two fractions.

$$= \frac{{}^1(x+5)(x-3)^1}{{}_1(x+6)(x+5)_1} \cdot \frac{{}^1(x+6)(x-4)}{{}_1(x-3)(x-5)}$$

STEP 3 Write the product in lowest terms.

$$= \frac{x-4}{x-5}$$

CHECK

Let $a = 0$ and substitute 0 into the original expression and the product to see if they are equal.

$$\frac{(0)^2+2 \cdot (0)-15}{(0)^2+11 \cdot (0)+30} \cdot \frac{(0)^2+2 \cdot (0)-24}{(0)^2-8 \cdot (0)+15} = \frac{(-15)(-24)}{30 \cdot 15} = \frac{24}{30} = \frac{4}{5}$$

$$\frac{(0)-4}{(0)-5} = \frac{-4}{-5} = \frac{4}{5} \; \checkmark$$

The two expressions are equal, so the product is correct.

> **Watch Out !**
>
> When using substitution to check a product, be sure that the number you substitute does not result in a zero denominator.

> **Need More HELP ?**
>
> To review how to factor trinomials, go to *Factoring Polynomials* in *Algebra* (p. 1658).

SOUTHWESTERN

Dividing Rational Expressions

To divide a rational expression $\frac{a}{b}$ by a rational expression $\frac{c}{d}$, multiply $\frac{a}{b}$ by the **multiplicative inverse**, or **reciprocal**, of the divisor: $\frac{a}{b} \div \frac{d}{c} = \frac{a}{b} \cdot \frac{c}{d}$, where b, c, and $d \neq 0$.

EXAMPLE 4

Divide $\frac{24s^3}{6s^2}$ by $\frac{12s}{20s^2}$.

METHOD 1

STEP 1 To divide, multiply the expression $\frac{24s^3}{6s^2}$ by the reciprocal of the divisor, $\frac{12s}{20s^2}$, where $s \neq 0$.

$$\frac{24s^3}{6s^2} \div \frac{12s}{20s^2} = \frac{24s^3}{6s^2} \cdot \frac{20s^2}{12s}$$

STEP 2 Write out the factors in the numerator and denominator of each fraction.

$$= \frac{2 \cdot 12 \cdot s^2 \cdot s}{2 \cdot 3 \cdot s^2} \cdot \frac{20 \cdot s \cdot s}{12 \cdot s}$$

STEP 3 Cancel out like factors and simplify the remaining factors.

$$= \frac{2 \cdot 12 \cdot s^2 \cdot s}{2 \cdot 3 \cdot s^2} \cdot \frac{20 \cdot s \cdot s}{12 \cdot s}$$

$$= \frac{20 \cdot s \cdot s}{3} = \frac{20s^2}{3}$$

METHOD 2

STEP 1 Multiply $\frac{24s^3}{6s^2}$ by the reciprocal of the divisor, $\frac{12s}{20s^2}$, where $s \neq 0$, and express the product as one fraction.

$$\frac{24s^3}{6s^2} \div \frac{12s}{20s^2}$$

$$= \frac{24s^3 \cdot 20s^2}{6s^2 \cdot 12s}$$

STEP 2 Use the Commutative Property of Multiplication to reorder the numeric and variable factors. Apply the Product Rule to multiply like bases in the numerator: $a^m \cdot a^n = a^{m+n}$.

$$= \frac{24 \cdot 20 \cdot s^3 \cdot s^2}{6 \cdot 12 \cdot s \cdot s^2}$$

$$= \frac{24 \cdot 20 \cdot s^5}{6 \cdot 12 \cdot s^3}$$

STEP 3 Use the Division Rule to divide like bases: $\frac{a^m}{a^n} = a^{m-n}$. Then simplify.

$$= \frac{24 \cdot 20 \cdot s^{5-3}}{6 \cdot 12} = \frac{480s^2}{72} = \frac{20s^2}{3}$$

CHECK

Let $s = 2$ and substitute 2 into the original expression and into the product to see if they are equal.

$$\frac{24(2)^3}{6(2)^2} \div \frac{12(2)}{20(2)^2} = \frac{192}{24} \cdot \frac{80}{24} = \frac{192 \cdot 80}{192 \cdot 3} = \frac{80}{3} \text{ and } \frac{20 \cdot (2)^2}{3} = \frac{80}{3} ✔$$

The two expressions are equal, so the product is correct.

EXAMPLE 5

Divide $\dfrac{8y + 20}{4}$ **by** $\dfrac{6y + 15}{3}$.

STEP 1 Multiply $\dfrac{8y + 20}{4}$ by the reciprocal of $\dfrac{6y + 15}{3}$, where $y \neq -\dfrac{5}{2}$.

$$\frac{8y + 20}{4} \div \frac{6y + 15}{3} = \frac{8y + 20}{4} \cdot \frac{3}{6y + 15}$$

STEP 2 Factor the numerator and denominator of each rational expression.

$$= \frac{4(2y + 5)}{4} \cdot \frac{3}{3(2y + 5)}$$

STEP 3 Cancel like factors, and simplify.

$$= \frac{\cancel{4}(\cancel{2y + 5})}{\cancel{4}} \cdot \frac{\cancel{3}}{\cancel{3}(\cancel{2y + 5})} = 1$$

CHECK

Let $y = 0$. $\dfrac{8(0) + 20}{4} \div \dfrac{6(0) + 15}{3} = \dfrac{20}{4} \div \dfrac{15}{3} = 5 \times \dfrac{3}{15} = \dfrac{15}{15} = 1$ ✔

Need More
HELP

If the denominator of a rational expression has the form $ax + b$, set $ax + b$ equal to 0, and solve for x. The resulting value of x must be excluded.

EXAMPLE 6

Divide $\dfrac{3r^3 - 9r^2}{r^2 - 9}$ **by** $\dfrac{6r^2}{r^2 + 6r + 9}$.

STEP 1 Multiply the dividend by the reciprocal of the divisor. Note that $r \neq 0$, -3, or 3.

$$\frac{3r^3 - 9r^2}{r^2 - 9} \div \frac{6r^2}{r^2 + 6r + 9} = \frac{3r^3 - 9r^2}{r^2 - 9} \times \frac{r^2 + 6r + 9}{6r^2}$$

STEP 2 Factor the numerator and denominator of each rational expression.

$$= \frac{3r^2(r - 3)}{(r - 3)(r + 3)} \times \frac{(r + 3)^2}{6r^2}$$

STEP 3 Cancel like factors, and simplify the result.

$$= \frac{3 \cdot \cancel{r^2} \cdot \cancel{(r - 3)}}{\cancel{(r - 3)}\cancel{(r + 3)}} \times \frac{(r + 3)^{\cancel{2}^{1}}}{6 \cdot \cancel{r^2}} = \frac{r + 3}{2}$$

CHECK

Let $r = 1$. $\dfrac{3(1)^3 - 9(1)^2}{(1)^2 - 9} \div \dfrac{6(1)^2}{(1)^2 + 6(1) + 9} = \dfrac{-6}{-8} \times \dfrac{16}{6} = 2$ and $\dfrac{(1) + 3}{2} = 2$ ✔

Need More
HELP

Remember—a perfect square trinomial can be factored into the square of a binomial.
$a^2 + 2ab + b^2 = (a + b)^2$

GOT TO KNOW!

Multiplying and Dividing Rational Expressions

If a and b are polynomials and $b \neq 0$, then $\dfrac{a}{b}$ is a rational expression.

To multiply rational expressions, use the rule $\dfrac{a}{b} \cdot \dfrac{c}{d} = \dfrac{a \cdot c}{b \cdot d}$ where b and $d \neq 0$.

To divide rational expressions, use the rule $\dfrac{a}{b} \div \dfrac{c}{d} = \dfrac{a}{b} \cdot \dfrac{d}{c}$, where b, d, and $c \neq 0$.

Adding and Subtracting Rational Expressions

Adding Rational Expressions

A rational expression has a polynomial in its numerator and denominator. To add two rational expressions, apply the rule $\frac{a}{b} + \frac{c}{d} = \frac{ad + bc}{bd}$, where bd is the **least common denominator (LCD)**, and neither b nor d equals zero. The LCD is a product of prime factors, where the exponent of each factor is the greatest exponent in either denominator.

Need More

HELP ?

To review polynomials, go to *Operations with Polynomials* in *Algebra* (p. 1598).

EXAMPLE 1

Add $\frac{2}{xy} + \frac{8}{xy}$, where $x \neq 0$ and $y \neq 0$.

METHOD 1

STEP 1 Find the LCD.

The denominators of the two rational expressions are equal, so the LCD is xy.

STEP 2 Combine the two fractions and simplify.

$$\frac{2}{xy} + \frac{8}{xy} = \frac{2+8}{xy} = \frac{10}{xy}$$

METHOD 2

STEP 1 Apply the Distributive Property $ab + ac = (b + c)a$.

$$\frac{2}{xy} + \frac{8}{xy} = (2 + 8)\frac{1}{xy}$$

STEP 2 Simplify.

$$= 10\frac{1}{xy} = \frac{10}{xy}$$

EXAMPLE 2

Need More

HELP ?

Remember—it is not necessary to find a LCD when multiplying or dividing rational expressions. The rules for multiplication and division are $\frac{a}{b} \cdot \frac{c}{d} = \frac{a \cdot c}{b \cdot d}$ and $\frac{a}{b} \div \frac{c}{d} = \frac{a}{b} \cdot \frac{d}{c} = \frac{ad}{bc}$ respectively.

Add $\frac{6}{5y^2} + \frac{1}{y^2}$, where $y \neq 0$.

STEP 1 Find the LCD.

The prime factors of $5y^2$ are $5 \cdot y \cdot y$, and the prime factors of y^2 are $y \cdot y$. Therefore, the LCD of these two expressions is $5y^2$.

STEP 2 Rewrite the second addend as an equivalent fraction whose denominator is $5y^2$ by multiplying $\frac{1}{y^2}$ by 1 in the form of $\frac{5}{5}$.

$$\frac{6}{5y^2} + \frac{1}{y^2} = \frac{6}{5y^2} + \frac{5}{5} \cdot \frac{1}{y^2}$$

$$= \frac{6}{5y^2} + \frac{5}{5y^2}$$

STEP 3 The denominators of the two fractions are alike, so combine the two fractions and simplify the numerator.

$$= \frac{6}{5y^2} + \frac{5}{5y^2}$$

$$= \frac{6+5}{5y^2} = \frac{11}{5y^2}$$

Check by substitution.

Let $y = 1$ and substitute 1 into the original expression and the sum to see if they're equal.

$$\frac{6}{5(1)^2} + \frac{1}{(1)^2} = \frac{6}{5} + 1 = \frac{11}{5} \text{ and } \frac{11}{5(1)^2} = \frac{11}{5} \checkmark$$

EXAMPLE 3

Add $\dfrac{a}{a-3} + \dfrac{3}{3-a}$.

There are two ways you can find the sum of these fractions.

The binomial denominators $3 - a$ and $a - 3$ are opposites. So, you can either multiply the first or second term by 1 in the form of $\dfrac{-1}{-1}$ to find an LCD in either case.

Combine the fractions and simplify.

METHOD 1	METHOD 2
$\dfrac{a}{a-3} + \dfrac{3}{3-a}$	$\dfrac{a}{a-3} + \dfrac{3}{3-a}$
$= \dfrac{-1}{-1} \cdot \dfrac{a}{a-3} + \dfrac{3}{3-a}$	$= \dfrac{a}{a-3} + \dfrac{3}{3-a} \cdot \dfrac{-1}{-1}$
$= \dfrac{-a}{3-a} + \dfrac{3}{3-a}$	$= \dfrac{a}{a-3} + \dfrac{-3}{a-3}$
$= \dfrac{-a+3}{3-a} = 1$	$= \dfrac{a-3}{a-3} = 1$

SEARCH

To see step-by-step videos of these problems, enter the page number into the SWadvantage.com Search Bar.

EXAMPLE 4

Add $\dfrac{x^2 + 5x}{x^2 + 2x - 15} + \dfrac{x^2 - 25}{x^2 - 9}$.

STEP 1 Factor the numerators and denominators of each fraction. The LCD contains three prime factors: $(x + 5)$, $(x + 3)$, and $(x - 3)$, where $x \neq 5$ and $x \neq \pm 3$.

STEP 2 Cancel the like factors $(x + 5)$ in the numerator and denominator of the first term.

STEP 3 The LCD of the remaining addends is $(x + 3)(x - 3)$. To add, multiply the first addend by 1 in the form of $\dfrac{x+3}{x+3}$, and combine the fractions into one fraction by multiplying their numerators.

STEP 4 Apply the Distributive Property, $a(b + c) = ab + ac$, to find the product of each term of the numerator and then combine like terms.

$$\dfrac{x^2 + 5x}{x^2 + 2x - 15} + \dfrac{x^2 - 25}{x^2 - 9}$$

$$= \dfrac{x(x + 5)}{(x + 5)(x - 3)} + \dfrac{(x + 5)(x - 5)}{(x + 3)(x - 3)}$$

$$= \dfrac{x\cancel{(x + 5)}}{\cancel{(x + 5)}(x - 3)} + \dfrac{(x + 5)(x - 5)}{(x + 3)(x - 3)}$$

$$= \dfrac{x}{(x - 3)} + \dfrac{(x + 5)(x - 5)}{(x + 3)(x - 3)}$$

$$= \dfrac{x}{x - 3} \cdot \dfrac{x + 3}{x + 3} + \dfrac{(x + 5)(x - 5)}{(x + 3)(x - 3)}$$

$$= \dfrac{x(x + 3) + (x + 5)(x - 5)}{(x + 3)(x - 3)}$$

$$= \dfrac{(x^2 + 3x) + (x^2 - 25)}{(x + 3)(x - 3)}$$

$$= \dfrac{2x^2 + 3x - 25}{(x + 3)(x - 3)}$$

Need More HELP?

To review how to factor the difference of two squares, $a^2 - b^2$, and a perfect square trinomial, $a^2 + 2ab + b^2$, go to *Factoring Polynomials* in *Algebra* (p. 1658).

Check by substitution.

Let $x = 0$ and substitute 0 into the original expression and the sum to see if they are equal.

$$\dfrac{(0)^2 + 5(0)}{(0)^2 + 2(0) - 15} + \dfrac{(0)^2 - 25}{(0)^2 - 9} = \dfrac{-25}{-9}$$

$$\dfrac{2(0)^2 + 3(0) - 25}{(0 + 3)(0 - 3)} = \dfrac{-25}{-9}$$

The two expressions are equal, so the product is correct. ✔

Need More
HELP ?

The rules for subtracting and adding rational expressions are similar. Each requires identifying an LCD before adding or subtracting.

$$\frac{a}{b} \pm \frac{c}{d} = \frac{ad \pm bc}{bd}$$

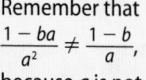

Watch Out !

Remember that $\frac{1-ba}{a^2} \neq \frac{1-b}{a}$, because a is not a common factor of the numerator $1 - ba$ and the denominator.

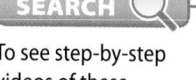

SEARCH

To see step-by-step videos of these problems, enter the page number into the SWadvantage.com Search Bar.

Subtracting Rational Expressions

To subtract rational expressions, apply the rule $\frac{a}{b} - \frac{c}{d} = \frac{ad - bc}{bd}$, where bd is the least common denominator (LCD) of the expressions, and $b \neq 0$ and $d \neq 0$.

EXAMPLE 5

Subtract $\frac{1}{a^2} - \frac{b}{a}$, where $a \neq 0$.

STEP 1 Find the LCD.

The LCD of the two expressions is a^2. Therefore, multiply $\frac{b}{a}$ by 1 in the form of $\frac{a}{a}$.

$$\frac{1}{a^2} - \frac{b}{a}$$
$$= \frac{1}{a^2} - \frac{b}{a} \cdot \frac{a}{a}$$
$$= \frac{1}{a^2} - \frac{ba}{a^2}$$

STEP 2 The denominators are alike, so combine the two fractions.

$$= \frac{1 - ba}{a^2}$$

Check by substitution.

Substitute $a = 1$ and $b = 2$ into the original expression and the difference to see if they are equal.

$$\frac{1}{1^2} - \frac{2}{1} = 1 - 2 = -1 \text{ and } \frac{1 - (1)(2)}{1^2} = -1$$

The expressions are equal, so the difference is correct. ✔

EXAMPLE 6

Subtract $\frac{3}{r - 5} - \frac{8}{5 - r}$, where $r \neq 5$.

STEP 1 The denominators are opposites of each other, not equal. So, to find a LCD, you can either multiply the first or the second term by 1 in the form of $\frac{-1}{-1}$.

The denominator in Method 1 is $5 - r$, and the denominator in Method 2 is $r - 5$. These expressions are opposites.

STEP 2 The denominators in each case are alike, so combine the fractions and simplify the differences.

METHOD 1

$$\frac{3}{r - 5} - \frac{8}{5 - r}$$
$$= \frac{-1}{-1} \cdot \frac{3}{r - 5} - \frac{8}{5 - r}$$
$$= \frac{-3}{-(r - 5)} - \frac{8}{5 - r}$$
$$= \frac{-3}{5 - r} - \frac{8}{5 - r}$$
$$= \frac{-3 - 8}{5 - r}$$
$$= \frac{-11}{5 - r}$$

METHOD 2

$$\frac{3}{r - 5} - \frac{8}{5 - r}$$
$$= \frac{3}{r - 5} - \frac{8}{5 - r} \cdot \frac{-1}{-1}$$
$$= \frac{3}{r - 5} - \frac{(-8)}{-(5 - r)}$$
$$= \frac{3}{r - 5} - \frac{(-8)}{r - 5}$$
$$= \frac{3 - (-8)}{r - 5}$$
$$= \frac{11}{r - 5}$$

EXAMPLE 7

Subtract. $\dfrac{x}{x^2 - 3x - 10} - \dfrac{2}{x^2 - 6x + 5}$

STEP 1 Find the LCD.

Factor each trinomial. The LCD is $(x - 5)(x + 2)(x - 1)$, where $x \neq 5$, $x \neq 1$, and $x \neq -2$.

STEP 2 Write each expression with the same denominator.

Multiply the first term by $\dfrac{(x - 1)}{(x - 1)}$ and the second term by $\dfrac{(x + 2)}{(x + 2)}$.

STEP 3 Combine the two rational expressions into one fraction whose LCD is $(x - 5)(x + 2)(x - 1)$.

STEP 4 Apply the Distributive Property to the two terms in the numerator of the difference, and combine like terms.

STEP 5 Factor the numerator.

$$\dfrac{x}{x^2 - 3x - 10} - \dfrac{2}{x^2 - 6x + 5}$$

$$= \dfrac{x}{(x - 5)(x + 2)} - \dfrac{2}{(x - 5)(x - 1)}$$

$$= \dfrac{x}{(x - 5)(x + 2)} \cdot \dfrac{(x - 1)}{(x - 1)} - \dfrac{2}{(x - 5)(x - 1)} \cdot \dfrac{(x + 2)}{(x + 2)}$$

$$= \dfrac{x(x - 1) - 2(x + 2)}{(x - 5)(x - 1)(x + 2)}$$

$$= \dfrac{x^2 - x - 2x - 4}{(x - 5)(x - 1)(x + 2)}$$

$$= \dfrac{x^2 - 3x - 4}{(x - 5)(x - 1)(x + 2)}$$

$$= \dfrac{(x + 1)(x - 4)}{(x - 5)(x - 1)(x + 2)}$$

Check by substitution.

Let $x = 0$ and substitute 0 into the original expression and the difference.

$$\dfrac{0}{0^2 - 3 \cdot 0 - 10} - \dfrac{2}{0^2 - 6 \cdot 0 + 5} = \dfrac{-2}{5} \text{ and } \dfrac{(0 - 1)(0 + 4)}{(0 - 5)(0 - 1)(0 + 2)} = -\dfrac{4}{10} = -\dfrac{2}{5}$$

The two expressions are equal. ✔

Need More

HELP?

To factor a trinomial of the form $1x^2 + bx + c$ that is not a perfect square, find the two factors of c whose sum is b.

Watch Out!

When distributing a negative number over a sum $(a + b)$, the signs of the terms within the parentheses change. That is, $-2(x + 2) = -2x - 4$.

GOT TO KNOW!

Adding and Subtracting Rational Expressions

- The least common denominator (LCD) of two rational expressions is a product of prime factors, where the exponent of each factor is the greatest exponent in either denominator.

- To add rational expressions, use the rule $\dfrac{a}{b} + \dfrac{c}{d} = \dfrac{ad + bc}{bd}$, where bd is the least common denominator, and b and $d \neq 0$.

- To subtract rational expressions, use the rule $\dfrac{a}{b} - \dfrac{c}{d} = \dfrac{ad - bc}{bd}$, where bd is the least common denominator, and b and $d \neq 0$.

Complex Fractions

SOUTHWESTERN

Simplifying Complex Fractions

A fraction $\frac{a}{b}$, where $b \neq 0$, is an indicated quotient that means $a \div b$, where a and b are rational expressions. Division of rational expressions is defined as $a \div b = a \times \frac{1}{b}$, where $\frac{1}{b}$ is the multiplicative inverse (reciprocal) of b.

A **complex fraction** is a fraction in which either a or b, or both, are **rational expressions** — polynomials whose exponents are positive integers or zero. Complex fractions have fractions as numerators and/or denominators.

EXAMPLE 1

Simplify the complex fraction $\dfrac{\frac{1}{2}}{\frac{3}{4}}$.

METHOD 1

STEP 1 Apply the definition of division: $a \div b = a \times \frac{1}{b}$, where $a = \frac{1}{2}$ and $b = \frac{3}{4}$.

To divide, multiply $\frac{1}{2}$ by the multiplicative inverse of $\frac{3}{4}$, which is $\frac{4}{3}$.

$$\frac{\left(\frac{1}{2}\right)}{\left(\frac{3}{4}\right)} = \frac{1}{2} \div \frac{3}{4}$$

$$= \frac{1}{2} \times \frac{4}{3}$$

STEP 2 Express the product in simplest form.

$$= \frac{4}{6}$$

$$= \frac{2}{3}$$

METHOD 2

STEP 1 Multiply both the numerator and denominator by the least common denominator (LCD) of both fractions. The LCD for 2 and 4 is 4, so multiply the fraction by 1 in the form of $\frac{4}{4}$.

$$\frac{\left(\frac{1}{2}\right)}{\left(\frac{3}{4}\right)} \cdot \frac{4}{4} = \frac{\left(\frac{1}{2}\right) \cdot 4}{\left(\frac{3}{4}\right) \cdot 4}$$

STEP 2 Find the products of the numerator and denominator and simplify.

$$= \frac{\left(\frac{4}{2}\right)}{\left(\frac{3 \cdot 4}{4}\right)} = \frac{2}{3}$$

The simplest form of $\dfrac{\frac{1}{2}}{\frac{3}{4}}$ is $\frac{2}{3}$.

EXAMPLE 2

Simplify the complex fraction $\dfrac{1+\frac{1}{x}}{1-\frac{1}{x}}$.

METHOD 1

STEP 1 Perform the indicated operations in the numerator and denominator of the complex fraction. The LCD of each term is x.

$$\frac{1+\frac{1}{x}}{1-\frac{1}{x}}$$

$$=\frac{\frac{x+1}{x}}{\frac{x-1}{x}}$$

STEP 2 Rewrite the complex fraction as a division problem and apply the definition of division. Multiply the first term by the reciprocal of $\frac{x-1}{x}$, which is $\frac{x}{x-1}$.

$$=\frac{x+1}{x}\div\frac{x-1}{x}$$

$$=\frac{x+1}{x}\cdot\frac{x}{x-1}$$

$$=\frac{(x+1)\cdot x}{x\cdot(x-1)}$$

STEP 3 Cancel like factors in the numerator and denominator and simplify. (Note: $x\neq0$ and $x\neq1$)

$$=\frac{(x+1)\cdot\cancel{x}}{\cancel{x}\cdot(x-1)}$$

$$=\frac{x+1}{x-1}$$

METHOD 2

STEP 1 Multiply both the numerator and denominator by x, the LCD of $1+\frac{1}{x}$ and $1-\frac{1}{x}$, $(x\neq0)$.

$$=\frac{x\cdot\left(1+\frac{1}{x}\right)}{x\cdot\left(1-\frac{1}{x}\right)}$$

STEP 2 Apply the Distributive Property $a(b+c)$ to the numerator and denominator where $a=x$, $b=1$, and $c=\frac{1}{x}$, and $x\neq1$. Cancel like factors in the products, $x\cdot\frac{1}{x}$.

$$=\frac{x\cdot1+x\cdot\frac{1}{x}}{x\cdot1-x\cdot\frac{1}{x}}$$

$$=\frac{x+1}{x-1}$$

Check by substitution.

Let $x=-1$ and substitute -1 into the original complex fraction and the simplified answer above.

$$\frac{1+\frac{1}{(-1)}}{1-\frac{1}{(-1)}}=\frac{1-1}{-2}=0$$

$$\frac{(-1+1)}{(-1-1)}=\frac{0}{-2}=0$$

✔ The two expressions are equal, so the simplification was correct.

Need More HELP ?

Remember—to add or to subtract two rational expressions, find the LCD of the denominators in each expression.

$$\frac{a}{b}\pm\frac{c}{d}=\frac{ad\pm bc}{bd}$$

Watch Out !

When multiplying rational expressions. be sure to use $\frac{a}{b}\cdot\frac{c}{d}=\frac{ac}{bd}$, where b and d are not zero.

SEARCH

To see step-by-step videos of these problems, enter the page number into the SWadvantage.com Search Bar.

EXAMPLE 3

Simplify the complex fraction $\dfrac{\left(\frac{1}{x+h} - \frac{1}{x}\right)}{h}$, $(x \neq 0 \text{ and } h \neq 0)$.

STEP 1 Find the LCD of the expression in the numerator. The LCD is $x(x + h)$. Write the numerator as a subtraction problem with this LCD.

$$\frac{\frac{1}{x+h} - \frac{1}{x}}{h} = \frac{\frac{x - (x + h)}{x(x + h)}}{h}$$

STEP 2 Rewrite the complex fraction as a division problem. Apply the definition of division to write the product of $\frac{1}{h}$ and $\frac{x - (x + h)}{x(x + h)}$.

$$= \frac{x - (x + h)}{x(x + h)} \div h$$

$$= \frac{x - (x + h)}{x(x + h)} \cdot \frac{1}{h}$$

STEP 3 Multiply the fraction by $\frac{1}{h}$, and simplify.

$$= \frac{1 \cdot x - (x + h)}{h \cdot x(x + h)}$$

$$= \frac{x - x - h}{h \cdot x(x + h)}$$

$$= \frac{-h}{h \cdot x(x + h)} = \frac{-1}{x(x + h)}$$

EXAMPLE 4

Simplify $\dfrac{\frac{3}{w^2 - 25} + w}{\frac{1}{w - 5}}$, $(w \neq \pm 5)$.

STEP 1 Find the LCD.
The LCD for $\frac{3}{w^2 - 25}$ and w is $w^2 - 25$.

STEP 2 Write both terms in the numerator using the LCD.

$$\frac{\frac{3}{w^2 - 25} + w}{\frac{1}{w - 5}} = \frac{\frac{3 + w(w^2 - 25)}{w^2 - 25}}{\frac{1}{w - 5}}$$

STEP 3 Multiply both the numerator and denominator of the complex fraction by the LCD, $w^2 - 25$.

$$= \frac{\frac{3 + w(w^2 - 25)}{w^2 - 25}}{\frac{1}{w - 5}} \cdot \frac{w^2 - 25}{w^2 - 25}$$

STEP 4 Cancel like factors and rewrite the terms in the numerator of the final answer.

$$= \frac{\left(\frac{3 + w^3 - 25w}{w^2 - 25}\right) \cdot (w^2 - 25)}{\left(\frac{1}{w - 5}\right) \cdot (w^2 - 25)^{(w + 5)}}$$

$$= \frac{w^3 - 25w + 3}{w + 5}$$

EXAMPLE 5

Write $\dfrac{(x+y)^{-1}}{x^{-1}+y^{-1}}$ as a fraction with positive exponents.

METHOD 1

STEP 1 To simplify this expression, apply the rule for Negative Exponents: $a^{-n} = \dfrac{1}{a^n}$, where $a \neq 0$. The result is a complex fraction.

$$\dfrac{(x+y)^{-1}}{x^{-1}+y^{-1}} = \dfrac{\frac{1}{x+y}}{\frac{1}{x}+\frac{1}{y}}$$

STEP 2 Write the denominator of the complex fraction as a rational number, where the LCD is xy.

$$= \dfrac{\frac{1}{x+y}}{\frac{y\cdot 1}{xy}+\frac{x\cdot 1}{xy}} = \dfrac{\frac{1}{x+y}}{\frac{y+x}{xy}}$$

STEP 3 Rewrite the complex fraction as a division problem. Apply the definition of division.

$$= \dfrac{1}{x+y} \div \dfrac{y+x}{xy}$$

$$= \dfrac{1}{x+y} \cdot \dfrac{xy}{y+x}$$

STEP 4 Write the product as one fraction in simplest form.

$$= \dfrac{xy}{(x+y)^2}$$

METHOD 2

STEP 1 Apply the rule for Negative Exponents: $a^{-n} = \dfrac{1}{a^n}$, where $a \neq 0$ and add the terms in the denominator of the complex fraction, where the LCD is xy.

$$\dfrac{(x+y)^{-1}}{x^{-1}+y^{-1}} = \dfrac{\frac{1}{x+y}}{\frac{1}{x}+\frac{1}{y}} = \dfrac{\frac{1}{x+y}}{\frac{y+x}{xy}}$$

STEP 2 Multiply both the numerator and denominator of the complex fraction by the LCD of the numerator and denominator, $xy(x+y)$, and cancel like factors.

$$= \dfrac{\frac{1}{x+y}}{\frac{y+x}{xy}} \cdot \dfrac{xy(x+y)}{xy(x+y)}$$

STEP 3 Simplify.

$$= \dfrac{xy}{(x+y)^2}$$

Watch Out !

Recall that
$(a+b)^{-n} \neq a^{-n} + b^{-n}$
So, in this problem,
$(x+y)^{-1} \neq x^{-1} + y^{-1}$
and, therefore,
$\dfrac{(x+y)^{-1}}{x^{-1}+y^{-1}} \neq 1.$

SEARCH

To see step-by-step videos of these problems, enter the page number into the SWadvantage.com Search Bar.

GOT TO KNOW!

Simplifying Complex Fractions

A complex fraction is the quotient of two rational expressions, where the numerator or denominator, or both, are also fractions.

Method 1	Method 2
Apply the definition of division $a \div b = a \times \dfrac{1}{b}$, where $\dfrac{1}{b}$ is the multiplicative inverse (reciprocal) of b ($b \neq 0$), and then simplify the result.	Multiply both numerator and denominator by the LCD of the numerator and denominator of the complex fraction and then simplify the result.

Exponential and Logarithmic Equations

What Came Before?
- Properties of exponents and logarithms
- Solving equations and problems

What's This About?
- Exponential growth and decay
- Solving exponential and logarithmic equations
- Using exponential equations to represent real-world problems

Practical Apps
- Mortgage interest compounds continuously, and the base e is used to find the balance at a specific time.
- The pH scale, which measures the acidity of a solution, is logarithmic.

Just for FUN!

Oh no, we're studying natural logs next.

eeeeeeeeee!!!!

CONTENTS	UPLOAD	DOWNLOAD	*Advanced Algebra*

You can find more practice problems online by visiting:
www.SWadvantage.com

Exponential Growth

Graphing Exponential Growth Functions

In equations like $y = 3^x$ or $y = \frac{1}{2} \cdot 4^x$, the variable x is an exponent. Equations like these, which can be written in general form as $y = ab^x$, are called **exponential functions** as long as $a \neq 0$, $b > 0$, and $b \neq 1$. When $a > 0$ and $b > 1$, the equation $y = ab^x$ is called an **exponential growth function** because the values of y grow as the values of x increase.

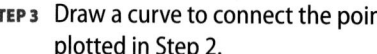

Watch Out

Be sure the values of a and b meet the qualifications for those numbers. If $a = 0$, the equation would be $y = 0$, which is a line, not an exponential function. If $b = 1$, then the equation would be $y = a$, which is also a line, not an exponential function. So we have to say $a \neq 0$ and $b \neq 1$ when we describe these numbers in $y = ab^x$.

EXAMPLE 1

Graph $y = 2^x$.

STEP 1 Make a table of values for x and y.

x	-2	-1	0	1	2	3
y	$\frac{1}{4}$	$\frac{1}{2}$	1	2	4	8

STEP 2 Plot the points from the table on a coordinate grid.

STEP 3 Draw a curve to connect the points you plotted in Step 2.

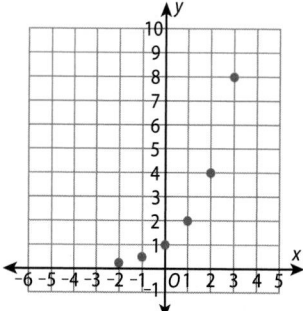

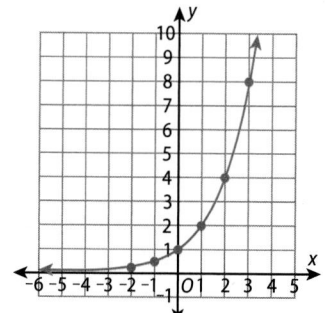

An **asymptote** is a line that a graph approaches more and more closely. As the values of x in the graph of $y = 2^x$ get smaller and smaller, the values of y get closer and closer to 0. This means that the line $y = 0$ is an asymptote of the graph of $y = 2^x$.

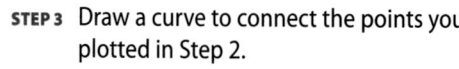

SEARCH

To see step-by-step videos of these problems, enter the page number into the SWadvantage.com Search Bar.

EXAMPLE 2

Graph $y = \frac{1}{2} \cdot 4^x$.

STEP 1 Make a table of values for x and y.

x	-2	-1	0	1	2
y	$\frac{1}{32}$	$\frac{1}{8}$	$\frac{1}{2}$	2	8

STEP 2 Plot the points from the table on a coordinate grid.

STEP 3 Draw a curve to connect the points you plotted in Step 2.

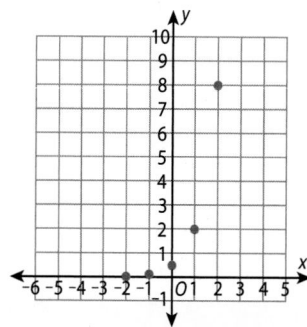

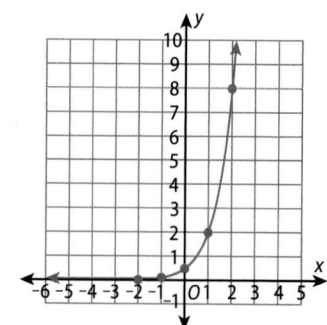

EXAMPLE 3

Graph $y = -\frac{1}{2} \cdot 3^x$.

STEP 1 Make a table of values for x and y.

x	-2	-1	0	1	2
y	$-\frac{1}{18}$	$-\frac{1}{6}$	$-\frac{1}{2}$	$-\frac{3}{2}$	$-\frac{9}{2}$

STEP 2 Plot the points from the table on a coordinate grid.

STEP 3 Draw a curve to connect the points you plotted in Step 2.

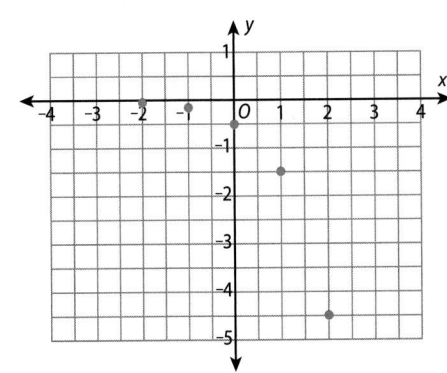

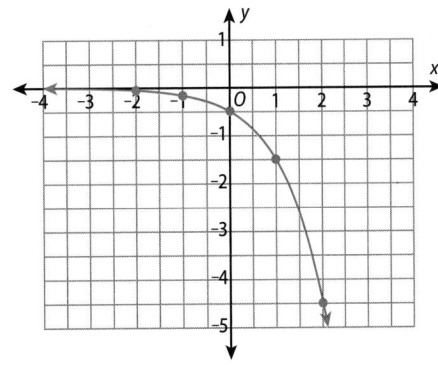

Try It This Way

You can use a graphing calculator to graph an exponential growth function. For example, to graph $y = -\frac{1}{2} \cdot 3^x$, go to the Y= screen and enter $(-)$ (1/2) $\times$ 3 $\wedge$ X,T,θ,n .

GOT TO KNOW!

Exponential Growth Functions

- The graph of an exponential growth function is in the form $y = ab^x$, where $a \neq 0$ and $b > 1$.
- The graph passes through the points $(0, a)$ and $(1, ab)$.
- The line $y = 0$ (the x-axis) is an asymptote of the graph of $y = ab^x$.

When $a > 0$

The y-values increase as you move from left to right.

The range is $y > 0$.

When $a < 0$

The y-values decrease as you move from left to right.

The range is $y < 0$.

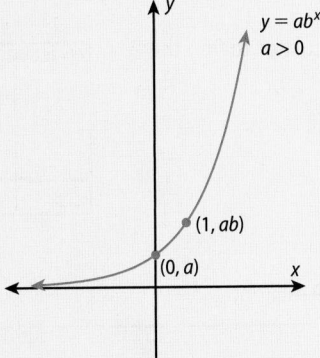

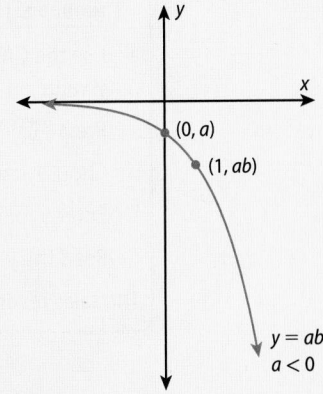

Modeling Exponential Growth

When a real-life quantity increases by a fixed percent each year, the amount y of the quantity after x years can be modeled by the function $y = a(1 + r)^x$, where a is the starting amount or **initial value**, r is the percent increase written as a decimal and $(1 + r)$ is the **growth factor**.

EXAMPLE 4

In an earlier year (to be called Year 1), the revenue from the sale of portable navigation systems was \$312 million. The sales revenue has grown at a rate of about 120% each year since Year 1.

a. Write an equation to model the situation, where y represents the sales revenue and x represents the number of years since Year 1.

Use the exponential growth equation.	$y = a(1 + r)^x$
Substitute 312 for the initial value a.	$y = 312(1 + r)^x$
The percent increase is 120% = 1.2.	
Substitute 1.2 for r.	$y = 312(1 + 1.2)^x$
Simplify the expression in the parentheses.	$y = 312(2.2)^x$

b. Use a graphing calculator to graph your equation.

Press the [Y=] key. Then enter 312 [×] 2.2 [^] [X,T,θ,n].

Use the [WINDOW] key to set a reasonable range of x- and y-values. In the graph shown, $-6 \leq x \leq 6$ and $-50 \leq y \leq 30{,}000$. The y scale is 10,000.

c. Use your model to estimate the revenue from sales in Year 6.

Year 6 is 5 years after Year 1, so find the value of y when $x = 5$.

METHOD 1

| Substitute 5 for x in the equation. | $y = 312(2.2)^5$ |
| Simplify. | $y \approx 16{,}079$ |

The sales revenue in Year 6 is about \$16,079 million.

METHOD 2

Use the CALC feature on a graphing calculator to find the y-value on the graph when $x = 5$.

Press [2nd] [TRACE] to go to the CALCULATE menu.

Choose *1: value* and press [ENTER].

Enter 5 for the value of x and press [ENTER].

Read the y-value displayed on the screen.

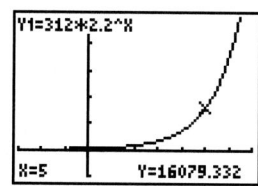

The sales revenue in Year 6 is about \$16,079 million.

Compound Interest

Compound interest is interest paid on the initial amount in an account and on previously earned interest. The equation $y = a(1 + r)^x$ needs to be modified slightly to model exponential growth that occurs more frequently than once a year. To find the value of an account that compounds interest n times a year for x years, use the equation $y = a\left(1 + \frac{r}{n}\right)^{nx}$.

EXAMPLE 5

Kyesha's grandmother gives her $12,000 to deposit in a college fund. Find the value of the account after 3 years for each interest rate.

a. 6% interest compounded quarterly

Find the value of the account that compounds 6% interest quarterly. (Four times a year)

Use the formula for compound interest.	$y = a\left(1 + \frac{r}{n}\right)^{nx}$.
Substitute 12,000 for a, the initial value.	$y = 12{,}000\left(1 + \frac{r}{n}\right)^{nx}$
Substitute 0.06 for r, 4 for n and 3 for x.	$y = 12{,}000\left(1 + \frac{0.06}{4}\right)^{4 \cdot 3}$
Simplify the expressions involving r, n, and x.	$y = 12{,}000(1 + 0.015)^{12}$
Simplify inside the parentheses first.	$y = 12{,}000(1.015)^{12}$
Simplify to find y.	$y \approx \$14{,}347.42$

b. 5% interest compounded monthly

Find the value of the account that compounds 5% interest monthly. (Twelve times a year)

Use the formula for compound interest.	$y = a\left(1 + \frac{r}{n}\right)^{nx}$.
Substitute 12,000 for a, the initial value.	$y = 12{,}000\left(1 + \frac{r}{n}\right)^{nx}$
Substitute 0.05 for r, 12 for n and 3 for x.	$y = 12{,}000\left(1 + \frac{0.05}{12}\right)^{12 \cdot 3}$
Simplify the expressions involving r, n, and x.	$y = 12{,}000(1 + 0.004)^{36}$
Simplify to find y.	$y \approx \$13{,}854.63$

Watch Out !

Remember to follow the Order of Operations when doing your calculations. Simplify inside the parentheses first, then raise that number to the power, then multiply by the initial amount.

Modeling Exponential Growth

	Growth (yearly)	Growth (n times a year)
Equation	$y = a(1 + r)^x$	$y = a\left(1 + \frac{r}{n}\right)^{nx}$
Initial Value	a	a
Percent increase (written as a decimal)	r	r
Number of compoundings per year	1	n
Number of years	x	x
Growth Rate	$(1 + r)$	$\left(1 + \frac{r}{n}\right)$

Exponential Decay

Graphing Exponential Decay Functions

An exponential function of the form $y = ab^x$, is an **exponential decay function** when $a > 0$ and $0 < b < 1$.

Need More HELP ?

For help simplifying negative exponents, go to *Integer and Rational Exponents* on page 1966.

SEARCH

To see step-by-step videos of these problems, enter the page number into the SWadvantage.com Search Bar.

EXAMPLE 1

Graph $y = \frac{1}{3}^x$.

STEP 1 Make a table of values for x and y.

x	-2	-1	0	1	2
y	9	3	1	$\frac{1}{3}$	$\frac{1}{9}$

STEP 2 Plot the points from the table on a coordinate grid.

STEP 3 Draw a curve to connect the points you plotted in Step 2.

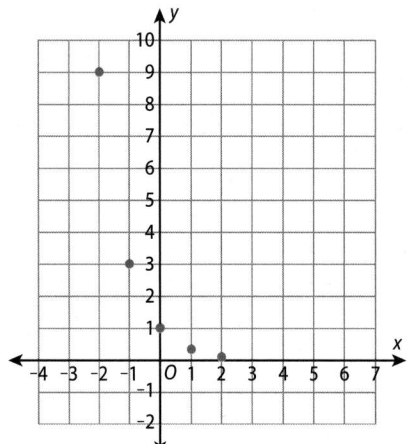

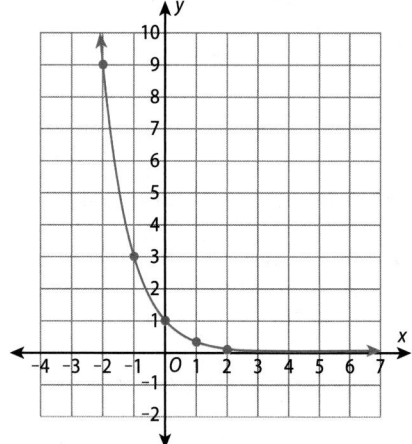

EXAMPLE 2

Tell whether the function represents *exponential growth* or *exponential decay*. Explain your reasoning.

a. $y = 2 \cdot 0.95^x$

The function represents exponential decay because the value of b is 0.95, which is less than 1.

b. $y = -4 \cdot \frac{3}{2}^x$

The function represents exponential growth because the value of b is $\frac{3}{2}$, which is greater than 1.

c. $y = 23 \cdot 4^x$

The function represents exponential growth because the value of b is 4, which is greater than 1.

d. $y = -2 \cdot \frac{3}{4}^x$

The function represents exponential decay because the value of b is $\frac{3}{4}$, which is less than 1.

Need More HELP ?

For help with exponential growth functions, go to *Exponential Growth* on page 1996.

EXAMPLE 3

Graph $y = -2 \cdot \frac{1}{4}^x$.

STEP 1 Make a table of values for x and y.

x	−1	0	1	2
y	−8	−2	$-\frac{1}{2}$	$-\frac{1}{8}$

STEP 2 Plot the points from the table on a coordinate grid.

STEP 3 Draw a curve to connect the points you plotted in Step 2.

> **Watch Out !**
>
> Remember to follow the order of operations when doing your calculations. Raise the number in parentheses to the power first, then multiply by a.

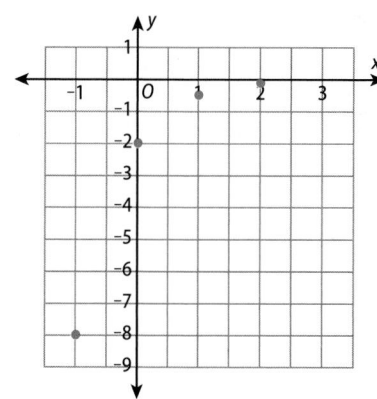

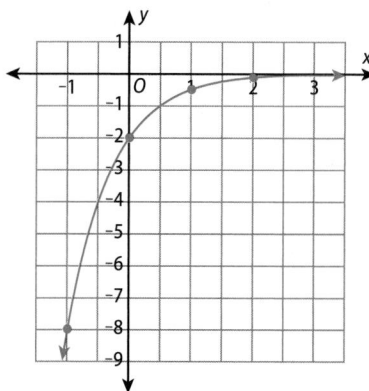

> **GOT TO KNOW !**

Comparing Exponential Growth and Exponential Decay

Exponential Growth

- In the equation $y = ab^x$, $b > 1$.

- When a is greater than 0, the graph of $y = ab^x$ rises from left to right.

- The graph passes through $(0, a)$ and $(1, ab)$.

- The graph below shows the graph of $y = ab^x$ when $a > 0$ and $b > 1$.

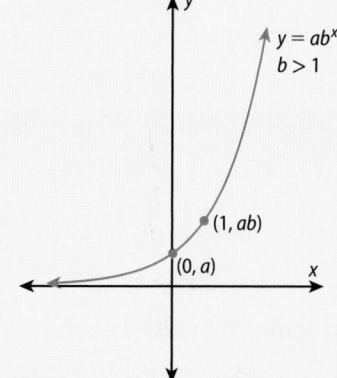

Exponential Decay

- In the equation $y = ab^x$, $0 < b < 1$.

- When a is greater than 0, the graph of $y = ab^x$ falls from left to right.

- The graph passes through $(0, a)$ and $(1, ab)$.

- The graph below shows the graph of $y = ab^x$ when $a > 0$ and $0 < b < 1$.

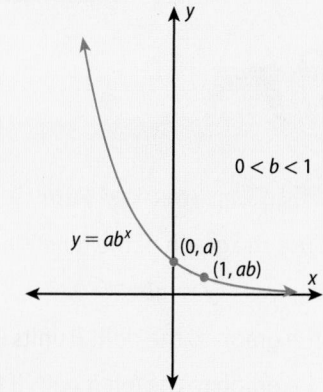

Translating Exponential Functions

To graph $y = ab^{x-h}$, you can sketch the graph of $y = ab^x$ and then move the graph horizontally by h units. To graph $y = ab^x + k$, you can sketch the graph of $y = ab^x$ and then move the graph vertically by k units.

Watch Out !

Observe that $k \neq 3$ in the equation $y = \frac{1}{2}^x - 3$. Instead, $k = -3$. It might help to write the equation in the form $y = ab^x + k$ as $y = \frac{1}{2}^x + (-3)$.

EXAMPLE 4

Graph $y = \left(\frac{1}{2}\right)^x - 3$. Then describe the asymptote.

STEP 1 Using the procedure shown in Example 1, graph $y = \left(\frac{1}{2}\right)^x$.
This graph is in blue on the graph to the right.

STEP 2 Graph $y = \left(\frac{1}{2}\right)^x - 3$.
The value of k in $y = \left(\frac{1}{2}\right)^x - 3$ is -3, so shift the graph of $y = \left(\frac{1}{2}\right)^x$ down (in the negative direction) 3 units.
The graph of $y = \left(\frac{1}{2}\right)^x - 3$ is in red on the graph to the right.

The asymptote is $y = -3$.

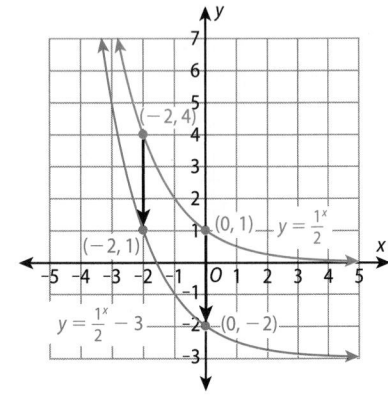

EXAMPLE 5

Graph $y = \left(\frac{1}{2}\right)^{x-3}$. Then describe the asymptote.

STEP 1 Using the procedure shown in Example 1, graph $y = \left(\frac{1}{2}\right)^x$.
This graph is in blue on the graph to the right.

STEP 2 Graph $y = \left(\frac{1}{2}\right)^{x-3}$.
The value of h in $y = \left(\frac{1}{2}\right)^{x-3}$ is 3, so shift the graph of $y = \left(\frac{1}{2}\right)^x$ to the right (in the positive direction) 3 units.
The graph of $y = \left(\frac{1}{2}\right)^{x-3}$ is in red on the graph to the right.

The asymptote is $y = 0$.

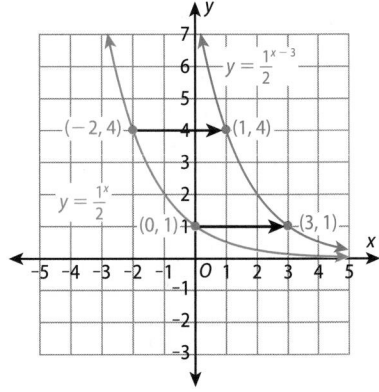

GOT TO KNOW!

Translating Exponential Functions

You can use the graph of the function $y = ab^x$ to graph $y = ab^{x-h}$ and $y = ab^x + k$.

$$y = ab^{x-h} \qquad\qquad y = ab^x + k$$

- Shift the graph to the right h units if $h > 0$.   • Shift the graph up k units if $k > 0$.

- Shift the graph to the left h units if $h < 0$.   • Shift the graph down k units if $k < 0$.

Modeling Exponential Decay

When a real-life quantity decreases by a fixed percent each year, the amount y of the quantity after x years can be modeled by the function $y = a(1 - r)^x$, where a is the starting amount or **initial value** , r is the percent decrease written as a decimal, and $(1 - r)$ is the **growth factor** .

EXAMPLE

Jeremy buys a new car for \$35,000. The value of the car decreases by 15% each year.

a. Write an equation to model the situation, where y represents the value of the car and x represents the number of years Jeremy has owned the car.

Use the exponential decay equation.	$y = a(1 - r)^x$
Substitute 35,000 for the initial value a.	$y = 35{,}000(1 - r)^x$
Substitute 0.15 for r.	$y = 35{,}000(1 - 0.15)^x$
Simplify the expression in the parentheses.	$y = 35{,}000(0.85)^x$

b. Find the value of the car after 4 years.

Use the model from part (a) to find the value of y when $x = 4$.

Substitute 4 for x in the equation.	$y = 35{,}000(0.85)^4$
Simplify.	$y \approx 18{,}270.22$

The value of the car after 4 years is \$18,270.22.

c. Estimate when the car will have a value of \$10,000.

STEP 1 Graph the equation $y = 35{,}000(0.85)^x$ on a graphing calculator.

STEP 2 The value of the car is \$10,000 when $y = 10{,}000$. Graph the equation $y = 10{,}000$.

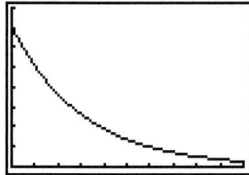

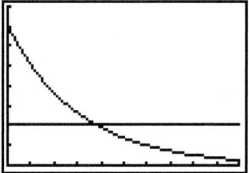

STEP 3 Press 2nd TRACE to go to the CALCULATE menu.
Choose 5:intersect and press ENTER .
Enter 5 for the value of x and press ENTER .
Press ENTER three times to choose the graphs and guess at the intersection.
Read the x value when the y value is 10,000.

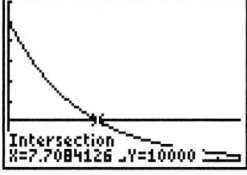

The car will have a value of \$10,000 when it is about 7.7 years old.

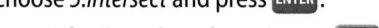

Base *e*

The Number *e*

Some numbers, like π and *i*, are represented by letters. This lesson is about an irrational number represented by the letter *e*.

There are different types of logarithms. Common logarithms, abbreviated *log*, are base 10, which means that **log *n* = *m*,** where $n = 10^m$. The **letter *e*** is the base for natural logarithms, which are abbreviated *ln*. This means that **ln *n* = *m*,** where $n = e^m$. The number *e* is approximately equal to 2.718.

Need More
HELP

For help simplifying exponential expressions, go to *Properties of Exponents* on page 1970.

EXAMPLE 1

Use a calculator to evaluate each expression below.

The e^x key on the calculator is above the [LN] key, so enter [2nd] [LN] to get e^x. Then enter the exponent, and press [ENTER].

		Keystrokes	**Value**
a.	e^3	[2nd] [LN] 3 [ENTER]	$e^3 \approx 20.08554$
b.	$e^{-0.8}$	[2nd] [LN] [(−)] 0.8 [ENTER]	$e^{-0.8} \approx 0.44933$
c.	$\dfrac{6e^2}{3e^5}$		

First simplify the expression. Then use a calculator to find the value of the simplified expression.

Simplify 6 ÷ 3. $\dfrac{6e^2}{3e^5} = \dfrac{2e^2}{e^5}$

Use the Quotient of Powers Property. $= 2e^{2-5}$

Simplify the expression. $= 2e^{-3}$

Enter [2] [×] [2nd] [LN] [(−)] [3] [ENTER]. The value of $\dfrac{6e^2}{3e^5} = 2e^{-3} \approx 0.099574$.

Natural logarithms—and thus *e*—are the basis of many interest and other business calculations. The equation $y = Pe^{rt}$ is used to find the amount in an account earning interest compounded continuously, where *P* is the initial or *principal* amount in the account, *r* is the interest rate written as a decimal, and *t* is the time in years.

EXAMPLE 2

Kelly opens an account with $500. How much will be in the account after 6 years if the account pays 8% interest compounded continuously?

STEP 1 Write the equation for continuously compounded interest. $y = Pe^{rt}$

STEP 2 Substitute 500 for *P*, 0.08 for *r*, and 6 for *t* in the equation. $y = 500e^{(0.08)6}$

STEP 3 Use your calculator to simplify. $y \approx 808.04$

The account will have $808.04 in it after 6 years.

EXAMPLE 3

The average price of a movie ticket can be modeled by the function $y = 2.85e^{0.047x}$ where y represents the cost of a ticket in dollars and x represents the number of years since a certain year (to be called Year 1).

SEARCH

To see step-by-step videos of these problems, enter the page number into the SWadvantage.com Search Bar.

a. **Graph the equation.**

Use a graphing calculator to graph the equation.

Press Y= 2.85 × 2nd LN 0.047 X,T,θ,*n* ENTER to enter the equation.

Then press GRAPH .

Make sure you have an appropriate viewing window. The graph shows the x-axis from -10 to 50, and the y-axis from 0 to 20.

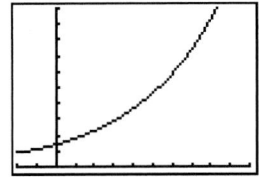

b. **Use the model to estimate the average price of a movie ticket in Year 16.**

METHOD 1

STEP 1   Find the value of x.

$x =$ Year 16 $-$ Year 1 $= 15$

STEP 2   Substitute 15 for x in the equation.

$y = 2.85e^{0.047(15)}$

STEP 3   Use your calculator to simplify.

$y \approx 5.77$

The average price of a movie ticket in Year 16 was about $5.77.

METHOD 2

Use the graph from part (a) and the CALC feature on a graphing calculator to find the value of the function when $x = 15$.

Press 2nd TRACE to go to the CALCULATE menu.

Choose *1:value* and press ENTER .

Enter 15 for the value of x and press ENTER .

Read the y value displayed on the screen.

The average price of a movie ticket in Year 16 was about $5.77.

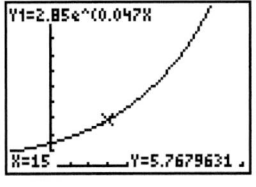

GOT TO KNOW!

Facts about e

- e is the base for natural logarithms, ln.
- $e \approx 2.718$
- To evaluate e^x on the calculator, enter 2nd LN to get e^x. Then enter the exponent, and press ENTER .

Logarithmic Functions

Graphing Logarithmic Functions

Equations written in the form $y = \log_b x$ where $b > 0$ are called **logarithmic functions**. The logarithmic function $y = \log_b x$ is the inverse of the exponential function $y = b^x$.

EXAMPLE 1

Need More

HELP ?

For help with inverse relationships, go to *Inverses of Non-linear Functions* on page 2094.

For help with the change-of-base formula, go to *Common Logarithms and Natural Logarithms* on page 1978.

Graph $y = \log_2 x$.

METHOD 1

Think of $y = \log_2 x$ as $2^y = x$ and plot points.

Choose friendly values for y first and then determine the x values, but remember to graph (x, y) points.

x	$\frac{1}{4}$	$\frac{1}{2}$	1	2	4	8
y	-2	-1	0	1	2	3

The graph is shown to the right.

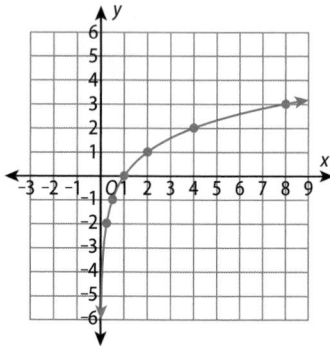

METHOD 2

Use the inverse relationship of $y = \log_2 x$ and $y = 2^x$.

Graph $y = 2^x$.

x	-2	-1	0	1	2	3
y	$\frac{1}{4}$	$\frac{1}{2}$	1	2	4	8

Then reflect the graph in the line $y = x$.

The graph is shown to the right.

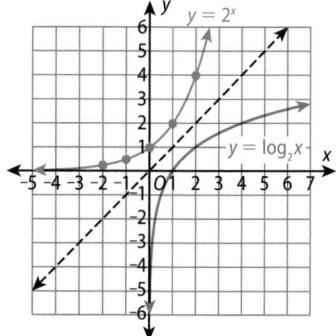

GOT TO KNOW!

Graphing Logarithmic Functions

The graph of $y = \log_b x$, where $b > 1$, has these characteristics:

- The graph of $y = \log_b x$ is the reflection of the graph of $y = b^x$ in the line $y = x$.
- The graph of $y = \log_b x$ includes $(1, 0)$ and $(b, 1)$.
- The y-axis is a vertical asymptote.
- The domain is $x > 0$ and the range is all real numbers.

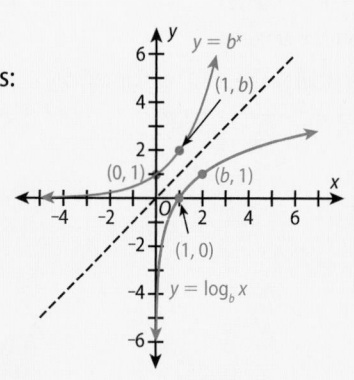

Using Logarithmic Functions

Logarithmic functions can be used to model many real-life situations, such as the energy released in an earthquake or the acidity of lakes and rivers.

EXAMPLE 2

The formula $m = 0.67 \log(0.37E) + 1.46$ can be used to find the magnitude m of an earthquake measured on the Richter scale, where E represents the amount of energy released by the earthquake measured in kilowatt hours.

a. **Use a calculator to find an earthquake's magnitude if it releases 15,500,000,000 kilowatt-hours of energy.**

Use the equation $m = 0.67 \log(0.37E) + 1.46$.

Substitute 15,500,000,000 for E. $m = 0.67 \log(0.37 \times 15{,}500{,}000{,}000) + 1.46$

Use a calculator to simplify. $m \approx 8.0$

The magnitude of the earthquake is about 8.0 on the Richter scale.

b. **Use the graph of the equation to find the amount of energy released by an earthquake that measures 6.8 on the Richter scale.**

STEP 1 Graph the related equation $y = 0.67 \log(0.37x) + 1.46$ on a graphing calculator.

Enter ▊Y=▊ 0.67 ▊×▊ ▊LOG▊ 0.37 ▊×▊ ▊X,T,θ,n▊ ▊)▊ ▊+▊ 1.46.

Adjust the viewing window.

In the graph below,
$0 < x < 500{,}000{,}000$ with an X scale of 5,000,000 and
$6.5 < y < 7$ with a Y scale of 0.1.

STEP 2 Find the equation for a measure of 6.8 on the Richter scale.

When the earthquake measures 6.8 on the Richter scale, $y = 6.8$.

Graph the line $y = 6.8$ on the same screen as the graph of $y = 0.67 \log(0.37x) + 1.46$.

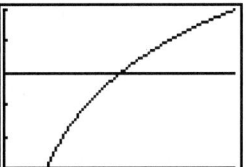

STEP 3 Find the intersection of the two graphs.

Press ▊2nd▊ ▊TRACE▊ to bring up the CALC screen.

Enter 5 to select *intersect*. Press ▊ENTER▊ three times to select the two graphs and make an estimated guess.

Read the *x*-value on the lower left of the screen when $y = 6.8$.

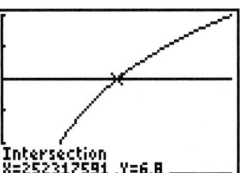

A 6.8 earthquake releases about 252,317,591 kilowatt-hours of energy.

SEARCH

To see step-by-step videos of these problems, enter the page number into the SWadvantage.com Search Bar.

Translating Logarithmic Functions Horizontally

To graph the function $y = \log_b(x - h)$, translate the graph of $y = \log_b x$ horizontally h units. This means if h is positive, you move the graph to the right h units. If h is negative, you move the graph to the left h units.

EXAMPLE 3

Watch Out !

Be careful not to confuse the functions $y = \log_2(x - 3)$ and $y = \log_2 x - 3$. When you evaluate $y = \log_2(x - 3)$ you find $y = \log_2(x - 3)$. When you evaluate $y = \log_2 x - 3$ you find $\log_2 x$ and then subtract 3 from this value.

Graph $y = \log_2(x - 3)$. Describe the vertical asymptote.

STEP 1 Graph $y = \log_2 x$.

Think of $y = \log_2 x$ as $2^y = x$ and plot points.

Choose friendly values for y first and then determine the x values, but remember to graph (x, y) points.

x	$\frac{1}{4}$	$\frac{1}{2}$	1	2	4	8
y	-2	-1	0	1	2	3

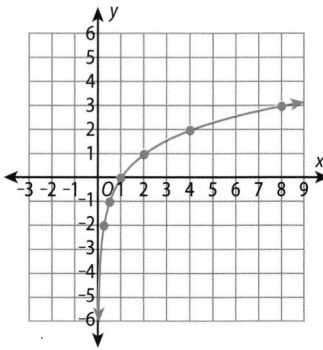

STEP 2 Shift the graph of $y = \log_2 x$ horizontally h units.

The value of h in $x - 3$ is positive 3. Shift the graph of $y = \log_2 x$ three units in the positive horizontal direction (to the right three units.)

The graph is shown to the right.

The vertical asymptote is $x = 3$.

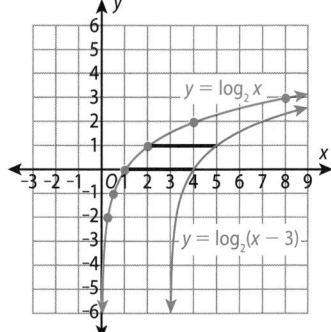

EXAMPLE 4

Try It This Way

You can use a graphing calculator to graph logarithmic functions of the form $y = \log_b(x - h)$.

Use the change-of-base formula to rewrite the function as $y = \frac{\log(x - h)}{\log b}$. Then enter this function into a graphing calculator.

Graph $y = \log_4(x + 2)$. Describe the vertical asymptote.

STEP 1 Graph $y = \log_4 x$.

Think of $y = \log_4 x$ as $4^y = x$. Create a table of values and then plot the points.

x	$\frac{1}{4}$	1	4	16
y	-1	0	1	2

STEP 2 Shift the graph of $y = \log_4 x$ horizontally h units.

Rewrite $x + 2$ in the form $x - h$ to get the correct value for h.
Because $x + 2 = x - (-2)$, the value of h is -2.
Shift the graph of $y = \log_4 x$ two units in the negative horizontal direction (to the left two units).

The graph is shown to the right.

The vertical asymptote is $x = -2$.

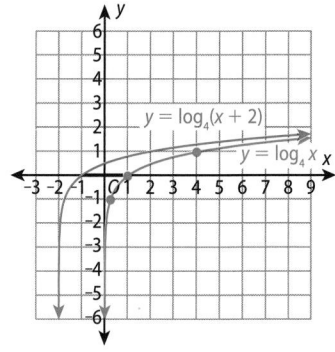

Translating Logarithmic Functions Vertically

To graph the function $y = \log_b x + k$, translate the graph of $y = \log_b x$ vertically k units. This means if k is positive, move the graph up k units. If k is negative, move the graph down k units.

EXAMPLE 5

Graph $y = \log_3 x - 2$. Describe the vertical asymptote.

STEP 1   Graph $y = \log_3 x$.

Think of $y = \log_3 x$ as $3^y = x$ and plot points.

Choose friendly values for y first and then determine the x values, but remember to graph (x, y) points.

x	$\frac{1}{9}$	$\frac{1}{3}$	1	3	9
y	-2	-1	0	1	2

The graph is shown to the right.

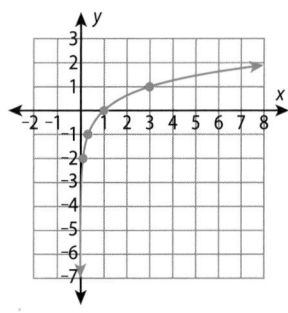

STEP 2   Shift the graph of $y = \log_3 x$ vertically k units.

Rewrite $y = \log_3 x - 2$ in the form $y = \log_b x + k$ to get the correct value for k. Because $y = \log_3 x - 2$ is the same thing as $y = \log_3 x + (-2)$, the value of k is -2. Shift the graph of $y = \log_3 x$ two units in the negative vertical direction (down two units).

The graph of the translation is shown to the right.

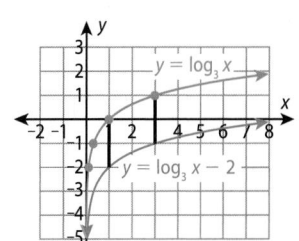

STEP 3   Describe the vertical asymptote.

The line $x = 0$ is a vertical asymptote.

SEARCH

To see step-by-step videos of these problems, enter the page number into the SWadvantage.com Search Bar.

GOT TO KNOW!

Translating Logarithmic Functions

The graph $y = \log_b(x - h) + k$ has the following characteristics:

- The graph is the graph of $y = \log_b x$ shifted h units in the horizontal direction and k units in the vertical direction.

- The line $x = h$ is a vertical asymptote.

- The domain of the function is $x > h$.

- The range of the function is all real numbers.

- If $b > 1$, the graph moves up to the right as x increases.

- If $0 < b < 1$, then the graph moves down to the right as x increases.

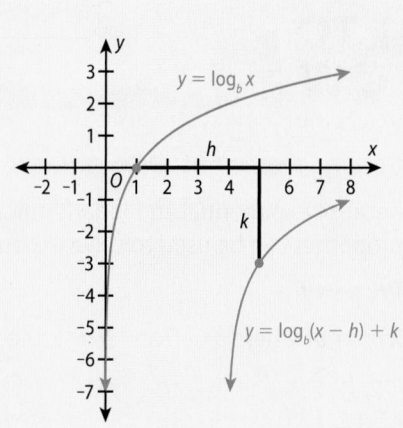

Solving Exponential Equations

When the powers in an exponential equation have the same base, the exponents are equal.

EXAMPLE 1

Solve $2^{3x} = 4^{x+1}$.

Write both expressions using the same base.	$2^{3x} = (2^2)^{x+1}$
Use a power property to simplify.	$2^{3x} = 2^{2(x+1)}$
Set the powers equal to each other.	$3x = 2(x+1)$
Use the distributive property to simplify.	$3x = 2x + 2$
Subtract $2x$ from each side to combine like terms.	$x = 2$
CHECK Substitute 2 for x in the original equation.	$2^{3 \cdot 2} \overset{?}{=} 4^{2+1}$
Simplify the exponents.	$2^6 \overset{?}{=} 4^3$
Simplify each expression.	$64 = 64$

When an exponential equation isn't easily written with the same base, you can solve the equation by taking a logarithm of each side.

EXAMPLE 2

Solve $4^x = 9$.

Write the equation.	$4^x = 9$
Take $\log_4$ of each side.	$\log_4 4^x = \log_4 9$
Simplify using $\log_b b^x = x$.	$x = \log_4 9$
Use the change-of-base formula.	$x = \dfrac{\log 9}{\log 4}$
Use a calculator to simplify.	$x \approx 1.585$
CHECK Substitute 1.585 for x in the original equation.	$4^{1.5858} \overset{?}{=} 9$
Use a calculator to simplify.	$9 = 9$

GOT TO KNOW!

Solving Exponential Equations

Because exponential and logarithmic functions are inverses of one another, the following properties can be used to solve exponential equations.

Property	Example
If $b^x = b^y$ where $b > 0$ and $b \neq 1$, then $x = y$.	$5^x = 25 \rightarrow 5^x = 5^2 \rightarrow x = 2$
$\log_b b^x = x$	$2^x = 7 \rightarrow \log_2 2^x = \log_2 7 \rightarrow x = \log_2 7$
$\ln e^x = x$	$e^x = 64 \rightarrow \ln e^x = \ln 64 \rightarrow x = \ln 64$

EXAMPLE 3

Solve $\frac{1}{2}e^x - 4 = 20$.

Write the original equation.	$\frac{1}{2}e^x - 4 = 20$
Add 4 to each side of the equation.	$\frac{1}{2}e^x = 24$
Multiply both sides of the equation by 2.	$e^x = 48$
Take the natural log of each side.	$\ln e^x = \ln 48$
Use a calculator to simplify.	$x \approx 3.87$

Need More HELP ?

For help with natural logarithms (ln) and common logarithms, go to *Common Logarithms and Natural Logarithms* on page 1978 and *Base* e on page 2004.

EXAMPLE 4

Solve $10^{2x-1} + 3 = 34$.

Write the original equation.	$10^{2x-1} + 3 = 34$
Subtract 3 from each side of the equation.	$10^{2x-1} = 31$
Take the common log of each side.	$\log 10^{2x-1} = \log 31$
Simplify.	$2x - 1 = \log 31$
Add 1 to both sides of the equation.	$2x = \log 31 + 1$
Divide both sides by 2.	$x = \dfrac{\log 31 + 1}{2}$
Use a calculator to simplify.	$x \approx 1.25$

EXAMPLE 5

The population of a city can be modeled by the equation $3762(0.96)^t = P$ where t is the number of years since a certain year and P is the population in thousands. According to this model, in how many years will the population of the city be about 2800 thousand?

SEARCH

To see step-by-step videos of these problems, enter the page number into the SWadvantage.com Search Bar.

METHOD 1

Solve the exponential equation.

Substitute 2800 for P in the equation.	$3762(0.96)^t = 2800$
Divide both sides by 3762.	$(0.96)^t = 0.74$
Take $\log_{0.96}$ of each side of the equation.	$t = \log_{0.96} 0.74$
Use the change-of-base property.	$t = \dfrac{\log 0.74}{\log 0.96}$
Use a calculator to simplify.	$t \approx 7.38$

In 7 years the population will be about 2800 thousand.

METHOD 2

Graph the expressions on a graphing calculator and find the point of intersection.

Graph Y1 = $3762(0.96)^x$ and Y2 = 2800 on the same screen.

Find the point of intersection. Read the value of x when y = 2800.

The population will be about 2800 thousand in 7.38 years.

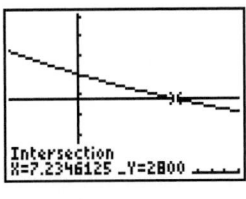

Intersection
X=7.2346125 _Y=2800

Solving Logarithmic Equations

When an equation involves logarithms, you use the relationships described in the *Got To Know!* box below to solve the equation.

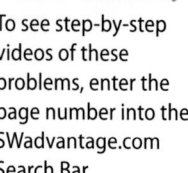

SEARCH

To see step-by-step videos of these problems, enter the page number into the SWadvantage.com Search Bar.

EXAMPLE 6

Solve $\log_2(4x - 3) = \log_2(2x + 5)$.

Write the original equation.	$\log_2(4x - 3) = \log_2(2x + 5)$
Set the logarithms equal to each other.	$4x - 3 = 2x + 5$
Add 3 to each side.	$4x = 2x + 8$
Subtract $2x$ from each side.	$2x = 8$
Divide each side by 2.	$x = 4$

CHECK Substitute 4 for x in the original equation. $\log_2(4 \cdot 4 - 3) \stackrel{?}{=} \log_2(2 \cdot 4 + 5)$

Simplify. Both sides of the equation are equal. $\log_2(13) = \log_2(13)$

EXAMPLE 7

Solve $\log_5(3x + 4) = 2$.

Write the equation.	$\log_5(3x + 4) = 2$
Make each side an exponent with base 5.	$5^{\log_5(3x + 4)} = 5^2$
Simplify using $b^{\log_b x} = x$.	$3x + 4 = 25$
Subtract 4 from each side.	$3x = 21$
Divide both sides by 3.	$x = 7$

CHECK Substitute 7 for x in the original equation. $\log_5(3 \cdot 7 + 4) \stackrel{?}{=} 2$

Simplify inside the parentheses. $\log_5(25) \stackrel{?}{=} 2$

Use $y = \log_b x \rightarrow b^y = x$. $5^2 = 25$

GOT TO KNOW!

Solving Logarithmic Equations

Because exponential and logarithmic functions are inverses of one another, the following properties can be used to solve logarithmic equations.

Property	Example
When b, x, and y are all positive and $b \neq 1$, if $\log_b x = \log_b y$, then $x = y$.	$\log_2(4x - 3) = \log_2(2x + 5) \rightarrow 4x - 3 = 2x + 5$
If $\ln x = y$, then $e^{\ln x} = e^y$ and $x = e^y$	$\ln x = 4 \rightarrow e^{\ln x} = e^4$ and $x = e^4$.
If $x = y$ and $b > 0$ and $b \neq 1$, then $b^x = b^y$.	$\log_5(3x + 4) = 2 \rightarrow 5^{\log_5(3x+4)} = 5^2$

EXAMPLE 8

Solve 5 + 2 ln x = 4.

Write the original equation.	$5 + 2\ln x = 4$
Subtract 5 from each side of the equation.	$2\ln x = -1$
Divide both sides of the equation by 2.	$\ln x = -\dfrac{1}{2}$
Make each side an exponent with base e.	$e^{\ln x} = e^{-\frac{1}{2}}$
Use $e^{\ln x} = x$ to simplify.	$x = e^{-\frac{1}{2}}$
Use a calculator to evaluate $e^{-\frac{1}{2}}$.	$x \approx 0.607$

A solution of a logarithmic equation that is not in the domain of the original equation is an **extraneous solution** . Check your answers to make sure there are no extraneous solutions.

EXAMPLE 9

Solve log $5x$ + log (x − 1) = 2.

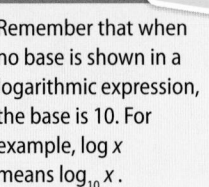

Watch Out !

Remember that when no base is shown in a logarithmic expression, the base is 10. For example, log x means $\log_{10} x$.

STEP 1 Write the equation without the logarithm.

Write the original equation.	$\log 5x + \log(x - 1) = 2$
Simplify using log a + log b = log ab.	$\log[5x(x-1)] = 2$
Simplify inside the parentheses.	$\log(5x^2 - 5x) = 2$
Rewrite, according to the definition of a logarithm.	$5x^2 - 5x = 10^2$
Simplify.	$5x^2 - 5x = 100$

STEP 2 Write the quadratic equation so that it can be factored.

Subtract 100 from both sides.	$5x^2 - 5x - 100 = 0$
Divide both sides by 5.	$x^2 - x - 20 = 0$
Factor.	$(x - 5)(x + 4) = 0$

STEP 3 Find the first factor.

| Set the first factor equal to zero. | $x - 5 = 0$ |
| Find the first possible solution. | $x = 5$ |

STEP 4 Find the second factor.

| Set the second factor equal to zero. | $x + 4 = 0$ |
| Find the first possible solution. | $x = -4$ |

STEP 5 Check the possible solutions for extraneous solutions.

Substitute 5 into the original equation.	$\log 5 \cdot 5 + \log(5 - 1) \stackrel{?}{=} 2$
Simplify.	$\log 25 + \log(4) = \log(25 \cdot 4) = \log 100 \stackrel{?}{=} 2$
Simplify.	$10^2 = 100$
Substitute -4 into the original equation.	$\log 5 \cdot (-4) + \log(-4 - 1) \stackrel{?}{=} 2$
Simplify.	$\log(-20) + \log(-5) \stackrel{?}{=} 2$

In log x, x must be positive, so the only solution is $x = 5$.

Exponential and Logarithmic Inequalities

SOUTHWESTERN

Watch Out !

Use infinity signs correctly. The symbol for infinity is ∞. This symbol is used to represent an unending list of positive numbers.

The symbol −∞ is used to represent an unending list of negative numbers.

Solving Exponential Inequalities

An inequality will usually have a number of solutions called intervals that represent a subset of real numbers. Parentheses and brackets are used to write solutions in interval notation.

- If the solution is > or <, parentheses are used. For example, $(3.2, \infty)$ means that the solution is larger than 3.2 and does not include 3.2. A parenthesis is always used with infinity because infinity is never reached (included).
- If the solution is ≥ or ≤, brackets are used. For example, $(-\infty, 4.5]$ means that the solution is 4.5 or smaller.

EXAMPLE 1

Solve $4^{x+1} > 32$.

Write the inequality.	$4^{x+1} > 32$
Write the numbers 4 and 32 with a base of 2.	$(2^2)^{x+1} > 2^5$
Use the power of a power property to simplify.	$2^{2(x+1)} > 2^5$
The powers are the same, so the exponents are equal.	$2(x+1) > 5$
Use the distributive property to simplify.	$2x + 2 > 5$
Subtract 2 from each side.	$2x > 3$
Divide both sides by 2.	$x > 1.5$

The solution is all numbers greater than 1.5. Using interval notation, we write the solution as $(1.5, \infty)$.

EXAMPLE 2

SEARCH

To see step-by-step videos of these problems, enter the page number into the SWadvantage.com Search Bar.

Solve $7^{3x-4} \leq 18$.

Write the inequality.	$7^{3x-4} \leq 18$
Take $\log_7$ of each side.	$\log_7 7^{3x-4} \leq \log_7 18$
Simplify using $\log_b b^x = x$.	$3x - 4 \leq \log_7 18$
Use the change-of-base formula.	$3x - 4 \leq \dfrac{\log 18}{\log 7}$
Use a calculator to simplify $\dfrac{\log 18}{\log 7}$.	$3x - 4 \leq 1.49$
Add 4 to each side.	$3x \leq 5.49$
Divide both sides by 3.	$x \leq 1.83$

The solution is all numbers less than and including 1.83. In interval notation, the solution is $(-\infty, 1.83]$.

GOT TO KNOW!

Interval Notation

Inequality	$a \leq x \leq b$	$a < x < b$	$a \leq x < b$	$a < x \leq b$	$x \leq b$	$x < b$	$x \geq b$	$x > b$
Notation	$[a, b]$	(a, b)	$[a, b)$	$(a, b]$	$(-\infty, b]$	$(-\infty, b)$	$[b, \infty)$	(b, ∞)

Remember that if you multiply or divide an inequality by a negative number, you need to switch the direction of the inequality symbol.

EXAMPLE 3

Solve $0.5^{3x-1} > 2^{x+4}$.

METHOD 1

Solve algebraically.

Write the original equation.	$0.5^{3x-1} > 2^{x+4}$
Write 0.5 as 2^{-1} so the bases are the same.	$(2^{-1})^{3x-1} > 2^{x+4}$
Use the power of a power property to simplify.	$2^{-1(3x-1)} > 2^{x+4}$
The powers are the same, so the exponents are equal.	$-1(3x-1) > x+4$
Use the distributive property to simplify.	$-3x+1 > x+4$
Subtract 1 from each side.	$-3x > x+3$
Subtract x from each side.	$-4x > 3$
Divide each side by -4. Change the direction of the inequality.	$x < -\dfrac{3}{4}$ or -0.75

The solution is $(-\infty, -0.75)$.

METHOD 2

Solve using a graphing calculator.

STEP 1 Enter [Y=] to enter the equations Y1 $= 0.5^{3x-1}$ and Y2 $= 2^{x+4}$.

Keystrokes for Y1: [0] [.] [5] [^] [(] [3] [×] [X,T,θ,n] [−] [1] [)]

Keystrokes for Y2: [2] [^] [(] [X,T,θ,n] [+] [4] [)]

STEP 2 Write each side of the inequality as a related inequality related to y.

Because each equation on the calculator is written with y on the left, write each inequality with y on the left.

In the inequality $0.5^{3x-1} > 2^{x+4}$, replace 2^{x+4} with y to get $0.5^{3x-1} > y$.

Rewrite this with y on the left as $y < 0.5^{3x-1}$.

In the inequality $0.5^{3x-1} > 2^{x+4}$, replace 0.5^{3x-1} with y to get $y > 2^{x+4}$.

STEP 3 Use the inequalities from Step 2 to determine the area to shade on the graph.

Because $y < 0.5^{3x-1}$, shade the y-values below the graph of $y = 0.5^{3x-1}$. Use the left arrow key to place the cursor to the left of Y1. Press the [ENTER] key until you see a line with shading below it.

Since $y > 2^{x+4}$, shade the y-values above the graph of $y = 2^{x+4}$. Use the left arrow key to place the cursor to the left of Y2. Press the [ENTER] key until you see a line with shading above it.

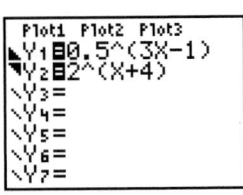

STEP 4 Graph the inequalities and determine the intersection.

Enter [2nd] [TABLE] to select the Calc feature. Press 5 to choose "intersect".

Press [ENTER] three times to find the point of intersection at $x = -0.75$.

Since both graphs are shaded to the left of $x = -0.75$, the solution is all x-values less than -0.75 or $(-\infty, -0.75)$.

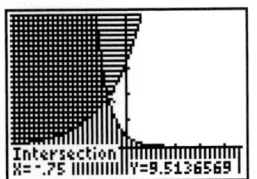

2015

Solving Logarithmic Inequalities

When an inequality involves logarithms, remember that the domain of $y = \log_a x$ is $x > 0$.

Watch Out !

Remember that the domain of a function may put other restrictions on the values of x. In Example 4, it would be incorrect to say the solution is $(-\infty, 32)$ because $\log_2 x$ is not defined when x is negative. Use the domain of the function to make sure you are not including undefined values.

EXAMPLE 4

Solve $\log_2 x < 5$.

STEP 1 Find the domain of the equation.

The domain of $\log_2 x$ is $x > 0$, so $x > 0$.

STEP 2 Solve the inequality.

Write the original equation.	$\log_2 x < 5$
Write each side as an exponent with a base of 2.	$2^{\log_2 x} < 2^5$
Rewrite using $b^{\log_b x} = x$	$x < 2^5$
Simplify.	$x < 32$

STEP 3 Write the solution.

Since $x > 0$ and $x < 32$, the inequality is written $0 < x < 32$.

In interval notation, the solution is $(0, 32)$.

EXAMPLE 5

Solve $\log(3x) \leq \log(x + 8)$.

STEP 1 Find the domain of the equation.

$3x$ must be positive, so $3x > 0$ when $x > 0$.

$x + 8$ must also be positive, so $x + 8 > 0$ when $x > -8$.

The intersection of $x > 0$ and $x > -8$ is $x > 0$, so x must be greater than 0.

STEP 2 Solve the inequality.

Write the original equation.	$\log(3x) \leq \log(x + 8)$
Logarithms with the same base are equal.	$3x \leq x + 8$
Simplify.	$x \leq 4$

STEP 3 Write the solution.

In interval notation, the solution is $(0, 4]$.

GOT TO KNOW !

Finding Restrictions on the Domain of Logarithmic Inequalities

The solution to a logarithmic inequality must always take into consideration the domain of the original function.

Function	$\log_a x$	$\log_a (x - n)$	$\log_a (x + n)$	$\log_a (mx)$	$\log_a (mx + n)$	$\log_a (mx - n)$
Domain	$x > 0$	$x - n > 0$	$x + n > 0$	$mx > 0$	$mx + n > 0$	$mx - n > 0$
Solve for x	$x > 0$	$x > n$	$x > -n$	$x > 0$	$x > -\dfrac{n}{m}$	$x > \dfrac{n}{m}$

EXAMPLE

Solve $10 + 3\ln(x + 1) \leq 16$.

STEP 1 Find the domain of the equation.

$x + 1$ must be positive, so $x + 1 > 0$ when $x > -1$.

STEP 2 Solve the inequality.

Write the original equation.	$10 + 3\ln(x + 1) \leq 16$
Subtract 10 from each side of the equation.	$3\ln(x + 1) \leq 6$
Divide both sides of the equation by 3.	$\ln(x + 1) \leq 2$
Make each side an exponent with base e.	$e^{\ln(x + 1)} \leq e^2$
Use $e^{\ln x} = x$ to simplify.	$x + 1 \leq e^2$
Subtract 1 from both sides.	$x \leq e^2 - 1$
Use a calculator to evaluate $e^2 - 1$.	$x \leq 6.39$

STEP 3 Write the solution.

We know $x > -1$ and $x \leq 6.39$. This inequality is written $-1 < x \leq 6.39$.

In interval notation, the solution is $(-1, 6.39]$.

Need More

HELP ?

For help with natural logarithms (ln) and common logarithms, go to *Common Logarithms and Natural Logarithms* on page 1978.

EXAMPLE

Solve $\log 2x + \log(3x - 2) \geq 1$.

STEP 1 Find the domain of the equation.

Write the equation without the logarithm.

$2x > 0$, so $x > 0$.

$3x - 2 > 0$, so when you solve for x, you get $x > \frac{2}{3}$. So, x must be $> \frac{2}{3}$.

STEP 2 Write the equation without the logarithm.

Write the original equation.	$\log 2x + \log(3x - 2) \geq 1$
Simplify using $\log a + \log b = \log ab$.	$\log[2x(3x - 2)] \geq 1$
Simplify inside the parentheses.	$\log(6x^2 - 4x) \geq 1$
Make each side an exponent with base 10 because $\log x = \log_{10} x$.	$10^{\log(6x^2 - 4x)} \geq 10^1$
Simplify.	$6x^2 - 4x \geq 10$

STEP 3 Factor the quadratic equation.

Subtract 10 from both sides.	$6x^2 - 4x - 10 \geq 0$
Divide both sides by 2 to make it easier to factor.	$3x^2 - 2x - 5 \geq 0$
Factor.	$(3x - 5)(x + 1) \geq 0$

STEP 4 Find the possible solutions.

$$3x - 5 \geq 0 \quad \text{or} \quad x + 1 \geq 0$$
$$x \geq \frac{5}{3} \quad \text{or} \quad x \geq -1$$

Because $\frac{5}{3}$ is greater than -1 and greater than $\frac{2}{3}$, the solution is $x \geq \frac{5}{3}$.

In interval notation, the solution is $[\frac{5}{3}, \infty)$.

SEARCH

To see step-by-step videos of these problems, enter the page number into the SWadvantage.com Search Bar.

Rational and Radical Functions

What Came Before?
- Operations with rational expressions
- Simplifying radical expressions

What's This About?
- Identifying the domain and range of rational and radical functions
- Finding asymptotes of rational functions
- Solving rational and radical equations and inequalities

Practical Apps
- Chemists use rational equations when mixing substances to achieve the desired concentration of a chemical.
- Engineers use radical equations to calculate the tensile stress on building materials.

just for FUN!

Q: What is $\sqrt{60s}$?

A: A sixties radical?

You can find more practice problems online by visiting:
www.SWadvantage.com

Rational Functions

Rational Functions

A **rational function** is a function of the form $y = \dfrac{p(x)}{q(x)}$, where $p(x)$ and $q(x)$ are polynomials and $q(x) \neq 0$. The graph of a rational function is a **hyperbola**. The graphs of a rational function usually contain an **asymptote**, a line that a graph approaches more and more closely. The domain and range of the function can help determine the asymptotes.

Ways to REMEMBER

Alphabetically, domain comes before range and x comes before y. That is one way to remember that the domain is the list of possible x-values and the range is the list of possible y-values.

Need More HELP?

For more help with hyperbolas and asymptotes, see *Graphing Hyperbolas* and *Equations for Hyperbolas* in *Conic Sections* on page 1932.

EXAMPLE 1

Graph $y = \dfrac{-3}{x}$.

STEP 1 Find the domain and range of the function.

The domain is all non-zero real numbers. ($x \neq 0$).

The range is all non-zero real numbers. ($y \neq 0$).

STEP 2 Identify the asymptotes.

Because $x \neq 0$, the y-axis is a vertical asymptote.

Because $y \neq 0$, the x-axis is a horizontal asymptote.

STEP 3 Make a table of values for x and y.

x	−6	−3	−1	1	3	6
y	0.5	1	3	−3	−1	−0.5

STEP 4 Graph the function.

Use dotted lines to draw the asymptotes $y = 0$ and $x = 0$ on a coordinate graph. Then plot the points from the table. Connect the points, being sure not to have the graph cross the asymptotes.

The graph of $y = \dfrac{-3}{x}$ is shown to the right.

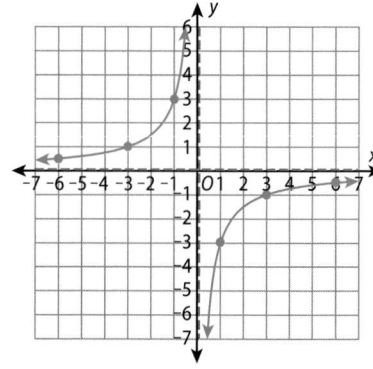

GOT TO KNOW!

Graphing Rational Functions

The graph of a rational function of the form $y = \dfrac{a}{x - h} + k$ is a hyperbola with the following characteristics.

- If $x = h$, the denominator is zero and the function is undefined. So, there is a vertical asymptote at $x = h$.

- The fractional portion of the function will never equal zero, so $y \neq k$. So, there is a horizontal asymptote at $y = k$.

- The graph has two symmetrical parts.

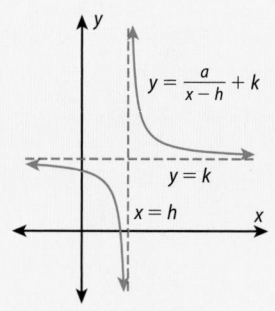

EXAMPLE 2

Graph $y = \dfrac{10}{x+3}$.

STEP 1 Find the domain and range of the function, and identify the asymptotes.

The domain is all real numbers except -3, so $x = -3$ is an asymptote.

The range is all real numbers except 0, so $y = 0$ is an asymptote.

STEP 2 Make a table of values for x and y.

x	−8	−5	−4	−2	−1	2	7
y	−2	−5	−10	10	5	2	1

STEP 4 Graph the function.

Draw the asymptotes $y = 0$ and $x = -3$ on a coordinate graph.

Then plot the points from the table.

Connect the points, being sure not to have the graph cross the asymptotes.

The graph of $y = \dfrac{10}{x+3}$ is shown to the right.

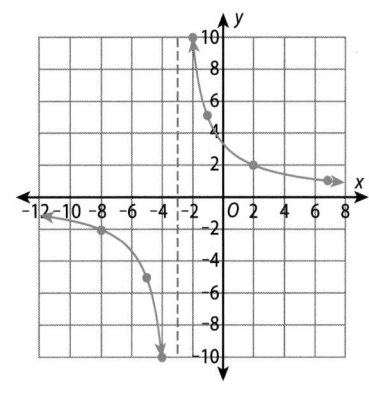

> **Need More**
> # HELP ?
> Remember, the only way a fraction will equal zero is if the numerator can be zero. In Example 2, the numerator will always be 10, so y will never equal zero.

EXAMPLE 3

Graph $y = \dfrac{-3}{x-1} + 2$.

STEP 1 Find the domain and range of the function, and identify the asymptotes.

The domain is all real numbers except 1, so $x = 1$ is an asymptote.

The range is all real numbers except 2, so $y = 2$ is an asymptote.

STEP 2 Make a table of values for x and y.

x	−2	0	2	4
y	3	5	−1	1

STEP 4 Graph the function.

Draw the asymptotes $x = 1$ and $y = 2$ on a coordinate graph.

Then plot the points from the table.

Connect the points, being sure not to have the graph cross the asymptotes.

The graph of $y = \dfrac{-3}{x-1} + 2$ is shown to the right.

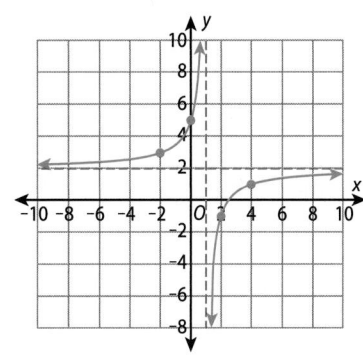

> **SEARCH** 🔍
> To see step-by-step videos of these problems, enter the page number into the SWadvantage.com Search Bar.

Asymptotes of Rational Functions

SOUTHWESTERN

Need More HELP ?

For help reviewing the degree of a polynomial, see *Graphing Polynomial Functions* in *Algebra* (p. 1624).

SEARCH

To see step-by-step videos of these problems, enter the page number into the SWadvantage.com Search Bar.

Rational Functions and Asymptotes

The last section showed how to graph a rational function of the form $y = \frac{p(x)}{q(x)}$, where $p(x)$ and $q(x)$ were linear polynomials and $q(x) \neq 0$. In this section, the rational functions will include higher-degree polynomials.

EXAMPLE 1

Graph $y = \frac{8}{x^2 + 4}$.

STEP 1 Find the *x*-intercepts.

The numerator will never equal 0, so there are no *x*-intercepts.

STEP 2 Identify the asymptotes.

The denominator has no restricted values, so there is no vertical asymptote.

The degree of the numerator (0) is less than the degree of the denominator (2), so the line $y = 0$ is a horizontal asymptote.

STEP 3 Make a table of values for *x* and *y*.

x	−2	−1	0	1	2
y	1	1.6	2	1.6	1

STEP 4 Graph the function.

Use dotted lines to draw the asymptote $y = 0$ on a coordinate graph.

Plot the points from the table.

Then, connect the points.

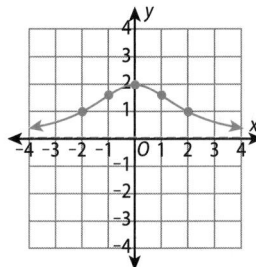

GOT TO KNOW!

Graphing Rational Functions

A rational function is of the form $f(x) = \frac{p(x)}{q(x)}$.

- $p(x)$ and $q(x)$ are polynomials with no common factors other than 1.
- The rational function can be represented by the general equation
$$f(x) = \frac{p(x)}{q(x)} = \frac{a_m x^m + a_{m-1} x^{m-1} + \ldots + a_1 x + a_0}{b_n x^n + b_{n-1} x^{n-1} + \ldots + b_1 x + b_0}.$$
- m is the degree of $p(x)$ and n is the degree of $q(x)$.

The graph of the rational function $f(x)$ has the following characteristics.

- The *x*-intercepts of the graph are the real zeros of $p(x)$.
- The graph has a vertical asymptote at each real zero of $q(x)$.
- The graph has at most one horizontal asymptote.

  If $m < n$, the line $y = 0$ is a horizontal asymptote.

  If $m = n$, the line $y = \frac{a_m}{b_n}$ is a horizontal asymptote.

  If $m > n$, the graph has no horizontal asymptote.

EXAMPLE 2

Identify the intercepts and asymptotes of the graph of $y = \frac{2x^2 - 8}{x^2 - 9}$. Then graph the function.

STEP 1 Find the *x*-intercepts.

Set the numerator equal to zero.	$2x^2 - 8 = 0$
Add 8 to both sides.	$2x^2 = 8$
Divide both sides by 2.	$x^2 = 4$
Take the square root of both sides.	$x = \pm 2$

The graph has *x*-intercepts at $x = 2$ and $x = -2$.

STEP 2 Identify the vertical asymptotes.

The denominator cannot equal zero, so the restricted values occur when $x^2 - 9 = 0$.

Set the denominator equal to zero.	$x^2 - 9 = 0$
Add 9 to both sides.	$x^2 = 9$
Take the square root of both sides.	$x = \pm 3$

The graph has vertical asymptotes at $x = 3$ and $x = -3$.

STEP 3 Identify the horizontal asymptotes.

The degree of the numerator (2) is the same as the degree of the denominator (2), so the line $y = \frac{a_m}{b_n}$ is a horizontal asymptote. The value of a_m is 2 and the value of b_n is 1, so the line $y = 2$ is a horizontal asymptote.

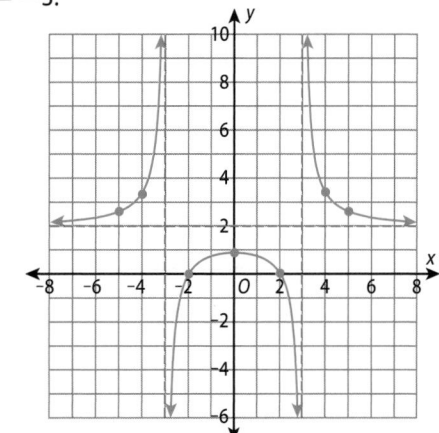

STEP 4 Graph the function.

METHOD 1

Graph the function on a coordinate grid. Make a table of values for *x* and *y*.

x	−5	−4	−2	0	2	4	5
y	$2\frac{5}{8}$	$3\frac{3}{7}$	0	$\frac{8}{9}$	0	$3\frac{3}{7}$	$2\frac{5}{8}$

Use dotted lines to draw the asymptotes $x = 3$, $x = -3$, and $y = 2$. Then connect the points on each side of the asymptotes and between the asymptotes.

The graph of $y = \frac{2x^2 - 8}{x^2 - 9}$ is shown to the right.

METHOD 2

Graph the function on a graphing calculator.
Press Y= and enter $(2x^2 - 8)/(x^2 - 9)$.

Use the asymptotes and intercepts as a guide to set an appropriate viewing window. Then press GRAPH.

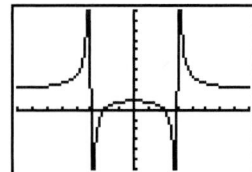

Watch **Out** !

Remember that when you introduce a square root symbol to solve an equation, there are two solutions—one positive root and one negative root. Check to make sure both solutions work in the situation.

Try It This Way

The asymptotes look like part of the graph because the calculator tries to connect all the values. To eliminate the asymptotes at integer values of *x*, you can change Xmin to −9.4 and Xmax to 9.4. Another method is to press MODE and select Dot mode. Press ENTER and GRAPH to see the graph in Dot mode, which shows only discrete points on the graph.

Factoring to Find Asymptotes

EXAMPLE 3

Identify the intercepts and asymptotes of the graph of $y = \dfrac{3x^2 + 4x - 4}{x^2 - 5x - 6}$**. Then, graph the function.**

STEP 1 Find the x-intercepts.

The numerator can be factored as $(3x - 2)(x + 2)$. This will equal zero when $x = \dfrac{2}{3}$ or $x = -2$, so the graph has x-intercepts at $x = \dfrac{2}{3}$ and $x = -2$.

STEP 2 Identify the vertical asymptotes.

The denominator cannot equal zero, so the restricted values occur when $x^2 - 5x - 6 = 0$. The denominator can be factored as $(x - 6)(x + 1)$, which will equal zero when $x = 6$ or $x = -1$, so the graph has vertical asymptotes at $x = 6$ and $x = -1$.

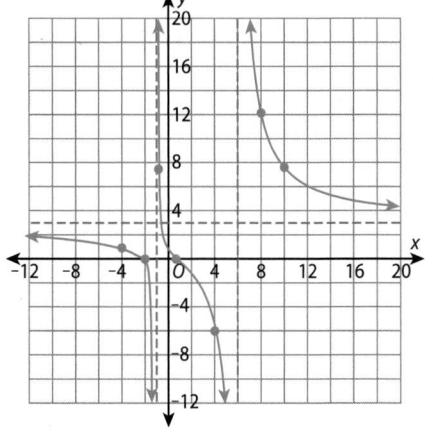

STEP 3 Identify the horizontal asymptotes.

The degree of the numerator (2) is the same as the degree of the denominator (2) so the horizontal asymptote is $y = \dfrac{a_m}{b_n} = 3$.

STEP 4 Graph the function.

Make a table of values for x and y.

x	−4	−2	−0.9	$\frac{2}{3}$	4	8	10
y	0.9	0	7.5	0	−6	12.2	7.6

Use dotted lines to draw the asymptotes $x = 6$, $x = -1$, and $y = 3$. Then connect the points on each side of the asymptotes and between the asymptotes. The graph is shown above.

EXAMPLE 4

Identify the intercepts and asymptotes of the graph of $y = \dfrac{x^2 - x - 2}{x - 1}$**. Then graph the function.**

STEP 1 Factor the numerator as $(x - 2)(x + 1)$. The graph has x-intercepts at $x = 2$ and $x = -1$.

STEP 2 The graph has a vertical asymptote when $x - 1 = 0$, so the line $x = 1$ is a vertical asymptote.

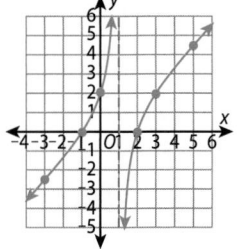

STEP 3 The degree of the numerator (2) is greater than the degree of the denominator (1), so there is no horizontal asymptote.

STEP 4 Make a table of values for x and y.

x	−3	−1	0	2	3	5
y	−2.5	0	2	0	2	4.5

Use dotted lines to draw the asymptote $x = 1$. Then plot the points in the table and connect the points on each side of the vertical asymptote. The graph is shown above.

EXAMPLE 5

The concentration c of a certain drug in a person's bloodstream t hours after receiving the drug is modeled by the equation $c = \dfrac{3t^2 + t}{t^3 + 50}$.

a. Find the intercepts and asymptotes of the function.

The numerator factors into $t(3t + 1)$, so the t-intercepts are $t = 0$ and $t = -1$.

The denominator equals zero when $t^3 = -50$ or $t = (-50)^{\frac{1}{3}} \approx 3.68$, so the line $t = -3.68$ is a vertical asymptote.

The degree of the numerator (2) is less than the degree of the denominator (3), so the line $c = 0$ is the horizontal asymptote.

b. Interpret the meaning of the horizontal asymptote in the context of the problem.

The horizontal asymptote shows that the concentration of the drug will eventually be zero.

c. Graph the function.

Graph the function on a graphing calculator.

Press [Y=] and enter the equation using these keystrokes:

Select an appropriate viewing window.

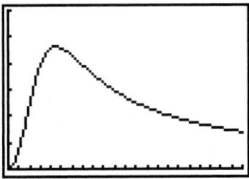

d. Use your graph to estimate the time when the concentration is the greatest.

To find the maximum concentration, press the [2nd] [TRACE] keys to get to the CALC menu. Press [4] to select MAXIMUM and then press [ENTER].

Use the arrow keys to highlight a point to the left of the maximum and press [ENTER].

Then use the arrow keys to highlight a point to the right of the maximum and press [ENTER].

Press [ENTER] again to guess the maximum value.

The calculator will display the maximum value on the bottom of the screen.

Maximum is $t \approx 4.49$ when $c \approx 0.46$.

The maximum concentration occurs about 4.5 hours after this drug is taken.

Need More

HELP ?

For help finding cube roots, go to *Other Roots* in *Radicals, Exponents, Logarithms, and Rational Expressions* on page 1954.

Rational Equations

Solving Rational Equations

A **rational equation** is an equation that contains fractional—or rational—expressions. When each side of the equation is a single rational expression, you can cross multiply.

Need More
HELP ?

Cross multiplication is a shorthand way of multiplying both sides of a rational equation by the same numbers— the denominators of both sides.

For example, multiply both sides of the equation in Example 1 by $4(x + 3)$. The expression $x + 3$ will cancel on the left side, and 4 will cancel on the right. The result is the same as the result of cross multiplying.

EXAMPLE 1

Solve $\frac{7}{x+3} = \frac{x}{4}$.

Each side of the equation contains one fraction, so you can solve by cross multiplying.

STEP 1 Write the equation. $\qquad\qquad\qquad\qquad\qquad\qquad \frac{7}{x+3} = \frac{x}{4}$

STEP 2 Cross multiply. $\qquad\qquad\qquad\qquad\qquad 7 \cdot 4 = x(x + 3)$

STEP 3 Multiply using the distributive property. $\qquad 28 = x^2 + 3x$

STEP 4 Subtract 28 from each side. $\qquad\qquad\quad 0 = x^2 + 3x - 28$

STEP 5 Factor. $\qquad\qquad\qquad\qquad\qquad\qquad 0 = (x + 7)(x - 4)$

STEP 6 Set both factors equal to 0, and solve. $\qquad x = -7$ or $x = 4$

CHECK Substitute -7 for x in the original equation. $\qquad$ Substitute 4 for x in the original equation.

$$\frac{7}{-7+3} \stackrel{?}{=} \frac{-7}{4} \qquad\qquad\qquad \frac{7}{4+3} \stackrel{?}{=} \frac{4}{4}$$

$$-\frac{7}{4} = -\frac{7}{4} \qquad\qquad\qquad\qquad \frac{7}{7} = \frac{4}{4} \ ✔$$

The solutions are -7 and 4.

When there are more than two terms in the equation, you can multiply each term by the lowest common denominator (LCD) of all the fractions in the equation.

Need More
HELP ?

Remember—the least common denominator is the smallest number that has each denominator as a factor.

EXAMPLE 2

Solve $\frac{2x}{3} - \frac{5}{6} = \frac{x}{2}$.

STEP 1 Write the equation. $\qquad\qquad\qquad\qquad\qquad\qquad \frac{2x}{3} - \frac{5}{6} = \frac{x}{2}$

STEP 2 Multiply each term by 6, the LCD of 3, 6 and 2. $\quad \frac{2x}{3}(6) - \frac{5}{6}(6) = \frac{x}{2}(6)$

STEP 3 Simplify. $\qquad\qquad\qquad\qquad\qquad\qquad\qquad 4x - 5 = 3x$

STEP 4 Subtract $4x$ from each side. $\qquad\qquad\qquad\qquad -5 = -1x$

STEP 5 Divide each side by -1. $\qquad\qquad\qquad\qquad\qquad 5 = x$

CHECK Substitute 5 for x in the original equation. $\qquad \frac{2 \cdot 5}{3} - \frac{5}{6} \stackrel{?}{=} \frac{5}{2}$

$\qquad\qquad$ Find a common denominator. $\qquad\qquad\qquad \frac{20}{6} - \frac{5}{6} \stackrel{?}{=} \frac{15}{6}$

$\qquad\qquad$ Simplify. $\qquad\qquad\qquad\qquad\qquad\qquad\qquad \frac{15}{6} = \frac{15}{6} \ ✔$

The solution is 5.

A solution of a transformed equation that is not a solution of the original equation is an **extraneous solution**. You should always check your answers in the original equation to be sure that the solution is not extraneous.

EXAMPLE 3

Solve $3 + \dfrac{8}{x-2} = \dfrac{4x}{x-2}$.

STEP 1	Write the original equation.	$3 + \dfrac{8}{x-2} = \dfrac{4x}{x-2}$
STEP 2	Multiply each term of the equation by $x-2$.	$3(x-2) + 8 = 4x$
STEP 3	Use the distributive property.	$3x - 6 + 8 = 4x$
STEP 4	Simplify.	$3x + 2 = 4x$
STEP 5	Subtract $3x$ from each side.	$2 = x$
CHECK	Substitute 2 for x in the original equation.	$3 + \dfrac{8}{2-2} \overset{?}{=} \dfrac{4 \cdot 2}{2-2}$
	Simplify.	$3 + \dfrac{8}{0} \overset{?}{=} \dfrac{8}{0}$

Division by zero is undefined, so 2 is an extraneous solution.

The original equation has no solution.

> **Watch Out !**
>
> Fractions with a zero in the denominator are undefined. Be careful not to confuse $\dfrac{0}{7}$, which equals zero, with $\dfrac{7}{0}$, which is undefined.

EXAMPLE 4

Solve $\dfrac{2}{x^2 - x} = \dfrac{1}{x-1}$.

Each side of the equation is written as a rational expression, so you can solve by cross multiplying.

STEP 1	Write the original equation.	$\dfrac{2}{x^2-x} = \dfrac{1}{x-1}$
STEP 2	Cross multiply.	$2(x-1) = x^2 - x$
STEP 3	Use the distributive property.	$2x - 2 = x^2 - x$
STEP 4	Subtract $2x$ from each side.	$-2 = x^2 - 3x$
STEP 5	Add 2 to each side.	$0 = x^2 - 3x + 2$
STEP 6	Factor.	$0 = (x-2)(x-1)$
STEP 7	Set both factors equal to 0, and solve.	$x = 2$ or $x = 1$
CHECK	Substitute 2 for x in the original equation.	$\dfrac{2}{2^2-2} \overset{?}{=} \dfrac{1}{2-1}$
	Simplify.	$\dfrac{2}{2} \overset{?}{=} \dfrac{1}{1}$
		$1 = 1 \ \checkmark$
	Substitute 1 for x in the original equation.	$\dfrac{2}{1^2-1} \overset{?}{=} \dfrac{1}{1-1}$

Division by zero is undefined, so 1 is an extraneous solution.

The only solution to the original equation is 2.

> **SEARCH**
>
> To see step-by-step videos of these problems, enter the page number into the SWadvantage.com Search Bar.

Solving More Complex Rational Equations

EXAMPLE 5

Solve $\dfrac{2x}{x-2} - \dfrac{4x-1}{3x+2} = \dfrac{17x+4}{3x^2-4x-4}$.

STEP 1 Write the original equation.

$$\dfrac{2x}{x-2} - \dfrac{4x-1}{3x+2} = \dfrac{17x+4}{3x^2-4x-4}$$

STEP 2 Factor $3x^2 - 4x - 4$.

$$\dfrac{2x}{x-2} - \dfrac{4x-1}{3x+2} = \dfrac{17x+4}{(3x+2)(x-2)}$$

STEP 3 Multiply each term by $(3x+2)(x-2)$.

$$\dfrac{2x(3x+2)(x-2)}{(x-2)} - \dfrac{(4x-1)(3x+2)(x-2)}{(3x+2)} = 17x+4$$

STEP 4 Simplify.

$$2x(3x+2) - (4x-1)(x-2) = 17x+4$$

STEP 5 Multiply using the distributive property.

$$6x^2 + 4x - (4x^2 - 8x - x + 2) = 17x+4$$

STEP 6 Distribute the negative inside the parentheses.

$$6x^2 + 4x - 4x^2 + 8x + x - 2 = 17x+4$$

STEP 7 Combine like terms.

$$2x^2 + 13x - 2 = 17x+4$$

STEP 8 Subtract $17x$ from each side.

$$2x^2 - 4x - 2 = 4$$

STEP 9 Subtract 4 from each side.

$$2x^2 - 4x - 6 = 0$$

STEP 10 Factor 2 out of each term.

$$2(x^2 - 2x - 3) = 0$$

STEP 11 Factor.

$$2(x-3)(x+1) = 0$$

STEP 12 The product will be zero when $x - 3 = 0$ or when $x + 1 = 0$.

$$x = 3 \text{ or } x = -1$$

CHECK Substitute 3 for x in the original equation.

$$\dfrac{2 \cdot 3}{3-2} - \dfrac{4 \cdot 3 - 1}{3 \cdot 3 + 2} \overset{?}{=} \dfrac{17 \cdot 3 + 4}{3(3^2) - 4 \cdot 3 - 4}$$

Simplify, and write with common denominators.

$$\dfrac{6}{1} - \dfrac{11}{11} \overset{?}{=} \dfrac{55}{11}$$

Both sides of the equation are equal.

$$\dfrac{55}{11} = \dfrac{55}{11} \checkmark$$

Substitute -1 for x in the original equation.

$$\dfrac{2 \cdot (-1)}{(-1)-2} - \dfrac{4 \cdot (-1) - 1}{3 \cdot (-1) + 2} \overset{?}{=} \dfrac{17 \cdot (-1) + 4}{3(-1)^2 - 4 \cdot (-1) - 4}$$

Simplify.

$$\dfrac{2}{3} - \dfrac{15}{3} \overset{?}{=} \dfrac{-13}{3}$$

Both sides of the equation are equal.

$$\dfrac{-13}{3} = \dfrac{-13}{3} \checkmark$$

The solutions are $x = 3$ and $x = -1$.

EXAMPLE 6

Solve $x - \dfrac{24}{x} = 5$.

STEP 1	Write the original equation.	$x - \dfrac{24}{x} = 5$
STEP 2	Multiply each term of the equation by x.	$x^2 - 24 = 5x$
STEP 3	Subtract $5x$ from each side.	$x^2 - 5x - 24 = 0$
STEP 4	Factor.	$(x - 8)(x + 3) = 0$
STEP 5	Set both factors equal to 0, and solve.	$x = 8$ or $x = -3$
CHECK	Substitute 8 for x in the original equation.	$8 - \dfrac{24}{8} \overset{?}{=} 5$
	Simplify.	$8 - 3 \overset{?}{=} 5$
		$5 = 5$ ✔
	Substitute -3 for x in the original equation.	$-3 - \dfrac{24}{-3} \overset{?}{=} 5$
	Simplify.	$-3 + 8 \overset{?}{=} 5$
		$5 = 5$ ✔

The solutions are 8 and -3.

SEARCH

To see step-by-step videos of these problems, enter the page number into the SWadvantage.com Search Bar.

EXAMPLE 7

Up to this point, a basketball player has made 37 out of 44 free throw shots. Solve the equation $\dfrac{90}{100} = \dfrac{37 + x}{44 + x}$ to find the number of consecutive free throws the player now needs to make in order to have a 90% free throw average.

STEP 1	Write the original equation.	$\dfrac{90}{100} = \dfrac{37 + x}{44 + x}$
STEP 2	Cross multiply.	$90(44 + x) = 100(37 + x)$
STEP 3	Use the distributive property.	$3960 + 90x = 3700 + 100x$
STEP 4	Subtract 3700 from each side.	$260 + 90x = 100x$
STEP 5	Subtract $90x$ from each side.	$260 = 10x$
STEP 6	Divide both sides by 10.	$26 = x$
CHECK	Substitute 26 for x in the original equation.	$\dfrac{90}{100} \overset{?}{=} \dfrac{37 + 26}{44 + 26}$
	Simplify.	$\dfrac{90}{100} \overset{?}{=} \dfrac{63}{70}$
	Cross multiply.	$90 \cdot 70 \overset{?}{=} 100 \cdot 63$
	Simplify.	$6300 = 6300$ ✔

The player has to make 26 consecutive free throw shots in order to have a 90% free throw average.

Need More HELP?

Remember that *per cent* means "out of 100." To write 90% as a fraction, you put 90 in the numerator and 100 in the denominator.

Rational Inequalities

Graphing Rational Inequalities

You use the methods for graphing rational equations to graph rational inequalities.

EXAMPLE 1

Graph $y < \dfrac{x^2 + 3x - 4}{x + 3}$.

STEP 1 Find the *x*-intercepts.

Identify when $y = 0$.	$x^2 + 3x - 4 = 0$
Factor.	$x^2 + 3x - 4 = (x + 4)(x - 1) = 0$
Set each factor equal to 0, and solve.	$x + 4 = 0$, so $x = -4$
	$x - 1 = 0$, so $x = 1$

STEP 2 Identify the asymptotes.

The value of *x* cannot be -3 because the denominator would equal zero and the function would be undefined. So there is a vertical asymptote at $x = -3$.

The degree of the numerator (2) is greater than the degree of the denominator (0), so there is no horizontal asymptote.

STEP 3 Make a table of values for *x* and *y*.

x	−5	−4	−3.5	−2	0	1	5
y	−3	0	4.5	−6	$-\dfrac{4}{3}$	0	4.5

STEP 4 Graph the function.

Use dotted lines to draw the asymptote $x = -3$ on a coordinate graph.

Plot the points from the table.

The inequality does not include the points on the graph because it is $<$, not $\leq$. Connect the points with a dotted line.

STEP 5 Shade the graph.

The graph includes the *y*-values that are less than the function, so shade the points below the graph of the function.

CHECK Choose a few points located in the shaded region. Substitute these points into the original inequality to confirm the graph is shaded correctly.

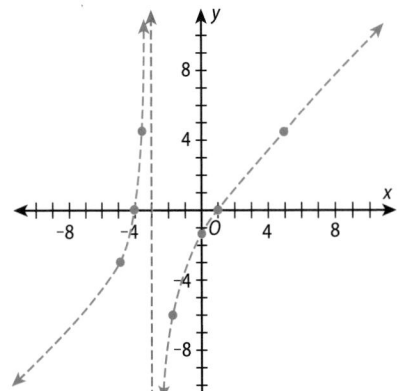

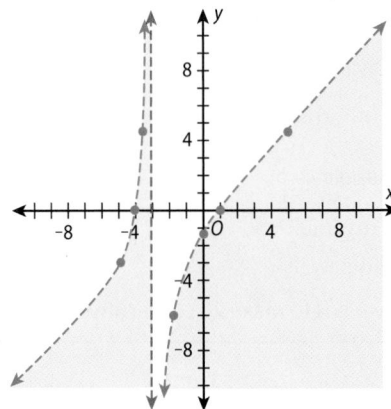

Solving Rational Inequalities

When you solve rational inequalities, your solution is often a range of values.

EXAMPLE 2

Solve $\frac{3x}{x+1} + \frac{6}{2x} \leq \frac{7}{x}$.

STEP 1 Determine the common denominator and the undefined values of x.

The common denominator is $2x(x+1)$. The undefined values occur at $x = -1$ and $x = 0$.

STEP 2 Multiply each term by the common denominator to clear the fractions.

Multiply by the common denominator.

$$\frac{3x \cdot 2x(x+1)}{x+1} + \frac{6 \cdot 2x(x+1)}{2x} \leq \frac{7 \cdot 2x(x+1)}{x}$$

Simplify.

$$3x \cdot 2x + 6(x+1) \leq 14(x+1)$$

Multiply.

$$6x^2 + 6x + 6 \leq 14x + 14$$

Combine like terms on one side of the inequality.

$$6x^2 - 8x - 8 \leq 0$$

Watch Out !

Remember that numbers that make a rational expression undefined cannot be included in the solution set.

STEP 3 Solve the related inequality.

Simplify.

$$2(3x^2 - 4x - 4) \leq 0, \text{ so } 3x^2 - 4x - 4 \leq 0$$

Factor the polynomial.

$$(3x + 2)(x - 2) \leq 0$$

Determine when the inequality equals zero.

$$x = -\frac{2}{3} \text{ and } x = 2$$

STEP 4 Test points from each interval formed by the zeros and the undefined values of x.

Interval	$(-\infty, -1)$	$(-1, -\frac{2}{3})$	$(-\frac{2}{3}, 0)$	$(0, 2)$	$(2, \infty)$
Choose a value of x in the interval to test in the original inequality.	$x = -2$	$x = -\frac{3}{4}$	$x = -\frac{1}{2}$	$x = 1$	$x = 3$
$\frac{3x}{x+1} + \frac{6}{2x} < \frac{7}{x}$	$4\frac{1}{2} \leq -3\frac{1}{2}$	$-13 \leq -9\frac{1}{3}$	$-9 \leq -14$	$4\frac{1}{2} \leq 7$	$3\frac{1}{4} \leq 2\frac{1}{3}$
Is the inequality *true* or *false*?	False	True	False	True	False

SEARCH

To see step-by-step videos of these problems, enter the page number into the SWadvantage.com Search Bar.

STEP 5 Determine the solution set of the inequality.

The inequality is true for points in the intervals $(-1, -\frac{2}{3})$ and $(0, 2)$.

Test the endpoints. The points $x = -\frac{2}{3}$ and $x = 2$ make the inequality true. The inequality is undefined at $x = -1$ and $x = 0$, so these points are not included in the solution.

The solution is $-1 < x \leq -\frac{2}{3}$ and $0 < x \leq 2$, or in interval notation $(-1, -\frac{2}{3}]$ and $(0, 2]$.

GOT TO KNOW!

Graphing Rational Inequalities

- Graph the inequality as you would a rational equation.

- Determine if the graph includes the boundary.

- Test points to determine how to shade the graph.

Solving Rational Inequalities

- Find the common denominator and any undefined values.

- Multiply each term by the common denominator to clear the fractions.

- Solve the related inequality.

- If necessary, test points in the intervals defined by the undefined values and the solutions to the inequality.

Radical Functions

Graphing Radical Functions

In this section, you will graph radical functions. A **radical function** is a function that contains a variable under a radical symbol, such as $y = \sqrt{x - 1}$ or $y = \sqrt[3]{2x}$. The expression under the radical symbol is called the **radicand**.

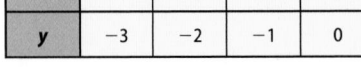

Find the domain and range of $y = \sqrt[3]{x} - 1$. Then graph the function.

STEP 1 Find the domain and range.

The radicand in an odd root can be any number, so the domain is all real numbers.

The value of y can be any number, so the range is all real numbers.

STEP 2 Make a table of values for x and y.

x	−8	−1	0	1	8
y	−3	−2	−1	0	1

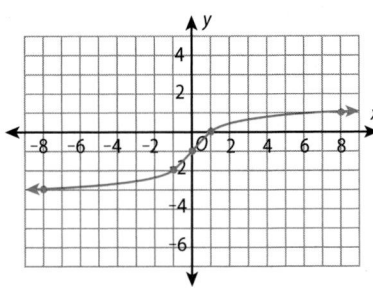

STEP 3 Graph the function.

Plot the points from the table on a coordinate grid. Then connect the points with a smooth curve.

The graph is to the right.

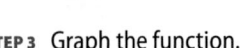

Find the domain and range of $y = 2\sqrt{x - 1}$. Then graph the function.

STEP 1 Find the domain and range.

The radicand is greater than or equal to zero, so $x - 1 \geq 0$ and the domain is $x \geq 1$.

The value of y will always be nonnegative, so the range is $y \geq 0$.

STEP 2 Make a table of values for x and y.

x	1	2	5	10
y	0	2	4	6

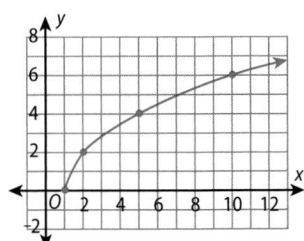

STEP 3 Graph the function.

Plot the points from the table on a coordinate grid. Then connect the points with a smooth curve.

The graph is to the right.

EXAMPLE 3

Find the domain and range of $y = \sqrt{x + 3} - 1$. Then graph the function.

STEP 1 Find the domain and range.

The radicand must be greater than or equal to zero, so $x + 3 \geq 0$ and the domain is $x \geq -3$.
When the radical is zero, the value of y will be -1, so the range is $y \geq -1$.

STEP 2 Make a table of values for x and y.

x	-3	-2	1	6
y	-1	0	1	2

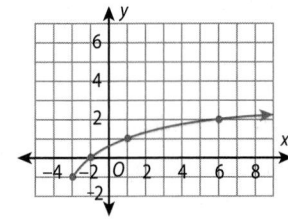

STEP 3 Graph the function.

Plot the points from the table on a coordinate grid. Then connect the points with a smooth curve. The graph of $y = \sqrt{x}$ has shifted 3 units to the left and 1 unit down.

Try It This Way

You can graph radical equations on a graphing calculator using the $\sqrt{}$ symbol (above the x^2 key). To graph cube roots, go to Y= and then press MATH and select option **4:³√(**. Be sure to put the radicand in parentheses.

EXAMPLE 4

Find the domain and range of $y = \sqrt[3]{x - 1} + 2$. Then graph the function.

STEP 1 Find the domain and range.

Because the root is an odd number, the domain and range are both all real numbers.

STEP 2 Make a table of values for x and y.

x	-7	0	1	2	9
y	0	1	2	3	4

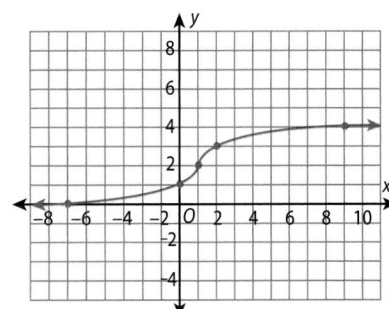

STEP 3 Graph the function.

Plot the points from the table on a coordinate grid. Then connect the points with a smooth curve. The graph of $y = \sqrt[3]{x}$ has shifted 1 unit to the right and 2 units up.

Square Root and Cube Root Functions

Graph of the Parent Function	$y = \sqrt{x}$	$y = \sqrt[3]{x}$
Standard Form of the Equation	$y = a\sqrt{x - h} + k$	$y = a\sqrt[3]{x - h} + k$
Domain and Range	$x \geq h$ and $y \geq k$	all real numbers
Graph of any radical function	Shift the graph of $y = a\sqrt{x}$ horizontally h units and vertically k units	Shift the graph of $y = a\sqrt[3]{x}$ horizontally h units and vertically k units

Radical Equations

Solving Radical Equations

When an equation contains radicals or rational exponents, you need to isolate the radical or exponent expression. Then, raise each side of the equation to the same power.

Need More

HELP ?

For help evaluating square roots and cube roots, see *Square Roots* (p. 1252) and *Other Roots* (p. 1254).

SEARCH 🔍

To see step-by-step videos of these problems, enter the page number into the SWadvantage.com Search Bar.

EXAMPLE 1

Solve $\sqrt[3]{x} + 4 = 0$.

STEP 1 Isolate the radical.

Subtract 4 from each side. $\qquad \sqrt[3]{x} = -4$

STEP 2 Solve for x.

Cube each side to eliminate the cube root. $\qquad \left(\sqrt[3]{x}\right)^3 = (-4)^3$

Simplify. $\qquad x = -64$

CHECK Substitute -64 for x in the original equation. $\qquad \sqrt[3]{-64} = -4$, so $\sqrt[3]{-64} + 4 = -4 + 4 = 0$.

The solution is -64.

EXAMPLE 2

Solve $2\sqrt{x + 12} - 3 = 5$.

STEP 1 Isolate the radical.

Add 3 to each side of the equation. $\qquad 2\sqrt{x + 12} = 8$

Divide each side by 2. $\qquad \sqrt{x + 12} = 4$

STEP 2 Solve for x.

Square both sides of the equation. $\qquad \left(\sqrt{x + 12}\right)^2 = (4)^2$

Simplify. $\qquad x + 12 = 16$

Subtract 12 from each side. $\qquad x = 4$

CHECK Substitute 4 into the original equation, and simplify. $\qquad 2\sqrt{4 + 12} - 3 \stackrel{?}{=} 5$

$$5 = 5 \; ✔$$

The solution is 4.

EXAMPLE 3

Solve $\sqrt[3]{5x} - \sqrt[3]{2x + 3} = 0$.

STEP 1 Isolate the radical.

Add $\sqrt[3]{2x + 3}$ to each side. $\qquad \sqrt[3]{5x} = \sqrt[3]{2x + 3}$

STEP 2 Solve for x.

Cube each side to eliminate the radical. $\qquad \left(\sqrt[3]{5x}\right)^3 = \left(\sqrt[3]{2x + 3}\right)^3$

Simplify. $\qquad 5x = 2x + 3$

$$3x = 3, \text{ so } x = 1$$

CHECK Substitute 1 for x in the original equation: $\sqrt[3]{5(1)} - \sqrt[3]{2(1) + 3} = \sqrt[3]{5} - \sqrt[3]{5} = 0$.

The solution is 1.

With rational exponents, you need to raise both sides of the equation to the power given by the reciprocal of the exponent to clear the exponent and any radicals. Always check your answer in the original equation. If a solution does not make the original equation true, it is an **extraneous solution** and should be omitted.

Need More

HELP?

Remember that a rational (or fractional) exponent represents a radical. For help with rational exponents, see *Integer and Rational Exponents* (p. 1966).

EXAMPLE 4

Solve $x = (x + 6)^{\frac{1}{2}}$.

Solve for x.

Raise each side to the power of 2, the reciprocal of $\frac{1}{2}$. $\qquad x^2 = ((x + 6)^{\frac{1}{2}})^2$

Simplify. $\qquad\qquad x^2 = x + 6$

Combine terms on one side to set equal to zero. $\qquad x^2 - x - 6 = 0$

Factor. $\qquad\qquad (x - 3)(x + 2) = 0$

Solve for x. $\qquad\qquad x = 3 \text{ or } x = -2$

CHECK Substitute the solutions into the original equation to check for extraneous solutions.

$3 \stackrel{?}{=} (3 + 6)^{\frac{1}{2}} \qquad -2 \stackrel{?}{=} (-2 + 6)^{\frac{1}{2}}$

$3 \stackrel{?}{=} \sqrt{9} \qquad\qquad -2 \stackrel{?}{=} \sqrt{4}$

$3 = 3 \qquad\qquad\quad -2 \neq 2$

One of the solutions does not check. It is an extraneous solution, so the only solution is 3.

Watch Out !

Raising each side of an equation to the same power can lead to solutions that do not make the original equation true. Always check your answer in the original equation to make sure there are no extraneous solutions.

EXAMPLE 5

Solve $x^{\frac{2}{3}} - 9 = 16$.

STEP 1 Isolate the term containing the exponent.

Add 9 to each side to isolate the exponential term. $\qquad x^{\frac{2}{3}} = 25$

STEP 2 Solve for x.

Raise each side to the $\frac{3}{2}$ power, the reciprocal of $\frac{2}{3}$. $\qquad \left(x^{\frac{2}{3}}\right)^{\frac{3}{2}} = (25)^{\frac{3}{2}}$

Simplify. $\qquad\qquad x = \sqrt{25^3}$

$\qquad\qquad x = 125$

CHECK Substitute 125 for x in the original equation. $\qquad 125^{\frac{2}{3}} - 9 = \sqrt[3]{125^2} - 9 = 25 - 9 = 16.$

The solution is 125.

GOT TO KNOW!

Solving Rational Equations

1. Isolate the radical on one side of the equation, if possible.

2. Raise each side of the equation to the same power to eliminate the radical.

3. To eliminate rational exponents, raise each side of the equation to the reciprocal of the rational exponent.

4. Always check your answer to make sure there are no extraneous solutions.

Radical Inequalities

Graphing Radical Inequalities

In this section, you will graph radical inequalities. A **radical inequality** is an inequality that contains a variable under a radical symbol, such as $y < \sqrt{x-1}$ or $y \geq \sqrt[2]{2x}$. The graph of a radical inequality is like the graph of a radical function, but it is shaded above or below the graph to represent the inequality.

EXAMPLE 1

Graph $y > -3\sqrt{x+2}$.

METHOD 1   **Plot points to graph the inequality.**

STEP 1 Find the domain and range of the related equation $y = -3\sqrt{x+2}$.

The radicand for a square root must be positive, so if $x + 2 \geq 0$, $x \geq -2$.

Because of the negative sign in front of the root, the range is $y \leq 0$.

STEP 2 Make a table of values for x and y using the related equation $y = -3\sqrt{x+2}$.

x	−2	−1	2	7
y	0	−3	−6	−9

STEP 3 Graph the related equation $y = -3\sqrt{x+2}$.

Plot the points from the table on a coordinate grid. Because the inequality is $y >$, it does not include the boundary, so connect the points with a dashed curve.

STEP 4 Shade the graph.

The inequality is y-values greater than $-3\sqrt{x+2}$, so shade above the boundary.

CHECK Choose a test point in the shaded region to substitute into the original inequality to confirm you shaded correctly. The point $(-1, 0)$ is in the shaded region.

$0 > -3\sqrt{-1+2}$ simplifies to $0 > -3$, which is a true statement, so the shading is correct.

METHOD 2   **Use a graphing calculator.**

STEP 1 Enter the inequality.

Press  and use these keystrokes to enter the radical expression.

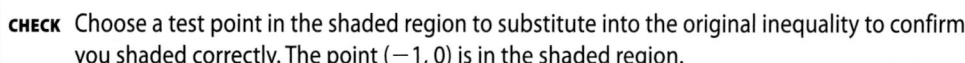

STEP 2 Shade the graph.

Use the left arrow key to highlight the area to the left of Y1. Because the inequality is $y >$ the radical expression, you want to shade points above the graph. Hit the ENTER key two times or until you see a line with shading above it. The icon next to the Y1 will look like this: ⬎.

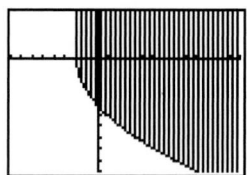

STEP 3 Graph the inequality.

Press the GRAPH key to display the graph.

EXAMPLE 2

Graph $y \leq \sqrt[3]{x - 4} + 1$.

STEP 1 Find the domain and range of the related equation $y = \sqrt[3]{x - 4} + 1$.

The domain and range include all real numbers.

STEP 2 Make a table of values for x and y using the related equation $y = \sqrt[3]{x - 4} + 1$.

x	−4	3	4	5
y	−1	0	1	2

STEP 3 Graph the related equation $y = \sqrt[3]{x - 4} + 1$.

Plot the points from the table on a coordinate grid. The inequality is $\leq$, so connect the points with a solid curve.

STEP 4 Shade the graph.

The inequality is $\leq$, so shade below the curve. Substitute a point from the shaded region into the original inequality to confirm you shaded correctly.

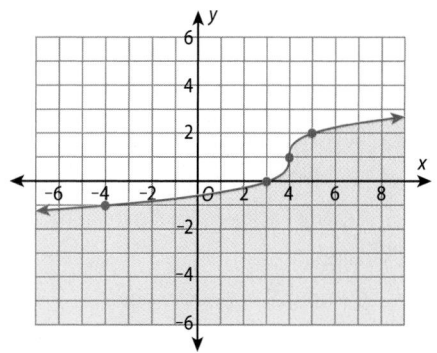

Need More

HELP ?

For help graphing radical functions, see *Radical Functions* (p. 2032).

SEARCH

To see step-by-step videos of these problems, enter the page number into the SWadvantage.com Search Bar.

Graphing Radical Inequalities

1. To graph a radical inequality, start by graphing the related radical equation.

2. Determine if the curve should be dashed (for $<$ and $>$) or solid (for $\leq$ and $\geq$).

3. Determine which side of the curve should be shaded.

Inequality	Where to Shade
$<$ or $\leq$	Shade below the curve
$>$ or $\geq$	Shade above the curve

4. Use a test point in the shaded region to check that the correct portion of the graph is shaded.

Solving Radical Inequalities

You solve radical inequalities the same way you solve radical equations, but if you multiply or divide by a negative, you need to change the direction of the inequality. If a solution does not make the original inequality true, it is an **extraneous solution** and should be omitted.

EXAMPLE 3

Solve $-2\sqrt{3x + 9} > -12$**.**

STEP 1 Find the domain of the function.

The radicand must be positive, so $3x + 9 \geq 0$, which means $x \geq -3$.

STEP 2 Solve the inequality for x.

Divide both sides by -2. Switch the inequality from $>$ to $<$.	$\sqrt{3x + 9} < 6$
Square each side to eliminate the square root.	$\left(\sqrt{3x + 9}\right)^2 < (6)^2$
Simplify.	$3x + 9 < 36$
Subtract 9 from both sides.	$3x < 27$
Divide both sides by 3.	$x < 9$

STEP 3 Write the solution.

The solution is $x < 9$, but the domain restricts x to values greater than -3.

The solution is $-3 \leq x < 9$. In interval notation, this is written $[-3, 9)$.

EXAMPLE 4

Solve $\sqrt{6x + 3} \geq \sqrt{2x - 5}$**.**

STEP 1 Find the domain of the function.

The radicands must be greater than or equal to zero.

$$6x + 3 \geq 0 \qquad\qquad 2x - 5 \geq 0$$
$$6x \geq -3 \qquad\qquad 2x \geq 5$$
$$x \geq -\frac{3}{6} = -\frac{1}{2} \qquad\qquad x \geq \frac{5}{2}$$

The intersection of these restrictions is $x \geq \frac{5}{2}$, so the domain is $x \geq \frac{5}{2}$.

STEP 2 Solve the inequality for x.

Square both sides to eliminate the square roots.	$\left(\sqrt{6x + 3}\right)^2 \geq \left(\sqrt{2x - 5}\right)^2$
Simplify.	$6x + 3 \geq 2x - 5$
Subtract 3 from both sides.	$6x \geq 2x - 8$
Subtract $2x$ from both sides.	$4x \geq -8$
Divide both sides by 4.	$x \geq -2$

STEP 3 Write the solution.

The solution is the intersection of $x \geq -2$ and the domain restriction $x \geq \frac{5}{2}$.

The solution is $x \geq \frac{5}{2}$. In interval notation, this is written $[\frac{5}{2}, \infty)$.

EXAMPLE 5

Solve $-5 > x - (1-x)^{\frac{1}{2}}$.

STEP 1 Find the domain of the function.

The radicand must be positive, so $1 - x \geq 0$, which means $x \leq 1$.

STEP 2 Solve the inequality for x.

Subtract x from each side of the original equation.	$-x - 5 > -(1-x)^{\frac{1}{2}}$
Divide each side by -1. Switch the inequality from $>$ to $<$.	$x + 5 < (1-x)^{\frac{1}{2}}$
Raise each side to the power of 2, the reciprocal of $\frac{1}{2}$.	$(x+5)^2 < \left((1-x)^{\frac{1}{2}}\right)^2$
Simplify.	$x^2 + 10x + 25 < 1 - x$
Combine terms on one side.	$x^2 + 11x + 24 < 0$
Factor.	$(x+8)(x+3) < 0$
Solve for x.	$x < -8$ or $x < -3$

STEP 3 Test points in each interval to determine the solution set.

Interval	$(-\infty, -8)$	$(-8, -3)$	$(-3, 1)$
Test Point	-15	-4	0
Test point in original inequality	$-5 > -15 - \sqrt{16}$ $-5 > -19$	$-5 > -4 - \sqrt{5}$ $-5 > -6.23$	$-5 > 0 - \sqrt{1}$ $-5 > -1$
Is the inequality *true* or *false*?	true	true	false

STEP 4 Write the solution.

The inequality is true in the intervals $(-\infty, -8)$ and $(-8, -3)$. When $x = -8$, the value of $x - (1-x)^{\frac{1}{2}} = -11$. The inequality $-5 > -11$ is true, so the solution includes -8.

The solution is $-\infty < x < -3$.

In interval notation, this is written $(-\infty, -3)$.

Watch Out !

In Example 6, the solution might appear to be $x < -8$. However, this solution misses the points greater than -8 but less than -3. When you have multiple intervals, always test points from each interval in the original inequality to make sure you include the entire solution.

GOT TO KNOW!

Solving Rational Inequalities

1. Isolate the radical on one side of the equation, if possible.

2. Raise each side of the equation to the same power to eliminate the radical.

3. To eliminate rational exponents, raise each side of the equation to the reciprocal of the rational exponent.

4. If you multiply or divide by a negative number, switch the direction of the inequality.

5. Always find the domain of the inequality to make sure your solution fits the domain.

6. Always check your answer to make sure there are no extraneous solutions.

7. When you have multiple solution points, test points in each interval.

Writing Models for Functions

What Came Before?
- Graphing quadratic functions
- Arithmetic sequences

What's This About?
- Calculating higher-order differences
- Using first-, second- and third-order differences to model linear, quadratic and cubic functions
- Modeling exponential equations using initial values and common ratios

Practical Apps
- Company profits may be modeled by quadratic and cubic functions.
- Biologists use an exponential growth equation to model a population of fruit flies over time.

just for FUN!

The cubic was afraid of coming home—she knew her parents were going to give her the 3rd degree.

You can find more practice problems online by visiting:
www.SWadvantage.com

Constant Differences

Constant Differences

When you subtract consecutive terms of a sequence, you are finding the **first-order differences** of the sequence. When you subtract the consecutive first-order differences, you get the **second-order differences**. When the differences are all the same, they are called **constant differences**. Constant differences can be used to model situations.

Need More
HELP ?

For help understanding sequences, go to *Arithmetic Sequences* (p. 1858) and *Geometric Sequences* (p. 1866).

EXAMPLE 1

Find the first-order and second-order differences for the sequence 2, 4, 8, 14, 22, 32. Tell if either difference results in a constant difference.

STEP 1 Find the first-order differences.

Write the sequence. Then start subtracting terms.

$4 - 2 = 2; 8 - 4 = 4; 14 - 8 = 6; 22 - 14 = 8; 32 - 22 = 10$

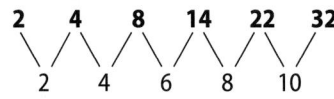

The first-order differences are 2, 4, 6, 8, and 10.
The differences are not all the same, so they are not constant differences.

STEP 2 Find the second-order differences.

Continue using the same diagram.

Find the difference of the first-order differences: $4 - 2 = 2; 6 - 4 = 2; 8 - 6 = 2; 10 - 8 = 2$

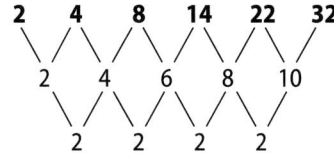

The second-order differences are all 2.

The differences are all the same, so the second-order differences are constant differences.

SEARCH 🔍

To see step-by-step videos of these problems, enter the page number into the SWadvantage.com Search Bar.

EXAMPLE 2

Find any constant differences for the sequence 1, 4, 7, 10, 13.

Write the sequence and start finding the differences.

Original sequence	**1**	**4**	**7**	**10**	**13**
First-order differences		3	3	3	3
Second-order differences		0	0	0	

The first-order differences are all 3, so the first-order differences are constant.

Once you find constant differences, you can stop. The remaining differences will always be zero. There is no need to find these differences.

EXAMPLE 3

Find any constant differences for the sequence 3, 3, 7, 16, 31, 53.

Original Sequence	**3**	**3**	**7**	**16**	**31**	**53**
First differences		0	4	9	15	22
Second differences			4	5	6	7
Third differences				1	1	1

The third-order differences are all 1, so the third-order differences are constant.

Ways to
REMEMBER

When something is *constant*, it is the same all the time. Use this to help remember that constant terms stay the same and constant differences result in differences that are the same number.

EXAMPLE 4

Find any constant differences for the sequence 1, 2, 4, 8, 16, 32.

Original Sequence	**1**	**2**	**4**	**8**	**16**	**32**
First-order differences		1	2	4	8	16
Second-order differences			1	2	4	8
Third-order differences				1	2	4
Fourth-order differences					1	2
Sixth-order differences						1

This sequence does not produce any constant differences.

GOT TO KNOW!

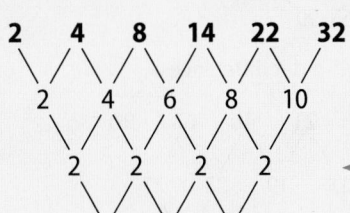

Constant Differences

When you subtract consecutive terms of a sequence, and the resulting differences are all the same, they are called constant differences. Some sequences have no constant differences.

Original Sequence	**2**	**4**	**8**	**14**	**22**	**32**
First differences		2	4	6	8	10
Second differences			2	2	2	2
Third differences				0	0	0

← These are constant differences.

← The second differences are constant, so there is no need to find third differences. The remaining differences will always be zero.

Second-Order Constant Differences

Second-Order Constant Differences

A sequence represented by a quadratic model will have second-order constant differences.

Need More
HELP ?

For help with finding second-order differences, go to *Constant Differences* (p. 2042).

EXAMPLE 1

Find the first six terms of the sequence generated by the quadratic model $a_n = n^2$. Then find the second-order differences for the sequence and tell whether they are constant.

STEP 1 Find the first six terms of the sequence.

Substitute the term number for n into the equation.

$a_1 = (1)^2 = 1$ $\qquad$ $a_4 = (4)^2 = 16$

$a_2 = (2)^2 = 4$ $\qquad$ $a_5 = (5)^2 = 25$

$a_3 = (3)^2 = 9$ $\qquad$ $a_6 = (6)^2 = 36$

STEP 2 Write the sequence generated by the quadratic model.

1, 4, 9, 16, 25, 36

STEP 3 Find the second-order differences.

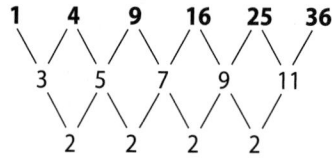

The second-order differences are constant.

SEARCH

To see step-by-step videos of these problems, enter the page number into the SWadvantage.com Search Bar.

EXAMPLE 2

Find the first six terms of the sequence generated by the quadratic model $a_n = 2n^2 + 5n - 12$. Then find the second-order differences for the sequence and tell whether they are constant.

STEP 1 Find the first six terms of the sequence.

Substitute the term number for n into the equation.

$a_1 = 2(1)^2 + 5 \cdot 1 - 12 = -5$ $\qquad$ $a_4 = 2(4)^2 + 5 \cdot 4 - 12 = 40$

$a_2 = 2(2)^2 + 5 \cdot 2 - 12 = 6$ $\qquad$ $a_5 = 2(5)^2 + 5 \cdot 5 - 12 = 63$

$a_3 = 2(3)^2 + 5 \cdot 3 - 12 = 21$ $\qquad$ $a_6 = 2(6)^2 + 5 \cdot 6 - 12 = 90$

STEP 2 Write the sequence generated by the quadratic model.

$-5, 6, 21, 40, 63, 90$

STEP 3 Find the second-order differences.

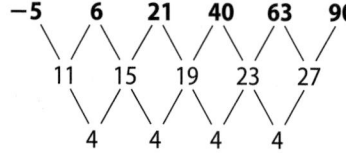

The second-order differences are constant.

If a sequence has second-order constant differences, you can write a quadratic model to represent the sequence.

EXAMPLE 3

The sequence 3, 5, 8, 12, 17, 23, . . . has second-order constant differences. Write the quadratic model for the sequence.

STEP 1 Write the first three terms in the form $an^2 + bn + c = a_n$.

Term (n)	a_n	$an^2 + bn + c$	$an^2 + bn + c = a_n$
1	3	$a(1)^2 + b \cdot 1 + c$	$a + b + c = 3$
2	5	$a(2)^2 + b \cdot 2 + c$	$4a + 2b + c = 5$
3	8	$a(3)^2 + b \cdot 3 + c$	$9a + 3b + c = 8$

Need More

HELP

For help with solving systems of equations, go to *Solving Systems by Substitution* (p. 1762) and *Solving Systems by Elimination* (p. 1766).

STEP 2 Use a system of three equations to solve for a, b, and c.

Write the system of equations.
$$a + b + c = 3$$
$$4a + 2b + c = 5$$
$$9a + 3b + c = 8$$

STEP 3 Eliminate one of the variables.

Rewrite the first equation to solve for one variable. $c = 3 - a - b$

Substitute $3 - a - b$ into the other equations for c. $4a + 2b + 3 - a - b = 5$
$$9a + 3b + 3 - a - b = 8$$

Simplify and combine constant terms. $3a + b = 2$
$$8a + 2b = 5$$

STEP 4 Use the new system of two equations to eliminate another variable.

Multiply the top equation by -2. $-6a - 2b = -4$
$$8a + 2b = 5$$

Add the two equations. $2a = 1$

Solve for a. $a = \frac{1}{2}$

STEP 5 Substitute a into an equation to find b.

Substitute $\frac{1}{2}$ into a two-variable equation. $8\left(\frac{1}{2}\right) + 2b = 5$

Simplify. $4 + 2b = 5$

Subtract 4 on each side. $2b = 1$

Divide by 2 on each side. $b = \frac{1}{2}$

STEP 6 Substitute a and b into an equation to find c.

Substitute $\frac{1}{2}$ for a and b in the equation $a + b + c = 3$. $\frac{1}{2} + \frac{1}{2} + c = 3$

Simplify. $c = 2$

STEP 7 Write the quadratic model.

Substitute for a, b, and c in the equation $a_n = an^2 + bn + c$. $a_n = \frac{1}{2}n^2 + \frac{1}{2}n + 2$

The quadratic model for the sequence 3, 5, 8, 12, 17, 23, . . . is $a_n = \frac{1}{2}n^2 + \frac{1}{2}n + 2$.

Try It

This Way

You can use the regression feature of a graphing calculator to find a quadratic model.

Enter the *x*-coordinates in one list (L1) and the *y*-coordinates in another list (L2).

Then press **STAT** and select CALC.

Choose 5:QuadReg to select a quadratic model, then press **2nd** **1** **,** **2nd** **2**

and press **ENTER**.

The values of *a*, *b*, and *c* in the quadratic model will be shown.

Using Ordered Pairs to Write a Quadratic Model

When a situation is modeled by a quadratic function, you can use three points to write an equation to model the situation.

EXAMPLE 4

The position of a free throw shot in basketball can be modeled by a quadratic function where the *x*-value represents the distance the player is from the back of the basket and the *y*-value represents the height of the ball. Find the equation of the path of the ball if the points $(-15, 7)$, $(-10, 10)$, and $(-5, 11)$ are on the graph.

STEP 1 Write a system of equations.

The equations are in the form $y = ax^2 + bx + c$. Substitute the *x*- and *y*-values for each point.

$$7 = (-15)^2a - 15b + c \rightarrow 7 = 225a - 15b + c$$
$$10 = (-10)^2a - 10b + c \rightarrow 10 = 100a - 10b + c$$
$$11 = (-5)^2a - 5b + c \rightarrow 11 = 25a - 5b + c$$

STEP 2 Write an expression for c. Then substitute the expression into the other equations.

$$7 = 225a - 15b + c \rightarrow c = -225a + 15b + 7$$

$$10 = 100a - 10b + -225a + 15b + 7 \qquad 11 = 25a - 5b + -225a + 15b + 7$$
$$10 - 7 = -125a + 5b \qquad\qquad 11 - 7 = -200a + 10b$$
$$3 = -125a + 5b \qquad\qquad 4 = -200a + 10b$$

STEP 3 Solve the system of two equations for one variable.

Multiply the top equation by -2 and then add the equations to eliminate one variable.

$$3 = -125a + 5b \rightarrow -6 = 250a - 10b$$
$$4 = -200a + 10b \qquad\underline{4 = -200a + 10b}$$
$$\qquad\qquad\qquad -2 = 50a$$

$$a = \frac{-2}{50} = \frac{-1}{25} \text{ or } -0.04$$

STEP 4 Use the system of two equations to solve for the remaining variable.

Substitute -0.04 into one of the original equations in STEP 3 and solve.

Substitute -0.04.	$3 = -125(-0.04) + 5b$
Simplify.	$3 = 5 + 5b$
Subtract 5 from each side.	$-2 = 5b$
Divide each side by 5.	$\frac{-2}{5} = b$

$$b = \frac{-2}{5} = -0.4$$

STEP 5 Substitute the values of *a* and *b* into one of the original equations.

Substitute -0.04 for *a* and -0.4 for *b*.	$c = -225(-0.04) + 15(-0.4) + 7$
Use a calculator to multiply.	$c = 9 + (-6) + 7$
Simplify.	$c = 10$

STEP 6 Write the quadratic model.

Substitute -0.04 for *a*, -0.4 for *b*, and 10 for *c* in the equation $y = ax^2 + bx + c$.

The equation to model the function is $y = -0.04x^2 - 0.4x + 10$.

EXAMPLE 5

The y-values in the points (30, 78), (40, 124), and (50, 180) represent the distance in feet needed to stop a car traveling on dry pavement at a speed of x miles per hour. The stopping distance is represented by a quadratic model. Find the equation to represent the stopping distance.

STEP 1   Write a system of equations.

The equations are in the form $y = ax^2 + bx + c$. Substitute the x- and y-values for each point.

$$78 = (30)^2a + 30b + c \rightarrow 78 = 900a + 30b + c$$
$$124 = (40)^2a + 40b + c \rightarrow 124 = 1600a + 40b + c$$
$$180 = (50)^2a + 50b + c \rightarrow 180 = 2500a + 50b + c$$

STEP 2   Write an expression for c. Then substitute the expression into the other equations.

$$78 = 900a + 30b + c \rightarrow c = -900a - 30b + 78$$
$$124 = 1600a + 40b - 900a - 30b + 78 \qquad 180 = 2500a + 50b - 900a - 30b + 78$$
$$46 = 700a + 10b \qquad\qquad 102 = 1600a + 20b$$

STEP 3   Solve the two-equation system for one variable.

Multiply the top equation by –2 and then add the equations to eliminate one variable.

$$46 = 700a + 10b \quad \rightarrow \quad -92 = -1400a - 20b$$
$$102 = 1600a + 20b \qquad \underline{102 = \quad 1600a + 20b}$$
$$\qquad\qquad\qquad\qquad 10 = \quad 200a$$

$$a = \frac{10}{200} = \frac{1}{20} \text{ or } 0.05$$

STEP 4   Solve the two-equation system for the remaining variable.

Substitute 0.05 into one of the original equations in STEP 3 and solve.

Substitute 0.05.	$46 = 700(0.05) + 10b$
Simplify.	$46 = 35 + 10b$
Subtract 35 from each side.	$11 = 10b$
Divide each side by 10.	$b = \frac{11}{10} = 1.1$

STEP 5   Substitute the values of a and b into the equation for c.

Substitute 0.05 for a and 1.1 for b.	$c = -900(0.05) - 30(1.1) + 78$
Simplify.	$c = -45 - 33 + 78 = -78 + 78 = 0$

STEP 6   Write the quadratic model.

Substitute 0.05 for a, 1.1 for b, and 0 for c in the equation $y = ax^2 + bx + c$.

The stopping distance can be modeled by the equation $y = 0.05x^2 + 1.1x$, where x is the speed in miles per hour and y is the distance needed to stop in feet.

SEARCH

To see step-by-step videos of these problems, enter the page number into the SWadvantage.com Search Bar.

GOT TO KNOW!

Modeling with Constant Differences

- When a sequence produces constant second-order differences, the terms of the sequence can be represented by a quadratic equation: $an^2 + bn + c = a_n$. Three terms of the sequence can be used to write and solve a system of equations to find the values of a, b, and c.

- When a situation is represented by a quadratic model, three points can be used to find the values of a, b, and c in the equation $y = ax^2 + bx + c$.

Third-Order Constant Differences

Third-Order Constant Differences

A sequence represented by a cubic equation will have third-order constant differences.

Need More
HELP ?

For help with finding third-order differences, go to *Constant Differences* (p. 2042).

EXAMPLE 1

Find the first six terms of the sequence generated by the cubic equation $a_n = n^3$. Then find the third-order differences for the sequence and tell whether they are constant.

STEP 1 Find the first six terms of the sequence.

Substitute the term number for n into the equation.

$a_1 = (1)^3 = 1$ $a_4 = (4)^3 = 64$

$a_2 = (2)^3 = 8$ $a_5 = (5)^3 = 125$

$a_3 = (3)^3 = 27$ $a_6 = (6)^3 = 216$

STEP 2 Write the sequence. Then find the third-order differences.

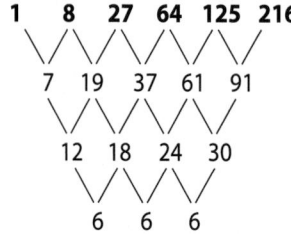

The third-order differences are 6 and are constant.

EXAMPLE 2

SEARCH

To see step-by-step videos of these problems, enter the page number into the SWadvantage.com Search Bar.

Find the first six terms of the sequence generated by the quadratic model $a_n = n^3 - 2n^2 + 4n - 3$. Then find the third-order differences for the sequence and tell whether they are constant.

STEP 1 Find the first six terms of the sequence.

Substitute the term number for n into the equation.

$a_1 = (1)^3 - 2(1)^2 + 4(1) - 3 = 0$ $a_4 = (4)^3 - 2(4)^2 + 4(4) - 3 = 45$

$a_2 = (2)^3 - 2(2)^2 + 4(2) - 3 = 5$ $a_5 = (5)^3 - 2(5)^2 + 4(5) - 3 = 92$

$a_3 = (3)^3 - 2(3)^2 + 4(3) - 3 = 18$ $a_6 = (6)^3 - 2(6)^2 + 4(6) - 3 = 165$

STEP 2 Write the sequence. Then find the third-order differences.

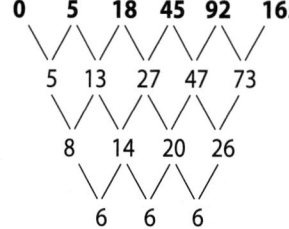

The third-order differences are 6 and are constant.

If a sequence has third-order constant differences, you can write a cubic equation to represent the sequence.

EXAMPLE 3

The first four terms of a sequence that has third-order constant differences are $-1, 5, 29, 83$. Write an equation to model the sequence.

STEP 1 Write the first three terms in the form $an^3 + bn^2 + cn + d = a_n$.

Term (n)	a_n	$an^3 + bn^2 + cn + d$	$an^3 + bn^2 + cn + d = a_n$
1	-1	$a(1)^3 + b(1)^2 + c(1) + d$	$a + b + c + d = -1$
2	5	$a(2)^3 + b(2)^2 + c(2) + d$	$8a + 4b + 2c + d = 5$
3	29	$a(3)^3 + b(3)^2 + c(3) + d$	$27a + 9b + 3c + d = 29$
4	83	$a(4)^3 + b(4)^2 + c(4) + d$	$64a + 16b + 4c + d = 83$

STEP 2 Write the system of equations in matrix form.

$$a + b + c + d = -1$$
$$8a + 4b + 2c + 1d = 5$$
$$27a + 9b + 3c + d = 29$$
$$64a + 16b + 4c + d = 83$$

$$\begin{bmatrix} 1 & 1 & 1 & 1 & -1 \\ 8 & 4 & 2 & 1 & 5 \\ 27 & 9 & 3 & 1 & 29 \\ 64 & 16 & 4 & 1 & 83 \end{bmatrix}$$

STEP 3 Enter the matrix in a graphing calculator.

Press **2nd** **x^{-1}** to get to the MATRIX feature. Press the right arrow until EDIT is highlighted and then press **ENTER**. The matrix in STEP 2 is a 4 × 5 matrix. Use the arrow keys to enter 4 × 5 matrix. Press **ENTER** and then the number for the first term of the matrix. Press **ENTER** and continue entering terms, pressing **ENTER** after typing each number.

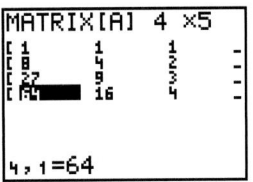

Need More
HELP?
For help with matrices, go to *Rows and Columns* (p. 1772).

STEP 4 Use a graphing calculator to solve the system.

Once the matrix is entered, press **2nd** **MODE** to return to the main screen. Press **CLEAR** if your screen is not empty. Press **2nd** **x^{-1}** to return to the MATRIX menu. Use the right arrow to select MATH. Use the down arrow until you highlight B:rref(. Press **ENTER**. Press **2nd** **x^{-1}** to return to the MATRIX menu. The matrix you entered should be [A]. Make sure the number in front of the matrix is highlighted and press **ENTER**. Then press **ENTER** again. The screen at the right shows the following solution.

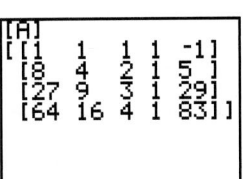

$$a = 2 \qquad b = -3 \qquad c = 1 \qquad d = -1$$

The equation for the sequence is $a_n = 2n^3 - 3n^2 + n - 1$.

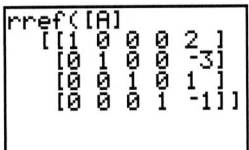

Using Ordered Pairs to Write a Cubic Equation

When a situation is modeled by a cubic function, you can use coordinate points to write a system of equations to model the situation.

SEARCH

To see step-by-step videos of these problems, enter the page number into the SWadvantage.com Search Bar.

EXAMPLE 4

The volume y of an open box is dependent on the height x of the box. The table shows the volume of the box for each given height.

x	1	2	3	4
y	64	72	48	16

Use these points to find an equation to represent the volume y in cubic inches in terms of the height x in inches.

STEP 1 Represent the data as ordered pairs. (1, 64), (2, 72), (3, 48), and (4, 16)

STEP 2 Use the coordinate points to write a system of four equations.

Substitute the x- and y- values into the equation $ax^3 + bx^2 + cx + d = y$.

x	y	$ax^3 + bx^2 + cx + d$	$ax^3 + bx^2 + cx + d = y$
1	64	$a(1)^3 + b(1)^2 + c(1) + d$	$a + b + c + d = 64$
2	72	$a(2)^3 + b(2)^2 + c(2) + d$	$8a + 4b + 2c + d = 72$
3	48	$a(3)^3 + b(3)^2 + c(3) + d$	$27a + 9b + 3c + d = 48$
4	16	$a(4)^3 + b(4)^2 + c(4) + d$	$64a + 16b + 4c + d = 16$

STEP 3 Write the system of equations in matrix form.

Write the system of equations and the related matrix.

$$a + b + c + d = 64$$
$$8a + 4b + 2c + 1d = 72$$
$$27a + 9b + 3c + d = 48$$
$$64a + 16b + 4c + d = 16$$

$$\begin{bmatrix} 1 & 1 & 1 & 1 & 64 \\ 8 & 4 & 2 & 1 & 72 \\ 27 & 9 & 3 & 1 & 48 \\ 64 & 16 & 4 & 1 & 16 \end{bmatrix}$$

The coefficients of the equations are the terms of the matrix.

STEP 4 Enter the matrix in a graphing calculator.

Enter the matrix into the calculator as described in Example 3.

STEP 5 Use a graphing calculator to solve the system of four equations.

In the matrix menu, choose MATH and use the down arrow until you highlight B:rref(.

Press ENTER and then return to the MATRIX menu to select matrix A.

Refer to Example 3 for more help.

STEP 6 Interpret the answer from the calculator.

In the resulting matrix, the 1s represent the position of the variable in the equation and the last column represents the value for that variable.

$a = 4$

$b = -40$

$c = 100$

$d = 0$

The equation for the volume of the box is $y = 4x^3 - 40x^2 + 100x$.

Watch Out !

Pay attention to the sign of each of the variables. For example, in Example 4, the value of b is negative, so in the equation, the x^2 term is negative.

EXAMPLE 5

A company's profit is represented by a cubic function where y represents the profit, in thousands of dollars, after x years. The table shows the profits for four years.

x	2	5	8	10
y	57	1122	4797	9497

Use these points to find an equation to represent the company's profits.

STEP 1 Use the coordinate points to write a system of four equations.

Substitute the x- and y-values into the equation $ax^3 + bx^2 + cx + d = y$.

x	y	$ax^3 + bx^2 + cx + d$	$ax^3 + bx^2 + cx + d = y$
2	57	$a(2)^3 + b(2)^2 + c(2) + d$	$8a + 4b + 2c + d = 57$
5	1122	$a(5)^3 + b(5)^2 + c(5) + d$	$125a + 25b + 5c + d = 1122$
8	4797	$a(8)^3 + b(8)^2 + c(8) + d$	$512a + 64b + 8c + d = 4797$
10	9497	$a(10)^3 + b(10)^2 + c(10) + d$	$1000a + 100b + 10c + d = 9497$

STEP 2 Write the system of equations in matrix form.

$8a + 4b + 2c + d = 57$
$125a + 25b + 5c + d = 1122$
$512a + 64b + 8c + d = 4797$
$1000a + 100b + 10c + d = 9497$

$$\begin{bmatrix} 8 & 4 & 2 & 1 & 57 \\ 125 & 25 & 5 & 1 & 1122 \\ 512 & 64 & 8 & 1 & 4797 \\ 1000 & 100 & 10 & 1 & 9497 \end{bmatrix}$$

STEP 3 Enter the matrix in a graphing calculator as described in Example 3. In the matrix menu, choose MATH and use the down arrow until you highlight B:rref(. Press ENTER and then return to the MATRIX menu to select matrix A. Refer to Example 3 for more help.

STEP 4 Interpret the answer from the calculator.

In the resulting matrix, the 1s represent the position of the variable in the equation and the last column represents the value for that variable.

$a = 10 \qquad b = -5 \qquad c = 0 \qquad d = -3$

The equation representing the company's profit y in thousands of dollars for year x is $y = 10x^3 - 5x^2 - 3$.

Watch Out !

Be sure to pay attention to the terms associated with each coefficient.

In Example 5, the coefficient for the x-term is 0, so there is no x-term in the equation. You might want to write the coefficient for every term to avoid errors:

$y = 10x^3 - 5x^2 + 0x - 3$

GOT TO KNOW!

Modeling with Constant Differences

- When a sequence produces constant third-order differences, the terms of the sequence can be represented by a cubic equation: $an^3 + bn^2 + cn + d = a_n$. The first four terms of the sequence can be used to write and solve a system of equations to find the values of a, b, c, and d.

- When a situation is represented by a cubic model, four points can be used to find the values of a, b, c, and d in the equation $ax^3 + bx^2 + cx + d = y$.

- To solve a system of four equations with four variables, represent the equations in a matrix and solve on a graphing calculator.

Modeling Exponential Growth Functions

Exponential growth functions are functions in the form $y = ab^x$, where a represents the initial amount and b represents the growth factor. When b is greater than 1, the equation is an **exponential growth function** because the values of y grow as the values of x increase.

Need More
HELP

The letters a and b in the equation $y = ab^x$ represent numbers. In order for an equation to represent an exponential function, the value of a cannot be 0 and the value of b cannot be 1. If $a = 0$ or $b = 1$, the equation would represent a line, not an exponential function.

EXAMPLE 1

Determine whether the data can be modeled by an exponential function. If so, write the exponential equation.

Decade	0	1	2	3	4	5
Cost	$0.25	$0.50	$1	$2	$4	$8

STEP 1 Divide each factor by the one before it to see if there is a constant growth factor.

$$\frac{0.50}{0.25} = 2; \frac{1}{0.5} = 2; \frac{2}{1} = 2; \frac{4}{2} = 2; \frac{8}{4} = 2$$

The quotients are all the same, so the data can be modeled by an exponential function.

STEP 2 Determine the values of a and b in the equation $y = ab^x$.

The constant factor from Step 1 is 2, so the value of b is 2.

When $x = 0$, $y = 0.25$. Substitute these values into $y = ab^x$ to get $0.25 = ab^0$ or $0.25 = a$.

STEP 3 Write the exponential function.

Substitute 0.25 for a and 2 for b in $y = ab^x$. $y = 0.25(2)^x$

The exponential function is $y = 0.25(2)^x$.

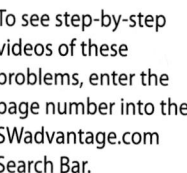
SEARCH

To see step-by-step videos of these problems, enter the page number into the SWadvantage.com Search Bar.

EXAMPLE 2

The second time a student plays a new electronic game she gets a score of 20. The sixth time she plays the game, she gets a score of 320. Write an exponential equation to model her scores.

STEP 1 Identify two points.

Let x represent the number of games played and y represent the score.
The points are (2, 20) and (6, 320).

STEP 2 Use the two points to write two equations in the form $y = ab^x$.

Substitute (2, 20) into $y = ab^x$.   Substitute (6, 320) into $y = ab^x$.
    $20 = ab^2$ $320 = ab^6$

STEP 3 Divide the two equations to solve for b.

Write the division. $\frac{320}{20} = \frac{ab^6}{ab^2}$

Simplify each side. $16 = b^4$

Take the fourth root of each side. $2 = b$

STEP 4 Use the value of b and either equation to solve for a.

In the equation $20 = ab^2$, substitute 2 for b. $20 = a(2)^2$, so $a = \frac{20}{4}$ or 5.

STEP 5 Write the exponential function.

Substitute 5 for a and 2 for b in $y = ab^x$. $y = 5(2)^x$

The exponential function is $y = 5(2)^x$.

EXAMPLE 3

The average major league baseball player's salary increases by about 8% every 5 years. In Year 10, the average player's salary, in thousands, was about $698.

a. Write an exponential function to model the player's salaries.

STEP 1 Identify the initial value a.

In Year 10, the average player's salary, in thousands, was about $698. Let x represent the number of years since Year 10. Then $x = 0$ represents Year 10.

Substitute 0 for x and 698 for y. $698 = ab^0 = a \times 1 = a$, so $698 = a$

STEP 2 Identify the growth factor b.

The salaries increase by about 8% each year, which written as a decimal is 0.08.

The salary each year is the whole amount from the year before $+$ 8%, so the growth factor is $1 + 0.08$, or 1.08.

STEP 3 Write the exponential function.

Substitute 698 for a and 1.08 for b in $y = ab^x$. $y = 698(1.08)^x$

The exponential function is $y = 698(1.08)^x$.

> **Watch Out!**
>
> When given the percent increase, remember to write the percent as a decimal. To do this, move the decimal point two places to the left and drop the percent sign.

b. Use your exponential model to estimate the average player's salary in Year 35 and in Year 5.

	Year 35	**Year 5**
Find the value of x.	Year 35 is 25 years since Year 10, so $x = 25$.	Year 5 is 5 years BEFORE Year 10, so $x = -5$.
Substitute for x in the equation and simplify.	$y = 698(1.08)^{25} \approx 4780$	$y = 698(1.08)^{-5} \approx 475$

If the growth continues at the same rate, the average baseball player's salary in Year 35 will be about $4780 thousands, or about $4.78 million.

The average baseball player's salary in Year 5 was about $475 thousands, or about $475,000.

GOT TO KNOW!

Exponential Growth Functions

- A set of data can be modeled by an exponential function if the y-values increase by a constant proportion.

- Divide each y-value by the value before it to find the growth factor.

- An exponential growth function is in the form:
  $y = ab^x$, where $a \neq 0$ and $b > 1$
  The initial value, or starting value, is represented by a. The growth rate is represented by b.

- When given the growth factor as a percent increase, use the function $y = a(1 + r)^x$, where $b = (1 + r)$. The percent increase r is written as a decimal and $(1 + r)$ is the growth factor.

Example:

Decade	0	1	2	3	4	5
Cost	$0.25	$0.50	$1	$2	$4	$8

$\times 2$ $\times 2$ $\times 2$ $\times 2$ $\times 2$

The initial value occurs when $x = 0$, so $a = 0.25$.

The growth rate b is 2.

The exponential model is $y = 0.25(2)^x$.

Modeling Exponential Decay

When a real-life quantity decreases by the same amount each year, the equation $y = ab^x$ is an **exponential decay function**, because the values of y decrease as the values of x increase. The growth rate b is the **rate of decay** and $0 < b < 1$.

SEARCH

To see step-by-step videos of these problems, enter the page number into the SWadvantage.com Search Bar.

EXAMPLE 4

The table shows the number of teams in each round of the NCAA Basketball Tournament.

Round	1	2	3	4	5	6
Teams	64	32	16	8	4	2

Determine if the number of teams in each round of the tournament can be modeled by an exponential function. If so, write a function to represent the number of teams y in each round x.

STEP 1 Determine if the data can be modeled by an exponential function.

Divide each factor by the one before it to see if there is a constant growth factor.

$$\frac{32}{64} = \frac{1}{2}; \quad \frac{16}{32} = \frac{1}{2}; \quad \frac{8}{16} = \frac{1}{2}; \quad \frac{4}{8} = \frac{1}{2}; \quad \frac{2}{4} = \frac{1}{2}$$

The quotients are all the same, so the data can be modeled by an exponential function.

STEP 2 Determine the values of a and b in the equation $y = ab^{x-1}$.

The rate of decay from Step 1 is $\frac{1}{2}$, so the value of b is $\frac{1}{2}$.

When $x = 0$, $y = 64$. Substitute these values into $y = ab^{x-1}$ to get $64 = ab^0$ or $64 = a$.

STEP 3 Write the exponential function.

Substitute 64 for a and $\frac{1}{2}$ for b in $y = ab^x$. $y = 64\left(\frac{1}{2}\right)^{x-1}$

The exponential function is $y = 64\left(\frac{1}{2}\right)^{x-1}$.

EXAMPLE 5

Watch Out !

The rate of decay will always be (1 minus the percent decrease). If you only multiply a by the percent decrease, you are only finding the amount of the decrease, not the total result after the decrease after x amount of time. Remember to multiply a by $(1 - r)$.

A car costs \$40,000. Each year, the value of the car decreases by 15%. Write an equation to represent the depreciation. Then find the value of the car after 6 years.

STEP 1 Identify the initial value a.

The initial cost of the car is \$40,000, so $a = 40{,}000$.

STEP 2 Identify the rate of decay b.

The value of the car decreases by 15% each year, so $b = (1 - 0.15)$ or 0.85.

STEP 3 Write the exponential function.

Substitute 40,000 for a and 0.85 for b in $y = ab^x$. $y = 40{,}000(0.85)^x$

The exponential function is $y = 40{,}000(0.85)^x$.

STEP 4 Find the value of the function when $x = 6$.

Substitute 6 for x. $y = 40{,}000(0.85)^6$

Simplify. $y \approx 15{,}086$

The value of the car after 6 years is about \$15,086.

EXAMPLE 6

The table shows the concentration of a stomach medication in a person's bloodstream in nanograms per milliliter t hours after the medication has reached its peak concentration.

Hours after peak concentration	1	2	3	4
Concentration (ng/mL)	389.1	307.4	242.8	191.8

Write an exponential function to model the concentration t hours after peak concentration.

STEP 1 Use two points to write two equations in the form $y = ab^t$.

Substitute $(1, 389.1)$ into $y = ab^t$.   Substitute $(2, 307.4)$ into $y = ab^t$.

$389.1 = ab^1$ $307.4 = ab^2$

STEP 2 Divide the two equations to solve for b.

Write the division. $\dfrac{307.4}{389.1} = \dfrac{ab^2}{ab^1}$

Simplify each side. $0.79 = b$

STEP 3 Use the value of b and either equation to solve for a.

In the equation $389.1 = ab^1$, substitute 0.79 for b. $389.1 = a(0.79)^1$, so $a = 492.5$.

STEP 4 Substitute 492.5 for a and 0.79 for b in $y = ab^t$.

The exponential function is $y = 492.5(0.79)^t$.

Try It This Way

You can use a graphing calculator to find an exponential model for a set of data. Enter the x-values in List 1 (L1) and the y-values in List 2 (L2). Then press the **STAT** key and choose CALC and then ExpReg. Press **ENTER** and then L1, L2 and then **ENTER** again. The values for a and b will be displayed.

Need More HELP?

For help solving exponential equations, go to *Exponential and Logarithmic Equations* (p. 2010).

GOT TO KNOW!

Exponential Decay Functions

- If a set of data can be modeled by an exponential decay function, the y-values decrease by a constant proportion.

- You can find the decay rate by dividing each y-value by the value before it.

- An exponential decay function is in the form:
$$y = ab^x$$
where a is the initial value ($a \neq 0$) and b is the rate of decay ($0 < b < 1$).

- When given the percent decrease, use the function $y = a(1 - r)^x$, where $b = (1 - r)$. The percent decrease r is written as a decimal and $(1 - r)$ is the rate of decay.

Example:

Round	0	1	2	3	4	5
Teams	64	32	16	8	4	2

$\div 2 \quad \div 2 \quad \div 2 \quad \div 2 \quad \div 2$

The initial value occurs when $x = 0$, so $a = 64$.

The growth rate b is $\dfrac{1}{2}$.

The exponential model is $y = 64\left(\dfrac{1}{2}\right)^x$.

Models for Power Functions

Writing Power Functions

A **power function** is a function in the form $y = ax^b$. There are two constants, a and b, so you can model a power function with two points.

Need More
HELP ?
For help solving exponential functions, see *Exponential and Logarithmic Functions* (p. 2010).

EXAMPLE 1

Write the power function that passes through the points (1, 2) and (2, 16).

STEP 1 Write a system of equations of the form $y = ax^b$.

Write the power function using (1, 2). $2 = a(1)^b$

Write the power function using (2, 16). $16 = a(2)^b$

STEP 2 Use one of the equations to solve for a.

Divide both sides of the first equation by 1^b. $\dfrac{2}{1^b} = a$

STEP 3 Substitute for a in the second equation, and then solve for b.

Substitute $\dfrac{2}{1^b}$ for a in $16 = a(2)^b$. $16 = \dfrac{2}{1^b}(2)^b$

Simplify. $16 = 2\left(\dfrac{2^b}{1^b}\right)$

Divide both sides by 2. $8 = \left(\dfrac{2^b}{1^b}\right)$

Simplify. $8 = 2^b$

STEP 4 Find the value of b.

METHOD 1

Rewrite 8 with a base of 2. $2^3 = 2^b$

Solve for b. $3 = b$

METHOD 2

Take $\log_2$ of each side. $\log_2 8 = b$

Use the change of base formula and solve. $\dfrac{\log 8}{\log 2} = b$

Use a calculator to simplify. $3 = b$

STEP 5 Find the value of a.

In Step 2, $a = \dfrac{2}{1^b}$. Substitute 3 for b and solve. $a = \dfrac{2}{1^3} = 2$

STEP 6 Substitute the values of a and b into $y = ax^b$.

Substitute 2 for a and 3 for b. $y = 2x^3$

The power function through the points (1, 2) and (2, 16) is $y = 2x^3$.

GOT TO KNOW!

Modeling Power Functions Given Two Points

- Power functions are in the form $y = ax^b$.

- Given two points, you can use a system of two equations to solve for a and b.

When you are given more than two points, you can decide whether a power model fits the points by finding the log of the *y*-values and the log of the *x*-values. If the points (log *x*, log *y*) fit a linear pattern, then the original points (*x*, *y*) can be modeled by a power function.

EXAMPLE 2

a. Determine if a power function is a good model for the data.

x	10	20	30	40	50
y	3.16	4.47	5.48	6.33	7.07

STEP 1 Take the log of the *x*- and *y*-values of the data.

log x	1	1.30	1.48	1.60	1.70
log y	0.50	0.65	0.74	0.80	0.85

STEP 2 Make a scatter plot of (log *x*, log *y*), and determine if the data represents a line.

Graph the points from the table in Step 1.

The points can be modeled by a line, so a power model is a good model for the original data.

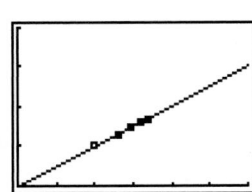

SEARCH

To see step-by-step videos of these problems, enter the page number into the SWadvantage.com Search Bar.

b. Model the data with a power function.

METHOD 1 Use two points from the transformed data to write an equation of the line.

Choose two points to find the slope.

$$m = \frac{0.65 - 0.50}{1.30 - 1.00}$$

Simplify.

$$m = \frac{0.15}{0.30} = 0.5$$

Substitute 0.5 for *m*.

$$\log y = 0.5\log x$$

Rewrite using the power property of logarithms.

$$\log y = \log x^{0.5}$$

Exponentiate each side to solve for *y*.

$$10^{\log y} = 10^{\log x^{0.5}}$$

Simplify.

$$y = x^{0.5}$$

The data is modeled by the power function $y = x^{0.5}$.

Need More HELP?

For help finding the slope of a line, go to *Rate of Change and Slope* in *Algebra* (p. 1536).

METHOD 2 Use a graphing calculator.

STEP 1 Enter the original data into the calculator.

Enter the original *x*-values in List 1 (L1) and the original *y*-values in List 2 (L2).

STEP 2 Use the regression feature of the calculator to find the power function.

Press **STAT** and then use the right arrow to highlight CALC. Use the down arrow until A:PwrReg is highlighted to select Power Regression. Press **ENTER**. Press **2nd** **1** to select L1. Then press **,** and **2nd** **2**. Press **ENTER**.

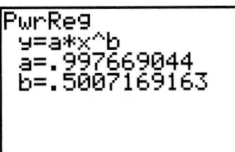

The calculator will display the equation $y = ax^b$ and the values of *a* and *b*. Substitute the values for *a* and *b* into the equation.

The data is modeled by the power function $y = x^{0.5}$.

Modeling Data Using Power Functions

SEARCH

To see step-by-step videos of these problems, enter the page number into the SWadvantage.com Search Bar.

EXAMPLE 3

a. Determine if a power function is a good model for the data.

x	1	2	3	4	5
y	1.5	6	13.5	24	37.5

STEP 1 Take the log of the x- and y-values of the data.

log x	0	0.30	0.48	0.60	0.70
log y	0.18	0.78	1.13	1.38	1.57

STEP 2 Make a scatter plot of (log x, log y) and determine if the data represents a line.

Graph the points from the table in Step 1.

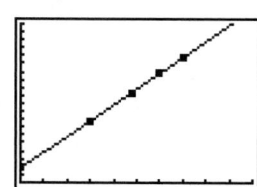

The points can be modeled by a line, so a power model is a good model for the original data.

b. Model the data with a power function.

Need More

HELP?

Remember that log x is short for $\log_{10} x$, so to solve log x for x, you raise both sides of the equation to the base 10.

METHOD 1 Use two points from the transformed data to write an equation of the line.

Choose two points to find the slope.

$$m = \frac{0.78 - 0.18}{0.30 - 0}$$

Simplify.

$$m = \frac{0.6}{0.3} = 2$$

The y-intercept is (0, 0.18) so log a = 0.18.

$$\log y = \log a + 2\log x$$

Substitute 2 for m and 0.18 for log a.

$$\log y = 0.18(2\log x)$$

Rewrite using the power property of logarithms.

$$\log y = 0.18(\log x^2)$$

Exponentiate each side to solve for y.

$$10^{\log y} = 10^{0.18}(10^{\log x^2})$$

Simplify.

$$y = 1.5x^2$$

The data is modeled by the power function $y = 1.5x^2$.

METHOD 2 Use a graphing calculator.

STEP 1 Enter the original data into the calculator.

Enter the original x-values in List 1 (L1) and the original y-values in List 2 (L2).

STEP 2 Use the regression feature of the calculator to find the power function.

Press **STAT** and then use the right arrow to highlight CALC. Use the down arrow until A:PwrReg is highlighted to select Power Regression. Press **ENTER**.

Press **2nd** **1** to select L1. Then press **,** and **2nd** **2**.

Press **ENTER**. Substitute the values for a and b into the equation $y = ax^b$.

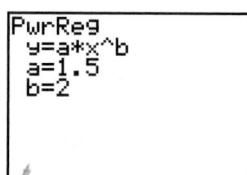

The data is modeled by the power function $y = 1.5x^2$.

EXAMPLE 4

The table shows the circulation of the top 10 magazines in the United States, where *x* represents the magazine's rank and *y* represents the circulation in millions. Model the data with a power function. Then estimate the circulation of the magazine ranked 15th.

x	1	2	3	4	5	6	7	8	9	10
y	20.5	20.4	15.1	13.2	9.0	7.6	5.1	4.6	4.5	4.3

STEP 1 Enter the data into the calculator.

Enter the original *x*-values in List 1 (L1) and the original *y*-values in List 2 (L2).

STEP 2 Use the regression feature of the calculator to find the power function.

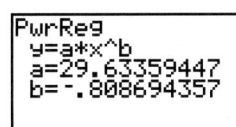

Press **STAT** and then use the right arrow to highlight CALC.

Use the down arrow until A:PwrReg is highlighted to select Power Regression. Press **ENTER**.

Press **2nd** **1** to select L1. Then press **,** and **2nd** **2**.

Press **ENTER**. Substitute the values for *a* and *b* into the equation $y = ax^b$.

The data is modeled by the power function $y = 29.6x^{-0.81}$.

STEP 3 Graph the equation $y = 29.6x^{-0.81}$ on a graphing calculator.

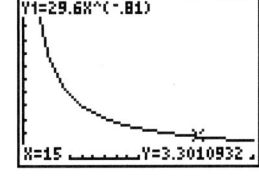

Press **2nd** **TRACE** to go to the CALCULATE menu.

Press **ENTER** to select 1: value.

The calculator will ask for an *x*-value. To find the circulation for the magazine with the 15th rank, find the value of *y* when $x = 15$, so enter 15 and press **ENTER**.

The circulation of the 15th ranked magazine is about 3.30 million.

Watch Out !

Be careful not to confuse a power function with an exponential function. A power function is in the form $y = ax^b$ where the constants are the coefficient of *x* and the exponent. An exponential function is of the form $y = ab^x$, where the constants are the base of the exponent and the initial value.

Modeling Power Functions

Power functions are in the form $y = ax^b$, where $a \neq 0$ and $b \neq 0$.

- A power function is a good model for a set of data (x, y) if the points $(\log x, \log y)$ can be modeled by a line.

- The slope of the line formed by the $(\log x, \log y)$ points is the value of *b* in $y = ax^b$.

- Use the *y*-intercept of the line formed by the $(\log x, \log y)$ points to find the value of *a* in $y = ax^b$. The value of *a* will be $10^{y\text{-intercept}}$.

- You can enter the data into a graphing calculator and use the Power Regression feature of the calculator to find the power function to model the data.

Analyzing Functions

What Came Before?
- Graphing linear functions
- Transformations in geometry

What's This About?
- Operations with functions
- Composition of functions
- Transformations of functions

Practical Apps
- Companies find their profit function by subtracting their cost function from their revenue function.
- The function used to convert Fahrenheit degrees to Celsius is the inverse of the function used to convert Celsius to Fahrenheit.

just for FUN!

Q: What type of function did Gandhi use?

A: A peacewise function.

CONTENTS	UPLOAD	DOWNLOAD	Advanced Algebra

You can find more practice problems online by visiting:
www.SWadvantage.com

Composing Functions

Evaluating Functions

The equation $f(x) = 3x + 2$ is written in function notation. The symbol $f(x)$ is read *the value of the function f at x,* or *f of x.* The name of the function is *f*, *x* represents the input, and $f(x)$ represents the *y*-value of the function for *x*. You can substitute numbers, other variables, or other functions for *x*.

Need More
HELP ?

The letter *f* is often used to represent a function, but you can use any letter to represent a function. Functions and their inputs can be represented by other letters like $g(x)$, $h(x)$, $f(a)$, or $d(t)$.

EXAMPLE 1

Given $f(x) = 2x - 1$, find $f(-4)$, $f(0)$, and $f(3)$.

STEP 1 Find $f(-4)$.

Substitute -4 for *x* in $2x - 1$. $f(-4) = 2(-4) - 1$

Multiply. $f(-4) = -8 - 1$

Simplify. $f(-4) = -9$

STEP 2 Find $f(0)$.

Substitute 0 for *x* in $2x - 1$. $f(0) = 2(0) - 1$

Multiply. $f(0) = 0 - 1$

Simplify. $f(0) = -1$

STEP 3 Find $f(3)$.

Substitute 3 for *x* in $2x - 1$. $f(3) = 2(3) - 1$

Multiply. $f(3) = 6 - 1$

Simplify. $f(3) = 5$

When you evaluate a function, you can use any letter to represent the independent variable. The functions $f(x) = x^2 - 4x + 3$, $f(a) = a^2 - 4a + 3$, and $f(t) = t^2 - 4t + 3$ all represent the same function. As you evaluate functions, it may be helpful to think of the function as $f(\ ) = (\ )^2 - 4(\ ) + 3$.

SEARCH

To see step-by-step videos of these problems, enter the page number into the SWadvantage.com Search Bar.

EXAMPLE 2

Given $g(x) = 3x + 4$, find $g(a)$, $g(x^2)$, and $g(t - 2)$.

STEP 1 Find $g(a)$.

Substitute *a* for *x* in $3x + 4$. $g(a) = 3(a) + 4$

Simplify. $g(a) = 3a + 4$

STEP 2 Find $g(x^2)$.

Substitute x^2 for *x* in $3x + 4$. $g(x^2) = 3(x^2) + 4$

Simplify. $g(x^2) = 3x^2 + 4$

STEP 3 Find $g(t - 2)$.

Substitute $t - 2$ for *x* in $3x + 4$. $g(t - 2) = 3(t - 2) + 4$

Use the distributive property. $g(t - 2) = 3t - 6 + 4$

Simplify. $g(t - 2) = 3t - 2$

Composition of Functions

One way of combining two functions is to form the composition of one function with another. If $f(x) = 2x + 3$ and $g(x) = x - 1$, the composition of f with g is represented by $f \circ g$ and means $f(g(x))$ or $f(x - 1)$. The notation $f \circ g$ is read f of g.

EXAMPLE 3

Given $f(x) = x + 2$ and $g(x) = x^2$, find $(f \circ g)(x)$.

Write $(f \circ g)(x)$ as $f(g(x))$. $(f \circ g)(x) = f(g(x))$

Substitute x^2 for $g(x)$. $= f(x^2)$

Substitute x^2 for x in $x + 2$. $= x^2 + 2$

$(f \circ g)(x) = (f(g(x)) = x^2 + 2$.

Watch Out !

The notation $(f \circ g)(x)$ does not mean $f(x) \cdot g(x)$. Notice that the circle between the f and g is not filled in, like the circle that represents multiplication.

EXAMPLE 4

Given $f(x) = x + 2$ and $g(x) = x^2$, find $(g \circ f)(x)$.

Write $(g \circ f)(x)$ as $g(f(x))$. $(g \circ f)(x) = g(f(x))$

Substitute $x + 2$ for $f(x)$. $= g(x + 2)$

Substitute $x + 2$ for x in x^2. $= (x + 2)^2$

Expand. $= (x + 2)(x + 2)$

Multiply. $= x^2 + 4x + 4$

$(g \circ f)(x) = (g(f(x)) = x^2 + 4x + 4$.

EXAMPLE 5

Given $d(t) = t^2 + 2t - 3$ and $h(t) = t - 1$, find $(d \circ h)(t)$.

Write $(d \circ h)(t)$ as $d(h(t))$. $(d \circ h)(t) = d(h(t))$

Substitute $t - 1$ for $h(t)$. $= d(t - 1)$

Substitute $t - 1$ for t in $t^2 + 2t - 3$. $= (t - 1)^2 + 2(t - 1) - 3$

Expand $(t - 1)^2$ and multiply $2(t - 1)$. $= (t - 1)(t - 1) + 2t - 2 - 3$

Multiply $(t - 1)(t - 1)$ and simplify. $= t^2 - 2t + 1 + 2t - 5 = t^2 - 4$

$(d \circ h)(t) = (d(h(t)) = t^2 - 4$.

GOT TO KNOW!

Understanding Composition of Functions

- The composition of function f with function g is written $(f \circ g)(x)$ which is read f of g of x.

- The notation $(f \circ g)(x) = f(g(x))$. Every x in function f is replaced by the expression for $g(x)$. If $f(x) = 2x + 3$ and $g(x) = x - 1$, then $(f \circ g)(x) = f(g(x)) = f(x - 1) = 2(x - 1) + 3 = 2x + 1$

- Given two functions f and g, a value in the domain of g might result in a value of $g(x)$ that is not in the domain of f.

The Domain of Composed Functions

EXAMPLE 6

Given $g(a) = \sqrt{a}$ and $h(a) = a - 2$.

a. Find $(g \circ h)(a)$.

Find $(g \circ h)(a)$.

Write $(g \circ h)(a)$ as $g(h(a))$. $\qquad$ $(g \circ h)(a) = g(h(a))$

Substitute $a - 2$ for $h(a)$. $\qquad\qquad = g(a - 2)$

Substitute $a - 2$ for a in $\sqrt{a}$. $\qquad = \sqrt{a - 2}$

$(g \circ h)(a) = (g(h(a)) = \sqrt{a - 2}$.

b. Find the domain of $(g \circ h)(a)$.

Find the domain of $(g \circ h)(a)$.

The domain of $(g \circ h)(a)$ is the domain of $\sqrt{a - 2}$. The value under the square root must be greater than or equal to zero, so $(a - 2) \geq 0$ or $a \geq 2$.

The domain is all numbers greater than 2, or $[2, \infty)$.

c. If possible, find $(g \circ h)(3)$.

Find $(g \circ h)(3)$.

Write $(g \circ h)(a)$. $\qquad\qquad$ $(g \circ h)(a) = \sqrt{a - 2}$

Substitute 3 for a in $\sqrt{a - 2}$. $\qquad = \sqrt{3 - 2}$

Simplify. $\qquad\qquad\qquad\qquad = \sqrt{1} = 1$

$(g \circ h)(3) = 1$.

d. If possible, find $(g \circ h)(0)$.

Find $(g \circ h)(0)$.

METHOD 1

Use the Domain from Part (b).

The domain from Part (b) is $a \geq 2$. Zero is not in the domain of $(g \circ h)(a)$, so $(g \circ h)(0)$ is undefined.

METHOD 2

Use Algebra.

Write $(g \circ h)(a)$. $\qquad\qquad$ $(g \circ h)(a) = \sqrt{a - 2}$

Substitute 0 for a in $\sqrt{a - 2}$. $\qquad = \sqrt{0 - 2}$

Simplify. $\qquad\qquad\qquad\qquad = \sqrt{-2}$

The value under the square root must be greater than or equal to zero, so $(g \circ h)(0)$ is undefined.

EXAMPLE 7

Given $f(x) = 2x + 4$ and $g(x) = \frac{1}{x}$. Find $(g \circ f)(-2)$, if possible.

Write $(g \circ f)(x)$.

$$(g \circ f)(x) = (g(f(x)) = \frac{1}{2x + 4}$$

Substitute -2 for x and simplify.

$$= \frac{1}{2(-2) + 4} = \frac{1}{0}$$

The denominator of a fraction cannot equal zero, so $(g \circ f)(-2)$ is undefined.

The Composition of Inverse Functions

When $(f \circ g)(x) = (g \circ f)(x)$, the functions f and g are inverses of one another.

Need More HELP?

For help with inverse functions, go to *Inverses of Linear Functions* and *Inverses of Non-Linear Functions* (p. 2090).

EXAMPLE 8

Given $f(x) = 2x + 4$ and $g(x) = \frac{1}{2}(x - 4)$.

a. Find $(f \circ g)(x)$.

Write $(f \circ g)(x)$ as $f(g(x))$.

$$(f \circ g)(x) = f(g(x)) = f\left(\frac{1}{2}(x - 4)\right) = f\left(\frac{1}{2}x - 2\right)$$

Substitute $\frac{1}{2}x - 2$ for x in $2x + 4$.

$$= 2\left(\frac{1}{2}x - 2\right) + 4$$

Apply the Distributive Property.

$$= x - 4 + 4$$

Simplify.

$$= x$$

$(f \circ g)(x) = (f(g(x)) = x$.

b. Find $(g \circ f)(x)$.

Write $(g \circ f)(x)$ as $g(f(x))$.

$$(g \circ f)(x) = g(f(x)) = g(2x + 4)$$

Substitute $2x + 4$ for x in $\frac{1}{2}(x - 4)$.

$$= \frac{1}{2}((2x + 4) - 4)$$

Simplify inside the parentheses.

$$= \frac{1}{2}(2x)$$

Multiply.

$$= x$$

$(g \circ f)(x) = (g(f(x)) = x$.

c. Tell whether f and g are inverse functions.

Because $(f \circ g)(x) = (g \circ f)(x)$, the functions are inverses.

GOT TO KNOW!

Composition of Inverse Functions

- When $(f \circ g)(x) = (g \circ f)(x)$, the functions f and g are inverses of each other.

- When two functions f and g are inverses of each other, $(f \circ g)(x) = x$ and $(g \circ f)(x) = x$.

EXAMPLE 9

Given $f(x) = x^2 - 3$ and $g(x) = \sqrt{x + 3}$, tell whether f and g are inverses of one another.

$(f \circ g)(x) = f(g(x)) = f\left(\sqrt{x + 3}\right) = \left(\sqrt{x + 3}\right)^2 - 3 = x + 3 - 3 = x$.

$(g \circ f)(x) = (g(f(x)) = g(x^2 - 3) = \sqrt{(x^2 - 3) + 3} = \sqrt{x^2} = x$.

Because $(f \circ g)(x) = (g \circ f)(x) = x$, the functions f and g are inverses of one another.

Adding and Subtracting Functions

Adding and Subtracting Functions

Functions can be combined to create new functions. For example, the notation $(f + g)(x)$ means to find the sum of $f(x) + g(x)$. The notation $(f - g)(x)$ means to find the difference of $f(x) - g(x)$. The domain of the combined functions is the numbers that are common to the domains of f and g.

SEARCH

To see step-by-step videos of these problems, enter the page number into the SWadvantage.com Search Bar.

EXAMPLE 1

Given $f(x) = 2x^2 + 3x - 2$ and $g(x) = 5x + 2$, find $(f + g)(x)$.

Write $(f + g)(x)$ as $f(x) + g(x)$.	$(f + g)(x) = f(x) + g(x)$
Substitute $2x^2 + 3x - 2$ for $f(x)$ and $5x + 2$ for $g(x)$.	$= 2x^2 + 3x - 2 + 5x + 2$
Combine like terms.	$= 2x^2 + 3x + 5x - 2 + 2$
Simplify.	$= 2x^2 + 8x$

$(f + g)(x) = 2x^2 + 8x.$

Need More HELP ?

For help evaluating functions, go to *Composition of Functions* (p. 2062).

EXAMPLE 2

Given $d(t) = \dfrac{1}{t}$ and $h(t) = \dfrac{3}{t^2}$, find $(d + h)(t)$ and the domain of $(d + h)(t)$.

STEP 1 Find $(d + h)(t)$.

Write $(d + h)(t)$ as $d(t) + h(t)$.	$(d + h)(t) = d(t) + h(t)$
Substitute $\dfrac{1}{t}$ for $d(t)$ and $\dfrac{3}{t^2}$ for $h(t)$.	$= \dfrac{1}{t} + \dfrac{3}{t^2}$
Write each fraction with a common denominator of t^2.	$= \dfrac{1}{t} \cdot \dfrac{t}{t} + \dfrac{3}{t^2}$
Simplify.	$= \dfrac{t}{t^2} + \dfrac{3}{t^2}$
Add.	$= \dfrac{t + 3}{t^2}$

STEP 2 Find the domain of $(d + h)(t)$.

Because the denominator of a fraction cannot equal zero, the domain of $(d + h)(t)$ is all real numbers, t, such that $t \neq 0$. This can be written $(-\infty, 0)$ and $(0, \infty)$.

EXAMPLE 3

Given $a(x) = x^2 - 6$ and $b(x) = \sqrt{x + 3}$, find $(a + b)(1)$.

Write $(a + b)(x)$ as $a(x) + b(x)$.	$(a + b)(x) = a(x) + b(x)$
Substitute $x^2 - 6$ for $a(x)$ and $\sqrt{x + 3}$ for $b(x)$.	$= x^2 - 6 + \sqrt{x + 3}$
No terms can be combined, so substitute 1 for x.	$(a + b)(1) = (1)^2 - 6 + \sqrt{1 + 3}$
Simplify.	$= 1 - 6 + 2 = -3$

$(a + b)(1) = -3.$

EXAMPLE 4

Given $f(x) = x^2$ and $g(x) = \sqrt{x-1}$, find $(f - g)(x)$ and the domain of $(f - g)(x)$.

STEP 1 Find $(f - g)(x)$.

Write $(f - g)(x)$ as $f(x) - g(x)$.

Substitute x^2 for $f(x)$ and $\sqrt{x-1}$ for $g(x)$.

$(f - g)(x) = f(x) - g(x)$

$= x^2 - \sqrt{x-1}$

$(f - g)(x) = x^2 - \sqrt{x-1}$.

STEP 2 Find the domain of $(f - g)(x)$.

The domain of f is $(-\infty, \infty)$. The number under the square root symbol must be non-negative, so the domain of g is $[1, \infty)$. The numbers in common to both are $[1, \infty)$, so the domain of $(f - g)(x)$ is $[1, \infty)$.

EXAMPLE 5

Given $a(x) = 2x + 1$ and $b(x) = x^2 + 2x - 3$, find $(a - b)(2)$.

METHOD 1

Subtract like terms.

Write $(a - b)(x)$ as $a(x) - b(x)$.

Substitute $2x + 1$ for $a(x)$ and $x^2 + 2x - 3$ for $b(x)$.

Distribute the negative and simplify.

Substitute 2 for x and simplify.

$(a - b)(2) = 0$

$(a - b)(x) = a(x) - b(x)$

$= 2x + 1 - (x^2 + 2x - 3)$

$= -x^2 + 4$

$(a - b)(2) = -(2)^2 + 4 = -4 + 4 = 0$

METHOD 2

Use a graphing calculator.

Enter $a(x)$ as Y1, $b(x)$ as Y2 and Y1 − Y2 as Y3. Graph Y3 and use the *trace* feature to estimate the value when $x = 2$.

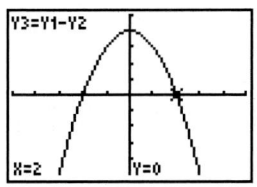

Watch Out !

When you subtract one function from another, you are subtracting each term of the function, not just the first term. In Example 5, if you wrote $g(x)$ without parentheses, the sign of the terms of $g(x)$ would be $-x^2 + 4x - 1$ instead of $-x^2 - 4x + 1$. Be sure to subtract each term of the second function.

Need More HELP ?

To enter Y1 − Y2, press **VARS** and then press the right arrow to choose Y-VARS. Press 1 to select Function. Press 1 to choose Y1. Repeat the procedure when you are ready to enter Y2.

GOT TO KNOW!

Adding and Subtracting Functions

Given two functions, f and g

The sum of f and g is represented by $(f + g)(x) = f(x) + g(x)$.	The difference of f and g is represented by $(f - g)(x) = f(x) - g(x)$.	The domain of $(f + g)$ or $(f - g)$ is all real numbers that the domains of f and g have in common.

Multiplying Functions

Multiplying Functions

The notation $(fg)(x)$ is used to represent the product of $f(x)$ and $g(x)$. The domain of $(fg)(x)$ contains the real numbers that are common to the domains of f and g.

EXAMPLE 1

Given $f(x) = -5$ and $g(x) = -2x - 1$, find $(fg)(x)$.

Write $(fg)(x)$ as $f(x) \cdot g(x)$.	$(fg)(x) = f(x) \cdot g(x)$
Substitute -5 for $f(x)$ and $-2x - 1$ for $g(x)$.	$= -5(-2x - 1)$
Apply the Distributive Property.	$= (-5)(-2x) + (-5)(-1)$
Simplify.	$= 10x + 5$

The product $(fg)(x)$ is $10x + 5$.

Watch Out !

The product of two functions $(f \cdot g)(x) = f(x) \cdot g(x)$ is different from the composition of f and g, which is written $(f \circ g)(x)$ and equals $(f(g(x))$. To avoid confusion, the product is often written as $(fg)(x)$, rather than $(f \cdot g)(x)$.

EXAMPLE 2

Given $f(x) = -2x$ and $g(x) = 3x + 4$, find $(fg)(x)$.

Write $(fg)(x)$ as $f(x) \cdot g(x)$.	$(fg)(x) = f(x) \cdot g(x)$
Substitute $-2x$ for $f(x)$ and $3x + 4$ for $g(x)$.	$= -2x(3x + 4)$
Apply the Distributive Property.	$= (-2x)(3x) + (-2x)(4)$
Simplify.	$= -6x^2 - 8x$

The product $(fg)(x)$ is $-6x^2 - 8x$.

SEARCH

To see step-by-step videos of these problems, enter the page number into the SWadvantage.com Search Bar.

EXAMPLE 3

Given $s(a) = -4$ and $t(a) = a^2 - 3a + 7$, find $(st)(a)$.

Write $(st)(a)$ as $s(a) \cdot t(a)$.	$(st)(a) = s(a) \cdot t(a)$
Substitute -4 for $s(a)$ and $a^2 - 3a + 7$ for $t(a)$.	$= -4(a^2 - 3a + 7)$
Apply the Distributive Property.	$= (-4)(a^2) + (-4)(-3a) + (-4)(7)$
Simplify each product.	$= -4a^2 + 12a - 28$

The product $(st)(a)$ is $-4a^2 + 12a - 28$.

EXAMPLE 4

Given $a(x) = 3x - 2$ and $b(x) = 2x - 5$, find $(ab)(x)$.

Write $(ab)(x)$ as $a(x) \cdot b(x)$.	$(ab)(x) = a(x) \cdot b(x)$
Substitute $3x - 2$ for $a(x)$ and $2x - 5$ for $b(x)$.	$= (3x - 2)(2x - 5)$
Multiply each term of $2x - 5$ by $3x$ and then by -2.	$= (3x)(2x) + (3x)(-5) + (-2)(2x) + (-2)(-5)$
Simplify each product.	$= 6x^2 - 15x - 4x + 10$
Combine any like terms.	$= 6x^2 - 19x + 10$

The product $(ab)(x)$ is $6x^2 - 19x + 10$.

EXAMPLE 5

Given $f(x) = -2x + 7$ and $g(x) = 4x^2 - 3x + 5$, find $(fg)(x)$.

Need More
HELP?
For help multiplying polynomials, go to *Multiplying Polynomials* on page 1608.

METHOD 1

Use the Distributive Property.

Write $(fg)(x)$ as $f(x) \cdot g(x)$.

$(fg)(x) = f(x) \cdot g(x)$

Substitute $-2x + 7$ for $f(x)$ and $4x^2 - 3x + 5$ for $g(x)$.

$= (-2x + 7)(4x^2 - 3x + 5)$

Use the Distributive Property to multiply each term of $-2x + 7$ by each term of $4x^2 - 3x + 5$.

$= (-2x)(4x^2) + (-2x)(-3x) + (-2x)(5) + (7)(4x^2) + (7)(-3x) + (7)(5)$

Simplify.

$= -8x^3 + 6x^2 - 10x + 28x^2 - 21x + 35$

Combine like terms

$= -8x^3 + 34x^2 - 31x + 35$

The product $(fg)(x)$ is $-8x^3 + 34x^2 - 31x + 35$.

METHOD 2

Write the terms vertically and multiply.

Write $(fg)(x)$ as $f(x) \cdot g(x)$.

$(fg)(x) = f(x) \cdot g(x)$

Substitute $-2x + 7$ for $f(x)$ and $4x^2 - 3x + 5$ for $g(x)$.

$= (-2x + 7)(4x^2 - 3x + 5)$

Write the terms vertically and multiply.

$$
\begin{array}{r}
4x^2 - 3x + 5 \\
\times \qquad -2x + 7 \\
\hline
\end{array}
$$

Multiply each term of $4x^2 - 3x + 5$ by 7.

$28x^2 - 21x + 35$

Multiply each term of $4x^2 - 3x + 5$ by $-2x$.

$-8x^3 + 6x^2 - 10x$

Add to combine like terms.

$-8x^3 + 34x^2 - 31x + 35$

The product $(fg)(x)$ is $-8x^3 + 34x^2 - 31x + 35$.

METHOD 3

Use a table to multiply.

There are two terms in *f* and three terms in *g*. Create a table that has two rows and three columns.

Write the terms of *f* with their signs next to the first column.

	$4x^2$	$-3x$	$+5$
$-2x$			
$+7$			

Write the terms of *g* with their signs above the first row.

Write the product of each pair of terms in the corresponding cells of the table.

	$4x^2$	$-3x$	$+5$
$-2x$	$-8x^3$	$+6x^2$	$-10x$
$+7$	$+28x^2$	$-21x$	$+35$

For example, the product of $-2x$ and 5 is $-10x$.

Add the products in each cell of the table.

$= -8x^3 + 6x^2 - 10x + 28x^2 - 21x + 35$

Combine like terms.

$= -8x^3 + 34x^2 - 31x + 35$

The product $(fg)(x)$ is $-8x^3 + 34x^2 - 31x + 35$.

GOT TO KNOW!

Multiplying Functions
- The expression $(fg)(x) = f(x) \cdot g(x)$.
- The domain of $(fg)(x)$ is the intersection of the domains of *f* and *g*.

SOUTHWESTERN

Evaluating Functions

When you evaluate combined functions, you need to make sure that the value is in the domain of the combined functions.

Need More

HELP ?

For help multiplying radical expressions, go to *Multiplying Radical Expressions* in *Advanced Algebra* (p. 1956).

EXAMPLE 6

Given $p(x) = \sqrt{x}$ and $q(x) = 2x^2 - 5x + 1$.

a. Find the domain of $(pq)(x)$.

The domain of $p(x)$ is $x \geq 0$, or $[0, \infty)$. The domain of $q(x)$ is all real numbers, or $(-\infty, \infty)$. The x-values the two functions have in common are $x \geq 0$, so the domain of $(fg)(x)$ is $x \geq 0$, or $[0, \infty)$.

b. Find $(pq)(9)$, if possible.

The value $x = 9$ is in the domain of $(fg)(x)$, so $(fg)(9)$ exists.

STEP 1 Find $(pq)(x)$.

Write $(pq)(x)$ as $p(x) \cdot q(x)$.

Substitute $\sqrt{x}$ for $p(x)$ and $2x^2 - 5x + 1$ for $q(x)$.

Multiply each term of $2x^2 - 5x + 1$ by $\sqrt{x}$.

$(pq)(x) = p(x) \cdot q(x)$

$= \sqrt{x}(2x^2 - 5x + 1)$

$= 2x^2\sqrt{x} - 5x\sqrt{x} + \sqrt{x}$

STEP 2 Find $(pq)(9)$.

Substitute 9 for x in $2x^2\sqrt{x} - 5x\sqrt{x} + \sqrt{x}$.

Multiply and simplify.

$= 2(9)^2\sqrt{9} - 5(9)\sqrt{9} + \sqrt{9}$

$= 162(3) - 45(3) + 3$

$= 486 - 135 + 3 = 354$

The value of $(pq)(9)$ is 354.

SEARCH 🔍

To see step-by-step videos of these problems, enter the page number into the SWadvantage.com Search Bar.

EXAMPLE 7

Given $f(x) = \sqrt{x}$ and $g(x) = 2\sqrt{x} - 3$.

a. Find the domain of $(fg)(x)$.

The domain of $f(x)$ is $x \geq 0$. The domain of $g(x)$ is $x \geq 0$. The domain of $(fg)(x)$ is $x \geq 0$, or $[0, \infty)$.

b. Find $(fg)(4)$, if possible.

The value $x = 9$ is in the domain of $(fg)(x)$, so $(fg)(9)$ exists.

STEP 1 Find $(fg)(x)$.

Write $(fg)(x)$ as $f(x) \cdot g(x)$.

Substitute $\sqrt{x}$ for $f(x)$ and $2\sqrt{x} - 3$ for $g(x)$.

Apply the Distributive Property.

Simplify.

$(fg)(x) = f(x) \cdot g(x)$

$= \sqrt{x}(2\sqrt{x} - 3)$

$= (2\sqrt{x})(\sqrt{x}) + (-3)(\sqrt{x})$

$= 2x - 3\sqrt{x}$

STEP 2 Find $(fg)(4)$.

Substitute 4 for x.

Simplify.

Simplify.

$= 2(4) - 3\sqrt{4}$

$= 8 - 3(2)$

$= 8 - 6 = 2$

The value of $(fg)(4)$ is 2.

EXAMPLE 8

Given $f(x) = \sqrt{x - 1}$ and $g(x) = \frac{1}{x}$.

a. Find the domain of $(fg)(x)$.

The domain of $f(x)$ is $x \geq 1$, or $[1, \infty)$. The domain of $g(x)$ is all x except $x \neq 0$, or $(-\infty, 0)$ and $(0, \infty)$.

The domain of $(fg)(x)$ is $x \geq 1$, or $[1, \infty)$.

b. Find $(fg)(3)$, if possible.

The value $x = 3$ is in the domain of $(fg)(x)$, so $(fg)(3)$ exists.

STEP 1 Find $(fg)(x)$.

Write $(fg)(x)$ as $f(x) \cdot g(x)$. $\qquad (fg)(x) = f(x) \cdot g(x)$

Substitute $\sqrt{x - 1}$ for $f(x)$ and $\frac{1}{x}$ for $g(x)$. $\qquad = \sqrt{x - 1}\left(\frac{1}{x}\right)$

Simplify. $\qquad = \frac{\sqrt{x - 1}}{x}$

STEP 2 Find $(fg)(3)$.

Substitute 3 for x. $\qquad = \frac{\sqrt{3 - 1}}{3}$

Simplify. $\qquad = \frac{\sqrt{2}}{3}$

The value of $(fg)(3)$ is $\frac{\sqrt{2}}{3}$.

c. Find $(fg)(-2)$, if possible.

The value $x = -2$ is not in $[1, \infty)$, the domain of $(fg)(x)$, so $(fg)(-2)$ is undefined.

Need More HELP?

For help evaluating functions, go to *Composition of Functions* on page 2062.

EXAMPLE 9

Given $g(x) = 3e^x$ and $h(x) = 2e^{3x} + 1$.

a. Find the domain of $(gh)(x)$.

The domain of $g(x)$ is all real numbers or $(-\infty, \infty)$. The domain of $h(x)$ is all real numbers or $(-\infty, \infty)$. The domain of $(gh)(x)$ is $(-\infty, \infty)$.

b. Find $(gh)(0)$, if possible.

The value $x = 0$ is in the domain of $(gh)(x)$, so $(gh)(0)$ exists.

STEP 1 Find $(gh)(x)$.

Write $(gh)(x)$ as $g(x) \cdot h(x)$. $\qquad (gh)(x) = g(x) \cdot h(x)$

Substitute $3e^x$ for $g(x)$ and $2e^{3x} + 1$ for $h(x)$. $\qquad = 3e^x(2e^{3x} + 1)$

Distribute $3e^x$. $\qquad = (3e^x)(2e^{3x}) + (3e^x)(1)$

Multiply. $\qquad = 6e^{x + 3x} + 3e^x$

Simplify. $\qquad = 6e^{4x} + 3e^x$

STEP 2 Find $(gh)(0)$.

Substitute 0 for x and simplify. $\qquad = 6e^{4(0)} + 3e^0 = 6 + 3 = 9$

The value of $(gh)(0)$ is 9.

Need More HELP?

For help simplifying functions with the base e, go to *Base* e on page 2004.

Dividing Functions

Dividing Functions

The notation $\left(\dfrac{f}{g}\right)(x)$ is used to represent the quotient of $f(x)$ and $g(x)$ and is equal to $\dfrac{f(x)}{g(x)}$. The domain of $\left(\dfrac{f}{g}\right)(x)$ contains the real numbers that are common to the domains of $f(x)$ and $g(x)$. The domain excludes any values of x that make $g(x) = 0$, because the denominator of a fraction cannot equal 0.

SEARCH 🔍

To see step-by-step videos of these problems, enter the page number into the SWadvantage.com Search Bar.

EXAMPLE 1

Given $f(x) = 4x + 6$ and $g(x) = -2$, find $\left(\dfrac{f}{g}\right)(x)$.

Write $\left(\dfrac{f}{g}\right)(x)$ as $\dfrac{f(x)}{g(x)}$.

$\left(\dfrac{f}{g}\right)(x) = \dfrac{f(x)}{g(x)}$

Substitute $4x + 6$ for $f(x)$ and -2 for $g(x)$.

$= \dfrac{4x + 6}{-2}$

Factor 2 out of the numerator and denominator.

$= \dfrac{2(2x + 3)}{2(-1)}$

Simplify.

$= \dfrac{(2x + 3)}{(-1)}$

Divide.

$= -2x - 3$

The quotient $\left(\dfrac{f}{g}\right)(x)$ is $-2x - 3$.

Need More

HELP ❓

For help factoring quadratics, go to *Factoring Polynomials* in *Algebra* (p. 1658).

EXAMPLE 2

Given $f(x) = 3x - 2$ and $g(x) = 3x^2 + 10x - 8$.

a. Find $\left(\dfrac{f}{g}\right)(x)$.

Write $\left(\dfrac{f}{g}\right)(x)$ as $\dfrac{f(x)}{g(x)}$

$\left(\dfrac{f}{g}\right)(x) = \dfrac{f(x)}{g(x)}$

Substitute $3x - 2$ for $f(x)$ and $3x^2 + 10x - 8$ for $g(x)$.

$= \dfrac{3x - 2}{3x^2 + 10x - 8}$

Factor the denominator.

$= \dfrac{3x - 2}{(3x - 2)(x + 4)}$

Simplify.

$= \dfrac{1}{x + 4}$

The quotient $\left(\dfrac{f}{g}\right)(x)$ is $\dfrac{1}{x + 4}$.

b. Find $\left(\dfrac{g}{f}\right)(x)$.

Write $\left(\dfrac{g}{f}\right)(x)$ as $\dfrac{g(x)}{f(x)}$.

$\left(\dfrac{g}{f}\right)(x) = \dfrac{g(x)}{f(x)}$

Substitute $3x^2 + 10x - 8$ for $f(x)$ and $3x - 2$ for $g(x)$.

$= \dfrac{3x^2 + 10x - 8}{3x - 2}$

Factor the numerator.

$= \dfrac{(3x - 2)(x + 4)}{(3x - 2)}$

Simplify.

$= x + 4$

The quotient $\left(\dfrac{g}{f}\right)(x)$ is $x + 4$.

Considering the Domain When Evaluating Functions

When you evaluate combined functions, you need to make sure that the value is in the domain of the combined functions.

EXAMPLE 3

Given $p(x) = 2x^2 - 5x - 3$ and $q(x) = 6x^2 - 5x - 4$.

a. Find $\left(\dfrac{p}{q}\right)(x)$.

Write $\left(\dfrac{p}{q}\right)(x)$ as $\dfrac{p(x)}{q(x)}$.

$$\left(\dfrac{p}{q}\right)(x) = \dfrac{p(x)}{q(x)}$$

Substitute $2x^2 - 5x - 3$ for $p(x)$ and $6x^2 - 5x - 4$ for $q(x)$.

$$= \dfrac{2x^2 - 5x - 3}{6x^2 - 5x - 4}$$

Factor the numerator and the denominator.

$$= \dfrac{(2x + 1)(x - 3)}{(2x + 1)(3x - 4)}$$

Simplify.

$$= \dfrac{(x - 3)}{(3x - 4)}$$

The quotient $\left(\dfrac{p}{q}\right)(x)$ is $\dfrac{(x - 3)}{(3x - 4)}$.

b. Find the domain of $\left(\dfrac{p}{q}\right)(x)$.

The domain of $p(x)$ is all real numbers. The domain of $q(x)$ is all real numbers, except for any values of x that make the denominator equal to 0. The denominator will be zero when $2x + 1 = 0$ or when $3x - 4 = 0$, the solutions of which are $x = -\dfrac{1}{2}$ and $x = \dfrac{4}{3}$.

The domain of $\left(\dfrac{p}{q}\right)(x)$ is all real numbers except $x = -\dfrac{1}{2}$ and $x = \dfrac{4}{3}$, or $\left(-\infty, -\dfrac{1}{2}\right), \left(-\dfrac{1}{2}, \dfrac{4}{3}\right)$ and $\left(\dfrac{4}{3}, \infty\right)$.

c. Find $\left(\dfrac{p}{q}\right)(0)$, if possible.

The domain includes $x = 0$, so $\left(\dfrac{p}{q}\right)(0)$ exists.

Substitute 0 for x in $\left(\dfrac{p}{q}\right)(x)$ and simplify.

$$\left(\dfrac{p}{q}\right)(0) = \dfrac{(0 - 3)}{(3 \cdot 0 - 4)} = \dfrac{-3}{-4} = \dfrac{3}{4}$$

The value of $\left(\dfrac{p}{q}\right)(0) = \dfrac{3}{4}$.

Watch Out !

When you are finding the values of x that make the denominator of $\left(\dfrac{f}{g}\right)(x)$ equal to zero, use the non-simplified version of the function. In Example 3, $x = -\dfrac{1}{2}$ also makes the denominator equal to zero and would be missed if you only looked at $\dfrac{(x - 3)}{(3x - 4)}$.

GOT TO KNOW!

Dividing Functions

- The expression $\left(\dfrac{f}{g}\right)(x) = \dfrac{f(x)}{g(x)}$.

- The domain of $\left(\dfrac{f}{g}\right)(x)$ is the intersection of the domains of $f(x)$ and $g(x)$, excluding any values that make $g(x) = 0$.

Considering the Domain When Evaluating Functions

SEARCH 🔍

To see step-by-step videos of these problems, enter the page number into the SWadvantage.com Search Bar.

EXAMPLE 4

Given $a(x) = \sqrt{x}$ and $b(x) = 4\sqrt{x^5}$.

a. Find the domain of $\left(\dfrac{a}{b}\right)(x)$.

The domain of $a(x)$ is $x \geq 0$, or $[0, \infty)$. The domain of $b(x)$ is $x \geq 0$, or $[0, \infty)$.

Now consider any values of x that make the denominator zero (when $b(x) = 0$). When the number inside the radical is zero, $b(x) = 0$, so $4\sqrt{x^5} = 0$ when $x = 0$. So $x \neq 0$.

The domain of $\left(\dfrac{a}{b}\right)(x)$ is $x > 0$, or $(0, \infty)$.

b. Find $\left(\dfrac{a}{b}\right)(x)$.

Need More
HELP ❓

For help simplifying radical expressions, go to *Dividing Radical Expressions* (p. 1962).

Write $\left(\dfrac{a}{b}\right)(x)$ as $\dfrac{a(x)}{b(x)}$.

$\left(\dfrac{a}{b}\right)(x) = \dfrac{a(x)}{b(x)}$

Substitute $\sqrt{x}$ for $a(x)$ and $4\sqrt{x^5}$ for $b(x)$.

$= \dfrac{\sqrt{x}}{4\sqrt{x^5}}$

Write each root with rational exponents.

$= \dfrac{x^{\frac{1}{2}}}{4x^{\frac{5}{2}}}$

Subtract the exponents and simplify.

$= \dfrac{x^{\frac{1}{2} - \frac{5}{2}}}{4} = \dfrac{x^{-\frac{4}{2}}}{4} = \dfrac{x^{-2}}{4}$

Write without negative exponents.

$= \dfrac{1}{4x^2}$

The quotient $\left(\dfrac{a}{b}\right)(x) = \dfrac{1}{4x^2}$.

c. Find $\left(\dfrac{a}{b}\right)(3)$, if possible.

Substitute 3 for x in $\dfrac{1}{4x^2}$.

$\left(\dfrac{a}{b}\right)(3) = \dfrac{1}{4(3)^2}$

Simplify.

$= \dfrac{1}{36}$

The value of $\left(\dfrac{a}{b}\right)(3) = \dfrac{1}{36}$.

EXAMPLE 5

Given $f(x) = \sqrt{x}$ and $g(x) = \sqrt{x - 4}$, find the domain of $\dfrac{f}{g}(x)$.

The domain of $f(x)$ is all numbers that make $x \geq 0$, which is $[0, \infty)$.

The domain of $g(x)$ is all numbers that make $x - 4 \geq 0$, which is $x \geq 4$, or $[4, \infty)$.

The domain cannot include any values that make $g(x) = 0$, so $x \neq 4$.

The numbers these three pieces have in common is all real numbers > 4, or $(4, \infty)$.

EXAMPLE 6

Given $f(x) = 8x^3 + 6x^2 + 4x + 15$ and $g(x) = 2x + 3$.

a. Find the domain of $\left(\dfrac{f}{g}\right)(x)$.

The domain of $f(x)$ is all real numbers or $(-\infty, \infty)$. The domain of $g(x)$ is all real numbers or $(-\infty, \infty)$.

Now consider any values of x that make the denominator zero. The denominator will be zero when $2x + 3 = 0$, or when $x = -\dfrac{3}{2}$. So $x \neq -\dfrac{3}{2}$.

The domain of $\left(\dfrac{f}{g}\right)(x)$ is $\left(-\infty, -\dfrac{3}{2}\right)$ and $\left(-\dfrac{3}{2}, \infty\right)$. $\left(\text{All real numbers except } -\dfrac{3}{2}.\right)$

b. Find $\left(\dfrac{f}{g}\right)(x)$.

Write $\left(\dfrac{f}{g}\right)(x)$ as $\dfrac{f(x)}{g(x)}$. $\qquad\qquad\qquad\qquad \left(\dfrac{f}{g}\right)(x) = \dfrac{f(x)}{g(x)}$

Substitute $8x^3 + 6x^2 + 4x + 15$ for $f(x)$ and $2x + 3$ for $b(x)$. $\qquad = \dfrac{8x^3 + 6x^2 + 4x + 15}{2x + 3}$

Use long division to divide $2x + 3$ into $8x^3 + 6x^2 + 4x + 15$.

Place $4x^2$ in the x^2 column, above $6x^2$.

Think: $2x \cdot ? = 8x^3$. $2x \cdot 4x^2 = 8x^3$.

Multiply $2x + 3$ by $4x^2$.

Subtract and pull down the next term.

$$
\begin{array}{r}
4x^2 \\
2x + 3 \overline{\smash{)}\ 8x^3 \ + \ 6x^2 \ + \ 1x \ + \ 15} \\
\underline{8x^3 \ + \ 12x^2 } \\
- \ 6x^2 \ + \ 1x
\end{array}
$$

Continue the long division just as you would for numbers.

Think: $2x \cdot ? = -6x^2$. $2x \cdot -3x = -6x^2$.

Multiply $2x + 3$ by $-3x$.

Subtract and pull down the next term.

Think: $2x \cdot 5 = 10x$, so multiply by 5.

Subtract.

$$
\begin{array}{r}
4x^2 \ - \ 3x \ + \ 5 \\
2x + 3 \overline{\smash{)}\ 8x^3 \ + \ 6x^2 \ + \ 1x \ + \ 15} \\
\underline{8x^3 \ + \ 12x^2 } \\
- \ 6x^2 \ + \ 1x \\
\underline{- \ 6x^2 \ - \ 9x } \\
+ \ 10x \ + \ 15 \\
\underline{10x \ + \ 15} \\
0
\end{array}
$$

The quotient $\left(\dfrac{f}{g}\right)(x) = 4x^2 - 3x + 5$.

c. Find $\left(\dfrac{f}{g}\right)(2)$, if possible.

Substitute 2 for x in $4x^2 - 3x + 5$. $\qquad \left(\dfrac{f}{g}\right)(2) = 4(2)^2 - 3(2) + 5$

Simplify. $\qquad\qquad\qquad\qquad\qquad\qquad = 16 - 6 + 5 = 15$

The value of $\left(\dfrac{f}{g}\right)(2) = 15$.

Need More

HELP ?

For help dividing polynomials, go to *Synthetic Division* in *Algebra* (p. 1678).

Piecewise Functions

Piecewise Functions

A function that is defined by two or more equations is called a **piecewise function**. One function is used for certain values of x and another is used for other values of x.

SEARCH

To see step-by-step videos of these problems, enter the page number into the SWadvantage.com Search Bar.

EXAMPLE 1

Given $f(x) = \begin{cases} 3x + 4 \text{ if } x < 0 \\ -x + 2 \text{ if } x \geq 0 \end{cases}$.

a. Find $f(-4)$.

When $x = -4$, use the function for values < 0.

Substitute -4 for x into $3x + 4$. $= 3(-4) + 4$

Simplify. $= -12 + 4 = -8$

The value of $f(-4) = -8$.

b. Find $f(3)$.

When $x = 3$, use the function for values ≥ 0.

Substitute 3 for x into $-x + 2$. $= -3 + 2$

Simplify. $= -1$

The value of $f(3) = -1$.

EXAMPLE 2

Given $g(x) = \begin{cases} x^2 + 3x + 5 \text{ if } x \leq 2 \\ 4 \text{ if } 2 < x \leq 4 \\ 2x - 5 \text{ if } x > 4 \end{cases}$.

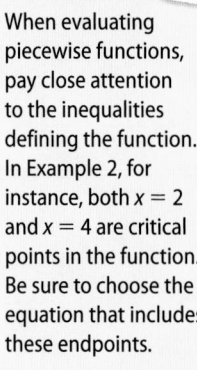

Watch Out!

When evaluating piecewise functions, pay close attention to the inequalities defining the function. In Example 2, for instance, both $x = 2$ and $x = 4$ are critical points in the function. Be sure to choose the equation that includes these endpoints.

a. Find $g(2)$.

When $x = 2$, use the function for values ≤ 2.

Substitute 2 for x into $x^2 + 3x + 5$. $g(2) = (2)^2 + 3(2) + 5$

Simplify. $= 4 + 6 + 5 = 15$

The value of $g(2) = 15$.

b. Find $g(6)$.

When $x = 6$, use the function for values > 4.

Substitute 6 for x into $2x - 5$. $g(6) = 2(6) - 5$

Simplify. $= 12 - 5 = 7$

The value of $g(6) = 7$.

c. Find $g(4)$.

When $x = 4$, use the function for values between $2 < x \leq 4$.

The function is a constant function. $g(4) = 4$

The value of $g(4) = 4$.

Graphing Piecewise Functions

EXAMPLE 3

Graph $f(x) = \begin{cases} 2 \text{ if } x < -1 \\ -2x + 3 \text{ if } x \geq -1 \end{cases}$.

STEP 1 Graph $f(x) = 2$ for $x < -1$. Use an open circle at $x = -1$ because this function does not include $x = -1$.

STEP 2 Graph $f(x) = -2x + 3$ for $x \geq -1$. Use a closed circle at $x = -1$ to include -1.

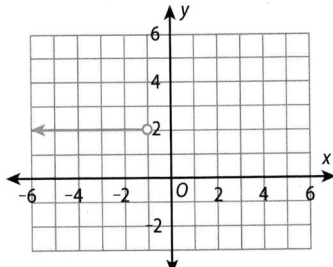

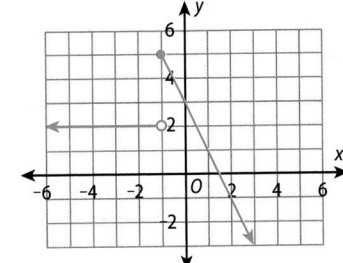

Need More
HELP ?
For help graphing linear functions, go to *Graphing From an Equation* in *Algebra* (p. 1528).

EXAMPLE 4

Graph $h(x) = \begin{cases} 0.25x^2 \text{ if } x \leq -3 \\ 1 \text{ if } -3 < x < 1 \\ 2x - 1 \text{ if } x \geq 1 \end{cases}$.

STEP 1 Graph $h(x) = 0.25x^2$ for $x \leq -3$. Use a closed circle at $x = -3$ because this function does include $x = -3$.

STEP 2 Graph $h(x) = 1$ for $-3 < x < 1$. Use open circles on each end so that the end points are not included.

STEP 3 Graph $h(x) = 2x - 1$ for $x \geq 1$. This point connects with the graph of $h(x) = 1$, so fill in the open circle at $x = 1$.

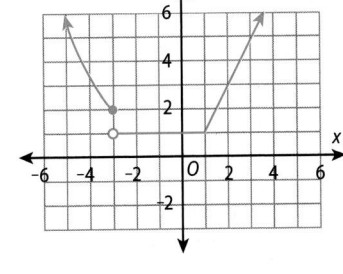

GOT TO KNOW!

Piecewise Functions

• A function that is defined by multiple equations is a piecewise function.

• Brackets are used to define the equations and the range of *x*-values for which each equation is defined.

• $\begin{cases} 2 \text{ if } x < -1 \\ -2x + 3 \text{ if } x \geq -1 \end{cases}$ ← This function is only defined for *x*-values < -1.
← This function includes the value $x = -1$ and all *x*-values greater than -1.

• The graph of a piecewise function will often have jumps or gaps in the graph.

Translating Functions

Translating Polynomial Functions

Shifts that move the graph to the left or right or up or down are called **transformations**.

EXAMPLE 1

The graph of $y = x^2$ is shown.

a. Describe how the graph of $y = x^2 + 3$ compares to the graph of $y = x^2$. Then graph $y = x^2 + 3$.

b. Describe how the graph of $y = x^2 - 1$ compares to the graph of $y = x^2$. Then graph $y = x^2 - 1$.

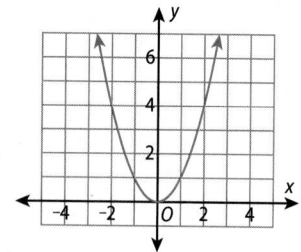

a. Because a quantity is being added to x^2, the graph of $y = x^2$ is shifted up. Because 3 is added to x^2, the graph is shifted up 3 units.

b. Because a quantity is being subtracted from x^2, the graph of $y = x^2$ is shifted down. Because 1 is being subtracted from x^2, the graph is shifted down 1 unit.

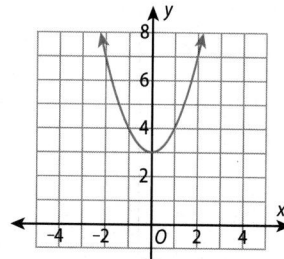

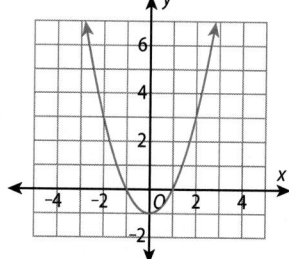

EXAMPLE 2

Describe how the graph of $y = (x - 2)^2$ compares to the graph of $y = x^2$. Then graph $y = (x - 2)^2$.

The graph of $y = (x - h)^2$ is the graph of $y = x^2$ translated h units horizontally. In this problem, h is positive 2, so the graph of $y = x^2$ is shifted two units to the right.

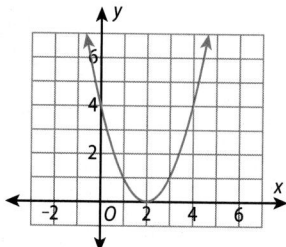

EXAMPLE 3

Describe how the graph of $y = (x + 4)^2 + 1$ compares to the graph of $y = x^2$. Then graph $y = (x + 4)^2 + 1$.

In the equation $y = (x + 4)^2 + 1$, h equals -4, so the graph of $y = x^2$ is translated 4 units to the left. Because the y value is increased by 1, the graph also shifts up 1 unit. Combined, the graph of $y = x^2$ is shifted left 4 units and up 1 unit.

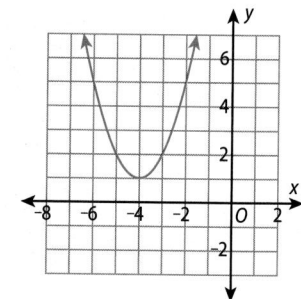

EXAMPLE 4

The graph of $y = x^3$ is shown.

a. Describe how the graph of $y = x^3 + 1$ compares to the graph of $y = x^3$. Then graph $y = x^3 + 1$.

b. Describe how the graph of $y = (x - 3)^3 - 2$ compares to the graph of $y = x^3$. Then graph $y = (x - 3)^3 - 2$.

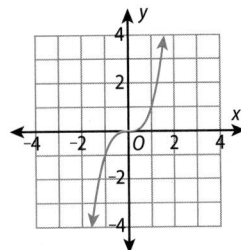

Need More
HELP ?
For help graphing polynomial functions, go to *Graphing Polynomial Functions* (p. 1624).

a. Because a quantity is being added to x^3, the graph of $y = x^3$ is shifted up. Because 1 is added to x^3, the graph is shifted up 1 unit.

b. Because 2 is subtracted, the graph of $y = x^3$ is shifted down 2 units. Because $h = 3$, the graph of $y = x^2$ is shifted right 3 units.

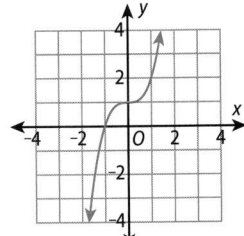

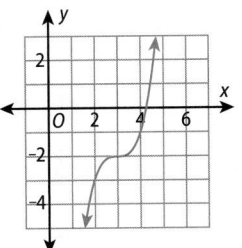

EXAMPLE 5

The graph of $y = x^3$ has been shifted vertically and horizontally. Write an equation to represent the graph.

The graph is shifted left 2 units and down 3 units.
The expression $(x + 2)^3$ shifts the graph left 2 units.
Subtracting 3 from $(x + 2)^3$ shifts the graph down 3 units.
The equation for the shifted graph is $y = (x + 2) - 3$.

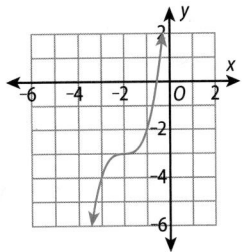

GOT TO KNOW!

Horizontal and Vertical Shifts

Vertical Shifts

- $g(x) = f(x) + k, k > 0$
  Shifts $f(x)$ up k units.

- $g(x) = f(x) - k, k > 0$
  Shifts $f(x)$ down k units.

Horizontal Shifts

- $g(x) = f(x - h), h > 0$
  Shifts $f(x)$ right h units.

- $g(x) = f(x - h), h < 0$
  Shifts $f(x)$ left h units.

Vertical and Horizontal Shifts

- $g(x) = f(x - h) + k, h > 0$ Shifts $f(x)$ right and up.
- $g(x) = f(x - h) - k, h > 0$ Shifts $f(x)$ right and down.
- $g(x) = f(x - h) + k, h < 0$ Shifts $f(x)$ left and up.
- $g(x) = f(x - h) - k, h < 0$ Shifts $f(x)$ left and down.

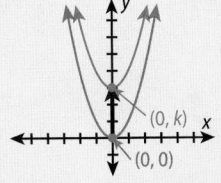

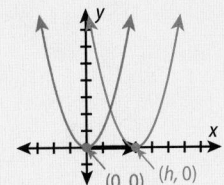

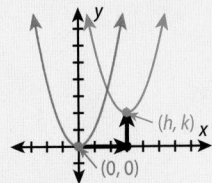

Translating Exponential Functions

The graph of $y = ab^{x-h}$ shifts the graph of $y = ab^x$ horizontally h units. The graph of $y = ab^x + k$ shifts the graph of $y = ab^x$ vertically by k units.

EXAMPLE 6

Use the graph of $y = \left(\frac{1}{2}\right)^x$ to graph $y = \left(\frac{1}{2}\right)^x - 3$.

Then describe the asymptote.

The value of k in $y = \left(\frac{1}{2}\right)^x - 3$ is negative 3, so shift the graph of $y = \left(\frac{1}{2}\right)^x$ down (in the negative direction) 3 units.

The asymptote is $y = -3$.

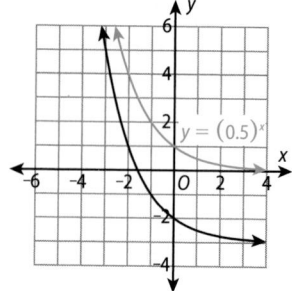

EXAMPLE 7

Use the graph of $y = 2^x$ to graph $y = 2^{x+1} + 2$.

The value of h in $y = 2^{x+1} + 2$ is -1, so shift the graph of $y = 2^x$ left 1 unit. The value of k in $y = 2^{x+1} + 2$ is positive 2, so shift the graph up 2 units.

The asymptote is $y = 2$.

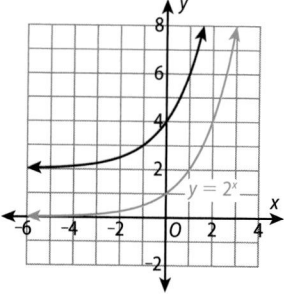

GOT TO KNOW!

Translating Exponential Functions

You can use the graph of $y = ab^x$ to graph $y = ab^{x-h}$, $y = ab^x + k$, and $y = ab^{x-h} + k$.

$y = ab^{x-h}$

- Shift to the right h units if $h > 0$.
- Shift to the left h units if $h < 0$.

$y = ab^x + k$

- Shift up k units if $k > 0$.
- Shift down k units if $k < 0$.

$y = ab^{x-h} + k$

- Shift right h units for $h > 0$ or left h units for $h < 0$.
- Shift up k units for $k > 0$ or down k units for $k < 0$.

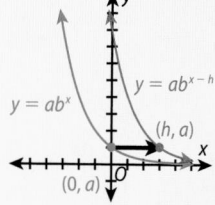

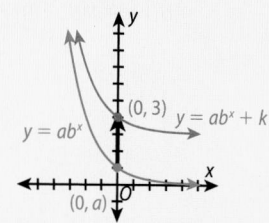

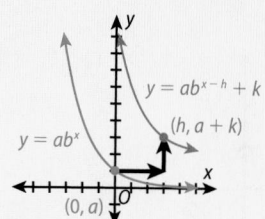

Translating Rational and Radical Functions

The graph of the rational function $y = \frac{a}{x - h} + k$ shifts the graph of $y = \frac{a}{x}$ horizontally h units and vertically k units. The graph of $y = \sqrt{x - h} + k$ shifts the graph of $y = \sqrt{x}$ horizontally h units and vertically k units.

Try It This Way

Use a graphing calculator to graph the standard function and the translated function on the same axes. You can also do this to check your graphs.

EXAMPLE 8

Use the graph of $y = \frac{1}{x}$ to graph $y = \frac{1}{x + 2} + 4$.

The value of h in $y = \frac{1}{x + 2} + 4$ is negative 2, so shift the graph of $y = \frac{1}{x}$ left 2 units.

The value of k in $y = \frac{1}{x + 2} + 4$ is positive 4, so shift the graph up 4.

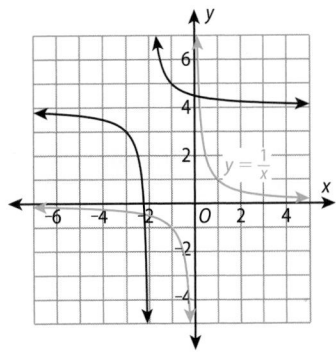

EXAMPLE 9

Use the graph of $y = \sqrt{x}$ to graph $y = \sqrt{x + 3} - 1$.

The value of h in $y = \sqrt{x + 3} - 1$ is negative 3, so shift the graph of $y = \sqrt{x}$ left 3 units.

The value of k is negative 1, so shift the graph down 1 unit.

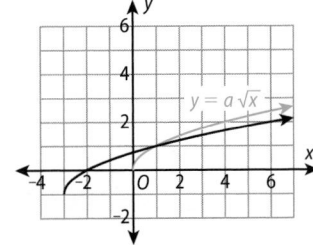

GOT TO KNOW!

Translating Rational and Radical Functions

You can use the graph of $y = \frac{a}{x}$ to graph $y = \frac{a}{x - h} + k$ and the graph of $y = a\sqrt{x}$ to graph $y = a\sqrt{x - h} + k$.

$$y = \frac{a}{x - h} + k$$

$$y = \sqrt{x - h} + k$$

- Shift to the right h units if $h > 0$ or left h units if $h < 0$.
- Shift up k units if $k > 0$ or down k units if $k < 0$.

- Shift to the right h units if $h > 0$ or left h units if $h < 0$.
- Shift up k units if $k > 0$ or down k units if $k < 0$.

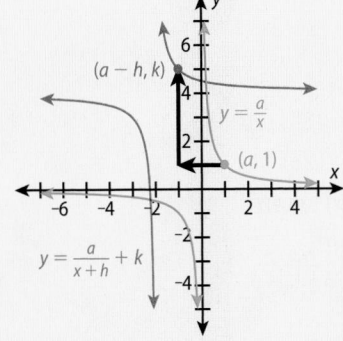

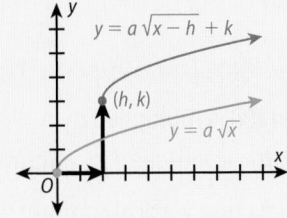

Stretching and Compressing Functions

Stretching and Compressing Functions

When you stretch or compress a function, the basic shape of the graph is changed. The graph can be stretched or compressed in a horizontal or vertical direction.

EXAMPLE 1

SEARCH

To see step-by-step videos of these problems, enter the page number into the SWadvantage.com Search Bar.

a. Graph $f(x) = x^2$, $g(x) = \frac{1}{2}x^2$, and $h(x) = 2x^2$ on the same axes.

METHOD 1

Create a table of values. Then use the points to graph the functions.

X	f(x)	g(x)	h(x)
0	0	0	0
1	1	$\frac{1}{2}$	2
−1	1	$\frac{1}{2}$	2
2	4	2	8
−2	4	2	8

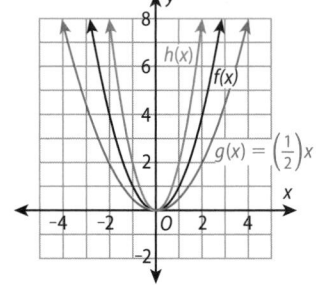

METHOD 2

Use a graphing calculator to graph the functions.

Press the [Y=] key and enter x^2 for Y1, $\frac{1}{2}x^2$ for Y2, and $2x^2$ for Y3. For Y2 you will need to type $\left(\frac{1}{2}\right)$ [×] x [^] 2 and for Y3 you will need to type 2 [×] x [^] 2.

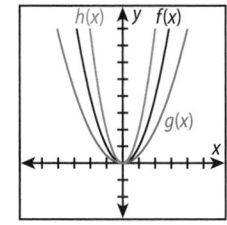

Need More

HELP ?

For help evaluating quadratic functions, go to *Order of Operations* in *Algebra* (p. 1418).

b. Compare the graph of $g(x) = \frac{1}{2}x^2$ to the graph of $f(x) = x^2$.

The graph of $g(x) = \frac{1}{2}f(x) = \frac{1}{2}x^2$ is a vertical compression of the graph of $f(x)$, because each y-value of $g(x)$ is $\frac{1}{2}$ the y-value of $f(x)$. So the graph of $g(x) = \frac{1}{2}f(x)$ is a vertical compression (or vertical shrink) of the graph of $f(x)$.

c. Compare the graph of $h(x) = 2x^2$ to the graph of $f(x) = x^2$.

The graph of $h(x) = 2f(x) = 2x^2$. This represents a vertical stretch of the graph of $f(x)$, because each y-value of $h(x)$ is 2 times the y-value of $f(x)$. So the graph of $h(x) = 2f(x)$ is a vertical stretch of the graph of $f(x)$.

GOT TO KNOW!

Stretching and Compressing Functions Vertically

When a function $f(x)$ is multiplied by a positive number c:

- the graph of $cf(x)$ is obtained by multiplying each y-value of $f(x)$ by c.

- the graph of $cf(x)$ is a vertical compression or shrink of the graph of $f(x)$ when $0 < c < 1$. The y-values of $cf(x)$ are c times less than the y-values of $f(x)$.

- the graph of $cf(x)$ is a vertical stretch of the graph of $f(x)$ when $c > 1$. The y-values of $cf(x)$ are c times greater than the y-values of $f(x)$.

EXAMPLE 2

a. **Graph $f(x) = x^2$, $g(x) = (3x)^2$, and $h(x) = \left(\frac{1}{4}x\right)^2$ on the same axes.**

   Use a graphing calculator to graph the functions.

   Press the [Y=] key and enter x^2 for Y1, $\left(\frac{1}{4}x\right)^2$ for Y2, and $(2x)^2$ for Y3. For Y2 you will need to type

   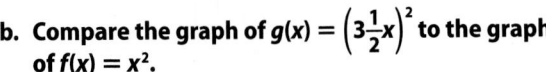 0.25 [×] *x* [)] [^] 2 and for Y3 you will

   need to type 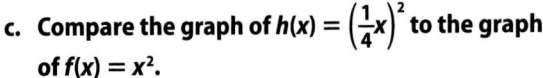 3 [×] *x* [)] [^] 2.

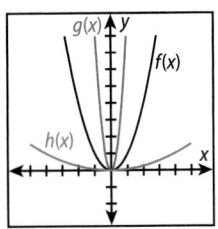

b. **Compare the graph of $g(x) = \left(3\frac{1}{2}x\right)^2$ to the graph of $f(x) = x^2$.**

   The graph of $g(x) = (3x)^2$ is a horizontal compression of the graph of $f(x) = x^2$ because for a given y-value, the x-value of $g(x)$ is $\frac{1}{3}$ the x-value of $f(x)$.

   So the graph of $g(x) = f(3x)$ is a horizontal compression (or horizontal shrink) of the graph of $f(x)$.

y-value	x-value in f(x)	x-value in g(x)
1	1	$\frac{1}{3}$
9	3	1
36	6	2

c. **Compare the graph of $h(x) = \left(\frac{1}{4}x\right)^2$ to the graph of $f(x) = x^2$.**

   The graph of $h(x) = \left(\frac{1}{4}x\right)^2$ is a horizontal stretch of the graph, because for a given y-value, the x-value of $h(x)$ is 4 times the x-value of $f(x)$.

   So the graph of $h(x) = f\left(\frac{1}{4}x\right)$ is a horizontal stretch of the graph of $f(x)$.

y-value	x-value in f(x)	x-value in g(x)
1	1	4
4	2	8
16	4	16

Ways to REMEMBER

The x-axis is the horizontal axis and the y-axis is the vertical axis on a coordinate grid. If a graph is stretched horizontally, the x-values will be greater than the x-values of the original function for a given y-value. If a graph is stretched vertically, the y-values for a given x will be greater than the y-values for that x in the original function.

GOT TO KNOW!

Stretching and Compressing Functions Horizontally

When the x-value of a function $f(x)$ is multiplied by a positive number c:

- the graph of $f(cx)$ is obtained by multiplying each x-value of $f(x)$ by $\frac{1}{c}$.

- the graph of $f(cx)$ is a horizontal compression or shrink of the graph of $f(x)$ when $c > 1$. For a given y-value, the x-value of $f(cx)$ will always be $\frac{1}{c}$ times the x-value of $f(x)$.

- the graph of $f(cx)$ is a horizontal stretch of the graph of $f(x)$ when $0 < c < 1$. For a given y-value, the x-value of $f(cx)$ will always be c times the y-value of $f(x)$.

Stretching and Compressing Other Functions

The graphs of other functions can also be stretched and compressed.

SEARCH

To see step-by-step videos of these problems, enter the page number into the SWadvantage.com Search Bar.

EXAMPLE 3

a. **Graph $f(x) = x^3 - 5$, $g(x) = (2x)^3 - 5$, and $h(x) = (0.5x)^3 - 5$ on the same axes.**

Use a graphing calculator to graph the functions.

Press the [Y=] key and enter $x^3 - 5$ for Y1, $(2x)^3 - 5$ for Y2, and $(0.5x)^3 - 5$ for Y3. For Y2 you will need to type [(] 2 [×] x [)] [^] 3 [−] 5 and for Y3 you will need to type [(] 0.5 [×] x [)] [^] 3 [−] 5.

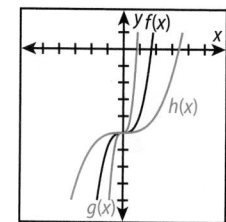

b. **Compare the graph of $y = (2x)^3 - 5$ to the graph of $y = x^3 - 5$.**

The graph of $g(x) = (2x)^3 - 5$ is a horizontal compression of the graph of $f(x) = x^3 - 5$ because for a given y-value, the x-value of $g(x)$ is $\frac{1}{2}$ the x-value of $f(x)$. So the graph of $g(x)$ is a horizontal compression (or horizontal shrink) of the graph of $f(x)$.

Need More

HELP?

For help entering functions on a graphing calculator, go to *Graphing Calculators* in *Algebra* (p. 1742).

c. **Compare the graph of $y = (0.5x)^3 - 5$ to the graph of $y = x^3 - 5$.**

The function $h(x) = (0.5x)^3 - 5$. The value of c is 0.5, so for a given y-value, the x-value of $h(x)$ is $\frac{1}{c}$ times the x-value of $f(x)$. Because $\frac{1}{c} = \frac{1}{0.5} = \frac{1}{\frac{1}{2}} = 2$, for a given y-value, the x-value of $h(x)$ is 2 times the x-value of $f(x)$. So the graph of $h(x) = (0.5x)^3 - 5$ is a horizontal stretch of the graph of $f(x)$.

EXAMPLE 4

a. **Graph $f(x) = 2^x - 1$, $g(x) = 0.25f(x)$, and $h(x) = f(3x)$ and $m(x) = 3f(x)$ on the same axes.**

Use a graphing calculator to graph the functions.

Press the [Y=] key and enter $2^x - 1$ for Y1, $0.25 \times (2^x - 1)$ for Y2, $(2^{3 \cdot x} - 1)$ for Y3 and $3 \times (2^x - 1)$ for Y4.

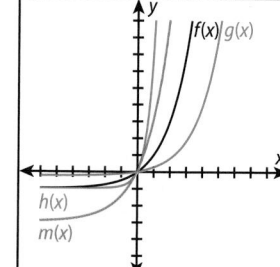

b. **Compare the graph of $g(x)$ to the graph of $f(x)$.**

The function $g(x) = 0.25f(x) = 0.25(2^x - 1)$. The graph of $g(x)$ is a vertical compression of the graph of $f(x)$ because each y-value of $g(x)$ is $\frac{1}{4}$ the y-value of $f(x)$.

c. **Compare the graph of $h(x)$ to the graph of $f(x)$.**

The graph of $h(x) = f(3x) = (2^{3 \cdot x} - 1)$. This is a horizontal compression of the graph of $f(x)$. In this case, the value of c is 3 and the value of $\frac{1}{c} = \frac{1}{3}$, so for a given y-value, the x-value of $h(x)$ is $\frac{1}{3}$ of the x-value of $f(x)$. So the graph of $h(x) = f(3x)$ is a horizontal compression of the graph of $f(x)$.

d. **Compare the graph of $m(x)$ to the graph of $f(x)$.**

The function $m(x) = 3f(x) = 3(2^x - 1)$. The graph of $m(x)$ is a vertical stretch of the graph of $f(x)$ because each y-value of $m(x)$ is 3 times the y-value of $f(x)$.

EXAMPLE 5

a. Graph $f(x) = \dfrac{1}{x-2}$ and $g(x) = f(3x)$ on the same axes.

Use a graphing calculator to graph the functions.

Press the [Y=] key and enter $\dfrac{1}{(x-2)}$ for Y1 and $\dfrac{1}{(3x-2)}$ for Y2. Make sure to use an appropriate viewing window so you get all branches of the graph.

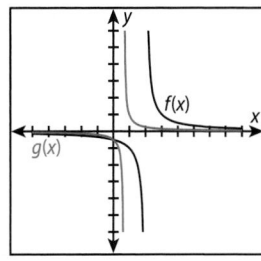

b. Make a table of values.

y-value	x-value in f(x)	x-value in g(x)
1	3	1
−2	$\dfrac{3}{2}$	$\dfrac{1}{2}$
−1	1	$\dfrac{1}{3}$
$\dfrac{1}{4}$	6	2

c. Using the graph and the table, compare the graph of $g(x)$ to the graph of $f(x)$.

The graph of $g(x) = f(3x) = \dfrac{1}{3x-2}$ is a horizontal compression of the graph of $f(x) = \dfrac{1}{x-2}$ because for a given y-value, the x-value of $g(x)$ is $\dfrac{1}{3}$ the x-value of $f(x)$.

EXAMPLE 6

a. Graph $f(x) = \sqrt{x} + 2$, $g(x) = 2f(x)$, $h(x) = \dfrac{1}{2}f(x)$ and $m(x) = f(4x)$ on the same axes.

Use a graphing calculator to graph the functions.

Press the [Y=] key and enter 2ND x^2 to get the square root symbol. Enter [√] $(x) + 2$ for Y1, $2 \times ($ [√] $(x) + 2)$ for Y2, $\left(\dfrac{1}{2}\right) \times ($ [√] $(x) + 2)$ for Y3, and [√] $(4x) + 2$ for Y4.

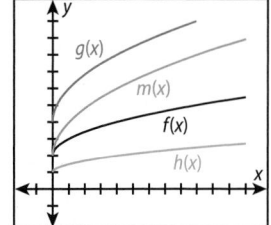

b. Compare the graph of $g(x)$ to the graph of $f(x)$.

The function $g(x) = 2f(x) = 2(\sqrt{x} + 2)$. The graph of $g(x)$ is a vertical stretch of the graph of $f(x)$ because each y-value of $g(x)$ is 2 times the y-value of $f(x)$.

c. Compare the graph of $h(x)$ to the graph of $f(x)$.

The function $h(x) = \dfrac{1}{2}f(x) = \dfrac{1}{2}(\sqrt{x} + 2)$. The graph of $h(x)$ is a vertical compression of the graph of $f(x)$ because each y-value of $h(x)$ is $\dfrac{1}{2}$ the y-value of $f(x)$.

d. Compare the graph of $m(x)$ to the graph of $f(x)$.

The graph of $m(x) = f(4x) = \sqrt{4x} + 2 = 2$. This is a horizontal compression of the graph of $f(x)$. The value of c is 4 and the value of $\dfrac{1}{c} = \dfrac{1}{4}$, so for a given y-value, the x-value of $h(x)$ is $\dfrac{1}{4}$ of the x-value of $f(x)$. So the graph of $h(x) =$ is a horizontal compression of the graph of $f(x)$.

Reflecting Functions

Reflecting Polynomial Functions

If you think of the x- and y-axis as a mirror, the graph of a function can be reflected in the axis to create a mirror image, or **reflection**, of the graph. If $g(x) = -f(x)$, the graph of $f(x)$ is reflected in the x-axis. If $g(x) = f(-x)$, the graph of $f(x)$ is reflected in the y-axis.

EXAMPLE 1

a. Graph $f(x) = (x + 2)^2 + 3$, $g(x) = -f(x)$, and $h(x) = f(-x)$ on the same axes.

Use a graphing calculator to graph the functions.

Press **Y=** and enter the equations.

Y1 = $(x + 2)$^2 + 3
Y2 = $-1*((x + 2)$^2 + 3)
Y3 = $(-x + 2)$^2 + 3

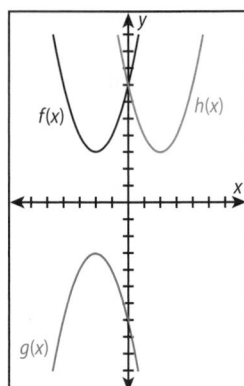

b. Compare the graph of $g(x)$ to the graph of $f(x)$.

The graph of $g(x) = -f(x) = -[(x + 2)^2 + 3]$. The graph of $g(x)$ is a reflection in the x-axis. The y-values of $g(x)$ are the opposite of the y-values of $f(x)$.

c. Compare the graph of $h(x)$ to the graph of $f(x)$.

The graph of $h(x) = f(-x) = (-x + 2)^2 + 3$. The graph of $h(x)$ is a reflection in the y-axis. The x-values of $h(x)$ are the opposite of the x-values of $f(x)$.

Watch Out !

You might be tempted to say that the graph of $-f(x)$ is a reflection over the x-axis. Think of the x-axis as a mirror. You see your reflection *in* the mirror. So we say that $-f(x)$ is a reflection **in** the x-axis and $f(-x)$ is a reflection **in** the y-axis.

EXAMPLE 2

The graph of $n(x) = m(-x)$. Describe how the graph of $n(x)$ compares to the graph of $m(x)$.

The x-values of $n(x)$ are opposite the x-values of $m(x)$.

The graph of $n(x)$ is a reflection in the y-axis.

GOT TO KNOW!

Reflecting Functions

Reflections in the x-axis

- The graph of $g(x) = -f(x)$ is a reflection of the graph of $f(x)$ in the x-axis.

- The y-values of $g(x)$ are opposite of the y-values of $f(x)$.

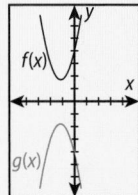

Reflections in the y-axis

- The graph of $g(x) = f(-x)$ is a reflection of the graph of $f(x)$ in the y-axis.

- The x-values of $g(x)$ are opposite of the x-values of $f(x)$.

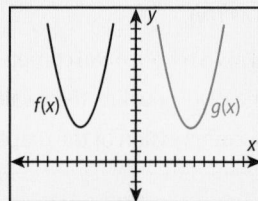

EXAMPLE 3

a. Describe how the graph of $g(x) = -[(x - 4)^2 - 2]$ compares to the graph of $f(x) = x^2$.

The graph of $g(x)$ shifts the graph of x^2 horizontally to the right 4 units, and vertically down 2 units. The graph is then reflected in the x-axis.

b. Use your description to sketch the graph of $g(x)$.

Need More

HELP ?

For help shifting graphs horizontally and vertically, go to *Translating Functions* (p. 2078).

STEP 1 To get the graph of $g(x)$, the graph of x^2 is shifted horizontally to the right 4 units and vertically down 2 units.

STEP 2 Then the shifted graph is reflected in the x-axis.

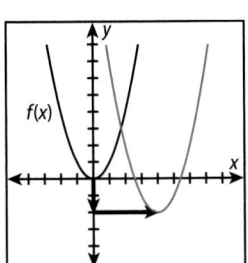

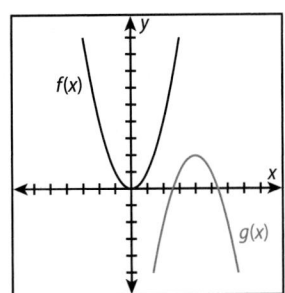

EXAMPLE 4

a. Graph $f(x) = (x + 4)^3$, $g(x) = f(-x)$, and $h(x) = -f(x)$ on the same axes.

Use a graphing calculator to graph the functions.

Press Y= and enter the equations.

Y1 = (x + 4)^3   Y2 = (-1*x + 4)^3   Y3 = -1*((x + 4)^3)^3

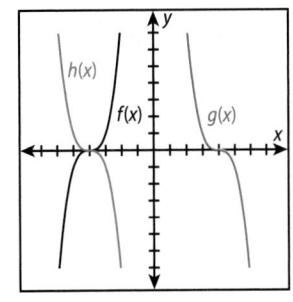

SEARCH 🔍

To see step-by-step videos of these problems, enter the page number into the SWadvantage.com Search Bar.

b. Compare the graph of $g(x)$ to the graph of $f(x)$.

The graph of $g(x) = f(-x) = (-x + 4)^3$. The graph of $g(x)$ is a reflection in the y-axis. The x-values of $g(x)$ are the opposite of the x-values of $f(x)$.

c. Compare the graph of $h(x)$ to the graph of $f(x)$.

The graph of $h(x) = -f(x) = -(x + 4)^3$. The graph of $h(x)$ is a reflection in the x-axis. The y-values of $h(x)$ are the opposite of the y-values of $f(x)$.

EXAMPLE 5

The graph of $f(x) = 0.5x^4 - 0.5x^3 - 3x^2 + 10$ is shown. Describe the graph of $-f(x)$.

The graph of $-f(x)$ is a reflection in the x-axis.

The y-values of $-f(x)$ are the opposite of the y-values of $f(x)$.

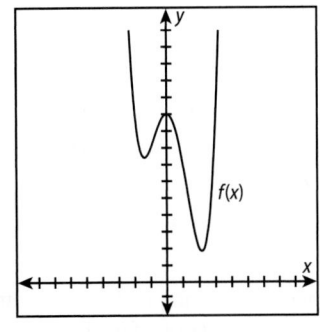

Reflecting Other Functions

The graphs of other functions can be reflected in the *x*- and *y*-axes.

EXAMPLE 6

SEARCH

To see step-by-step videos of these problems, enter the page number into the SWadvantage.com Search Bar.

a. Graph $f(x) = 2e^x + 1$, $g(x) = -f(x)$, and $h(x) = f(-x)$ on the same axes.

Use a graphing calculator to graph the functions. Press **Y=** and enter the equations.

$Y1 = 2*e^{(x)} + 1$ 　　$Y2 = -(2*e^{(x)} + 1)$ 　　$Y3 = 2*e^{(-x)} + 1$

b. Compare the graph of $g(x)$ to the graph of $f(x)$.

The graph of $g(x) = -f(x) = -(2e^x + 1)$. The graph of $g(x)$ is a reflection in the *x*-axis. The *y*-values of $g(x)$ are the opposite of the *y*-values of $f(x)$.

c. Compare the graph of $h(x)$ to the graph of $f(x)$.

The graph of $h(x) = f(-x) = 2e^{-x} + 1$. The graph of $h(x)$ is a reflection in the *y*-axis. The *x*-values of $h(x)$ are the opposite of the *x*-values of $f(x)$.

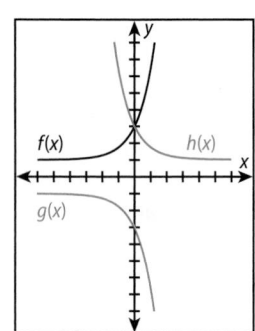

EXAMPLE 7

Need More

HELP ?

For help with exponential functions, go to *Exponential Growth* (p. 1996) and *Exponential Decay* (p. 2000).

a. Graph $f(x) = \left(-\frac{1}{4}\right)(2^x) + 1$, $g(x) = -f(x)$, and $h(x) = f(-x)$ on the same axes.

Use a graphing calculator to graph the functions. Press **Y=** and enter the equations.

$Y1 = \left(-\frac{1}{4}\right)*2^{(x)} + 1$, $Y2 = -\left(\left(-\frac{1}{4}\right)*2^{(x)} + 1\right)$ and

$Y3 = \left(-\frac{1}{4}\right)*2^{(-x)} + 1$

b. Compare the graph of $g(x)$ to the graph of $f(x)$.

The graph of $g(x) = -f(x) = -\left(\left(-\frac{1}{4}\right)*2^x + 1\right)$. The graph of $g(x)$ is a reflection in the *x*-axis. The *y*-values of $g(x)$ are the opposite of the *y*-values of $f(x)$.

c. Compare the graph of $h(x)$ to the graph of $f(x)$.

The graph of $h(x) = f(-x) = \left(-\frac{1}{4}\right)*2^{(-x)} + 1$. The graph of $h(x)$ is a reflection in the *y*-axis. The *x*-values of $h(x)$ are the opposite of the *x*-values of $f(x)$.

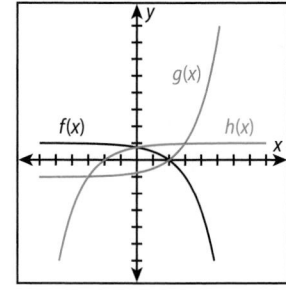

EXAMPLE 8

The graph of $f(x) = \sqrt{x^2 + 1}$ is shown. Write the equation for the reflection of the graph of $f(x)$ in the *y*-axis.

When the graph of $f(x)$ is reflected in the *y*-axis, the resulting graph $g(x) = f(-x)$. Substitute $(-x)$ for x in $\sqrt{x^2 + 1}$ and simplify.

$\sqrt{(-x)^2 + 1} = \sqrt{x^2 + 1}$

Because the graph of $f(x)$ is symmetric about the *y*-axis, the equation for the reflection of $f(x)$ in the *y*-axis is $f(x)$.

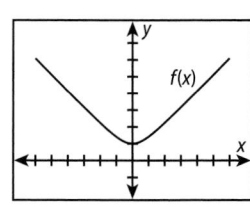

EXAMPLE 9

a. Given $f(x) = \sqrt{x}$, write an equation for the graph of $g(x)$, the reflection of $f(x)$ in the x-axis. Then write an equation for $h(x)$, the reflection of $f(x)$ in the y-axis.

When $f(x)$ is reflected in the x-axis, the resulting graph is represented by $-f(x)$. So $g(x) = -f(x) = -\sqrt{x}$.

When $f(x)$ is reflected in the y-axis, the resulting graph is represented by $f(-x)$. So $h(x) = f(-x) = \sqrt{-x}$.

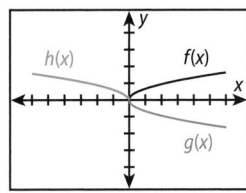

Need More HELP?

Remember that $f(3x)$ means to substitute $3x$ for every x in $f(x)$. For help with evaluating functions, go to *Composition of Functions* (p. 2062).

b. Describe the graphs of $g(x)$ and $h(x)$ in comparison to $f(x)$.

The graph of $g(x)$ has y-values that are the opposite of the y-values of $f(x)$.

The graph of $h(x)$ has x-values that are the opposite of the x-values of $f(x)$.

c. Graph $f(x)$, $g(x)$, and $h(x)$ on the same axes.

The graph is at the right above.

EXAMPLE 10

a. Given $f(x) = \dfrac{1}{3x - 2}$, write an equation for the graph of $g(x)$, the reflection of $f(x)$ in the x-axis.

When $f(x)$ is reflected in the x-axis, the resulting graph is represented by $-f(x)$. So $g(x) = -f(x) = -\dfrac{1}{3x - 2}$.

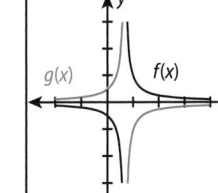

b. Describe the graph of $g(x)$ in comparison to $f(x)$. Then graph $f(x)$ and $g(x)$ on the same axes.

The graph of $g(x)$ has y-values that are the opposite of the y-values of $f(x)$.

EXAMPLE 11

a. Given $f(x) = \dfrac{-1}{x}$, write an equation for the graph of $g(x)$, the reflection of $f(x)$ in the y-axis.

When $f(x)$ is reflected in the y-axis, the resulting graph is represented by $f(-x)$.

Substitute $-x$ for x in $\dfrac{-1}{x}$. $f(-x) = \dfrac{-1}{-x} = \dfrac{1}{x}$

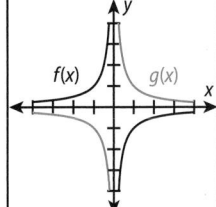

b. Describe the x- and y-coordinates of the graph of $g(x)$ in comparison to $f(x)$.

The graph of $g(x)$ has x-values that are the opposite of the x-values of $f(x)$. Because $f(-x) = \dfrac{1}{x} = -f(x)$, the graph of $g(x)$ is also the reflection of $f(x)$ in the x-axis.

c. Graph $f(x)$ and $g(x)$ on the same axes.

The graph is at the right above.

Inverses of Linear Functions

Inverses of Linear Functions

The **inverse** of a linear function will have the range of the original function as its domain and the domain of the original function as its range. This means that if the point (x, y) is on the original function, the point (y, x) is on the graph of the inverse. The inverse of a linear function $f(x)$ is denoted by $f^{-1}(x)$, which is read *f inverse of x* or *the inverse of f(x)*.

> **Watch Out** !
>
> The -1 in $f^{-1}(x)$ is not an exponent. It is notation to represent the inverse of the function $f(x)$, not $\frac{1}{f(x)}$ or $\frac{1}{f}$.

EXAMPLE 1

a. Create a table of values for $f(x) = 2x - 5$. Then graph $f(x)$.

Select x-values to use in the table. You can use any numbers that are in the domain of the function.

x	2	3	4	5	6
y = f(x)	−1	1	3	5	7

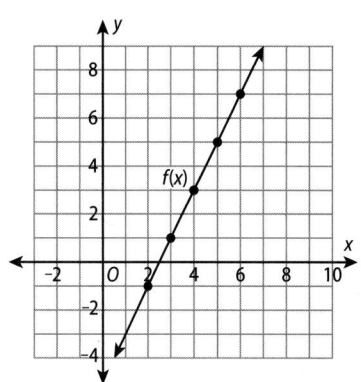

b. Create a table of values for $f^{-1}(x)$. Then graph $f^{-1}(x)$.

Switch the x- and y-coordinates from the table in part (a). These are the coordinates for $f^{-1}(x)$.

x	−1	1	3	5	7
y = f⁻¹(x)	2	3	4	5	6

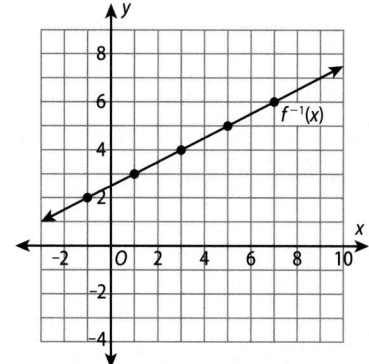

> **Need More HELP?**
>
> For help graphing linear equations, go to *Graphing from a Table of Values* (p. 1524) and *Graphing from an Equation* (p. 1528) in *Algebra*.

c. Describe the relationship between the graphs of $f(x)$ and $f^{-1}(x)$.

The graph of $f^{-1}(x)$ is a reflection of the graph of $f(x)$. The line of reflection is $y = x$.

GOT TO KNOW!

Inverses of Linear Functions

- The inverse of a linear function $f(x)$ is represented by the notation $f^{-1}(x)$.
- The graph of $f^{-1}(x)$ is a reflection of the graph of $f(x)$. The line of reflection is $y = x$.
- The x- and y-values of $f(x)$ are interchanged to generate the x- and y-values of $f^{-1}(x)$.
- The equation of the inverse function can be found by switching the x and y in the original equation and solving for y.

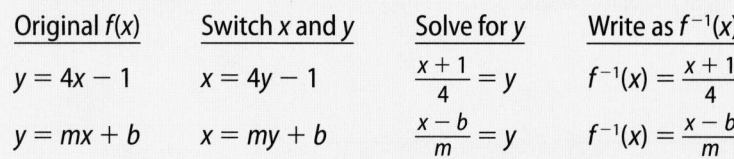

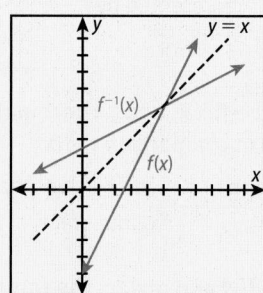

Original $f(x)$	Switch x and y	Solve for y	Write as $f^{-1}(x)$
$y = 4x - 1$	$x = 4y - 1$	$\frac{x + 1}{4} = y$	$f^{-1}(x) = \frac{x + 1}{4}$
$y = mx + b$	$x = my + b$	$\frac{x - b}{m} = y$	$f^{-1}(x) = \frac{x - b}{m}$

EXAMPLE 2

Find an equation for the inverse of $f(x) = 4x + 2$.

METHOD 1

Use points on the graph of $f^{-1}(x)$ to find the equation of the inverse.

STEP 1 Find two points on the graph of $f^{-1}(x)$.

Choose two coordinate points on the graph of $f(x)$.   (0, 2) and (1, 6)

Switch the x- and y-coordinates.   (2, 0) and (6, 1)

STEP 2 Find the slope of the line through (2, 0) and (6, 1).

$$m = \frac{y_2 - y_1}{x_2 - x_1} = \frac{1 - 0}{6 - 2} = \frac{1}{4}$$

STEP 3 Use a point and the slope to write the equation for the inverse.

Substitute the slope for m in $y = mx + b$. $y = \frac{1}{4}x + b$

Substitute 2 for x and 0 for y. $0 = \left(\frac{1}{4}\right)2 + b$

Solve for b. $-\frac{1}{2} = b$

STEP 4 Write the equation for the inverse.

Substitute $\frac{1}{4}$ for m and $-\frac{1}{2}$ for b in $y = mx + b$. $y = \frac{1}{4}x - \frac{1}{2}$

The equation for $f^{-1}(x) = \frac{1}{4}x - \frac{1}{2}$.

METHOD 2

Switch x and y in the original equation and solve for y.

Write the equation for $f(x)$. $y = 4x + 2$

Switch x and y. $x = 4y + 2$

Subtract 2 from each side. $x - 2 = 4y$

Divide both sides by 4. $\frac{x - 2}{4} = y$

Write in $y = mx + b$ form. $y = \frac{1}{4}x - \frac{1}{2}$

The equation for $f^{-1}(x) = \frac{1}{4}x - \frac{1}{2}$.

Need More HELP?
For help writing linear equations, go to *Writing an Equation of a Line* in *Algebra* (p. 1554).

SEARCH
To see step-by-step videos of these problems, enter the page number into the SWadvantage.com Search Bar.

EXAMPLE 3

Given $f(x) = -\frac{1}{2}x - 6$, find $f^{-1}(x)$.

Write the equation for $f(x)$. $y = -\frac{1}{2}x - 6$

Switch x and y. $x = -\frac{1}{2}y - 6$

Add 6 on each side. $x + 6 = -\frac{1}{2}y$

Multiply both sides by -2. $-2(x + 6) = y$

Write in $y = mx + b$ form. $y = -2x - 12$

The equation for $f^{-1}(x) = -2x - 12$.

Graphing Inverse Functions

The graph of $f^{-1}(x)$ is a reflection of the graph of $f(x)$. The line of reflection is $y = x$.

EXAMPLE 4

Given $f(x) = x + 3$.

a. Find $f^{-1}(x)$.

Write the equation for $f(x)$.	$y = x + 3$
Switch x and y.	$x = y + 3$
Subtract 3 from each side.	$x - 3 = y$

The equation for $f^{-1}(x) = x - 3$.

b. Graph $f(x)$ and $f^{-1}(x)$ on the same axes.

METHOD 1

Use the y-intercept and the slope.

STEP 1 Graph $f(x)$.

The y-intercept for $f(x)$ is 3 and the slope is 1.

Start at (0, 3) and go up 1 and right 1.
Connect the points.

STEP 2 Graph $f^{-1}(x)$.

The y-intercept for $f^{-1}(x)$ is -3 and the slope is 1.

Start at (0, -3) and go up 1 and right 1.
Connect the points.

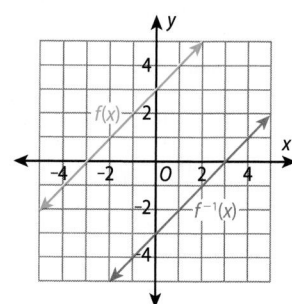

METHOD 2

Use a graphing calculator.

Enter $x + 3$ for Y1.

Press `2nd` `PRGM` to select the DRAW feature.

Use the down arrow to select 8: DRAW INV.

Press `ENTER`.

Press `VARS` and then the right arrow to select

Y-VARS. Then press `ENTER`.

Press `ENTER` to select Y1.

Then press `ENTER` again to display the graphs.

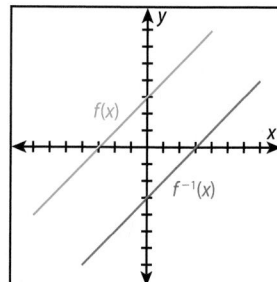

c. Describe the relationship between the graphs of $f(x)$ and $f^{-1}(x)$.

The graph of $f^{-1}(x)$ is a reflection of the graph of $f(x)$.

The line $y = x$ is the line of reflection.

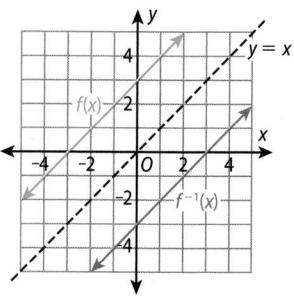

SEARCH

To see step-by-step videos of these problems, enter the page number into the SWadvantage.com Search Bar.

Try It This Way

The graph of $f^{-1}(x)$ is a reflection of $f(x)$ in the line $y = x$. For every point (x, y) on the graph of $f(x)$, the point (y, x) will be on the graph of $f^{-1}(x)$. Determine a few (x, y) points on $f(x)$, then graph the corresponding (y, x) points to graph $f^{-1}(x)$.

Verifying Linear Functions Are Inverses

Two functions, $f(x)$ and $g(x)$, are inverses of one another if $f(g(x)) = g(f(x)) = x$.

EXAMPLE 5

Given $f(x) = \frac{1}{2}x + 1$ and $g(x) = 2x - 2$. Tell whether the two functions are inverses of one another.

STEP 1 Find $f(g(x))$.

Substitute $g(x)$ for x in $f(x)$.　　　　$f(g(x)) = f(2x - 2)$

Replace each x in $\frac{1}{2}x + 1$ with $2x - 2$.　$= \frac{1}{2}(2x - 2) + 1$

Apply the Distributive Property.　　　$= \left(\frac{2x}{2} - \frac{2}{2}\right) + 1$

Simplify.　　　　　　　　　　　$= x - 1 + 1$

Add $-1 + 1$.　　　　　　　　　$= x$

STEP 2 Find $g(f(x))$.

Substitute $f(x)$ for x in $g(x)$.　　　$g(f(x)) = g\left(\frac{1}{2}x + 1\right)$

Replace each x in $2x - 2$ with $\frac{1}{2}x + 1$.　$= 2\left(\frac{1}{2}x + 1\right) - 2$

Apply the Distributive Property.　　　$= \left(\frac{2x}{2} + 2\right) - 2$

Simplify.　　　　　　　　　　　$= x + 2 - 2$

Simplify $2 - 2$.　　　　　　　　$= x$

Because $f(g(x)) = g(f(x)) = x$, the two functions are inverses of one another.

Need More

HELP

Remember that
$f(2x - 1)$ means to
substitute $2x - 1$
for every x in $f(x)$.
For help with
evaluating functions,
go to *Composition of
Functions* in *Advanced
Algebra* (p. 2061).

EXAMPLE 6

Given $f(x) = -x + 3$ and $g(x) = 3x - 1$. Tell whether the two functions are inverses of one another.

STEP 1 Find $f(g(x))$.

Substitute $g(x)$ for x in $f(x)$.　　　$f(g(x)) = f(3x - 1)$

Replace each x in $-x + 3$ with $3x - 1$.　$= -(3x - 1) + 3$

Distribute the negative sign.　　　　$= -3x + 1 + 3$

Simplify.　　　　　　　　　　　$= -3x + 4$

Because $f(g(x))$ is not equal to x, $f(x)$ and $g(x)$ are not inverses of each other.

Verifying Linear Functions Are Inverses

Two functions are inverses of one another if:

• for every x in the domain of g, $f(g(x)) = x$.

• for every x in the domain of f, $g(f(x)) = x$.

Inverses of Non-Linear Functions

Inverses of Non-Linear Functions

The inverse of a non-linear function might not be a function. You can use a horizontal line test on the graph of $f(x)$ to determine if $f^{-1}(x)$ is a function. If $f^{-1}(x)$ is not a function, you might be able to restrict the domain of $f(x)$ so that $f^{-1}(x)$ is a function. Otherwise the inverse of $f(x)$ is a relation.

Need More

HELP ?

For help graphing quadratic functions, go to *Properties of Quadratic Functions* in *Algebra* (p. 1690).

EXAMPLE 1

Given $f(x) = x^2$.

a. Determine if the inverse of $f(x)$ is a function.

Graph the function.

Determine if any horizontal line intersects the graph of $f(x)$ more than once.

Because a horizontal line crosses $f(x)$ more than once, the inverse of $f(x)$ is not a function.

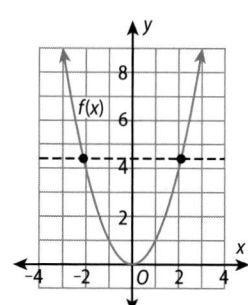

b. Graph $f(x)$, the inverse of $f(x)$ and $y = x$ on the same axes.

Graph the inverse and the line $y = x$ on the same graph as $f(x)$.

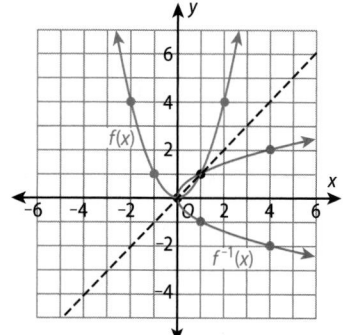

METHOD 1

Use a table of values.

Create a table of values for $f(x)$. Plot the (x, y) points and connect them.

x	-2	-1	0	1	2
y	4	1	0	1	4

Use the same values to plot the points (y, x) and connect them to get the graph of the inverse of $f(x)$.

Graph the line $y = x$. It has a slope of 1 and a y-intercept of 0.

METHOD 2

Use a graphing calculator.

Enter x^2 for Y1 and x for Y2.

Press 2nd PRGM to select the DRAW feature.

Use the down arrow to select 8:DRAW INV. Press ENTER.

Press VARS and then the right arrow to select Y-VARS. Then press ENTER.

Press ENTER again to select Y1.

Then press ENTER again to display the graphs.

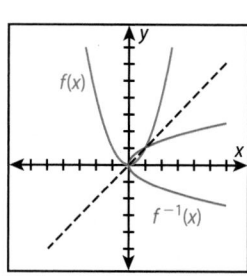

c. Describe the relationship between the graph of $f(x)$ and its inverse.

The graph of the inverse of $f(x)$ is a reflection of the graph of $f(x)$. The line $y = x$ is the line of reflection.

EXAMPLE 2

Given $f(x) = x^2 + 1$ for $x \geq 0$.

a. Determine if the inverse of $f(x)$ is a function.

On the graph of $f(x) = x^2 + 1$ for $x \geq 0$, no horizontal line crosses the graph more than once, so the inverse of $f(x)$ is a function.

b. Find the equation for the inverse of $f(x)$.

Find the equation for the inverse of $f(x)$.

Replace $f(x)$ with y.	$y = x^2 + 1$
Switch x and y.	$x = y^2 + 1$
Subtract 1 from each side.	$x - 1 = y^2$
Take the square root of both sides.	$\pm\sqrt{x-1} = y$

$f(x)$ is restricted to $x \geq 0$, so $f^{-1}(x)$ is only the positive square root, $\sqrt{x-1}$.

SEARCH

To see step-by-step videos of these problems, enter the page number into the SWadvantage.com Search Bar.

EXAMPLE 3

Given $f(x) = \frac{1}{2}x^3 - 2$.

a. Determine if the inverse of $f(x)$ is a function.

No horizontal line intersects the graph of $f(x)$ more than once, so the inverse of $f(x)$ is a function.

b. Find the equation for the inverse of $f(x)$.

Find the equation for the inverse of $f(x)$.

Replace $f(x)$ with y.	$y = \frac{1}{2}x^3 - 2$
Switch x and y.	$x = \frac{1}{2}y^3 - 2$
Add 2 to each side.	$x + 2 = \frac{1}{2}y^3$
Multiply both sides by 2.	$2x + 4 = y^3$
Take the cube root of both sides.	$\sqrt[3]{2x + 4} = y$

The equation for $f^{-1}(x) = \sqrt[3]{2x + 4}$.

Need More

HELP ?

For help solving cubic equations, go to *Solving Higher-Order Polynomial Equations* in *Algebra* (p. 1720).

GOT TO KNOW!

Inverses of Non-Linear Functions

- The inverse of a non-linear function $f(x)$ may or may not be a function. If it is a function, it is represented by the notation $f^{-1}(x)$, and read *f inverse* or *the inverse of f of x*.

- If no horizontal line intersects the graph of $f(x)$ more than once, then the inverse of $f(x)$ is a function.

- The graph of the inverse of $f(x)$ is a reflection of the graph of $f(x)$. The line of reflection is $y = x$.

- For every (x, y) point on the graph of $f(x)$, the point (y, x) is on the graph of $f^{-1}(x)$.

- The equation of the inverse function can be found by switching the x and y in the original equation and solving for y.

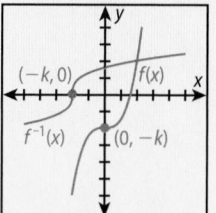

Inverses of Exponential and Logarithmic Functions

If two functions are inverses of one another, then $f(g(x)) = g(f(x)) = x$.

EXAMPLE 4

Determine whether $f(x) = \ln(x - 1)$ and $g(x) = e^x + 1$ are inverses of one another.

STEP 1 Find $f(g(x))$.

Substitute $g(x)$ for x in $f(x)$. $\qquad\qquad f(g(x)) = f(e^x + 1)$

Replace each x in $\ln(x - 1)$ with $e^x + 1$. $\qquad = \ln(e^x + 1 - 1)$

Simplify. $\qquad\qquad\qquad\qquad\qquad\qquad = \ln(e^x) = x$

STEP 2 Find $g(f(x))$.

Substitute $f(x)$ for x in $g(x)$. $\qquad\qquad g(f(x)) = g(\ln(x - 1))$

Replace each x in $e^x + 1$ with $\ln(x - 1)$. $\qquad = e^{\ln(x - 1)} + 1$

Simplify. $\qquad\qquad\qquad\qquad\qquad\qquad = (x - 1) + 1 = x$

Because $f(g(x) = g(f(x) = x$, the two functions are inverses of one another.

Need More

HELP

For help solving equations involving natural logarithms, e, logs, and exponential functions, go to *Exponential and Logarithmic Equations* (p. 2010).

Remember: $\ln(e^x) = x$ and $e^{\ln(x)} = x$.

SEARCH

To see step-by-step videos of these problems, enter the page number into the SWadvantage.com Search Bar.

EXAMPLE 5

Given $f(x) = 2^x$.

a. Find the equation for $f^{-1}(x)$.

Replace $f(x)$ with y. $\qquad\qquad\qquad y = 2^x$

Switch x and y. $\qquad\qquad\qquad\qquad x = 2^y$

Take $\log_2$ of each side $\qquad\qquad \log_2 x = \log_2 2^y$

Simplify using $\log_b b^x = b$. $\qquad\quad \log_2 x = y$

The equation for $f^{-1}(x) = \log_2 x$.

b. Graph the function.

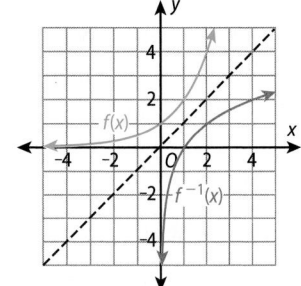

EXAMPLE 6

Given $f(x) = \log_8 x - 2$. Find the equation for $f^{-1}(x)$.

Replace $f(x)$ with y. $\qquad\qquad\qquad y = \log_8 x - 2$

Switch x and y. $\qquad\qquad\qquad\qquad x = \log_8 y - 2$

Add 2 to each side. $\qquad\qquad\qquad x + 2 = \log_8 y$

Raise each side to the base 8. $\qquad 8^{x + 2} = 8^{\log_8 y}$

Simplify. $\qquad\qquad\qquad\qquad\qquad 8^{x + 2} = y$

The equation for $f^{-1}(x) = 8^{x + 2}$.

EXAMPLE 7

Given $f(x) = \dfrac{4}{x-3}$.

a. Find the equation for $f^{-1}(x)$.

Write the equation for $f(x)$, replacing $f(x)$ with y.

$$y = \frac{4}{x-3}$$

Switch x and y.

$$x = \frac{4}{y-3}$$

Multiply each side by $y - 3$.

$$x(y-3) = 4$$

Divide each side by x.

$$y - 3 = \frac{4}{x}$$

Add 3 to each side.

$$y = \frac{4}{x} + 3$$

The equation for $f^{-1}(x) = \dfrac{4}{x} + 3$ where $x \neq 0$.

b. Find the domain and range of $f(x)$ and $f^{-1}(x)$.

The domain of $f(x)$ is all real numbers except $x = 3$.
The domain of $f^{-1}(x)$ is all real numbers except $x = 0$.
Thus, the range of $f(x) = $ all real numbers except $x = 0$, and the range of $f^{-1}(x) = $ all real numbers except $x = 3$.

c. Graph $f(x)$, $f^{-1}(x)$ and $y = x$ on the same axes.

The graph is at the right.

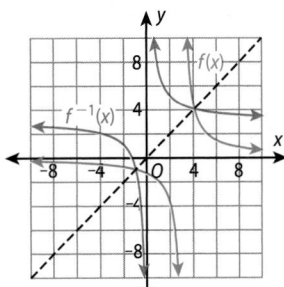

Try It This Way

Enter the equation for $f(x)$ in a graphing calculator for Y1. Use the DRAW feature and select DRAW INV from the menu.

Press **ENTER** and then press **VARS**, select Y-VARS, select 1 for function, and then select the function Y1.

Press **ENTER** again and the calculator will display the graph of $f(x)$ and $f^{-1}(x)$.

EXAMPLE 8

Given $f(x) = \sqrt{x+2}$.

a. Find the domain and range of $f(x)$ and $f^{-1}(x)$.

Find the domain and range of $f(x)$ and $f^{-1}(x)$.

The domain of $f(x)$ is all real numbers such that $x + 2 \geq 0$ or $x \geq -2$. The range of $f(x)$ is all real numbers y such that $y \geq 0$. The domain of $f^{-1}(x) = $ the range of $f(x) = $ all real numbers x such that $x \geq 0$. The range of $f^{-1}(x) = $ the domain of $f(x) = $ all real numbers y such that $y \geq -2$.

b. Find the equation for $f^{-1}(x)$.

Find the equation for $f^{-1}(x)$.

Switch the x and y in the equation of $f(x)$ and solve for y to find the equation for $f^{-1}(x)$.

Replace $f(x)$ with y.

$$y = \sqrt{x+2}$$

Switch x and y.

$$x = \sqrt{y+2}$$

Square both sides.

$$x^2 = y + 2$$

Subtract 2 from each side.

$$x^2 - 2 = y$$

The equation for $f^{-1}(x) = x^2 - 2$ for $x \geq 0$.

Parent Functions

Parent Functions

The functions in this section are called **parent functions** because they are the most basic form of a number of related graphs with similar features. The related graphs are created by combinations of translations, stretches, compressions, or reflections of the parent functions. Understanding the characteristics of these basic graphs will help you analyze the shapes of more complicated graphs.

GOT TO KNOW!

Parent Functions

The basic parent functions are shown below.

Identity Function	**Square Function**	**Cube Function**
$y = x$	$y = x^2$	$y = x^3$

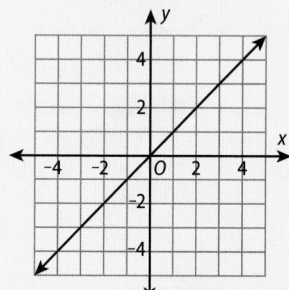
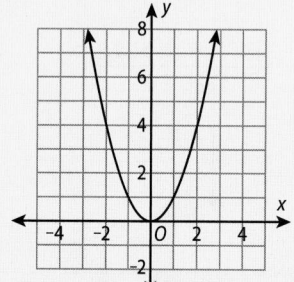
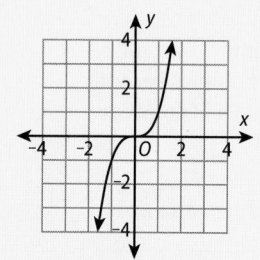

Square Root Function	**Reciprocal Function**	**Cube Root Function**
$y = \sqrt{x}$	$y = \dfrac{1}{x}$	$y = \sqrt[3]{x}$

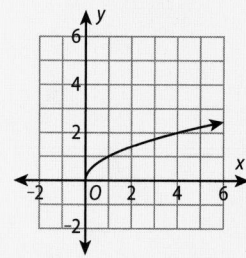
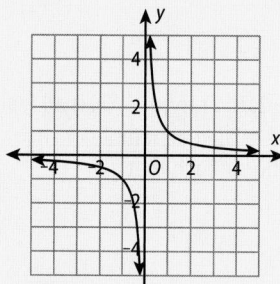
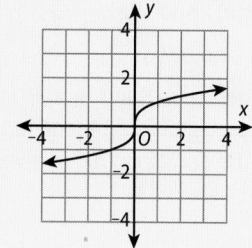

Absolute Value Function	**Exponential Function**	**Natural Logarithm Function**
$y = |x|$	$y = e^x$	$y = \ln x$

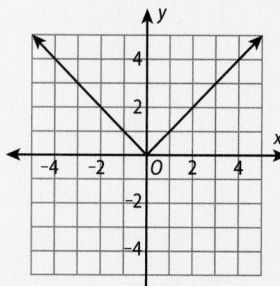
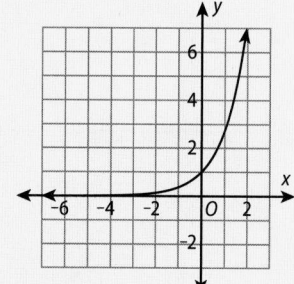
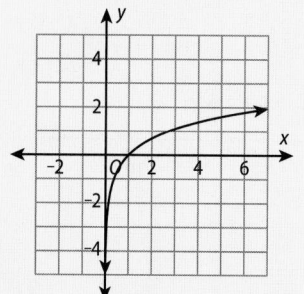

EXAMPLE 1

The graph of a function is shown.

a. Identify the parent function of the graph.

The graph is a line, so the parent function is the identity function $y = x$.

b. Describe how the parent function is modified to get the graph.

The graph of $y = x$ is shifted down 3 units. For a given x-value, the y-values of this function are twice as much as the y-values of $y = x$, so the graph is stretched by 2.

c. Write an equation for the function in the graph.

The equation is in the form $y = mx + b$ with a slope of 2 and a y-intercept of -3. The equation of the graph is $y = 2x - 3$.

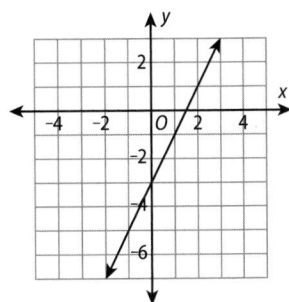

Need More

HELP ❓

For help graphing linear equations, go to *Slope-Intercept Form of a Linear Equation* in *Algebra* (p. 1540).

SEARCH 🔍

To see step-by-step videos of these problems, enter the page number into the SWadvantage.com Search Bar.

EXAMPLE 2

The graph of a function is shown.

a. Identify the parent function of the graph.

The graph is a parabola, so the parent function is the square function $y = x^2$.

b. Describe how the parent function is modified to get the graph.

The graph of $y = x^2$ is shifted up 1 unit and left 4 units.

c. Write an equation for the function in the graph.

The equation is in the form $y = (x - c)^2 + k$, with $c = -4$ and $k = 1$. The equation of the graph is $y = (x + 4)^2 + 1$.

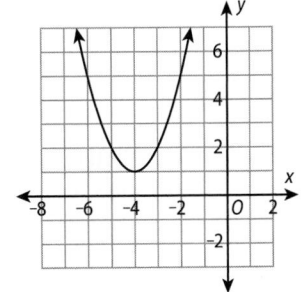

Need More

HELP ❓

To relate the graph of a parabola to its equation, see *Graphing Parabolas* (p. 1910) and *Equations for Parabolas* (p. 1916).

EXAMPLE 3

The graph of a function is shown.

a. Identify the parent function of the graph.

The graph is a parabola, so the parent function is the square function $y = x^2$.

b. Describe how the parent function is modified to get the graph.

For a given y-value, the x-value of the function shown is $\frac{1}{3}$ of the x-value of the parent function. Therefore, the graph is a horizontal compression of the parent function. It is also shifted down 2.

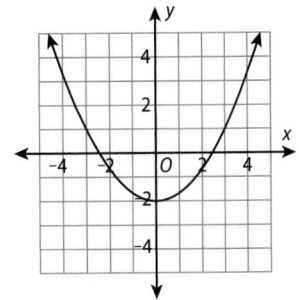

Try It

This Way

Check your answer by graphing your equation on a graphing calculator and comparing it to the given graph.

Need More

HELP

For help with rational functions, go to *Rational Functions* (p. 2020).

EXAMPLE 4

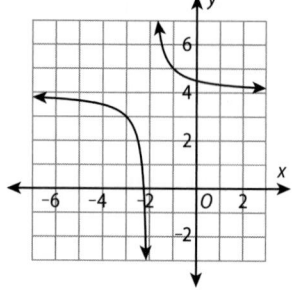

a. Identify the parent function of the graph.

The graph has two separate "branches", so the parent function is the reciprocal function $y = \frac{1}{x}$.

b. Describe how the parent function is modified to get the graph.

The graph of $y = \frac{1}{x}$ is shifted up 4 units and left 2 units.

c. Write an equation for the function in the graph.

The equation is in the form $y = \frac{1}{x - c} + k$, where $c = -2$ and $k = 4$.

The equation of the graph is $y = \frac{1}{x + 2} + 4$.

Need More

HELP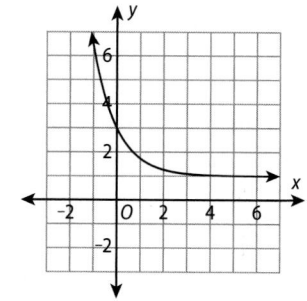

For help with exponential functions with a base of *e*, go to *Base* e (p. 2004).

EXAMPLE 5

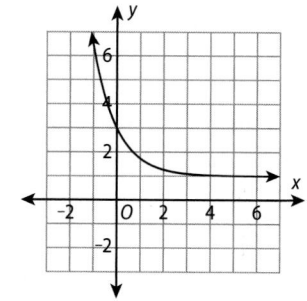

a. Identify the parent function of the graph.

The graph is an exponential function, so the parent function is $y = e^x$.

b. Describe how the parent function is modified to get the graph.

The graph of $y = e^x$ is shifted up 1 unit. It is also a reflection of $y = e^x$ in the *x*-axis, so for every (x, y) on $y = e^x$, the point $(-x, y)$ is on the given function.

For a given *x*, the *y*-value of the given function is two times the *y*-value for that *x* in the parent function. This means that the graph of the parent function is stretched vertically by 2.

c. Write an equation for the function in the graph.

The equation is in the form $y = ae^{cx} + k$, with $a = 2$, $c = -1$ and $k = 1$.
The equation of the graph is $y = 2e^{-x} + 1$.

Need More

HELP

For help writing equations when a graph is compressed or stretched, go to *Stretching and Compressing Functions* (p. 2082).

EXAMPLE 6

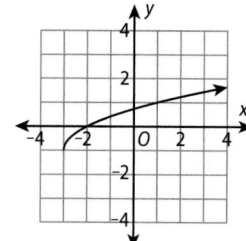

a. Identify the parent function of the graph.

The parent function is the square root function $y = \sqrt{x}$.

b. Describe how the parent function is modified to get the graph.

The graph is the graph of $y = \sqrt{x}$ shifted to the left 3 units. It is also shifted down 1.

c. Write an equation for the function in the graph.

The equation is in the form $y = \sqrt{x - a} + k$, with $a = -3$ and $k = -1$.
The equation of the graph is $y = \sqrt{x + 3} - 1$.

EXAMPLE 7

a. Identify the parent function of the graph.

The parent function is the absolute value equation, $y = |x|$.

b. Describe how the parent function is modified to get the graph.

The graph of $y = |x|$ is shifted up 3 units and right 4 units.

c. Write an equation for the function in the graph.

The equation is in the form $y = |x - c| + k$, with $c = 4$ and $k = 3$.
The equation of the graph is $y = |x - 4| + 3$.

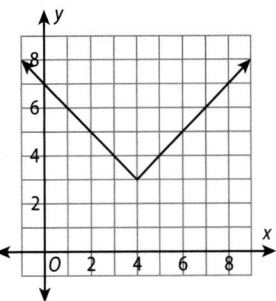

Need More
HELP ?

For help with absolute value functions, go to *Absolute Value* in *Algebra* (p. 1386).

EXAMPLE 8

a. Identify the parent function of the graph.

The graph is logarithmic, so the parent function is the natural logarithm function $y = \ln x$.

b. Describe how the parent function is modified to get the graph.

The graph of $y = \ln x$ is shifted up 1 unit and right 5 units.

c. Write an equation for the function in the graph.

The equation is in the form $y = \ln(x - c) + k$, with $c = 5$ and $k = 1$. The equation of the graph is $y = \ln(x - 5) + 1$.

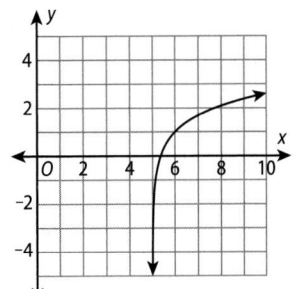

Need More
HELP ?

For help with natural logarithmic functions, go to *Common Logs and Natural Logs* (p. 1978).

EXAMPLE 9

a. Identify the parent function of the graph.

The parent function is the cube function $y = x^3$.

b. Describe how the parent function is modified to get the graph.

The graph of $y = x^3$ is shifted down 2 units and right 3 units.

c. Write an equation for the function in the graph.

The equation is in the form $y = (x - c)^3 + k$, with $c = 3$ and $k = -2$.
The equation of the graph is $y = (x - 3)^3 - 2$.

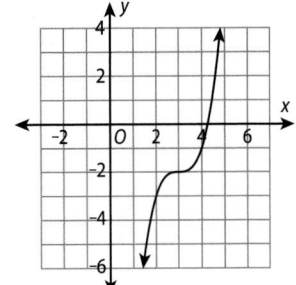

SEARCH

To see step-by-step videos of these problems, enter the page number into the SWadvantage.com Search Bar.

EXAMPLE 10

Identify the parent function for the equation.

a. $y = \dfrac{6}{x} - 2$ **b.** $y = -2(x + 5)^2$ **c.** $y = 0.5(x - 4)$ **d.** $y = (0.25)e^{2x} + 1a$

    reciprocal function   square function   identity function   exponential function

Advanced Algebra

Formulas

Conic Sections

Circles	$(x - h)^2 + (y - k)^2 = r^2$	$\dfrac{(x - h)^2}{r^2} + \dfrac{(y - k)^2}{r^2} = 1$
	Horizontal Axis	**Vertical Axis**
Ellipse	$\dfrac{(x - h)^2}{a^2} + \dfrac{(y - k)^2}{b^2} = 1$	$\dfrac{(x - h)^2}{b^2} + \dfrac{(y - k)^2}{a^2} = 1$
Hyperbola	$\dfrac{(x - h)^2}{a^2} - \dfrac{(y - k)^2}{b^2} = 1$	$\dfrac{(x - h)^2}{b^2} - \dfrac{(y - k)^2}{a^2} = 1$
Parabola	$x - h = \dfrac{1}{4p}(y - k)^2$	$y - k = \dfrac{1}{4p}(x - h)^2$

Variation

Inverse Variation	$y = \dfrac{k}{x}$ or $k = xy$
Direct Variation	$y = kx$, or $k = \dfrac{y}{x}$
Joint Variation	$y = kxz$ or $k = \dfrac{y}{xz}$
Power Function	$y = ax^b$

Interest

Simple Interest	$I = Prt$
Compound Interest	$A = P\left(1 + \dfrac{r}{n}\right)^{nt}$

Exponential Models

Growth	$A(t) = a(1 + r)^t$
Decay	$A(t) = a(1 - r)^t$

Sequences and Series

	Arithmetic	**Geometric**
First term	a or a_1	a or a_1
Number of terms	n	n
Constant	difference, d	ratio, r
Sequence, explicit	$a_n = a_1 + (n - 1)d$	$a_n = a_1 r^{n-1}$, if $r \neq 0$
Sequence, recursive	$a_n = a_{n-1} + d$	$a_n = r \cdot a_{n-1}$
Partial Sum of Sequence (Sum of finite series)	$S_n = \dfrac{n(a_1 + a_n)}{2}$; $S_n = \dfrac{n[2a_1 + (n-1)d]}{2}$	$S_n = \dfrac{a_1(1 - r^n)}{1 - r}$, if $r \neq 1$
Sum of Infinite Series	None	$S = \dfrac{a_1}{1 - r}$, if $|r| < 1$
Fibonacci sequence	$a_n = \dfrac{\left(1 + \sqrt{5}\right)^n - \left(1 - \sqrt{5}\right)^n}{2^n \sqrt{5}}$	

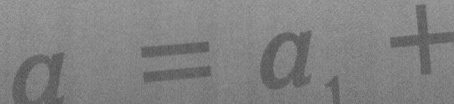

Cramer's Rule

| 2 equations in 2 variables | $x = \dfrac{\det(M_x)}{\det(M_c)} = \dfrac{\begin{vmatrix} c & b \\ f & e \end{vmatrix}}{\begin{vmatrix} a & b \\ d & e \end{vmatrix}}$ and $y = \dfrac{\det(M_y)}{\det(M_c)} = \dfrac{\begin{vmatrix} a & c \\ d & f \end{vmatrix}}{\begin{vmatrix} a & b \\ d & e \end{vmatrix}}$ | 3 equations in 3 variables | $x = \dfrac{\det(M_x)}{\det(M_c)}, y = \dfrac{\det(M_y)}{\det(M_c)}, z = \dfrac{\det(M_z)}{\det(M_c)}$ |

Properties of Logarithms

	Exponential	For all b	Common logs	Natural logs
Zero	$b^0 = 1, b \neq 0$	$\log_b 1 = 0$	$\log 1 = 0$	$\ln 1 = 0$
One	$b^1 = b$	$\log_b b = 1$	$\log 10 = 1$	$\ln e = 1$
Product	$b^x \cdot b^y = b^{x+y}$	$\log_b(xy) = \log_b x + \log_b y$	$\log(xy) = \log x + \log y$	$\ln(xy) = \ln x + \ln y$
Quotient	$b^{\frac{x}{y}} = b^{x-y}, y \neq 0$	$\log_b\left(\dfrac{x}{y}\right) = \log_b x - \log_b y$	$\log\left(\dfrac{x}{y}\right) = \log x - \log y$	$\ln\left(\dfrac{x}{y}\right) = \ln x - \ln y$
Reciprocal	$b^{\frac{1}{y}} = b^{-y}, y \neq 0$	$\log_b\left(\dfrac{1}{y}\right) = -\log_b y$	$\log\left(\dfrac{1}{y}\right) = -\log y$	$\ln\left(\dfrac{1}{y}\right) = -\ln y$
Power	$(b^x)^y = b^{xy}$	$\log_b x^y = y \log_b x$	$\log x^y = y \log x$	$\ln x^y = y \ln x$
Change of Base		$\log_b x = \dfrac{\log x}{\log b} = \dfrac{\ln x}{\ln b}$		

Properties of Radicals

Exponents	$a^{\frac{1}{n}} = \sqrt[n]{a}, n \neq 0$	$a^{\frac{m}{n}} = \left(\sqrt[n]{a}\right)^m = \sqrt[n]{a^m}, n \neq 0$
Product Rule	$\sqrt{a \cdot b} = \sqrt{a} \cdot \sqrt{b}$	$\sqrt[n]{a} \cdot \sqrt[n]{b} = \sqrt[n]{ab}$
Quotient Rule	$\dfrac{\sqrt{a}}{\sqrt{b}} = \sqrt{\dfrac{a}{b}}, b \neq 0$	$\dfrac{\sqrt[n]{a}}{\sqrt[n]{b}} = \sqrt[n]{\dfrac{a}{b}}, b \neq 0$

Go For It!

Transformations of Functions

Reflections

$g(x) = -f(x)$	over x-axis
$g(x) = f(-x)$	over y-axis

Dilations

$g(x) = f(cx)$	horizontal
	$0 < c < 1$: stretch
	$c > 1$: shrink
$g(x) = c \cdot f(x)$	vertical
	$0 < c < 1$: shrink
	$c > 1$: stretch

Translations

$g(x) = f(x - h) + k$	$h > 0$: right h units
$g(x) = ab^{x-h} + k$	$h < 0$: left h units
$g(x) = \dfrac{a}{x - h} + k$	$k > 0$: up k units
$g(x) = \sqrt{x - h} + k$	$k < 0$: down k units

Advanced Algebra

Solving Word Problems

Step 1	Read the problem carefully. Determine what number or numbers need to be found.
Step 2	Represent one unknown number with a suitable variable.
Step 3	Use conditions stated in the problem to write expressions for other numbers.
Step 4	Use additional conditions to find the relationship between expressions. Write the expressions algebraically. Connect them with the appropriate sign (=, <, >, ≤, or ≥.)
Step 5	Solve the equation or inequality.
Step 6	Check to see if the resulting solution matches the conditions stated in the problem.

Word Problem Formulas

Distance	$d = rt$	d = distance r = rate t = time
Consecutive Number	$A = n + (n + 1)$ $B = n(n + 2)$	n = the first of two consecutive numbers $n + 1$ = the next consecutive number $n + 2$ = the next consecutive odd or even number A = sum of two consecutive numbers B = product of two consecutive odd (or even) numbers
Digit	$A(u + t + h) = u + 10t + 100h$	A = number multiplied by the sum of the digits u = the ones digit of the given number t = the tens digit of the given number h = the hundreds digit of the given number
Coin	$0.25q + 0.1d + 0.05n + 0.01p = A$	q = number of quarters d = number of dimes n = number of nickels p = number of pennies A = total worth
Lever	$\ell_1 w_1 = \ell_2 w_2$	ℓ_1 = length from fulcrum to first weight w_1 = first weight ℓ_2 = length from fulcrum to second weight w_2 = second weight
Work	$\frac{1}{a} + \frac{1}{b} = \frac{1}{n}$	a = length of time it takes person A to complete a task b = length of time it takes person B to complete a task n = length of time it would take A and B to complete the task together

Word Problem Formulas (continued)

Mixture	Use this table format.			
	Concentration	Volume	Percent Substance	Total Volume Substance
	1	V	$a\%$	$0.01(a)(V)$
	2	Total $- V$	$b\%$	$0.01(b)(\text{Total} - V)$
	Final	Total	$c\%$	$0.01(c)(\text{Total})$

Parent Functions

Linear (Identity)

$y = x$

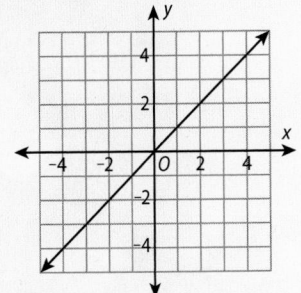

Quadratic (Squared)

$y = x^2$

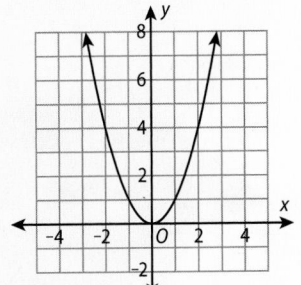

Cubic (Cubed)

$y = x^3$

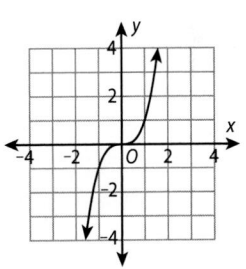

Rational (Reciprocal)

$y = \dfrac{1}{x}$

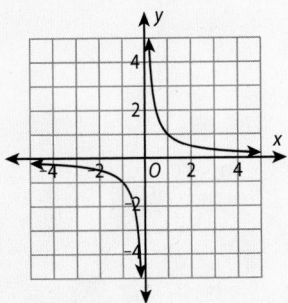

Radical (Square Root)

$y = \sqrt{x}$

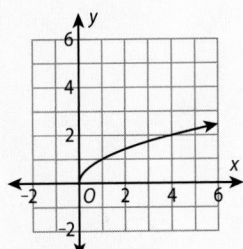

Cube Root

$y = \sqrt[3]{x}$

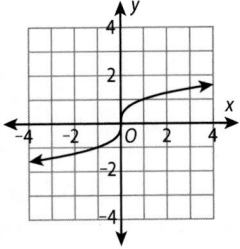

Absolute Value

$y = |x|$

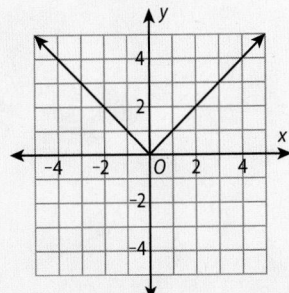

Exponential

$y = e^x$

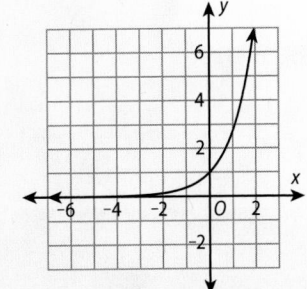

Natural Logarithm

$y = \ln x$

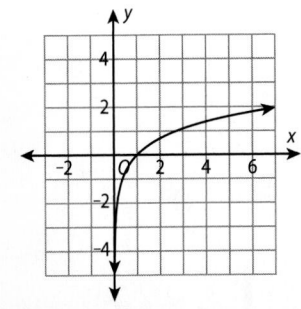

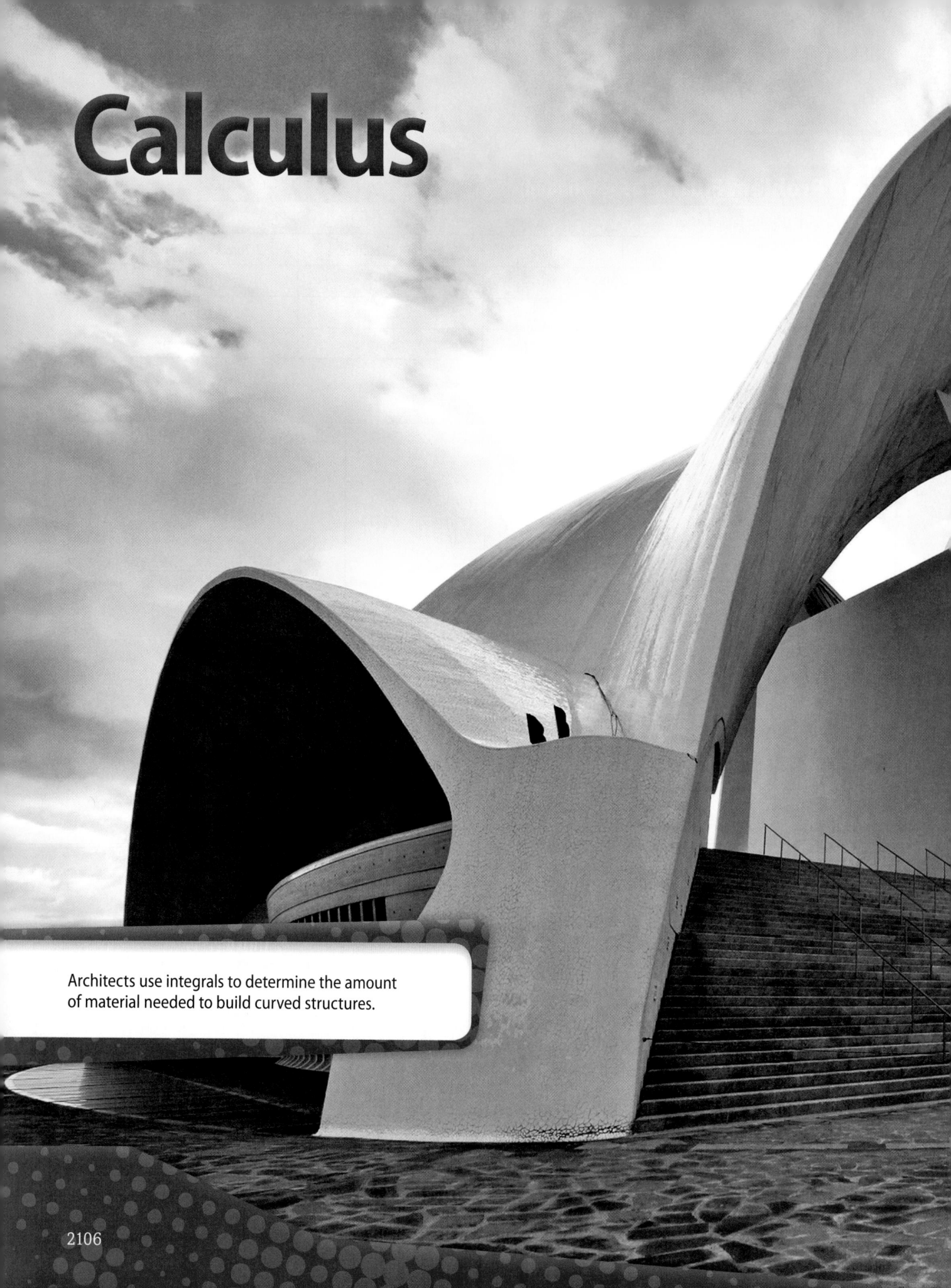

Calculus

Architects use integrals to determine the amount
of material needed to build curved structures.

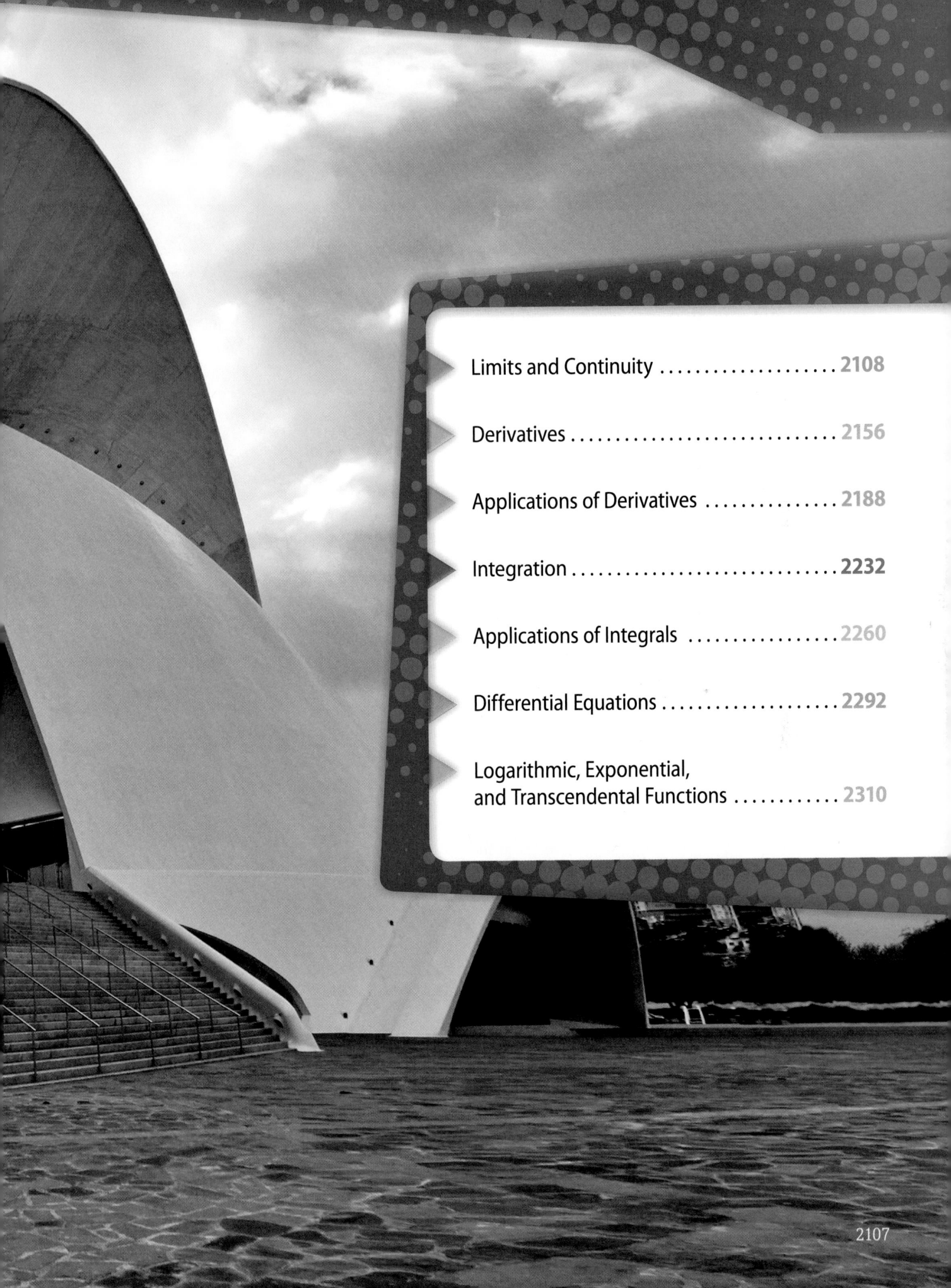

Limits and Continuity

What Came Before?
- Graphing functions
- Operations with functions, including composition

What's This About?
- Defining and finding limits
- Discovering continuity and its importance
- Finding and analyzing a function's behavior around asymptotes

Practical Apps
- In Physics, limits are used to describe a falling object's vertical position.
- Credit card companies use calculus to set the minimum payments due on credit card statements at the exact time the statement is processed.

Just for FUN!

TEACHER:

$$\lim_{x \to 8} \frac{1}{x-8} = \infty$$

Now you try one.

STUDENT:

$$\lim_{x \to 5} \frac{1}{x-5} = \text{ro}$$

CONTENTS	UPLOAD	DOWNLOAD	Calculus

You can find more practice problems online by visiting:
www.SWadvantage.com

What Is a Limit?

GOT TO KNOW!

What is a Limit?

The answer to any limit problem is a *y* value.

Understanding Limits

In algebra, it is common to find an exact value of a function $f(x)$. Because $y = f(x)$, this value is sometimes called the "*y* value" of the function. When finding a specific *y* value of a function, all that you need is the corresponding *x* value.

But what happens if the function is more than just a simple curve? What if the function jumps around, has holes in it, or has fascinating behavior such as shooting up toward infinity or bouncing up and down forever? What if the function is undefined at a particular *x* value? What does "undefined" mean to different functions at different points? To describe the behavior of the *y* values of such functions, you can use a *limit*.

Intuitive Definition of a Limit

Let's start by understanding the meaning of limit. The **limit** of a function $f(x)$ is a number L on the *y*-axis such that if *x* is in the neighborhood of a number *c*, then $f(x)$ is in the neighborhood of L.

L is the limit as *x* approaches *c*. For a different number *c*, there may be a different L.

The notation for a limit looks like this:

$$\lim_{x \to c} f(x) = L$$

You should read the statement like this: "The limit of $f(x)$ as *x* approaches *c* is L."

EXAMPLE 1

Find $\lim\limits_{x \to -1} \dfrac{x^3 + 5x^2 + 10x + 6}{x + 1}$.

To solve this problem, you need to find the *y* value of the function as *x* approaches -1.

The function is undefined at $x = -1$ because this value would cause division by zero. The exclusion of $x = -1$ creates a hole at the point $(-1, 3)$, as seen in the graph at the right, but the behavior of the graph can still be defined.

To find $\lim\limits_{x \to -1} f(x)$, look at the *y* values of the curve as *x* approaches *c* from both the left and the right. (You will read about the importance of both directions in *Left- and Right-Hand Limits*.)

In this case, as the *x* values approach -1, the *y* value approaches 3.

Therefore, $\lim\limits_{x \to -1} f(x) = 3$.

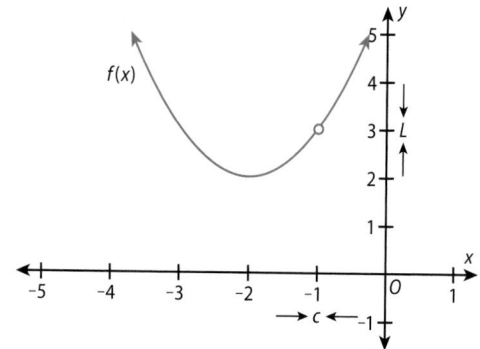

EXAMPLE 2

Given: $f(x) = \begin{cases} x^2 + 4x + 4, & x \neq -2 \\ 1, & x = -2 \end{cases}$

Find: $\lim\limits_{x \to -2} f(x)$

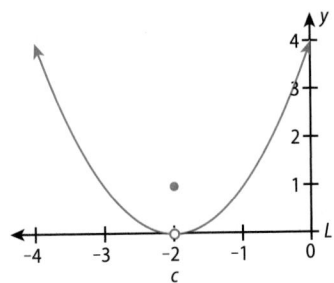

SEARCH

To see step-by-step videos of these problems, enter the page number into the SWadvantage.com Search Bar.

A limit and the function's value are not necessarily the same. In this example, the function is defined at c. The graph shows that $f(-2) = 1$, but the value that the function approaches as x gets closer and closer to -2 is 0.

Therefore, $\lim\limits_{x \to -2} f(x) = 0$.

Simple Polynomials

There are still occasions when you use limits for smoothly changing functions. Simple polynomials, for example, have no undefined values or breaks in their graphs. Finding the limits of such functions is straightforward because the limit is the same as the function's value.

EXAMPLE 3

Find $\lim\limits_{x \to 4} 3x + 1.$

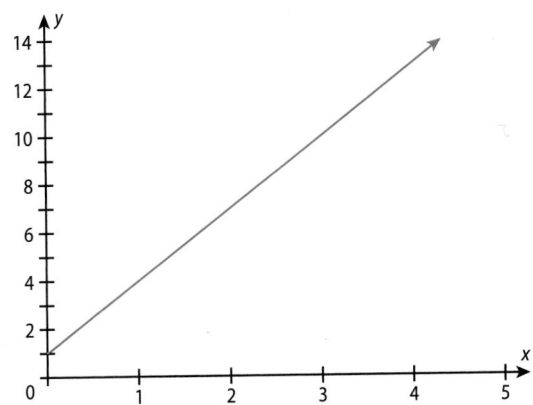

As seen in the graph above, $\lim\limits_{x \to 4} f(x) = 13$. Notice that $f(4)$ also equals 13. For all simple polynomials, $f(c) = L$, which means you can determine the limit by substituting c into the function.

Definition of a Limit

A formal definition of a limit is much more involved than our intuitive definition. As a result, people used some of the techniques of calculus to solve problems long before mathematicians could prove that the techniques were correct. It was only in the late nineteenth century that the mathematician A. L. Cauchy developed an early form of the Epsilon-Delta Definition of a limit, which is the backbone of calculus today. Briefly, this definition is as follows:

$$\lim_{x \to c} f(x) = L \text{ if and only if for each } \varepsilon > 0,$$

there exists $\delta > 0$ such that

$$\text{if } 0 < |x - c| < \delta, \text{ then } |f(x) - L| < \varepsilon.$$

What does the definition mean? Compare the blue numbers in the definition above to those in graph below.

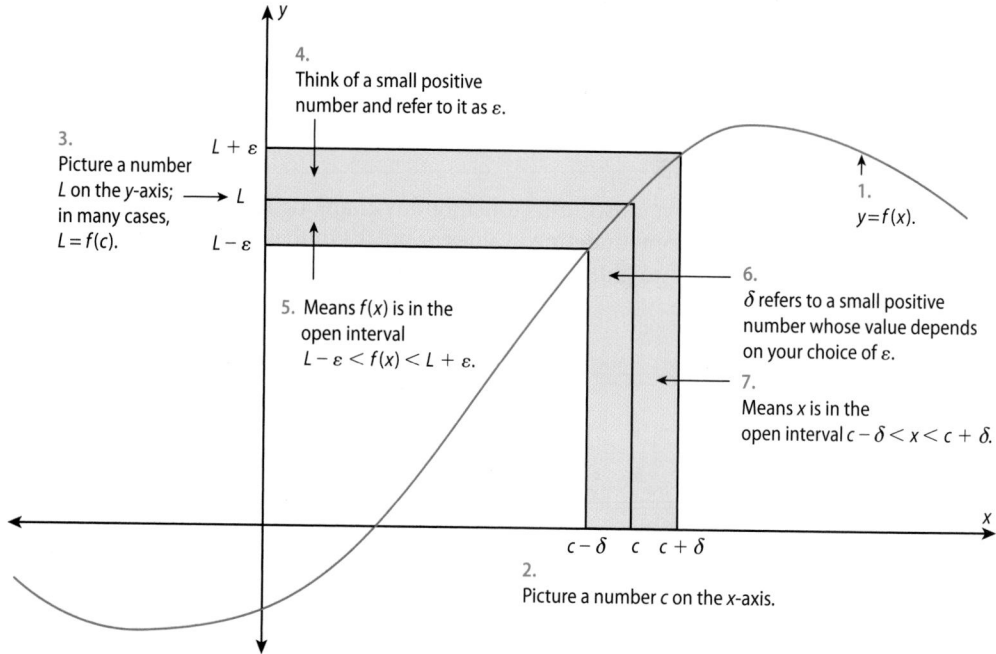

We use the Epsilon-Delta Definition of a limit to answer the question, "How close is close enough?" Regardless of how small the separation ε we choose along the y-axis, there is a corresponding separation δ along the x-axis such that if x is between $c - \delta$ and $c + \delta$, then $f(x)$ is between $L - \varepsilon$ and $L + \varepsilon$. To understand how this applies to problems, let's work a couple of examples.

Using the Formal Definition of a Limit

For formal proofs of limits using the Epsilon-Delta Definition, we must show that for any given positive number ε, we can find a positive number δ such that

$$\left|f(x) - L\right| < \varepsilon \quad \text{if} \quad 0 < |x - c| < \delta$$

As you work through the example below, notice that the goal is to manipulate the ε inequality so that it looks similar to the δ inequality.

You can then prove the limit by identifying the value of δ for which the Epsilon-Delta statement holds true.

EXAMPLE 4

Use the formal definition of a limit to prove the following:

$$\lim_{x \to 1} 2x + 1 = 3$$

STEP 1 Identify the terms $f(x)$, L, and c needed to apply the Epsilon-Delta Definition of a limit.

From the limit equation, we can identify:

$f(x) = 2x + 1$

$L = 3$

$c = 1$

We will show that given any positive number ε, a positive number δ can be found such that:

$$\underset{f(x)}{\left|(2x + 1) - \underset{L}{3}\right|} < \varepsilon \quad \text{if} \quad 0 < |x - \underset{c}{1}| < \delta$$

STEP 2 Simplify and rearrange the ε inequality to a form similar to the δ inequality.

Write the ε inequality using $f(x)$ and L.	$\left|(2x + 1) - 3\right| < \varepsilon$
Simplify.	$\left|2x - 2\right| < \varepsilon$
Factor out 2.	$\left|2(x - 1)\right| < \varepsilon$
Divide both sides by 2.	$\left|x - 1\right| < \frac{\varepsilon}{2}$

STEP 3 Compare the ε inequality to the δ inequality, and choose a value of δ.

Write the revised the Epsilon-Delta Definition.	$(x - 1) < \frac{\varepsilon}{2}$ if $0 < |x - 1| < \delta$
Choose a value of δ that makes the δ inequality true.	$\delta = \frac{\varepsilon}{2}$

If we choose $\delta = \frac{\varepsilon}{2}$, then $|x - 1| < \delta$ becomes $|x - 1| < \frac{\varepsilon}{2}$, which is the same as the ε inequality.

According to the Epsilon-Delta Definition of limits, then, this proves the limit equation: $\lim_{x \to 1} 2x + 1 = 3$.

Limits by Tables

One way to approximate a limit is to use a table of values. To do this, choose x values close to c, approaching from both the left and the right. Then look at the function's output values to determine if the y values are approaching a distinct value as x approaches c.

SEARCH

To see step-by-step videos of these problems, enter the page number into the SWadvantage.com Search Bar.

EXAMPLE 1

Use a table of values to determine $\lim\limits_{x \to 0} \frac{\sin x}{x}$.

Notice that you cannot find the limit by substituting zero into the function because that would cause division by zero.

Since algebraic substitution will not produce the answer, a table of values may help illustrate the problem and lead to the answer.

Remember that a limit is the y value, L, that the function approaches as x gets close to c.

x	−1	−0.5	−0.1	−0.05	0	0.05	0.1	0.5	1
$f(x)$	0.8415	0.9589	0.9983	0.9996	?	0.9996	0.9983	0.9589	0.8415

Look at the y values as x approaches 0 from both the left and the right.

In this case, as the x values get closer to 0 from both the left and the right, the y values get closer and closer to 1.

Therefore, $\lim\limits_{x \to 0} \frac{\sin x}{x} = 1$.

The graph of the function $f(x) = \frac{\sin x}{x}$ is below. Notice that the y value does approach 1 as x approaches 0.

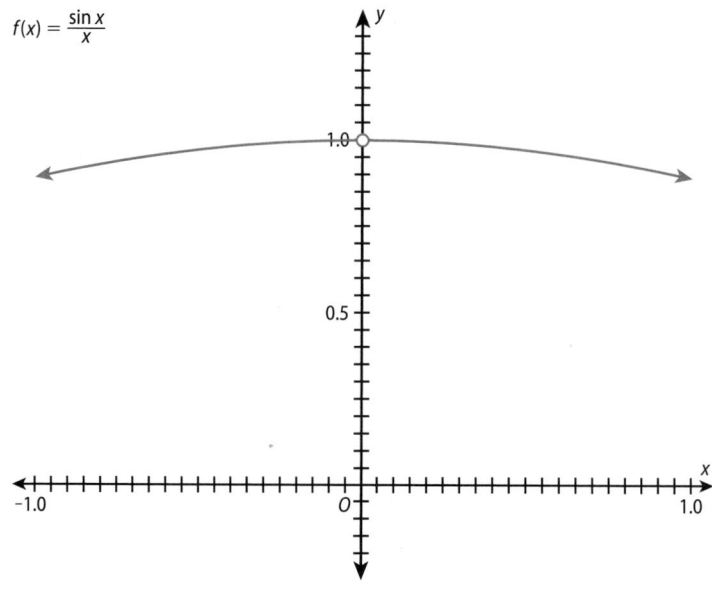

$f(x) = \frac{\sin x}{x}$

EXAMPLE 2

Create a table of values to determine the limit of $f(x) = \dfrac{x^3 + 5x^2 + 10x + 6}{x + 1}$ as x approaches -1.

STEP 1 Create a table, and fill in values of x that get close to the given value c from both sides.

x	−1.5	−1.1	−1.01	−1.001	−1	−0.999	−0.99	−0.9	−0.5
f(x)									

STEP 2 Calculate the values for $f(x)$ at each point, and fill in the table as shown below.

x	−1.5	−1.1	−1.01	−1.001	−1	−0.999	−0.99	−0.9	−0.5
f(x)	2.25	2.81	2.98	2.998	?	3.002	3.02	3.21	4.25

STEP 3 Study the table to determine if the function values approach the same number from the right and left.

In this case, the function is approaching 3 from both the left and the right.

Therefore, the limit of $f(x)$ as x approaches -1 is 3.

Try It This Way

Calculating the $f(x)$ terms for a table can be time-consuming. To make the job easier, type the function into a graphing calculator. Then use the tracing feature to find $f(x)$ values.

EXAMPLE 3

Create a table of values to determine the limit of $f(x) = \dfrac{x + 3}{x^2 + 2x - 3}$ as x approaches -3.

Create a table. Write values of x that get close to -3 from both sides. Calculate the values for $f(x)$ at each point.

x	−3.5	−3.1	−3.01	−3.001	−3	−2.999	−2.99	−2.9	−2.5
f(x)	−0.22	−0.244	−0.2493	−0.2499	?	−0.2501	−0.2506	−0.256	−0.28

Determine if the function values approach the same number from the right and left. In this case, the function is approaching -0.25 from both the left and the right.

Therefore, the limit of $f(x)$ as x approaches -3 is -0.25.

GOT TO KNOW!

Using Your Calculator to Make Tables

You can use a graphing calculator to create a table of values.

- To do this, enter the function into **Y =**. Next, choose the table settings. A convenient start value is the c value.

- Then choose a small value for how much the x values will change. This is shown on the calculator by the symbol Δ. How small is small? That depends on the function. Experiment with different values. Try starting with 0.1.

- Finally, go to the table to see the values already calculated for you. *Note:* Calculators list tables vertically, so move the cursor up to view values to the left and down to view values to the right.

SW SOUTHWESTERN

Limits by Graphs

A limit can often be found by looking at the graph of the function and determining the *y* value that the function approaches. This method can be the quickest way to reach a conclusion about a limit value. When graphing functions, be sure to double check conclusions algebraically or with a table of values to reduce errors caused by misleading graphs.

EXAMPLE 4

Use the graph of the function below.

$$f(x) = \begin{cases} (x+2)^3 + 1 & x \neq -2 \\ 2, & x = -2 \end{cases}$$

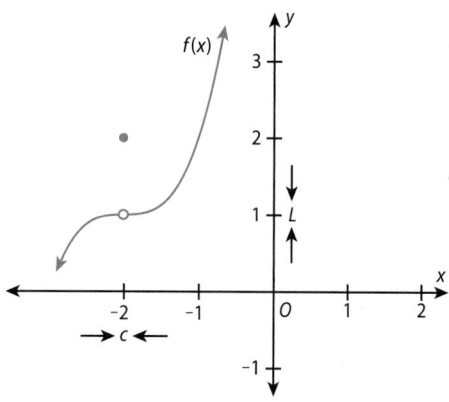

a. Find the limit of $f(x)$ as x approaches -2.

This piecewise function is a smooth curve that "jumps" at $x = -2$, as shown in the graph above. This is an example where the function value differs from the limit value at a given point.

As the x values get closer to -2 from the left and the right, the y values get closer to 1.

Here $f(-2) = 2$, but the limit of $f(x)$ as x approaches -2 is 1.

b. Find the limit of $f(x)$ as x approaches -1.

There is nothing special happening on the graph when $x = -1$. Here the function value and the limit value are the same. As seen in the graph above, $f(-1) = 2$.

Also, as the function approaches -1 from the left and the right, the y values approach 2.

Therefore, the limit of $f(x)$ as x approaches -1 is 2.

There are several different types of graphical behaviors that cause interesting limits. These include asymptotes, undefined values, and jumps in piecewise functions. Example 5 shows each of these types of behavior.

EXAMPLE 5

Use the graph below.

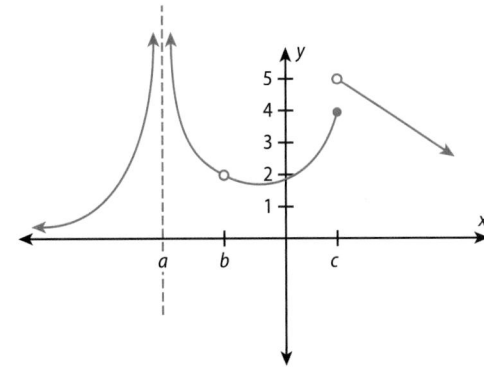

SEARCH

To see step-by-step videos of these problems, enter the page number into the SWadvantage.com Search Bar.

a. Find the limit of $f(x)$ as x approaches a.

To find the limit of $f(x)$ as x approaches a, study the graph as x approaches a from the left and from the right. As the function gets closer and closer to a from either side, the y values increase without bound.

Because the function is approaching infinity from both sides, the limit of $f(x)$ as x approaches a is infinity.

The limit does not exist.

b. Find the limit of $f(x)$ as x approaches b.

To find the limit of $f(x)$ as x approaches b, study the graph as it approaches b from the left and from the right. The function does not exist at b, but the limit does.

As the function gets closer and closer to b from either side, the y values approach 2.

Therefore, the limit of $f(x)$ as x approaches b is 2.

c. Find the limit of $f(x)$ as x approaches c.

To find the limit of $f(x)$ as x approaches c, study the graph as x approaches c from the left and from the right. As the function gets closer and closer to c from the left, the function approaches 4.

As the function gets closer and closer to c from the right, the function approaches 5.

Because the function approaches different values from each side, the limit does not exist.

Need More

HELP ?

Example 5(a): To learn more about infinite limits, go to *Infinite Limits* on page 2136.

Example 5(c): For more about limits that do not exist, go to *Left- and Right-Hand Limits* on page 2132.

Calculating Limits Algebraically

Direct Substitution

Need More HELP?

For more about continuous functions, go to *Continuity at a Point* on page 2144.

Sometimes the function value and the limit are the same. When this is the case, you can determine the limit by direct substitution of the *x* value into the given function. Functions of this type are *continuous* at *c*.

See the *Got To Know!* box at the bottom of the page for a list of limit rules.

EXAMPLE 1

Find: $\lim\limits_{x \to 2} 4$

Use the Constant Rule for limits. $\qquad \lim\limits_{x \to 2} 4 = 4$

Look at the graph of the function at the right to see why the limit of the constant function as *x* approaches 2 is the same as the constant value. Notice that for the given constant function $y = 4$, the limit as *x* approaches <u>any</u> value is 4.

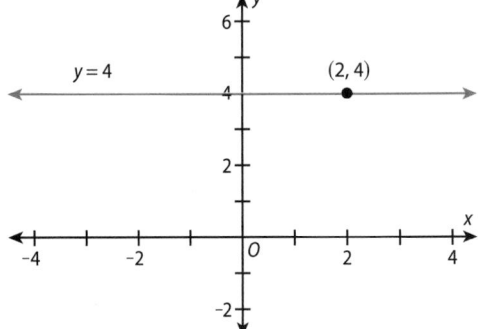

EXAMPLE 2

Find: $\lim\limits_{x \to 1} 2(x + 1)$

Use the Constant Multiple Rule for limits. $\qquad \lim\limits_{x \to 1} 2(x + 1) = 2 \lim\limits_{x \to 1} (x + 1)$

Use direct substitution. $\qquad\qquad\qquad\qquad\qquad\qquad\quad = 2(1 + 1)$

Simplify. $\qquad\qquad\qquad\qquad\qquad\qquad\qquad\qquad = 4$

GOT TO KNOW!

Limit Rules

Let *n* be a positive integer, *k* be a constant, and *f* and *g* be functions which have limits at $x = c$. Then the following rules hold:

1. Constant Rule
$$\lim\limits_{x \to c} k = k$$

2. Constant Multiple Rule
$$\lim\limits_{x \to c} kf(x) = k \lim\limits_{x \to c} f(x)$$

3. Sum Rule
$$\lim\limits_{x \to c} [f(x) + g(x)] = \lim\limits_{x \to c} f(x) + \lim\limits_{x \to c} g(x)$$

4. Difference Rule
$$\lim\limits_{x \to c} [f(x) - g(x)] = \lim\limits_{x \to c} f(x) - \lim\limits_{x \to c} g(x)$$

5. Product Rule
$$\lim\limits_{x \to c} [f(x) \cdot g(x)] = \lim\limits_{x \to c} f(x) \cdot \lim\limits_{x \to c} g(x)$$

6. Quotient Rule
$$\lim\limits_{x \to c} \frac{f(x)}{g(x)} = \frac{\lim\limits_{x \to c} f(x)}{\lim\limits_{x \to c} g(x)}, \text{ if } \lim\limits_{x \to c} g(x) \neq 0$$

7. Power Rule
$$\lim\limits_{x \to c} [f(x)]^n = \left[\lim\limits_{x \to c} f(x) \right]^n$$

8. *n*th Root Rule
$$\lim\limits_{x \to c} \sqrt[n]{f(x)} = \sqrt[n]{\lim\limits_{x \to c} f(x)}, \text{ if } \lim\limits_{x \to c} f(x) > 0$$

Finding the Limit of Polynomial Functions

Polynomial functions are continuous functions whose graphs are smooth curves. The graph at the right shows the smooth curve of a polynomial function $p(x)$. Notice the point drawn on the graph at the point $x = 2$.

In Example 3, you can see how to find the limit of the polynomial function in the graph at $x = 2$ by applying several of the limit rules.

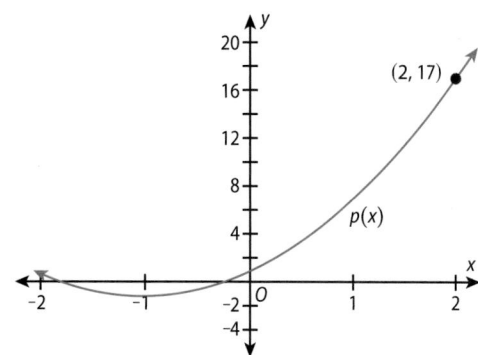

EXAMPLE 3

Find: $\lim\limits_{x \to 2} (2x^2 + 4x + 1)$

Use the Sum Rule for limits.	$\lim\limits_{x \to 2} (2x^2 + 4x + 1) = \lim\limits_{x \to 2} 2x^2 + \lim\limits_{x \to 2} 4x + \lim\limits_{x \to 2} 1$
Use the Constant Multiple Rule.	$= 2 \lim\limits_{x \to 2} x^2 + 4 \lim\limits_{x \to 2} x + \lim\limits_{x \to 2} 1$
Use the Power Rule.	$= 2 \left(\lim\limits_{x \to 2} x \right)^2 + 4 \lim\limits_{x \to 2} x + \lim\limits_{x \to 2} 1$
Use the Constant Rule.	$= 2 \left(\lim\limits_{x \to 2} x \right)^2 + 4 \lim\limits_{x \to 2} x + 1$
Use direct substitution.	$= 2(2)^2 + 4(2) + 1$
Simplify.	$= 17$

SEARCH

To see step-by-step videos of these problems, enter the page number into the SWadvantage.com Search Bar.

You can see that the limit as x approaches 2 in Example 3 is the same as the function's value at $x = 2$. This is always the case for limits of polynomial functions. You can use direct substitution to evaluate all polynomial limits.

EXAMPLE 4

Find: $\lim\limits_{x \to 0} (x^3 - 2x^2 + x - 3)$

The graph of the function is shown at the right. Because you are finding the limit of a polynomial function, you can use direct substitution as follows.

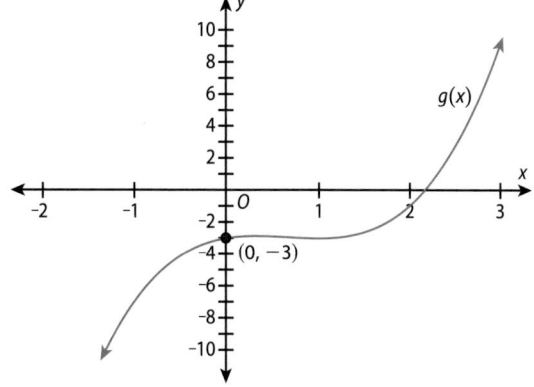

Use direct substitution.	$\lim\limits_{x \to 0} (x^3 - 2x^2 + x - 3) = (0)^3 - 2(0)^2 + (0) - 3$
Simplify.	$= -3$

Finding the Limit of Radical and Composite Functions

You can use direct substitution to find radical limits as long as the result is a real number when you substitute c into the function.

Composite limits can be found using direct substitution when the limit of the function exists. See the *Got To Know!* box at the bottom of the page for both of these limit rules.

EXAMPLE 5

Find: $\lim\limits_{x \to 4} \sqrt{x}$

Use direct substitution.	$\lim\limits_{x \to 4} \sqrt{x} = \sqrt{4}$
Simplify.	$= 2$

EXAMPLE 6

Find: $\lim\limits_{x \to 1} \sqrt{x^2 + 8}$

STEP 1 Identify $g(x)$ and $f(x)$.

$g(x) = x^2 + 8$ and $f(x) = \sqrt{x}$

STEP 2 Find $\lim\limits_{x \to c} g(x) = L$.

$$\lim\limits_{x \to 1} g(x) = \lim\limits_{x \to 1} (x^2 + 8)$$

Use direct substitution. $= (1)^2 + 8$

Simplify. $= 9$

STEP 3 Find $f(L)$.

$$f(L) = \sqrt{L}$$

Use direct substitution. $= \sqrt{9}$

Simplify. $= 3$

STEP 4 State the limit.

$$\lim\limits_{x \to 1} \sqrt{x^2 + 8} = 3$$

GOT TO KNOW!

Limits of Radicals

Let n be a positive integer. Then $\lim\limits_{x \to c} \sqrt[n]{x} = \sqrt[n]{c}$, for all c when n is odd, and $c > 0$ when n is even.

Limits of Composite Functions

If f and g are functions, and $\lim\limits_{x \to c} g(x) = L$ and $\lim\limits_{x \to c} f(x) = f(L)$, then $\lim\limits_{x \to c} f(g(x)) = f\left(\lim\limits_{x \to c} g(x)\right) = f(L)$.

Finding the Limit of Rational Functions

Often you can find the limit of rational functions using direct substitution. If substituting in the c value does not cause the denominator to be zero, then direct substitution is a very straightforward method for finding the limit. You can use direct substitution to find the limit of a rational function for any value of c other than the x values of the vertical asymptotes or holes in the graphs of the function.

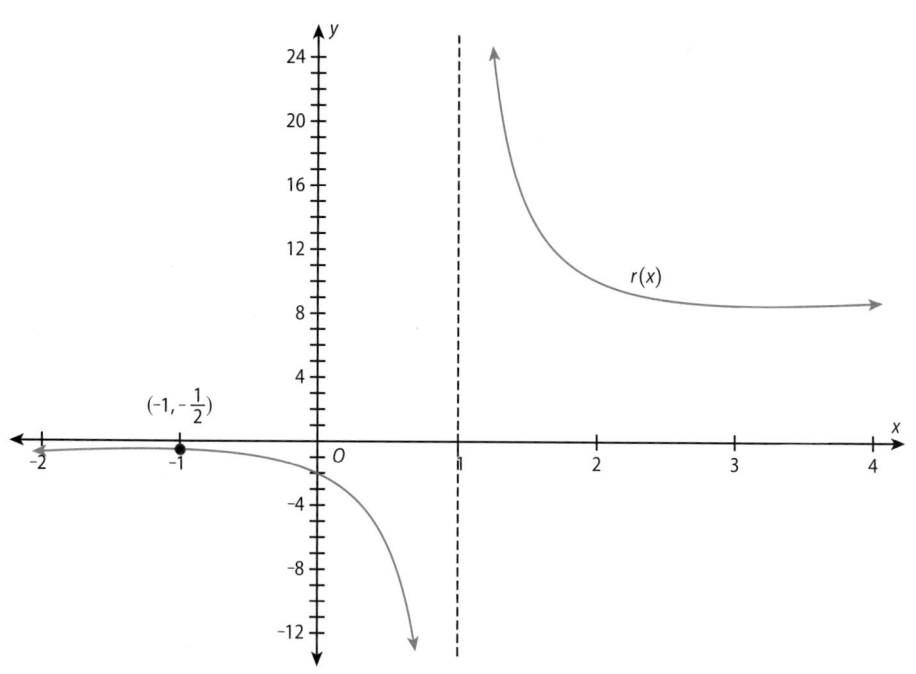

EXAMPLE 7

Find the limit of $r(x)$ as x approaches -1 if $r(x) = \dfrac{x^2 + 2x + 2}{x - 1}$.

When the value $x = -1$ is substituted into the denominator, the value is not zero. Therefore, direct substitution may be used to solve this problem.

Use direct substitution.
$$\lim_{x \to -1} r(x) = \frac{x^2 + 2x + 2}{x - 1} = \frac{(-1)^2 + 2(-1) + 2}{(-1) - 1}$$

Simplify.
$$= \frac{1 - 2 + 2}{-2} = -\frac{1}{2}$$

Notice that if the problem in Example 7 had asked for the limit as x approaches 1, direct substitution would fail. Substituting 1 for x would cause the denominator to be zero.

EXAMPLE 8

Find: $\displaystyle\lim_{x \to 0} \dfrac{\sqrt[3]{(x + 27)}}{x - 2}$

As in Example 7, first check the denominator's value when the value $x = 0$ is substituted into the equation. Because the value is not zero, direct substitution may be used.

Use direct substitution.
$$\lim_{x \to 0} \frac{\sqrt[3]{(x + 27)}}{x - 2} = \frac{\sqrt[3]{((0) + 27)}}{(0) - 2} = -\frac{3}{2}$$

Finding the Limits of Trigonometric Functions

You can also use direct substitution to find the limits of the six basic trigonometric functions. For each defined value of a trigonometric function, a limit exists that is the same as the function value at that specific point. Where the functions are undefined, the limit does not exist. Recall from trigonometry that undefined behavior happens with tangent, secant, cosecant, and cotangent functions.

Need More HELP?

For help with values of trigonometric functions, go to *Trigonometric Ratios* in *Trigonometry* (Book 1, p. 902).

EXAMPLE 9

Find: $\lim\limits_{x \to \pi} \sin(x)$

Use direct substitution. $\lim\limits_{x \to \pi} \sin(x) = \sin \pi$

Simplify. $= 0$

EXAMPLE 10

Find: $\lim\limits_{x \to \pi} \cos(x)$

Use direct substitution. $\lim\limits_{x \to \pi} \cos(x) = \cos \pi$

Simplify. $= -1$

EXAMPLE 11

Find: $\lim\limits_{x \to \frac{\pi}{2}} \tan(x)$

Use direct substitution. $\lim\limits_{x \to \frac{\pi}{2}} \tan(x) = \tan \frac{\pi}{2}$

Simplify. $= \text{undefined}$

Since the value of $\tan \frac{\pi}{2}$ is undefined, the limit of $\tan(x)$ as x approaches $\frac{\pi}{2}$ does not exist.

GOT TO KNOW!

Trigonometric Limits

If c is in the domain of the given trigonometric function, then the following rules hold:

$\lim\limits_{x \to c} \sin(x) = \sin(c)$ $\lim\limits_{x \to c} \csc(x) = \csc(c)$

$\lim\limits_{x \to c} \cos(x) = \cos(c)$ $\lim\limits_{x \to c} \sec(x) = \sec(c)$

$\lim\limits_{x \to c} \tan(x) = \tan(c)$ $\lim\limits_{x \to c} \cot(x) = \cot(c)$

Putting All of the Limit Rules Together

The following examples demonstrate how to use multiple limit rules to find limits of given functions.

EXAMPLE 12

Find: $\lim\limits_{x\to 0} \dfrac{(\sin(x^2) + 2)}{(\cos(x^2))}$

Since $\cos(0)^2$ does not equal zero, the Quotient Rule of limits may be used.

$$\lim_{x\to 0} \frac{(\sin(x^2) + 2)}{(\cos(x^2))} = \frac{\lim\limits_{x\to 0}(\sin(x^2) + 2)}{\lim\limits_{x\to 0}(\cos(x^2))}$$

Use the Sum Rule.

$$= \frac{\lim\limits_{x\to 0}(\sin(x^2)) + \lim\limits_{x\to 0} 2}{\lim\limits_{x\to 0}(\cos(x^2))}$$

Use the Constant Rule.

$$= \frac{\lim\limits_{x\to 0}(\sin(x^2)) + 2}{\lim\limits_{x\to 0}(\cos(x^2))}$$

Use direct substitution.

$$= \frac{\sin((0)^2) + 2}{(\cos(0)^2)}$$

Simplify.

$$= \frac{\sin 0 + 2}{\cos 0}$$

$$= \frac{0 + 2}{1}$$

$$= 2$$

$$\lim_{x\to 0} \frac{(\sin(x^2) + 2)}{(\cos(x^2))} = 2$$

SEARCH

To see step-by-step videos of these problems, enter the page number into the SWadvantage.com Search Bar.

EXAMPLE 13

Let $f(x)$, $g(x)$, and $h(x)$ be polynomial functions. Find $\lim\limits_{x\to a} [3f(x)g(x) - (h(x))^2]$.

Use the Difference Rule.

$$\lim_{x\to a} [3f(x)g(x) - [h(x)]^2] = \lim_{x\to a} 3f(x)g(x) - \lim_{x\to a} [h(x)]^2$$

Use the Constant Multiple Rule.

$$= 3 \lim_{x\to a} f(x)g(x) - \lim_{x\to a} [h(x)]^2$$

Use the Product Rule.

$$= 3 \lim_{x\to a} f(x) \lim_{x\to a} g(x) - \lim_{x\to a} [h(x)]^2$$

Use the Power Rule.

$$= 3 \lim_{x\to a} f(x) \lim_{x\to a} g(x) - \left[\lim_{x\to a} h(x)\right]^2$$

Use direct substitution.

$$= 3f(a)g(a) - [h(a)]^2$$

$$\lim_{x\to a} [3f(x)g(x) - [h(x)]^2] = 3f(a)g(a) - [h(a)]^2$$

Limits of Indeterminate Forms

Using Algebra to Find Limits

As seen in the previous topic, direct substitution is a helpful technique for evaluating limits. Unfortunately, direct substitution does not work for all types of functions. We have seen how it is possible to find limits using tables and graphs. Is it also possible to find a limit algebraically when the value of the function does not exist?

Direct substitution fails if it produces a fraction in the form $\frac{0}{0}$. A rational function in which the limit of the numerator and the denominator both equal zero as x approaches c is called an **indeterminate form**. The Examples show techniques for algebraically finding the limits of indeterminate forms of rational functions.

When asked to find the limit of a rational function, the first thing to try is direct substitution. When direct substitution produces an indeterminate form, algebraic techniques or trigonometric formulas are needed to manipulate the equation, if possible, until the denominator is no longer 0 when c replaces x. First try factoring techniques.

Factoring Techniques for Evaluating Limits

EXAMPLE 1

Evaluate: $\displaystyle\lim_{x\to-2}\frac{x^2-3x-10}{x+2}$

Direct substitution fails because it produces $\frac{0}{0}$.

Factor the numerator.

$$\lim_{x\to-2}\frac{x^2-3x-10}{x+2}=\lim_{x\to-2}\frac{(x+2)(x-5)}{x+2}$$

Cancel like factors.

$$\lim_{x\to-2}\frac{\cancel{(x+2)}(x-5)}{\cancel{x+2}}=\lim_{x\to-2}(x-5)$$

Use direct substitution.

$$=((-2)-5)$$

Simplify.

$$=-7$$

Need More

HELP ?

For help with factoring, go to *Factoring Polynomials* in *Algebra* (starting on p. 1658).

EXAMPLE 2

Evaluate: $\displaystyle\lim_{x\to-1}\frac{x^3+1}{x+1}$

Direct substitution fails because it produces $\frac{0}{0}$.

Factor the numerator.

$$\lim_{x\to-1}\frac{x^3+1}{x+1}=\lim_{x\to-1}\frac{(x+1)(x^2-x+1)}{x+1}$$

Cancel like factors.

$$\lim_{x\to-1}\frac{\cancel{(x+1)}(x^2-x+1)}{\cancel{x+1}}=\lim_{x\to-1}x^2-x+1$$

Use direct substitution.

$$=(-1)^2-(-1)+1$$

Simplify.

$$=3$$

You saw in an earlier topic how to use graphs and tables to find a limit. The next example shows three methods of solving the same problem: algebraic factoring, graphing, and creating a table. Each method is an effective tool for finding approximate limits of indeterminate forms of rational functions, but at times the algebraic method is the most precise approach.

EXAMPLE 3

Evaluate: $\lim\limits_{x \to -4} \dfrac{2x^2 + 9x + 4}{x^2 - x - 20}$

SEARCH

To see step-by-step videos of these problems, enter the page number into the SWadvantage.com Search Bar.

METHOD 1 **Algebraic Factoring**

Direct substitution fails because it produces $\dfrac{0}{0}$.

Factor the numerator and denominator.

$$\lim\limits_{x \to -4} \frac{2x^2 + 9x + 4}{x^2 - x - 20} = \lim\limits_{x \to -4} \frac{(2x + 1)(x + 4)}{(x - 5)(x + 4)}$$

Cancel like factors.

$$\lim\limits_{x \to -4} \frac{(2x + 1)\cancel{(x + 4)}}{(x - 5)\cancel{(x + 4)}} = \lim\limits_{x \to -4} \frac{(2x + 1)}{(x - 5)}$$

Use direct substitution.

$$= \frac{2(-4) + 1}{(-4) - 5}$$

Simplify.

$$= \frac{7}{9}$$

METHOD 2 **Graphing**

Graph the given function. Study the graph as the x values approach -4 from the left and the right. For this function, the y value approaches $\dfrac{7}{9}$ as x approaches -4. Notice that it would be difficult to determine the exact fraction value of y just by looking at a graph unless the hole is labeled as shown. This is one reason why the algebraic technique is a more precise approach to calculating limits.

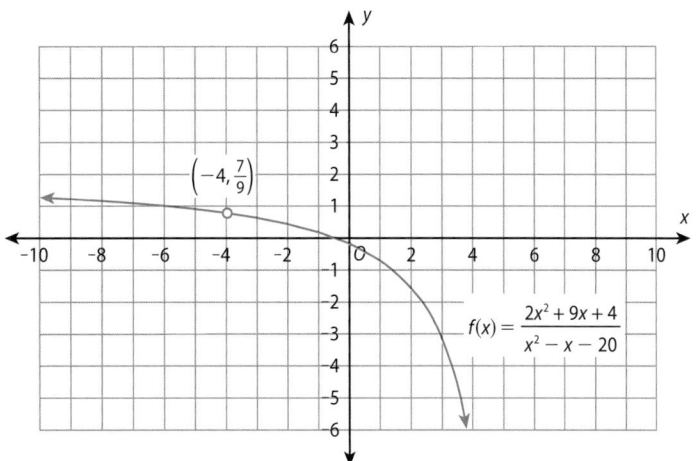

$$f(x) = \frac{2x^2 + 9x + 4}{x^2 - x - 20}$$

METHOD 3 **Table of Values**

Create a table to show values of $f(x)$ using x values that get closer and closer to -4. Study the table to determine the y value that $f(x)$ approaches. For this function, as x approaches -4, $f(x)$ approaches 0.778. This decimal value is approximately $\dfrac{7}{9}$. As in Method 2, this approximate value demonstrates that the algebraic method, if possible, may yield a more precise result when solving a limit problem.

x	-5	-4.1	-4.01	-4.001	-4	-3.999	-3.99	-3.9	-3
$f(x)$	0.9	0.7912	0.7791	0.7779	?	0.7776	0.7764	0.7640	0.625

Deciding How to Factor When Evaluating Limits

When factoring an indeterminate form, sometimes identifying common factors you can use to cancel the denominator is not clear. The following examples show two other possible ways to factor. First, consider whether factoring -1 from the numerator might produce a factor like the denominator. Also, think about whether there might be more than one method of factoring the numerator.

EXAMPLE 4

Evaluate: $\lim\limits_{x \to 2} \dfrac{2-x}{x^2+2x-8}$

Direct substitution fails because it produces $\dfrac{0}{0}$.

Factor the denominator.	$\lim\limits_{x \to 2} \dfrac{2-x}{x^2+2x-8} = \lim\limits_{x \to 2} \dfrac{2-x}{(x-2)(x+4)}$
Factor -1 from the numerator.	$= \lim\limits_{x \to 2} \dfrac{-(x-2)}{(x-2)(x+4)}$
Cancel like factors.	$= \lim\limits_{x \to 2} \dfrac{-1}{(x+4)}$
Use direct substitution.	$= \dfrac{-1}{2+4}$
Simplify.	$= -\dfrac{1}{6}$

Watch Out !

Sometimes you can factor polynomials more than one way. In Example 5, $x^6 - 1$ could instead have been factored as

$(x^2 - 1)(x^4 + x^2 + 1)$.

To decide which factored form to use, look at the rest of the expression. Determine if factoring in either way will allow you to cancel a pair of factors.

EXAMPLE 5

Evaluate: $\lim\limits_{x \to 1} \dfrac{x^6 - 1}{x^3 - 1}$

Direct substitution fails because it produces $\dfrac{0}{0}$.

Factor the numerator as the difference of two squares.	$\lim\limits_{x \to 1} \dfrac{x^6 - 1}{x^3 - 1} = \lim\limits_{x \to 1} \dfrac{(x^3 - 1)(x^3 + 1)}{x^3 - 1}$
Cancel like factors.	$\lim\limits_{x \to 1} \dfrac{(x^3 - 1)(x^3 + 1)}{x^3 - 1} = \lim\limits_{x \to 1} x^3 + 1$
Use direct substitution.	$= (1)^3 + 1$
Simplify.	$= 2$

Limits Involving Trigonometric Factoring

Trigonometric functions also appear in indeterminate forms of limits. Factoring these functions may produce limits that may be evaluated using direct substitution. The following examples demonstrate some common trigonometric factoring techniques.

EXAMPLE 6

Evaluate: $\lim\limits_{x \to \frac{\pi}{2}} \dfrac{\cos^2 x}{\sin x - 1}$

Direct substitution fails because it produces $\frac{0}{0}$.

Use a trigonometric identity to rewrite the numerator.

Factor the numerator using the difference of two squares.

Factor -1 from the numerator.

Cancel like factors.

Use direct substitution.

Simplify.

$$\lim_{x \to \frac{\pi}{2}} \frac{\cos^2 x}{\sin x - 1} = \lim_{x \to \frac{\pi}{2}} \frac{1 - \sin^2 x}{\sin x - 1}$$

$$= \lim_{x \to \frac{\pi}{2}} \frac{(1 - \sin x)(1 + \sin x)}{\sin x - 1}$$

$$= \lim_{x \to \frac{\pi}{2}} \frac{-1(\sin x - 1)(1 + \sin x)}{\sin x - 1}$$

$$= \lim_{x \to \frac{\pi}{2}} -1(1 + \sin x)$$

$$= -1\left(1 + \sin \frac{\pi}{2}\right)$$

$$= -2$$

SEARCH

To see step-by-step videos of these problems, enter the page number into the SWadvantage.com Search Bar.

EXAMPLE 7

Evaluate: $\lim\limits_{x \to \pi} \dfrac{\cos^2 x + 2\cos x + 1}{\cos x + 1}$

Direct substitution fails because it produces $\frac{0}{0}$.

Factor the numerator.

Cancel like factors.

Use direct substitution.

Simplify.

$$\lim_{x \to \pi} \frac{\cos^2 x + 2\cos x + 1}{\cos x + 1} = \lim_{x \to \pi} \frac{(\cos x + 1)(\cos x + 1)}{\cos x + 1}$$

$$\lim_{x \to \pi} \frac{(\cos x + 1)(\cos x + 1)}{\cos x + 1} = \lim_{x \to \pi} (\cos x + 1)$$

$$= \cos \pi + 1$$

$$= 0$$

Conjugate Technique

Another technique for finding the limit of indeterminate forms involves rationalizing the numerator. To do this, the rational function must be multiplied by a form of 1 that involves the conjugate of the numerator. Remember that the conjugate of a binomial such as $a + b$ is $a - b$.

EXAMPLE 8

Evaluate: $\lim\limits_{x \to -1} \dfrac{\sqrt{x + 2} - 1}{x + 1}$

METHOD 1 **Algebraic Rationalizing**

Direct substitution fails because it produces $\dfrac{0}{0}$.

Multiply by the conjugate form of 1.

$$\lim_{x \to -1} \frac{\sqrt{x + 2} - 1}{x + 1} = \lim_{x \to -1} \frac{\sqrt{x + 2} - 1}{x + 1} \cdot \frac{(\sqrt{x + 2} + 1)}{(\sqrt{x + 2} + 1)}$$

Use the Distributive Property of Multiplication.

$$= \lim_{x \to -1} \frac{(\sqrt{x + 2})^2 + \sqrt{x + 2} - \sqrt{x + 2} - 1}{(x + 1)(\sqrt{x + 2} + 1)}$$

Simplify the numerator.

$$= \lim_{x \to -1} \frac{\cancel{x + 1}}{\cancel{(x + 1)}(\sqrt{x + 2} + 1)}$$

Cancel like factors.

$$= \lim_{x \to -1} \frac{1}{(\sqrt{x + 2} + 1)}$$

Use direct substitution.

$$= \frac{1}{(\sqrt{(-1) + 2} + 1)}$$

Simplify.

$$= \frac{1}{2}$$

METHOD 2 **Graphing**

By studying the graph below, you can determine that the *y* value approaches 0.5 as the *x* values approach −1 from the left and from the right. Therefore, the limit as *x* approaches −1 is 0.5, as determined using the algebraic technique in Method 1.

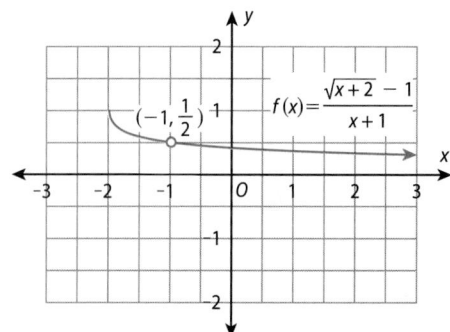

EXAMPLE 9

Evaluate: $\lim\limits_{x \to 12} \dfrac{\sqrt{x-3}-3}{x-12}$

SEARCH

To see step-by-step videos of these problems, enter the page number into the SWadvantage.com Search Bar.

METHOD 1 **Algebraic Rationalizing**

Direct substitution fails because it produces $\dfrac{0}{0}$.

Multiply by the conjugate form of 1.

$$\lim_{x \to 12} \frac{\sqrt{x-3}-3}{x-12} = \lim_{x \to 12} \left[\frac{\sqrt{x-3}-3}{x-12} \cdot \frac{\sqrt{x-3}+3}{\sqrt{x-3}+3} \right]$$

Use the Distributive Property of Multiplication.

$$= \lim_{x \to 12} \frac{\left(\sqrt{x-3}\right)^2 + 3\sqrt{x-3} - 3\sqrt{x-3} - 9}{(x-12)\left(\sqrt{x-3}+3\right)}$$

Simplify the numerator.

$$= \lim_{x \to 12} \frac{x-12}{(x-12)\left(\sqrt{x-3}+3\right)}$$

Cancel like factors.

$$= \lim_{x \to 12} \frac{1}{\left(\sqrt{x-3}+3\right)}$$

Use direct substitution.

$$= \frac{1}{\left(\sqrt{(12)-3}+3\right)}$$

Simplify.

$$= \frac{1}{6}$$

METHOD 2 **Table of Values**

By looking at the table of values below, you can determine that the y values approach 0.1667, which is approximately $\dfrac{1}{6}$, as x approaches 12.

x	13	12.1	12.01	12.001	12	11.999	11.99	11.9	11
f(x)	0.1623	0.1662	0.1666	0.1667	?	0.1667	0.1667	0.1671	0.1716

GOT TO KNOW!

Strategies for Finding Indeterminate Limits

1. Direct substitution will fail, so try these methods.

2. Try algebraic factoring. Look for common factors that will cancel and allow for direct substitution.

3. If trigonometric functions are present, use identities and factoring to change the form of the function.

4. Rationalize the fraction by using conjugates.

5. If algebraic techniques fail, try graphing the function or creating a table of values to approximate the value of the limit by using values of x that are *very close to c*.

Special Trigonometric Limits

The previous lesson showed how to find limits of indeterminate forms by algebraically factoring or rationalizing rational functions. For some functions, these methods will not work because there are no algebraic or trigonometric identities that can help. In this instance, geometry and advanced limit theorems are necessary.

The following examples show how to use two special trigonometric formulas, shown in the *Got To Know!* box on the next page, to algebraically determine the limit of specific trigonometric functions.

Need More

HELP ?

For help with finding the limit of a sine function using a table and a graph, go to *Using Tables and Graphs to Find Limits* on page 2114.

EXAMPLE 1

Evaluate: $\displaystyle\lim_{x\to 0} \frac{\sin 3x}{x}$

METHOD 1

Algebraic

Multiply by a useful form of 1.

$$\lim_{x\to 0} \frac{\sin 3x}{x} = \lim_{x\to 0}\left[\left(\frac{3}{3}\right)\frac{\sin 3x}{x}\right]$$

Use the Constant Multiple Rule for limits.

$$= 3\lim_{x\to 0} \frac{\sin(3x)}{(3x)}$$

Use a special trigonometric formula.

$$= 3(1)$$

Simplify.

$$= 3$$

$$\lim_{x\to 0} \frac{\sin 3x}{x} = 3$$

METHOD 2

Graphing

The graph below shows the function $f(x) = \dfrac{\sin 3x}{x}$.

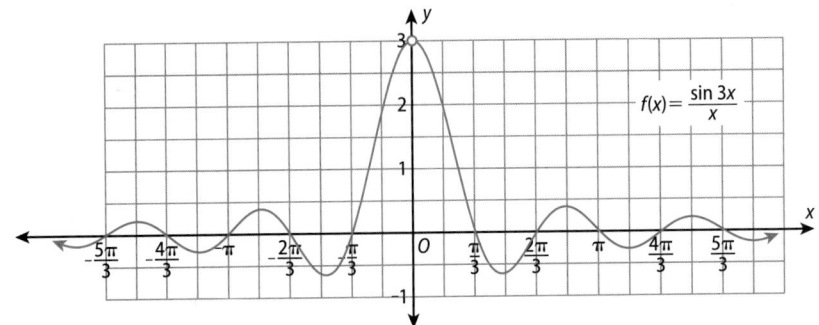

Notice that the *y* value approaches 3 as the *x* value approaches 0 from the left and from the right. Therefore, the limit of *y* as *x* approaches 0 is 3.

EXAMPLE 2

Find: $\lim\limits_{x \to 0} \dfrac{\sin 5x}{3x}$

Multiply by a useful form of 1.

Apply the Commutative Property of Multiplication so that the equation matches the sine formula.

Use the Constant Multiple Rule for limits.

Use a special trigonometric formula.

Simplify.

$\lim\limits_{x \to 0} \dfrac{\sin 5x}{3x} = \dfrac{5}{3}$

$$\lim\limits_{x \to 0} \dfrac{\sin 5x}{3x} = \lim\limits_{x \to 0} \left[\left(\dfrac{5}{5} \right) \dfrac{\sin 5x}{3x} \right]$$

$$= \lim\limits_{x \to 0} \left[\left(\dfrac{5}{3} \right) \dfrac{\sin 5x}{5x} \right]$$

$$= \left(\dfrac{5}{3} \right) \lim\limits_{x \to 0} \dfrac{\sin 5x}{5x}$$

$$= \dfrac{5}{3} (1)$$

$$= \dfrac{5}{3}$$

SEARCH

To see step-by-step videos of these problems, enter the page number into the SWadvantage.com Search Bar.

EXAMPLE 3

Find: $\lim\limits_{x \to 0} \dfrac{\sin^2(4x)}{x}$

Use a trigonometric identity.

Factor the difference of two squares.

Multiply by a useful form of 1.

Apply the Constant Multiple Rule for limits.

Apply the Product Rule for limits.

Use a special trigonometric formula.

Simplify.

$\lim\limits_{x \to 0} \dfrac{\sin^2(4x)}{x} = 0$

$$\lim\limits_{x \to 0} \dfrac{\sin^2(4x)}{x} = \lim\limits_{x \to 0} \dfrac{1 - \cos^2(4x)}{x}$$

$$= \lim\limits_{x \to 0} \dfrac{(1 + \cos(4x))(1 - \cos(4x))}{x}$$

$$= \dfrac{4}{4} \lim\limits_{x \to 0} \dfrac{(1 + \cos(4x))(1 - \cos(4x))}{x}$$

$$= 4 \lim\limits_{x \to 0} \dfrac{(1 + \cos(4x))(1 - \cos(4x))}{4x}$$

$$= 4 \lim\limits_{x \to 0} (1 + \cos(4x)) \cdot \lim\limits_{x \to 0} \dfrac{(1 - \cos(4x))}{4x}$$

$$= 4 \lim\limits_{x \to 0} (1 + \cos(4x)) \cdot 0$$

$$= 0$$

GOT TO KNOW!

Formulas for Special Trigonometric Limits

Sine $\lim\limits_{a \to 0} \dfrac{\sin a}{a} = 1$

Cosine $\lim\limits_{a \to 0} \dfrac{1 - \cos a}{a} = 0$

Left- and Right-Hand Limits

One-Sided Limits3

The graph at the right shows the greatest integer function, $f(x) = [x]$. The domain of this function is all real numbers, but does the limit exist everywhere? You easily can locate the limit at $x = \frac{3}{2}$, for example, because you can see from the graph that $\lim\limits_{x \to \frac{3}{2}} [[x]] = 1$. But $\lim\limits_{x \to 1} [[x]]$ causes problems because of the break in the graph.

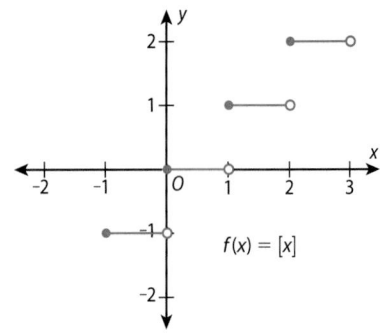

$f(x) = [x]$

The y values as x approaches 1 from the left-hand side are 0, but the y values as x approaches 1 from the right-hand side are 1. Since the y values do not approach the same number as x approaches 1 from the left and from the right, the limit does not exist at $x = 1$.

Even though the limit does not exist at $x = 1$, you can still describe the behavior of the graph using one-sided limits. These one-sided limits have their own special notation.

Left-Hand Limit Notation: $\lim\limits_{x \to c^-} f(x)$ "the limit as x approaches c from the left"

Right-Hand Limit Notation: $\lim\limits_{x \to c^+} f(x)$ "the limit as x approaches c from the right"

EXAMPLE 1

Find: $\lim\limits_{x \to 1^-} [[x]]$

Examine the graph above. Just to the left of $x = 1$, $f(x)$ is 0.

You can conclude that $\lim\limits_{x \to 1^-} [[x]] = 0$.

EXAMPLE 2

Find: $\lim\limits_{x \to 1^+} [[x]]$

Examine the graph above. Just to the right of $x = 1$, $f(x)$ is 1.

You can conclude that $\lim\limits_{x \to 1^+} [[x]] = 1$.

GOT TO KNOW!

Limits That Do Not Exist

For a limit to exist, the y value must approach the same number, L, as x approaches c from the left and from the right.

If the left- and right-hand limits are not equal, the limit does not exist. This is commonly abbreviated DNE.

The graph below shows another function that has a break. Use this graph for Examples 3, 4, and 5.

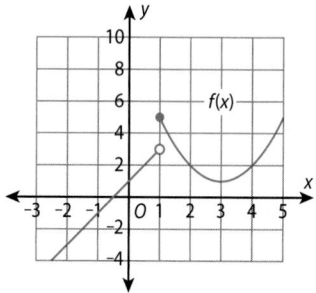

EXAMPLE 3

Find: $\lim\limits_{x \to 1^-} f(x)$

Use the graph above to find the y value as x approaches 1 from the *left*.

The y value of $f(x)$ as x approaches 1 from the left is 3.

Therefore, $\lim\limits_{x \to 1^-} f(x) = 3$.

EXAMPLE 4

Find: $\lim\limits_{x \to 1^+} f(x)$

Use the graph above to find the y value as x approaches 1 from the *right*.

The y value of $f(x)$ as x approaches 1 from the right is 5.

Therefore, $\lim\limits_{x \to 1^+} f(x) = 5$.

EXAMPLE 5

Find: $\lim\limits_{x \to 1} f(x)$

Use the graph and examples above.

For the limit to exist, the left- and right-hand limits must equal each other.

$\lim\limits_{x \to 1^-} f(x) = 3$

$\lim\limits_{x \to 1^+} f(x) = 5$

Since $3 \neq 5$, then $\lim\limits_{x \to 1^-} f(x) \neq \lim\limits_{x \to 1^+} f(x)$.

Therefore, $\lim\limits_{x \to 1} f(x) = $ DNE.

Piecewise Defined Functions

Left- and right-hand limits are commonly used to determine the existence of the limit of piecewise defined functions. The following examples show such limits.

EXAMPLE 6

Given: $g(x) = \begin{cases} \sin(x^2 + \pi), & x < 0 \\ 3x + 2, & x \geq 0 \end{cases}$

a. Find: $\lim\limits_{x \to 0^-} g(x)$

To find the limit of $g(x)$ as x approaches 0 from the left, use the function defined for all values less than (left of) 0.

Insert the correct function. $\qquad \lim\limits_{x \to 0^-} g(x) = \lim\limits_{x \to 0^-} \sin(x^2 + \pi)$

Use direct substitution. $\qquad\qquad\qquad = \sin((0)^2 + \pi)$

Simplify. $\qquad\qquad\qquad\qquad\qquad = 0$

Need More HELP ?

To find the limit as $x \to 0$, compare the left-hand and right-hand limits. Since $0 \neq 2$, then the limit as $x \to 0$ does not exist.

b. Find: $\lim\limits_{x \to 0^+} g(x)$

To find the limit of $g(x)$ as x approaches 0 from the right use the function defined for all values greater than (right of) 0.

Insert the correct function. $\qquad \lim\limits_{x \to 0^+} g(x) = \lim\limits_{x \to 0^+} (3x + 2)$

Use direct substitution. $\qquad\qquad\qquad = 3(0) + 2$

Simplify. $\qquad\qquad\qquad\qquad\qquad = 2$

EXAMPLE 7

Given: $h(x) = \begin{cases} x, & x < 1 \\ -x + 2, & x \geq 1 \end{cases}$

Find: $\lim\limits_{x \to 1} h(x)$

To determine the limit of this piecewise function, you must find and compare the left- and right-hand limits.

STEP 1 Find the left-hand limit.

$$\lim\limits_{x \to 1^-} h(x) = \lim\limits_{x \to 1^-} x$$
$$= 1$$

STEP 2 Find the right-hand limit.

$$\lim\limits_{x \to 1^+} h(x) = \lim\limits_{x \to 1^+} (-x + 2)$$
$$= 1$$

STEP 3 Compare the left- and right-hand limits.

Since $\lim\limits_{x \to 1^-} h(x) = \lim\limits_{x \to 1^+} h(x) = 1$, you can conclude that $\lim\limits_{x \to 1} h(x) = 1$.

EXAMPLE 8

Given: $f(x) = \dfrac{|x-1|}{x-1}$

Find: $\lim\limits_{x \to 1} f(x)$

Use algebra to rewrite $f(x)$ as a piecewise function created by the absolute value.

$$f(x) = \begin{cases} \dfrac{-(x-1)}{x-1}, & x < 1 \\ \dfrac{(x-1)}{x-1}, & x \geq 1 \end{cases}$$

STEP 1 Simplify the function

$$f(x) = \begin{cases} -1, & x < 1 \\ 1 & x \geq 1 \end{cases}$$

STEP 2 Evaluate the left-hand limit.

$$\lim\limits_{x \to 1^-} f(x) = -1$$

STEP 3 Evaluate the right-hand limit.

$$\lim\limits_{x \to 1^+} f(x) = 1$$

STEP 4 Compare the left- and right-hand limits.

Since $\lim\limits_{x \to 1^-} f(x) \neq \lim\limits_{x \to 1^+} f(x)$, you can conclude that $\lim\limits_{x \to 1} f(x) =$ DNE.

SEARCH

To see step-by-step videos of these problems, enter the page number into the SWadvantage.com Search Bar.

One-Sided Limits Using Tables

Another way to find left- and right-hand limits is to use a table of values. When finding only the left-hand or right-hand limit, you just need to include values in the table for $f(x)$ approaching from one direction.

Need More HELP?

For help with using a table of values, go to *Using Tables and Graphs to Find Limits* on page 2114.

EXAMPLE 9

Use a table to find $\lim\limits_{x \to 2^+} \sqrt{x-2}$.

STEP 1 Make a table.

Write x values in the table near $x = 2$, approaching from the right (greater than 2). Use a calculator to determine the values of $f(x)$.

x	2.01	2.02	2.03	2.04	2.05
f(x)	0.1	0.1414	0.1732	0.2	0.2236

STEP 2 Evaluate the behavior of the $f(x)$ values.

As the x values in the table approach 2 from the right, the y values approach 0. Therefore, you can conclude that $\lim\limits_{x \to 2^+} \sqrt{x-2} = 0$.

Infinite Limits

Unbounded Functions

Rational functions often have limit behavior that does not exist. This is caused by the vertical asymptotes found in such functions. The function $f(x) = \frac{1}{x^2}$ is a good example. The graph and the table below both show that as x approaches 0 from the left, the y values increase without bound. As x approaches zero from the right, the y values again increase without bound. You indicate these infinite limits symbolically as follows.

$$\lim_{x \to 0^-} f(x) = \infty \qquad \text{and} \qquad \lim_{x \to 0^+} f(x) = \infty$$

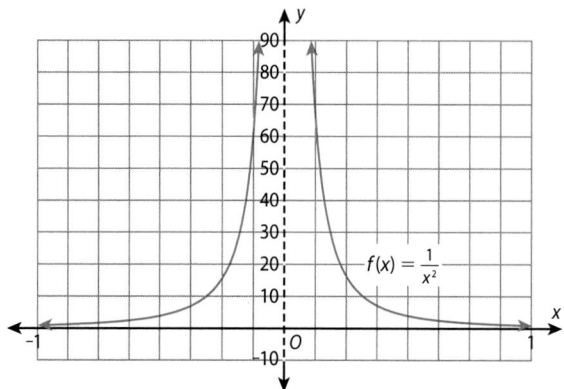

x	-1	-0.1	-0.01	-0.001	0	0.001	0.01	0.1	1
$f(x)$	1	100	10,000	1,000,000	?	1,000,000	10,000	100	1

EXAMPLE 1

Find: $\lim\limits_{x \to -4} \dfrac{1}{(x+4)^2}$

By looking at the graph of $g(x)$ at the right, you can see that the y values increase without bound as x approaches -4 from the left and from the right.

Therefore, the limit of $g(x)$ as x approaches -4 is infinity.

$$\lim_{x \to -4} \frac{1}{(x+4)^2} = \infty$$

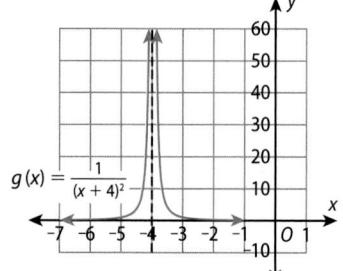

GOT TO KNOW!

Infinity

Infinity (∞) is a behavior, not a value. Stating that the limit of a given function is infinity is simply a specific way of saying that the limit does not exist.

EXAMPLE 2

Find: $\lim\limits_{x \to 1} \dfrac{-3}{(x-1)^2}$

By looking at the graph of $h(x)$ at the right, you can see that the y values decrease without bound as x approaches 1 from the left and the right.

Therefore, the limit of $h(x)$ as x approaches 1 is negative infinity.

$$\lim\limits_{x \to 1} \dfrac{-3}{(x-1)^2} = -\infty$$

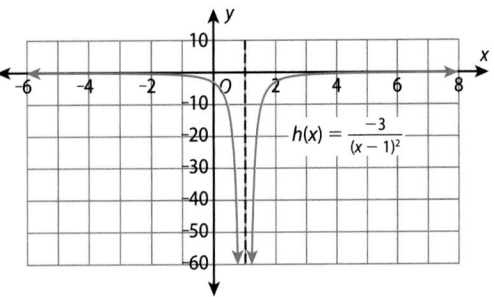

$h(x) = \dfrac{-3}{(x-1)^2}$

Try It This Way

You can use a calculator to solve Example 2 by making a table of values. Look at the y values as x gets close to one. The numbers will be very large negative values. Thus, the limit is negative infinity.

EXAMPLE 3

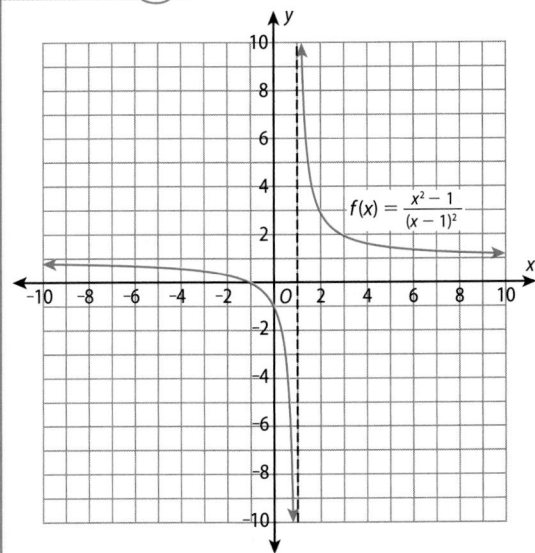

$f(x) = \dfrac{x^2 - 1}{(x-1)^2}$

a. Find $\lim\limits_{x \to 1^-} \dfrac{x^2 - 1}{(x-1)^2}$.

By looking at the graph above, you can see that the y values decrease without bound as x approaches 1 from the left.

Therefore, $\lim\limits_{x \to 1^-} \dfrac{x^2 - 1}{(x-1)^2} = -\infty$.

b. Find $\lim\limits_{x \to 1^+} \dfrac{x^2 - 1}{(x-1)^2}$.

By looking at the graph above, you can see that the y values increase without bound as x approaches 1 from the right.

Therefore, $\lim\limits_{x \to 1^-} \dfrac{x^2 - 1}{(x-1)^2} = \infty$.

SEARCH

To see step-by-step videos of these problems, enter the page number into the SWadvantage.com Search Bar.

Limits and Vertical Asymptotes

Identifying Vertical Asymptotes

Functions that have vertical asymptotes approach positive or negative infinity as the x values approach the asymptotes from the left- and right-hand sides. This behavior indicates whether the limit of the function is positive or negative infinity.

To find the vertical asymptotes of a given function, first factor the numerator and the denominator. Any x value that would cause the denominator to be 0 is either a hole in the graph or an asymptote.

Next, cancel any like factors. If this eliminates the division by 0, then the function has a hole in the graph for that x value. If it does not eliminate the division by 0, the function has an asymptote for that x value.

You can identify an asymptote by setting the denominator equal to 0 and solving for x. This simplified equation is the equation of a vertical asymptote.

SEARCH 🔍

To see step-by-step videos of these problems, enter the page number into the SWadvantage.com Search Bar.

EXAMPLE 1

Determine all vertical asymptotes of $f(x) = \dfrac{3x}{x^2 + x - 2}$.

STEP 1 Factor the denominator.

$$\frac{3x}{x^2 + x - 2} = \frac{3x}{(x + 2)(x - 1)}$$

STEP 2 Determine the asymptote equations.

Set the denominator equal to 0. $(x + 2)(x - 1) = 0$

Solve for x. $x = -2, 1$

Therefore, the vertical asymptotes of $f(x)$ are $x = -2$ and $x = 1$.

EXAMPLE 2

Determine all vertical asymptotes of $g(x) = \dfrac{x^3 + 8}{x^2 - 3x - 10}$.

STEP 1 Factor the numerator and the denominator.

$$\frac{x^3 + 8}{x^2 - 3x - 10} = \frac{(x + 2)(x^2 - 2x + 4)}{(x + 2)(x - 5)}$$

STEP 2 Cancel like factors.

$$= \frac{\cancel{(x + 2)}(x^2 - 2x + 4)}{\cancel{(x + 2)}(x - 5)}$$

$$= \frac{(x^2 - 2x + 4)}{(x - 5)}$$

Need More HELP ?

Cancelling a factor of $(x + 2)$ from the denominator indicates that there is a hole in the graph at $x = -2$.

STEP 3 Determine the asymptote equations.

Set the denominator equal to 0. $(x - 5) = 0$

Solve for x. $x = 5$

Therefore, the vertical asymptote of $g(x)$ is $x = 5$.

Infinite Limits

Once you have found the vertical asymptotes of a function, you can determine whether the infinite limits on either side of the asymptote are positive or negative infinity using a graph or a table of values.

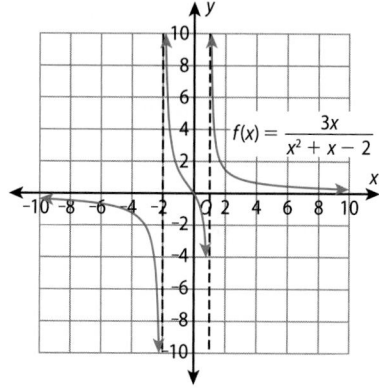

$$f(x) = \frac{3x}{x^2 + x - 2}$$

EXAMPLE 3

Find: $\lim\limits_{x \to -2^-} \dfrac{3x}{x^2 + x - 2}$

In Example 1, you saw how to determine that a vertical asymptote for this function occurs at $x = -2$. You can conclude that the limit as x approaches -2 from the left is either positive or negative infinity.

Using the graph above, you can see that the function decreases without bound as x approaches -2 from the left.

Therefore, $\lim\limits_{x \to -2^-} \dfrac{3x}{x^2 + x - 2} = -\infty$.

EXAMPLE 4

Find: $\lim\limits_{x \to -2^+} \dfrac{3x}{x^2 + x - 2}$

As in Example 3, you can see from the graph above that the function increases without bound as x approaches -2 from the right.

Therefore, $\lim\limits_{x \to -2^+} \dfrac{3x}{x^2 + x - 2} = \infty$.

EXAMPLE 5

Find: $\lim\limits_{x \to -2} \dfrac{3x}{x^2 + x - 2}$

Use the limit values found in Example 3 and 4.

$\lim\limits_{x \to -2^-} \dfrac{3x}{x^2 + x - 2} = -\infty$ and $\lim\limits_{x \to -2^+} \dfrac{3x}{x^2 + x - 2} = \infty$

Since the left-hand limit does not equal the right-hand limit, $\lim\limits_{x \to -2} \dfrac{3x}{x^2 + x - 2} = $ DNE.

Try It This Way

You can also determine whether the limit in Example 3 is positive or negative infinity by using a calculator to find $f(x)$ for values of x very close to -2, approaching from the left (less than -2).

End Behavior

Previous lessons have explained how to determine the limit of a function as x approaches a specific value. This lesson explains how to determine a limit as x approaches positive or negative infinity.

To look at a function as x approaches negative infinity means to study the graph as the x values decrease without bound. This is the left "end" of the function. Conversely, to look at a function as x approaches positive infinity means to study the graph as the x values increase without bound. This is the right "end" of the function.

Watch Out !

Sometimes graphs of polynomials, such as the one in Example 1, have a shape similar to those with an asymptote, even though there is none. To determine if there is an asymptote, consider both the graph and the function.

EXAMPLE 1

Find $\lim\limits_{x \to -\infty} x^3 - 2x^2 - 4x + 1$ and $\lim\limits_{x \to \infty} x^3 - 2x^2 - 4x + 1$.

METHOD 1

Use a graph.

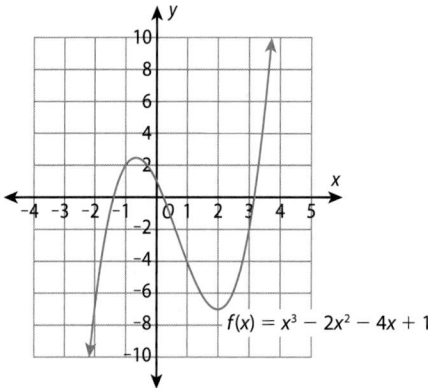

$f(x) = x^3 - 2x^2 - 4x + 1$

Studying the graph, you can see that as the x values approach negative infinity (the left side of the graph), the y values decrease without bound. As the x values approach positive infinity (the right side of the graph), the y values increase without bound.

Therefore, $\lim\limits_{x \to -\infty} x^3 - 2x^2 - 4x + 1 = -\infty$ and $\lim\limits_{x \to \infty} x^3 - 2x^2 - 4x + 1 = \infty$.

METHOD 2

Use a table.

Use a calculator to find $f(x)$ for values of x that get very large in the positive and negative direction to approximate infinity or negative infinity.

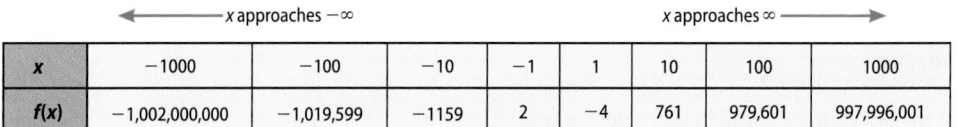

	← x approaches $-\infty$							x approaches ∞ →
x	-1000	-100	-10	-1	1	10	100	1000
$f(x)$	$-1{,}002{,}000{,}000$	$-1{,}019{,}599$	-1159	2	-4	761	$979{,}601$	$997{,}996{,}001$

You can see from the table that $f(x)$ becomes larger negative values as x approaches negative infinity. As x approaches positive infinity, $f(x)$ becomes larger positive values.

Therefore, $\lim\limits_{x \to -\infty} x^3 - 2x^2 - 4x + 1 = -\infty$ and $\lim\limits_{x \to \infty} x^3 - 2x^2 - 4x + 1 = \infty$.

EXAMPLE 2

Use the graph below.

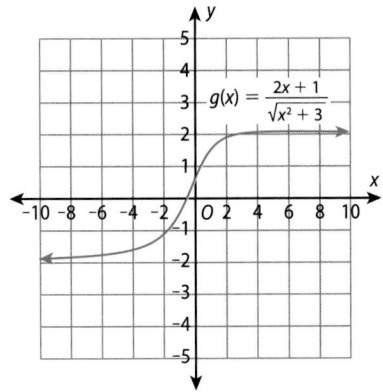

$g(x) = \dfrac{2x + 1}{\sqrt{x^2 + 3}}$

a. Find $\displaystyle\lim_{x \to -\infty} \dfrac{2x + 1}{\sqrt{x^2 + 3}}$.

Since the y values tend toward -2 as x decreases without bound, $\displaystyle\lim_{x \to -\infty} \dfrac{2x + 1}{\sqrt{x^2 + 3}} = -2$.

b. Find $\displaystyle\lim_{x \to \infty} \dfrac{2x + 1}{\sqrt{x^2 + 3}}$.

Since the y values tend toward 2 as x increases without bound, $\displaystyle\lim_{x \to \infty} \dfrac{2x + 1}{\sqrt{x^2 + 3}} = 2$.

SEARCH

To see step-by-step videos of these problems, enter the page number into the SWadvantage.com Search Bar.

EXAMPLE 3

Use the table of values below.

	← x approaches −∞					x approaches ∞ →		
x	−1000	−100	−10	−1	1	10	100	1000
f(x)	1.9989	1.9899	1.8889	undefined	2.5	2.0909	2.0099	2.001

a. Find $\displaystyle\lim_{x \to \infty} \dfrac{1}{x + 1} + 2$.

Since the y values tend toward 2 as x increases without bound, $\displaystyle\lim_{x \to \infty} \dfrac{1}{x + 1} + 2 = 2$.

b. Find $\displaystyle\lim_{x \to -\infty} \dfrac{1}{x + 1} + 2$.

Since the y values tend toward 2 as x decreases without bound, $\displaystyle\lim_{x \to -\infty} \dfrac{1}{x + 1} + 2 = 2$.

Evaluating Limits at Infinity

It is possible to determine the limits at infinity of rational functions algebraically as well as graphically or numerically. When direct substitution into the function produces the indeterminate form $\frac{\infty}{\infty}$, divide the numerator and denominator by the highest power of x to simplify the function. Then find the limit of the function.

Using the result of the limit, you can determine whether the graph has horizontal asymptotes.

Limit Does Not Exist	**Limit is 0**	**Limit is a Number**
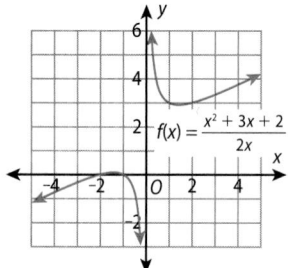	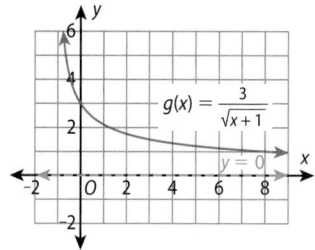	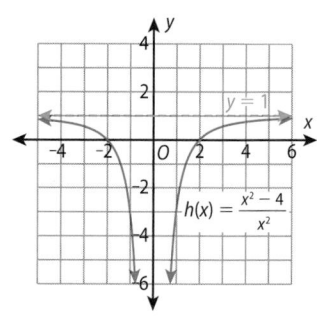
No horizontal asymptote	Horizontal asymptote at $y = 0$	Horizontal asymptote at $y = $ limit (In this case, $y = 1$.)

GOT TO KNOW!

Rules for Finding Limits at Infinity for Rational Functions

1. If the degree of the numerator is **greater than** the degree of the denominator, then the limit DNE (does not exist).

   • There is no horizontal asymptote.

2. If the degree of the numerator is **less than** the degree of the denominator, then the limit is 0.

   • There is a horizontal asymptote at $y = 0$, the x-axis.

3. If the degree of the numerator is **equal to** the degree of the denominator, then the limit is the leading coefficient of the numerator divided by the leading coefficient of the denominator.

   • There is a horizontal asymptote at $y = $ limit.

EXAMPLE 4

Find: $\lim\limits_{x\to\infty} \dfrac{2x^3}{2x+1}$

Direct substitution gives $\dfrac{\infty}{\infty}$.

Divide the numerator and denominator by x^3.

$$\lim\limits_{x\to\infty} \dfrac{2x^3}{2x+1} = \lim\limits_{x\to\infty} \dfrac{\frac{2x^3}{x^3}}{\frac{2x+1}{x^3}}$$

Simplify.

$$= \lim\limits_{x\to\infty} \dfrac{2}{\frac{2}{x^2}+\frac{1}{x^3}}$$

The limit of a number divided by ∞ is 0.

$$= \dfrac{2}{0+0}$$

Simplify.

$$= \text{undefined}$$

Therefore, $\lim\limits_{x\to\infty} \dfrac{2x^3}{2x+1} = \text{DNE}$, and there is no horizontal asymptote. (See rule 1 on page 2142.)

GOT TO KNOW!

Limit of a Number Divided by ∞

Any number divided by ∞ is approximately 0: $\lim\limits_{x\to\infty} \dfrac{a}{x} = 0$.

Imagine the size of a piece of pizza that has been divided into infinite pieces.

EXAMPLE 5

Find: $\lim\limits_{x\to\infty} \dfrac{5x}{4x^2 - 3x + 2}$

Direct substitution gives $\dfrac{\infty}{\infty}$.

Divide the numerator and denominator by x^2.

$$\lim\limits_{x\to\infty} \dfrac{5x}{4x^2 - 3x + 2} = \lim\limits_{x\to\infty} \dfrac{\frac{5x}{x^2}}{\frac{4x^2 - 3x + 2}{x^2}}$$

Simplify.

$$= \lim\limits_{x\to\infty} \dfrac{\frac{5}{x}}{4 - \frac{3}{x} + \frac{2}{x^2}}$$

The limit of a number divided by ∞ is 0.

$$= \dfrac{0}{4 - 0 + 0}$$

Simplify.

$$= 0$$

Therefore, $\lim\limits_{x\to\infty} \dfrac{5x}{4x^2 - 3x + 2} = 0$, and there is a horizontal asymptote at $y = 0$. (See rule 2.)

EXAMPLE 6

Find: $\lim\limits_{x\to\infty} \dfrac{4x + 7}{-x - 3}$

Direct substitution gives $\dfrac{\infty}{\infty}$.

Divide the numerator and denominator by x.

$$\lim\limits_{x\to\infty} \dfrac{4x + 7}{-x - 3} = \lim\limits_{x\to\infty} \dfrac{\frac{4x + 7}{x}}{\frac{-x - 3}{x}}$$

Simplify.

$$= \lim\limits_{x\to\infty} \dfrac{4 + \frac{7}{x}}{-1 - \frac{3}{x}}$$

The limit of a number divided by ∞ is 0.

$$= \dfrac{4 + 0}{-1 - 0}$$

Simplify.

$$= -4$$

Therefore, $\lim\limits_{x\to\infty} \dfrac{4x + 7}{-x - 3} = -4$, and there is a horizontal asymptote at $y = -4$. (See rule 3.)

SEARCH

To see step-by-step videos of these problems, enter the page number into the SWadvantage.com Search Bar.

Continuity at a Point

What Is Continuity?

This lesson explores the concept of *continuity* at a point. Temperature is an example of a continuous function of time. If you plot the temperature at each moment for several days, you see a smooth graph. If you plot the amount of money in your wallet at each moment over several days, you might see a series of horizontal lines, sometimes stepping up, sometimes stepping down. This function is not continuous.

In exploring the limit of $f(x)$ as $x \to c$, the emphasis was on functional values close to c rather than what happens to the function at $x = c$. We now consider the following cases.

If $\lim_{x \to c} f(x) = f(c)$, then f is **continuous** at $x = c$.

If $\lim_{x \to c} f(x) \neq f(c)$, then f is **discontinuous** at $x = c$.

Geometrically, the criterion for continuity is to be able to draw the curve without lifting the pencil; there should be no holes or breaks. For this to happen, the left- and right-hand limits must both equal the function's value at c.

Types of Discontinuity

The following examples show four different types of discontinuity: holes, jumps, breaks, and poles. These fall into the following two categories.

A **removable discontinuity** implies that you can make the function continuous by defining or changing the function value $f(c)$.

A **non-removable discontinuity** implies that you cannot make the function continuous by any value $f(c)$.

SEARCH

To see step-by-step videos of these problems, enter the page number into the SWadvantage.com Search Bar.

EXAMPLE 1

Given $f(x) = \dfrac{x^2 - 2x - 3}{x + 1}$, identify the type of discontinuity at $x = -1$.

The function $f(x)$ is undefined at $x = -1$. As seen in the graph of $f(x)$ at the right, there is a hole discontinuity at the point $(-1, -4)$. If this point were defined, the function would be continuous.

Therefore, at $x = -1$, $f(x)$ has a removable discontinuity.

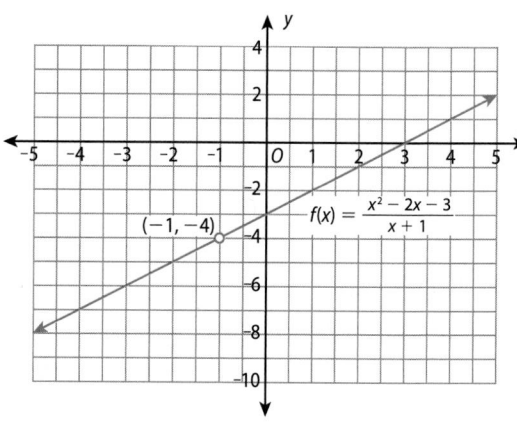

EXAMPLE 2

Given $g(x) = \begin{cases} x^2 + 2x + 3, & x \neq -1 \\ 4, & x = -1 \end{cases}$, identify the type of discontinuity at $x = -1$.

The function $g(x)$ is defined at $x = -1$. As seen in the graph of $g(x)$ at the right, the function has a *jump* discontinuity at $x = -1$. If this jump value were changed to fill the hole at $(-1, 2)$, the function would be continuous.

Therefore, at $x = -1$, $g(x)$ has a removable discontinuity.

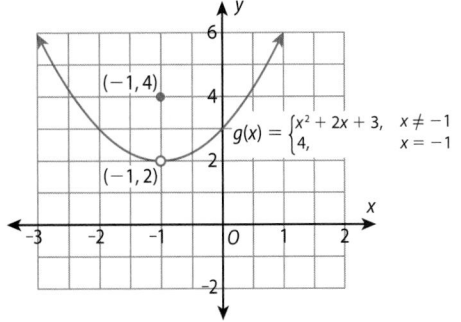

Try It This Way

If you can move your finger along the graph of the function from one side of the point to the other and only cross a hole, the discontinuity is removable at that point.

EXAMPLE 3

Given $h(x) = \begin{cases} 2, & x \geq -1 \\ 1, & x < -1 \end{cases}$, identify the type of discontinuity at $x = -1$.

The function $h(x)$ is defined for all values of x. As seen in the graph of $h(x)$ at the right, the function has a *break* discontinuity at $x = -1$. There is no value for $h(x)$ that would connect this break and create a continuous function.

Therefore, at $x = -1$, $h(x)$ has a non-removable discontinuity.

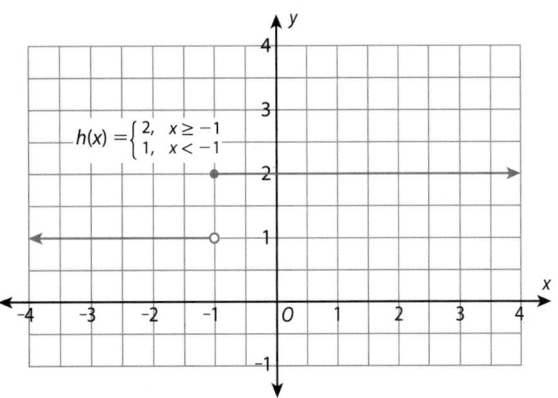

EXAMPLE 4

Given $j(x) = \dfrac{1}{x+1}$, identify the type of discontinuity at $x = -1$.

The function $j(x)$ is undefined at $x = -1$. As seen in the graph of $j(x)$ at the right, the function has a vertical asymptote at $x = -1$. No defined value of $j(x)$ would make this function continuous.

Therefore, at $x = -1$, $j(x)$ has a non-removable discontinuity.

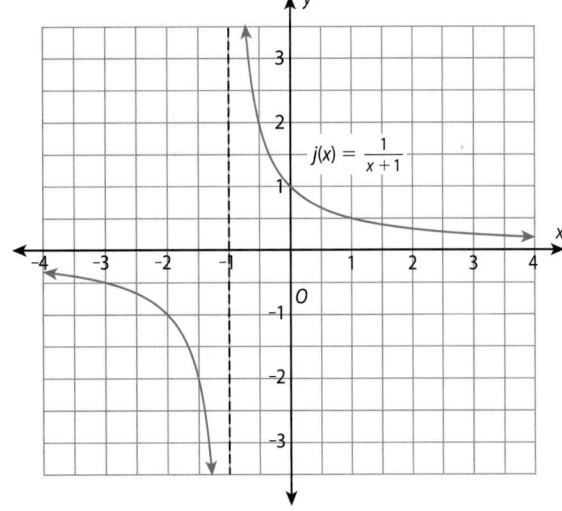

The type of discontinuity shown in Example 4, for which a limit does not exist, is called an infinite discontinuity. It is also sometimes called a pole discontinuity.

Determining Continuity at a Point

You can use simple tests to determine if a function is continuous at a given point. The following examples show how to apply these tests.

The graph of $f(x)$ below seems to be continuous at $x = 0$, but you need algebraic proof to confidently make such a statement. See Example 5 for this proof.

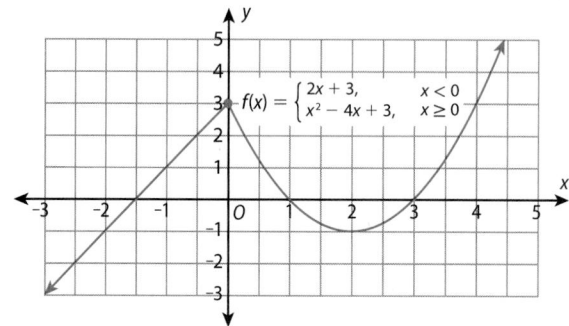

EXAMPLE 5

Determine if $f(x) = \begin{cases} 2x + 3, & x < 0 \\ x^2 - 4x + 3, & x \geq 0 \end{cases}$ **is continuous at $x = 0$. If not, state why.**

STEP 1 Determine if $f(0)$ is defined.

$f(0) = (0)^2 - 4(0) + 3 = 3$

STEP 2 Determine if $\lim\limits_{x \to 0} f(x)$ exists.

$\lim\limits_{x \to 0^-} f(x) = \lim\limits_{x \to 0^-} (2x + 3) = 2(0) + 3 = 3$

$\lim\limits_{x \to 0^+} f(x) = \lim\limits_{x \to 0^+} (x^2 - 4x + 3) = (0)^2 - 4(0) + 3 = 3$

$\therefore \lim\limits_{x \to 0} f(x) = 3$

STEP 3 Determine if $\lim\limits_{x \to 0} f(x) = f(0)$.

$\lim\limits_{x \to 0} f(x) = 3 \quad \text{and} \quad f(0) = 3$

$\therefore \lim\limits_{x \to 0} f(x) = f(0)$

Because all three tests are true, $f(x)$ is continuous at $x = 0$.

Need More HELP

Remember—in advanced math classes, the symbol $\therefore$ in problems means "therefore."

Three Tests for Continuity at a Point

1. $f(c)$ is defined.

2. $\lim\limits_{x \to c} f(x)$ exists; the left- and right-hand limit equal each other.

3. $\lim\limits_{x \to c} f(x) = f(c)$

If any of these three tests fail, the function is discontinuous at $x = c$.

SEARCH

To see step-by-step videos of these problems, enter the page number into the SWadvantage.com Search Bar.

EXAMPLE 6

Determine if $r(x) = \dfrac{3x - 4}{3x^2 + 2x - 8}$ is continuous at $x = -2$. If not, state why.

Use the three tests for continuity at a point.

STEP 1 Determine if $r(-2)$ is defined. $r(-2) = \dfrac{3(-2) - 4}{3(-2)^2 + 2(-2) - 8} = \dfrac{-10}{0} =$ undefined

Because $r(c)$ is undefined, it is not necessary to proceed any further with the tests for continuity.

Since $r(-2)$ is undefined, the function $r(x) = \dfrac{3x - 4}{3x^2 + 2x - 8}$ is not continuous at $x = -2$.

EXAMPLE 7

Determine if $p(x) = \begin{cases} -x - 1, & x < 0 \\ \sin x, & x \geq 0 \end{cases}$ is continuous at $x = 0$. If not, state why.

Use the three tests for continuity at a point.

STEP 1 Determine if $p(0)$ is defined. $P(0) = \sin(0) = 0$

STEP 2 Determine if $\lim\limits_{x \to 0} p(x)$ exists. $\lim\limits_{x \to 0^-} p(x) = \lim\limits_{x \to 0^-} (-x - 1) = -(0) - 1 = -1$

$\lim\limits_{x \to 0^+} p(x) = \lim\limits_{x \to 0^+} \sin x = \sin(0) = 0$

Because $\lim\limits_{x \to 0^-} p(x) \neq \lim\limits_{x \to 0^+} p(x)$, $\lim\limits_{x \to 0} p(x)$ DNE.

Since $\lim\limits_{x \to 0} p(x)$ DNE, it is not necessary to proceed with the third test.

The function $p(x)$ is not continuous at $x = 0$.

EXAMPLE 8

Determine if $k(x) = \begin{cases} |x - 3|, & x \neq 3 \\ 4, & x = 3 \end{cases}$ is continuous at $x = 3$. If not, state why.

Use the three tests for continuity at a point.

STEP 1 Determine if $k(3)$ is defined. $k(3) = 4$

STEP 2 Determine if $\lim\limits_{x \to 3} k(x)$ exists. $\lim\limits_{x \to 3^-} k(x) = \lim\limits_{x \to 3^-} |x - 3|$

$= \lim\limits_{x \to 3^-} -(x - 3) = -((3) - 3) = 0$

$\lim\limits_{x \to 3^+} k(x) = \lim\limits_{x \to 3^+} |x - 3|$

$= \lim\limits_{x \to 3^+} (x - 3) = (3) - 3 = 0$

$\therefore \lim\limits_{x \to 3} k(x) = 0$

STEP 3 Determine if $\lim\limits_{x \to 3} k(x) = k(3)$. $\lim\limits_{x \to 3} k(x) = 0$ and $k(3) = 4$

$\therefore \lim\limits_{x \to 3} k(x) \neq k(3)$

Therefore, $k(x)$ is not continuous at $x = 3$.

Finding Constants That Make a Function Continuous

Some advanced problems will test your knowledge of continuity by giving a function and asking you to find constant values such that the function is continuous. To solve this type of problem, use the three tests for continuity, and solve for the constant values. These problems must be solved algebraically instead of graphically because there is no given function to graph.

SEARCH

To see step-by-step videos of these problems, enter the page number into the SWadvantage.com Search Bar.

EXAMPLE 9

Find the constant a such that $f(x) = \begin{cases} ax, & x \leq 2 \\ x^2 - 4x + 3, & x > 2 \end{cases}$ is a continuous function at $x = 2$.

STEP 1 Determine if $f(2)$ is defined. $\quad f(2) = 2a$

Although you do not yet know the value of $2a$, you do know that a is a constant and you can conclude that $2a$ is defined.

STEP 2 Determine if $\lim\limits_{x \to 2} f(x)$ exists.

Find the limit from the left. $\qquad \lim\limits_{x \to 2^-} f(x) = \lim\limits_{x \to 2^-} a(x) = a(2) = 2a$

Find the limit from the right. $\qquad \lim\limits_{x \to 2^+} f(x) = \lim\limits_{x \to 2^+} (x^2 - 4x + 3) = (2)^2 - 4(2) + 3 = -1$

Determine the value of a $\qquad \lim\limits_{x \to 2^-} f(x) = \lim\limits_{x \to 2^+} f(x)$
for which the limit exists. $\qquad\qquad 2a = -1$
$\qquad\qquad\qquad\qquad\qquad a = -\dfrac{1}{2}$

STEP 3 Verify that if $a = -\dfrac{1}{2}$, the defined value at $x = 2$ equals the limit of $f(x)$ as x approaches 2.

$$f(2) \stackrel{?}{=} \lim\limits_{x \to 2} f(x)$$

Substitute. $\qquad\qquad\qquad 2a \stackrel{?}{=} -1$

Let $a = -\dfrac{1}{2}$. $\qquad\qquad 2\left(-\dfrac{1}{2}\right) \stackrel{?}{=} -1$

Simplify. $\qquad\qquad\qquad -1 = -1 \checkmark$

Therefore, if $a = -\dfrac{1}{2}$, the function $f(x)$ is continuous at $x = 2$.

GOT TO KNOW!

Continuous Functions

To find a constant a that makes a function continuous at a point $x = c$:

• Find the left-hand and right-hand limits at the point $x = c$.

• Set the two one-sided limits equal to each other and solve for a.

EXAMPLE 10

Find the constant a such that $g(x) = \begin{cases} \cos ax, & x \le \pi \\ \dfrac{\pi - x}{2}, & x > \pi \end{cases}$ is a continuous function at $x = \pi$.

STEP 1 Determine if $g(\pi)$ is defined. $\qquad g(\pi) = \cos a\pi$

STEP 2 Determine if $\lim\limits_{x \to \pi} g(x)$ exists.

Find the limit from the left. $\qquad \lim\limits_{x \to \pi^-} g(x) = \lim\limits_{x \to \pi^-} \cos ax = \cos a\pi$

Find the limit from the right. $\qquad \lim\limits_{x \to \pi^+} g(x) = \lim\limits_{x \to \pi^+} \dfrac{\pi - x}{2} = \dfrac{\pi - (\pi)}{2} = 0$

Determine the value of a $\qquad \lim\limits_{x \to \pi^-} g(x) = \lim\limits_{x \to \pi^+} g(x)$
for which the limit exists.

Substitute. $\qquad\qquad\qquad\quad \cos a\pi = 0$

Apply a trigonometric property. $\qquad a\pi = \dfrac{\pi}{2}$

Simplify. $\qquad\qquad\qquad\qquad\quad a = \dfrac{1}{2}$

STEP 3 Verify that if $a = \dfrac{1}{2}$, the defined value at $x = \pi$ equals the limit of $g(x)$ as x approaches π.

$$g(\pi) \stackrel{?}{=} \lim\limits_{x \to \pi} g(x)$$

Substitute. $\qquad \cos \dfrac{\pi}{2} \stackrel{?}{=} 0$

Simplify. $\qquad\qquad 0 = 0 \checkmark$

Therefore, if $a = \dfrac{1}{2}$, the function $g(x)$ is continuous at $x = \pi$.

EXAMPLE 11

Find the constants a and b such that $h(x) = \begin{cases} 1, & x \le -1, \\ ax + b, & -1 < x < 2 \\ 10, & x \ge 2 \end{cases}$ is continuous at $x = -1$ and 2.

This is a more challenging question and requires two points to be considered.

STEP 1 Set the defined function at $x = -1$ equal to the limit as x $\qquad h(-1) = \lim\limits_{x \to -1} h(x)$
approaches -1. $\qquad\qquad\qquad\qquad\qquad\qquad\qquad\qquad 1 = a(-1) + b$

STEP 2 Set the defined function at $x = 2$ equal to the limit as x $\qquad h(2) = \lim\limits_{x \to 2} h(x)$
approaches 2. $\qquad\qquad\qquad\qquad\qquad\qquad\qquad\qquad 10 = a(2) + b$

STEP 3 Use systems of equations to solve for a and b. $\qquad 10 = 2a + b$

Subtract one equation from the other. $\qquad\qquad\qquad \underline{-(1 = -a + b)}$

Subtract. $\qquad\qquad\qquad\qquad\qquad\qquad\qquad\qquad 9 = 3a$

Simplify to solve for a. $\qquad\qquad\qquad\qquad\qquad\qquad a = 3$

Substitute a into one of the original equations. $\qquad 10 = 2(3) + b$

Simplify to solve for b. $\qquad\qquad\qquad\qquad\qquad\qquad b = 4$

Therefore, if $a = 3$ and $b = 4$, the function $h(x)$ is continuous at $x = -1$ and 2.

Need More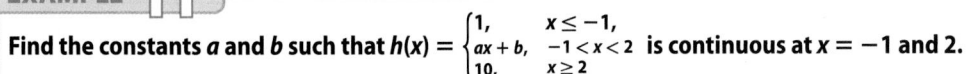

HELP ?

For help with solving
systems of equations,
go to *Solving a System
by Substitution* in
Algebra (p. 1568).

Continuity on an Interval

Continuity on an Open Interval

The previous topic discussed continuity of a function at a given point. This topic takes a closer look at continuity of a function on intervals. Many functions, such as polynomial and trigonometric functions, are continuous at every point in their domains. When describing the continuity of a function, it is therefore useful to first identify the function's domain. You can then describe the continuity of the function along intervals within the domain.

An **open interval** is a continuous set of real numbers that does not contain its endpoints. In order for a function to be continuous everywhere in an open interval, it must be continuous at every point in the interval. It does not have to be continuous at the endpoints.

Need More HELP?

For more about polynomials, go to *Operations with Polynomials* in *Algebra* (starting on p. 1598).

EXAMPLE 1

Describe the continuity of the function $f(x) = \tan x$.

STEP 1 Identify the domain.

The domain is the set of all real numbers, $x \neq \frac{\pi}{2} + n\pi$.

STEP 2 Identify intervals in the domain.

The function is discontinuous at each asymptote: $\ldots, -\frac{\pi}{2}, \frac{\pi}{2}, \frac{3\pi}{2}, \ldots$. It has open intervals between the asymptotes.

STEP 3 Determine continuity on the intervals.

The function is continuous at all points other than the asymptotes. It is therefore continuous on the open intervals between the asymptotes.

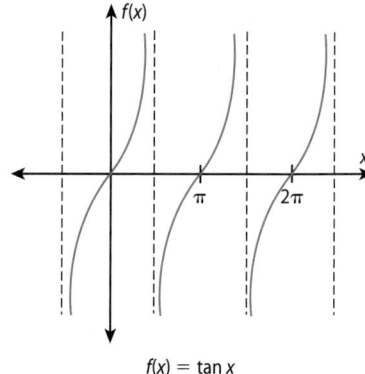

$f(x) = \tan x$

EXAMPLE 2

Describe the continuity of the function $g(x) = \frac{x^2 - 4}{x - 2}$.

STEP 1 Identify the domain.

The domain is the set of all real numbers, $x \neq 2$.

STEP 2 Identify intervals in the domain.

Because the function has a hole, it is discontinuous at $x = 2$. It has open intervals at $(-\infty, 2)$ and $(2, \infty)$.

STEP 3 Determine continuity on the intervals.

The function is continuous at all points other than the hole. It is therefore continuous on the open intervals $(-\infty, 2)$ and $(2, \infty)$.

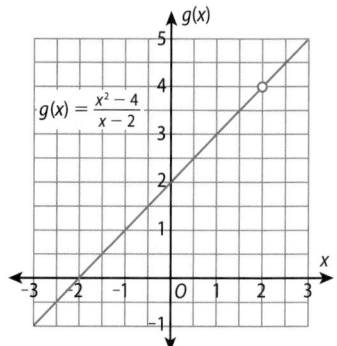

$g(x) = \frac{x^2 - 4}{x - 2}$

GOT TO KNOW!

Continuity on an Open Interval

A function is continuous on an open interval (a, b) if it is continuous at every point in (a, b).

Continuity on a Closed Interval

A **closed interval** is a set of real numbers that contains its endpoints. A function is continuous on a closed interval if it is continuous at each point in the interval and at both endpoints. A function might also have a **half-open interval**, which is a continuous set of real numbers that contains only one endpoint. A function continuous on a half-open interval must be continuous at each point in the interval and continuous at one of the endpoints.

EXAMPLE 3

Describe the continuity of $f(x) = \begin{cases} 2, & -3 \le x \le -1 \\ x^2 + 1, & -1 < x \le 2 \end{cases}$.

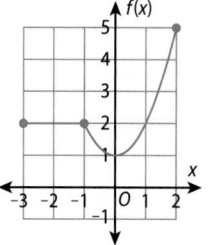

STEP 1   Identify the domain. $[-3, 2]$

STEP 2   Identify intervals in the domain. $[-3, -1]$ and $(-1, 2]$

STEP 3   Determine continuity on the intervals and at each endpoint.

The function is continuous at each point on the open intervals $(-3, -1)$ and $(-1, 2)$.

Check continuity at $x = -3$. $f(-3) = \lim\limits_{x \to -3^+} 2 = 2$

Check continuity at $x = -1$. $f(-1) = \lim\limits_{x \to -1^-} 2 = \lim\limits_{x \to -1^+} (x^2 + 1) = 2$

Check continuity at $x = 2$. $f(2) = \lim\limits_{x \to -2^-} (x^2 + 1) = 5$

Because $f(x)$ is continuous on the open intervals and at each endpoint, it is continuous on the entire closed interval $[-3, 2]$.

SEARCH

To see step-by-step videos of these problems, enter the page number into the SWadvantage.com Search Bar.

EXAMPLE 4

Describe the continuity $f(x) = \sqrt{x}$.

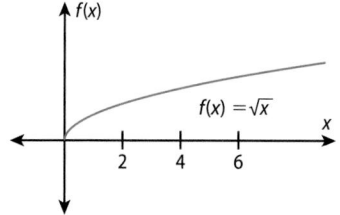

STEP 1   Identify the domain. $[0, \infty)$

STEP 2   Identify the interval in the domain. $[0, \infty)$

STEP 3   Determine continuity on the interval and at the endpoint.

The function is continuous at each point on $(0, \infty)$.

Check continuity at $x = 0$. $f(0) = \lim\limits_{x \to 0^+} \sqrt{x} = 0$

Because $f(x)$ is continuous on the open interval and at the endpoint, it is continuous on the half-open interval $[0, \infty)$.

GOT TO KNOW!

Continuity on a Closed Interval or a Half-Open Interval

A function is continuous on a closed interval [a, b] if it is continuous on (a, b) and	A function is continuous on a half closed interval [a, b) if it is continuous on (a, b) and	A function is continuous on a half closed interval (a, b] if it is continuous on (a, b) and
$\lim\limits_{x \to a^+} f(x) = f(a)$ and $\lim\limits_{x \to b^-} f(x) = f(b)$	$\lim\limits_{x \to a^+} f(x) = f(a)$	$\lim\limits_{x \to b^-} f(x) = f(b)$

Properties of Continuity

The following examples show the use of properties of continuity to describe the continuity of combined functions. The *Got to Know!* box lists these properties.

SEARCH 🔍

To see step-by-step videos of these problems, enter the page number into the SWadvantage.com Search Bar.

EXAMPLE 5

Describe the continuity of $h(x) = x - \cos x + \sin x$.

Apply the sum and difference properties of continuity.

Because each term of $h(x)$ is continuous everywhere, the entire function $h(x)$ is continuous everywhere.

EXAMPLE 6

Describe the continuity of $j(x) = (4x)(\sin x)$.

Apply the product property of continuity.

Because both $4x$ and $\sin x$ are continuous everywhere, the function $j(x)$ is continuous everywhere.

EXAMPLE 7

Describe the continuity of $k(x) = \frac{x-1}{x+2}$.

Apply the quotient property of continuity.

Because both $x - 1$ and $x + 2$ are continuous everywhere, the function $k(x)$ is continuous everywhere with one exception: $x \neq -2$.

EXAMPLE 8

Describe the continuity of $g(x) = 5\sqrt{x}$.

The function $\sqrt{x}$ is continuous on the half-open interval $[0, \infty)$.

Applying the constant multiple property of continuity, $g(x)$ is also continuous on $[0, \infty)$.

GOT TO KNOW!

Properties of Continuity

If a is a real number, and the functions $f(x)$ and $g(x)$ are continuous at a point c, then the following functions are also continuous at c.

Constant Multiple: af **Product:** fg

Sum: $f + g$ **Quotient:** $\frac{f}{g}, g(c) \neq 0$

Difference: $f - g$

Continuity of Composite Functions

To find the continuity of a composite function $f(g(x))$, first determine the continuity of $g(x)$, and then determine if the function f restricts the continuity.

Need More

HELP ?

For more about composite functions, go to *Composition of Functions* in *Advanced Algebra* (p. 2062).

EXAMPLE 9

Describe the continuity of $h(x) = \sin x^2$.

STEP 1 Write the function as a composite.

$f(g(x)) = \sin x^2$, where $g(x) = x^2$ and $f(x) = \sin g(x)$

STEP 2 Determine the continuity of $g(x)$.

Because $g(x)$ is a polynomial, it is continuous everywhere.

STEP 3 Determine the continuity of $f(x)$.

The sine function is continuous everywhere. Therefore, $f(x)$ has the same continuity as $g(x)$.

The function $h(x)$ is continuous everywhere.

EXAMPLE 10

Describe the continuity of $h(x) = \dfrac{1}{\sqrt{1-x^2}}$.

STEP 1 Write the function as a composite.

$f(g(x)) = \dfrac{1}{\sqrt{1-x^2}}$,

where $g(x) = \sqrt{1-x^2}$ and $f(x) = \dfrac{1}{g(x)}$

STEP 2 Determine the continuity of $g(x)$.

Because $g(x)$ is a radical, $1 - x^2 \geq 0$.

Therefore, $g(x)$ is continuous on the closed interval $[-1, 1]$.

STEP 3 Determine the continuity of $f(x)$.

$f(x)$ has the same continuity as $g(x)$ except where the denominator is 0.

$$\sqrt{1-x^2} \neq 0$$
$$x \neq \pm 1$$

The function $h(x)$ is continuous on the open interval $(-1, 1)$.

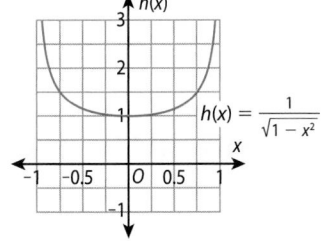

$h(x) = \dfrac{1}{\sqrt{1-x^2}}$

GOT TO KNOW!

Continuity of Composite Functions

If a function $g(x)$ is continuous at a point c, and the function $f(x)$ is continuous at $g(c)$, then the composite function $(f \circ g)(x) = f(g(x))$ is continuous at c.

Intermediate Value Theorem

SEARCH

To see step-by-step videos of these problems, enter the page number into the SWadvantage.com Search Bar.

Continuous Functions on a Closed Interval

Continuous functions have graphs that are smooth curves with no holes, poles, jumps, or breaks. If a function is continuous on a closed interval, then it must contain every y value on the interval and the endpoints.

In the real world, there are endless examples of these types of functions. A car's speed, for example, is a continuous function on a closed interval. If a car's speed increases from 0 to 50 mph in 30 seconds, then the car must have traveled every speed between 0 mph and 50 mph during the time interval 0 to 30 seconds.

The graphs below show examples of continuous functions on a closed interval.

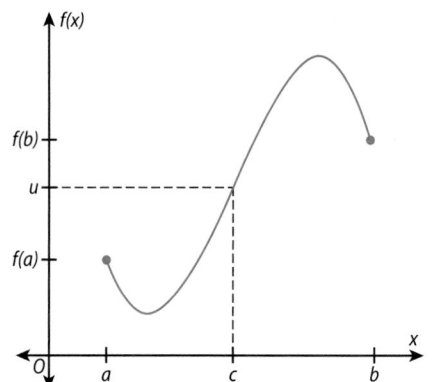
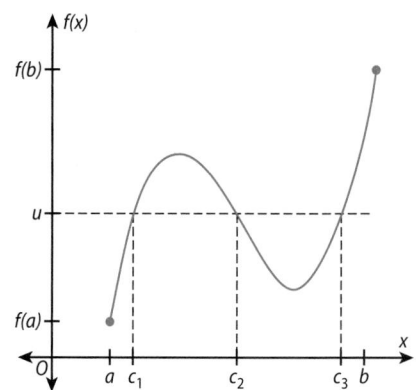

Intermediate Value Theorem

The functions shown on the graphs have a closed interval with endpoints a and b. These endpoints correspond to the y values $f(a)$ and $f(b)$.

Intermediate Value Theorem
If f is a continuous function on a closed interval $[a, b]$, and u is a value between $f(a)$ and $f(b)$, then there exists at least one value c on $[a, b]$ such that $f(c) = u$.

Notice in the graph on the left that the curve extends below $f(a)$ and above $f(b)$. The Intermediate Value Theorem only says that an x value for any y value between $f(a)$ and $f(b)$ must exist. Notice that the theorem does not say that only one x value exists for a certain u. The graph on the right side shows an example of three x values for a single u.

Watch Out !

The Intermediate Value Theorem is an *existence theorem*. You can use it to determine the existence of a value c, but the theorem does not help you determine what that value is.

EXAMPLE 1

Show that there is at least one value c on the interval $[-1, 1]$ such that $f(c) = 3$ if $f(x) = x^2 - 2x + 1$.

STEP 1 Calculate $f(x)$ at the left endpoint.

$$f(-1) = (-1)^2 - 2(-1) + 1 = 4$$

STEP 2 Calculate $f(x)$ at the right endpoint.

$$f(1) = (1)^2 - 2(1) + 1 = 0$$

STEP 3 Apply the Intermediate Value Theorem.

Since $f(-1) > 3 > f(1)$, there must at least one value c on $[-1, 1]$ such that $f(c) = 3$.

The Intermediate Value Theorem and Zeros

One common use for the Intermediate Value Theorem is to identify intervals on which zeros of given functions are located. Recall that a *zero* is a value of x for which $f(x) = 0$. Since zeros occur between positive and negative values of the function, you can use the Intermediate Value Theorem to state the existence of at least one zero between a and b if $f(a)$ and $f(b)$ have opposite signs. Zeros can also occur at the endpoints of an interval.

EXAMPLE 2

Show that $g(x) = x^3 - 2x - 2$ has a zero in the interval [0, 2].

STEP 1 Calculate $g(x)$ at the left endpoint.

$$g(0) = (0)^3 - 2(0) - 2 = -2$$

STEP 2 Calculate $g(x)$ at the right endpoint.

$$g(2) = (2)^3 - 2(2) - 2 = 2$$

STEP 3 Use the Intermediate Value Theorem to identify a zero.

Since $g(0) < 0$ and $g(2) > 0$, there must exist at least one value c on [0, 2] such that $g(c) = 0$.

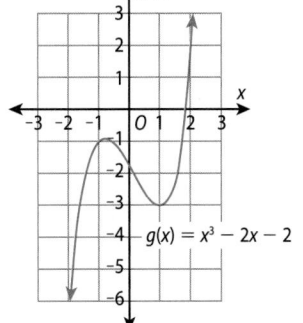

EXAMPLE 3

Show that a solution exists to the equation $\cos x + 4 \sin x + 1 = 0$ in the interval $\left[-\frac{\pi}{2}, 0\right]$.

STEP 1 Calculate $f(x)$ at the left endpoint.

$$f\left(-\frac{\pi}{2}\right) = \cos\left(-\frac{\pi}{2}\right) + 4\sin\left(-\frac{\pi}{2}\right) + 1 = -3$$

STEP 2 Calculate $f(x)$ at the right endpoint.

$$f(0) = \cos(0) + 4\sin(0) + 1 = 2$$

STEP 3 Use the Intermediate Value Theorem to identify a zero.

Since $f\left(-\frac{\pi}{2}\right) < 0$ and $f(0) > 0$, there must be at least one value c on $\left[-\frac{\pi}{2}, 0\right]$ such that $f(c) = 0$. Since a zero is a solution to the equation, a solution to the equation exists in the interval $\left[-\frac{\pi}{2}, 0\right]$.

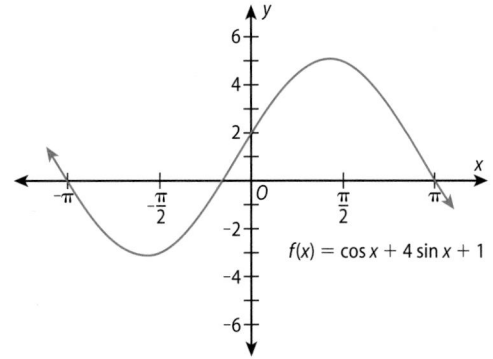

GOT TO KNOW!

Special Case of the Intermediate Value Theorem: Zeros

If f is a continuous function on [a, b], and $f(a)$ and $f(b)$ have opposite signs, there must be at least one c on [a, b] such that $f(c) = 0$.

Derivatives

What Came Before?
- Limits and continuity
- Finding rates of change by using slope

What's This About?
- Defining and understanding the derivative of a function
- Rules of differentiation
- Differentiation of trigonometric functions and higher order derivatives

Practical Apps
- Companies use derivatives to figure out how to maximize profits and minimize costs.
- Chemists use derivatives of exponential decay equations to determine the half-life of elements.

just for FUN!

Q: What's the derivative of cow?

A: Prime rib!

Slope of a Tangent

You can find the average rate of change between two points by drawing a secant between the points and calculating the slope, as shown on the graph at the right. Recall that the slope is Δy divided by Δx, which is sometimes called the rise divided by the run.

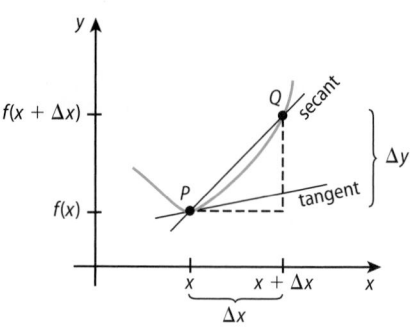

Calculus describes how to find the rate of change of a function at an instant. The instantaneous rate of change of $f(x)$ at point P is the slope of the tangent at P. Drawing the tangent with the correct slope would be difficult, but you can approximate the slope using a secant. On the graph, a secant is drawn from the point P to a nearby point Q. The slope of the secant m_{sec} is the change in the y values divided by the change in the x values.

$$m_{sec} = \frac{\Delta y}{\Delta x} = \frac{f(x + \Delta x) - f(x)}{\Delta x}$$

From the graph, you can see that as Q moves closer to P (as Δx gets smaller), the secant gets closer to the tangent. The slope of the tangent, then, is the limit as Δx approaches zero.

$$m_{tan} = \lim_{\Delta x \to 0} m_{sec} = \lim_{\Delta x \to 0} \frac{f(x + \Delta x) - f(x)}{\Delta x}$$

SEARCH

To see step-by-step videos of these problems, enter the page number into the SWadvantage.com Search Bar.

Try It This Way

To understand the slope of a tangent, draw a smooth curve on a piece of paper.

Mark a point of tangency on the curve. Place a ruler on the point of tangency and one other point on the curve. The edge of the ruler represents the secant.

Now move the second point closer to the point of tangency. Keep moving until the two points are essentially the same point. The edge of the ruler now represents the tangent.

EXAMPLE 1

Find the slope of the tangent to $y = x^2$ at the points (1, 1) and (0, 0).

STEP 1 Find the equation for the slope.

Use the definition of the slope of the tangent.	$m_{tan} = \lim\limits_{\Delta x \to 0} \dfrac{f(x + \Delta x) - f(x)}{\Delta x}$
Substitute the function into the definition.	$= \lim\limits_{\Delta x \to 0} \dfrac{(x + \Delta x)^2 - x^2}{\Delta x}$
Expand $(x + \Delta x)^2$.	$= \lim\limits_{\Delta x \to 0} \dfrac{x^2 + 2x\Delta x + (\Delta x)^2 - x^2}{\Delta x}$
Subtract like terms.	$= \lim\limits_{\Delta x \to 0} \dfrac{2x\Delta x + (\Delta x)^2}{\Delta x}$
Use the Distributive Property.	$= \lim\limits_{\Delta x \to 0} \dfrac{\Delta x(2x + \Delta x)}{\Delta x}$
Cancel Δx.	$= \lim\limits_{\Delta x \to 0} (2x + \Delta x)$
Find the limit.	$= 2x$

STEP 2 Find the value of the slope at (1, 1). $2x = 2(1) = 2$

STEP 3 Find the value of the slope at (0, 0). $2x = 2(0) = 0$

The slope of the tangent line to $y = x^2$ at (1, 1) is 2. The slope at (0, 0) is 0.

Notice in Example 1 that the equation for the slope is the same at all points on the function, but the actual slope is different for different points along the function.

Definition of a Derivative

An important concept in calculus is instantaneous changes in functions. The slope of a tangent describes these changes. The slope, called the derivative of the function, is defined in the *Got To Know!* box. The process of finding a derivative is called **differentiation**. Often, the derivative is written as $f'(x)$, which is read "f prime of x."

Common Derivative Notations

Notation	How It Is Read
$f'(x)$	f prime of x
y'	y prime
$\dot{y}$	y dot
$\dfrac{dy}{dx}$	the derivative of y with respect to x
$\dfrac{d}{dx}(f)$	the derivative of f with respect to x

EXAMPLE 2

Use the definition of a derivative to find $f'(x)$ if $f(x) = 5x + 6$.

Use the definition of a derivative.

$$f'(x) = \lim_{\Delta x \to 0} \frac{f(x + \Delta x) - f(x)}{\Delta x}$$

Substitute the function into the definition.

$$= \lim_{\Delta x \to 0} \frac{5(x + \Delta x) + 6 - (5x + 6)}{\Delta x}$$

Use the Distributive Property.

$$= \lim_{\Delta x \to 0} \frac{5x + 5\Delta x + 6 - 5x - 6}{\Delta x}$$

Subtract like terms.

$$= \lim_{\Delta x \to 0} \frac{5\Delta x}{\Delta x}$$

Cancel Δx and find the limit.

$$= \lim_{\Delta x \to 0} \frac{5\Delta x}{\Delta x} = 5$$

$$f'(x) = 5$$

Notice that the function described in Example 2, $f(x) = 5x + 6$, is a linear equation. The derivative is a constant, 5. Just as the slope of a linear equation is a constant, the derivative of a linear equation is a constant.

EXAMPLE 3

Use the definition of a derivative to find $f'(x)$ if $f(x) = x^2 - 4$.

Use the definition of a derivative.

$$f'(x) = \lim_{\Delta x \to 0} \frac{f(x + \Delta x) - f(x)}{\Delta x}$$

Substitute the function into the definition.

$$= \lim_{\Delta x \to 0} \frac{(x + \Delta x)^2 - 4 - (x^2 - 4)}{\Delta x}$$

Use the Distributive Property.

$$= \lim_{\Delta x \to 0} \frac{x^2 + 2x\Delta x + (\Delta x)^2 - 4 - x^2 + 4}{\Delta x}$$

Combine like terms.

$$= \lim_{\Delta x \to 0} \frac{2x\Delta x + (\Delta x)^2}{\Delta x}$$

Use the Distributive Property.

$$= \lim_{\Delta x \to 0} \frac{\Delta x(2x + \Delta x)}{\Delta x}$$

Cancel Δx. Then find the limit.

$$= \lim_{\Delta x \to 0} (2x + \Delta x) = 2x$$

$$f'(x) = 2x$$

Definition of a Derivative

The **derivative** of a function f at x is $f'(x) = \lim\limits_{\Delta x \to 0} \dfrac{f(x + \Delta x) - f(x)}{\Delta x}$ provided the limit exists.

Derivative at a Point

The derivative of a function has the same *equation* for any point. For most functions, however, the *value* of the derivative is different for different points. The following examples show how to find the derivative at a certain point.

EXAMPLE 4

Use the definition of a derivative to find $f'(x)$ at (1, 10) and at $\left(\frac{1}{2}, 3\right)$ if $f(x) = 8x^3 + 2x$.

STEP 1 Find the derivative $f'(x)$.

Use the definition of a derivative.

$$f'(x) = \lim_{\Delta x \to 0} \frac{f(x + \Delta x) - f(x)}{\Delta x}$$

Substitute the function into the definition.

$$= \lim_{\Delta x \to 0} \frac{8(x + \Delta x)^3 + 2(x + \Delta x) - (8x^3 + 2x)}{\Delta x}$$

Use the Distributive Property. Subtract like terms of $8x^3$ and $-2x$.

$$= \lim_{\Delta x \to 0} \frac{24x^2 \Delta x + 24x(\Delta x)^2 + 8(\Delta x)^3 + 2\Delta wx}{\Delta x}$$

Cancel Δx. Then find the limit.

$$= \lim_{\Delta x \to 0} 24x^2 + 24x\Delta x + 8(\Delta x)^2 + 2 = 24x^2 + 2$$

STEP 2 Find the value of the derivative at (1, 10).

$$f'(1) = 24(1)^2 + 2 = 26$$

STEP 3 Find the value of the derivative at $\left(\frac{1}{2}, 3\right)$.

$$f'\left(\frac{1}{2}\right) = 24\left(\frac{1}{2}\right)^2 + 2 = 8$$

The derivative of $f(x) = 8x^3 + 2x$ at (1, 10) is 26 and at $\left(\frac{1}{2}, 3\right)$ is 8.

EXAMPLE 5

Use the definition of a derivative to find $f'(x)$ at (3, 2) if $f(x) = \frac{6}{x}$.

STEP 1 Find the derivative $f'(x)$.

Use the definition of a derivative.

$$f'(x) = \lim_{\Delta x \to 0} \frac{f(x + \Delta x) - f(x)}{\Delta x}$$

Substitute the function into the definition.

$$= \lim_{\Delta x \to 0} \frac{\frac{6}{x + \Delta x} - \frac{6}{x}}{\Delta x}$$

Combine terms in the numerator.

$$= \lim_{\Delta x \to 0} \frac{\frac{6x - 6(x + \Delta x)}{x(x + \Delta x)}}{\Delta x}$$

Simplify.

$$= \lim_{\Delta x \to 0} \frac{-6\Delta x}{x(x + \Delta x)(\Delta x)}$$

Cancel Δx. Then find the limit.

$$= \lim_{\Delta x \to 0} \frac{-6}{x(x + \Delta x)} = -\frac{6}{x^2}$$

STEP 2 Find the derivative at (3, 2).

$$f'(3) = -\frac{6}{(3)^2} = -\frac{2}{3}$$

The derivative of $f(x) = \frac{6}{x}$ at (3, 2) is $-\frac{2}{3}$.

Instantaneous Rate of Change

Differentiation describes the rate of change of one variable with respect to another. This has many applications in everyday life, such as the rate of change of distance with respect to time, the rate of change in pressure with respect to volume, and the rate of change in cost with respect to availability.

EXAMPLE 6

The distance (in meters) along a straight path that an object moves from a starting point during time t (in seconds) is described by the function $f(t) = t^2 + 6t$. Use the definition of a derivative to find the instantaneous rate of change of the distance (in units m/s) at $t = 10$ s.

STEP 1 Find the derivative $f'(t)$.

Use the definition of a derivative.

$$f'(t) = \lim_{\Delta t \to 0} \frac{f(t + \Delta t) - f(t)}{\Delta t}$$

Substitute the function into the definition.

$$= \lim_{\Delta t \to 0} \frac{(t + \Delta t)^2 + 6(t + \Delta t) - (t^2 + 6t)}{\Delta t}$$

Simplify and cancel like terms. Then find the limit.

$$= \lim_{\Delta t \to 0} \frac{2t\Delta t + (\Delta t)^2 + 6\Delta t}{\Delta t} = 2t + 6$$

STEP 2 Find the value of the derivative at $t = 10$ s.

$$f'(10) = 2(10) + 6 = 26$$

The instantaneous rate of change of the distance at $t = 10$ seconds is 26 m/s.

EXAMPLE 7

The value V of a car decreases since the number of years t it was bought according to the equation $V(t) = 500t^2 - 4500t + 25,000$. What is the instantaneous rate of change (in dollars per year, \$/y) in the value of the car after 4 years?

STEP 1 Find the derivative $f'(t)$.

Use the definition of a derivative.

$$V'(t) = \lim_{\Delta t \to 0} \frac{V(t + \Delta t) - V(t)}{\Delta t}$$

Substitute the function into the definition.

$$= \lim_{\Delta t \to 0} \left[\frac{500(t + \Delta t)^2 - 4500(t + \Delta t) + 25,000 - (500t^2 - 4500t + 25,000)}{\Delta t} \right]$$

Simplify the numerator, and cancel like terms.

$$= \lim_{\Delta t \to 0} \frac{1000t\Delta t + 500(\Delta t)^2 - 4500\Delta t}{\Delta t}$$

Simplify. Then find the limit.

$$= \lim_{\Delta t \to 0} (1000t + 500\Delta t - 4500) = 1000t - 4500$$

STEP 2 Find the value of the derivative at $t = 4$ y.

$$V'(4) = 1000(4) - 4500 = -500$$

The instantaneous rate of change in the value of the car at $t = 4$ years is $-\$500$/y.

SEARCH

To see step-by-step videos of these problems, enter the page number into the SWadvantage.com Search Bar.

Approximate Rate of Change

Using a Table to Find an Approximate Rate of Change

Differentiation is useful for finding the instantaneous rate of change of a function only if you know the exact form of the function. If you do not know the exact form of the function, you can still find its approximate rate of change using the difference quotient, $\dfrac{f(x + \Delta x) - f(x)}{\Delta x}$.

If you look back at the definition of a derivative, you see that the limit of the difference quotient is the derivative of the function. You can use the difference quotient without taking a limit to find an approximate value of a derivative.

EXAMPLE 1

Find the approximate rate of change of the function $f(x)$ at $x = 2$ using the table at the right.

x	0	1	2	3	4
f(x)	2	5	14	29	50

Watch Out !

When you use the difference quotient with different methods, you should not expect to obtain the same answer. The answers will probably be different because they are approximations.

METHOD 1

Use values of x to the left and right of $x = 2$.

$$\frac{f(x + \Delta x) - f(x)}{\Delta x} = \frac{f(3) - f(1)}{3 - 1}$$

Substitute $f(3)$ and $f(1)$. Simplify the numerator.

$$= \frac{29 - 5}{2}$$

Simplify.

$$= 12$$

The approximate rate of change of $f(x)$ at $x = 2$ is 12.

METHOD 2

Use $x = 2$ and a value to the right of $x = 2$.

$$\frac{f(x + \Delta x) - f(x)}{\Delta x} = \frac{f(3) - f(2)}{3 - 2}$$

Substitute $f(3)$ and $f(2)$. Simplify the numerator.

$$= \frac{29 - 14}{1}$$

Simplify.

$$= 15$$

The approximate rate of change of $f(x)$ at $x = 2$ is 15.

METHOD 3

Use $x = 2$ and a value to the left of $x = 2$.

$$\frac{f(x + \Delta x) - f(x)}{\Delta x} = \frac{f(2) - f(1)}{2 - 1}$$

Substitute $f(2)$ and $f(1)$. Simplify the numerator.

$$= \frac{14 - 5}{1}$$

Simplify.

$$= 9$$

The approximate rate of change of $f(x)$ at $x = 2$ is 9.

GOT TO KNOW !

Difference Quotient

Use the difference quotient to find an approximate rate of change from a table of values.

$$\frac{f(x + \Delta x) - f(x)}{\Delta x}$$

EXAMPLE 2

Use the table at the right to find an approximate value of f'(x) at x = 9.

x	0	2	4	8	10
f(x)	−1	15	55	207	319

Use x = 8 and x = 10 in the difference quotient.

$$\frac{f(x + \Delta x) - f(x)}{\Delta x} = \frac{f(10) - f(8)}{10 - 8}$$

Substitute f(10) and f(8). Simplify the numerator.

$$= \frac{319 - 207}{2}$$

Simplify.

$$= 56$$

The approximate value of f'(x) at x = 9 is 56.

SEARCH

To see step-by-step videos of these problems, enter the page number into the SWadvantage.com Search Bar.

EXAMPLE 3

The position x (in meters) of an object is a function of the time t (in seconds). The velocity of the object is the rate of change of its position with respect to time. Use the table of values to find the approximate velocity of the object at t = 2.5 s.

t(s)	1	2	3	4	5
x(m)	2	11	26	47	74

Use t = 2 and t = 3 in the difference quotient.

$$\frac{f(t + \Delta t) - f(t)}{\Delta t} = \frac{f(3) - f(2)}{3 - 2}$$

Substitute f(3) and f(2). Simplify the numerator.

$$= \frac{26 - 11}{1}$$

Simplify.

$$= 15$$

The approximate velocity at t = 2.5 s is 15 m/s.

EXAMPLE 4

The table shows the revenue r (in thousands of dollars) of a company as a function of time t (in years). Find the approximate rate of change of the revenue in the 30th year.

t(y)	1	5	10	15	30
r($1000)	100	300	245	250	439

Use t = 15 and t = 30 in the difference quotient.

$$\frac{f(t + \Delta t) - f(t)}{\Delta t} = \frac{f(30) - f(15)}{30 - 15}$$

Substitute f(30) and f(15). Simplify the numerator.

$$= \frac{439 - 250}{15}$$

Simplify.

$$= 13 \text{ (rounded to 2 significant figures)}$$

The approximate rate of change of the revenue in t = 30 is $13,000/y.

Need More
HELP ?

For help with tangents, go to *Definition of a Derivative* on page 2158.

Using a Graph to Find an Approximate Rate of Change

If you do not know the form of a function, but you have a graph of it, you can find the approximate rate of change at a point using the slope of the tangent.

In some cases, the tangent at a certain point is drawn on the graph, and the slope that you calculate will be the exact rate of change.

If the tangent is not drawn, you can place a ruler on the graph to estimate the tangent. The slope you determine by this method is the approximate rate of change. Since the derivative of a function is the slope of the tangent at a point, this method also provides an estimate of the derivative.

EXAMPLE 5

Use the graph at the right to find the rate of change of $f(x)$ at the point (1, 2).

STEP 1 Choose points on the tangent that have convenient values of Δy and Δx.

Use the points (2, 3) and (0, 1).

STEP 2 Calculate the slope of the line.

$$\text{slope} = \frac{\Delta y}{\Delta x} = \frac{3 - 1}{2 - 0} = 1$$

The approximate rate of change of $f(x)$ at (1, 2) is 1.

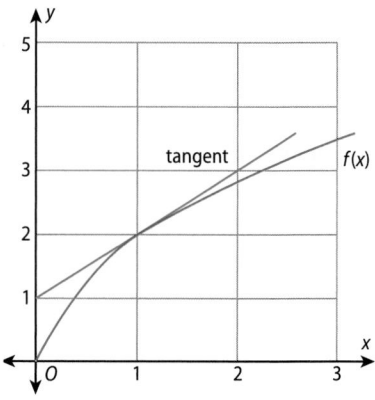

EXAMPLE 6

SEARCH

To see step-by-step videos of these problems, enter the page number into the SWadvantage.com Search Bar.

Use the graph at the right to find the derivative of $f(x)$ at the point (2, 1).

STEP 1 Choose points on the tangent that have convenient values of Δy and Δx.

Use the points (2, 1) and (0, 2).

STEP 2 Calculate the slope of the line.

$$\text{slope} = \frac{\Delta y}{\Delta x} = \frac{1 - 2}{2 - 0} = -\frac{1}{2}$$

The derivative of $f(x)$ at (1, 2) is $-\frac{1}{2}$.

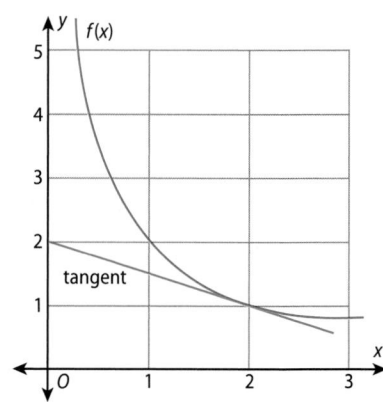

EXAMPLE 7

Use the graph at the right to find the approximate rate of change of $f(x)$ at the point $(-1, -2)$.

STEP 1 Use a ruler to connect two points that form a tangent at $(-1, -2)$.

Use the points $(-2, -4)$ and $(0, 0)$.

STEP 2 Calculate the slope of the line.

$$\text{slope} = \frac{\Delta y}{\Delta x} = \frac{-4 - 0}{-2 - 0} = 2$$

The approximate rate of change of $f(x)$ at $(-1, -2)$ is 2.

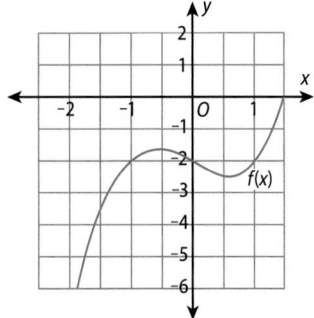

Watch Out !

Be careful to place the ruler so that it touches the function curve at just one point.

EXAMPLE 8

Use the graph at the right to find the approximate derivative of $f(x)$ at the point $(-1, 0)$.

STEP 1 Use a ruler to connect two points that form a tangent at $(-1, 0)$.

Use the points $(-2, 4)$ and $(0, -4)$.

STEP 2 Calculate the slope of the line.

$$\text{slope} = \frac{\Delta y}{\Delta x} = \frac{4 - (-4)}{-2 - 0} = -4$$

The derivative of $f(x)$ at $(-1, 0)$ is -4.

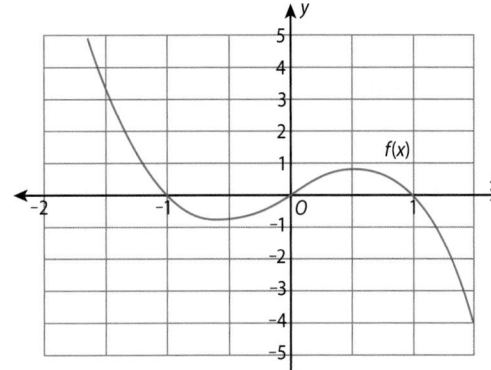

EXAMPLE 9

Use the graph in Example 8 to find the approximate derivative of $f(x)$ at the point $(1, 0)$.

STEP 1 Use a ruler to connect two points that form a tangent at $(1, 0)$.

Use the points $\left(\frac{1}{2}, 2\right)$ and $\left(\frac{3}{2}, -2\right)$.

STEP 2 Calculate the slope of the line.

$$\text{slope} = \frac{\Delta y}{\Delta x} = \frac{2 - (-2)}{\frac{1}{2} - \frac{3}{2}} = -4$$

The derivative of $f(x)$ at $(1, 2)$ is -4.

Differentiability and Continuity

Differentiability Implies Continuity

If a function is differentiable at a point c, then it is also continuous at that point. In order to prove that a function is continuous at a point, you can either show that it meets the three conditions for continuity at that point, or you can show that its derivative exists at that point.

SEARCH

To see step-by-step videos of these problems, enter the page number into the SWadvantage.com Search Bar.

Conditions for continuity:

- $f(x)$ is defined
- $\lim_{x \to c} f(x)$ exists
- $\lim_{x \to c} f(x) = f(c)$

Definition of a Derivative:

$$f'(c) = \lim_{\Delta x \to 0} \frac{f(x + \Delta x) - f(x)}{\Delta x}$$

at $x = c$

EXAMPLE 1

Show that $f(x) = 3x^2 + 1$ is continuous at the point $x = 1$.

METHOD 1

Show that the function meets the conditions for continuity at $x = 1$.

Show that $f(1)$ is defined. $f(1) = 3(1)^2 + 1 = 4$

Show that $\lim_{x \to 1} f(x)$ exists. $\lim_{x \to 1} f(x) = \lim_{x \to 1} (3x^2 + 1) = 3(1)^2 + 1 = 4$

Show that $\lim_{x \to 1} f(x) = f(1)$ $4 = 4$

Because the function meets the three conditions for continuity, it is continuous at $x = 1$.

METHOD 2

Show that the derivative exists at $x = 1$.

STEP 1 Find the derivative.

Use the definition of a derivative. $f'(x) = \lim_{\Delta x \to 0} \dfrac{f(x + \Delta x) - f(x)}{\Delta x}$

Substitute $f(x) = 3x^2 + 1$. $= \lim_{\Delta x \to 0} \dfrac{3(x + \Delta x)^2 + 1 - (3x^2 + 1)}{\Delta x}$

Simplify the numerator. Cancel Δx. $= \lim_{\Delta x \to 0} \dfrac{6x\Delta x + 3(\Delta x)^2}{\Delta x}$

Simplify and find the limit. $= \lim_{\Delta x \to 0} (6x + 3\Delta x) = 6x$

STEP 2 Find $f'(1)$.

$6(1) = 6$

Because the derivative exists at $x = 1$, the function is continuous at $x = 1$.

GOT TO KNOW!

Differentiability Implies Continuity

If a function is differentiable at a point, then the function is continuous at that point.

Continuity Does Not Imply Differentiability

Some functions are continuous but not differentiable at a point. Examples include functions that have a vertical tangent line at a point or functions that have a corner or cusp.

EXAMPLE 2

Show that $f(x) = |x|$ is continuous but not differentiable at $x = 0$.

STEP 1 Show that the function is continuous at $x = 0$.

Show that $f(0)$ is defined. $\qquad\qquad$ $f(0) = |0| = 0$

Show that $\lim\limits_{x \to 0} f(x)$ exists by taking one-sided limits. $\qquad$ $\lim\limits_{x \to 0^+} |0| = \lim\limits_{x \to 0^-} |0| = 0$

Show that $\lim\limits_{x \to 0} f(x) = f(0)$. $\qquad\qquad$ $0 = 0$

Because the function meets the three conditions for continuity, it is continuous at $x = 0$.

STEP 2 Show that the function is not differentiable at $x = 0$.

Use the limit of the difference quotient. $\qquad$ $f'(x) = \lim\limits_{\Delta x \to 0} \dfrac{f(x + \Delta x) - f(x)}{\Delta x}$

Insert $f(x) = |x|$. $\qquad\qquad\qquad\qquad\quad$ $= \lim\limits_{\Delta x \to 0} \dfrac{|x + \Delta x| - |x|}{\Delta x}$

Evaluate for $f'(0)$ and simplify. $\qquad\qquad$ $= \lim\limits_{\Delta x \to 0} \dfrac{|0 + \Delta x| - |0|}{\Delta x} = \lim\limits_{\Delta x \to 0} \dfrac{|\Delta x|}{\Delta x}$

Evaluate the left-hand limit. $\qquad$ $\lim\limits_{\Delta x \to 0^-} \dfrac{|\Delta x|}{\Delta x} = -1$

Evaluate the right-hand limit. $\qquad$ $\lim\limits_{\Delta x \to 0^+} \dfrac{|\Delta x|}{\Delta x} = 1$

Since the left- and right-hand limits do not agree, the derivative does not exist at $x = 0$.

Need More HELP

For more about one-sided limits, go to *Left- and Right-Hand Limits* on page 2132.

EXAMPLE 3

Show that $g(x) = \sqrt[3]{x}$ is continuous but not differentiable at $x = 0$.

STEP 1 Show that the function is continuous at $x = 0$.

Show that $g(0)$ is defined. $\qquad$ $g(0) = \sqrt[3]{0} = 0$

Show that $\lim\limits_{x \to 0} g(x)$ exists. $\qquad$ $\lim\limits_{x \to 0} g(0) = \lim\limits_{x \to 0} \sqrt[3]{0} = 0$

Show that $\lim\limits_{x \to 0} g(x) = g(0)$. $\qquad$ $0 = 0$

Because the function meets the three conditions for continuity, it is continuous at $x = 0$.

STEP 2 Show that the function is not differentiable at $x = 0$.

Use the limit of the difference quotient. $\qquad$ $g'(x) = \lim\limits_{\Delta x \to 0} \dfrac{g(x + \Delta x) - g(x)}{\Delta x}$

Insert $g(x) = \sqrt[3]{x}$. $\qquad\qquad\qquad\qquad$ $= \lim\limits_{\Delta x \to 0} \dfrac{\sqrt[3]{x + \Delta x} - \sqrt[3]{x}}{\Delta x}$

Evaluate for $g'(0)$. $\qquad\qquad$ $g'(0) = \lim\limits_{\Delta x \to 0} \dfrac{\sqrt[3]{0 + \Delta x} - \sqrt[3]{0}}{\Delta x}$

Simplify and find the limit. $\qquad\qquad$ $= \lim\limits_{\Delta x \to 0} \dfrac{1}{(\Delta x)^{2/3}}$ Does Not Exist

The function is continuous but not differentiable at $x = 0$.

Need More HELP

For more about simplifying radical expressions, go to *Dividing Radical Expressions* in *Advanced Algebra*. (page 1962).

Local Linearity

To see an example of local linearity, graph $y = x^2$ on a graphing calculator and zoom in until the parabolic curve looks like a line.

Tangent Line Approximation

If you zoom in toward a certain point on the graph of a function, the function looks like a straight line. The linear appearance of a function at a certain point is called **local linearity**.

The slope of this zoomed-in portion of the function is very close to the slope of the tangent line at that point. Recall that the derivative of a function at a certain point is the slope of the tangent line at that point. Because of this similar behavior, you can approximate the value of a function using the tangent line for values close to the point of tangency, as shown in the graph. Using a tangent line to approximate a function's value at a certain point is called **tangent line approximation**.

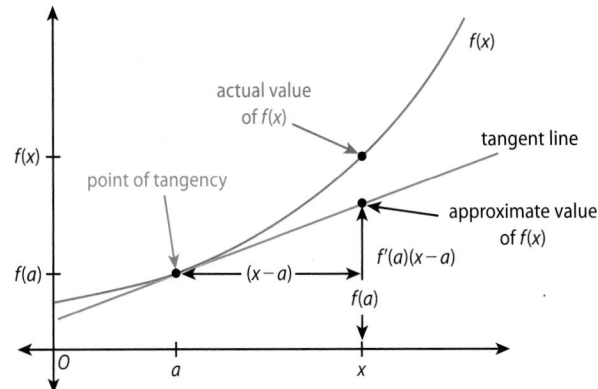

The point-slope formula of a line with a slope m is $y - y_1 = m(x - x_1)$. Applying this to a function $f(x)$ at a point $(a, f(a))$, using the derivative as the slope, provides an approximation of the function: $f(x) \approx f(a) + f'(a)(x - a)$.

EXAMPLE 1

What is the tangent line approximation for a function $f(t)$ close to the point (0, 0) if the derivative of the function is $f'(t) = 2t + 6$?

STEP 1 Determine the derivative at $t = 0$. $\qquad\qquad f'(0) = 2(0) + 6 = 6$

STEP 2 Use the derivative to approximate the function $f(t)$ at (0, 0).

Use the formula for tangent line approximation. $\qquad f(t) \approx f(a) + f'(a)(t - a)$

Rewrite the approximation for $a = 0$. $\qquad\qquad\qquad \approx f(0) + f'(0)(t - 0)$

Substitute $f(0) = 0$, $f'(0) = 6$, and $a = 0$. $\qquad\qquad \approx 0 + 6(t - 0)$

Simplify. $\qquad\qquad\qquad\qquad\qquad\qquad\qquad\qquad \approx 6t$

The tangent line approximation at (0, 0) is $f(t) \approx 6t$.

Tangent Line Approximation

Given the derivative $f'(a)$ of a function at a point $(a, f(a))$, the approximate function at that point is

$$f(x) \approx f(a) + f'(a)(x - a).$$

Error of the Tangent Line Approximation

The tangent line approximation does not usually provide the actual value of the function. You can calculate the error $E(x)$ by subtracting the approximation from the actual value of the function: $E(x) = f(x) - [f(a) + f'(a)(x - a)]$.

$E(x)$ at the point where you calculate the approximation should be zero. If you use the tangent line approximation at another point, $E(x)$ will generally increase the farther you are from that point.

EXAMPLE 2

The derivative of a function is $f'(x) = 15x^2$.

a. What is the tangent line approximation for the function close to the point $(1, -1)$?

STEP 1 Determine the derivative at $x = 1$. $\qquad f'(1) = 15(1)^2 = 15$

STEP 2 Use the derivative to approximate the function $f(x)$ at $(1, -1)$.

Use the formula for tangent line approximation. $\qquad f(x) \approx f(a) + f'(a)(x - a)$

Rewrite the approximation for $a = 1$. $\qquad \approx f(1) + f'(1)(x - 1)$

Substitute $f(1) = -1, f'(1) = 15$, and $a = 1$. $\qquad \approx -1 + 15(x - 1)$

Simplify. $\qquad \approx 15x - 16$

The tangent line approximation at $(1, -1)$ is $f(x) \approx 15x - 16$.

b. If the actual function is $f(x) = 5x^3 - 6$, what is the tangent line approximation error at $(1, -1)$?

Use the error formula. $\qquad E(x) = f(x) - [f(a) + f'(a)(x - a)]$

Substitute $f(x)$ and the approximation. $\qquad = 5x^3 - 6 - (15x - 16)$

Substitute $x = 1$. Then simplify. $\qquad = 5(1)^3 - 6 - [15(1) - 16] = 0$

Because the tangent line approximation was calculated at $(1, -1)$, the error at that point is 0.

c. What is the tangent line approximation error at $(2, 34)$?

Use the error formula. $\qquad E(x) = f(x) - [f(a) + f'(a)(x - a)]$

Substitute $f(x)$ and the approximation. $\qquad = 5x^3 - 6 - (15x - 16)$

Substitute $x = 2$. $\qquad = 5(2)^3 - 6 - [15(2) - 16] = 20$

Because the tangent line approximation was calculated at $(1, -1)$, the error at $(2, 34)$ is not 0. When the approximation is applied to the point $(2, 34)$, the error is $E(x) = 20$.

GOT TO KNOW!

Error of the Tangent Line Approximation

Given the tangent line approximation for a function $f(x)$ at a point $(a, f(a))$ and the derivative of the function at that point $f'(a)$, the error of using that approximation at any point on the function is:

$$E(x) = f(x) - [f(a) + f'(a)(x - a)].$$

Constant, Sum, and Difference Rules

Simple Derivative Rules

Finding the derivative of a function using the limit of the difference quotient can be laborious. This method, however, reveals useful formulas for some common derivatives that make finding the derivative much simpler. For these special cases, you can use derivative rules such as the ones listed in the *Got To Know!* box below. It is useful when expressing these rules to use the derivative notation $\frac{d}{dx} f(x)$.

EXAMPLE 1

Find the derivative of $f(x) = 6$.

METHOD 1

Use the definition of a derivative.

Begin with the derivative of the function.
$$f'(6) = \lim_{\Delta x \to 0} \frac{f(x + \Delta x) - f(x)}{\Delta x}$$

The value of $f(x)$ is 6 everywhere.
$$= \lim_{\Delta x \to 0} \frac{6 - 6}{\Delta x}$$

Simplify.
$$= 0$$

Therefore $f'(x) = 0$ for all values of x.

METHOD 2

Use the constant rule for derivatives.
$$\frac{d}{dx}(6) = 0$$

This method also shows that $f'(x) = 0$ for all values of x.

Try It This Way

Graph the function $f(x) = 6$ on a graphing calculator. Notice that the slope of the constant line is always zero. This shows that the derivative of a constant function is zero.

GOT TO KNOW!

Constant, Sum, and Difference Differentiation Rules

Constant Rule: The derivative of any constant is zero.

If c is a real number, then
$$\frac{d}{dx}(c) = 0.$$

Constant Multiple Rule: The derivative of the product of a constant and a function is the constant times the derivative of the function.

If c is a real number and $f(x)$ is a differentiable function, then
$$\frac{d}{dx}[cf(x)] = c\frac{d}{dx}f(x).$$

Sum Rule: The derivative of sums is the sum of the derivatives.

If $f(x)$ and $g(x)$ are differentiable functions, then
$$\frac{d}{dx}[f(x) + g(x)] = \frac{d}{dx}f(x) + \frac{d}{dx}g(x).$$

Difference Rule: The derivative of a difference is the difference of the derivatives.

If $f(x)$ and $g(x)$ are differentiable functions, then
$$\frac{d}{dx}[f(x) - g(x)] = \frac{d}{dx}f(x) - \frac{d}{dx}g(x).$$

EXAMPLE 2

The derivative of $f(x) = 4x^2 - 9$ is $f'(x) = 8x$. Find the derivative of $7f(x)$.

Substitute $f(x)$. $\frac{d}{dx}[7f(x)] = \frac{d}{dx}[7(4x^2 - 9)]$

Use the constant multiple rule of derivatives. $= 7\frac{d}{dx}(4x^2 - 9)$

Insert the derivative of $4x^2 - 9$. Then simplify. $= 7(8x) = 56x$

The derivative of $7f(x)$ is $56x$.

SEARCH

To see step-by-step videos of these problems, enter the page number into the SWadvantage.com Search Bar.

EXAMPLE 3

The derivative of $f(x) = x^6 + 4x$ is $f'(x) = 6x^5 + 4$, and the derivative of $g(x) = 2x^5 - 3x$ is $g'(x) = 10x^4 - 3$.

a. Find the derivative of $f(x) + g(x)$.

Substitute $f(x)$ and $g(x)$. $\frac{d}{dx}[f(x) + g(x)] = \frac{d}{dx}[(x^6 + 4x) + (2x^5 - 3x)]$

Use the sum rule of derivatives. $= \frac{d}{dx}(x^6 + 4x) + \frac{d}{dx}(2x^5 - 3x)$

Insert the derivatives. $= 6x^5 + 4 + 10x^4 - 3$

Simplify. $= 6x^5 + 10x^4 + 1$

The derivative of $f(x) + g(x)$ is $6x^5 + 10x^4 + 1$.

b. Find the derivative of $f(x) - g(x)$.

Substitute $f(x)$ and $g(x)$. $\frac{d}{dx}[f(x) + g(x)] = \frac{d}{dx}[(x^6 + 4x) - (2x^5 - 3x)]$

Use the difference rule of derivatives. $= \frac{d}{dx}(x^6 + 4x) - \frac{d}{dx}(2x^5 - 3x)$

Insert the derivatives. $= 6x^5 + 4 - (10x^4 - 3)$

Simplify. $= 6x^5 - 10x^4 + 7$

The derivative of $f(x) - g(x)$ is $6x^5 - 10x^4 + 7$.

EXAMPLE 4

The derivative of $f(x) = 4x^3 + 7x$ is $f'(x) = 12x^2 + 7$ and the derivative of $g(x) = 9x^2 - x$ is $g'(x) = 18x - 1$. Find the derivative of $8x^3 + 18x^2 + 12x - 18$.

Factor out 2 and rearrange to get $f(x)$ and $g(x)$. $\frac{d}{dx}[(8x^3 + 18x^2 + 12x - 18)] = \frac{d}{dx}2[(4x^3 + 7x) + (9x^2 - x) - 9]$

Use the constant multiple rule. $= 2\frac{d}{dx}[(4x^3 + 7x) + (9x^2 - x) - 9]$

Use the sum and difference rules. $= 2\left[\frac{d}{dx}(4x^3 + 7x) + \frac{d}{dx}(9x^2 - x) - \frac{d}{dx}9\right]$

Insert the derivatives. Use the constant rule. $= 2[12x^2 + 7 + 18x - 1 - 0]$

Simplify. $= 2[12x^2 + 18x + 6]$

Use the distributive property. $= 24x^2 + 36x + 12$

The derivative of $8x^3 + 18x^2 + 12x - 9$ is $24x^2 + 36x + 12$.

Power, Product, and Quotient Rules

Power Rule for Derivatives

One of the most powerful formulas for simplifying the differentiation process is the power rule for derivatives. This formula allows you to quickly take the derivative of any power without using the definition of a derivative equation.

When you take the derivative of a power function, multiply the function by the exponent, and then reduce the exponent by one. This means that the instantaneous rate of change of a quartic function is a cubic function, the instantaneous rate of change of a cubic function is a quadratic function, and so on.

Ways to REMEMBER

Product Rule: Try the phrase "1d2 plus 2d1" to remember the formula.

Quotient Rule: Try the phrase "low-dee-high minus high-dee-low all over low low" to remember the formula.

EXAMPLE 1

Find: $\dfrac{d}{dx}(x^7)$

Use the power rule for derivatives. $\qquad \dfrac{d}{dx}(x^7) = 7\dfrac{d}{dx}(x^{7-1})$

Simplify. $\qquad\qquad\qquad\qquad\qquad\qquad = 7x^6$

EXAMPLE 2

Find: $\dfrac{d}{dx}\left(x^{\frac{3}{2}}\right)$

Use the power rule for derivatives. $\qquad \dfrac{d}{dx}\left(x^{\frac{3}{2}}\right) = \dfrac{3}{2}x^{\frac{3}{2}-1}$

Simplify. $\qquad\qquad\qquad\qquad\qquad\qquad = \dfrac{3}{2}x^{\frac{1}{2}}.$

GOT TO KNOW!

Power, Product, and Quotient Differentiation Rules

1) **Power Rule**

   If n is a real number then

   $\dfrac{d}{dx}(x^n) = nx^{n-1}$.

2) **Product Rule**

   If $f(x)$ and $g(x)$ are differentiable functions, then

   $\dfrac{d}{dx}[f(x)g(x)] = f(x)g'(x) + g(x)f'(x)$.

3) **Quotient Rule**

   If $f(x)$ and $g(x)$ are differentiable functions where $g(x) \neq 0$ then

   $\dfrac{d}{dx}\left[\dfrac{f(x)}{g(x)}\right] = \dfrac{g(x)f'(x) - f(x)g'(x)}{(g(x))^2}$.

EXAMPLE 3

Find: $\frac{d}{dx}\left(\frac{1}{x}\right)$

Rewrite the fraction as a power of x. $\quad\quad \frac{d}{dx}\left(\frac{1}{x}\right) = \frac{d}{dx}(x^{-1})$

Use the power rule for derivatives. $\quad\quad\quad = -1x^{-1-1}$

Simplify and rewrite. $\quad\quad\quad\quad\quad\quad = -x^{-2} = -\frac{1}{x^2}$

EXAMPLE 4

Find: $\frac{d}{dx}\sqrt{x}$

Rewrite the fraction as a power of x. $\quad\quad \frac{d}{dx}\sqrt{x} = \frac{d}{dx}\left(x^{\frac{1}{2}}\right)$

Use the power rule for derivatives. $\quad\quad\quad = \frac{1}{2}x^{\frac{1}{2}-1}$

Simplify. $\quad\quad\quad\quad\quad\quad\quad\quad\quad = \frac{1}{2}x^{-\frac{1}{2}}$

Need More HELP?

For more about fractional exponents, see *Properties of Exponents* in *Advanced Algebra* (p. 1970).

EXAMPLE 5

Find: $\frac{d}{dx}(3x^3)$

Use the constant multiple rule for derivatives. $\quad\quad \frac{d}{dx}(3x^3) = 3\frac{d}{dx}(x^3)$

Use the power rule for derivatives. $\quad\quad\quad\quad = 3 \cdot 3x^{3-1}$

Simplify. $\quad\quad\quad\quad\quad\quad\quad\quad\quad\quad\quad = 9x^2$

EXAMPLE 6

Find the derivative of $y = 3x^2 + 2x + 1$.

Use the sum rule for derivatives. $\quad\quad \frac{dy}{dx} = \frac{d}{dx}(3x^2) + \frac{d}{dx}(2x) + \frac{d}{dx}(1)$

Use the constant rule for derivatives. $\quad\quad\quad = \frac{d}{dx}(3x^2) + \frac{d}{dx}(2x) + 0$

Use the constant multiple rule for derivatives. $\quad\quad = 3\frac{d}{dx}(x^2) + 2\frac{d}{dx}(x)$

Use the power rule for derivatives. $\quad\quad\quad = 3(2x) + 2(1)$

Simplify. $\quad\quad\quad\quad\quad\quad\quad\quad\quad\quad = 6x + 2$

SEARCH

To see step-by-step videos of these problems, enter the page number into the SWadvantage.com Search Bar.

Notice that the derivative of the quadratic function in Example 6 is a linear function.

Product Rule for Derivatives

You can use the product rule to find the derivative of a function that involves the multiplication of two functions. For some functions, it is easier to apply the product rule before you simplify. For other functions, simplifying is easier than using the product rule.

EXAMPLE 7

Find the derivative of $y = 3x^{-3}(2x + 1)$.

<table>
<tr><td>Insert the function into the equation.</td><td>$\dfrac{dy}{dx} = \dfrac{d}{dx}[3x^{-3}(2x + 1)]$</td></tr>
<tr><td>Use the product rule for derivatives.</td><td>$= 3x^{-3}\dfrac{d}{dx}[(2x + 1)] + (2x + 1)\dfrac{d}{dx}(3x^{-3})$</td></tr>
<tr><td>Use the sum rule for derivatives.</td><td>$= 3x^{-3}\dfrac{d}{dx}(2x) + 3x^{-3}\dfrac{d}{dx}(1) + (2x + 1)\dfrac{d}{dx}(3x^{-3})$</td></tr>
<tr><td>Use the constant multiple rule and the constant rule.</td><td>$= 6x^{-3}\dfrac{d}{dx}x + 0 + 3(2x + 1)\dfrac{d}{dx}(x^{-3})$</td></tr>
<tr><td>Use the power rule for derivatives.</td><td>$= 6x^{-3}(1) + 3(2x + 1)(-3)x^{-4}$</td></tr>
<tr><td>Simplify.</td><td>$= -12x^{-3} - 9x^{-4}$</td></tr>
<tr><td></td><td>$= \dfrac{-12}{x^3} - \dfrac{9}{x^4}$</td></tr>
</table>

Watch Out !

The derivative of a product is not a product of the derivatives.

EXAMPLE 8

Find the derivative of $y = (3x^{-3})(x^{-6} - 3x)$.

METHOD 1

Simplify the function before taking the derivative.

<table>
<tr><td>Insert the function into the equation.</td><td>$\dfrac{dy}{dx} = \dfrac{d}{dx}[3x^{-3}(x^{-6} - 3x)]$</td></tr>
<tr><td>Use the distributive property.</td><td>$= \dfrac{d}{dx}(3x^{-9} - 9x^{-2})$</td></tr>
<tr><td>Use the difference and the constant rules.</td><td>$= 3\dfrac{d}{dx}(x^{-9}) - 9\dfrac{d}{dx}(x^{-2})$</td></tr>
<tr><td>Use the power rule for derivatives.</td><td>$= -27x^{-10} + 18x^{-3}$</td></tr>
</table>

METHOD 2

Use the product rule before simplifying.

<table>
<tr><td>Insert the function into the equation.</td><td>$\dfrac{dy}{dx} = \dfrac{d}{dx}[3x^{-3}(x^{-6} - 3x)]$</td></tr>
<tr><td>Use the product rule for derivatives.</td><td>$= (3x^{-3})\dfrac{d}{dx}(x^{-6} - 3x) + (x^{-6} - 3x)\dfrac{d}{dx}(3x^{-3})$</td></tr>
<tr><td>Use the constant multiple and difference rules.</td><td>$= (3x^{-3})\dfrac{d}{dx}(x^{-6}) - 3(3x^{-3})\dfrac{d}{dx}(x) + 3(x^{-6} - 3x)\dfrac{d}{dx}(x^{-3})$</td></tr>
<tr><td>Use the power rule for derivatives.</td><td>$= (-6)(3x^{-3})x^{-7} - 3(3x^{-3})(1) + (-3)(3)(x^{-6} - 3x)x^{-4}$</td></tr>
<tr><td>Simplify.</td><td>$= -27x^{-10} + 18x^{-3}$</td></tr>
<tr><td></td><td>$= \dfrac{-27}{x^{10}} + \dfrac{18}{x^3}$</td></tr>
</table>

Quotient Rule for Derivatives

If you apply the quotient rule, you might find that the procedure gets complicated. Like the product rule, however, the quotient rule can greatly simplify the differentiation process for some functions.

EXAMPLE 9

Use the quotient rule to find the derivative of $\frac{x}{\sqrt{x}}$.

Insert the function. Rewrite the radical as an exponent.

$$\frac{dy}{dx} = \frac{d}{dx}\left(\frac{x}{\sqrt{x}}\right) = \frac{d}{dx}\left(\frac{x}{x^{\frac{1}{2}}}\right)$$

Use the quotient rule for derivatives.

$$= \frac{x^{\frac{1}{2}}\frac{d}{dx}(x) - x\frac{d}{dx}\left(x^{\frac{1}{2}}\right)}{\left(x^{\frac{1}{2}}\right)^2}$$

Use the power rule for derivatives.

$$= \frac{x^{\frac{1}{2}}(1) - \frac{1}{2}x\left(x^{-\frac{1}{2}}\right)}{\left(x^{\frac{1}{2}}\right)^2}$$

Simplify.

$$= \frac{1}{2}x^{-\frac{1}{2}}$$

$$= \frac{1}{2x^{\frac{1}{2}}}$$

SEARCH

To see step-by-step videos of these problems, enter the page number into the SWadvantage.com Search Bar.

EXAMPLE 10

Find the derivative of $y = \frac{12x^3}{(x^4 + 2)}$.

Insert the function in the equation.

$$\frac{dy}{dx} = \frac{d}{dx}\left[\frac{12x^3}{(x^4 + 2)}\right]$$

Use the quotient rule for derivatives.

$$= \frac{(x^4 + 2)\frac{d}{dx}(12x^3) - 12x^3\frac{d}{dx}(x^4 + 2)}{(x^4 + 2)^2}$$

Use the sum rule for derivatives.

$$= \frac{(x^4 + 2)\frac{d}{dx}(12x^3) - 12x^3\frac{d}{dx}(x^4) - 12x^3\frac{d}{dx}(2)}{(x^4 + 2)^2}$$

Use the distributive property.

$$= \frac{x^4\frac{d}{dx}(12x^3) + 2\frac{d}{dx}(12x^3) - 12x^3\frac{d}{dx}(x^4) - 12x^3\frac{d}{dx}(2)}{(x^4 + 2)^2}$$

Use the constant multiple rule.

$$= \frac{12x^4\frac{d}{dx}(x^3) + 24\frac{d}{dx}(x^3) - 12x^3\frac{d}{dx}(x^4) - 12x^3\frac{d}{dx}(2)}{(x^4 + 2)^2}$$

Use the power rule and constant rule.

$$= \frac{36x^4x^2 + 72x^2 - 48x^3x^3 - 0}{(x^4 + 2)^2}$$

Simplify the numerator.

$$= \frac{-12x^6 + 72x^2}{(x^4 + 2)^2}$$

Expand the denominator.

$$= \frac{-12x^6 + 72x^2}{x^8 + 4x^4 + 4}$$

Chain Rule

Derivatives of Composite Functions

A composite is a function that is composed of another function: $f(g(x))$. The rules for derivatives presented so far will not work for many composite functions. To differentiate composite functions, first identify the outer and inner functions.

outer function

$f(g(x))$

inner function

The Chain Rule describes how to find the derivative of a composite function. Let $u = g(x)$ be the inner function. Then the derivative of the composite function is the derivative of the outer function with respect to u multiplied by the derivative of the inner function with respect to x.

> ### Ways to REMEMBER
>
> When taking the derivative of a composite function, think about eating a chocolate covered peanut. The outer function is the chocolate and the inner function is the peanut. The derivative of this delicious treat is the derivative of the outer chocolate times the derivative of the inner peanut.

EXAMPLE 1

Find the derivative of $y = (x + 4)^2$.

METHOD 1

Expand the function and then find the derivative.

Use the FOIL method to expand the function. $y = (x + 4)^2 = x^2 + 8x + 16$

Use the Power Rule to find the derivative. $\dfrac{dy}{dx} = 2x + 8$

METHOD 2

Use the Chain Rule to find the derivative.

STEP 1 Determine the layers of functions. $y = u^2 \qquad u = x + 4$

STEP 2 Differentiate the outer and inner functions.

Differentiate the outer function. $\dfrac{dy}{du} = \dfrac{d}{du}(u^2) = 2u$

Differentiate the inner function. $\dfrac{du}{dx} = \dfrac{d}{dx}(x + 4) = 1$

STEP 3 Apply the Chain Rule. $\dfrac{dy}{dx} = \dfrac{dy}{du}\dfrac{du}{dx}$

Substitute the derivatives. $= (2u)(1) = 2u$

Substitute for u, and simplify. $= 2(x + 4) = 2x + 8$

Using both methods, the derivative of $y = (x + 4)^2$ is $2x + 8$.

GOT TO KNOW!

Chain Rule

For a composite function $y = f(g(x))$, let $y = f(u)$, and $u = g(x)$. If $f(u)$ is differentiable at u, and $g(x)$ is differentiable at x, then

$$\frac{dy}{dx} = \frac{dy}{du}\frac{du}{dx} \text{ or equivalently, } \frac{d}{dx}[f(g(x))] = f'(g(x)) \cdot g'(x).$$

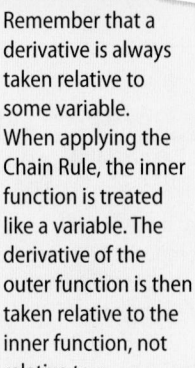

EXAMPLE 2

Use the Chain Rule to find the instantaneous rate of change of $y = \sqrt{x^2 + 2x + 3}$.

STEP 1 Determine the layers of functions.

$$y = u^{\frac{1}{2}} \qquad u = x^2 + 2x + 3$$

STEP 2 Differentiate the outer and inner functions.

Differentiate the outer function.
$$\frac{dy}{du} = \frac{d}{du}(u^{\frac{1}{2}}) = \frac{1}{2}u^{-\frac{1}{2}} = \frac{1}{2\sqrt{u}}$$

Differentiate the inner function.
$$\frac{du}{dx} = \frac{d}{dx}(x^2 + 2x + 3) = 2x + 2$$

STEP 3 Apply the Chain Rule.

Insert the derivatives.
$$\frac{dy}{dx} = \frac{dy}{du}\frac{du}{dx} = \frac{1}{2\sqrt{u}}(2x + 2)$$

Substitute for u, and simplify.
$$= \left(\frac{1}{2\sqrt{x^2 + 2x + 3}}\right)(2x + 2) = \frac{x + 1}{\sqrt{x^2 + 2x + 3}}$$

The following example uses the Chain Rule to find a tangent line. Recall that the slope at a point is the derivative. You can therefore use the point-slope equation to find the tangent line equation. Notice the use of the notation $\left.\dfrac{dy}{dx}\right|_c$, which means the derivative at a point c.

EXAMPLE 3

Write the equation of the tangent line to $f(x) = \dfrac{1}{(3x^4 - 5)^2}$ at $x = 0$.

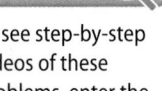

STEP 1 Determine the layers of functions.

$$y = u^{-2} \qquad u = 3x^4 - 5$$

STEP 2 Differentiate the outer and inner functions.

Differentiate the outer function.
$$\frac{dy}{du} = \frac{d}{du}(u^{-2}) = -2u^{-3} = \frac{-2}{u^3}$$

Differentiate the inner function.
$$\frac{du}{dx} = \frac{d}{dx}(3x^4 - 5) = 12x^3$$

STEP 3 Apply the Chain Rule.

Insert the derivatives. Then substitute u.
$$\frac{dy}{dx} = \frac{dy}{du}\frac{du}{dx} = \frac{-2}{u^3}(12x^3) = \frac{-24x^3}{(3x^4 - 5)^3}$$

STEP 4 Evaluate the derivative at $x = 0$.
$$\left.\frac{dy}{dx}\right|_0 = \frac{-24(0)^3}{(3(0)^4 - 5)^3} = 0$$

STEP 5 Find the equation of the tangent line.

Use $x_1 = 0$, $y_1 = f(0) = \dfrac{1}{(-5)^2}$, and $m = \left.\dfrac{dy}{dx}\right|_0$ in the point-slope equation.
$$y - \frac{1}{(-5)^2} = 0(x - 0)$$

Simplify.
$$y = \frac{1}{(-5)^2} = \frac{1}{25}$$

The equation of the tangent line at $x = 0$ is $y = \dfrac{1}{25}$.

SOUTHWESTERN

Derivatives of Multiple-Function Composites

You can extend the Chain Rule for a composite of multiple functions. The derivative of the composite function is the product of the derivative of each function with respect to the next inner function.

EXAMPLE 4

Find the derivative of $y = \left(3 - \frac{1}{x}\right)^{-1}$.

STEP 1 Determine the layers of functions.

$$y = u^{-1} \qquad u = 3 - v \qquad v = \frac{1}{x}$$

STEP 2 Differentiate each function.

Differentiate y with respect to u. $\qquad \frac{dy}{du} = \frac{d}{du}(u^{-1}) = -u^{-2}$

Differentiate u with respect to v. $\qquad \frac{du}{dv} = \frac{d}{dv}(3 - v) = -1$

Differentiate v with respect to x. $\qquad \frac{dv}{dx} = \frac{d}{dx}\left(\frac{1}{x}\right) = \frac{d}{dx}(x^{-1}) = -x^{-2}$

STEP 3 Apply the Chain Rule.

Insert the derivatives. $\qquad \dfrac{dy}{dx} = \dfrac{dy}{du}\dfrac{du}{dv}\dfrac{dv}{dx}$

$$= (-u^{-2})(-1)(-x^{-2})$$

Substitute u and v. $\qquad = \left(\dfrac{-1}{\left(3 - \frac{1}{x}\right)^2}\right)(-1)\left(\dfrac{-1}{x^2}\right)$

Simplify. $\qquad = \dfrac{-1}{x^2\left(3 - \frac{1}{x}\right)^2}$

GOT TO KNOW!

Chain Rule for a Three-Function Composite

For a composite function $y = f(g(h(x)))$, let $y = f(u)$, and $u = g(v)$, and $v = h(x)$. If $f(u)$ is differentiable at u, $g(v)$ is differentiable at v, and $h(x)$ is differentiable at x, then

$$\frac{dy}{dx} = \frac{dy}{du}\frac{du}{dv}\frac{dv}{dx},$$

or equivalently, $\frac{d}{dx}[f(g(h(x)))] = f'(g(h(x))) \cdot g'(h(x)) \cdot h'(x)$.

Using Multiple Derivative Rules

The following examples show how to take the derivative of functions using more than one derivative technique.

EXAMPLE 5

Find the derivative of $f(x) = (x^2 + 12)\left(\sqrt{2x^2 - 1}\right)$.

Use the Product Rule.

$$f'(x) = (x^2 + 12)\frac{d}{dx}\left(\sqrt{2x^2 - 1}\right) + \left(\sqrt{2x^2 - 1}\right)\frac{d}{dx}(x^2 + 12)$$

Use the Chain Rule and the Power Rule.

$$= (x^2 + 12)\left[\frac{1}{2}(2x^2 - 1)^{-\frac{1}{2}}(4x)\right] + \left(\sqrt{2x^2 - 1}\right)(2x)$$

Simplify in radical form.

$$= \frac{2x(x^2 + 12)}{\sqrt{2x^2 - 1}} + 2x\sqrt{2x^2 - 1}$$

Write with a common denominator.

$$= \frac{2x(x^2 + 12)}{\sqrt{2x^2 - 1}} + \frac{2x(2x^2 - 1)}{\sqrt{2x^2 - 1}}$$

Combine fractions.

$$= \frac{2x(x^2 + 12) + 2x(2x^2 - 1)}{\sqrt{2x^2 - 1}}$$

Simplify.

$$= \frac{6x^3 + 22x}{\sqrt{2x^2 - 1}}$$

Need More

HELP ?

The previous examples demonstrate how to apply the Chain Rule by explicitly showing each step. Once you are familiar with the Chain Rule, you can skip most of the steps and simply write down the derivative, as shown on the examples on this page.

EXAMPLE 6

Find the derivative of $f(x) = \dfrac{x}{(x^4 - 1)^3}$.

Use the Quotient Rule.

$$f'(x) = \frac{(x^4 - 1)^3\frac{d}{dx}(x) - (x)\frac{d}{dx}(x^4 - 1)^3}{[(x^4 - 1)^3]^2}$$

Use the Power Rule and the Chain Rule.

$$= \frac{(x^4 - 1)^3(1) - (x)[3(x^4 - 1)^2(4x^3)]}{[(x^4 - 1)^3]^2}$$

Simplify.

$$= \frac{(x^4 - 1)^3 - (12x^4)(x^4 - 1)^2}{(x^4 - 1)^6}$$

Factor out the common factor.

$$= \frac{(x^4 - 1)^2[(x^4 - 1) - (12x^4)]}{(x^4 - 1)^6}$$

Cancel the common factor.

$$= \frac{(x^4 - 1) - (12x^4)}{(x^4 - 1)^4}$$

Simplify.

$$= \frac{-11x^4 - 1}{(x^4 - 1)^4}$$

SEARCH 🔍

To see step-by-step videos of these problems, enter the page number into the SWadvantage.com Search Bar.

Derivatives of Trigonometric Functions

The derivative of each trigonometric function is also a trigonometric function. To see this in action, place a straight edge on the graph of a trigonometric function such as sine to model the tangent line. If you move the straight edge to model the tangent line at different x values, it will oscillate periodically just like other trigonometric functions.

The following examples show how to use trigonometric derivatives with other derivative rules.

EXAMPLE 1

Find: $\frac{d}{dx}(\sin^2 x)$

Rewrite the function.	$\frac{d}{dx}(\sin^2 x) = \frac{d}{dx}[(\sin x)^2]$
Use the Chain Rule.	$= (2\sin x)\frac{d}{dx}(\sin x)$
Use a trig formula.	$= 2\sin x(\cos x)$

EXAMPLE 2

Find: $\frac{d}{dx}(3x \cos x)$

Use the Product Rule.	$\frac{d}{dx}(3x \cos x) = (3x)\frac{d}{dx}(\cos x) + \cos x\frac{d}{dx}(3x)$
Use a trig formula.	$= 3x(-\sin x) + (\cos x)\frac{d}{dx}(3x)$
Use the Constant Multiple Rule.	$= 3x(-\sin x) + 3\cos x\frac{d}{dx}(x)$
Use the Power Rule.	$= 3x(-\sin x) + 3(\cos x)(1)$
Simplify.	$= -3x \sin x + 3\cos x$

Need More HELP?

The words *trigonometry* and *trigonometric* are often shortened to trig.

SEARCH

To see step-by-step videos of these problems, enter the page number into the SWadvantage.com Search Bar.

Derivatives of Trigonometric Functions

$\frac{d}{dx}(\sin x) = \cos x$ $\frac{d}{dx}(\csc x) = -\csc x \cot x$

$\frac{d}{dx}(\cos x) = -\sin x$ $\frac{d}{dx}(\sec x) = \sec x \tan x$

$\frac{d}{dx}(\tan x) = \sec^2 x$ $\frac{d}{dx}(\cot x) = -\csc^2 x$

EXAMPLE 3

Find: $\frac{d}{dx}(\tan 4x)$

Use the Chain Rule and a trig formula.	$\frac{d}{dx}(\tan 4x) = (\sec^2 4x)\frac{d}{dx}(4x)$
Use the Constant Multiple and Power Rules.	$= (\sec^2 4x)(4)$
Simplify.	$= 4\sec^2 4x$

Watch Out !

Because trig identities allow the same function to be expressed in different ways, there will be many ways to write the derivatives of trig functions.

EXAMPLE 4

Find: $\frac{d}{dx}[(\sec 3x)(1 - \sin 3x)]$

Use the Product Rule.
$$\frac{d}{dx}[(\sec 3x)(1 - \sin 3x)]$$
$$= (\sec 3x)\frac{d}{dx}(1 - \sin 3x) + (1 - \sin 3x)\frac{d}{dx}(\sec 3x)$$

Use the Chain Rule and trig formulas. $= (\sec 3x)(-\cos 3x)(3) + (1 - \sin 3x)(\sec 3x \tan 3x)(3)$

Use the Commutative Property. $= -3(\sec 3x)(\cos 3x) + 3(1 - \sin 3x)(\sec 3x \tan 3x)$

Use the Distributive Property. $= -3(\sec 3x)(\cos 3x) + 3(\sec 3x \tan 3x - \sin 3x \sec 3x \tan 3x)$

Use trig identities. $= -3(1) + 3\left(\sec 3x \tan 3x - \sin 3x \frac{1}{\cos 3x}\frac{\sin 3x}{\cos 3x}\right)$

Simplify. $= -3 + 3\left(\sec 3x \tan 3x - \frac{\sin^2 3x}{\cos^2 3x}\right)$

Use a trig identity. $= -3 + 3(\sec 3x \tan 3x - \tan^2 3x)$

Need More HELP ?

For more about trigonometric identities, go to *Fundamental Identities* in *Trigonometry* (Book 1, p. 996).

EXAMPLE 5

Find: $\frac{d}{dx}\sqrt{\csc(1 - x)}$

Note that the function is a multiple-function composite.

Rewrite with a fractional exponent. $\frac{d}{dx}\sqrt{\csc(1 - x)} = \frac{d}{dx}[\csc(1 - x)]^{\frac{1}{2}}$

Use the Chain Rule and trig formulas. $= \frac{1}{2}[\csc(1 - x)]^{-\frac{1}{2}}[-\csc(1 - x)\cot(1 - x)(-1)]$

Multiply. $= \frac{1}{2}\csc(1 - x)^{\frac{1}{2}}\cot(1 - x)$

Write in radical form. $= \frac{1}{2}\sqrt{\csc(1 - x)}\cot(1 - x)$

SOUTHWESTERN

Trigonometric Tangent Lines

The slope of a line tangent to a function is the derivative of the function. The graph at the right shows an example. For trigonometric functions, you must use trigonometric derivative formulas to find the slope. You can then use this slope to write the equation of the tangent line at a certain point. In the examples below, the notation y' is used for the derivative of y with respect to x.

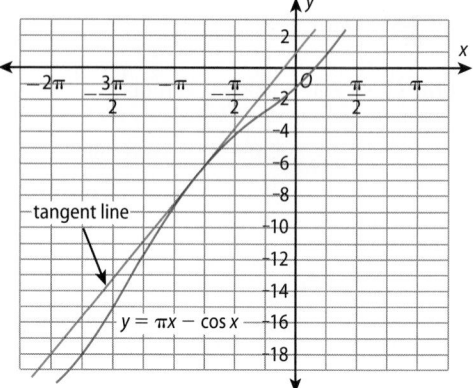

tangent line

$y = \pi x - \cos x$

EXAMPLE 6

Write the equation of the line tangent to $y = \pi x - \cos x$ when $x = -\pi$.

STEP 1 Determine the slope of the tangent line at $x = -\pi$.

Find the slope of the tangent line. $y' = \pi + \sin x$

Evaluate the slope at $x = -\pi$. $y'(-\pi) = \pi + \sin(-\pi) = \pi + (0) = \pi$

STEP 2 Determine the y value at $x = -\pi$. $y(-\pi) = \pi(-\pi) - \cos(-\pi) = -\pi^2 - (-1) = -\pi^2 + 1$

STEP 3 Find the equation of the tangent line.

Use the point-slope equation. $y - y_1 = m(x - x_1)$

Substitute. $y - (-\pi^2 + 1) = \pi(x - (-\pi))$

Simplify. $y = \pi x + 1$

Watch Out !

Don't confuse the functional notation $y(0)$ with the variable y multiplied by 0. Although they look the same, the functional notation means the function y evaluated at the point $x = 0$. You can only tell the difference by looking at how they are used in a problem.

EXAMPLE 7

Write the equation of the line tangent to $y = \sin^2 x - \sin x + 1$ when $x = 0$.

STEP 1 Determine the slope of the tangent line at $x = 0$.

Find the slope of the tangent line. $y' = 2(\sin x)(\cos x) - \cos x$

Evaluate the slope at $x = 0$. $y'(0) = 2(\sin(0))(\cos(0)) - \cos(0) = 2(0)(1) - 1 = -1$

STEP 2 Determine the y value at $x = 0$. $y(0) = \sin^2(0) - \sin(0) + 1 = 0 - 0 + 1 = 1$

STEP 3 Find the equation of the tangent line.

Use the point-slope equation. $y - y_1 = m(x - x_1)$

Substitute. $y - (1) = (-1)(x - (0))$

Simplify. $y = -x + 1$

EXAMPLE 8

Find the instantaneous rate of change of $y = \frac{4x+1}{\sin x}$ when $x = \frac{\pi}{2}$.

The instantaneous rate of change is the derivative of a function at a certain point.

STEP 1 Find the derivative y'.

Use the quotient rule.

$$y' = \frac{(\sin x)\frac{d}{dx}(4x+1) - (4x+1)\frac{d}{dx}(\sin x)}{(\sin x)^2}$$

Differentiate.

$$= \frac{(\sin x)(4) - (4x+1)(\cos x)}{(\sin x)^2}$$

STEP 2 Evaluate y' at $\frac{\pi}{2}$.

Substitute

$$y'\left(-\frac{\pi}{2}\right) = \frac{\left(\sin\left(-\frac{\pi}{2}\right)\right)(4) - \left(4\left(-\frac{\pi}{2}\right)+1\right)\left(\cos\left(-\frac{\pi}{2}\right)\right)}{\left(\sin\left(-\frac{\pi}{2}\right)\right)^2}$$

Differentiate and simplify.

$$= \frac{(-1)(4) - \left(4\left(-\frac{\pi}{2}\right)+1\right)(0)}{(-1)^2} = \frac{-4-0}{1} = -4$$

Need More

HELP ?

For trigonometric values of special angles, see *Trigonometric Ratios of Special Angles* in *Trigonometry* (Book 1, p. 910).

EXAMPLE 9

The total number of people in a store for $0 \le t \le 9$ hr is given by $P(t) = \left(10\sqrt{t}\right)[\sin^2 \pi t + \cos^2 t]$. Find the approximate rate of people entering or leaving the store $P'(t)$, in people/hr, when $t = 1$ hr.

STEP 1 Find the derivative $P'(t)$.

Use the product rule.

$$P'(t) = \left(10\sqrt{t}\right)\frac{d}{dt}[\sin^2 \pi t + \cos^2 t] + [\sin^2 \pi t + \cos^2 t]\frac{d}{dt}\left(10\sqrt{t}\right)$$

Use the Chain Rule.

$$= \left(10\sqrt{t}\right)\left[2\sin \pi t \cdot \frac{d}{dt}\sin \pi t + 2\cos t \cdot \frac{d}{dt}\cos t\right]$$
$$+ [\sin^2 \pi t + \cos^2 t]\frac{d}{dt}\left(10\sqrt{t}\right)$$

Use the Chain Rule again.

$$= \left(10\sqrt{t}\right)\left[2\sin \pi t \cdot \cos \pi t \frac{d}{dt}\pi t + 2\cos t \cdot (-\sin t)\right]$$
$$+ [\sin^2 \pi t + \cos^2 t]\frac{d}{dt}\left(10\sqrt{t}\right)$$

Use the constant multiple and power rules.

$$= \left(10\sqrt{t}\right)[2\sin \pi t \cdot (\cos \pi t)(\pi)$$
$$+ 2\cos t \cdot (-\sin t)] + [\sin^2 \pi t + \cos^2 t]5t^{-\frac{1}{2}}$$

STEP 2 Evaluate $P'(t)$ at $t = 1$.

Substitute.

$$P'(1) = \left(10\sqrt{1}\right)2\sin\pi \cdot (\cos \pi)(\pi) + 2\cos t(1) \cdot (-\sin(1))$$
$$+ [\sin^2 \pi + \cos^2(1)]5(1)^{-\frac{1}{2}}$$

Use a calculator to simplify.

$$P'(1) \approx -7.633$$

Therefore, people are leaving the store at a rate of approximately 7.633 people/hr at $t = 1$ hr.

SEARCH

To see step-by-step videos of these problems, enter the page number into the SWadvantage.com Search Bar.

Higher Order Derivatives

Determining Higher Order Derivatives

You can take the derivative of a derivative function. This new function is called a **higher order derivative**. These higher order derivatives are called the first derivative, the second derivative, the third derivative, and so on until the nth derivative. The first derivative, $f'(x)$, describes the rate of change of the original function. The second derivative, $f''(x)$, describes the rate of change of the first derivative, which is the rate of change of the rate of change.

The second derivative has many practical applications. One familiar example is acceleration. Suppose $f'(x)$ describes velocity, which is the rate of change of position. Then $f''(x)$ describes acceleration, which is the rate of change of velocity. Another example is sales. If $f'(x)$ describes the increase or decrease in sales, then $f''(x)$ describes how the increase or decrease in sales is increasing or decreasing.

EXAMPLE 1

Find the third derivative of $y = 4\sqrt{x + 1}$.

STEP 1 Find the first derivative.

Rewrite using a fractional exponent. $\qquad y = 4(x + 1)^{\frac{1}{2}}$

Use the Chain Rule. $\qquad y' = 4\left(\frac{1}{2}\right)(x + 1)^{-\frac{1}{2}}(1) = 2(x + 1)^{-\frac{1}{2}}$

STEP 2 Differentiate the first derivative to find the second derivative.

Use the Chain Rule. $\qquad y'' = 2\left(-\frac{1}{2}\right)(x + 1)^{-\frac{3}{2}}(1) = -(x + 1)^{-\frac{3}{2}}$

STEP 3 Differentiate the second derivative to find the third derivative.

Use the Chain Rule. $\qquad y''' = -\left(-\frac{3}{2}\right)(x + 1)^{-\frac{5}{2}}(1) = \frac{3}{2}(x + 1)^{-\frac{5}{2}}$

$y''' = \frac{3}{2}(x + 1)^{-\frac{5}{2}}$

Need More

HELP ?

Recall the Chain Rule.
$$\frac{dy}{dx} = \frac{dy}{du}\frac{du}{dx}$$
For more about the derivatives of composite functions, go to *Chain Rule* on page 2176.

GOT TO KNOW!

Notation For Higher Derivatives

1st derivative	$f'(x)$	$\frac{dy}{dx}$	y'	y prime
2nd derivative	$f''(x)$	$\frac{d^2y}{dx^2}$	y''	y double prime
3rd derivative	$f'''(x)$	$\frac{d^3y}{dx^3}$	y'''	y triple prime
4th derivative	$f^{(4)}(x)$	$\frac{d^4y}{dx^4}$	$y^{(4)}$	y quadruple prime
10th derivative	$f^{(10)}(x)$	$\frac{d^{10}y}{dx^{10}}$	$y^{(10)}$	
nth derivative	$f^{(n)}(x)$	$\frac{d^ny}{dx^n}$	$y^{(n)}$	

Polynomial and Trigonometric Higher Order Derivatives

Each time you take the derivative of a polynomial, its degree decreases by one. If you take the derivative enough times, the higher order derivative will eventually be zero.

The derivatives of trigonometric functions, however, are trigonometric functions. Higher order derivatives are not eventually zero. Trigonometric functions and their higher order derivatives can even repeat themselves. In some cases, you can use the repeating pattern to determine higher order derivatives without working through many derivations.

EXAMPLE 2

Find the fifth derivative of $f(x) = x^4 + 3x^3 - 7x + 2$.

Differentiate five times.

$$f'(x) = 4x^3 + 9x^2 - 7$$
$$f''(x) = 12x^2 + 18x$$
$$f'''(x) = 24x + 18$$
$$f^{(4)}(x) = 24$$
$$f^{(5)}(x) = 0$$

SEARCH

To see step-by-step videos of these problems, enter the page number into the SWadvantage.com Search Bar.

EXAMPLE 3

Find: $\dfrac{d^4}{dx^4}(\sin x)$

Differentiate four times.

$$\frac{dy}{dx} = \frac{d}{dx}(\sin x) = \cos x$$
$$\frac{d^2y}{dx^2} = \frac{d}{dx}(\cos x) = -\sin x$$
$$\frac{d^3y}{dx^3} = \frac{d}{dx}(-\sin x) = -\cos x$$
$$\frac{d^4y}{dx^4} = \frac{d}{dx}(-\cos x) = \sin x$$

EXAMPLE 4

Find $y^{(12)}$ if $y = \sin 3x$.

STEP 1 Find lower derivatives to look for a pattern.

$$y' = 3 \cos 3x$$
$$y'' = -3^2 \sin 3x$$
$$y''' = -3^3 \cos 3x$$
$$y^{(4)} = 3^4 \sin 3x$$
$$y^{(5)} = -3^5 \cos 3x$$

STEP 2 Examine the pattern to solve the problem.

The second, third, fourth, and fifth derivatives repeat. Only the power of 3 changes. Counting through the derivatives reveals that $y^{(12)}$ is similar to $y^{(4)}$ with a different power of 3.

Therefore, $y^{(12)} = 3^{12}\sin 3x$.

Derivatives of Inverse Functions

Finding the Derivative of an Inverse Function

Need More
HELP ?

For more about inverse functions, go to *Inverses of Linear Functions* and *Inverses of Non-Linear Functions* in *Advanced Algebra* (pp. 2090, 2094).

An inverse function, $f^{-1}(x)$, is a reflection of the original function about the line $y = x$.

As the graph at the right shows, the slope of a function at a point (a, b) and the slope of the inverse function at (b, a) are reciprocals.

Because the derivative is the slope at a certain point, you can use this property to find the derivative of an inverse function at the point. First find the corresponding x value for $f(x)$. Then find the derivative of the $f(x)$ at this point. The reciprocal is the derivative of the inverse function.

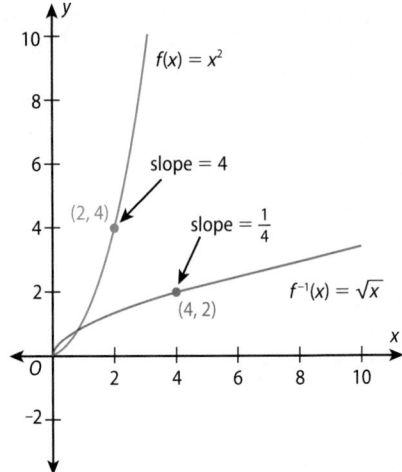

EXAMPLE 1

Find $\frac{d}{dx}\left(f^{-1}(x)\right)$ at $x = 1$ if $f(x) = \sqrt{x} - 1$.

STEP 1 You are given the x value for the inverse function. Find the corresponding x value for $f(x)$.

Set $f(x)$ equal to 1. Then solve for x.

$$f(x) = \sqrt{x} - 1 = 1$$
$$\sqrt{x} = 2$$
$$x = 4$$

STEP 2 Find the derivative of $f(x)$ at $x = 4$.

$$f'(x) = \frac{1}{2}x^{-\frac{1}{2}}$$
$$f'(4) = \frac{1}{2}(4)^{-\frac{1}{2}} = \frac{1}{4}$$

STEP 3 Find the reciprocal.

$$\frac{d}{dx}\left(f^{-1}(1)\right) = \frac{1}{\frac{d}{dx}(f(4))} = \frac{1}{\frac{1}{4}} = 4$$

Therefore, the derivative of the inverse function at $x = 1$ is 4.

GOT TO KNOW!

Derivative of an Inverse Function

The derivative of an inverse function at x is the reciprocal of the derivative of the original function evaluated at the inverse's y value.

$$\frac{d}{dx}\left(f^{-1}(x)\right) = \frac{1}{\frac{d}{dx}\left(f(f^{-1}(x))\right)}$$

EXAMPLE 2

Find $\frac{d}{dx}(f^{-1}(x))$ at $x = 3$ if $f(x) = x^3 + 2$.

STEP 1 You are given the x value for the inverse function. Find the corresponding x value for $f(x)$.

Set $f(x)$ equal to 3. Then solve for x.
$$f(x) = x^3 + 2 = 3$$
$$x^3 = 1$$
$$x = \sqrt[3]{1} = 1$$

STEP 2 Find the derivative of $f(x)$ at $x = 1$.
$$f'(x) = 3x^2$$
$$f'(1) = 3(1)^2 = 3$$

STEP 3 Find the reciprocal.
$$\frac{d}{dx}(f^{-1}(3)) = \frac{1}{\frac{d}{dx}(f(1))}$$
$$= \frac{1}{3}$$

Therefore, the derivative of the inverse function at $x = 3$ is $\frac{1}{3}$.

SEARCH

To see step-by-step videos of these problems, enter the page number into the SWadvantage.com Search Bar.

EXAMPLE 3

Find $\frac{d}{dx}(f^{-1}(x))$ at $x = 2$ if $f(x) = x^4 + 4$.

You are given the x value for the inverse function. Find the corresponding x value for $f(x)$.

Set $f(x)$ equal to 2. $f(x) = x^4 + 4 = 2$

Solve for x. $x = \sqrt[4]{-2}$

The x value of $f(x)$ does not exist at this point. This indicates that there is no derivative of the inverse function at $x = 2$.

EXAMPLE 4

Use the table to find $\frac{d}{dx}(f^{-1}(x))$ at $x = 5$.

x	$f(x)$	$f^{-1}(x)$	$f'(x)$
1	5	2	4
5	−3	1	6

STEP 1 Use the table to find the value of the inverse function at $x = 5$. $f^{-1}(5) = 1$

STEP 2 Find the derivative of $f(x)$ at $x = 1$. $f'(1) = 4$

STEP 3 Find the reciprocal. $\frac{d}{dx}(f^{-1}(5)) = \dfrac{1}{\frac{d}{dx}(f(1))} = \frac{1}{4}$

Therefore, the derivative of the inverse function at $x = 5$ is $\frac{1}{4}$.

Applications of Derivatives

What Came Before?

- Finding and evaluating derivatives
- Applying the Power, Product, Quotient, and Chain Rules of differentiation

What's This About?

- Finding relationships between a function and its first and second derivatives
- Finding the equation of a line tangent to a curve
- Solving problems involving optimization

Practical Apps

- Optimization is used by economists when dealing with supply and demand.
- Physics uses position functions and their derivatives to describe an object's path, velocity, and acceleration.

Just for FUN!

Delta's doorbell rings.

DELTA: "Epsilon! What are you doing here?"

EPSILON: "Oh, I was just in the neighborhood."

CONTENTS	UPLOAD	DOWNLOAD	Calculus

Topics	Vocabulary	Pages
Relationships Between f, f', f''	*critical value* *critical point* *inflection point*	2190–2197
Position, Velocity, and Acceleration	*displacement* *speed*	2198–2201
Curve Sketching	*local maximum* *local minimum* *absolute maximum* *absolute minimum* *inflection point*	2202–2207
Implicit Differentiation	*explicit* *implicit* *implicit differentiation*	2208–2211
Tangent and Normal Lines	*normal line*	2212–2213
Related Rates	*related rates*	2214–2219
Optimization		2220–2227
Mean Value Theorem		2228–2229
Extreme Value Theorem		2230–2231

You can find more practice problems online by visiting:
www.SWadvantage.com

Relationships between f, f', f''

SOUTHWESTERN

The Relationship between f and f'

A function's first derivative is the slope of the tangent line at any given point. Look at the tangent lines on the graph at the right. If the function is increasing on an interval, the slope is positive. The first derivative of the function is therefore positive for the interval. If the function is decreasing on an interval, the slope is negative, and the first derivative is negative. If the function is constant, its slope is zero and the first derivative is zero.

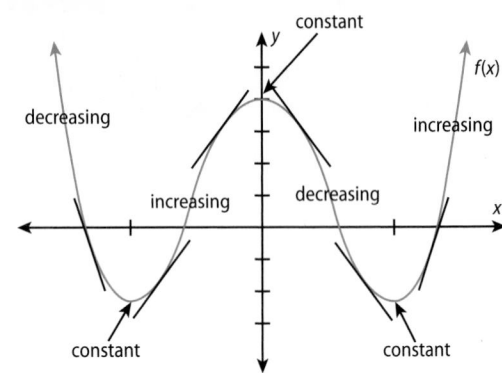

SEARCH

To see step-by-step videos of these problems, enter the page number into the SWadvantage.com Search Bar.

EXAMPLE 1

Determine whether the function $f(x) = 3x^4 - 7x^2 + 5$ is increasing, decreasing, or constant at the point $x = -1$.

Find the first derivative. $f'(x) = 12x^3 - 14x$

Substitute $x = -1$. $f'(-1) = 12(-1)^3 - 14(-1) = 2$

Because $f'(-1)$ is positive, the function is increasing at $x = -1$.

EXAMPLE 2

Determine whether the function $f(x) = x^5 - 3x^2 - 3$ is increasing, decreasing, or constant at the point $x = 1$.

Find the first derivative. $f(x) = 5x^4 - 6x$

Substitute $x = 1$. $f'(1) = 5(1)^4 - 6(1) = -1$

Because $f'(1)$ is negative, the function is decreasing at $x = 1$.

EXAMPLE 3

Determine whether the function $f(x) = \sin x - x$ is increasing, decreasing, or constant at the point $x = 0$.

Find the first derivative. $f'(x) = \cos x - 1$

Substitute $x = 0$. $f'(0) = \cos (0) - 1 = 0$

Because $f'(0)$ is zero, the function is constant at $x = 0$.

GOT TO KNOW!

Relationship between f and f'

f	Increasing	Constant	Decreasing
f'	Positive	Zero	Negative

Critical Points

When a function f is defined at a point c, and the first derivative of the function at that point is zero or does not exist (or is undefined), then c is a **critical value** and the ordered pair $(c, f(c))$ is a **critical point** of the function. Critical points indicate where the graphical behavior of a function changes.

EXAMPLE 4

Find the critical points of $y = \frac{1}{3}x^3 - \frac{5}{2}x^2 + 6x + \frac{1}{2}$.

STEP 1 Find the derivative.

$$y' = x^2 - 5x + 6$$

STEP 2 Find the zeros of the derivative.

Set the derivative equal to zero. $x^2 - 5x + 6 = 0$

Factor. $(x - 2)(x - 3) = 0$

Solve for x. $x = 2, 3$

Therefore, y has critical points at $x = 2$ and $x = 3$.

EXAMPLE 5

Find the critical points of $\frac{1}{(x - 2)^2}$

STEP 1 Find the derivative.

Write with a negative exponent to make differentiating easier. $y = (x - 2)^{-2}$

Use the Power Rule and Chain Rule. $y' = -2(x - 2)^{-3}(1) = -2(x - 2)^{-3}$

STEP 2 Find the zeros of the derivative.

Set the derivative equal to zero. $y' = \frac{-2}{(x - 2)^3} = 0$

By inspection, you can see that there are no values of x that cause the derivative to be zero. When $x = 2$, however, the denominator is zero so that the derivative is undefined at that point. Therefore y has a critical point at $x = 2$.

Need More

HELP ?

Remember: a function is undefined for any value of x that causes the denominator to be zero.

EXAMPLE 6

Find the critical points of $y = 3\cos(2x)$.

STEP 1 Find the derivative. $y' = 3(-\sin(2x))(2) = -6\sin(2x)$

STEP 2 Find the zeros of the derivative.

Set the derivative equal to zero. $-6\sin(2x) = 0$

Divide. $\sin(2x) = 0$

Determine where the sine function is zero. $2x = 0, \pm\pi, \pm2\pi, \pm3\pi, \pm4\pi, \dots$

Divide by 2. $x = 0, \pm\frac{\pi}{2}, \pm\pi, \pm\frac{3\pi}{2}, \pm2\pi, \dots$

Therefore, y has an infinite number of critical points.

Sign Charts with First Derivatives

A sign chart is a number line that identifies the intervals between critical points of a function. You can describe the increasing and decreasing behavior of a function by testing values within each of these intervals.

EXAMPLE 7

Try It This Way

You can also use a graphing calculator to identify critical points of a function. Graph the function and observe changes in the y values as you trace the x values. A critical point is where the y value is infinite or where it changes from increasing to decreasing and visa versa.

Use a sign chart to identify the intervals on which $f(x) = x^3 - x^2 - 8x + 10$ is increasing and decreasing.

STEP 1 Find the critical points of the function.

Find the derivative and set it equal to zero. $f'(x) = 3x^2 - 2x - 8 = 0$

Factor. $(3x + 4)(x - 2) = 0$

Solve for x. $x = -\dfrac{4}{3}, 2$

STEP 2 Create a number line and mark the critical points.

STEP 3 Choose a value on each interval and test it for positive or negative derivative values.

$f'(-2) = 3(-2)^2 - 2(-2) - 8 = 8$

$f'(0) = 3(0)^2 - 2(0) - 8 = -8$

$f'(3) = 3(3)^2 - 2(3) - 8 = 13$

STEP 4 Mark the number line intervals with $+$ or $-$ on each interval. Label the function as increasing for each $+$ interval and decreasing for each $-$ interval.

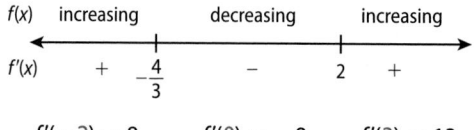

The function is increasing on $\left(-\infty, -\dfrac{4}{3}\right)$ and $(2, \infty)$ because $f'(x) > 0$ on these intervals.

The function is decreasing on $\left(-\dfrac{4}{3}, 2\right)$ because $f'(x) < 0$ on this interval.

EXAMPLE 8

Use a sign chart to find the intervals on which $g(x) = \dfrac{x}{(x+1)^2}$ is increasing and decreasing.

STEP 1 Find the critical points of the function.

Differentiate using the Quotient Rule.

$$g'(x) = \frac{(x+1)^2\,(1) - (x)[2(x+1)(1)]}{(x+1)^4}$$

Simplify, and set the derivative equal to zero.

$$= \frac{1-x}{(x+1)^3} = 0$$

Set the numerator equal to 0.　　　　　　$1 - x = 0$

Solve for x.　　　　　　　　　　　　$x = 1$

Therefore, $g(x)$ has one critical point at $x = -1$ because the derivative is undefined there. It has another critical point at $x = 1$ because its derivative is zero there.

STEP 2 Create a number line and mark the critical points.

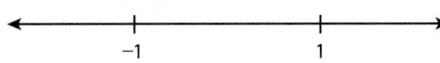

STEP 3 Choose a value on each interval and test it for positive or negative derivative values.

$$g'(-2) = \frac{1-(-2)}{(-2+1)^3} = -3$$

$$g'(0) = \frac{1-(0)}{(0+1)^3} = 1$$

$$g'(2) = \frac{1-(2)}{(2+1)^3} = -\frac{1}{27}$$

STEP 4 Mark the number line intervals with $+$ or $-$ on each interval.

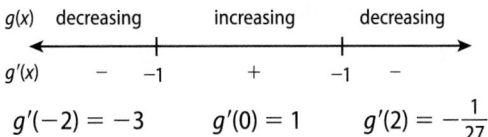

The function is decreasing on $(-\infty, -1)$ and $(1, \infty)$ because $g'(x) < 0$ on these intervals.

The function is increasing on $(-1, 1)$ because $g'(x) > 0$ on this interval.

Need More HELP ?

For help with finding solutions to quadratic equations, go to *Zeroes and Roots* in *Algebra* (p. 1628).

SEARCH

To see step-by-step videos of these problems, enter the page number into the SWadvantage.com Search Bar.

The Relationship between f and f''

A function's second derivative describes how the function's increasing or decreasing behavior is changing. Graphically, this describes the concavity of a function.

When $f''(x) > 0$, the rate of change is increasing and the graph of $f(x)$ is concave up. When $f''(x) < 0$, the rate of change is decreasing and the graph of $f(x)$ is concave down.

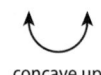

concave up

concave down

Inflection Points

The point at which a function changes concavity is called an **inflection point** and is found where the second derivative changes signs. Possible inflection points occur where the second derivative is zero or undefined. You can use a sign chart to identify inflection points.

EXAMPLE 9

Describe the concavity of $f(x) = 4x^2 + 23x - 15$.

Find $f'(x)$.　　　$f'(x) = 8x + 23$

Find $f''(x)$.　　　$f''(x) = 8$

Since $f''(x)$ is positive for all values of x, $f(x)$ is concave up on $(-\infty, \infty)$.

EXAMPLE 10

Use the graph at the right to determine the sign of y'' on (a, b).

Since the graph is concave up on (a, b), y'' is positive for all values of x on (a, b).

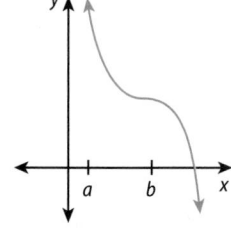

GOT TO KNOW!

Relationship between f and f''

f	Concave upwards	Possible inflection point	Concave downwards
f''	Positive	Zero or undefined	Negative

Sign Charts with Second Derivatives

Recall that a sign chart with first derivatives shows intervals where a function is increasing or decreasing. A similar sign chart with second derivatives shows intervals where a function is concave up or concave down. You can identify the intervals by finding inflection points.

EXAMPLE 11

Use a sign chart to identify the intervals on which $g(x) = x^4 - 4x^2 + 3$ is concave up and concave down. Then identify the function's inflection points.

STEP 1 Find the second derivative of the function.

Find the first derivative. $g'(x) = 4x^3 - 8x$

Find the second derivative. $g''(x) = 12x^2 - 8$

STEP 2 Find the possible inflection points.

Set the second derivative to zero. $12x^2 - 8 = 0$

Factor. $4(3x^2 - 2) = 0$

Solve for x. $x = \pm\sqrt{\dfrac{2}{3}}$

STEP 3 Create a number line and mark the possible inflection points.

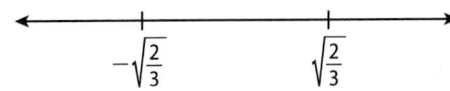

$$-\sqrt{\dfrac{2}{3}} \qquad \sqrt{\dfrac{2}{3}}$$

STEP 4 Choose a value on each interval and test it for positive or negative second derivative.

$g''(-1) = 12(-1)^2 - 8 = 4$

$g''(0) = 12(0)^2 - 8 = -8$

$g''(1) = 12(1)^2 - 8 = 4$

STEP 5 Mark the number line intervals with $+$ or $-$ on each interval.

$g(x)$ concave up   concave down   concave up

$g''(x)$ $+$ $-\sqrt{\dfrac{2}{3}}$ $-$ $\sqrt{\dfrac{2}{3}}$ $+$

$g''(-1) = 4$ $g''(0) = -8$ $g''(1) = 4$

The function is concave up on $\left(-\infty, -\sqrt{\dfrac{2}{3}}\right)$ and $\left(\sqrt{\dfrac{2}{3}}, \infty\right)$ because $g''(x) > 0$ on these intervals.

The function is concave down on $\left(-\sqrt{\dfrac{2}{3}}, \sqrt{\dfrac{2}{3}}\right)$ because $g''(x) < 0$ on this interval.

The function has inflection points at $x = \pm\sqrt{\dfrac{2}{3}}$ because $g''(x)$ changes signs at these points.

Watch Out

Finging where f'' is zero does not guarantee an inflection point. You must check to see if f'' changes signs.

You can also use a graph to make a sign chart. This is a good way to organize the information about the function and its derivatives.

Using First and Second Derivative Graphs

A graph of a function's first derivative identifies where the function is increasing or decreasing. A graph of a function's second derivative identifies where the function is concave up or concave down.

EXAMPLE 12

a. Use the graph at the right of y'' to determine where y is concave up.

$y'' > 0$ on $(2, \infty)$

y is concave up from $(2, \infty)$.

b. Use the graph at the right of y'' to determine where y is concave down.

$y'' < 0$ on $(-\infty, 2)$

y is concave down from $(-\infty, 2)$.

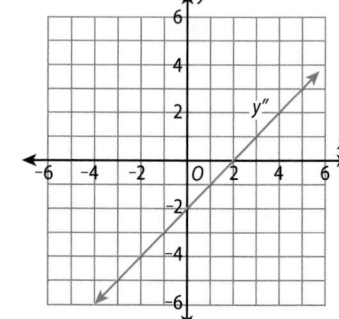

EXAMPLE 13

a. Use the graph of $f'(x)$ at the right to determine where $f(x)$ is increasing.

$f'(x) > 0$ on $(-\infty, -1)$ and $(1, \infty)$

$f(x)$ is increasing from $(-\infty, -1)$ and $(1, \infty)$.

b. Use the graph of $f'(x)$ at the right to determine where $f(x)$ is decreasing.

$f'(x) < 0$ on $(-1, 1)$

$f(x)$ is decreasing from $(-1, 1)$.

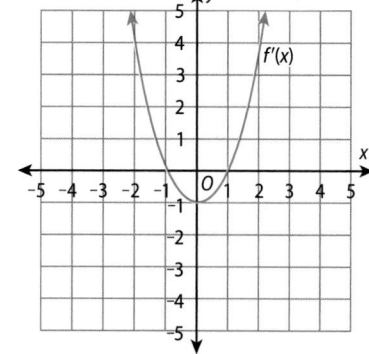

EXAMPLE 14

Use the graph of $f'(x)$ above in Example 13 to determine where $f(x)$ is concave up.

Since $f''(x)$ is the derivative of $f'(x)$, you can identify it on the graph as the slope of the tangent line. So, $f''(x)$ is positive when $f'(x)$ is increasing.

Therefore, $f''(x) > 0$ on $(0, \infty)$ and $f(x)$ is concave up from $(0, \infty)$.

Using a Table of Signs for Derivatives of a Function

The first derivative of a function indicates critical points of a function and increasing or decreasing behavior of the function on an interval. The second derivative indicates inflection points and concavity of the function on an interval. You can use a table of signs for derivatives of a function to describe behavior of the function.

x	−2	−1.5	−1	−0.5	0	0.5	1	1.5	2	2.5	3
g'(x)	+	+	undefined	−	−	−	0	+	0	−	−
g''(x)	+	+	undefined	+	0	−	−	−	−	−	−

EXAMPLE 15

Use the table to determine where $g(x)$ is both concave down and decreasing.

The function is concave down and decreasing where $g'(x) < 0$ and $g''(x) < 0$.

Therefore, $g(x)$ is both concave down and decreasing on $(0, 1)$ and $(2, \infty)$.

EXAMPLE 16

Use the table to determine where $g(x)$ has an inflection point.

The function has an inflection point where $g''(x)$ changes signs.

Therefore $g(x)$ has an inflection point at $x = 0$.

EXAMPLE 17

Use the table to determine where $g(x)$ has critical points point.

The function has critical points where $g'(x)$ is zero or undefined.

Therefore, $g(x)$ has critical points at $x = -1, 1$, and 2.

EXAMPLE 18

Use the table to determine where $g'(x)$ is increasing.

The function $g'(x)$ is increasing where its derivative, $g''(x)$, is positive.

Therefore $g'(x)$ is increasing on $(-\infty, -1)$, and $(-1, 0)$.

EXAMPLE 19

Use the table to determine where $g'(x)$ has critical points.

The function $g'(x)$ has critical points where its derivative, $g''(x)$, is zero or undefined.

Therefore $g'(x)$ has critical points at $x = -1$, and 0.

SEARCH

To see step-by-step videos of these problems, enter the page number into the SWadvantage.com Search Bar.

Position, Velocity, and Acceleration

Describing Motion

First and second derivatives are useful for relating the position, the velocity, and the acceleration of an object. An object's position is its distance from a starting point. Position functions are often labeled as $x(t)$ or $s(t)$. A change in position is called **displacement**. To calculate displacement, subtract the final position from the initial position: $\Delta x = x_f - x_i$. The position and displacement of an object are often expressed in the unit meters (m).

EXAMPLE 1

The position of an object is described by the equation $x(t) = 4t^2 + t$. Find the object's displacement between time $t = 3$ and $t = 4$.

STEP 1 Find the initial and final positions.

$$x(3) = 4(3)^2 + (3) = 39$$
$$x(4) = 4(4)^2 + (4) = 68$$

STEP 2 Find the displacement. $\Delta x = x_f - x_i$

Substitute. $= x(4) - x(3)$

Simplify. $= 68 - 39 = 29$

Position and Velocity

The rate of change of position with respect to time is velocity. Average velocity is the change in position divided by the change in time.

$$v_{avg} = \frac{\Delta x}{\Delta t} = \frac{x_f - x_i}{t_f - t_i}$$

The instantaneous velocity of an object is the derivative of its position function: $v(t) = x'(t)$. If the position is expressed in meters (m) and time is expressed in seconds (s), then velocity is expressed in meters per second (m/s).

EXAMPLE 2

Given the position equation $x(t) = 5t^2 + 6t - 8$, find the equation for velocity.

Differentiate the position equation. $v(t) = x'(t) = 10t + 6$

EXAMPLE 3

Given the position equation $x(t) = \sqrt{3t^3 + 2t^2 + 1}$, find the equation for velocity.

Differentiate using the Chain Rule. $v(t) = x'(t) = \frac{1}{2}(3t^3 + 2t^2 + 1)^{-\frac{1}{2}}(9t^2 + 4t)$

Simplify. $= \frac{9t^2 + 4t}{2\sqrt{3t^3 + 2t^2 + 1}}$

Velocity and Acceleration

The rate at which the velocity of an object changes with respect to time is its acceleration. Average acceleration is the change in velocity divided by the change in time.

$$a_{avg} = \frac{\Delta v}{\Delta t} = \frac{v_f - v_i}{t_f - t_i}$$

The instantaneous acceleration of an object is the derivative of its velocity: $a(t) = v'(t)$. If velocity is expressed in meters per second (m/s), then acceleration is expressed in meters per second per second (m/s/s). This unit is commonly written in the simplified form m/s².

EXAMPLE 4

The velocity of an object is described by the equation $v(t) = (25.2)t - (0.7)t^2$. Find the instantaneous acceleration of the object at $t = 4.5$ s.

Find the derivative of the velocity. $a(t) = v'(t) = 25.2 - (2.8)t$

Substitute $t = 4.5$. $a(4.5) = 25.2 - (2.8)(4.5) = 12.6$

The instantaneous acceleration at $t = 4.5$ s is 12.6 m/s².

SEARCH

To see step-by-step videos of these problems, enter the page number into the SWadvantage.com Search Bar.

EXAMPLE 5

The velocity of an object is described by the equation $v(t) = 3t^5 + 2t^3 - 11t + 4$, in m/s.

a. Find the object's average acceleration from $t = 0$ s to $t = 1$ s.

STEP 1 Find the velocity at each time.

$v(0) = 3(0)^5 + 2(0)^3 - 11(0) + 4 = 4$

$v(1) = 3(1)^5 + 2(1)^3 - 11(1) + 4 = -2$

STEP 2 Find the average acceleration. $a_{avg} = \frac{v_f - v_i}{t_f - t_i} = \frac{(-2) - (4)}{1 - 0} = -6$

The average acceleration is -6 m/s². A negative acceleration is sometimes called *deceleration*.

b. Find the object's instantaneous acceleration at $t = 0.5$ s.

Differentiate the velocity equation. $v'(t) = 15t^4 + 6t^2 - 11$

Evaluate at $t = 0.5$ s. $v'(0.5) = 15(0.5)^4 + 6(0.5)^2 - 11 \approx -9$ m/s²

Therefore, the instantaneous acceleration at $t = 0.5$ s is approximately -9 m/s².

Need More

HELP ?

For help with rounding answers to the correct number of significant digits, go to *Precision and Error* in *Measurement* (Book 1, page 600).

EXAMPLE 6

Using the graph of velocity at the right, determine when acceleration is positive on the interval [0, 4].

Since acceleration is the derivative of velocity, acceleration is positive where the graph of velocity is increasing.

Therefore, the acceleration is positive on (2, 4).

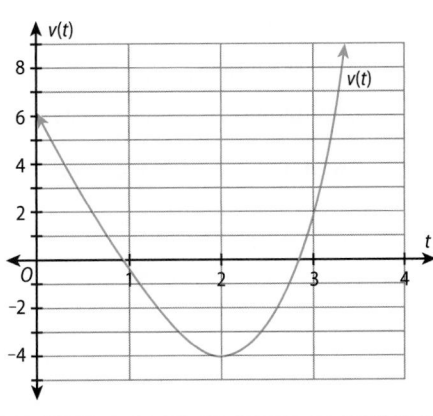

Position, Velocity, And Acceleration

$v(t) = x'(t)$

$a(t) = v'(t) = x''(t)$

Position and Acceleration

You can also find the acceleration equation from the position function. Velocity is the first derivative of position, and acceleration is the first derivative of velocity. Therefore, acceleration is the second derivative of position. It is the rate of change of the rate of change of position: $a(t) = v'(t) = x''(t)$.

EXAMPLE 7

The position of an object is described by the equation $x(t) = t^4 - t^3 - t + 4$. Find the time, t, when the object's acceleration is zero.

STEP 1 Find the acceleration equation.

Take the first derivative of position. $x'(t) = 4t^3 - 3t^2 - 1$

Take the derivative again. $x''(t) = 12t^2 - 6t$

The acceleration is $a(t) = 12t^2 - 6t$.

STEP 2 Find the time when the acceleration is zero.

Set $a(t)$ equal to zero. $12t^2 - 6t = 0$

Factor. $6t(2t - 1) = 0$

Solve for t. $t = 0, \frac{1}{2}$

Therefore, the object's acceleration is zero when $t = 0$ and $t = \frac{1}{2}$.

EXAMPLE 8

Find the velocity and acceleration of an object with the position function $x(t) = 3\sin t - 2\cos t$.

Differentiate to find the velocity. $v(t) = x'(t) = 3\cos t + 2\sin t$

Differentiate again to find the acceleration. $a(t) = x''(t) = -3\sin t + 2\cos t$

EXAMPLE 9

SEARCH

To see step-by-step videos of these problems, enter the page number into the SWadvantage.com Search Bar.

An object has the position function $x(t) = 4 - \frac{1}{t^2}$. Find the velocity and acceleration at time $t = 2$.

STEP 1 Find the velocity and acceleration equations.

Differentiate to find the velocity. $v(t) = x'(t) = -(-2)t^{-3} = 2t^{-3}$

Differentiate again to find the acceleration. $a(t) = x''(t) = 2(-3)t^{-4} = -6t^{-4}$

STEP 2 Find the velocity and acceleration at $t = 2$.

Substitute $t = 2$ into the velocity equation. $v(2) = \frac{2}{(2)^3} = \frac{1}{4}$

Substitute $t = 2$ into the acceleration equation. $a(2) = -\frac{6}{(2)^4} = -\frac{3}{8}$

EXAMPLE 10

A penny is thrown upward from the top of a 100-ft-tall building. The height of the penny is described by the equation $h(t) = -16t^2 + 64t + 100$. Assume up is the positive direction.

a. At what time is the velocity of the penny zero?

Find $v(t)$ and set it equal to zero. $v(t) = h'(t) = -32t + 64 = 0$

Solve for t. $t = 2$

Therefore, the velocity is zero at $t = 2$ s.

b. What is the maximum height of the penny?

The maximum height occurs when the velocity is zero.

Find $h(t)$ when $v(t) = 0$. $h(2) = -16(2)^2 + 64(2) + 100 = 164$ ft

c. At what time does the penny hit the ground?

The penny hits the ground when $h(t) = 0$.

Set the height equation to zero. $h(t) = -16t^2 + 64t + 100 = 0$

Use the quadratic formula. $t = \dfrac{-64 \pm \sqrt{64^2 - 4(-16)(100)}}{2(-16)}$

Solve for t. $\approx -1.2, 5.2$

Therefore, the penny hits the ground after approximately 5.2 s.

d. What is the penny's acceleration? $a(t) = v'(t) = -32$

Because the acceleration is a constant, the acceleration at all times as the penny is rising and falling is -32 ft/s^2.

Need More
HELP ?
For more help solving quadratics using the quadratic formula, go to *The Quadratic Formula* in *Algebra* (p. 1710).

Watch Out !

When solving problems involving time, as in Example 10(c), only times that are positive are possible solutions.

Speed

Speed is the absolute value of velocity. Velocity is a vector quantity with both magnitude and direction, but speed is a scalar quantity. It has magnitude but not direction. The odometer on a car is a measure of speed. It shows how fast the car is traveling but not the direction.

When velocity and acceleration have the same sign, speed is increasing. When velocity and acceleration have opposite signs, speed is decreasing.

EXAMPLE 11

Find when the speed of the penny in Example 10 is increasing.

The speed of the penny is increasing when the velocity and acceleration have the same sign.

As the penny rises, its velocity is upward, which is positive. At $t = 2$ s, the penny has zero velocity. As the penny falls, its velocity is downward, which is negative. The acceleration of the penny is negative for all values of t. The penny hits the ground at $t = 5.2$, and its velocity there is again zero.

Therefore, the speed of the penny is increasing for $2 < t < 5.2$.

GOT TO KNOW !

Speed

Speed is increasing.

$v(t)$	+	−
$a(t)$	+	−

Speed is decreasing.

$v(t)$	+	−
$a(t)$	−	+

Curve Sketching

Extrema

The high and low points of a graph are called *extrema*.

local maximum (relative maximum) — any high point

local minimum (relative minimum) — any low point

absolute maximum — highest point on a closed interval

absolute minimum — lowest point on a closed interval

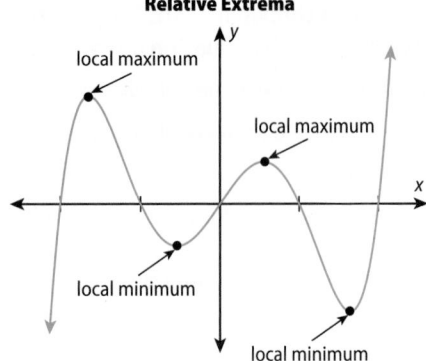

Relative Extrema

Extrema occur at *critical points* of the function, where the derivative is zero or undefined.

One way to identify extrema on a closed interval is by comparing the y values of the function at the critical points and the endpoints of the interval.

SEARCH

To see step-by-step videos of these problems, enter the page number into the SWadvantage.com Search Bar.

EXAMPLE 1

Find the extrema of $f(x) = \frac{1}{3}x^3 - x^2 - 3x + 4$ on the interval $[-4, 4]$.

STEP 1 Find the critical points of $f(x)$.

Set the derivative of f equal to zero. $\qquad f'(x) = x^2 - 2x - 3 = 0$

Factor. $\qquad\qquad\qquad\qquad\qquad\qquad (x - 3)(x + 1) = 0$

Solve for x. $\qquad\qquad\qquad\qquad\qquad\qquad\qquad x = 3, -1$

STEP 2 Evaluate $f(x)$ at each critical point and endpoint.

Evaluate $f(x)$ at critical points. $\qquad f(3) = -5 \qquad f(-1) = 5\frac{2}{3}$

Evaluate $f(x)$ at the endpoints. $\qquad f(-4) = -21\frac{1}{3} \qquad f(4) = -2\frac{2}{3}$

Therefore, the maximum is $f(-1) = 5\frac{2}{3}$, and the minimum is $f(-4) = -21\frac{1}{3}$.

EXAMPLE 2

Find the extrema of $f(x) = x^3 + 3x^2 + 1$ on the interval $[-2, 1]$.

STEP 1 Find the critical points of f.

Set the derivative of f equal to zero. $\qquad f'(x) = 3x^2 + 6x = 0$

Factor. $\qquad\qquad\qquad\qquad\qquad\qquad\qquad x(3x + 6) = 0$

Solve for x. $\qquad\qquad\qquad\qquad\qquad\qquad\qquad x = 0, -2$

STEP 2 Evaluate f at each critical point and endpoint.

Evaluate $f(x)$ at critical points. $\qquad f(0) = 1 \qquad f(-2) = 5$

Evaluate $f(x)$ at the other endpoint. $\qquad f(1) = 5$

Therefore, the maxima are $f(-2) = f(1) = 5$, and the minimum is $f(0) = 1$.

First Derivative Test

The First Derivative Test determines if a critical value is a local minimum or a local maximum. If the derivative changes from negative to positive at a critical point, the point is a local minimum. If the derivative changes from positive to negative at a critical point, the point is a local maximum. If the sign of the derivative does not change at the critical point, then the point is neither a local maximum nor a local minimum.

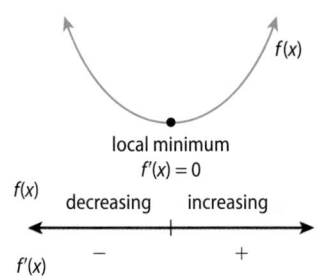
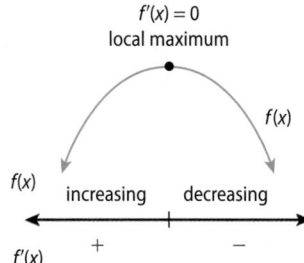

EXAMPLE 3

Find where the relative extrema of $g(x) = 2\sin x - x$ are on $[-\pi, \pi]$.

STEP 1 Find the critical values of $g(x)$.

Set $g'(x)$ equal to zero. $\qquad\qquad g'(x) = 2\cos x - 1 = 0$

Solve for $\cos x$. $\qquad\qquad\qquad\qquad \cos x = \dfrac{1}{2}$

Identify solutions on the interval $[-\pi, \pi]$. $\qquad x = -\dfrac{\pi}{3}, \dfrac{\pi}{3}$

STEP 2 Create a sign chart using the critical values.

$g(x)$ decreasing increasing decreasing

$g'(x)$ $\quad-\quad -\dfrac{\pi}{3}\quad +\quad -\dfrac{\pi}{3}\quad -$

Therefore, $g(x)$ has a relative minimum at $-\dfrac{\pi}{3}$ since $g'(x)$ changes from negative to positive at this point. There is a relative maximum at $\dfrac{\pi}{3}$ since $g'(x)$ changes from positive to negative at this point.

Need More

HELP ?

To make a sign chart, test a value within each interval to determine if the derivative is positive or negative. For more review of creating a sign chart using critical values, go to *Relationships Between f, f', f"* (p. 2190).

GOT TO KNOW!

The First Derivative Test For Extrema

$f(c)$ is a local maximum if $f'(x)$ changes from positive to negative at $x = c$.

$f(c)$ is a local minimum if $f'(x)$ changes from negative to positive at $x = c$.

Second Derivative Test and Inflection Points

If the second derivative of a function is positive at a critical point, then a graph of the function is concave up and the point is a local minimum. If the second derivative is negative at a critical point, then a graph of the function is concave down and the point is a local maximum. If the second derivative is zero at a critical point or if the first derivative is undefined, then the second derivative test fails and other means are necessary to determine if the point is a maximum or minimum.

The second derivative also identifies an **inflection point**, where the concavity of a function changes. Possible inflection points are where the second derivative is zero or is undefined.

GOT TO KNOW!

Inflection Point

If the concavity of a function $f(x)$ changes from positive to negative or from negative to positive at $f(c)$, then $(c, f(c))$ is an inflection point.

Possible inflection points are where $f''(x) = 0$ or $f''(x)$ is undefined.

EXAMPLE 4

Use the Second Derivative Test to find the relative extrema of $y = x^3 - 3x^2 - 45x + 24$.

STEP 1 Find the critical points of the function.

Find y' and set it equal to zero. $\qquad y' = 3x^2 - 6x - 45 = 0$

Factor. $\qquad\qquad\qquad\qquad\qquad (3x + 9)(x - 5) = 0$

Solve for x. $\qquad\qquad\qquad\qquad\qquad\qquad x = -3, 5$

STEP 2 Use the Second Derivative Test.

Find y''. $\qquad\qquad\qquad\qquad y'' = 6x - 6$

Test y'' at the critical points. $\qquad y''(-3) = -24 \qquad y''(5) = 24$

Since the second derivative is negative at $x = -3$, there is a local maximum at $x = -3$. Since the second derivative is positive at $x = 5$, there is a local minimum at $x = 5$.

EXAMPLE 5

Identify any inflection points of the function $y = 3x^5 - 5x^3$.

STEP 1 Identify possible inflection points.

Find y'. $\qquad\qquad\qquad\qquad\qquad y' = 15x^4 - 15x^2$

Find y'' and set it equal to zero. $\qquad y'' = 60x^3 - 30x = 0$

Factor. $\qquad\qquad\qquad\qquad\qquad\qquad x(2x^2 - 1) = 0$

Solve for x. $\qquad\qquad\qquad\qquad\qquad\qquad x = 0, \pm\dfrac{\sqrt{2}}{2}$

STEP 2 Test values of y'' on either side of possible inflection points to identify changes in concavity.

$$y''(-1) = -1 \qquad y''\left(-\frac{1}{4}\right) = \frac{14}{64} \qquad y''\left(\frac{1}{4}\right) = -\frac{14}{64} \qquad y''(1) = 1$$

The function has inflection points at $x = 0, \pm\dfrac{\sqrt{2}}{2}$ because concavity changes at each point.

SEARCH

To see step-by-step videos of these problems, enter the page number into the SWadvantage.com Search Bar.

GOT TO KNOW!

The Second Derivative Test For Extrema

$f(c)$ is a local maximum if $f'(x) = 0$ and $f''(x) < 0$ at $x = c$.

$f(c)$ is a local minimum if $f'(x) = 0$ and $f''(x) > 0$ at $x = c$.

Curve Sketching

You can combine the first and second derivative tests with your knowledge of other properties of functions to sketch graphs. Sketching graphs by hand can bring out important characteristics that might be difficult to observe on a calculator.

Steps for Curve Sketching:

1. Define the domain of the function.
2. Determine if the function has symmetry about either axis.
3. Find the x- and y-intercepts.
4. Find any vertical and horizontal asymptotes.
5. Find the first and second derivatives to identify extrema and inflection points.
6. Create a sign chart relating the first and second derivatives to the function.
7. Sketch the graph.

EXAMPLE  6

Sketch the graph of $f(x) = x^3 + 1$.

STEP 1 Identify the domain, symmetry, and intercepts of the function.

The domain of the function is all real values of x.

There is no symmetry because neither $-x$ nor $-y$ can replace x or y without changing the function.

Find the x- and y-intercepts. $0 = x^3 + 1$ $y = (0)^3 + 1$

$x = -1$ $y = 1$

STEP 2 Identify any asymptotes. There are no vertical or horizontal asymptotes.

STEP 3 Identify where the first and second derivatives are zero or undefined.

Find $f'(x)$ and $f''(x)$. Set them equal to zero. $f'(x) = 3x^2 = 0$ $f''(x) = 6x = 0$

Solve for x. $x = 0$ $x = 0$

Test points in f' in each interval. $f'(-1) = 3$ $f(2) = 12$

Because f' is positive in both cases, f increases on each interval and $x = 0$ is not an extrema.

STEP 4 Create a sign chart.

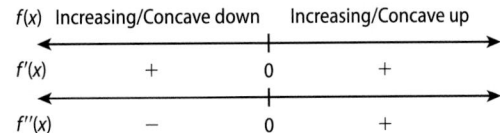

STEP 5 Sketch the graph.

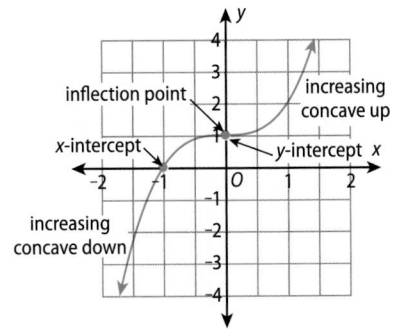

Need More

HELP ?

For help with identifying vertical and horizontal asymptotes, go to *Asymptotes of Rational Functions* in *Advanced Algebra* (p. 1502).

Rational and Trigonometric Curve Sketching

EXAMPLE 7

SEARCH

To see step-by-step videos of these problems, enter the page number into the SWadvantage.com Search Bar.

Sketch the graph of $y = \dfrac{4}{x^2 + 3}$.

STEP 1 Identify the domain, symmetry, and intercepts of the function.

The domain of the function is all real values of x.

There is vertical symmetry because $-x$ can replace x without changing the function.

Find the x- and y-intercepts. $\qquad y = \dfrac{4}{(0)^2 + 3} = \dfrac{4}{3} \qquad 0 = \dfrac{4}{x^2 + 3}$

There are no x-intercepts because there are no values of x for which $y = 0$.

STEP 2 Identify any asymptotes.

There are no vertical asymptotes.

There is a horizontal asymptote at $y = 0$ because the degree of the numerator is less than the degree of the denominator.

STEP 3 Identify where the first derivative is zero or undefined.

Rewrite y to make differentiating easier. $\qquad y = 4(x^2 + 3)^{-1}$

Use the Power Rule and Chain Rule. $\qquad y' = -4(x^2 + 3)^{-2}(2x) = -8x(x^2 + 3)^{-2}$

The critical point of y is at $x = 0$ since this is where y' is equal to zero.

STEP 4 Identify where the second derivative is zero or undefined.

Use the Product Rule. $\qquad y'' = (-8x)[-2(x^2 + 3)^{-3}(2x)] + (x^2 + 3)^{-2}(-8)$

Simplify, and set equal to zero. $\qquad = \dfrac{24(x + 1)(x - 1)}{(x^2 + 3)^3} = 0$

Solve for x. $\qquad x = -1, 1$

STEP 5 Create a sign chart. Test values to determine concavity, increasing, and decreasing.

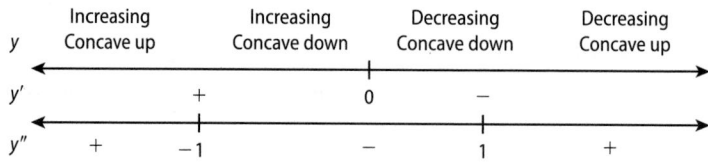

STEP 6 Sketch the graph.

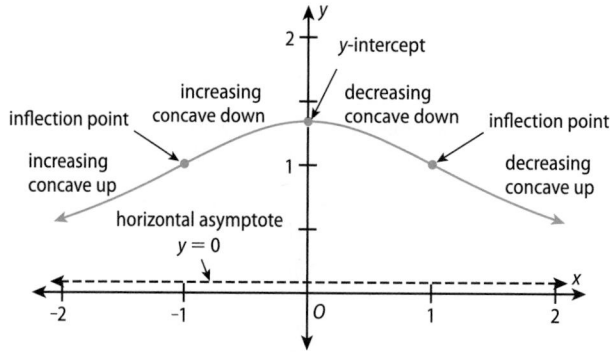

EXAMPLE 8

Sketch the graph of $y = \dfrac{\sin x}{1 + \cos x}$ from $[-\pi, \pi]$.

STEP 1 Identify the domain, symmetry, and intercepts of the function.

The domain of the function is all real values of x except $x = -\pi, \pi$.

There is symmetry about the origin since $y(-x) = -y(x)$.

Find the x- and y-intercepts.

$$y = \frac{\sin(0)}{1 + \cos(0)} = 0 \qquad 0 = \frac{\sin x}{1 + \cos x}$$

$$x = 0$$

STEP 2 Identify any asymptotes.

There are vertical asymptotes at $x = -\pi, \pi$.

There is no horizontal asymptote.

STEP 3 Identify where the first derivative is zero or undefined.

Use the Quotient Rule. $\qquad y' = \dfrac{(1 + \cos x)(\cos x) - (\sin x)(-\sin x)}{(1 + \cos x)^2}$

Simplify. $\qquad = \dfrac{\cos x + \cos^2 x + \sin^2 x}{(1 + \cos x)^2} = \dfrac{\cos x + 1}{(1 + \cos x)^2} = \dfrac{1}{1 + \cos x}$

$\qquad = (1 + \cos x)^{-1}$

The critical points of y are $x = -\pi, \pi$ since this is where y' is undefined.

STEP 4 Identify where the second derivative is zero or undefined.

Use the Chain Rule. $\qquad y'' = -(1 + \cos x)^{-2} \cdot (0 - \sin x) = \dfrac{\sin x}{(1 + \cos x)^2}$

There is a possible inflection point at $x = 0$ since y'' is zero at this point.

STEP 5 Create a sign chart. Test values to determine concavity, increasing, and decreasing.

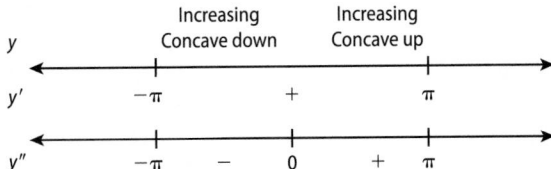

STEP 6 Sketch the graph.

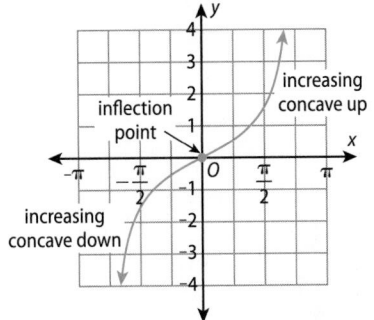

Need More

HELP ?

For help with finding the solutions to trigonometric equations, go to *Solving Trigonometric Equations* in *Trigonometry* (Book 1, pp. 1032, 1036).

Implicit Differentiation

Explicit and Implicit Equations

A mathematical relationship between variables is **explicit** if one variable is solved in terms of the other, such as $y = 3x - 2$. A relationship is **implicit** if an equation relates the variables but one variable is not solved in terms of the other. Examples include $xy = 10$ and $x^2 + y^2 = 1$. An implicit relationship may or may not describe a function. If solving for y is difficult or not possible, you can use **implicit differentiation** in which you take the derivative of both sides of the equation with respect to x and then solve for $\frac{dy}{dx}$. When you use implicit differentiation with respect to x for terms that include y, you must use the Chain Rule.

SEARCH

To see step-by-step videos of these problems, enter the page number into the SWadvantage.com Search Bar.

EXAMPLE 1

Find $\frac{dy}{dx}$ for $xy = 10$.

METHOD 1

Solve by explicit differentiation.

Solve the equation for y.	$y = 10x^{-1}$
Use the Power Rule.	$\frac{dy}{dx} = -10x^{-2} = -\frac{10}{x^2}$

METHOD 2

Solve by implicit differentiation.

Differentiate each side with respect to x.	$\frac{d}{dx}[xy] = \frac{d}{dx}[10]$
Use the Constant Rule.	$\frac{d}{dx}[xy] = 0$
Use the Product Rule.	$x\frac{d}{dx}[y] + y\frac{d}{dx}[x] = 0$
Use the Power Rule to differentiate x.	$x\frac{d}{dx}[y] + y(1) = 0$
Use the Chain Rule and Power Rule.	$x(1)\frac{dy}{dx} + y = 0$
Solve for $\frac{dy}{dx}$ using y from the original equation.	$\frac{dy}{dx} = -\frac{y}{x}$
Substitute y from the original equation and simplify.	$\frac{dy}{dx} = -\frac{10x^{-1}}{x} = -\frac{10}{x^2}$

GOT TO KNOW!

Implicit Differentiation

- Differentiate both sides of the equation with respect to x.
- Solve for $\frac{dy}{dx}$.

Using Implicit Differentiation

Implicit differentiation is useful for finding the slope of a tangent line for implicit equations. You can also use it to find the instantaneous rate of change of an implicit equation.

EXAMPLE 2

Find the slope of the tangent line of $x^2 + y^2 = 5$ at the point $(-2, 1)$, as shown in the graph at the right.

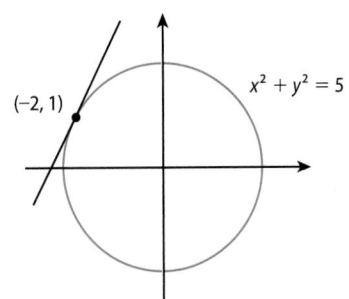

Differentiate each side with respect to x.
$$\frac{d}{dx}[x^2 + y^2] = \frac{d}{dx}[5]$$

Use the Constant Rule.
$$\frac{d}{dx}[x^2 + y^2] = 0$$

Use the Sum Rule.
$$\frac{d}{dx}[x^2] + \frac{d}{dx}[y^2] = 0$$

Use the Power Rule.
$$2x + \frac{d}{dx}[y^2] = 0$$

Use the Chain Rule.
$$2x + 2y\frac{dy}{dx} = 0$$

Solve for $\frac{dy}{dx}$.
$$\frac{dy}{dx} = -\frac{x}{y}$$

Substitute values of x and y. Then simplify.
$$\frac{dy}{dx} = -\frac{(-2)}{1} = 2$$

Need More

HELP ?

Remember that the slope of the tangent line and the instantaneous rate of change are both derivatives.

EXAMPLE 3

Find the instantaneous rate of change of $3x^2 + 2xy + 3y^2 = 4$.

Differentiate each side with respect to x.
$$\frac{d}{dx}[3x^2 + 2xy + 3y^2] = \frac{d}{dx}[4]$$

Use the Constant Rule.
$$\frac{d}{dx}[3x^2 + 2xy + 3y^2] = 0$$

Use the Sum Rule.
$$\frac{d}{dx}[3x^2] + \frac{d}{dx}[2xy] + \frac{d}{dx}[3y^2] = 0$$

Use the Power Rule.
$$6x + \frac{d}{dx}[2xy] + \frac{d}{dx}[3y^2] = 0$$

Use the Product and Chain Rules.
$$6x + \left[2x\frac{dy}{dx} + 2y(1)\right] + \frac{d}{dx}[3y^2] = 0$$

Use the power and chain rules.
$$6x + \left[2x\frac{dy}{dx} + y(2)\right] + 6y\frac{dy}{dx} = 0$$

Solve for $\frac{dy}{dx}$ and simplify.
$$\frac{dy}{dx} = \frac{-6x - 2y}{2x + 6y} = -\frac{3x + y}{x + 3y}$$

Watch Out !

When you use implicit differentiation, the solution can be expressed in terms of x and y.

The Second Derivative and Implicit Differentiation

If a derivative is written in terms of two variables, you can use implicit differentiation again to find the second derivative.

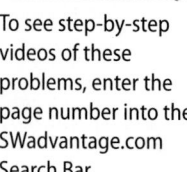
EXAMPLE 4

Find $\dfrac{d^2y}{dx^2}$ if $x^2 + y^2 = 5$.

From Example 2, you know that $\dfrac{dy}{dx} = -\dfrac{x}{y}$. Differentiate this to find the second derivative.

Differentiate each side with respect to x.
$$\frac{d^2y}{dx^2} = \frac{d}{dx}\left[-\frac{x}{y}\right]$$

Use the Quotient Rule and Chain Rule.
$$= \frac{y(-1) - (-x)\frac{dy}{dx}}{y^2}$$

Substitute $\dfrac{dy}{dx}$.
$$= \frac{-y + x\left(-\frac{x}{y}\right)}{y^2}$$

Use the original equation to simplify the numerator.
$$= \frac{-y^2 - x^2}{y^3} = \frac{-5}{y^3}$$

EXAMPLE 5

Use implicit differentiation to find $\dfrac{d^2y}{dx^2}$ at the point (1, 6) if $xy = 5 + x$.

STEP 1 Use implicit differentiation to find the first derivative.

Differentiate each side with respect to x.
$$\frac{d}{dx}[xy] = \frac{d}{dx}[5 + x]$$

Differentiate, using the Chain Rule for the y term.
$$x\frac{dy}{dx} + y\frac{d}{dx}[x] = \frac{d}{dx}[5] + \frac{d}{dx}[x]$$

Use the Power Rule and Constant Rule.
$$x\frac{dy}{dx} + y(1) = 0 + 1$$

Solve for $\dfrac{dy}{dx}$.
$$\frac{dy}{dx} = \frac{1 - y}{x}$$

STEP 2 Use implicit differentiation to find the second derivative.

Differentiate each side with respect to x.
$$\frac{d^2y}{dx^2} = \frac{d}{dx}\left[\frac{1 - y}{x}\right]$$

Use the Quotient Rule and Chain Rule.
$$= \frac{x\left[(0) - \frac{dy}{dx}\right] - (1 - y)(1)}{x^2}$$

Substitute $\dfrac{dy}{dx}$ and simplify.
$$= \frac{-x\left[\frac{1-y}{x}\right] - 1 - y}{x^2} = \frac{2y - 2}{x^2}$$

Substitute x and y values. Simplify.
$$= \frac{2(6) - 2}{(1)^2} = 10$$

Trigonometric Implicit Differentiation

Trigonometric equations may also be differentiated implicitly. The chain rule will often be used more than once because with trigonometric expressions there are often functions existing inside the trigonometric functions.

EXAMPLE 6

Find the instantaneous rate of change of sin(x + y) = x.

Differentiate each side with respect to x.

$$\frac{d}{dx}[\sin(x + y)] = \frac{d}{dx}[x]$$

Use the Power Rule.

$$\frac{d}{dx}[\sin(x + y)] = 1$$

Use the Chain Rule and differentiate sine.

$$(\cos(x + y))\left(1 + \frac{dy}{dx}\right) = 1$$

Divide.

$$\left(1 + \frac{dy}{dx}\right) = \frac{1}{\cos(x + y)}$$

Subtract.

$$\frac{dy}{dx} = \frac{1}{\cos(x + y)} - 1$$

Need More

HELP ?

For help with the derivatives of trigonometric functions, go to *Derivatives of Trigonometric Functions* (p. 2180).

EXAMPLE 7

Find the instantaneous rate of change of cos x + xy + sin y = 1.

Differentiate each side with respect to x.

$$\frac{d}{dx}[\cos x + xy + \sin y] = \frac{d}{dx}[1]$$

Use the Sum Rule.

$$\frac{d}{dx}[\cos x] + \frac{d}{dx}[xy] + \frac{d}{dx}[\sin y] = \frac{d}{dx}[1]$$

Use the Constant Rule.

$$\frac{d}{dx}[\cos x] + \frac{d}{dx}[xy] + \frac{d}{dx}[\sin y] = 0$$

Differentiate cosine.

$$-\sin x + \frac{d}{dx}[xy] + \frac{d}{dx}[\sin y] = 0$$

Use the Product and Chain Rules.

$$-\sin x + x\frac{dy}{dx} + y + \frac{d}{dx}[\sin y] = 0$$

Use the Chain Rule and differentiate sine.

$$-\sin x + x\frac{dy}{dx} + y + (\cos y)\frac{dy}{dx} = 0$$

Isolate the $\frac{dy}{dx}$ terms.

$$x\frac{dy}{dx} + (\cos y)\frac{dy}{dx} = -y + \sin x$$

Factor out the $\frac{dy}{dx}$.

$$\frac{dy}{dx}[x + \cos y] = -y + \sin x$$

Solve for $\frac{dy}{dx}$.

$$\frac{dy}{dx} = \frac{-y + \sin x}{x + \cos y}$$

Tangent and Normal Lines

Tangent Line Slopes

The slope of the line tangent to a curve at a given point is the derivative of the curve evaluated at the given point.

EXAMPLE 1

Find the slope of the tangent line to the curve $y = x^2 + 3x - 2$ at $(-1, -4)$.

Find the derivative of y. $y' = 2x + 3$

Evaluate the derivative at $x = -1$. $y'(-1) = 2(-1) + 3 = 1$

Therefore, the slope of the tangent line at $(-1, -4)$ is 1.

Tangent Line Equations

Need More

HELP ?

For help with point-slope form, go to *Point-Slope Form of Linear Equations* in *Algebra* (p. 1544).

The graph at the right shows a curve with a tangent line drawn at a point. You can find the equation of the tangent using the point-slope equation of a line. The slope of the line is the derivative evaluated at the given point.

EXAMPLE 2

Write the equation of the line tangent to the curve $y = 2x^3 + 7x^2 - 2$ at $(-3, 7)$.

STEP 1 Find the slope of the tangent line.

Find the derivative of y. $y' = 6x^2 + 14x$

Evaluate the derivative
at $x = -3$. $y'(-3) = 6(-3)^2 + 14(-3) = 12$

STEP 2 Use the slope to find the equation of the tangent line.

Use point-slope form of the equation. $y - y_1 = m(x - x_1)$

Substitute values for $x_1, y_1,$ and the slope. $y - (7) = 12(x - (-3))$

Simplify. $y - 7 = 12x + 36$

Solve for y. $y = 12x + 43$

GOT TO KNOW!

Tangent Line Equation

The equation of the line tangent to a curve y at the point (x_1, y_1) is:

$$y - y_1 = y'(x_1)(x - x_1)$$

Normal Line Equations

A **normal line** is a line that is perpendicular to the tangent line of a curve at the point of tangency. Remember from algebra that the slopes of perpendicular lines are negative reciprocals.

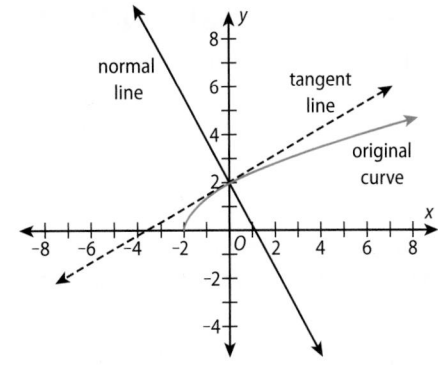

EXAMPLE 3

Find the slope of the normal line to the curve $y = \sin x$ at $x = \frac{\pi}{3}$.

Find y'.	$y' = \cos x$
Evaluate y' at the given x.	$y'\left(\frac{\pi}{3}\right) = \cos\left(\frac{\pi}{3}\right) = \frac{1}{2}$
Find the negative reciprocal.	$-\dfrac{1}{y'\left(\frac{\pi}{3}\right)} = -\dfrac{1}{\frac{1}{2}} = -2$

EXAMPLE 4

Write the equation of the normal line to the curve $y = \sqrt{2x + 4}$ at (0, 2).

STEP 1 Find the slope of the normal line.

Rewrite y as an exponent.	$y = (2x + 4)^{\frac{1}{2}}$
Find the derivative of y.	$y' = \frac{1}{2}(2x + 4)^{-\frac{1}{2}}(2) = (2x + 4)^{-\frac{1}{2}}$
Evaluate the derivative at $x = 0$.	$y'(0) = (2(0) + 4)^{-\frac{1}{2}} = \frac{1}{2}$
Find the negative reciprocal.	$-\dfrac{1}{y'(0)} = -\dfrac{1}{\frac{1}{2}} = -2$

STEP 2 Use the slope to find the equation of the normal line.

Use the point–slope form of an equation.	$y - y_1 = m(x - x_1)$
Substitute the values of x_1, y_1 and the slope.	$y - (2) = -2(x - (0))$
Solve for y.	$y = -2x + 2$

SEARCH

To see step-by-step videos of these problems, enter the page number into the SWadvantage.com Search Bar.

GOT TO KNOW!

Normal Line Equation

The equation of the normal line to a curve y at the point (x_1, y_1) is:

$$y - y_1 = -\frac{1}{y'(x_1)}(x - x_1)$$

Related Rates

Using the Chain Rule to Relate Rates of Change

Related rates problems use the Chain Rule to relate the rates of change of two quantities. Drawing sketches is useful when solving this type of problem. You can then relate the quantities with an equation and use the Chain Rule to solve the problem.

EXAMPLE 1

A 15-ft ladder is resting against the side of a shed. The top of the ladder begins to slide straight down the side of the shed at a rate of 0.3 ft/s. How fast is the base of the ladder moving away from the shed when the top of the ladder is 12 ft above the ground?

STEP 1 Identify given and unknown information. Draw and label a picture.

Given: $z = 15$ ft $\dfrac{dy}{dt} = -0.3$ ft/s $y = 12$ ft

Find: $\dfrac{dx}{dt}$ when $y = 12$ ft

STEP 2 Write an equation relating the quantities.

Use the Pythagorean theorem. $x^2 + y^2 = 15^2$

STEP 3 Differentiate to relate the rates of change.

Differentiate with respect to time. $\dfrac{d}{dt}[x^2 + y^2] = \dfrac{d}{dt}[15^2]$

Use the Sum Rule and the Constant Rule. $\dfrac{d}{dt}[x^2] + \dfrac{d}{dt}[y^2] = 0$

Use the Chain Rule. $2x\dfrac{dx}{dt} + 2y\dfrac{dy}{dt} = 0$

Solve for the unknown rate. $\dfrac{dx}{dt} = \dfrac{1}{2x}\left[-2y\dfrac{dy}{dt}\right]$

STEP 4 Solve for any missing information.

Use the Pythagorean theorem to find x. $x^2 = 15^2 - y^2$

Substitute the given value of y. $= 225 - (12)^2 = 81$

Simplify. $x = 9$

STEP 5 Find the unknown rate.

Substitute known quantities into the rate equation. $\dfrac{dx}{dt} = \dfrac{1}{2(9)}[-2(12)(-0.3)]$

Simplify. $= 0.4$

Therefore, the base of the ladder is moving away from the shed at a rate of 0.4 ft/s when the top of the ladder is 12 ft above the ground.

Need More
HELP

Remember the Pythagorean theorem: The sum of the square of the sides of a right triangle is equal to the square of the hypotenuse.

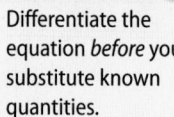

Watch Out

Differentiate the equation *before* you substitute known quantities.

(figure: right triangle with vertical side labeled y, horizontal side labeled x, and hypotenuse labeled $z = 15$ ft ladder; arrows indicate the top sliding down and the base moving away)

EXAMPLE 2

Two cars are traveling away from the same restaurant and leave at the same time. One car travels north at 65 mph and the other travels east at 50 mph. How fast is the distance between the two cars changing after 2 hours?

SEARCH

To see step-by-step videos of these problems, enter the page number into the SWadvantage.com Search Bar.

STEP 1 Identify given and unknown information. Draw and label a picture.

Given: $\dfrac{dx}{dt} = 50$ mph $\qquad \dfrac{dy}{dt} = 65$ mph $\qquad \Delta t = 2$ h

Find: $\dfrac{dz}{dt} =$ when $t = 2$ h

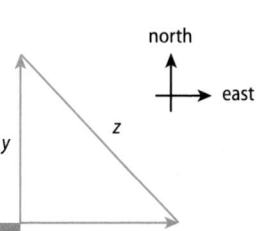

STEP 2 Write an equation relating the quantities.

Use the Pythagorean theorem. $\qquad\qquad x^2 + y^2 = z^2$

STEP 3 Differentiate to relate the rates of change.

Differentiate with respect to time. $\qquad \dfrac{d}{dt}[x^2 + y^2] = \dfrac{d}{dt}[z^2]$

Use the Sum Rule. $\qquad\qquad \dfrac{d}{dt}[x^2] + \dfrac{d}{dt}[y^2] = \dfrac{d}{dt}[z^2]$

Use the Chain Rule. $\qquad\qquad 2x\dfrac{dx}{dt} + 2y\dfrac{dy}{dt} = 2z\dfrac{dz}{dt}$

Solve for the unknown rate. $\qquad\qquad \dfrac{dz}{dt} = \dfrac{1}{z}\left[x\dfrac{dx}{dt} + y\dfrac{dy}{dt}\right]$

STEP 4 Solve for any missing information.

Use the relationship distance = (rate)(time) to find x and y.

Calculate x. $\qquad\qquad x = (50)(2) = 100$

Calculate y. $\qquad\qquad y = (65)(2) = 130$

Use the Pythagorean theorem to find z. $\qquad z = \sqrt{x^2 + y^2} = \sqrt{(100)^2 + (130)^2} \approx 164$

STEP 5 Find the unknown rate.

Substitute known quantities into the rate equation. $\qquad \dfrac{dz}{dt} = \dfrac{1}{(164)}[(100)(50) + (130)(65)] \approx 82$

The distance between the two cars is changing at a rate of approximately 82 mph after 2 hours.

Solving Related Rates Problems

1. Identify given and unknown information, and assign variables to quantities.

2. Draw a picture with labels.

3. Write an equation relating the quantities.

4. Differentiate with respect to time to relate the rates of change.

5. Solve for the unknown quantity.

6. Use given information to determine any missing information.

7. Substitute known information into the rates equation.

SOUTHWESTERN

Rates Involving Circles and Spheres

Related rates problems often involve circles or spheres. You can relate a change in radius of a circle to a change in its circumference or area. You can relate a change in the radius of a sphere to a change in its surface area or volume.

Need More HELP ?

Remember:

Circumference of a circle $= 2\pi r$

Area of a circle $= \pi r^2$

Surface area of a sphere $= 4\pi r^2$

Volume of a sphere $= \frac{4}{3}\pi r^3$

EXAMPLE 3

A snowball is melting and creating a circular puddle. When the radius of the puddle is 16 cm, the radius is increasing at a rate of 2 cm/min. How fast is the area of the puddle increasing when the radius is 16 cm?

STEP 1 Identify given and unknown information. Draw and label a picture.

Given: $\frac{dr}{dt} = 2$ cm/min

Find: $\frac{dA}{dt}$ when $r = 16$ cm

A is the area of the circle.

$r = 16$ cm

STEP 2 Write an equation relating the quantities.

Use the equation for the area of a circle. $\qquad A = \pi r^2$

STEP 3 Differentiate to relate the rates of change.

Differentiate with respect to time. $\qquad \frac{dA}{dt} = \frac{d}{dt}[\pi r^2]$

Use the Constant Multiple Rule. $\qquad \frac{dA}{dt} = \pi \frac{d}{dt}[r^2]$

Use the Power and Chain Rules. $\qquad \frac{dA}{dt} = 2\pi r \frac{dr}{dt}$

STEP 4 Find the unknown rate.

Substitute known quantities into the rate equation. $\qquad \frac{dA}{dt} = 2\pi(16)(2) = 64\pi$

Therefore, the area of the puddle is increasing at a rate of 64π cm²/min when the radius is 16 cm.

EXAMPLE 4

The circumference of a circle is $C = 2\pi r$. In Example 3, how fast is C changing when $r = 16$ cm?

STEP 1 Identify given and known information.

Given: $C = 2\pi r$ $\qquad \frac{dr}{dt} = 2$ cm/min when $r = 16$ cm

Find: $\frac{dC}{dt}$ when $r = 16$ cm

STEP 2 Use related rates to find the unknown rate.

Differentiate with respect to time. $\qquad \frac{dC}{dt} = 2\pi \frac{dr}{dt}$

Substitute the known quantity. $\qquad = 2\pi(2) = 4\pi$

The circumference of the puddle is increasing at a rate of 4π cm/min when the radius is 16 cm.

SEARCH

To see step-by-step videos of these problems, enter the page number into the SWadvantage.com Search Bar.

EXAMPLE 5

A spherical weather balloon is being inflated. When the radius of the balloon is 3 ft, the radius is increasing at a rate of 2 ft/min. Find the rate at which the volume of the balloon is increasing when the radius is 3 ft.

STEP 1 Draw a picture and label the given information using appropriate variables.

Given: 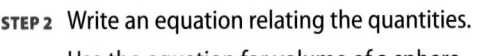 $\frac{dr}{dt} = 2$ ft/min when $r = 3$ ft

Find: $\frac{dV}{dt}$ when $r = 3$ ft

V is the volume of the balloon.

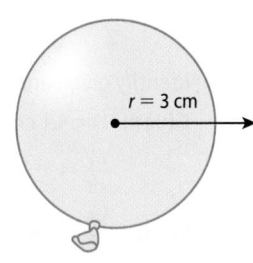

$r = 3$ cm

STEP 2 Write an equation relating the quantities.
Use the equation for volume of a sphere. $V = \frac{4}{3}\pi r^3$

STEP 3 Differentiate to relate the rates of change.
Differentiate with respect to time. $\frac{dV}{dt} = \frac{4}{3}\pi \frac{d}{dt}[r^3]$

Use the Power and Chain Rules. Simplify. $= \frac{4}{3}\pi(3r^2)\frac{dr}{dt} = 4\pi r^2 \frac{dr}{dt}$

STEP 4 Find the unknown rate.
Substitute known quantities. Simplify. $\frac{dV}{dt} = 4\pi(3)^2(2) = 72\pi$

Therefore, the volume of the balloon is increasing at a rate of 72π ft³/min when the radius is 3 ft.

EXAMPLE 6

For the balloon in Example 5, find the rate that the area of the cross section through the center of the balloon is changing when the radius is 3 ft.

STEP 1 Identify given and known information.
Given: $\frac{dr}{dt} = 2$ ft/min when $r = 3$ ft

Find: $\frac{dA}{dt}$ when $r = 3$ ft

STEP 2 Write an equation relating the quantities.
Use the equation for the area of a circle. $A = \pi r^2$

STEP 3 Use related rates to find the unknown rate.
Differentiate with respect to time. $\frac{dA}{dt} = \pi \frac{d}{dt}[r^2]$

Use the Power and Chain Rules. Simplify. $= \pi(2r)\frac{dr}{dt} = 2\pi r \frac{dr}{dt}$

Substitute the known quantities. $= 2\pi(3)(2) = 12\pi$

Therefore, the area of the cross section of the balloon extending through its center is increasing at a rate of 12π ft³/min when the radius is 3 ft.

Rates Involving Cones and Cylinders

EXAMPLE 7

A child is holding a conical ice cream cone with a radius of 4.1 cm and a height of 12.3 cm in the sun. The ice cream is leaking out a hole in the bottom of the cone at a rate of 2 cm³/min. How fast is the height of ice cream in the cone decreasing when the height of the ice cream is 5 cm?

STEP 1 Identify given and unknown information. Draw and label a picture.

Given: $r = 4.1$ cm when $h = 12.3$ cm

$$\frac{dV}{dt} = -2 \text{ cm}^3/\text{min}$$

Find: $\frac{dh}{dt}$ when $h = 5$ cm

r is the radius of the ice cream.

h is the height of the ice cream.

r = 4.1 cm

h = 12.3 cm

STEP 2 Write an equation relating the quantities.

Use the equation for the volume of a cone. $V = \frac{1}{3}\pi r^2 h$

Use a ratio of given information to eliminate r. $\frac{r}{h} = \frac{4.1}{12.3}$

Solve for r. $r = \frac{1}{3}h$

Substitute h in the volume equation. $V = \frac{1}{3}\pi\left(\frac{1}{3}h\right)^2 h = \frac{1}{27}\pi h^3$

STEP 3 Differentiate to relate the rates of change.

Differentiate with respect to time. $\frac{dV}{dt} = \frac{1}{27}\pi\frac{d}{dt}[h^3]$

Use the Power Rule. $= \frac{1}{27}\pi\left(3h^2\frac{dh}{dt}\right)$

Simplify. $= \frac{\pi h^2}{9}\frac{dh}{dt}$

Solve for the unknown rate. $\frac{dh}{dt} = \frac{9}{\pi h^2}\frac{dV}{dt}$

STEP 4 Find the unknown rate.

Substitute known quantities. Simplify. $\frac{dh}{dt} = \frac{9}{\pi(5)^2}(-2) = -\frac{18}{25\pi}$

The ice cream height in the cone is decreasing at a rate of $-\frac{18}{25\pi}$ cm/min when the height is 5 cm.

EXAMPLE 8

The circumference of a cylinder is decreasing at a rate of 4π cm/s, and the radius of the cylinder is decreasing at a rate twice as fast as the height. How fast is the volume of the cylinder changing when the height of the cylinder is 24 cm and the radius is 16 cm?

SEARCH

To see step-by-step videos of these problems, enter the page number into the SWadvantage.com Search Bar.

STEP 1 Identify given and unknown information. Draw and label a picture.

Given: $\dfrac{dC}{dt} = -4\pi$ cm/s $\qquad \dfrac{dr}{dt} = 2\dfrac{dh}{dt}$

Find: $\dfrac{dV}{dt}$ when $h = 24$ cm and $r = 16$ cm

C is the circumference of the cylinder.

V is the volume of the cylinder.

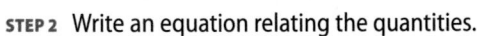

$r = 16$ cm

$h = 24$ cm

STEP 2 Write an equation relating the quantities.

Use the equation for the volume of a cylinder. $\qquad V = \pi r^2 h$

STEP 3 Differentiate to relate the rates of change.

Differentiate with respect to time. $\qquad \dfrac{dV}{dt} = \pi\dfrac{d}{dt}[r^2 h]$

Use the Chain Rule and Power Rule. $\qquad \dfrac{dV}{dt} = \pi\left[r^2\dfrac{dh}{dt} + 2hr\dfrac{dr}{dt}\right]$

STEP 4 Solve for any missing information.

Use the circumference equation to find the rate of change of r. $\qquad C = 2\pi r$

Differentiate with respect to time. $\qquad \dfrac{dC}{dt} = 2\pi\dfrac{dr}{dt}$

Solve for $\dfrac{dr}{dt}$. $\qquad \dfrac{dr}{dt} = \dfrac{1}{2\pi}\dfrac{dC}{dt}$

Use the given relationship of $\dfrac{dr}{dt}$ and $\dfrac{dh}{dt}$. $\qquad \dfrac{dC}{dt} = 2\pi\left(2\dfrac{dh}{dt}\right)$

Simplify. $\qquad = 4\pi\dfrac{dh}{dt}$

Solve for $\dfrac{dh}{dt}$. $\qquad \dfrac{dh}{dt} = \dfrac{1}{4\pi}\dfrac{dC}{dt}$

STEP 5 Find the unknown rate.

Substitute $\dfrac{dh}{dt}$ into the rate equation. $\qquad \dfrac{dV}{dt} = \pi\left[r^2\dfrac{1}{4\pi}\dfrac{dC}{dt} + 2hr\dfrac{1}{2\pi}\dfrac{dC}{dt}\right]$

Substitute known quantities into the equation. $\qquad \dfrac{dV}{dt} = \pi\left[(16)^2\dfrac{1}{4\pi}(-4\pi) + 2(24)(16)\dfrac{1}{2\pi}(-4\pi)\right]$

Simplify. $\qquad = -1792\pi$

Therefore, the volume of the cylinder is decreasing at a rate of -1792π cm³/s when the height is 24 cm and the radius is 16 cm.

Optimization

Absolute Maximum and Minimum

On a closed interval, a function always has a highest point and and a lowest point. These are called the absolute maximum and absolute minimum points. These points occur either at the endpoints of the interval or where the derivative of the function is zero.

EXAMPLE 1

Find the absolute minimum value of $y = x^2 + 3x + 1$ on $[-3, 3]$.

STEP 1 Find the critical points of the function.

Differentiate y.	$y' = 2x + 3$
Set y' equal to zero.	$2x + 3 = 0$
Solve for x.	$x = -\dfrac{3}{2}$

STEP 2 Evaluate the function at the endpoints and critical points.

Evaluate y at the endpoint $x = -3$.	$y = (-3)^2 + 3(-3) + 1 = 1$
Evaluate y at the critical point $x = -\dfrac{3}{2}$.	$y = \left(-\dfrac{3}{2}\right)^2 + 3\left(-\dfrac{3}{2}\right) + 1 = -\dfrac{5}{4}$
Evalute y at the endpoint $x = 3$.	$y = (3)^2 + 3(3) + 1 = 19$

The minimum value of the function on the interval $[-3, 3]$ is $-\dfrac{5}{4}$ and occurs when $x = -\dfrac{3}{2}$.

EXAMPLE 2

Find the absolute maximum value of $f(x) = x^3 - 12x - 3$ on $[-3, 5]$.

STEP 1 Find the critical points of the function.

Differentiate y.	$f'(x) = 3x^2 - 12$
Set y' equal to zero.	$3x^2 - 12 = 0$
Solve for x.	$x = \pm 2$

STEP 2 Evaluate the function at the endpoints and the critical points.

Evaluate f at the endpoint $x = -3$.	$f(-3) = (-3)^3 - 12(-3) - 3 = 6$
Evaluate f at the critical point $x = -2$.	$f(-2) = (-2)^3 - 12(-2) - 3 = 13$
Evaluate f at the critical point $x = 2$.	$f(2) = (2)^3 - 12(2) - 3 = -19$
Evaluate f at the endpoint $x = 5$.	$f(5) = (5)^3 - 12(5) - 3 = 62$

The maximum value of the function on $[-3, 5]$ is 62 and occurs at the right endpoint $x = 5$.

GOT TO KNOW!

Finding Absolute Maximum and Minimum Values

1. Find the critical points by setting the derivative of the function to zero.

2. Compare the value of the function at the endpoints of the interval and at critical points.

Recognizing Minimum and Maximum Problems

Some word problems ask you to find values using terms such as *fastest, heaviest, slowest,* or *strongest.* Terms such as these that refer to extreme values indicate that you need to solve the problem by identifying a maximum or a minimum. This type of problem is called an optimization problem.

EXAMPLE 3

The amount of traffic T moving through an intersection is described by $T(t) = \dfrac{t}{0.1t^2 + 10}$, in hundreds of cars per hour, where t is the time since 12 A.M. Find t when traffic is heaviest.

STEP 1 Determine the endpoints by identifying the domain.

The domain is defined as one day. Since there are 24 hours in a day, the domain is [0, 24].

STEP 2 Find the critical points of the function.

Differentiate T.
$$T'(t) = \frac{(0.1t^2 + 10)(1) - t(0.2t)}{(0.1t^2 + 10)^2}$$

Simplify and set T' equal to zero.
$$T'(t) = \frac{-0.1t^2 + 10}{(0.1t^2 + 10)^2} = 0$$

Identify t when the numerator is equal to zero. $-0.1t^2 + 10 = 0$

Solve for values of t within the domain. $t = 10$

In the interval [0, 24], the only critical point is at $t = 10$.

STEP 3 Evaluate the function at the endpoints and the critical point.

Evaluate T at the endpoint $t = 0$. $T(0) = \dfrac{(0)}{0.1(0)^2 + 10} = 0$

Evaluate T at the critical point $t = 10$. $T(10) = \dfrac{(10)}{0.1(10)^2 + 10} = 0.5$

Evaluate T at the endpoint $t = 24$. $T(24) = \dfrac{(24)}{0.1(24)^2 + 10} = 0.4$

The maximum value of $T = 0.5$ hundred cars per hour occurs when $t = 10$ h. Therefore, the traffic is the heaviest through the intersection at 10 A.M.

SEARCH

To see step-by-step videos of these problems, enter the page number into the SWadvantage.com Search Bar.

GOT TO KNOW!

Solving Optimization Problems

1. Identify given and unknown information. Assign variables if the problem doesn't provide them.

2. Draw a picture if it seems helpful.

3. Write an equation relating the quantities.

4. If the equation has more than one variable, use substitution to reduce the equation to one variable.

5. Determine the endpoints by identifying the domain.

6. Differentiate to find the critical points.

7. Test the endpoints and critical points or use the first derivative test to determine maximum and minimum values.

Optimization Problems

When you solve an optimization problem, first interpret the problem to determine what information is given and what you are asked to find. Determine the endpoints by finding the domain. Then, differentiate to find the critical points. You can identify the maximum or minimum value of the function at these points.

EXAMPLE 4

The outside air temperature during a 24-hour period is described by the function $f(t) = 20 \sin\left(\frac{\pi}{12}t - 3\right) + 75$ in degrees Celsius, where t is hours since 12 A.M. At what time of day is the temperature the warmest?

STEP 1 Determine the endpoints by identifying the domain.

The domain is defined as one day. Since there are 24 hours in a day, the domain is [0, 24].

STEP 2 Find the critical points of the function.

Differentiate $f(t)$. $\qquad\qquad\qquad\qquad\qquad\qquad f'(t) = \frac{20\pi}{12}\cos\left(\frac{\pi}{12}t - 3\right)$

Set $f'(t)$ equal to zero. $\qquad\qquad \frac{20\pi}{12}\cos\left(\frac{\pi}{12}t - 3\right) = 0$

Divide by the constant. $\qquad\qquad\qquad \cos\left(\frac{\pi}{12}t - 3\right) = 0$

Find the inverse trigonometric function. $\qquad\quad \frac{\pi}{12}t - 3 = \cos^{-1}(0)$

Evaluate inverse cosine. $\qquad\qquad\qquad\quad \frac{\pi}{12}t - 3 = -\frac{\pi}{2}, \frac{\pi}{2}$

Solve for t. $\qquad\qquad\qquad\qquad\qquad\qquad\qquad t \approx 5.5, 17.5$

The function has critical points at approximately $t = 5.5$ h and $t = 17.5$ h.

STEP 3 Evaluate the function at the endpoints and the critical points.

Evaluate f at the endpoint $t = 0$. $\qquad\qquad f(0) = 20\sin\left(\frac{\pi}{12}(0) - 3\right) + 75 \approx 72.2$

Evaluate f at the critical point $t = 5.5$ h. $\qquad f(5.5) \approx 20\sin\left(\frac{\pi}{12}(5.5) - 3\right) + 75 \approx 55$

Evaluate f at the critical point $t = 17.5$ h. $\quad f(17.5) \approx 20\sin\left(\frac{\pi}{12}(17.5) - 3\right) + 75 \approx 95$

Evaluate f at the endpoint $t = 24$ h. $\qquad f(24) \approx 20\sin\left(\frac{\pi}{12}(24) - 3\right) + 75 \approx 72.2$

The maximum value of $f(t) = 95°C$ occurs when $t \approx 17.5$ h.

Therefore, the outside temperature is the hottest at about 17.5 hours past 12 A.M. This is equivalent to about 5:30 P.M.

Volume

The maximum or minimum area of geometric shapes can be found using the techniques for finding absolute maximum and minimum values. For volume problems, the endpoints of the interval are defined by the dimensions of the shape.

SEARCH

To see step-by-step videos of these problems, enter the page number into the SWadvantage.com Search Bar.

EXAMPLE 5

A soup company wants to create a cylindrical can with a surface area of 204π in.². Find the dimensions that will maximize the volume of the can.

STEP 1 Identify given and unknown information. Draw and label a picture.

Given: surface area = 240π in.²

Find: r and h when the volume is a maximum

A_s is the surface area of the cylinder.

V is the volume of the cylinder.

STEP 2 Write an equation relating the quantities.

Use the equation for the volume of a cylinder.

$V = 2\pi r^2 h$

Use the equation for the surface area of a cylinder.

$A_s = 2\pi r^2 + 2\pi rh$

Substitute the given value of the surface area.

$204\pi = 2\pi r^2 + 2\pi rh$

Solve the surface area equation for h.

$h = \frac{204\pi}{2\pi r} - r = \frac{102}{r} - r$

Substitute into the volume equation. Simplify.

$V = 2\pi r^2\left(\frac{102}{r} - r\right) = 204\pi r - 2\pi r^3$

STEP 3 Determine the endpoints by identifying the domain of r.

The smallest possible r is zero. The largest possible r is when h is zero.

Substitute $h = 0$ into the surface area equation.

$102 = r^2 + r(0)$

Solve for r.

$r \approx 10.0995$

STEP 4 Find the critical points of the function.

Differentiate V and set it equal to zero.

$V' = 204\pi - 6\pi r^2 = 0$

Solve for r in the domain.

$r \approx 5.831$

STEP 5 Evaluate the function at the endpoints and the critical point.

Evaluate V at the endpoint $r = 0$.

$V = 204\pi(0) - 2\pi(0)^3 = 0$

Evaluate V at the critical point $r \approx 5.831$.

$V \approx 204\pi(5.831) - 2\pi(5.831)^3 \approx 2491$

Evaluate V at the endpoints $r \approx 10.0995$.

$V \approx 204\pi(10.0995) - 2\pi(10.0995)^3 \approx 0$

The greatest volume is about 2491 in.³ when $r \approx 5.831$ in.

STEP 6 Solve for the other dimension.

Use the surface area equation to find h.

$h = \frac{102}{5.831} - 5.831 \approx 11.662$

The dimensions of the can with maximum volume are approximately $r = 5.831$ in. and $h = 11.662$ in.

Area

Optimization problems that involve the maximum area of an object often ask you to determine the values of the sides of a rectangle or the radius and height of a cylinder or cone when the area is maximized.

EXAMPLE 6

A farmer is creating a rectangular fence using 300 ft of fencing. What are the dimensions of the maximum area he can enclose with this amount of fencing?

STEP 1 Draw a picture and label all given quantities.

Given: The perimeter is equal to 300 ft.

Find: x and y for a maximum area

STEP 2 Write an equation relating the quantities.

Use the equation for the perimeter of a rectangle.	$2x + 2y = 300$
Simplify the perimeter equation and solve for y.	$y = 150 - x$
Use the equation for the area of a rectangle.	$A = xy$
Substitute y in the area equation.	$A = x(150 - x)$
Simplify.	$= 150x - x^2$

STEP 3 Determine the endpoints by identifying the domain of x.

The smallest possible x is zero. The largest possible x is when y is zero.

Use the equation for the perimeter of a rectangle. $\qquad x = 150 - (0) = 150$

STEP 4 Find the critical points of the function.

Differentiate A and set it equal to zero. $\qquad A' = 150 - 2x = 0$

Solve for x. $\qquad x = 75$

STEP 5 Evaluate the function at the endpoints and the critical point.

Evaluate A at the endpoint $x = 0$. $\qquad A = 150(0) - (0)^2 = 0$

Evaluate A at the critical point $x = 75$. $\qquad A = 150(75) - (75)^2 = 5625$

Evaluate A at the endpoint $x = 150$. $\qquad A = 150(150) - (150)^2 = 0$

The area is 5625 ft^2 when $x = 75$ ft.

STEP 6 Solve for the other dimension.

Use the perimeter equation to find y. $\qquad y = 150 - (75) = 75$

Therefore, the dimensions of the fence that can be made with 300 ft of fencing and a maximum area are 75 ft $\times$ 75 ft.

EXAMPLE 7

Find the dimensions of the rectangle with the largest possible area that is bounded by the parabolic curve $y = 9 - x^2$ and the x-axis.

SEARCH

To see step-by-step videos of these problems, enter the page number into the SWadvantage.com Search Bar.

STEP 1 Identify given and unknown information. Draw and label a picture.

Given: $y = 9 - x^2$

Find: x and y values for which A is maximum

A is the area of the rectangle.

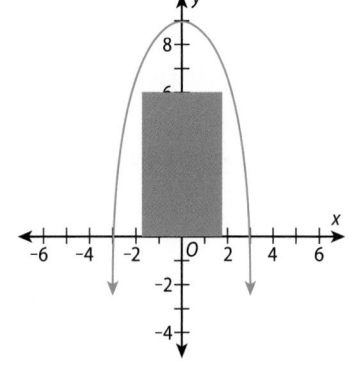

STEP 2 Write an equation relating the quantities.

Use the equation for the area of a rectangle. $A = (\text{base})(\text{height})$

Substitute base $= 2x$ and height $= y$. $= 2xy$

Substitute y from the parabola equation. $= 2x(9 - x^2) = 18x - 2x^3$

STEP 3 Determine the endpoints by identifying the domain of x.

The smallest possible x is zero. The largest possible x is when y is zero.
Use the parabolic equation to find x when y is 0. $0 = 9 - x^2$

Solve for x. $x = \pm 3$

STEP 4 Find the critical points of the function.

Differentiate A and set it equal to zero. $A' = 18 - 6x^2 = 0$

Solve for x. $x = \pm\sqrt{3} \approx 1.732$

Eliminate the negative value of x because it is outside the domain.

STEP 5 Evaluate the function at the endpoints and the critical point.

Evaluate A at the endpoint $x = 0$. $A = 18(0) - 2(0)^3 = 0$

Evaluate A at the critical point $x \approx 1.732$. $A = 18(1.732) - 2(1.732)^3 = 20.785$

Evaluate A at the endpoint $x = 3$. $A = 18(3) - 2(3)^3 = 0$

The greatest area is 20.785 when $x \approx 1.732$.

STEP 6 Solve for the other dimension.

Use the parabola equation to find y. $y \approx 9 - (1.732)^2$

Solve for y. ≈ 6

The total base of the rectangle is $2x = 2(1.732) \approx 3.5$.

Therefore, the dimensions of the rectangle with the largest possible area that is bounded by the parabolic curve $y = 9 - x^2$ and the x-axis are approximately 3.5×6.

Distance

Optimization problems involving distance can include traveling distance as well as the distance between two points.

EXAMPLE 8

Find the points on the curve $y = x^2 + 5$ that are closest to the point (0, 7).

STEP 1 Identify given and unknown information. Draw and label a picture.

    Given: $y = x^2 + 5$

    Find: x and y on the curve that minimizes the distance to (0, 7)

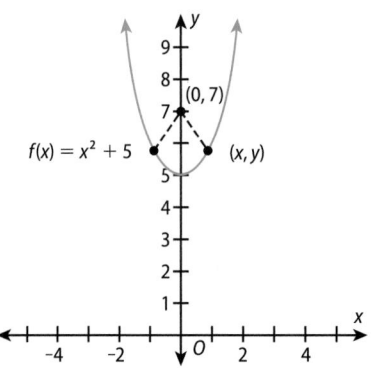

STEP 2 Write an equation relating the quantities.

Use the distance equation.

$$d = \sqrt{(x - x_1)^2 + (y - y_1)^2}$$

Substitute (0, 7) for (x_1, y_1).

$$= \sqrt{(x - 0)^2 + (y - 7)^2}$$

Use the equation for the parabola. Simplify.

$$= \sqrt{(x)^2 + ((x^2 + 5) - 7)^2} = \sqrt{x^4 - 3x^2 + 4}$$

STEP 3 Find the critical points.

Since the d has a minimum value wherever the radicand is a minimum, we only need to find the critical value of $R = x^4 - 3x^2 + 4$.

Differentiate the radicand equation and set equal to zero.

$$R' = 4x^3 - 6x = 0$$

Factor x.

$$x(4x^2 - 6) = 0$$

Solve for x.

$$x = 0, -\frac{\sqrt{6}}{2}, \frac{\sqrt{6}}{2}$$

STEP 4 Evaluate the function at the critical points.

Evaluate d at $x = 0$.

$$d = \sqrt{(0)^4 - 3(0)^2 + 4} = 2$$

Evaluate d at $x = \pm\frac{\sqrt{6}}{2}$.

$$d = \sqrt{\left(\frac{\pm\sqrt{6}}{2}\right)^4 - 3\left(\frac{\pm\sqrt{6}}{2}\right)^2 + 4} \approx 1\frac{3}{4}.$$

The minimum distance is at the points $x = \pm\frac{\sqrt{6}}{2}$.

STEP 5 Solve for the other dimension.

Use the equation for the parabola to find y.

$$y = \left(\frac{\pm\sqrt{6}}{2}\right)^2 + 5 = 3\frac{1}{4}$$

The points on the curve $y = x^2 + 5$ closest to (0, 7) are $\left(-\frac{\sqrt{6}}{2}, 3\frac{1}{4}\right)$ and $\left(\frac{\sqrt{6}}{2}, 3\frac{1}{4}\right)$.

EXAMPLE 9

A farmer is riding a tractor in the middle of a pasture. The tractor is 2 miles from a dirt road that leads to the barn, and the barn is 6 miles down the road. His tractor can travel an average of 4 mph on pastureland and 8 mph on the dirt road. How far from the barn should the farmer drive to the road so that he reaches the barn in the least amount of time?

SEARCH

To see step-by-step videos of these problems, enter the page number into the SWadvantage.com Search Bar.

STEP 1 Identify given and unknown information. Draw and label a picture.

Given: $x + r = 6$

rate on pasture $= 4$ mph

rate on road $= 8$ mph

Find: r so that t is minimum

t is the time the farmer travels.

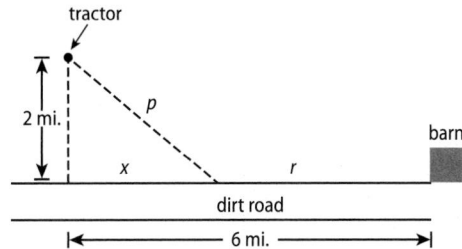

STEP 2 Write an equation relating the quantities.

Identify the distance traveled on pasture. $p = \sqrt{(x)^2 + (2)^2} = \sqrt{x^2 + 4}$

Identify the distance traveled on the road. $r = 6 - x$

Find the time as the distance divided by the rate for each part of the trip. $t = \dfrac{\sqrt{x^2 + 4}}{4} + \dfrac{6 - x}{8}$

STEP 3 Determine the endpoints by identifying the domain of x.

The farmer could drive straight to the road and the x value would be zero, or the farmer could drive straight to the barn and the x value would be 6. Therefore, the domain is [0, 6].

STEP 4 Find the critical points of the function.

Differentiate the time equation and set it equal to zero. $t' = \dfrac{1}{4}\left(\dfrac{1}{2}(x^2+4)^{-\frac{1}{2}}(2x)\right) - \dfrac{1}{8} = 0$

Simplify. $\dfrac{x}{4\sqrt{x^2+4}} - \dfrac{1}{8} = 0$

Multiply by the common denominator. $2x - \sqrt{x^2+4} = 0$

Solve for x. $x \approx 1.155$

Watch Out !

If a distance involves a square root, you should exclude the negative answer because distances must be positive.

STEP 5 Evaluate the time function at the endpoints and the critical point.

Evaluate t at the endpoint $x = 0$. $t(0) = \dfrac{\sqrt{(0)^2+4}}{4} + \dfrac{6-(0)}{8} = 1.25$

Evaluate t at the critical point $x \approx 1.155$. $t(1.155) = \dfrac{\sqrt{(1.155)^2+4}}{4} + \dfrac{6-(1.155)}{8} = 1.183$

Evaluate t at the endpoint $x = 6$. $t(6) = \dfrac{\sqrt{(6)^2+4}}{4} + \dfrac{6-(6)}{8} = 1.581$

The least time is $t \approx 1.183$ h when $x \approx 1.155$.

STEP 6 Evaluate the distance from the barn.

Use the equation for the distance r. $r = 6 - (1.155) \approx 4.845$

The farmer should drive to a point on the road that is a distance about 4.845 mi from the barn.

Mean Value Theorem

Understanding the Mean Value Theorem

You can use the Mean Value Theorem to identify a point where the instantaneous rate of change of a function equals the average rate of change over an interval.

SEARCH

To see step-by-step videos of these problems, enter the page number into the SWadvantage.com Search Bar.

EXAMPLE 1

Find the value c on $[0, 8]$ such that $f'(c) = \dfrac{f(b) - f(a)}{b - a}$ for the function $f(x) = x^{\frac{2}{3}} + 1$.

STEP 1 Differentiate the given function.

Use the Power Rule. $\qquad\qquad f'(x) = \dfrac{2}{3}x^{-\frac{1}{3}}$

STEP 2 Evaluate the derivative at c. $\qquad f'(c) = \dfrac{2}{3}c^{-\frac{1}{3}}$

STEP 3 Find the slope over the entire interval.

Evaluate the function at $b = 8$. $\qquad\qquad f(b) = f(8) = 8^{\frac{2}{3}} + 1 = 5$

Evaluate the function at $a = 0$. $\qquad\qquad f(a) = f(0) = 0^{\frac{2}{3}} + 1 = 1$

Substitute terms in the slope formula. $\qquad \dfrac{f(b) - f(a)}{b - a} = \dfrac{5 - 1}{8 - 0} = \dfrac{1}{2}$

STEP 4 Set the derivative (Step 2) equal to the slope (Step 3). $\qquad \dfrac{2}{3}c^{-\frac{1}{3}} = \dfrac{1}{2}$

STEP 5 Solve for c.

Divide both sides by $\dfrac{2}{3}$. $\qquad\qquad\qquad\qquad c^{-\frac{1}{3}} = \dfrac{3}{4}$

Raise both sides to the power of -3. $\qquad\qquad \left(c^{-\frac{1}{3}}\right)^{-3} = \left(\dfrac{3}{4}\right)^{-3}$

Simplify. $\qquad\qquad\qquad\qquad\qquad\qquad c = \left(\dfrac{4}{3}\right)^3 \approx 2.4$

GOT TO KNOW!

The Mean Value Theorem

If f is a continuous function on $[a, b]$ and differentiable on (a, b), then there exists at least one value c on (a, b) such that

$$f'(c) = \dfrac{f(b) - f(a)}{b - a}$$

Instantaneous rate $\quad=\quad$ Average rate of
of change at $x = c$ $\qquad$ change over the
$\qquad\qquad\qquad$ entire interval

EXAMPLE 2

Find the value *c* on $\left[0, \frac{\pi}{2}\right]$ such that $g'(c) = \frac{g(b) - g(a)}{b - a}$ for the function $g(x) = \sin(2x)$.

STEP 1 Differentiate the given function at *c*.

Use the Chain Rule. $\qquad\qquad\qquad\qquad g'(c) = 2\cos(2c)$

STEP 2 Find the slope over the entire interval.

Evaluate the function at $b = \frac{\pi}{2}$. $\qquad\qquad g(b) = g\left(\frac{\pi}{2}\right) = \sin\left(2\left(\frac{\pi}{2}\right)\right) = 0$

Evaluate the function at $a = 0$. $\qquad\qquad g(b) = g(0) = \sin(2(0)) = 0$

Substitute terms in the slope formula. $\qquad \dfrac{g(b) - g(a)}{b - a} = \dfrac{0 - 0}{\frac{\pi}{2} - 0} = 0$

STEP 3 Set the derivative (Step 1) equal to the slope (Step 2). $\qquad\qquad 2\cos(2c) = 0$

STEP 4 Solve for *c*. $\qquad\qquad\qquad\qquad\qquad c = \dfrac{\pi}{4}$

Applying the Mean Value Theorem

The Mean Value Theorem is often used to prove other theorems. You can also use it, however, in real world situations to show that there must have been an instant in time when a specific instantaneous rate of change was reached based on the behavior over an interval.

EXAMPLE 3

A car traveling on a straight highway passes a speed radar and is clocked at 55 mph. The same car passes another speed radar 6 minutes later 10 miles down the road and is clocked at 65 mph. Use the Mean Value Theorem to prove that the car must have traveled faster than the speed limit of 70 mph during some point between the two radars.

> **Need More**
> **HELP ?**
> Remember: Average velocity is the slope of position.

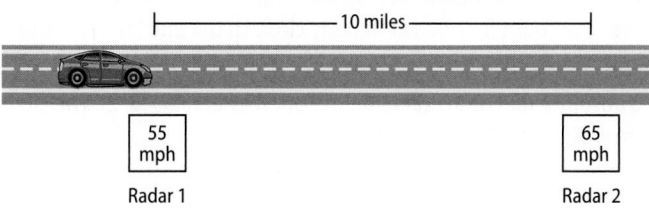

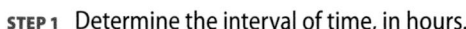

STEP 1 Determine the interval of time, in hours.

Identify *t* when the car passes the first radar. $\qquad t = 0$

Identify *t* when the car passes the second radar. $\qquad t = 6 \text{ min} \times \dfrac{1 \text{ hr}}{60 \text{ min}} = 0.1 \text{ h}$

The time interval is [0, 0.1].

STEP 2 Find the car's average speed between the two radars.

Let *f* represent the position of the car in miles.

Find the slope between the two points. $\qquad \dfrac{f(0.1) - f(0)}{0.1 - 0} = \dfrac{10 - 0}{0.1 - 0} = 100$

Since the average rate of change over the interval is 100 mph, the mean value theorem states that there must be at least one time between the two radars when the car traveled 100 mph and therefore broke the speed limit of 70 mph.

Extreme Value Theorem

Extrema on Open and Closed Intervals

An open interval is one that does not include the endpoints. A closed interval does include the endpoints. The Extreme Value Theorem states that a continuous function always has an extreme maximum value and an extreme minimum value over a closed interval.

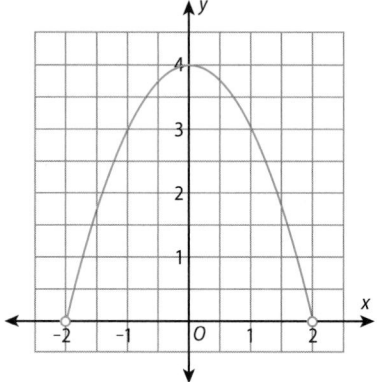

EXAMPLE 1

Find the absolute maximum value of the graph above on the open interval $(-2, 2)$.

The absolute maximum value is the highest y-value on the graph. By looking at the graph, you can see that the absolute maximum value is $y = 4$ and occurs when $x = 0$.

This function has an absolute maximum value of $y = 4$ on the open interval of $(-2, 2)$.

EXAMPLE 2

Find the absolute minimum value of the graph above on the open interval $(-2, 2)$.

Since this function is defined on an open interval, the endpoints are not part of the function. Although it is possible to account for points infinitely close to the endpoints, the function never includes these minimum endpoints.

This function has no absolute minimum value on the open interval $(-2, 2)$. This does not violate the Extreme Value Theorem because the interval is open.

EXAMPLE 3

Find the absolute minimum value of the graph above on the closed interval $[-2, 2]$.

If you evaluate the function over the closed interval $[-2, 2]$, then the endpoints are included. The absolute minimum value is the lowest y-value on the graph. You can see that the absolute minimum value is $y = 0$, which occurs when $x = -2$ and $x = 2$.

This function has an absolute minimum value of $y = 0$ on the closed interval $[-2, 2]$.

Discontinuous Functions

The Extreme Value Theorem does not guarantee absolute extrema for discontinuous functions. The following examples show why.

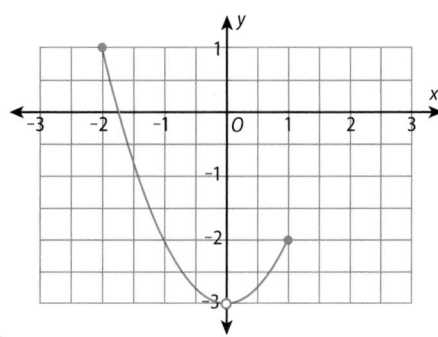

EXAMPLE 4

Find the absolute maximum value of the graph above on the closed interval $[-2, 1]$.

The absolute maximum value is the greatest y-value on the graph. You can see that the absolute maximum value occurs at the left endpoint of the closed interval. The y-value at the left endpoint is 1.

The absolute maximum value of the function is $y = 1$.

EXAMPLE 5

Find the absolute minimum value of the graph above on the closed interval $[-2, 1]$.

In theory, this function is discontinuous at its lowest point on the curve. The function's y-values will get infinitely close to -3 but will never reach that value.

Since this function is discontinuous at its lowest point, it does not have an absolute minimum value on the closed interval $[-2, 1]$.

EXAMPLE 6

The graph at the right shows the same function as above except the point at $x = 0$ is now included. Find the absolute minimum value of the function on the closed interval $[-2, 1]$.

This function is now continuous at its lowest point on the curve. The lowest value of y on the closed interval $[-2, 1]$ is $y = -3$.

The absolute minimum value on the closed interval $[-2, 1]$ is $y = -3$.

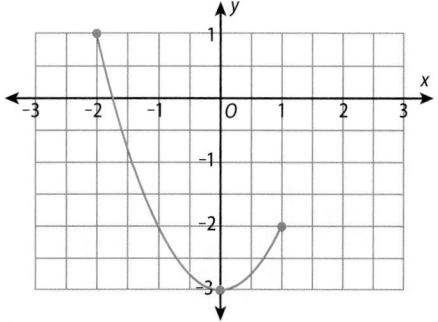

SEARCH

To see step-by-step videos of these problems, enter the page number into the SWadvantage.com Search Bar.

Integration

What Came Before?
- Partial sums
- Derivatives and differentiation

What's This About?
- Using Riemann Sums to find the area under a curve
- Applying the Fundamental Theorem of Calculus
- Evaluating integrals by using substitution and integration by parts

Practical Apps
- Architects use integrals to determine the amount of material needed to build curved structures.
- Integration can be used by accountants to determine costs when marginal cost is known.

Just for FUN!

The functions sin x, cos x, and e^x go to a party. While sin x and cos x are enjoying the party, e^x is just sitting in the corner.

cos x: "Why don't you integrate like us?"

e^x: "It wouldn't make a difference."

CONTENTS | UPLOAD | DOWNLOAD | *Calculus*

You can find more practice problems online by visiting:
www.SWadvantage.com

Antidifferentiation and Indefinite Integrals

Antidifferentiation is the process of identifying a function if you know its derivative. A more common name for antidifferentiation is **integration**. The integral notation is

$$\int f(x)dx = F(x) + C,$$

where $F(x) + C$ is a *general solution* to the integral because it is true for any constant C.

SEARCH

To see step-by-step videos of these problems, enter the page number into the SWadvantage.com Search Bar.

EXAMPLE 1

Find the general solution of the equation $y' = 4$.

The general solution is a function whose derivative is 4. One example is $y = 4x$.

Since the derivative of a constant is zero, the following are examples of functions that also have a derivative of 4. Notice that each function is identical except for the constant term.

$$y = 4x + 1 \qquad y = 4x - 3 \qquad y = 4x - \pi \qquad y = 4x + \frac{1}{2}$$

Therefore, the general solution to the equation $y' = 4$ is $y = 4x + C$.

EXAMPLE 2

Find and graph three solutions to $y = \int 2\, dx$.

Find the general solution. $\int 2\, dx = 2x + C$

Use three arbitrary values for C. $y = 2x - 1 \qquad y = 2x + 0 \qquad y = 2x + 1$

Graph the three functions. (Notice that the slope of each is 2.)

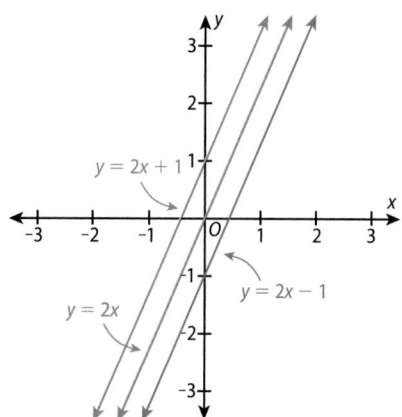

Basic Integration Properties

Zero	$\int 0\, dx = C$	**Sum or Difference** $\int [f(x) \pm g(x)]dx = \int f(x)dx \pm \int g(x)dx$
Constant	$\int k\, dx = kx + C$	**Power**
Constant Multiplier	$\int [k\, f(x)]dx = k \int f(x)dx$	$\int x^n\, dx = \dfrac{x^{n+1}}{n+1} + C$

Solving Integration Problems

Just as multiplication is the inverse operation of division, integration is the inverse of differentiation. To solve integration problems, look at the derivative inside the integral, and think about which function has that derivative. The properties of differentiation also apply to integration. For example, you can bring constants outside an integral sign, and the integral of a sum is the sum of an integral. You can use differentiation to check integration solutions.

EXAMPLE 3

Find the general solution of $\int (x + 3)dx$. Check your answer using differentiation.

STEP 1 Solve the integral.

Expand into the sum of integrals. $\qquad\qquad \int (x + 3)dx = \int x\, dx + \int 3\, dx$

Integrate. $\qquad\qquad\qquad\qquad\qquad\qquad\qquad = \frac{x^2}{2} + 3x + C$

STEP 2 Check the answer. $\qquad \frac{d}{dx}\left(\frac{x^2}{2} + 3x + C\right) = \frac{2x}{2} + 3 = x + 3\ \checkmark$

> ## Watch **Out** !
> When you find the solution to more than one integral at a time, there is no need to add two constants. Although the solution to each integral will include a constant, because the constants can be any number, it is common practice to write the sum of the constants as C.

EXAMPLE 4

Find the general solution of $\int 4x\, dx$. Check your answer using differentiation.

STEP 1 Solve the integral.

Bring the constant outside the integral. $\qquad \int 4x\, dx = 4\int x\, dx$

Integrate. $\qquad\qquad\qquad\qquad\qquad\qquad\qquad = 4\left(\frac{x^2}{2}\right) + C$

Simplify. $\qquad\qquad\qquad\qquad\qquad\qquad\qquad = 2x^2 + C$

STEP 2 Check the answer. $\qquad \frac{d}{dx}(2x^2 + C) = 4x\ \checkmark$

EXAMPLE 5

Find the general solution of $\int (x^2 + 3x - 12)dx$. Check your answer using differentiation.

STEP 1 Solve the integral.

Expand the integral. $\qquad\qquad \int (x^2 + 3x - 12)dx = \int x^2\, dx + \int 3x\, dx - \int 12\, dx$

Bring the constants outside the integrals. $\qquad\qquad\qquad = \int x^2\, dx + 3\int x\, dx - 12\int dx$

Integrate. $\qquad\qquad\qquad\qquad\qquad\qquad\qquad\qquad\quad = \frac{x^3}{3} + 3\left(\frac{x^2}{2}\right) - 12x + C$

STEP 2 Check the answer. $\quad \frac{d}{dx}\left(\frac{x^3}{3} + 3\left(\frac{x^2}{2}\right) - 12x + C\right) = \frac{3x^2}{3} + 3\left(\frac{2x}{2}\right) - 12 = x^2 + 3x - 12\ \checkmark$

> ## Watch **Out** !
> The integral $\int dx$ means $\int 1\, dx$, not $\int 0\, dx$.

Rewriting Before Integrating

Before integrating, it is helpful to rewrite some functions using simple algebra techniques to make integration easier or, in some cases, possible. Rewrite terms that have exponents in the denominator or terms that include radicals. If possible, multiply the function inside the integral.

Watch Out !

The integral of a quotient is *not* the integral of the numerator over the integral of the denominator.

EXAMPLE 6

Evaluate: $\int \frac{1}{x^4}\, dx$

Rewrite using a negative exponent. $\int \frac{1}{x^4}\, dx = \int x^{-4}\, dx$

Integrate. $= \frac{x^{-3}}{-3} + C$

Simplify. $= -\frac{1}{3x^3} + C$

EXAMPLE 7

Evaluate: $\int \sqrt[3]{x^2}\, dx$

Rewrite using a fractional exponent. $\int \sqrt[3]{x^2}\, dx = \int x^{\frac{2}{3}}\, dx$

Integrate. $= \frac{x^{\frac{5}{3}}}{\frac{5}{3}} + C$

Change back to radical form. $= \frac{\sqrt[3]{x^5}}{\frac{5}{3}} + C$

Simplify. $= \frac{3x\sqrt[3]{x^2}}{5} + C$

EXAMPLE 8

Evaluate: $\int \frac{x^2 - 5x}{x}\, dx$

Expand into the sum of integrals. $\int \frac{x^2 - 5x}{x}\, dx = \int \frac{x^2}{x}\, dx + \int \frac{-5x}{x}\, dx$

Divide by x. $= \int x\, dx + \int -5\, dx$

Integrate. $= \frac{x^2}{2} - 5x + C$

EXAMPLE 9

Evaluate: $\int (x+2)(x-1)\,dx$

Multiply. $\int (x+2)(x-1)\,dx = \int (x^2 + x - 2)\,dx$

Expand. $= \int x^2\,dx + \int x\,dx - \int 2\,dx$

Integrate. $= \dfrac{x^3}{3} + \dfrac{x^2}{2} - 2x + C$

EXAMPLE 10

Evaluate: $\int \dfrac{(x-4)^2}{x^{-1}}\,dx$

Rewrite with a positive exponent. $\int \dfrac{(x-4)^2}{x^{-1}}\,dx = \int x(x-4)^2\,dx$

Multiply. $= \int [x(x^2 - 8x + 16)]\,dx$

Use the Distributive Property. $= \int (x^3 - 8x^2 + 16x)\,dx$

Expand. $= \int x^3\,dx - 8\int x^2\,dx + 16\int x\,dx$

Integrate. $= \dfrac{x^4}{4} - 8\left(\dfrac{x^3}{3}\right) + 16\left(\dfrac{x^2}{2}\right) + C$

Simplify. $= \dfrac{x^4}{4} - \dfrac{8x^3}{3} + 8x^2 + C$

EXAMPLE 11

Evaluate: $\int \dfrac{2(x-4)}{\sqrt{x}}\,dx$

Rewrite with a negative fractional exponent. $\int \dfrac{2(x-4)}{\sqrt{x}}\,dx = \int (2x^{-\frac{1}{2}}(x-4)\,dx$

Use the Distributive Property. $= \int (2x^{\frac{1}{2}} - 8x^{-\frac{1}{2}})\,dx$

Expand. $= 2\int x^{\frac{1}{2}}\,dx - 8\int x^{-\frac{1}{2}}\,dx$

Integrate. $= 2\left(\dfrac{x^{\frac{3}{2}}}{\frac{3}{2}}\right) - 8\left(\dfrac{x^{\frac{1}{2}}}{\frac{1}{2}}\right) + C$

Simplify. $= \dfrac{4x^{\frac{3}{2}}}{3} - 16x^{\frac{1}{2}} + C$

Change back to radical form. $= \dfrac{4x\sqrt{x}}{3} - 16\sqrt{x} + C$

Integral Solutions through a Particular Point

You can find a particular solution to an integral if you know a point on the curve of the function. First, find the general solution to the integral. Then, determine the particular solution using the given x- and y-values to calculate C.

SEARCH 🔍

To see step-by-step videos of these problems, enter the page number into the SWadvantage.com Search Bar.

EXAMPLE 12

Find the solution to the equation $y' = (2x^2 - 3)$ that passes through the point $(0, -1)$.

STEP 1 Find the general solution.

Write the function as an integral. $\qquad y = \int(2x^2 - 3)dx$

Expand the integral. $\qquad = 2\int x^2\,dx - \int 3\,dx$

Integrate. $\qquad = 2\left(\dfrac{x^3}{3}\right) - 3x + C$

STEP 2 Determine C.

Substitute the point $(0, -1)$ for x and y. $\qquad -1 = 2\left(\dfrac{(0)^3}{3}\right) - 3(0) + C$

Solve for C. $\qquad -1 = C$

STEP 3 Write the particular solution. $\qquad y = 2\left(\dfrac{x^3}{3}\right) - 3x - 1$

EXAMPLE 13

Find the solution to $y' = \dfrac{x-1}{x^3}$ that passes through the point $\left(1, \dfrac{3}{2}\right)$.

STEP 1 Find the general solution.

Write the function as an integral by integrating y'. $\qquad y = \int \dfrac{x-1}{x^3}\,dx$

Rewrite with a negative exponent. $\qquad = \int x^{-3}(x-1)dx$

Use the Distributive Property. $\qquad = \int(x^{-2} - x^{-3})dx$

Integrate. $\qquad = \dfrac{x^{-1}}{-1} - \dfrac{x^{-2}}{-2} + C$

Simplify. $\qquad = -x^{-1} + \dfrac{1}{2}x^{-2} + C$

STEP 2 Determine C.

Substitute the point $\left(1, \dfrac{3}{2}\right)$ for x and y. $\qquad \dfrac{3}{2} = \dfrac{(1)^{-1}}{-1} - \dfrac{(1)^{-2}}{-2} + C$

Solve for C. $\qquad 2 = C$

STEP 3 Write the particular solution. $\qquad y = -x^{-1} + \dfrac{1}{2}x^{-2} + 2$

EXAMPLE 14

Find the solution to $f'(x) = \dfrac{3}{\sqrt[3]{x}}$ that passes through $f(0) = -3$.

STEP 1 Find the general solution.

Write the function as an integral by integrating $f'(x)$.

$$f(x) = \int \frac{3}{\sqrt[3]{x}}\, dx$$

Rewrite with a negative rational exponent.

$$= \int 3x^{-\frac{1}{3}}\, dx$$

Integrate.

$$= 3\frac{x^{\frac{2}{3}}}{\frac{2}{3}} + C$$

Simplify.

$$= \frac{9}{2}x^{\frac{2}{3}} + C$$

STEP 2 Determine C.

Substitute the point $(0, -3)$ for x and y.

$$(-3) = \frac{9}{2}(0)^{\frac{2}{3}} + C$$

Solve for C.

$$-3 = C$$

STEP 3 Write the particular solution.

$$y = \frac{9}{2}x^{\frac{2}{3}} - 3$$

> **Watch Out !**
>
> Sometimes problems use the notation $f(x)$ for the function that is inside the integral sign, and sometimes $f(x)$ is used for the solution. Consider what the problem is asking to identify $f(x)$ in each case.

EXAMPLE 15

Find the solution to the equation $y' = x^{-\frac{1}{2}}(x-1)^2$ that passes through the point $\left(1, \dfrac{16}{15}\right)$.

STEP 1 Find the general solution.

Write the function as an integral by integrating y'.

$$y = \int x^{-\frac{1}{2}}(x-1)^2\, dx$$

Multiply the binomials.

$$= \int (x)^{-\frac{1}{2}}(x^2 - 2x + 1)\, dx$$

Use the Distributive Property.

$$= \int \left(x^{\frac{3}{2}} - 2x^{\frac{1}{2}} + x^{-\frac{1}{2}}\right) dx$$

Integrate.

$$= \frac{x^{\frac{5}{2}}}{\frac{5}{2}} - \frac{2x^{\frac{3}{2}}}{\frac{3}{2}} + \frac{x^{\frac{1}{2}}}{\frac{1}{2}} + C$$

Simplify.

$$= \frac{2}{5}x^{\frac{5}{2}} - \frac{4}{3}x^{\frac{3}{2}} + 2x^{\frac{1}{2}} + C$$

STEP 2 Determine C.

Substitute the point $\left(1, \frac{16}{15}\right)$ for x and y.

$$\frac{16}{15} = \frac{2}{5}(1)^{\frac{5}{2}} - \frac{4}{3}(1)^{\frac{3}{2}} + 2(1)^{\frac{1}{2}} + C$$

Solve for C.

$$0 = C$$

STEP 3 Write the particular solution.

$$y = \frac{2}{5}x^{\frac{5}{2}} - \frac{4}{3}x^{\frac{3}{2}} + 2x^{\frac{1}{2}}$$

Riemann Sums

Area Under a Curve

As a preparation for learning about integrals, it is useful to investigate how to calculate the area bounded by the curve of a function and the *x*-axis. You can approximate this area by dividing it into geometric shapes, such as rectangles and trapezoids, and adding the areas.

EXAMPLE 1

Approximate the area under the curve at the right on [0, 3] using the sum of the areas of the rectangles.

Each rectangle's area, A_i, is the product of its base and height.

$$A_1 = (0.5)(3) = 1.5$$
$$A_2 = (0.5)(1.5) = 0.75$$
$$A_3 = (1)(1.3) = 1.3$$
$$A_4 = (0.5)(1.5) = 0.75$$
$$A_5 = (0.5)(2.5) = 1.25$$
$$A_{total} = 1.5 + 0.75 + 1.3 + 0.75 + 1.25 \approx 5.6$$

An approximation for the area under the curve from [0, 3] is 5.6.

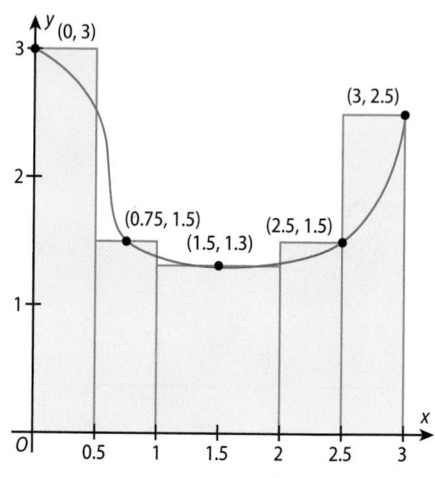

Need More HELP?

For help with summation notation, go to *Arithmetic Series* in *Advanced Algebra* (p. 1862).

You can also express the total area of the shapes under the curve using summation notation.

If the bases of the rectangles are different, as in Example 1, the total area for *n* rectangles is $A = \sum_{i=1}^{n} b_i h_i$, where *b* is the width of the base and *h* is the height of each rectangle. If the bases of the rectangles are all the same, as in Example 2 below, then the calculation is simplified by bringing *b* outside the summation: $A = b \sum_{i=1}^{n} h_i$.

EXAMPLE 2

Approximate the area under the curve $y = 6 - x^2$, shown at the right, on [0, 2] using the sum of the areas of the rectangles. Is the approximation an overestimate or an underestimate?

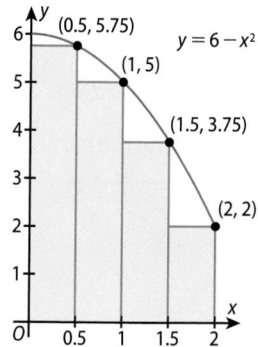

Express the total area using summation notation.
$$A = b \sum_{i=1}^{4} h_i$$

Expand the summation.
$$= b(h_1 + h_2 + h_3 + h_4)$$

Substitute the base and the heights.
$$= (0.5)(5.75 + 5 + 3.75 + 2)$$

Simplify.
$$\approx 8.25$$

Since the areas of the rectangles all lay below the curve, this is an underestimate of the actual area.

EXAMPLE 3

Approximate the area under the curve $y = 6 - x^2$, shown at the right, on [0, 2] using the sum of the areas of the rectangles. Is the approximation an overestimate or an underestimate?

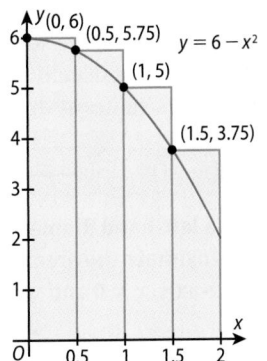

Express the total area using summation notation.	$A = b\sum_{i=1}^{4} h_i$
Expand the summation.	$= b(h_1 + h_2 + h_3 + h_4)$
Substitute the base and the heights.	$= (0.5)[(6 + 5.75 + 5 + 3.75)$
Simplify.	≈ 10.25

Since the areas of the rectangles all lay above the curve, this is an overestimate of the actual area.

SEARCH

To see step-by-step videos of these problems, enter the page number into the SWadvantage.com Search Bar.

You can also use trapezoids to approximate the area under a curve. The area of a trapezoid is usually expressed with the trapezoid drawn so that its parallel sides are horizontal. To use it for approximating the area under a curve, consider the trapezoid as if its bases are vertical and its height is horizontal, as shown at the right. Notice that if two trapezoids are side-by-side under a curve, they share a side.

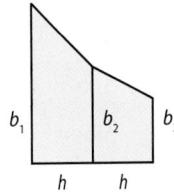

EXAMPLE 4

Approximate the area under the curve $y = 6 - x^2$, shown below, on [0, 2] using the sum of the areas of the trapezoids.

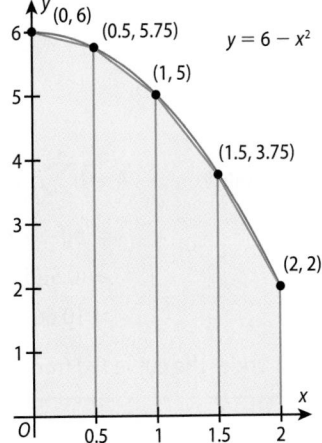

Add the areas of the trapezoids.	$A = \frac{1}{2}((b_1 + b_2)h) + \frac{1}{2}((b_2 + b_3)h) + \frac{1}{2}((b_3 + b_4)h) + \frac{1}{2}((b_4 + b_5)h)$
Factor.	$= \frac{h}{2}(b_1 + b_2 + b_2 + b_3 + b_3 + b_4 + b_4 + b_5)$
Simplify.	$= \frac{h}{2}(b_1 + 2b_2 + 2b_3 + 2b_4 + b_5)$
Substitute the base and heights.	$= \frac{(0.5)}{2}[(6) + 2(5.75) + 2(5) + 2(3.75) + (2)]$
Simplify.	$= 9.25$

Left-Hand Riemann Sums

If you divide the area between the curve of a function and the x-axis on a closed interval into rectangles, the sum of the rectangles' areas is called a **Riemann sum**. For convenience, the interval is usually divided into equal parts. For a left-hand Riemann sum, you use the function's values at the left-hand side of each subinterval as the rectangle's height.

EXAMPLE 5

Use a left-hand Riemann sum with six equal subintervals to approximate the area bound by the curve $f(x) = 0.5x^3 - x^2 - 2x + 6$, the x-axis, $x = 0$ and $x = 3$. The graph is shown at the right.

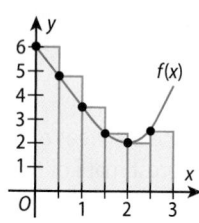

STEP 1 Find the x-values at the left-hand points of the rectangles.

Divide the interval into equal parts.

$$\text{width} = \frac{(\text{right endpoint}) - (\text{left endpoint})}{\text{number of subintervals}}$$

Substitute.

$$= \frac{3 - 0}{6}$$

Simplify.

$$= 0.5$$

The x-values at the left-hand points of the rectangles are 0, 0.5, 1, 1.5, 2, and 2.5.

STEP 2 Calculate the height of each rectangle.

$$f(0) = (0.5)(0)^3 - (0)^2 - 2(0) + 6 = 6$$
$$f(0.5) = (0.5)(0.5)^3 - (0.5)^2 - 2(0.5) + 6 \approx 4.81$$
$$f(1) = (0.5)(1)^3 - (1)^2 - 2(1) + 6 = 3.5$$
$$f(1.5) = (0.5)(1.5)^3 - (1.5)^2 - 2(1.5) + 6 \approx 2.44$$
$$f(2) = (0.5)(2)^3 - (2)^2 - 2(2) + 6 = 2$$
$$f(2.5) = (0.5)(2.5)^3 - (2.5)^2 - 2(2.5) + 6 \approx 2.56$$

STEP 3 Find the total area of the rectangles.

Write the area using summation notation.

$$A = b\sum_{i=1}^{6} h_i$$

Expand the summation.

$$= b(h_1 + h_2 + h_3 + h_4 + h_5 + h_6)$$

Substitute the base and heights.

$$\approx (0.5)(6 + 4.81 + 3.5 + 2.44 + 2 + 2.56)$$

Simplify.

$$\approx 10.66$$

The left-hand approximation of the area under the curve $f(x)$ from $x = 0$ to $x = 3$ is 10.66.

Riemann Sum

If f is a function on $[a, b]$ divided into n subintervals so that Δx_i is the width and x_i^* is any point in the ith subinterval, then the sum of the rectangles is:

$$\sum_{i=1}^{n} f(x_i^*)\Delta x_i$$

Right-Hand Riemann Sums

For a right-hand Riemann sum, you calculate the area of rectangles using the function's values at the right-hand side of each subinterval as the rectangle's height.

Use a right–hand Riemann sum with six equal subintervals to approximate the area bound by the curve $f(x) = 0.5x^3 - x^2 - 2x + 6$, the x-axis, $x = 0$ and $x = 3$. The graph is shown at the right.

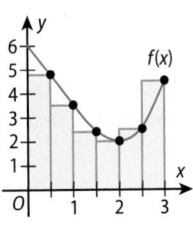

> **Watch Out** !
> The right-hand approximation does not always result in an overestimate of the total area under the curve.

STEP 1 Find the x-values at the right-hand points of the rectangles.

Divide the interval into equal parts. $\text{width} = \dfrac{(\text{right endpoint}) - (\text{left endpoint})}{\text{number of subintervals}}$

Substitute. $= \dfrac{3 - 0}{6}$

Simplify. $= 0.5$

The x-values at the right-hand points of the rectangles are 0.5, 1, 1.5, 2, 2.5, and 3.0.

STEP 2 Calculate the height of each rectangle.

$f(0.5) = (0.5)(0.5)^3 - (0.5)^2 - 2(0.5) + 6 \approx 4.81$

$f(1) = (0.5)(1)^3 - (1)^2 - 2(1) + 6 = 3.5$

$f(1.5) = (0.5)(1.5)^3 - (1.5)^2 - 2(1.5) + 6 \approx 2.44$

$f(2) = (0.5)(2)^3 - (2)^2 - 2(2) + 6 = 2$

$f(2.5) = (0.5)(2.5)^3 - (2.5)^2 - 2(2.5) + 6 \approx 2.56$

$f(3) = (0.5)(3)^3 - (3)^2 - 2(3) + 6 = 4.5$

STEP 3 Find the total area of the rectangles.

Write the area using summation notation. $A = b\displaystyle\sum_{i=1}^{6} h_i$

Expand the summation. $= b(h_1 + h_2 + h_3 + h_4 + h_5 + h_6)$

Substitute the base and heights. $\approx (0.5)(4.81 + 3.5 + 2.44 + 2 + 2.56 + 4.5)$

Simplify. ≈ 9.91

The right-hand approximation of the area under the curve $f(x)$ from $x = 0$ to $x = 3$ is 9.91.

GOT TO KNOW!

Left-Hand and Right-Hand Riemann Sums

Left-Hand Riemann Sum

$$\sum_{i=1}^{n} f(x_{i-1})\Delta x_i$$

where x_{i-1} is the left endpoint of each subinterval.

Right-Hand Riemann Sum

$$\sum_{i=1}^{n} f(x_i)\Delta x_i$$

where x_i is the right endpoint of each subinterval.

Midpoint Riemann Sums

To approximate the area under a curve using a midpoint Riemann sum, use the function's value at the midpoint of each subinterval as the rectangle's height. The first midpoint's *x-value* is half the width of the subinterval added to the interval's left endpoint.

SEARCH

To see step-by-step videos of these problems, enter the page number into the SWadvantage.com Search Bar.

EXAMPLE 7

Use a midpoint Riemann sum with six equal subintervals to approximate the area bound by the curve $f(x) = 0.5x^3 - x^2 - 2x + 6$, the *x*-axis, $x = 0$ and $x = 3$. The graph is shown at the right.

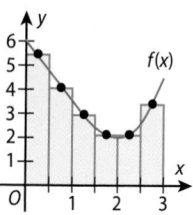

STEP 1 Find the *x*-values at the midpoints of the rectangles.

Divide the interval into parts.	$\text{width} = \dfrac{(\text{right endpoint}) - (\text{left endpoint})}{\text{number of subintervals}}$
Substitute.	$= \dfrac{3 - 0}{6}$
Simplify.	$= 0.5$

The *x*-values at the midpoints of the rectangles are 0.25, 0.75, 1.25, 1.75, 2.25, and 2.75.

STEP 2 Calculate the height of each rectangle.

$f(0.25) = (0.5)(0.25)^3 - (0.25)^2 - 2(0.25) + 6 \approx 5.45$

$f(0.75) = (0.5)(0.75)^3 - (0.75)^2 - 2(0.75) + 6 \approx 4.15$

$f(1.25) = (0.5)(1.25)^3 - (1.25)^2 - 2(1.25) + 6 \approx 2.91$

$f(1.75) = (0.5)(1.75)^3 - (1.75)^2 - 2(1.75) + 6 \approx 2.12$

$f(2.25) = (0.5)(2.25)^3 - (2.25)^2 - 2(2.25) + 6 \approx 2.13$

$f(2.75) = (0.5)(2.75)^3 - (2.75)^2 - 2(2.75) + 6 \approx 3.34$

STEP 3 Find the total area of the rectangles.

Write the area using summation notation.	$A = b\sum_{i=1}^{6} h_i$
Expand the summation.	$= b(h_1 + h_2 + h_3 + h_4 + h_5 + h_6)$
Substitute the base and heights.	$\approx (0.5)(5.45 + 4.15 + 2.91 + 2.12 + 2.13 + 3.34)$
Simplify.	≈ 10.05

The midpoint approximation of the area under the curve $f(x)$ from $x = 0$ to $x = 3$ is 10.05.

GOT TO KNOW!

Midpoint Riemann Sum

$$\sum_{i=1}^{n} f\left(x_{i-1} + \frac{\Delta x_i}{2}\right) \Delta x_i$$

where $x_{i-1} + \dfrac{\Delta x_i}{2}$ is the midpoint of each subinterval.

Trapezoidal Rule

If you divide the area between the curve of a function and the *x*-axis on a closed interval into trapezoids instead of rectangles, you can use the Trapezoidal Rule to approximate the total area. The area of each trapezoid is $\frac{1}{2}$(subinterval width)(sum of the heights). If the widths of the trapezoids are chosen equal, then the total area of all trapezoids is the product of half the subinterval width and the sum of the two side heights of all trapezoids.

Need More
HELP ?

For more with finding the area of a trapezoid, go to *Areas of Trapezoids* in *Measurement* (Book 1, p. 540).

EXAMPLE 8

The table below has *x* and *f(x)* values for the function **f(x) = 0.5x³ − x² − 2x + 6.**

x	0	0.5	1	1.5	2	2.5	3
f(x)	6	4.81	3.5	2.44	2	2.56	4.5

Use trapezoids to approximate the area under the curve *f(x)*, shown on the graph at the right, on the interval [0, 3] with six equal subintervals.

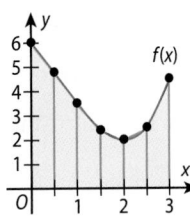

Write the Trapezoidal Rule for 6 subintervals.

$$A_{total} = \frac{1}{2}\left(\frac{b-a}{6}\right)[f(x_0) + 2f(x_1) + 2f(x_2) + 2f(x_3) + 2f(x_4) + 2f(x_5) + f(x_6)]$$

Substitute the endpoints.

$$= \frac{1}{2}\left(\frac{3-0}{6}\right)[f(x_0) + 2f(x_1) + 2f(x_2) + 2f(x_3) + 2f(x_4) + 2f(x_5) + f(x_6)]$$

Substitute the *x*-values.

$$= \frac{1}{4}[f(0) + 2f(0.5) + 2f(1) + 2f(1.5) + 2f(2) + 2f(2.5) + f(3)]$$

Substitute the *y*-values.

$$\approx \frac{1}{4}[6 + 9.62 + 7 + 4.88 + 4 + 5.12 + 4.5]$$

Simplify.

$$\approx 10.3$$

The approximate area between the curve $f(x) = 0.5x^3 − x^2 − 2x + 6$ and the *x*-axis on the interval [0, 3] is 10.3.

Trapezoidal Rule (with equal subintervals)

If *f* is a continuous function on [*a*, *b*], then the approximate area bound by the function and the *x*-axis on the closed interval [*a*, *b*] with *n* subintervals is

$$= \frac{1}{2}\left(\frac{b-a}{n}\right)[f(x_0) + 2f(x_1) + 2f(x_2) + \ldots + 2f(x_{n-1}) + (x_n)]$$

Fundamental Theorem of Calculus

Definite Integral

A definite integral defines the area under a curve bound by the x-axis and the lines $x = a$ and $x = b$ when the function is continuous and non-negative. If you use a Riemann sum to approximate this area, increasing the number of rectangles brings the approximation closer to the actual value. It follows that as the number of rectangles approaches infinity, the limit of the Riemann sum is the definite integral.

The notation for a definite integral on $[a, b]$ is $\int_a^b f(x)dx$. The notation for the solution, $F(x)\big|_a^b$, means you evaluate the antiderivative at the interval's endpoints, $F(b) - F(a)$.

EXAMPLE 1

Calculate the area under the curve $y = 3x$ on the interval [0, 2], shown on the graph at the right.

METHOD 1

Use a midpoint Riemann sum with 4 rectangles.

STEP 1 Identify the x values of the midpoints.

$x = 0.25, 0.75, 1.25, 1.75$

STEP 2 Calculate the y values of the midpoints.

$y = 3(0.25) = 1.75 \qquad y = 3(0.75) = 2.25$

$y = 3(1.25) = 3.75 \qquad y = 3(1.75) = 5.25$

STEP 3 Find the total area of the rectangles.

$$A = b\sum_{i=1}^{4} h_i = b(h_1 + h_2 + h_3 + h_4)$$

Substitute the base and heights.

$= (0.5)(1.75 + 2.25 + 3.75 + 5.25)$

Simplify.

$= 6.5$

A Riemann approximation of the area under the curve $y = 3x$ is 6.5.

METHOD 2

Use a definite integral.

Write the area as an integral.

$A = \int_0^2 3x\,dx$

Integrate.

$= 3\left(\frac{x^2}{2}\right)\Big|_0^2$

Evaluate at the endpoints.

$= 3\left(\frac{2^2}{2}\right) - 3\left(\frac{0^2}{2}\right) = 6$

The actual area under the curve $y = 3x$ is 6.

Try It This Way

Use a graphing calculator to see a visual representation of this definite integral.

First type the function $3x$ into the Y= function.

Then select CALC (2nd TRACE).

Next, select $\int f(x)dx$.

When the calculator asks for the Lower Limit, type in 0, ENTER. When the calculator asks for the Upper Limit, type in 2, ENTER.

GOT TO KNOW!

Fundamental Theorem of Calculus

Let F be the antiderivative of a function f on the closed interval $[a, b]$. If f is continuous on $[a, b]$, then:

$$\int_a^b f(x)dx = F(b) - F(a)$$

EXAMPLE 2

Determine the area under the curve $y = 2x$ on the interval [2, 5], shown on the graph at the right.

METHOD 1

Use a midpoint Riemann sum with 3 rectangles.

STEP 1 Identify the x values of the midpoints.

$x = 2.5, 3.5, 4.5$

STEP 2 Calculate the y values of the midpoints.

$y = 2(2.5) = 5$
$y = 2(3.5) = 7$
$y = 2(4.5) = 9$

STEP 3 Find the total area of the rectangles.

$A = b \sum_{i=1}^{3} h_i = b(h_1 + h_2 + h_3)$

Substitute the base and heights.

$= (1)(5 + 7 + 9)$

Simplify.

$= 21$

METHOD 2

Use the formula for the area of a trapezoid.

Write the formula for the area.

$A = \frac{1}{2}h(b_1 + b_2)$

Substitute the width h and heights b_1 and b_2.

$= \frac{1}{2}(3)(4 + 10) = 21$

METHOD 3

Use a definite integral.

Write the area as an integral.

$A = \int_{2}^{5} 2x\, dx$

Integrate.

$= 2\left(\frac{x^2}{2}\right)\Big|_{2}^{5}$

Evaluate at the endpoints.

$= 2\left(\frac{5^2}{2}\right) - 2\left(\frac{2^2}{2}\right)$

Simplify.

$= 21$

The Riemann approximation of the area under the curve is 21. The trapezoid formula and definite integral define the actual area under the curve $y = 2x$ as 21.

EXAMPLE 3

Evaluate $\int_{-4}^{4}\sqrt{16 - x^2}\, dx$ using the graph of the function and a geometric formula.

Write the formula for the area of a semicircle.

$A = \frac{1}{2}\pi r^2$

Substitute the radius r.

$= \frac{1}{2}\pi(4)^2 = 8\pi$

$\int_{-4}^{4}\sqrt{16 - x^2}\, dx = 8\pi$

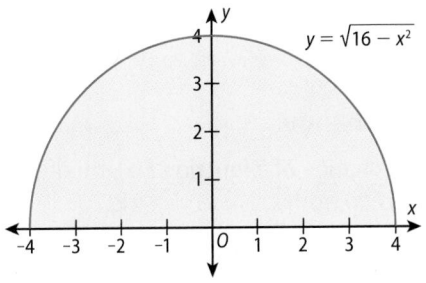

Accumulation of Change

If a function represents a rate of change, the definite integral of the function is the total change. For example, if a function represents velocity (the rate of change of position), the definite integral of the function is the total change in position. The integral of the rate of change of a population is the total change in population. Notice that the total change of these functions may be positive, negative, or zero, unlike area, which is always positive.

EXAMPLE 4

Watch Out !

The definite integral only represents an area when the function is positive.

Evaluate $\int_{-2}^{2} 3x\, dx$, shown on the graph at the right.

Integrate.

$$\int_{-2}^{2} 3x\, dx = 3\left(\frac{x^2}{2}\right)\Big|_{-2}^{2}$$

Evaluate at the endpoints.

$$= 3\left(\frac{2^2}{2}\right) - 3\left(\frac{(-2)^2}{2}\right)$$

Simplify.

$$= 0$$

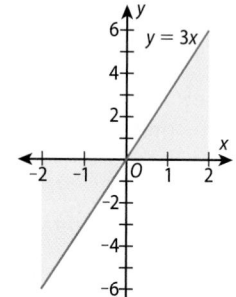

Notice that you could calculate the area between the curve $y = 3x$ and the x axis from -2 to 2 by finding the area of two triangles, each with an area of 6. The total area from -2 to 2 is then 12. The definite integral, however, is 0. In this case, the integral does not represent a total area since the function is negative on $[-2, 0]$. The integral $\int_{-2}^{2} 3x\, dx = 0$ represents the accumulation of change.

EXAMPLE 5

Evaluate $\int_{0}^{3}(x^2 - 2)dx$, shown on the graph at the right.

Integrate.

$$\int_{0}^{3}(x^2 - 2)dx = \left(\frac{x^3}{3} - 2x\right)\Big|_{0}^{3}$$

Evaluate at the endpoints.

$$= \left(\frac{3^3}{3} - 2(3)\right) - \left(\frac{0^3}{3} - 2(0)\right)$$

Simplify.

$$= 3$$

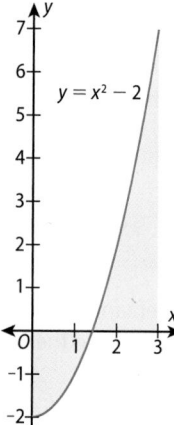

GOT TO KNOW !

Accumulation of Change

If $F'(x)$ is the rate of change of a function $F(x)$, then the total change in $F(x)$ from $x = a$ to $x = b$ is:

$$\int_{a}^{b} F'(x)dx = F(b) - F(a)$$

EXAMPLE 6

Let $P(t)$ represent a population of bacteria that is growing at a rate of t^5 million bacteria per hour after t hours. Find the total change in population of bacteria during the first 2 hours.

Write an accumulation of change integral. $\int_a^b P'(t)dt = \int_0^2 t^5\,dt$

Integrate. $= \dfrac{t^6}{6}\Big|_0^2$

Evaluate at the endpoints. $= \dfrac{2^6}{6} - \dfrac{0^6}{6} \approx 10.7$

The total bacteria population change during the first 2 hours is about 10.7 million bacteria.

EXAMPLE 7

The function $C'(x) = x^2 - 12x + 40$ describes the cost in dollars per unit to make a product. If the fixed cost is \$350, what is the total cost to make 60 units?

Write an accumulation of change integral. Total cost $=$ Fixed cost $+ \int_a^b C'(x)dx$

Substitute. $= 350 + \int_0^{60}(x^2 - 12x + 40)dx$

Integrate. $= 350 + \left[\dfrac{x^3}{3} - 12\left(\dfrac{x^2}{2}\right) + 40x\right]_0^{60}$

Evaluate at the endpoints. $= 350 + \dfrac{60^3}{3} - 6(60)^2 + 40(60)$

$- \left[\dfrac{0^3}{3} - 6(0)^2 + 40(0)\right] = 53{,}150$

The total cost to make 60 units is \$53,150.

EXAMPLE 8

$V(t)$ represents the amount of water in a tank that has sprung a leak and is losing water at a rate of $\sqrt{t}$ gallons per minute. If the tank initially held 40 gallons, how much is in it after 5 minutes?

STEP 1 Determine the change in volume.

Write an accumulation of change integral. $\int_a^b V'(t)dt = \int_0^5 \sqrt{t}\,dt$

Integrate. $= \dfrac{2t^{\frac{3}{2}}}{3}\Big|_0^5$

Evaluate at the endpoints. $= \dfrac{2(5)^{\frac{3}{2}}}{3} - \dfrac{2(0)^{\frac{3}{2}}}{2} \approx 7.5$

The total change in the volume of water during the first 5 minutes is about 7.5 gallons.

STEP 2 Calculate the amount of water remaining.

Subtract from the initial amount. Amount left $=$ initial amount $-$ amount of change

Substitute. $= 40 - 7.5 \approx 32.5$

The amount of water left in the tank after the first 5 minutes is about 32.5 gallons.

Trigonometric Rules for Integration

Finding the Integral of Trigonometric Functions

Once you know the derivative formulas for trigonometric functions, the integral formulas are easy to learn because of the inverse relationship between them. For example, the antiderivative of $\cos x$ is $\sin x$ because the derivative of $\sin x$ is $\cos x$.

SEARCH

To see step-by-step videos of these problems, enter the page number into the SWadvantage.com Search Bar.

EXAMPLE 1

Evaluate: $\int_0^\pi 2\sin x\, dx$

Integrate.

$$\int_0^\pi 2\sin x\, dx = -2\cos x\Big|_0^\pi$$

Evaluate at the endpoints.

$$= (-2)\cos \pi - (-2)\cos(0)$$

Simplify.

$$= (-2)(-1) - (-2)(1) = 4$$

EXAMPLE 2

Evaluate: $\int_{-\pi}^\pi 4\sec x \tan x\, dx$

Integrate.

$$\int_{-\pi}^\pi 4\sec x \tan x\, dx = 4\sec x\Big|_{-\pi}^\pi$$

Evaluate at the endpoints.

$$= 4\sec \pi - 4\sec(-\pi)$$

Simplify.

$$= 4(-1) - 4(-1) = 0$$

EXAMPLE 3

Evaluate: $\int_0^{2\pi}(3x + \cos x)dx$

Expand.

$$\int_0^{2\pi}(3x + \cos x)dx = 3\int_0^{2\pi} x\, dx + \int_0^{2\pi} \cos x\, dx$$

Integrate.

$$= \left(3\left(\frac{x^2}{2}\right) + \sin x\right)\Big|_0^{2\pi}$$

Evaluate at the endpoints.

$$= \left(3\left(\frac{(2\pi)^2}{2}\right) + \sin(2\pi)\right) - \left(3\left(\frac{0^2}{2}\right) + \sin(0)\right)$$

Simplify.

$$= (6\pi^2 + 0) - (0 + 0) = 6\pi^2$$

GOT TO KNOW!

Trigonometric Integrals

$\int \sin x\, dx = -\cos x$ $\int \sec x \tan x\, dx = \sec x$

$\int \cos x\, dx = \sin x$ $\int \csc^2 x\, dx = -\cot x$

$\int \sec^2 x\, dx = \tan x$ $\int \csc x \cot x\, dx = -\csc x$

EXAMPLE 4

Evaluate: $\int_{-\pi/4}^{\pi/4} \frac{1}{\cos^2 x} dx$

Rewrite using a trig identity. $\quad \int_{-\pi/4}^{\pi/4} \frac{1}{\cos^2 x} dx = \int_{-\pi/4}^{\pi/4} \sec^2 x \, dx$

Integrate. $\quad = \tan x \Big|_{-\pi/4}^{\pi/4}$

Evaluate at the endpoints. $\quad = \tan\left(\frac{\pi}{4}\right) - \tan\left(-\frac{\pi}{4}\right)$

Simplify. $\quad = (1) - (-1) = 2$

Need More

HELP?

For help with trigonometric identities, go to *Fundamental Identities* in *Trigonometry* (Book 1, p. 996).

EXAMPLE 5

Evaluate: $\int_{\pi/4}^{\pi/6} \frac{\cos x}{\sin^2 x} dx$

Rewrite the integral. $\quad \int_{\pi/6}^{\pi/4} \frac{\cos}{\sin^2 x} dx = \int_{\pi/6}^{\pi/4} \left(\frac{1}{\sin x}\right)\left(\frac{\cos x}{\sin x}\right) dx$

Use trig identities. $\quad = \int_{\pi/6}^{\pi/4} \csc x \cot x \, dx$

Integrate. $\quad = -\csc x \Big|_{\pi/6}^{\pi/4}$

Evaluate at the endpoints. $\quad = \left(-\csc x \frac{\pi}{4}\right) - \left(-\csc x \frac{\pi}{6}\right)$

Simplify. $\quad = -\sqrt{2} - (-2) = 2 - \sqrt{2}$

EXAMPLE 6

Evaluate: $\int_0^{\pi/4} \frac{1}{2 - 2\sin^2 x} dx$

Factor. $\quad \int_0^{\pi/4} \frac{1}{2 - 2\sin^2 x} dx = \int_0^{\pi/4} \frac{1}{2(1 - \sin^2 x)} dx$

Use a trig identity. $\quad = \int_0^{\pi/4} \frac{1}{2(\cos^2 x)} dx$

Use a trig identity. $\quad = \frac{1}{2} \int_0^{\pi/4} \sec^2 x \, dx$

Integrate. $\quad = \frac{1}{2} \tan x \Big|_0^{\pi/4}$

Evaluate at the endpoints. $\quad = \frac{1}{2}\left[\tan \frac{\pi}{4} - \tan(0)\right]$

Simplify. $\quad = \frac{1}{2}[1 - 0] = \frac{1}{2}$

u-Substitution

Composite Functions

You can use the Chain Rule in reverse to solve an integral of the form $\int f(g(x))g'(x)dx$. First, identify $g(x), f(g(x))$, and $g'(x)$. The solution is the antiderivative of $f(g(x))$.

SEARCH

To see step-by-step videos of these problems, enter the page number into the SWadvantage.com Search Bar.

EXAMPLE 1

Evaluate: $\int 8x(4x^2 + 3)dx$

METHOD 1

Use simple integration.

Multiply. $\qquad \int 8x(4x^2 + 3)dx = \int(32x^3 + 24x)dx$

Integrate. $\qquad\qquad\qquad = 32\left(\frac{x^4}{4}\right) + 24\left(\frac{x^2}{2}\right)$

Simplify. $\qquad\qquad\qquad = 8x^4 + 12x^2 + C$

METHOD 2

Use composite integration.

STEP 1 Identify $g(x), f(g(x))$, and $g'(x)$. $\quad g(x) = 4x^2 + 3 \qquad f(g(x)) = g(x) \qquad g'(x) = 8x$

STEP 2 Write the composite integral. $\quad \int 8x(4x^2 + 3)dx = \int g'(x)g(x)dx$

Integrate. $\qquad\qquad\qquad\qquad\qquad = \frac{(g(x))^2}{2} + C$

Substitute $4x^2 + 3$ for $g(x)$. $\qquad\quad = \frac{(4x^2 + 3)^2}{2} + C$

Simplify. $\qquad\qquad\qquad\qquad\qquad = 8x^4 + 12x^2 + C$

Need More

HELP ?

Remember that all constants are collectively labeled *C* when writing the solution to an indefinite integral.

EXAMPLE 2

Evaluate: $\int 2x\sqrt{x^2 - 7}\ dx$

STEP 1 Identify $g(x), f(g(x))$, and $g'(x)$. $\quad g(x) = x^2 - 7 \qquad f(g(x)) = f(g(x))^{\frac{1}{2}} \qquad g'(x) = 2x$

STEP 2 Write the composite integral. $\quad \int 2x\sqrt{x^2 - 7}\ dx = \int g'(x)(g(x))^{\frac{1}{2}}\ dx$

Integrate. $\qquad\qquad\qquad\qquad\qquad = \frac{2}{3}(g(x))^{\frac{3}{2}} + C$

Substitute $x^2 - 7$ for $g(x)$. $\qquad\quad = \frac{2}{3}(x^2 - 7)^{\frac{3}{2}} + C$

GOT TO KNOW!

Composite Integration

If $f(g(x))$ and $g'(x)$ are continuous on an interval, and F is an antiderivative of f, then:

$$\int f(g(x))g'(x)dx = F(g(x)) + C$$

EXAMPLE 3

Evaluate: $\int 8\sin 8x\,dx$

STEP 1 Identify $g(x)$, $f(g(x))$, and $g'(x)$. $g(x) = 8x$ $f(g(x)) = \sin(g(x))$ $g'(x) = 8$

STEP 2 Use composite integration.

Write the integral as a composite. $\int 8\sin 8x\,dx = \int g'(x)\sin(g(x))dx$

Integrate. $= -\cos(g(x)) + C$

Substitute $8x$ for $g(x)$. $= -\cos 8x + C$

> **Watch Out !**
> Even though you may be able to identify a composite function and a derivative function within an integral, you can only use composite integration if both of these functions are continuous on the interval.

Some integrals almost have the form $\int f(g(x))g'(x)dx$, but $g'(x)$ is missing a constant multiple. In this case, you can multiply and divide by the constant before using composite integration.

EXAMPLE 4

Evaluate: $\int \dfrac{x}{\sqrt[3]{5x^2 + 1}}\,dx$

STEP 1 Identify $g(x)$, $f(g(x))$, and $g'(x)$. $g(x) = 5x^2 + 1$ $f(g(x)) = (g(x))^{-\frac{1}{3}}$ $g'(x) = 10x$

STEP 2 Use composite integration.

Multiply and divide by 10. $\int \dfrac{x}{\sqrt[3]{5x^2 + 1}}\,dx = \dfrac{1}{10}\int \dfrac{10x}{\sqrt[3]{5x^2 + 1}}\,dx$

Write the integral as a composite. $= \dfrac{1}{10}\int (g(x))^{-\frac{1}{3}}g'(x)dx$

Integrate. $= \left(\dfrac{1}{10}\right)\dfrac{3}{2}(g(x))^{\frac{2}{3}} + C$

Substitute $5x^2 + 1$ for $g(x)$. $= \dfrac{3}{20}(5x^2 + 1)^{\frac{2}{3}} + C$

EXAMPLE 5

Evaluate: $\int 7x^2(4x^3 + 3)^{\frac{2}{3}}dx$

STEP 1 Identify $g(x)$, $f(g(x))$, and $g'(x)$. $g(x) = 4x^3 + 3$ $f(g(x)) = (g(x))^{\frac{2}{3}}$ $g'(x) = 12x^2$

STEP 2 Use composite integration.

Multiply and divide by 12. $\int 7x^2(4x^3 + 3)^{\frac{2}{3}}\,dx = \dfrac{7}{12}\int 12x^2(4x^3 + 3)^{\frac{2}{3}}\,dx$

Write the integral as a composite. $= \dfrac{7}{12}\int g'(x)(g(x))^{\frac{2}{3}}\,dx$

Integrate. $= \left(\dfrac{7}{12}\right)\dfrac{3}{5}(g(x))^{\frac{5}{3}} + C$

Substitute $4x^3 + 3$ for $g(x)$. $= \dfrac{7}{20}(4x^3 + 3)^{\frac{5}{3}} + C$

> **Watch Out !**
> Notice that you can only multiply and divide by a constant and bring it outside the integral. This method cannot be used with variables.

Change of Variables

Instead of using the $f(g(x))$ notation to solve composite integrals, you can simplify the form by changing variables. Let u equal $g(x)$ and $du = g'(x)dx$. The integral is then $\int f(u)du$, and its solution is $F(u) + C$, where $F(u)$ is the antiderivative of $f(u)$. Remember that this process, called *u*-substitution, can only be used if $f(g(x))$ and $g'(x)$ are continuous.

EXAMPLE 6

Use *u*–substitution to find $\int 3x^2 \sqrt{x^3 - 2}\, dx$.

STEP 1 Identify u and du. $u = x^3 - 2$ $du = 3x^2\, dx$

STEP 2 Use *u*-substitution.

Rewrite the integral in terms of u. $\int 3x^2 \sqrt{x^3 - 2}\, dx = \int u^{\frac{1}{2}}\, du$

Integrate. $= \frac{2u^{\frac{3}{2}}}{3} + C$

Substitute $x^3 - 2$ for $g(x)$. $= \frac{2(x^3 - 2)^{\frac{3}{2}}}{3} + C$

EXAMPLE 7

Use *u*–substitution to find $\int x^6 \cos(x^7)dx$.

STEP 1 Identify u and du. $u = x^7$ $du = 7x^6 dx$

STEP 2 Use *u*-substitution.

Multiply and divide by 7. $\int x^6 \cos(x^7)dx = \frac{1}{7}\int 7x^6 \cos(x^7)dx$

Rewrite the integral in terms of u. $= \frac{1}{7}\int \cos u\, du$

Integrate. $= \frac{1}{7} \sin u + C$

Substitute x^7 for $g(x)$. $= \frac{1}{7} \sin(x^7) + C$

GOT TO KNOW!

u-Substitution

If $f(g(x))$ and $g'(x)$ are continuous on an interval, $u = g(x)$, and $F(u)$ is the antiderivative of $f(u)$, then:

$$\int f(g(x))g'(x)dx = \int f(u)du = F(u) + C$$

EXAMPLE 8

Use *u*–substitution to find $\int (1 + 2x)^4\, dx$.

STEP 1 Identify *u* and *du*. $u = 1 + 2x$ $du = 2\, dx$

STEP 2 Use *u*-substitution.

Multiply and divide by 2. $\int (1 + 2x)^4\, dx = \frac{1}{2}\int 2(1 + 2x)^4\, dx$

Rewrite the integral in terms of *u*. $= \frac{1}{2}\int u^4\, du$

Integrate. $= \frac{1}{2}\left(\frac{u^5}{5}\right) + C$

Substitute $1 + 2x$ for $g(x)$. $= \frac{(1 + 2x)^5}{10} + C$

SEARCH

To see step-by-step videos of these problems, enter the page number into the SWadvantage.com Search Bar.

Often you can choose from different substitutions when you apply *u*-substitution to an integral. Although one method may be easier than another, all methods of substitution should lead to the same solution for the integral, as Example 9 shows.

EXAMPLE 9

Use *u*–substitution to find $\int \cos x \sin x\, dx$.

METHOD 1

Let $u = \sin x$.

STEP 1 Identify *u* and *du*. $u = \sin x$ $du = \cos x\, dx$

STEP 2 Rewrite the integral in terms of *u*. $\int \cos x \sin x\, dx = \int u\, du$

Integrate. $= \frac{u^2}{2} + C$

Substitute $\sin x$ for $g(x)$. $= \frac{\sin^2 x}{2} + C$

METHOD 2

Let $u = \cos x$.

STEP 1 Identify *u* and *du*. $u = \cos x$ $du = -\sin x\, dx$

STEP 2 Rewrite the integral in terms of *u*. $\int \cos x \sin x\, dx = -\int u\, du$

Integrate. $= -\frac{u^2}{2} + C$

Substitute $\cos x$ for $g(x)$. $= \frac{-\cos^2 x}{2} + C$

Apply the identity $\sin^2 x + \cos^2 x = 1$. $= \frac{\sin^2 x - 1}{2} + C$

Write all constants collectively as C. $= \frac{\sin^2 x}{2} + C$

Need More

HELP?

When solving problems involving trigonometric functions, the solutions can be written in different ways. For a review of trigonometric identities, go to *Fundamental Identities* in *Trigonometry* (Book 1, p. 998).

Definite Integrals

When solving a definite integral using *u*–substitution, you can change the upper and lower bounds to represent the function *u*. If you use this method, you can solve the entire problem with respect to *u*. You do not need to substitute *x* back into the problem.

EXAMPLE 10

Evaluate: $\int_0^1 2x(x^2 + 12)^4\, dx$

METHOD 1

Leave the upper and lower bounds in terms of *x*.

STEP 1 Identify *u* and *du*. $u = x^2 + 12$ $du = 2x\, dx$

STEP 2 Use *u*-substitution.

Rewrite the integral in terms of *u*. $\int_0^1 2x(x^2 + 12)^4\, dx = \int_{x=0}^{x=1} u^4\, du$

Integrate. $= \frac{u^5}{5}\Big|_{x=0}^{x=1}$

Substitute *u*. $= \frac{(x^2 + 12)^5}{5}\Big|_0^1$

Evaluate at the endpoints. $= \frac{(1^2 + 12)^5}{5} - \frac{(0^2 + 12)^5}{5} = 24492.2$

METHOD 2

Change the upper and lower bounds in terms of *u*.

STEP 1 Identify *u* and *du*. $u = x^2 + 12$ $du = 2x\, dx$

STEP 2 Change the bounds of the interval.

Evaluate the new lower bound. $u = x^2 + 12 = (0)^2 + 12 = 12$

Evaluate the new upper bound. $u = x^2 + 12 = (1)^2 + 12 = 13$

STEP 3 Use *u*-substitution.

Rewrite the integral in terms of *u*. $\int_0^1 2x(x^2 + 12)^4\, dx = \int_{12}^{13} u^4\, du$

Integrate. $= \frac{u^5}{5}\Big|_{12}^{13}$

Evaluate at the endpoints. $= \frac{(13)^5}{5} - \frac{(12)^5}{5} = 24492.2$

GOT TO KNOW!

Definite Integrals and *u*–Substitution

If $f(g(x))$ and $g'(x)$ are continuous on an interval, and $u = g(x)$, then:

$$\int_a^b f(g(x))g'(x)dx = \int_{g(a)}^{g(b)} f(u)du$$

EXAMPLE 11

Evaluate: $\int_0^{\frac{\pi}{3}} \sin 3x\, dx$

STEP 1 Identify u and du. $\quad u = 3x \quad\quad du = 3\, dx$

STEP 2 Change the bounds of the interval.

Evaluate the new lower bound. $\quad u = 3x = 3(0) = 0$

Evaluate the new upper bound. $\quad u = 3x = 3\left(\frac{\pi}{3}\right) = \pi$

STEP 3 Use u-substitution.

Multiply and divide by 3. $\quad\quad \int_0^{\frac{\pi}{3}} \sin 3x\, dx = \frac{1}{3} \int_0^{\frac{\pi}{3}} 3\sin 3x\, dx$

Rewrite the integral in terms of u. $\quad\quad = \frac{1}{3} \int_0^{\pi} \sin u\, du$

Integrate. $\quad\quad = \frac{1}{3}(-\cos u)\Big|_0^{\pi}$

Evaluate at the endpoints. $\quad\quad = -\frac{1}{3}(\cos \pi - \cos 0)$

Simplify. $\quad\quad = -\frac{1}{3}[(-1) - 1] = \frac{2}{3}$

SEARCH

To see step-by-step videos of these problems, enter the page number into the SWadvantage.com Search Bar.

EXAMPLE 12

Evaluate: $\int_1^2 \dfrac{x^3}{\sqrt[3]{2x^4 + 1}}\, dx$

STEP 1 Identify u and du. $\quad u = 2x^4 + 1 \quad\quad du = 8x^3\, dx$

STEP 2 Change the bounds of the interval.

Evaluate the new lower bound. $\quad u = 2x^4 + 1 = 2(1)^4 + 1 = 3$

Evaluate the new upper bound. $\quad u = 2x^4 + 1 = 2(2)^4 + 1 = 33$

STEP 3 Use u-substitution.

Multiply and divide by 3. $\quad\quad \int_1^2 \dfrac{x^2}{\sqrt[3]{2x^4 + 1}}\, dx = \frac{1}{8} \int_1^2 \dfrac{8x^3}{\sqrt[3]{2x^4 + 1}}\, dx$

Rewrite the integral in terms of u. $\quad\quad = \int_3^{33} u^{-\frac{1}{3}}\, du$

Integrate. $\quad\quad = \frac{1}{8}\left(\dfrac{3u^{\frac{2}{3}}}{2}\right)\Bigg|_3^{33}$

Evaluate at the endpoints. $\quad\quad = \frac{3}{16}\left(33^{\frac{2}{3}} - 3^{\frac{2}{3}}\right) \approx 1.539$

Integration by Parts

Finding the Integral of Products

If an integral includes the product of two functions, but it does not fit the u-substitution style, you can often use **integration by parts** to solve the integral: $\int u\,dv = uv - \int v\,du$. When identifying the u and v parts of the integral, try one of the following techniques:

- Choose the most complicated part of the integrand as dv. Let the remaining part be u.
- Choose u to be the part of the integrand whose derivative is a simpler function than u. Let the remaining part be dv.

Integration by parts is most useful for solving problems when the integrand is the product of a polynomial and one of the following types of functions: $\sin ax$, $\cos ax$, e^{ax}, or $\ln x$.

EXAMPLE 1

Find: $\int xe^x dx$

STEP 1 Determine u and dv. Then find du and v.

$$u = x \qquad dv = e^x\,dx$$
$$du = dx \qquad v = \int dv = \int e^x dx = e^x$$

STEP 2 Use integration by parts.

Apply $\int u\,dv = uv - \int v\,du$. $\int(x)(e^x dx) = (x)(e^x) - \int e^x dx$

Integrate. $= xe^x - e^x + C$

EXAMPLE 2

Find: $\int x \sin x\,dx$

STEP 1 Determine u and dv. Then find du and v.

$$u = x \qquad dv = \sin x\,dx$$
$$du = dx \qquad v = \int dv = \int \sin x dx = -\cos x$$

STEP 2 Use integration by parts.

Apply $\int u\,dv = uv - \int v\,du$. $\int(x)(\sin x\,dx) = (x)(-\cos x) - \int(-\cos x)dx$

Integrate. $= -x\cos x + \sin x + C$

Integration by Parts

If u and v are functions of x and their derivatives are continuous, then:

$$\int u\,dv = uv - v\int du$$

EXAMPLE 3

Find: $\int \sin^2 x \, dx$

STEP 1 Determine u and dv. Then find du and v.

$u = \sin x \qquad dv = \sin x \, dx$

$du = \cos x \, dx \qquad v = \int dv = \int \sin x \, dx = -\cos x$

STEP 2 Use integration by parts.

Apply $\int u \, dv = uv - \int v \, du$.	$\int(\sin x)(\sin x \, dx) = (\sin x)(-\cos x) - \int(-\cos x)(\cos x)dx$
Simplify.	$= -\sin x \cos x + \int \cos^2 x \, dx$
Apply $\sin^2 x + \cos^2 x = 1$.	$= -\sin x \cos x + \int(1 - \sin^2 x)dx$
Rewrite as the difference of integrals.	$= -\sin x \cos x + \int dx - \int \sin^2 x \, dx$
Add $\int \sin^2 x \, dx$ to both sides.	$2\int \sin^2 x \, dx = -\sin x \cos x + \int dx$
Divide by 2 and integrate.	$\int \sin^2 x \, dx = -\frac{1}{2}\sin x \cos x + \frac{1}{2}x + C$

Need More

HELP ?

Remember: $\int 1 \, dx$ is always written as $\int dx$.

EXAMPLE 4

Find: $\int e^{-x} \cos x \, dx$

STEP 1 Use integration by parts.

Determine u and dv. Then find du and v. $\qquad u = e^{-x} \qquad dv = \cos x \, dx$

$\qquad\qquad\qquad\qquad\qquad\qquad\qquad\qquad\qquad du = -e^{-x} dx \quad v = \int dv = \int \cos x \, dx = \sin x$

Apply $\int u \, dv = uv - \int v \, du$.	$\int(e^{-x})(\cos x \, dx) = (e^{-x})(\sin x) - \int(\sin x)(-e^{-x})dx$
Simplify.	$= e^{-x}\sin x + \int e^{-x}\sin x \, dx$

STEP 2 Use integration by parts for $\int \sin x \, e^{-x} dx$.

Determine u and dv. Then find du and v. $\qquad u = e^{-x} \qquad dv = \sin x \, dx$

$\qquad\qquad\qquad\qquad\qquad\qquad\qquad\qquad\qquad du = -e^{-x} dx \quad v = \int dv = \int \sin x \, dx = -\cos x$

Apply $\int u \, dv = uv - \int v \, du$.	$\int(e^{-x})(\sin x \, dx) = (e^{-x})(-\cos x) - \int(-\cos x)(-e^{-x})dx$
Simplify.	$= e^{-x}\cos x - \int e^{-x}\cos x \, dx$

STEP 3 Combine the integration by parts equations.

Add Step 1 and Step 2 results.	$\int e^{-x}\cos x \, dx = e^{-x}\sin x - e^{-x}\cos x - \int e^{-x}\cos x \, dx$
Add $\int \cos x \, dx \, e^{-x} dx$ to both sides.	$2\int e^{-x}\cos x \, dx = e^{-x}\sin x - e^{-x}\cos x$
Divide by 2.	$\int e^{-x}\cos x \, dx = \frac{1}{2}e^{-x}(\sin x - \cos x)$

SEARCH 🔍

To see step-by-step videos of these problems, enter the page number into the SWadvantage.com Search Bar.

Ways to

REMEMBER

Use **LIATE** when trying to decide what to let u equal.

In order of preference, let:

$u = $ **L**n x

$u = $ **I**nverse trig function

$u = $ **A**lgebraic function (polynomial)

$u = $ **T**rigonometric function

$u = $ **E**xponential function

Applications of Integrals

What Came Before?

- The Fundamental Theorem of Calculus
- Rules for integration

What's This About?

- Finding the area under a curve or between two curves
- Integration of functions representing particle movement
- Finding the volume of solids of revolution

Practical Apps

- Manufacturing companies use integrals to evaluate the volume of irregular figures.
- Integrals are also used by physicists to find the moment of inertia of a spinning object.

just for FUN!

There are only $\frac{2}{3}\int_1^2 2x\,dx$ types of people in the world—those who know how to integrate and those who don't.

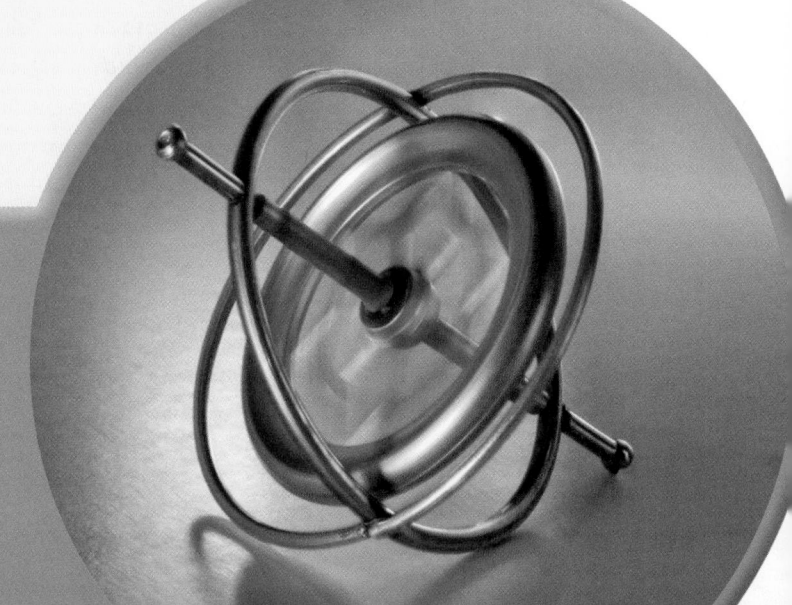

CONTENTS　　**UPLOAD**　　**DOWNLOAD**　　*Calculus*

You can find more practice problems online by visiting:
www.SWadvantage.com

Area Between Two Curves

Bounded Regions

A definite integral represents the area bounded by the curve of a function and the x-axis on an interval. You can find the area between two curves by subtracting the area formed by the lower curve from the area formed by the upper curve, as shown by the graphs below.

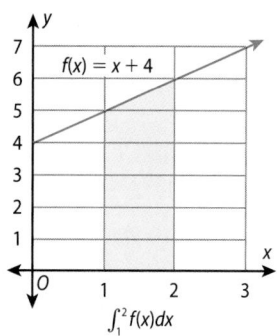

$\int_1^2 f(x)dx$

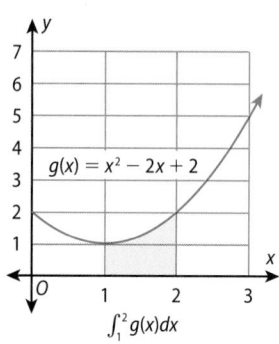

$\int_1^2 g(x)dx$

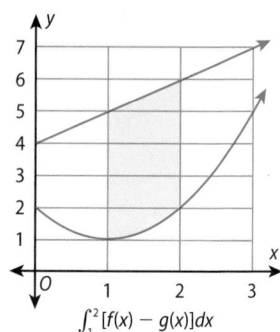

$\int_1^2 [f(x) - g(x)]dx$

EXAMPLE 1

Using the graphs shown above, find the area of the region bounded by the curves $f(x) = x + 4$ and $g(x) = x^2 - 2x + 2$ and the vertical lines $x = 1$ and $x = 2$.

Apply the area formula.

$$A = \int_1^2 [(x + 4) - (x^2 - 2x + 2)]dx$$

Simplify.

$$= \int_1^2 (-x^2 + 3x + 2)dx$$

Integrate.

$$= \left[\frac{-x^3}{3} + \frac{3x^2}{2} + 2x \right]_1^2$$

Evaluate at the endpoints.

$$= \left[\frac{-(2)^3}{3} + \frac{3(2)^2}{2} + 2(2) \right] - \left[\frac{-(1)^3}{3} + \frac{3(1)^2}{2} + 2(1) \right]$$

Simplify.

$$= \frac{25}{6}$$

Ways to REMEMBER

Use the phrase, "top minus bottom" to remember the *Area Between Two Curves* formula.

GOT TO KNOW!

Area Between Two Curves

If $f(x)$ and $g(x)$ are continuous on $[a, b]$ and $g(x) \leq f(x)$, then the area between the curves, bounded by $x = a$ and $x = b$, is:

$$A = \int_a^b f(x)dx - \int_a^b g(x)dx = \int_a^b [f(x) - g(x)]dx$$

EXAMPLE 2

Find the area of the region bounded by the curves of $g(x) = x + 1$ and $f(x) = 8 - x^2$ and the vertical lines $x = 0$ and $x = 2$. Assume $g(x) \leq f(x)$ on the interval.

Apply the area formula.	$A = \int_0^2 [(8 - x^2) - (x + 1)]dx$
Simplify.	$= \int_0^2 (-x^2 - x + 7)dx$
Integrate.	$= \left[\dfrac{-x^3}{3} - \dfrac{x^2}{2} + 7x \right]_0^2$
Evaluate at the endpoints.	$= \left[\dfrac{-(2)^3}{3} - \dfrac{(2)^2}{2} + 7(2) \right] - \left[\dfrac{-0^3}{3} - \dfrac{0^2}{2} + 7(0) \right]$
Simplify.	$= \dfrac{28}{3}$

SEARCH

To see step-by-step videos of these problems, enter the page number into the SWadvantage.com Search Bar.

EXAMPLE 3

Find the area of the region bounded by the curves of $y = -0.5x^2 + 3$ and $y = 0.25x^3 - 2$ and the vertical lines $x = 0$ and $x = 1$.

Graph the functions to identify the upper and lower functions.

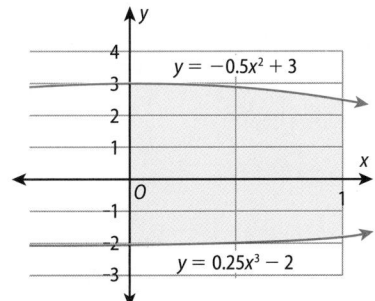

Watch Out !

The equation for finding the area between two curves does not change if the curve of one or both functions is below the x-axis. You should always subtract the lower function from the upper function in the integral.

Apply the area formula.	$A = \int_0^1 [(-0.5x^2 + 3) - (0.25x^3 - 2)]dx$
Simplify.	$= \int_0^1 (-0.25x^3 - 0.5x^2 + 5)dx$
Integrate.	$= \left[-0.25\left(\dfrac{x^4}{4}\right) - 0.5\left(\dfrac{x^3}{3}\right) + 5x \right]_0^1$
Evaluate at the endpoints.	$= \left[-0.25\left(\dfrac{1^4}{4}\right) - 0.5\left(\dfrac{1^3}{3}\right) + 5(1) \right]$
	$\quad - \left[-0.25\left(\dfrac{0^4}{4}\right) - 0.5\left(\dfrac{0^3}{3}\right) + 5(0) \right]$
Simplify.	≈ 4.8

Intersecting Curves

Bounded regions may also be defined by intersecting functions. To find the area of such regions, you must determine the intersection points. These intersection points serve as the lower and upper bounds of integration.

EXAMPLE 4

Find the area of the region bounded by the curves $y = x^2$ and $y = 4$.

STEP 1 Graph the functions to identify the upper and lower functions.

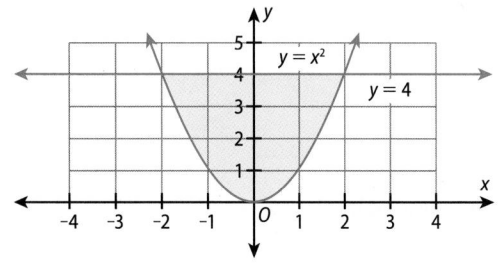

STEP 2 Calculate the x-values of the intersection points.

Set the two functions equal to each other. $x^2 = 4$

Solve for x. $x = \pm 2$

STEP 3 Calculate the area of the bounded region.

Apply the area formula. $A = \int_{-2}^{2}(4 - x^2)dx$

Integrate. $= \left[4x - \frac{x^3}{3}\right]_{-2}^{2}$

Evaluate at the endpoints. $= \left[4(2) - \frac{(2)^3}{3}\right] - \left[4(-2) - \frac{(-2)^3}{3}\right] = \frac{32}{3}$

EXAMPLE 5

Find the area of the region bounded by the curves $f(x) = x$ and $g(x) = x^2$. Assume $g(x) \leq f(x)$.

STEP 1 Calculate the x-values of the intersection points.

Set the two functions equal to each other. $x = x^2$

Set the terms equal to zero. $x^2 - x = 0$

Factor. $x(x - 1) = 0$

Solve for x. $x = 0, 1$

STEP 2 Calculate the area of the bounded region.

Apply the area formula. $A = \int_{0}^{1}(x - x^2)dx$

Integrate. $= \left[\frac{x^2}{2} - \frac{x^3}{3}\right]_{0}^{1}$

Evaluate at the endpoints. $= \left[\frac{1^2}{2} - \frac{1^3}{3}\right] - \left[\frac{0^2}{2} - \frac{0^3}{3}\right] = \frac{1}{6}$

Curves that Intersect Between Endpoints

The curves shown on the graph at the right cross at intersection points within an interval. When this happens, the upper function becomes the lower function, and the lower function becomes the upper function. To find the area when functions cross, you need two separate integrals, each with a different integrand.

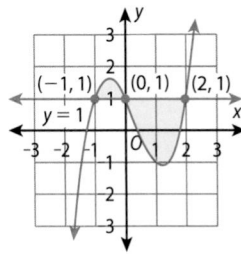

EXAMPLE 6

Using the graph above, find the area of the region bound by $y = x^3 - x^2 - 2x + 1$ and $y = 1$ on the interval $[-1, 2]$.

Need More

HELP ?

For more help with finding the intersection of curves, go to *Systems with Zero, One, or Many Solutions* in *Algebra* (p. 1580).

STEP 1 Calculate the *x*-values of the intersection points.

Set the two functions equal to each other.	$x^3 - x^2 - 2x + 1 = 1$
Subtract 1 from both sides.	$x^3 - x^2 - 2x = 0$
Factor.	$x(x - 2)(x + 1) = 0$
Solve for *x*.	$x = -1, 0, 2$

STEP 2 Calculate the area from $x = -1$ to $x = 0$.

Apply the area formula to both regions.	$A = \int_{-1}^{0}[(x^3 - x^2 - 2x + 1) - (1)]dx$
Simplify.	$= \int_{-1}^{0}(x^3 - x^2 - 2x)dx$
Integrate.	$= \left[\dfrac{x^4}{4} - \dfrac{x^3}{3} - \dfrac{2x^2}{2}\right]_{-1}^{0}$
Evaluate at the endpoints.	$= \left[\dfrac{0^4}{4} - \dfrac{0^3}{3} - \dfrac{2(0)^2}{2}\right] - \left[\dfrac{(-1)^4}{4} - \dfrac{(-1)^3}{3} - \dfrac{2(-1)^2}{2}\right]$
Simplify.	$= \dfrac{5}{12}$

STEP 3 Calculate the area from $x = 0$ to $x = 2$.

Apply the area formula to both regions.	$A = \int_{0}^{2}[(1) - (x^3 - x^2 - 2x + 1)]dx$
Simplify.	$= \int_{0}^{2}(-x^3 + x^2 + 2x)dx$
Integrate.	$= \left[\dfrac{-x^4}{4} + \dfrac{x^3}{3} + \dfrac{2x^2}{2}\right]_{0}^{2}$
Evaluate at the endpoints.	$= \left[\dfrac{-(2)^4}{4} + \dfrac{(2)^3}{3} + \dfrac{2(2)^2}{2}\right] - \left[\dfrac{-(0)^4}{4} + \dfrac{(0)^3}{3} + \dfrac{2(0)^2}{2}\right]$
Simplify.	$= \dfrac{8}{3}$

STEP 4 Calculate the total area.

Add the two areas.	$A_{total} = A_1 + A_2$
Substitute A_1 and A_2.	$= \dfrac{5}{12} + \dfrac{8}{3}$
Write with a common denominator.	$= \dfrac{5}{12} + \dfrac{32}{12} = \dfrac{37}{12}$

Second Fundamental Theorem of Calculus

Differentiating an Integral as a Function of x

The Second Fundamental Theorem of Calculus states that if you integrate a continuous function and then take its derivative, you end up with the original function. You can use the theorem to find the derivative of an integral whose upper bound is x instead of a constant.

EXAMPLE 1

Use the Second Fundamental Theorem of Calculus to evaluate, if possible.

a. $\dfrac{d}{dx} \int_{-2}^{x} \sqrt{4 - t^2}\ dt$ **on** $(-2, 2)$

Since is $f(t) = \sqrt{4 - t^2}$ is continuous on $(-2, 2)$, you can use the Second Fundamental Theorem.

$\dfrac{d}{dx} \int_{-2}^{x} \sqrt{4 - t^2}\ dt = \sqrt{4 - x^2}$ for all values of x on $(-2, 2)$

b. $\dfrac{d}{dx} \int_{1}^{x} \dfrac{1}{t^2}\ dt$ **for** $x > 1$

Since $f(t) = \dfrac{1}{t^2}$ is continuous for all $x > 1$, you can use the Second Fundamental Theorem.

$\dfrac{d}{dx} \int_{1}^{x} \dfrac{1}{t^2}\ dt = \dfrac{1}{x^2}$ for all $x > 1$

c. $\dfrac{d}{dx} \int_{\pi}^{x} \cos(2\pi t)dt$

Since $f(t) = \cos(2\pi t)$ is continuous for all real x, you can use the Second Fundamental Theorem.

$\dfrac{d}{dx} \int_{\pi}^{x} \cos(2\pi t)dt = \cos(2\pi x)$

d. $\dfrac{d}{dx} \int_{-\frac{\pi}{2}}^{x} \tan t\ dt$ **on the interval** $\left(-\dfrac{\pi}{2}, \dfrac{\pi}{2}\right)$

Since $\tan t$ is continuous within the interval, you can use the Second Fundamental Theorem.

$\dfrac{d}{dx} \int_{-\frac{\pi}{2}}^{x} \tan t\ dt = \tan x$ on the interval $\left(-\dfrac{\pi}{2}, \dfrac{\pi}{2}\right)$

e. $\dfrac{d}{dx} \int_{-\pi}^{x} \tan t\ dt$ **on the interval** $\left(-\pi, \dfrac{\pi}{2}\right)$

Since $\tan t$ is not continuous at $x = -\dfrac{\pi}{2}$ within the interval, you cannot use the Second Fundamental Theorem to solve the problem.

GOT TO KNOW!

Second Fundamental Theorem of Calculus

If the function f is continuous on an open interval containing a, then for every value x on the interval:

$$\frac{d}{dx} \int_{a}^{x} f(t)dt = f(x)$$

Using the Chain Rule to Differentiate an Integral

When the upper bound of an integral is a function other than x, you can use the Chain Rule combined with the Second Fundamental Theorem to find the derivative of the integral.

$$\frac{d}{dx} \int_a^{g(x)} f(t)dt = f(g(x))g'(x)$$

EXAMPLE 2

Use the Second Fundamental Theorem of Calculus to evaluate, if possible.

a. $\dfrac{d}{dx} \int_1^{x^2} \sqrt{1 + t^2} \, dt$

STEP 1 Identify $g(x)$, $f(g(x))$, and $g'(x)$.

$$g(x) = x^2 \qquad f(g(x)) = \sqrt{1 + (x^2)^2} = \sqrt{1 + x^4} \qquad g'(x) = 2x$$

STEP 2 Apply the Second Fundamental Theorem and the Chain Rule.

$$\frac{d}{dx} \int_1^{x^2} \sqrt{1 + t^2} \, dt = 2x\sqrt{1 + x^4}$$

b. $\dfrac{d}{dx} \int_{5x^3}^3 \sqrt{3 + 4t^2} \, dt$

STEP 1 Rewrite the integral. $\qquad \dfrac{d}{dx} \int_{5x^3}^3 \sqrt{3 + 4t^2} \, dt = -\dfrac{d}{dx} \int_3^{5x^3} \sqrt{3 + 4t^2} \, dt$

STEP 2 Identify $g(x)$, $f(g(x))$, and $g'(x)$.

$$g(x) = 5x^3 \qquad f(g(x)) = \sqrt{3 + 4(5x^3)^2} = \sqrt{3 + 100x^6} \qquad g'(x) = 15x^2$$

STEP 3 Apply the Second Fundamental Theorem and the Chain Rule.

$$\frac{d}{dx} \int_{5x^3}^3 \sqrt{3 + 4t^2} \, dt = -15x^2\sqrt{3 + 100x^6}$$

GOT TO KNOW!

Bounds of a Function

You can exchange the bounds of a function by placing a negative sign in front of the function.

$$\int_a^b f(x)dx = -\int_b^a f(x)dx$$

EXAMPLE 3

Let $h(x) = \int_2^{g(x)} f(t)dt$. Use the table at the right to find $h'(1)$.

x	f(x)	f'(x)	g(x)	g'(x)
1	10	−4	2	2
2	−1	3	6	7

STEP 1 Find $h'(x)$.

Use the Second Fundamental Theorem. $\qquad \dfrac{d}{dx} \int_2^{g(x)} f(t)dt = f(g(x))g'(x)$

STEP 2 Find $h'(1)$.

Evaluate at $x = 1$. $\qquad\qquad\qquad\qquad \dfrac{d}{dx} \int_2^{g(x)} f(t)dt = f(g(1))g'(1)$

Substitute $g(1)$ from the table. $\qquad\qquad\qquad\quad = f(2)g'(1)$

Substitute $f(2)$ from the table. $\qquad\qquad\qquad\quad = (-1)g'(1)$

Substitute $g'(1)$ from the table. $\qquad\qquad\qquad\quad = (-1)(2)$

Simplify. $\qquad\qquad\qquad\qquad\qquad\qquad\quad = -2$

SEARCH

To see step-by-step videos of these problems, enter the page number into the SWadvantage.com Search Bar.

Mean Value Theorem for Integrals

Area Under the Curve

The Mean Value Theorem for Integrals states that on a given closed interval $[a, b]$ there exists at least one value c between a and b such that the area of a rectangle formed by the base from a to b and the function's height at c is the same as the area under the curve from a to b. The graph at the right demonstrates this concept.

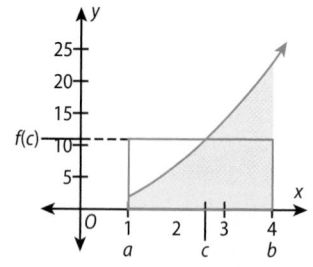

Problems related to the Mean Value Theorem for Integrals often require you to determine the value of c that is guaranteed to exist by the theorem. In the next lesson, you will learn that c indicates the value $f(c)$, which is the mean (average) value of the function over the interval.

EXAMPLE 1

Find the value of c guaranteed by the Mean Value Theorem for Integrals for $f(x) = 6x$ over the interval $[2, 5]$.

STEP 1 Calculate the definite integral.

Integrate. $\qquad\qquad\qquad\qquad \int_2^5 6x\, dx = [3x^2]_2^5$

Evaluate at the endpoints. $\qquad\qquad\quad = 3(5)^2 - 3(2)^2$

Simplify. $\qquad\qquad\qquad\qquad\qquad = 63$

STEP 2 Calculate $f(c)$.

Use the Mean Value Theorem. $\qquad \int_2^5 6x\, dx = f(c)(5 - 2)$

Substitute the integral's value. $\qquad 63 = f(c)(5 - 2)$

Solve for $f(c)$ and simplify. $\qquad\quad f(c) = 21$

STEP 3 Calculate c.

Replace x with c in the function. $\qquad f(c) = 21 = 6c$

Solve for c. $\qquad\qquad\qquad\qquad\qquad c = \dfrac{21}{6} = \dfrac{7}{2}$

$c = \dfrac{7}{2}$

The Mean Value Theorem for Integrals

If f is continuous on the closed interval $[a, b]$, then there exists at least one value c on the closed interval $[a, b]$ such that:

$$\int_a^b f(x)\,dx = f(c)(b - a)$$

EXAMPLE 2

Find the value of *c* guaranteed by the Mean Value Theorem for Integrals for *f*(*x*) = *x*³ + 1 on [2, 3].

STEP 1 Calculate the definite integral.

Integrate.

$$\int_2^3 (x^3 + 1)dx = \left[\frac{1}{4}x^4 + x\right]_2^3$$

Evaluate at the endpoints.

$$= \left[\frac{1}{4}3^4 + 3\right] - \left[\frac{1}{4}2^4 + 2\right] = \frac{69}{4}$$

STEP 2 Calculate *f*(*c*).

Use the Mean Value Theorem.

$$\int_2^3 (x^3 + 1)dx = f(c)(3 - 2)$$

Substitute the integral's value.

$$\frac{69}{4} = f(c)(3 - 2)$$

Solve for *f*(*c*) and simplify.

$$f(c) = \frac{69}{4}$$

STEP 3 Calculate *c*.

Replace *x* with *c* in the function.

$$f(c) = \frac{69}{4} = c^3 + 1$$

Solve for *c*.

$$c = \sqrt[3]{\frac{69}{4} - 1} \approx 2.53$$

SEARCH

To see step-by-step videos of these problems, enter the page number into the SWadvantage.com Search Bar.

EXAMPLE 3

Find the value of *c* guaranteed by the Mean Value Theorem for Integrals for *f*(*x*) = sin *x* over the interval $\left[-\frac{\pi}{4}, \frac{\pi}{4}\right]$.

STEP 1 Calculate the definite integral.

Integrate.

$$\int_{-\frac{\pi}{4}}^{\frac{\pi}{4}} \sin x\, dx = [-\cos x]_{-\frac{\pi}{4}}^{\frac{\pi}{4}}$$

Evaluate at the endpoints.

$$= -\left[\cos \frac{\pi}{4}\right] + \left[\cos\left(-\frac{\pi}{4}\right)\right] = 0$$

STEP 2 Calculate *f*(*c*).

Use the Mean Value Theorem.

$$\int_{-\frac{\pi}{4}}^{\frac{\pi}{4}} \sin x\, dx = f(c)\left(\frac{\pi}{4} - \left(-\frac{\pi}{4}\right)\right)$$

Substitute the integral's value.

$$0 = f(c)\left(\frac{\pi}{4} - \left(-\frac{\pi}{4}\right)\right)$$

Solve for *f*(*c*) and simplify.

$$f(c) = 0$$

STEP 3 Calculate *c*.

Replace *x* with *c* in the function.

$$f(c) = 0 = \sin c$$

Solve for *c*.

$$c = \sin^{-1}(0) = 0$$

Need More HELP?

For help with inverse trigonometric functions, go to *Inverse Sine Functions* in *Trigonometry* (Book 1, p. 1022).

Average Value of a Function

Finding the Average Value

The Mean Value Theorem guarantees the existence of at least one value c on a closed interval such that the area of a rectangle with the base $b - a$ and height $f(c)$ has the same value as the area under the curve from a to b. As the graph at the right shows, the value of $f(c)$ is the **average value of a function**. Notice that the function shown on the graph has two points where $f = f_{avg}$ on the interval $[-2, 1]$.

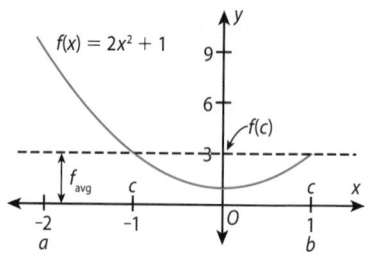

EXAMPLE 1

Look at the graph of $f(x) = 2x^2 + 1$ on $[-2, 1]$ shown above.

a. Find the average value of $f(x)$ on the interval.

Use the average value definition.
$$f(c) = \frac{1}{b-a} \int_a^b f(x)dx$$

Substitute $f(x)$ and the endpoints.
$$= \frac{1}{1-(-2)} \int_{-2}^1 (2x^2 + 1)dx$$

Integrate.
$$= \frac{1}{3}\left[\frac{2}{3}x^3 + x\right]_{-2}^1$$

Evaluate at the endpoints.
$$= \frac{1}{3}\left[\left(\frac{2}{3}(1)^3 + 1\right) - \left(\frac{2}{3}(-2)^3 + (-2)\right)\right]$$

Simplify.
$$= 3$$

Therefore, the average value of $f(x) = 2x^2 + 1$ on $[-2, 1]$ is 3.

b. Find all values of x where the function equals its average value.

Replace x with c in the original function.
$$f(c) = 3 = 2c^2 + 1$$

Solve for c.
$$c = \sqrt{1}$$

Simplify.
$$= -1, 1$$

Therefore, $f(x)$ is equal to its average value when $x = -1$ and $x = 1$.

Watch Out !

Remember to include both positive and negative solutions when taking the square root of a number.

Average Value of a Function

If f is an continuous function on $[a, b]$, then the average value $f(c)$ is:
$$f(c) = \frac{1}{b-a} \int_a^b f(x)dx$$

EXAMPLE 2

Find the average value of $f(x) = \sin x$ on the interval $\left[0, \frac{2\pi}{3}\right]$.

Use the average value definition.
$$f(c) = \frac{1}{b-a}\int_a^b f(x)\,dx$$

Substitute $f(x)$ and the endpoints.
$$= \frac{1}{\frac{2\pi}{3}-0}\int_0^{\frac{2\pi}{3}} \sin x\,dx$$

Integrate.
$$= \frac{3}{2\pi}\left[-\cos x\right]_0^{\frac{2\pi}{3}}$$

Evaluate at the endpoints.
$$= \frac{3}{2\pi}\left[-\cos\left(\frac{2\pi}{3}\right) + \cos(0)\right]$$

Simplify.
$$= \frac{9}{4\pi}$$

Therefore, the average value of $f(x) = \sin x$ on $\left[0, \frac{2\pi}{3}\right]$ is $\frac{9}{4\pi}$.

SEARCH

To see step-by-step videos of these problems, enter the page number into the SWadvantage.com Search Bar.

EXAMPLE 3

Find the average value of $y = x^2\sqrt{x^3+1}$ on the interval [0, 3].

STEP 1 Set up the average value integral.

Use the average value definition.
$$f(c) = \frac{1}{b-a}\int_a^b f(x)\,dx$$

Substitute $f(x)$ and the endpoints.
$$= \frac{1}{3-0}\int_0^3 \left[x^2\sqrt{x^3+1}\right]dx$$

Simplify.
$$= \frac{1}{3}\int_0^3 \left[x^2\sqrt{x^3+1}\right]dx$$

STEP 2 Use u-substitution to solve the integral.

Identify u and du.
$$u = x^3 + 1 \qquad du = 3x^2\,dx$$

Solve for the endpoints in terms of u.
$$u = (0)^3 + 1 = 1$$
$$u = (3)^3 + 1 = 28$$

Rewrite the integral in terms of u.
$$f(c) = \frac{1}{3}\left[\frac{1}{3}\int_1^{28} u^{\frac{1}{3}}\,du\right]$$

Integrate.
$$= \frac{1}{9}\left[\frac{3}{4}u^{\frac{4}{3}}\right]_1^{28}$$

Evaluate at the endpoints.
$$= \frac{1}{12}\left(28^{\frac{4}{3}} - 1^{\frac{4}{3}}\right)$$

Simplify.
$$\approx 7$$

Therefore, the average value of $y = x^2\sqrt{x^3+1}$ is approximately 7.

Need More HELP?

For more help with using substitution to solve an integral, go to *u-Substitution* on page 2252.

Motion Along a Line

SOUTHWESTERN

Velocity and Position

When describing motion along a straight line, three important functions are position, velocity, and acceleration. Velocity is the derivative of an object's position equation: $v(t) = x'(t)$. The integral of an object's velocity equation is its position: $x(t) = \int v(t)dt$. The change in position over a time interval is called **displacement**: $\Delta x(t) = \int_{t_1}^{t_2} v(t)dt$. An object's position at a certain time is the sum of its starting position and its displacement: $x(t) = x_{initial} + \Delta x(t)$.

EXAMPLE 1

The position of a particle moving along the x-axis is given by $x(t) = t^2 - 4t - 3$.

a. What is the position of the particle at $t = 0$?

Set $t = 0$ in the position equation. $x(0) = 0^2 - 4(0) - 3 = -3$

b. What is the velocity of the particle?

Take the derivative of the position equation. $v(t) = \dfrac{d}{dt}x(t)$

Substitute the position equation. $= \dfrac{d}{dt}[t^2 - 4t - 3]$

Differentiate. $= 2t - 4$

EXAMPLE 2

A particle starts at $x = 2$ and moves along the x-axis with a velocity of $v(t) = 2t - 4$.

a. What is the particle's displacement during the first 3 seconds?

Find the integral of velocity. $\Delta x(t) = \int_0^3 v(t)dt = \int_0^3 (2t - 4)dt$

Integrate. $= \left[\dfrac{2t^2}{2} - 4t\right]_0^3$

Evaluate at the endpoints. $= [(3)^2 - 4(3)] - [(0)^2 - 4(0)]$

Simplify. $= -3$

b. What is the particle's position after the first 3 seconds?

Add the initial position and the integral of velocity. $x(t) = x_{initial} + \Delta x(t)$

Substitute the initial position and displacement. $= 2 + (-3)$

Simplify. $= -1$

GOT TO KNOW!

Velocity and Position

Velocity is the derivative of position. $v(t) = x'(t)$

Position is the antiderivative of velocity. $x(t) = \int v(t)dt$

Position $\xrightarrow[\text{integrate}]{\text{differentiate}}$ Velocity

EXAMPLE 3

A particle moves along the *x*-axis so that its velocity at any time $t \geq 0$ is given by $v(t) = \cos t$. At $t = \pi$, the position of the particle is $x(\pi) = 1$. Find the equation for the position $x(t)$ at any time *t*.

STEP 1 Calculate the position from the velocity.

$$x(t) = \int v(t)dt = \int \cos t \, dt$$

Integrate.

$$= \sin t + C$$

STEP 2 Determine the constant of integration.

Evaluate the equation for $t = \pi$.

$$x(\pi) = \sin(\pi) + C$$

Given $x(\pi) = 1$. Substitute $\sin \pi = 0$.

$$1 = 0 + C$$

Solve for *C*.

$$C = 1$$

The position at any time *t* is given by $x(t) = \sin t + 1$.

SEARCH

To see step-by-step videos of these problems, enter the page number into the SWadvantage.com Search Bar.

Area Under a Velocity Graph

You can use the graph of an object's velocity, as shown at the right, to calculate its position and its displacement, Δx. The area between the velocity graph and the *x*-axis during a time interval is the displacement (change in position). Notice that A_1 is above the axis and A_2 is below the axis. To calculate the total displacement, add the area above the axis and subtract the area below the axis. For the graph at the right, $\Delta x = A_1 - A_2$.

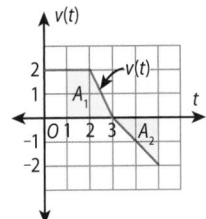

If you know the object's starting position, you can calculate the position at any time by adding the displacement to the starting position.

Need More

HELP ?

For help finding the area of bounded regions, go to *Fundamental Theorem of Calculus* (p. 2246).

EXAMPLE 3

An object is moving along the *x*-axis. The graph above shows its velocity from $t = 0$ to $t = 5$. Use the graph to find $x(5)$ if $x(1) = -3$.

STEP 1 Calculate the displacement.

Since the position at $t = 1$ is known, we need to calculate the displacement after that time.

Find the area of the trapezoid from $t = 1$ to $t = 3$.

$$\int_1^3 v(t)dt = A_1 = \frac{1}{2}(2)(1 + 2) = 3$$

Find the area of the triangle from $t = 3$ to $t = 5$.

$$\int_3^5 v(t)dt = A_2 = \frac{1}{2}(2)(2) = 2$$

Find the total displacement from the areas.

$$\int_1^5 v(t)dt = \int_1^3 v(t)dt - \int_3^5 v(t)dt$$
$$= 3 - 2 = 1$$

STEP 2 Calculate the position at $t = 5$.

Add the initial position and displacement.

$$x(5) = x(1) + \int_1^5 v(t)dt$$

Substitute.

$$= -3 + 1$$

Simplify.

$$= -2$$

Acceleration and Velocity

Acceleration is the derivative of an object's velocity equation: $a(t) = v'(t)$. The integral of an object's acceleration equation is its velocity: $v(t) = \int a(t)dt$.

EXAMPLE 5

The acceleration of a particle moving along the x-axis is $a(t) = 3 + \sin t$. Find $v(t)$ if $v(0) = -4$.

STEP 1 Calculate the velocity from the acceleration.

  Integrate.

$$v(t) = \int a(t)dt = \int (3 + \sin t)dt$$
$$= 3t - \cos t + C$$

STEP 2 Determine the constant of integration.

  Evaluate the equation for $t = 0$.

  Given $v(0) = -4$. Substitute $\cos(0) = 1$

  Solve for C.

$$v(0) = 3(0) - \cos(0) + C$$
$$-4 = 0 - 1 + C$$
$$C = -3$$

The velocity at any time t is given by $v(t) = 3t - \cos t - 3$.

Watch Out !

Don't forget the constant, C, when integrating an indefinite integral.

EXAMPLE 6

The acceleration of a particle moving along the x-axis is $a(t) = 6t - 4$.

a. **Find the velocity equation if $v(4) = 37$.**

STEP 1 Find $v(t)$ by integrating $a(t)$.

  Integrate.

$$v(t) = \int a(t)dt = \int (6t - 4)dt$$
$$= 3t^2 - 4t + C$$

STEP 2 Determine the constant of integration.

  Evaluate the equation for $t = 4$.

  Solve for C.

$$v(4) = 3(4)^2 - 4(4) + C = 37$$
$$C = 5$$

The velocity equation is $v(t) = 3t^2 - 4t + 5$.

b. **Find the position equation if $x(1) = -6$.**

STEP 1 Find $x(t)$ by integrating $v(t)$.

  Integrate.

$$x(t) = \int v(t)dt = \int (3t^2 - 4t + 5)dt$$
$$= t^3 - 2t^2 + 5t + C$$

STEP 2 Determine the constant of integration.

  Evaluate the equation for $t = 1$.

  Solve for C.

$$x(1) = (1)^3 - 2(1)^2 + 5(1) + C = -6$$
$$C = -10$$

The position equation is $x(t) = t^3 - 2t^2 + 5t - 10$.

GOT TO KNOW!

Acceleration and Velocity

Acceleration is the derivative of velocity. $a(t) = v'(t)$

Velocity is the antiderivative of acceleration. $v(t) = \int a(t)dt$

Velocity $\underset{\text{integrate}}{\overset{\text{differentiate}}{\rightleftarrows}}$ Acceleration

Changing Speed and Direction

The speed of an object is the absolute value of its velocity. When an object is moving along a straight line, its speed and direction may change.

- **Speed is increasing** when velocity and acceleration have the same sign.
- **Speed is decreasing** when velocity and acceleration have opposite signs.
- An object is **changing direction** when its $v(t)$ is zero *and* $a(t)$ is nonzero.

Need More

HELP ?

For more about identifying turning points of a function, see *Curve Sketching* (p. 2202).

EXAMPLE

The velocity of a particle moving along the x-axis is $v(t) = t^2 + 3t - 4$. When $t = 0$, the position of the particle is $x = 2$.

a. **At what time does the particle change direction?**

STEP 1 Set the velocity equal to zero. $t^2 + 3t - 4 = 0$

Factor. $(t + 4)(t - 1) = 0$

Solve for t. $t = -4, 1$

Since time must be positive, the $v(t) = 0$ only when $t = 1$.

STEP 2 Verify that acceleration is nonzero at this time.

Differentiate the velocity. $a(t) = v'(t) = 2t + 3$

Evaluate for $t = 1$. $a(1) = 2(1) + 3 = 5$

Since $v(1) = 0$ and $a(1) \neq 0$, the particle changes direction at $t = 1$.

b. **What is the particle's position when it changes direction?**

Add the initial position and the displacement. $x(t) = x(0) + \int_0^1 v(t)dt$

Substitute $x(0)$ and $v(t)$. $= 2 + \int_0^1 (t^2 + 3t - 4)dt$

Integrate. $= 2 + \left[\frac{t^3}{3} + \frac{3t^2}{2} - 4t\right]_0^1$

Evaluate at the endpoints. $= 2 + \left[\frac{1^3}{3} + \frac{3(1)^2}{2} - 4(1)\right] - \left[\frac{0^3}{3} + \frac{3(0)^2}{2} - 4(0)\right]$

Simplify. $= -\frac{1}{6}$

SEARCH

To see step-by-step videos of these problems, enter the page number into the SWadvantage.com Search Bar.

c. **Is the particle's speed increasing, decreasing, or zero at $t = 2$?**

STEP 1 Calculate the velocity at $t = 2$. $v(2) = (2)^2 + 3(2) - 4 = 6$

STEP 2 Calculate the acceleration at $t = 2$. $a(2) = 2(2) + 3 = 7$

Since velocity and acceleration have the same sign, the particle's speed is increasing at $t = 2$.

d. **What is the particle's speed at $t = \frac{1}{2}$?**

Calculate the velocity at that time. $v\left(\frac{1}{2}\right) = \left(\frac{1}{2}\right)^2 + 3\left(\frac{1}{2}\right) - 4 = -\frac{9}{4}$

Find the absolute value of the velocity. $\text{speed} = \left|v\left(\frac{1}{2}\right)\right| = \left|-\frac{9}{4}\right| = \frac{9}{4}$

Distance

Distance is how far an object travels during a time interval. It is important not to confuse displacement and distance. Displacement depends on direction, but distance does not. Recall that displacement is the integral of velocity between two times. Distance is the integral of speed between two times: $\int_{t_1}^{t_2} |v(t)|\,dt$.

To integrate the absolute value of the velocity function, you have to divide the integral into parts. Add the integral for time intervals when the velocity is positive. Subtract the integral for time intervals when the velocity is negative. You can identify these time intervals by determining when the velocity is zero.

To calculate distance from a graph, add areas above the x-axis and areas below the x-axis.

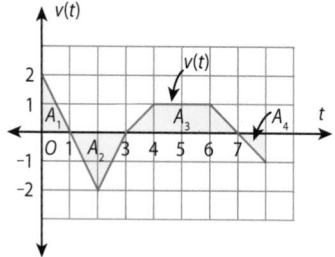

EXAMPLE 8

The graph above shows the velocity of a particle for time $0 \le t \le 8$.

a. **Use the graph to find the total distance traveled by the particle from $t = 0$ to $t = 8$.**

STEP 1 Determine each of the four areas.

In each case, use the formula for a triangle or a trapezoid.

$A_1 = \frac{1}{2}(1)(2) = 1$ $\qquad A_3 = \frac{1}{2}(1)(2 + 4) = 3$

$A_2 = \frac{1}{2}(2)(2) = 2$ $\qquad A_4 = \frac{1}{2}(1)(1) = \frac{1}{2}$

STEP 2 The distance is the sum of the areas.

$\text{Distance} = A_1 + A_2 + A_3 + A_4 = 1 + 2 + 3 + \frac{1}{2} = 6\frac{1}{2}$

b. **Find the displacement of the particle between $t = 0$ and $t = 8$.**

To calculate displacement, add areas above the x-axis. Subtract areas below the x-axis.

$\text{Displacement} = A_1 - A_2 + A_3 - A_4 = 1 - 2 + 3 - \frac{1}{2} = 1\frac{1}{2}$

GOT TO KNOW!

Distance as the Integral of Speed

$\text{Distance} = \int |v(t)|\,dt$

EXAMPLE 9

A particle moves along the *x*-axis so that its velocity at any time $t \geq 0$ is given by $v(t) = 3t^2 - 6t - 9$. If the position of the particle is 4 when $t = 0$, find the total distance traveled from $t = 0$ to $t = 5$.

METHOD 1

Use the integral of the speed.

STEP 1 Identify possible times when the particle changes direction.

Set the velocity equation equal to zero. $3t^2 - 6t - 9 = 0$

Factor. $3(t + 1)(t - 3) = 0$

Solve for *t*. $t = -1, 3$

Because time must be positive, the only possible turning point on [0, 5] is $t = 3$.

STEP 2 Use acceleration to verify that the particle changes direction at $t = 3$.

Differentiate the velocity equation. $a(t) = v'(t) = 6t - 6$

Find the acceleration at $t = 3$. $a(3) = 6(3) - 6 = 12$

Because $v(3) = 0$ and $a(3)$ is nonzero, the object changes direction at $t = 3$.

STEP 3 Determine whether the velocity is positive or negative on each interval.

Calculate the velocity at any time within the interval to determine the sign of the velocity.

On (0, 3), choose $t = 2$: $v(2) = 3(2)^2 - 6(2) - 9 = -9$ negative

On (3, 5), choose $t = 4$: $v(4) = 3(4)^2 - 6(4) - 9 = 15$ positive

STEP 4 Find the distance.

Subtract the integral if the velocity is negative. Add the integral if the velocity is positive.

Divide the integral into parts. $\text{distance} = \int |v(t)| dt = -\int_0^3 v(t) dt + \int_3^5 v(t) dt$

Substitute $v(t)$. $= -\int_0^3 (3t^2 - 6t - 9) dt + \int_3^5 (3t^2 - 6t - 9) dt$

Integrate. $= -[t^3 - 3t^2 - 9t]_0^3 + [t^3 - 3t^2 - 9t]_3^5$

Evaluate at the endpoints. $= -[(3)^3 - 3(3)^2 - 9(3)] + [(0)^3 - 3(0)^2 - 9(0)]$
    $+ [(5)^3 - 3(5)^2 - 9(5)] - [(3)^3 - 3(3)^2 - 9(3)] = 59$

METHOD 2

Use the position function.

STEP 1 Find the position equation. $x(t) = \int v(t) dt = \int (3t^2 - 6t - 9) dt$

Integrate. $= t^3 - 3t^2 - 9t + C$

STEP 2 Determine the constant of integration.

Evaluate for $x(0) = 4$. $x(0) = (0)^3 - 3(0)^2 - 9(0) + C = 4$

Solve for *C*. $C = 4$

The position equation is $x(t) = t^3 - 3t^2 - 9t + 4$.

STEP 3 Identify times when the particle changes direction.

Using the same process as Method 1, we know the particle changes direction at $t = 3$.

STEP 4 Find the distance along (0, 3) and (3, 5).

$\text{distance} = |x(3) - x(0)| + |x(5) - x(3)|$
    $= |(-23) - (4)| + |(9) - (-23)| = 59$

Try It This Way

You can use a graphing calculator to see the area under the curve that represents the total distance traveled.

In **Y=** , enter the absolute value of the velocity function. (The absolute value feature is under **MATH** , **NUM** .)

Next, graph the function, and then use **2nd** , **TRACE** to bring up the **CALC** menu.

Choose $\int f(x) dx$ to integrate. Type in the lower bound, **ENTER** , and the upper bound, **ENTER** .

Watch as the calculator shades the area under the curve and finally calculates the numerical answer.

Volume of Solids: Disk Method

SOUTHWESTERN

Solids of Revolution

If a bounded region is revolved about a line, the resulting shape is a **solid of revolution**. The line about which it revolves is the **axis of revolution**. Imagine cutting the solid into slices perpendicular to the axis of revolution, as shown on the graph at the right. Each slice is a right circular cylinder, or **disk**. The volume of a cylinder is the product of the circular area and its thickness. As the number of slices approaches infinity, the slices become infinitely thin. The volume of the solid is then the sum of the volumes of the slices. The graph shows a solid produced by revolving the region bounded by $y = 3x$ on [1, 3].

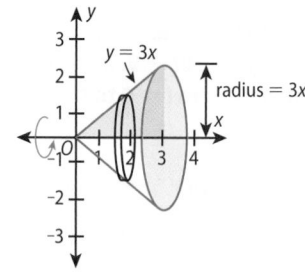

You can determine the volume of the solid of revolution by integrating all of the areas of the disks within the bounded region: $V = \int_a^b A(x)dx$. Since each circular area is $\pi(\text{radius})^2$, if you write the radius R as a function of x, the volume becomes $V = \pi\int_a^b [R(x)]^2 \, dx$.

SEARCH

To see step-by-step videos of these problems, enter the page number into the SWadvantage.com Search Bar.

EXAMPLE 1

Find the volume of the solid generated by revolving the region bounded by $y = 3x$, the x-axis, $x = 0$, and $x = 3$ about the x-axis.

Calculate the volume using $R(x) = 3x$.	$V = \pi\int_0^3 [3x]^2 \, dx$
Simplify.	$= 9\pi\int_0^3 x^2 \, dx$
Integrate.	$= (3\pi x^3)\big|_0^3$
Evaluate at the endpoints.	$= 3\pi(3)^3 - 3\pi(0)^3 = 81\pi$

EXAMPLE 2

Find the volume of the solid generated by revolving the region bounded by $y = 2\sqrt{x}$, the x-axis, $x = 2$, and $x = 5$ about the x-axis.

Calculate the volume using $R(x) = 2\sqrt{x}$.	$V = \pi\int_2^5 [2\sqrt{x}]^2 \, dx$
Simplify.	$= 4\pi\int_2^5 x \, dx$
Integrate.	$= 2\pi x^2\big|_2^5$
Evaluate at the endpoints.	$= 2\pi(5^2 - 2^2) = 42\pi$

GOT TO KNOW!

Volume of a Solid of Revolution: Disk Method (x-axis)

$V = \pi\int_a^b [R(x)]^2 \, dx$

EXAMPLE 3

Find the volume of the solid generated by revolving the region bounded by $y = \sqrt{\cos x}$, the x-axis, $x = -\frac{\pi}{2}$, and $x = \frac{\pi}{2}$ about the x-axis.

Calculate the volume using $R(x) = \sqrt{\cos x}$. $V = \pi \int_{-\frac{\pi}{2}}^{\frac{\pi}{2}} (\sqrt{\cos x})^2 \, dx$

Simplify. $= \pi \int_{-\frac{\pi}{2}}^{\frac{\pi}{2}} \cos x \, dx$

Integrate. $= \pi (\sin x) \Big|_{-\frac{\pi}{2}}^{\frac{\pi}{2}}$

Evaluate at the endpoints. $= \pi \left[\sin\left(\frac{\pi}{2}\right) - \sin\left(-\frac{\pi}{2}\right) \right]$

Simplify. $= 2\pi$

> **Watch Out !**
> Remember that you can only use the volume formula for solids of revolution if the function is continuous over the interval.

EXAMPLE 4

The graph at the right shows the region in the first quadrant bounded by $y = -x^2 + 4x - 3$ and the x-axis.

Find the volume of the solid generated by revolving the region about the x-axis.

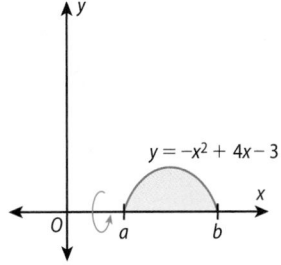

$y = -x^2 + 4x - 3$

STEP 1 Find the boundaries of the region.

Find the x–intercepts by setting the function equal to zero. $-x^2 + 4x - 3 = 0$

Factor. $-(x - 1)(x - 3) = 0$

Solve for x. $x = 1, 3$

STEP 2 Find the volume of the solid of revolution.

Use the disk method formula. $V = \pi \int_{-1}^{3} (-x^2 + 4x - 3)^2 \, dx$

Expand the squared function. $= \pi \int_{-1}^{3} (x^4 - 8x^3 + 22x^2 - 24x + 9) \, dx$

Integrate. $= \pi \left(\frac{x^5}{5} - 2x^4 + \frac{22x^3}{3} - 12x^2 + 9x \right) \Big|_{1}^{3}$

Evaluate at the endpoints. $= \pi \left(\frac{(3)^5}{5} - 2(3)^4 + \frac{22(3)^3}{3} - 12(3)^2 + 9(3) \right)$

$- \pi \left(\frac{(1)^5}{5} - 2(1)^4 + \frac{22(1)^3}{3} - 12(1)^2 + 9(1) \right)$

Simplify. $= \frac{16\pi}{15}$

> **Watch Out !**
> Do not forget to square the function that represents the radius.

SW SOUTHWESTERN

Revolving About the *y*-Axis

You can also create solids of revolution by revolving regions about the *y*-axis. The graph at the right shows a solid formed by revolving the region formed by $y = x^2$ about the *y*-axis between $y = 0$ and $y = 2$.

To find the volume of such solids, imagine slicing cross sections of the solid perpendicular to the *y*-axis. The volume of the solid is then the integral with respect to *y* instead of *x*.

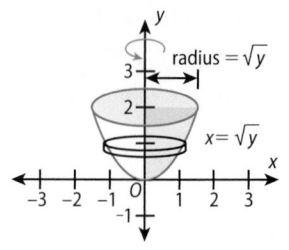

SEARCH 🔍

To see step-by-step videos of these problems, enter the page number into the SWadvantage.com Search Bar.

EXAMPLE 5

Find the volume of the solid created by rotating the region bounded by the graph of $y = x^2$, the line $y = 2$, and the *y*-axis, about the *y*-axis.

STEP 1 Write the function in terms of *y*.

Use the given function *y*. $y = x^2$

Solve for *x*. $x = \sqrt{y}$

STEP 2 Find the volume of the solid of revolution.

Use the disk method in terms of *y*. $V = \int_a^b [R(y)]^2 \, dy$

Substitute the endpoints and the radius. $= \pi \int_0^2 \left(\sqrt{y}\right)^2 dy$

Simplify. $= \pi \int_0^2 y \, dy$

Integrate. $= \pi \left(\dfrac{y^2}{2}\right)\Big|_0^2$

Evaluate at the endpoints. $= \pi \left(\dfrac{2^2}{2} - \dfrac{0^2}{2}\right)$

Simplify. $= 2\pi$

GOT TO KNOW!

Volume of a Solid of Revolution: Disk Method (*y*-axis)

$V = \pi \int_a^b [R(y)]^2 \, dy$

Dividing Lines

Some solids of revolution problems involve finding a line that divides a volume in half. If you could slice the volume at this line, you would create two solids with equal volumes. To determine the value of k, you can integrate each volume along its interval. Since the dividing line $x = k$ creates two solids of equal volume, set up a volume equation for each region and find the value of k for which they are equal.

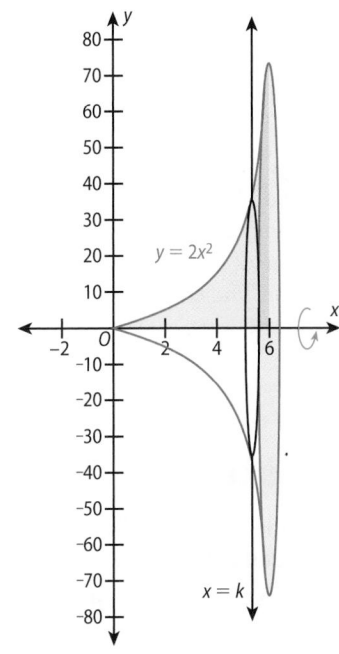

Watch Out !

The line that divides a volume in half is not necessarily the line that is halfway between the upper and lower bounds.

EXAMPLE 6

The graph above shows a region in the first quadrant that is bounded by the x-axis, the graph of $y = 2x^2$, and the line $x = 6$. The vertical line $x = k$ divides the region into two regions such that when these two regions are revolved about the x-axis, the solids of revolution created have equal volumes. Find the value of k.

Set the two volumes equal to each other.	$\pi \int_a^k [R(x)]^2\, dx = \pi \int_k^b [R(x)]^2\, dx$
Substitute the endpoints and radius for each region.	$\pi \int_0^k (2x^2)^2\, dx = \pi \int_k^6 (2x^2)^2\, dx$
Simplify.	$\int_0^k x^4\, dx = \int_k^6 x^4\, dx$
Integrate.	$\left(\dfrac{x^5}{5}\right)\Big|_0^k = \left(\dfrac{x^5}{5}\right)\Big|_k^6$
Evaluate at the endpoints.	$\left(\dfrac{k^5}{5}\right) - \left(\dfrac{0^5}{5}\right) = \left(\dfrac{6^5}{5}\right) - \left(\dfrac{k^5}{5}\right)$
Simplify.	$\left(\dfrac{k^5}{5}\right) = \left(\dfrac{7776}{5}\right) - \left(\dfrac{k^5}{5}\right)$
Multiply both sides by 5.	$k^5 = 7776 - k^5$
Add k^5 to both sides.	$2k^5 = 7776$
Divide both sides by 2.	$k^5 = 3888$
Solve.	$k = \sqrt[5]{3888} \approx 5.2$

Therefore, the line that divides the volume of the solid in half is approximately $k = 5.2$.

Volume of Solids: Washer and Shell Method

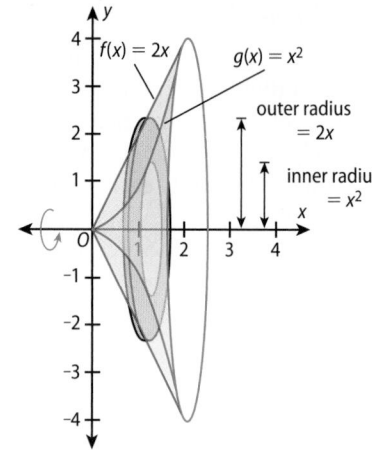

Washers

When a solid of revolution is formed by a bounded region that has space between itself and its axis of rotation, a hole is created in the middle of the solid. The cross section of such a solid has the shape of a washer, as shown by the graph at the right.

To find the area of the washer, subtract the area of the inner circle from the area of the outer circle. The volume of the solid is the integral of the area of the washer. The endpoints are the intersections of the two functions.

EXAMPLE 1

Find the volume of the solid, shown in the graph above, formed by revolving the region bounded by $f(x) = 2x$ and $g(x) = x^2$ about the x-axis.

STEP 1 Determine the endpoints of the region.

Set the functions equal to each other.	$x^2 = 2x$
Subtract $2x$.	$x^2 - 2x = 0$
Factor.	$x(x - 2) = 0$
Solve for x.	$x = 0, 2$

STEP 2 Find the volume of the solid.

Use the washer formula for the volume.	$V = \pi \int_a^b (f(x))^2 - (g(x))^2 \, dx$
Substitute endpoints and the radius functions.	$= \pi \int_0^2 [(2x)^2 - (x^2)^2] dx$
Simplify.	$= \pi \int_0^2 (4x^2 - x^4) dx$
Integrate.	$= \pi \left[\frac{4x^3}{3} - \frac{x^5}{5} \right]_0^2$
Evaluate at the endpoints.	$= \pi \left[\frac{4}{3}(2)^3 - \frac{1}{5}(2)^5 \right] - \pi \left[\frac{4}{3}(0)^3 - \frac{1}{5}(0)^5 \right]$
Simplify.	$= \frac{64\pi}{15}$

GOT TO KNOW!

Volume of a Solid of Revolution: Washer Method

Revolution about the x-axis —

$V = \pi \int_a^b (f(x))^2 - (g(x))^2 \, dx$

where $f(x)$ is the outer radius and $g(x)$ is the inner radius on $[a, b]$

Revolution about the y-axis —

$V = \pi \int_a^b (f(y))^2 - (g(y))^2 \, dy$

where $f(y)$ is the outer radius and $g(y)$ is the inner radius on $[a, b]$

EXAMPLE 2

The graph at the right shows the region bound by $g(x) = x$, the y-axis, and the line $f(x) = 3$. Find the volume of the solid of revolution formed by revolving this region about the x-axis.

Since there is a space between the shaded region and the axis of rotation, use the washer method.

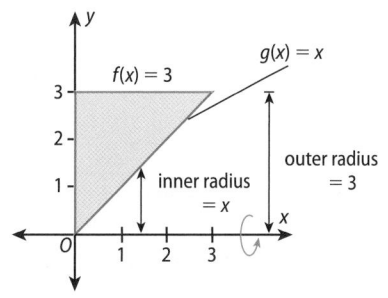

SEARCH 🔍

To see step-by-step videos of these problems, enter the page number into the SWadvantage.com Search Bar.

Use the washer formula for the volume. $V = \pi \int_0^3 [(3)^2 - (x)^2] dx$

Simplify. $= \pi \int_0^3 (9 - x^2) dx$

Integrate. $= \pi \left[9x - \frac{x^3}{3} \right]_0^3$

Evaluate at the endpoints. $= \pi \left[9(3) - \frac{1}{3}(3)^3 \right] - \pi \left[9(0) - \frac{1}{3}(0)^3 \right] = 18\pi$

EXAMPLE 3

Find the volume of the solid formed by rotating the region bounded by $y = x^3$ and $y = \sqrt{x}$ about the x-axis.

STEP 1 Graph the bounded region to determine the inner radius and outer radius of the washer.

The graph shows that $\sqrt{x} > x^3$ on the entire bounded interval. Thus, $f(x) = \sqrt{x}$ is the outer radius and $g(x) = x^3$ is the inner radius.

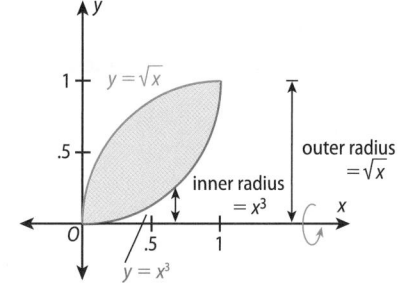

Watch Out ⚠️

Make sure that you integrate the square of the outer function minus the square of the inner function and not the other way around.

STEP 2 Determine the endpoints of the region.

Set the functions equal to each other. $x^3 = \sqrt{x}$

Square both sides. $x^6 = x$

Subtract x from both sides. $x^6 - x = 0$

Factor. $x(x^5 - 1) = 0$

Solve for x. $x = 0, 1$

STEP 3 Find the volume of the solid.

Use the washer formula for the volume. $V = \pi \int_0^1 [(\sqrt{x})^2 - (x^3)^2] dx$

Simplify. $= \pi \int_0^1 (x - x^6) dx$

Integrate. $= \pi \left[\frac{x^2}{2} - \frac{x^7}{7} \right]_0^1$

Evaluate at the endpoints. $= \pi \left[\frac{1}{2}(1)^2 - \frac{1}{7}(1)^2 \right] - \pi \left[\frac{1}{2}(0)^2 - \frac{1}{7}(0)^2 \right]$

Simplify. $= \frac{5\pi}{14}$

y-Axis Washers

As with the disk method, you can use the washer method to calculate the volume of a solid formed by revolving a region about the y-axis. First, write the function in terms of y, and then integrate with respect to y over the interval of y.

EXAMPLE 4

Find the volume of the solid formed by rotating the region bounded by the x-axis, $x = 2$, and $y = \sqrt{2x}$ about the y-axis.

STEP 1 Write the function in terms of y.

Use the given function. $y = \sqrt{2x}$

Solve for x. $x = \dfrac{y^2}{2}$

STEP 2 Determine the endpoints of the region.

Since the x-axis forms one of the boundaries of the region, the lower bound is $y = 0$.

To find the upper bound, calculate the y-value of the intersection point of $x = \dfrac{y^2}{2}$ and $x = 2$.

Set the two functions equal to each other. $\dfrac{y^2}{2} = 2$

Solve for y. $y = \pm 2$

To form the volume, you revolve only the cross-sectional area in the first quadrant. Thus, the upper bound of the integral is $y = 2$.

STEP 3 Graph the region to be rotated.

Since there is a space between the shaded region and the axis of rotation, use the washer method to find the volume of the solid.

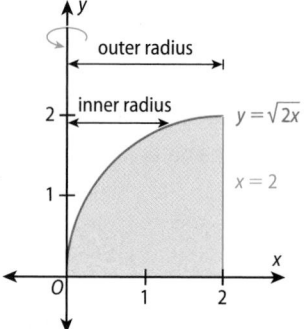

STEP 4 Find the volume of the solid of revolution.

Use the washer method formula. $V = \pi \int_0^2 \left[(2)^2 - \left(\dfrac{y^2}{2} \right)^2 \right] dy$

Simplify. $= \pi \int_0^2 \left[4 - \dfrac{y^4}{4} \right] dy$

Integrate. $= \pi \left[4y - \dfrac{y^5}{20} \right]_0^2$

Evaluate at the endpoints. $= \pi \left[4(2) - \dfrac{(2)^5}{20} \right] - \pi \left[4(0) - \dfrac{(0)^5}{5} \right]$

Simplify. $= \dfrac{32\pi}{5}$

Watch Out !

When revolving about the y-axis, all functions must be in terms of y, and the upper and lower bounds must be y-values.

Using More Than One Integral

When a region does not have the same inner and outer radius on the entire interval of integration, you need more than one integral to calculate the volume of the solid of revolution.

The graph at the right shows an example. The region from $y = 0$ to $y = 3$ has a radius of $x = 1$. Revolving this region forms a disk. The region from $y = 3$ to $y = 4$ has an inner radius and an outer radius. Revolving this region forms a washer.

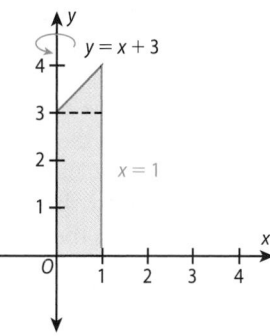

EXAMPLE 5

The graph above shows a region bounded by the x-axis, $x = 1$, and $y = x + 3$. Find the volume of the solid formed by revolving the region about the y-axis.

SEARCH

To see step-by-step videos of these problems, enter the page number into the SWadvantage.com Search Bar.

STEP 1 Write the function in terms of y.

Use the given function y. $y = x + 3$

Solve for x. $x = y - 3$

STEP 2 Determine the endpoints of the region.

Since the x-axis forms one of the boundaries of the region that is to be revolved, the lower bound is $y = 0$.

To find the upper bound, calculate the y-value of the intersection point of $x = y - 3$ and $x = 1$.

Set the two functions equal to each other. $y - 3 = 1$

Solve for y. $y = 4$

STEP 3 Find the volume of the solid of revolution.

The graph above shows that the solid does not have the same radius from $y = 0$ to $y = 4$. For this reason, you must use two separate regions for the integration of the area. The first region will use the disk method to find the volume from $y = 0$ to $y = 3$. The second region will use the washer method to find the volume from $y = 3$ to $y = 4$.

Add the volumes of the disk and the washer.

$$V = \pi \int_a^b [R(y)]^2\, dy + \pi \int_b^c [f(y))^2 - (g(y)]^2\, dy$$

Substitute the endpoints and functions.

$$= \pi \int_0^3 (1)^2\, dy + \pi \int_3^4 [(1)^2 - (y - 3)^2]dy$$

Simplify.

$$= \pi \int_0^3 dy + \pi \int_3^4 (-y^2 + 6y - 8)dy$$

Integrate.

$$= \pi (y)_0^3 + \pi \left(-\frac{y^3}{3} + 3y^2 - 8y\right)\Big|_3^4$$

Evaluate.

$$= \pi(3 - 0) + \pi\left(-\frac{(4)^3}{3} + 3(4)^2 - 8(4)\right)$$

$$-\pi\left(-\frac{(3)^3}{3} + 3(3)^2 - 8(3)\right)$$

Simplify.

$$= \frac{11\pi}{3}$$

Cylindrical Shells

The shell method is a way to find the volume of a solid of revolution by treating it as the sum of infinite cylindrical shells inside one another. The shells are parallel to the axis of rotation instead of perpendicular as in the disk and washer methods. For example, in the graph at the right, revolving a rectangular slice of the shaded area about the y-axis forms the cylindrical shell.

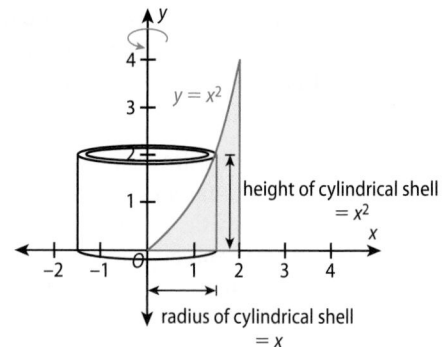

The sum of the volumes all such shells equals the volume of the solid of revolution: $V = 2\pi \int_a^b xf(x)dx$. To find the volume of the solid, substitute the function for $f(x)$ in the integrand, and then integrate over the interval. Finding the volume of a solid formed by revolving about the x-axis is solved in the same way, except the integral is written in terms of y.

EXAMPLE 6

Use the shell method to find the volume of the solid created by revolving $y = x^2$ from $x = 0$ to $x = 2$ about the y-axis, as shown in the graph above.

Use the shell method formula for y-axis rotation.	$V = 2\pi \int_a^b xf(x)dx$
Substitute the endpoints and the radius.	$= 2\pi \int_0^2 x(x^2)dx$
Simplify.	$= 2\pi \int_0^2 x^3\, dx$
Integrate.	$= 2\pi \left(\frac{x^4}{4}\right)\Big\|_0^2$
Evaluate at the endpoints.	$= 2\pi \left(\frac{(2)^4}{4}\right) - 2\pi \left(\frac{(0)^4}{4}\right)$
Simplify.	$= 8\pi$

GOT TO KNOW!

Volume of a Solid of Revolution: Shell Method

Horizontal axis of revolution —

$V = 2\pi \int_a^b yf(y)dy$

where y is the average radius, and $f(y)$ is the height of any shell on $[a, b]$

Vertical axis of revolution —

$V = 2\pi \int_a^b xf(x)dx$

where x is the average radius, and $f(x)$ is the width of any shell on $[a, b]$

EXAMPLE 7

Find the volume of the solid formed by rotating the region bounded by the *x*-axis, *x* = 1, and *y* = *x* + 3 about the *y*-axis, as shown in the graph at the right.

The method of finding this volume using the sum of two separate integrals was used in Example 5. In this example, the shell method is used. This method allows you to calculate the volume with a more direct approach.

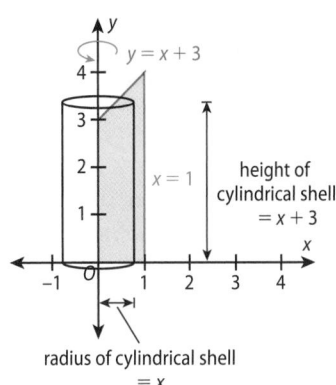

Use the shell method formula for *y*-axis rotation.

$$V = 2\pi \int_a^b x f(x)\,dx$$

Substitute the endpoints and the function.

$$= 2\pi \int_0^1 x(x + 3)\,dx$$

Simplify.

$$= 2\pi \int_0^1 (x^2 + 3x)\,dx$$

Integrate.

$$= 2\pi \left(\frac{x^3}{3} + \frac{3x^2}{2} \right)\Big|_0^1$$

Evaluate at the endpoints.

$$= 2\pi \left(\frac{(1)^3}{3} + \frac{3(1)^2}{2} \right) - 2\pi \left(\frac{(0)^3}{3} + \frac{3(0)^2}{2} \right)$$

Simplify.

$$= \frac{11\pi}{3}$$

Watch Out ⚠

The constant when using the disk and washer methods is π. The constant when using the shell method is 2π.

EXAMPLE 8

Find the volume of the solid formed by revolving the region shown in the graph at the right bounded by the graphs of *y* = *x*3 · 2*x* · 2, *x* · 0, and *x* · 2 about the *y*-axis.

It would be impossible to calculate the volume of this solid using the washer method since the inner and outer radii are formed by the same function. The shell method is needed to find the volume.

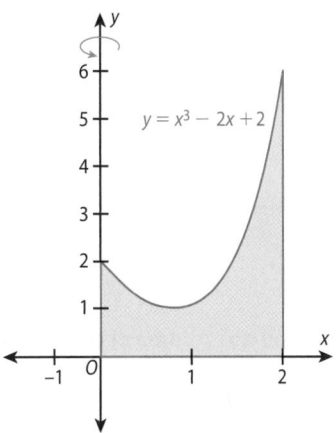

SEARCH 🔍

To see step-by-step videos of these problems, enter the page number into the SWadvantage.com Search Bar.

Use the shell method formula for *y*-axis rotation.

$$V = 2\pi \int_a^b x f(x)\,dx$$

Substitute the radius and the function.

$$= 2\pi \int_0^2 [x(x^3 - 2x + 2)]\,dx$$

Simplify.

$$= 2\pi \int_0^2 (x^4 - 2x^2 + 2x)\,dx$$

Integrate.

$$= 2\pi \left(\frac{x^5}{5} - \frac{2x^3}{3} + x^2 \right)\Big|_0^2$$

Evaluate at the endpoints.

$$= 2\pi \left(\frac{(2)^5}{5} - \frac{2(2)^3}{3} + (2)^2 \right)$$

$$- 2\pi \left(\frac{(0)^5}{5} - \frac{2(0)^3}{3} + (0)^2 \right)$$

Simplify.

$$= \frac{152\pi}{15}$$

Disks Revolved About a Line

When a solid of revolution is formed by revolving a bounded region about a line other than the *x*- or *y*-axis, the equation for the radius of the solid is the difference of the line of revolution and the boundary curve.

EXAMPLE 1

Find the volume of the solid created by revolving the region bounded by $y = x^2$, $x = 2$, and the *x*-axis about the line $x = 2$.

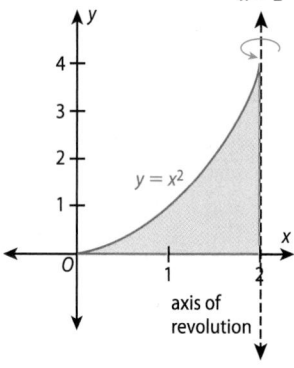

STEP 1 Find the radius of the solid.

Write the function $y = x^2$ in terms of *y*. $x = \sqrt{y}$

Use line − curve to determine the radius. $R(x) = 2 - \sqrt{y}$

STEP 2 Find the volume of the solid.

Use the disk method with respect to *y*.

$$V = \pi \int_0^4 (2 - \sqrt{y})^2 \, dy$$

Expand.

$$= \int_0^4 (4 - 4y^{\frac{1}{2}} + y) \, dy$$

Integrate.

$$= \pi \left(4y - \frac{8y^{\frac{3}{2}}}{3} + \frac{y^2}{2} \right) \Bigg|_0^4$$

Evaluate at the endpoints.

$$= \pi \left(4(4) - \frac{8(4)^{\frac{3}{2}}}{3} + \frac{(4)^2}{2} \right) - \pi \left(4(0) - \frac{8(0)^{\frac{3}{2}}}{3} + \frac{(0)^2}{2} \right)$$

Simplify.

$$= \frac{8\pi}{3}$$

Need More
HELP ?
Remember—You can use the disk method to find the volume of a solid that has no gap between the bounded region and the line of rotation. For more help with the disk method, go to *Volume of Solids: Disk Method* (p. 2278).

EXAMPLE 2

Find the volume of the solid created by revolving the region bounded by the curve $y = -x$, $y = -1$, and the *y*-axis about the line $y = -1$.

STEP 1 Use line − curve to find the radius. $R(x) = -1 - (-x) = x - 1$

STEP 2 Find the volume of the solid.

Use the disk method with respect to *x*.

$$V = \pi \int_0^1 (x - 1)^2 \, dx$$

Expand and simplify.

$$= \pi \int_0^1 (x^2 - 2x + 1) \, dx$$

Integrate.

$$= \pi \left[\frac{x^3}{3} - x^2 + x \right]_0^1$$

Evaluate.

$$= \frac{\pi}{3}$$

Washers Revolved About a Line

To use the washer method to find the volume of a solid revolved about a line other than the x- or y-axis, you must find equations for the inner and outer radii. Each radius is the difference between the line of revolution and the curve that defines the solid.

EXAMPLE 3

Find the volume of the solid created by revolving the region bounded by the curve $y = x$, $x = 1$, and the x-axis about the line $x = 2$.

STEP 1 Use line − curve to determine the radii.

Outer radius = $(2 - y)$

Inner radius = $(2 - 1)$

STEP 2 Find the volume of the solid.

Use the washer method formula.

$V = \pi \int_0^1 [(2 - y)^2 - (2 - 1)^2]dy$

Expand and simplify.

$= \pi \int_0^1 (y^2 - 4y + 3)dy$

Integrate.

$= \pi \left[\dfrac{y^3}{3} - 2y^2 + 3y \right]_0^1$

Evaluate.

$= \dfrac{4\pi}{3}$

Need More

HELP ?

Remember—You can use the washer method to find the volume of a solid that has a gap between the bounded region and the line of rotation. For more help with the washer method, go to *Volume of Solids: Washer and Shell Method* (p. 2282).

EXAMPLE 4

Find the volume of the solid created by revolving the region bounded by the curves $y = x^2$ and $y = x$ about the line $y = -4$, shown on the graph at the right.

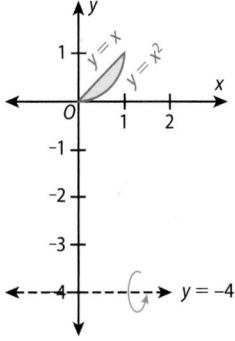

SEARCH

To see step-by-step videos of these problems, enter the page number into the SWadvantage.com Search Bar.

STEP 1 Use line − curve to determine the radii.

Outer radius = $(-4 - x)$

Inner radius = $(-4 - x^2)$

STEP 2 Find the volume of the solid.

Use the washer method formula.

$V = \pi \int_0^1 [(-4 - x)^2 - (-4 - x^2)^2]dx$

Expand and simplify.

$= \pi \int_0^1 (-x^4 - 7x^2 + 8x)dx$

Integrate.

$= \pi \left[-\dfrac{x^5}{5} - \dfrac{7x^3}{3} + 4x^2 \right]_0^1$

Evaluate.

$= \dfrac{22\pi}{15}$

Solids with Known Cross Sections

Base of a Cross Section

To find the volume of a solid with a known cross section, assume the solid lies on the plane of the figure and extends along either the *x*-axis or the *y*-axis. The cross section is perpendicular to the axis. The figures below show an area along the *x*-axis.

The cross sections in the figure extend out of the page. It is convenient to let the base of the cross section be vertical, between the *x*-axis and the function that defines the region, as shown by the square in the figure. The base can instead be between two functions, as shown by the semicircle. For any cross-sectional shape, the volume of the solid is the integral of the cross section's area along the interval: $V = \int_a^b A(x)\,dx$.

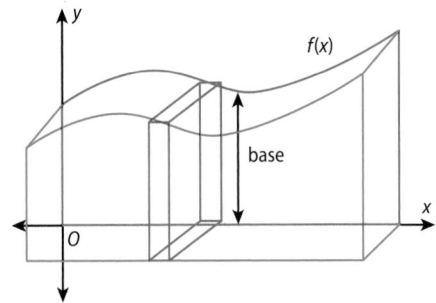

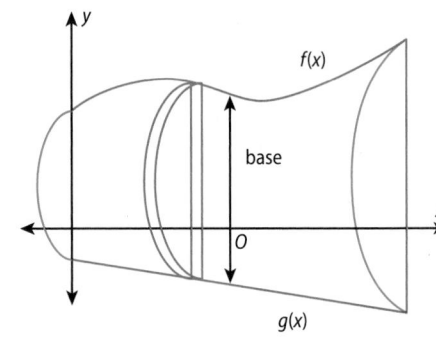

SEARCH

To see step-by-step videos of these problems, enter the page number into the SWadvantage.com Search Bar.

EXAMPLE 1

The region bounded by $f(x) = x + 1$, the *x*-axis, the *y*-axis, and the line $x = 4$ forms the base of a solid with a square cross section perpendicular to the *x*-axis. Find the volume of the solid.

Find the base of the cross sections.	base $= f(x) = x + 1$
Write the equation for the cross section area.	area $= (\text{base})^2 = (x + 1)^2$
Integrate the area of the cross sections.	volume $= \int_0^4 (x + 1)^2\,dx = \dfrac{124}{3}$

EXAMPLE 2

The region bounded by $f(x) = x + 1$, the *x*-axis, the *y*-axis, and the line $x = 4$ forms the base of a solid with semicircular cross sections perpendicular to the *x*-axis. Find the volume of the solid.

The area of a semicircle is one-half the area of a circle, $\pi(\text{radius})^2$. The base of the semicircle is the distance between $f(x)$ and the *x*-axis, and the radius of the semicircular cross section is one-half the base length.

Find the cross section radius from the base length.	radius $= \dfrac{f(x)}{2} = \dfrac{x + 1}{2}$
Write the equation for the cross section area.	area $= \dfrac{1}{2}\pi r^2 = \dfrac{1}{2}\pi\left(\dfrac{x+1}{2}\right)^2 = \dfrac{\pi}{8}(x+1)^2$
Integrate the area of the cross sections.	volume $= \dfrac{\pi}{8}\int_0^4 (x + 1)^2\,dx = \dfrac{31\pi}{6}$

EXAMPLE 3

The region bounded by $y = x + 1$, the *x*-axis, the *y*-axis, and the line $x = 4$ forms the base of a solid with right isosceles triangle cross sections perpendicular to the *x*-axis. Find the volume of the solid.

Find the base of the cross sections. 　　　　　base $= f(x) = x + 1$

Write the equation for the cross section area. 　area $= \frac{1}{2}(\text{base})^2 = \frac{1}{2}(x + 1)^2$

Integrate the area of the cross sections. 　　　volume $= \frac{1}{2}\int_0^4 (x + 1)^2\, dx = \frac{62}{3}$

EXAMPLE 4

The region bounded by $y = x + 1$, $y = -x - 1$, the *y*-axis, and the line $x = 3$ forms the base of a solid with equilateral triangle cross sections perpendicular to the *x*-axis. Find the volume of the solid.

Find the base of the cross sections. 　　　base $= f(x) - g(x) = (x + 1) - (-x - 1) = 2x + 2$

Write the equation for the cross section area. 　area $= \frac{1}{2}(\text{base})(\text{height}) = \frac{1}{2}(2x + 2)\left(\frac{\sqrt{3}}{2}(2x + 2)\right)$

$$= \frac{\sqrt{3}}{4}(2x + 2)^2$$

Integrate the area of the cross sections. 　　volume $= \frac{\sqrt{3}}{4}\int_0^4 (2x + 2)^2\, dx = \frac{124\sqrt{3}}{3}$

Need More

HELP ?

For help with finding the height of an equilateral triangle, go to *Special Triangles and Angles* in *Trigonometry* (Book 1, p. 898).

EXAMPLE 5

The region bounded by $y = x$, $y = -x$, and $y = 3$ forms the base of a solid with square cross sections perpendicular to the *y*-axis. Find the volume of the solid.

Find the base of the cross sections. 　　　base $= f(y) - g(y) = (y) - (-y) = 2y$

Write the equation for the cross section area. 　area $= (\text{base})^2 = (2y)^2$

Integrate the area of the cross sections. 　　volume $= \int_0^3 (2y)^2\, dy = 36$

GOT TO KNOW!

Volumes of Solids with Known Cross Sections

Square: 　　　$V = \int (\text{base})^2\, dx$ 　　　　Right Isosceles Triangle: 　$V = \frac{1}{2}\int (\text{base})^2\, dx$

Semicircle: $V = \frac{\pi}{8}\int (\text{base})^2\, dx$ 　　Equilateral Triangle: 　　$V = \frac{\sqrt{3}}{4}\int (\text{base})^2\, dx$

Differential Equations

What Came Before?
- Rules for differentiation
- Evaluating integrals

What's This About?
- Defining and graphing slope fields
- Solving differential equations
- Using differential equations to model growth and decay

Practical Apps
- Radioactive materials decay at specific rates. Differential equations can be used to determine the amount of material left after a known amount of time.
- Forensic experts use Newton's Law of Cooling, which is a differential equation, to determine time of death at a homicide scene.

just for FUN!

Q: What's the most polite and respectful thing in math?

A: A deferential equation.

You can find more practice problems online by visiting:
www.SWadvantage.com

Differential Equations

SOUTHWESTERN

General Solutions to Differential Equations

A **differential equation** is an equation relating a function and one or more of its derivatives.

The **order** of a differential equation is the power of the highest derivative in the equation. For example, $\frac{dy}{dx} = 6x$ and $y' + 3x - 8 = 0$ are first-order differential equations, but $\frac{d^2y}{dx^2} - 4y = 0$ and $y'' + 2x = 4y$ are second-order differential equations.

A function is a solution to a differential equation if the equation is true when the function and its derivatives are substituted in the equation. You can solve simple differential equations by integrating both sides. A general solution to a differential equation includes an unknown constant C.

Try It This Way

To quickly see many possible solutions to the differential equation $y' = 2x$, use a graphing calculator to graph:

$y = x^2$,

$y = x^2 + 1$,

$y = x^2 + 2$,

$y = x^2 + 3$,

$y = x^2 - 1$,

$y = x^2 - 2$, and

$y = x^2 - 3$ in a standard viewing window.

EXAMPLE 1

Find the general solution to the following differential equations. Check your solutions.

a. $\frac{dy}{dx} = 2x$

Write the equation in differential form.	$dy = 2x\,dx$
Write the integral for both sides.	$\int dy = \int 2x\,dx$
Integrate.	$y = x^2 + C$

CHECK   Differentiate both sides of the equation. $\frac{d}{dx}(y) = \frac{d}{dx}(x^2 + C)$

$$\frac{dy}{dx} = 2x \checkmark$$

b. $\frac{dy}{dx} = \sin x$

Write the equation in differential form.	$dy = \sin x\,dx$
Write the integral for both sides.	$\int dy = \int \sin x\,dx$
Integrate.	$y = -\cos x + C$

CHECK   Differentiate both sides of the equation. $\frac{d}{dx}(y) = \frac{d}{dx}(-\cos x + C)$

$$\frac{dy}{dx} = \sin x \checkmark$$

c. $\frac{dy}{dx} = 3x^2 - 2x + 5$

Write the equation in differential form.	$dy = (3x^2 - 2x + 5)dx$
Write the integral for both sides.	$\int dy = \int (3x^2 - 2x + 5)dx$
Integrate.	$y = x^3 - x^2 + 5x + C$

CHECK   Differentiate both sides of the equation. $\frac{d}{dx}(y) = \frac{d}{dx}(x^3 - x^2 + 5x + C)$

$$\frac{dy}{dx} = 3x^2 - 2x + 5 \checkmark$$

Initial Value Problems

After you find the general solution to a differential equation, you can determine a particular solution if you know a value of the function at a specific point. This type of problem is called an **initial value problem**. The initial value enables you to determine the value of the constant C.

When finding a particular solution, you usually need to know the same number of initial values as the order of the equation. For example, to determine the constant in a first-order differential equation, you only need to know one initial value. For a second-order differential equation, you need to know two initial values.

EXAMPLE 2

Find the solution to the differential equation $y' = 4x^3 - 2x$ if $y(2) = 18$.

STEP 1 Find the general solution.

Write the equation in differential form.	$dy = (4x^3 - 2x)dx$
Write the integral for both sides.	$\int dy = \int (4x^3 - 2x)dx$
Separate the integrals.	$\int dy = 4\int x^3\, dx - 2\int x\, dx$
Integrate.	$y = x^4 - x^2 + C$

STEP 2 Determine the value of C.

Apply the initial condition.	$y(2) = 18$
Substitute.	$(2)^4 - (2)^2 + C = 18$
Simplify.	$16 - 4 + C = 18$
Solve for C.	$C = 6$

The solution to the differential equation is $y = x^4 - x^2 + 6$.

SEARCH

To see step-by-step videos of these problems, enter the page number into the SWadvantage.com Search Bar.

EXAMPLE 3

Find the solution to the differential equation $y' = 6\cos x$ if $y(\pi) = 5$.

STEP 1 Find the general solution.

Write the equation in differential form.	$dy = (6\cos x)dx$
Write the integral for both sides.	$\int dy = \int (6\cos x)dx$
Integrate.	$y = 6\sin x + C$

STEP 2 Determine the value of C.

Apply the initial condition.	$y(\pi) = 5$
Substitute.	$6\sin(\pi) + C = 5$
Simplify.	$6(0) + C = 5$
Solve for C.	$C = 5$

The solution to the differential equation is $y = 6\sin x + 5$.

Second-Order Differential Equations

The method you use to find the solution to a second-order differential equation depends on the form of the equation. In the simplest case, the equation consists of only a second-order derivative equal to a constant. To solve this type of equation, you can integrate twice to find the function. If you know two initial values, you can determine the particular solution to the equation.

When integrating a first-order differential equation, the equation is usually written in differential form so that you integrate with respect to dy on one side and dx on the other. For second-order differential equations, you use prime notation and integrate with respect to dx, but the result is the same: $\int y''\,dx = y' + C$ and $\int y'\,dx = y + C$.

EXAMPLE 4

The graph shows the position s of a ball that is thrown up with an initial velocity v of 64 ft/s from the top of a cliff 100 ft from a canyon floor. The acceleration due to gravity is -32 ft/s². Find the equation of the position as a function of time t.

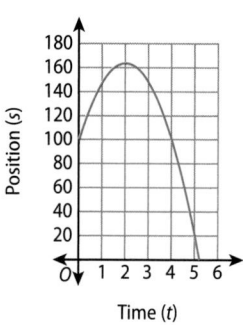

STEP 1 Write the differential equation and initial values.

The acceleration is a second-order differential equation.	$a(t) = s''(t) = -32$
The initial position is 100.	$s(0) = 100$
The initial velocity is 64.	$v(0) = s'(0) = 64$

STEP 2 Find the general velocity equation.

The velocity is the integral of the acceleration.	$\int s''(t)\,dt = \int(-32)\,dt$
Integrate.	$s'(t) = -32t + C_1$

STEP 3 Find the particular velocity equation.

Use the initial condition for the velocity.	$s'(0) = 64$
Substitute.	$-32(0) + C_1 = 64$
Solve for C_1.	$C_1 = 64$

Therefore the particular velocity equation is $s'(t) = -32t + 64$.

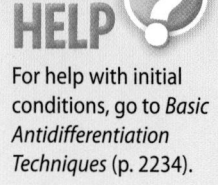

Need More

HELP

For help with initial conditions, go to *Basic Antidifferentiation Techniques* (p. 2234).

STEP 4 Find the general position equation.

The position is the integral of the velocity.	$\int s'(t)\,dt = \int(-32t + 64)\,dt$
Integrate.	$s(t) = -16t^2 + 64t + C_2$

STEP 5 Find the particular position equation.

Use the initial condition for the position.	$s(0) = 100$
Substitute.	$-16(0)^2 + 64(0) + C_2 = 100$
Solve for C_2.	$C_2 = 100$

Therefore the particular position equation is $s(t) = -16t^2 + 64t + 100$.

Verifying Solutions to Differential Equations

You can determine whether a given function is a solution to a differential equation by first differentiating the function to determine y' and y'', and then substituting these values into the differential equation. If the equation is true, the function is a solution. In some cases, you have to determine values of constants that will make a function a solution to an equation.

EXAMPLE 5

Determine whether $y = \sin x$ is a solution to the differential equation $y'' + y' = 0$.

STEP 1 Find the derivatives.

$$y' = \frac{d}{dx}(y) = \frac{d}{dx}(\sin x) = \cos x$$

$$y'' = \frac{d}{dx}(y') = \frac{d}{dx}(\cos x) = -\sin x$$

STEP 2 Substitute in the equation.

$$y'' + y' = -\sin x + \cos x \neq 0$$

Therefore $y = \sin x$ is not a solution to the differential equation.

SEARCH

To see step-by-step videos of these problems, enter the page number into the SWadvantage.com Search Bar.

EXAMPLE 6

Determine whether $y = e^{2x} + 2e^{3x}$ is a solution to the differential equation $y'' - 5y' + 6y = 0$.

STEP 1 Find the derivatives.

$$y' = \frac{d}{dx}(e^{2x} + 2e^{3x}) = 2e^{2x} + 6e^{3x}$$

$$y'' = \frac{d}{dx}(2e^{2x} + 6e^{3x}) = 4e^{2x} + 18e^{3x}$$

STEP 2 Substitute in the equation.

$$y'' - 5y' + 6y = (4e^{2x} + 18e^{3x}) - 5(2e^{2x} + 6e^{3x})$$
$$+ 6(e^{2x} + 2e^{3x}) = 0$$

Therefore $y = e^{2x} + 2e^{3x}$ is a solution to the differential equation.

EXAMPLE 7

Find all values of A so that $y = \sqrt{6 + Ax}$ is a solution to $y' - \frac{4}{y} = 0$.

STEP 1 Determine y'.

$$\frac{d}{dx}(y) = \frac{d}{dx}\sqrt{6 + Ax}$$

Differentiate. Write y' in terms of y.

$$y' = \frac{A}{2\sqrt{6 + Ax}} = \frac{A}{2y}$$

STEP 2 Determine values of A that make the differential equation true.

Rewrite the differential equation.

$$y' = \frac{4}{y}$$

Substitute y'.

$$\frac{A}{2y} = \frac{4}{y}$$

Solve for A.

$$A = 8$$

Therefore $y = \sqrt{6 + Ax}$ is a solution to the differential equation if $A = 8$.

Slope Fields

Sketching a Slope Field

A **slope field** is a graph of the slopes determined by a differential equation at multiple points. Sketching a small line segment at points on the graph that represent the corresponding slope at each point creates a slope field. The graph of a slope field is a useful way to visualize the general solutions to a differential equation.

EXAMPLE 1

Need More
HELP ?

For help with sketching line segments with a given slope, go to *Rate of Change and Slope* in *Algebra* (p. 1536).

Sketch a slope field for the differential equation $y' = x$.

STEP 1 Make a table of values for points on a Cartesian coordinate plane.

STEP 2 Sketch small line segments at each point with the slope found in STEP 1.

(x, y)	$y' = x$
$(-1, 1)$	-1
$(-1, 0)$	-1
$(-1, -1)$	-1
$(0, 1)$	0
$(0, 0)$	0
$(0, -1)$	0
$(1, 1)$	1
$(1, 0)$	1
$(1, -1)$	1

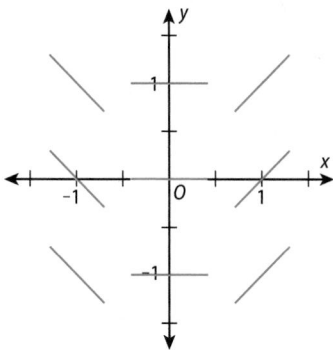

EXAMPLE 2

Sketch a slope field for the differential equation $y' = x + y$.

STEP 1 Make a table of values for points on a Cartesian coordinate plane.

STEP 2 Sketch small line segments at each point with the slope found in STEP 1.

(x, y)	$y' = x + y$
$(-1, 1)$	0
$(-1, 0)$	-1
$(-1, -1)$	-2
$(0, 1)$	1
$(0, 0)$	0
$(0, -1)$	-1
$(1, 1)$	2
$(1, 0)$	1
$(1, -1)$	0

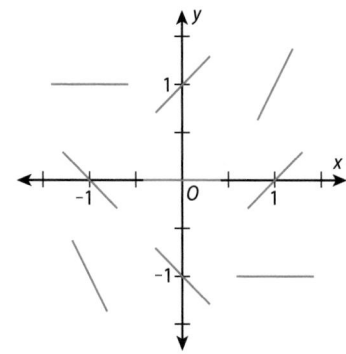

EXAMPLE 3

Sketch a slope field for the differential equation $y' = -\dfrac{x}{y}$.

STEP 1 Make a table of values for points on on a Cartesian coordinate plane.

(x, y)	$y' = -\dfrac{x}{y}$
$(-1, 2)$	$\frac{1}{2}$
$(-1, 1)$	1
$(-1, 0)$	undefined
$(-1, -1)$	-1
$(-1, -2)$	$-\frac{1}{2}$
$(0, 2)$	0
$(0, 1)$	0
$(0, 0)$	undefined
$(0, -1)$	0
$(0, -2)$	0
$(1, 2)$	$-\frac{1}{2}$
$(1, 1)$	-1
$(1, 0)$	undefined

(x, y)	$y' = -\dfrac{x}{y}$
$(1, -1)$	1
$(1, -2)$	$\frac{1}{2}$
$(-2, 2)$	1
$(-2, 1)$	2
$(-2, 0)$	undefined
$(-2, -1)$	-2
$(-2, -2)$	-1
$(2, 2)$	-1
$(2, 1)$	-2
$(2, 0)$	undefined
$(2, -1)$	2
$(2, -2)$	1

STEP 2 Sketch small line segments at each point with the slope found in STEP 1.

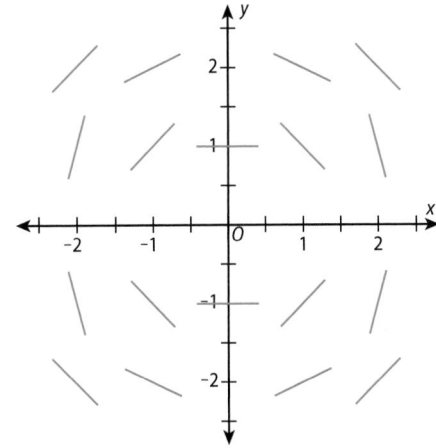

SEARCH

To see step-by-step videos of these problems, enter the page number into the SWadvantage.com Search Bar.

EXAMPLE 4

Sketch a slope field for the differential equation $y' = xy$.

STEP 1 Make a table of values for several points on a Cartesian coordinate plane.

(x, y)	$y' = xy$
$(-1, 2)$	-2
$(-1, 1)$	-1
$(-1, 0)$	0
$(-1, -1)$	1
$(-1, -2)$	2
$(0, 2)$	0
$(0, 1)$	0
$(0, 0)$	0
$(0, -1)$	0
$(0, -2)$	0
$(1, 2)$	2
$(1, 1)$	1
$(1, 0)$	0

(x, y)	$y' = xy$
$(1, -1)$	-1
$(1, -2)$	-2
$(-2, 2)$	-4
$(-2, 1)$	-2
$(-2, 0)$	0
$(-2, -1)$	2
$(-2, -2)$	4
$(2, 2)$	4
$(2, 1)$	2
$(2, 0)$	0
$(2, -1)$	-2
$(2, -2)$	-4

STEP 2 Sketch small line segments at each point with the slope found in STEP 1.

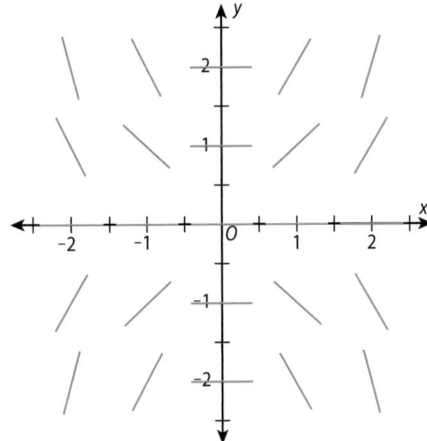

Initial Conditions

It is possible to graph a particular solution to a differential equation using slope fields and an initial condition. The method shown in the following examples gives a rough sketch of the solution curve. You need to use advanced methods or a graphing calculator to sketch the exact curve.

Use the slope field for $\frac{dy}{dx} = 2x$ and the initial condition $f(0) = 1$ to sketch the solution curve to the differential equation. Verify that the sketch matches the particular solution $y = x^2 + 1$.

Start with a slope field of $\frac{dy}{dx} = 2x$, as shown at the right. Begin at the point (0, 1) and trace a smooth curve following the slope segments to sketch the solution curve passing through the point (0, 1). Extend the curve for values of x greater than and less than 0 for a complete sketch of the solution curve.

The sketch is a parabola with a vertex at the point (0, 1), which matches the particular solution $y = x^2 + 1$.

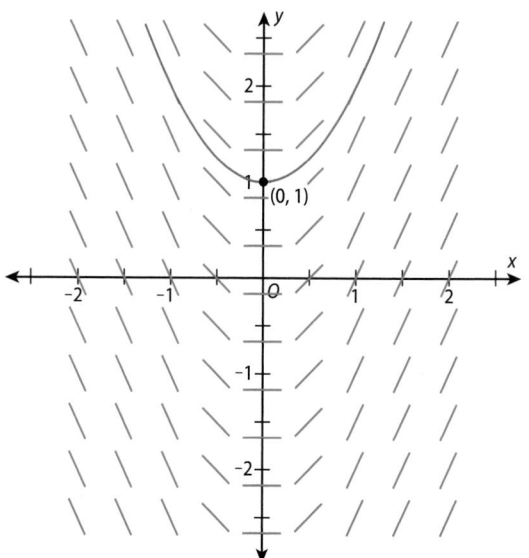

EXAMPLE 6

Use the slope field created by $\frac{dy}{dx} \cdot 2x + y$ and the initial condition $f(1) \cdot 1$ to sketch the solution curve to the differential equation.

Start with a slope field of $\frac{dy}{dx} = 2x + y$ as shown at the right. Begin at the point (1, 1) and trace a smooth curve following the slope segments to sketch the solution curve passing through the point (1, 1). Extend the curve for values of x greater than and less than 1 for a complete sketch of the solution curve.

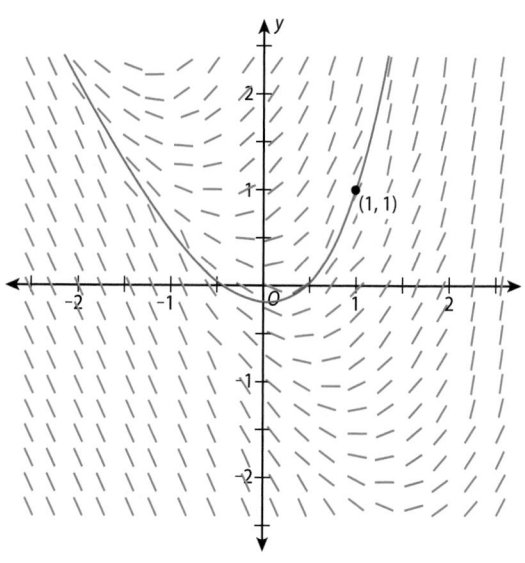

To graph a particular solution, imagine that the graph of the slope field represents flowing water. When your pencil comes near a slope segment it pushes your pencil in the direction it is flowing until your pencil gets to the next segment that pushes it in its own direction, and so on.

Euler's Method

The previous page shows how to use a slope field to sketch the particular solution to a differential equation. Euler's method uses a similar procedure to find a numerical approximation of a particular solution using points along a slope field. This method provides a way to estimate the solution to a differential equation that is difficult or impossible to solve.

To use Euler's method, you start at a given point (x_0, y_0). The next point is x_0 plus any step size you choose, Δx, so that $x_1 = x_0 + \Delta x$. The corresponding y-value approximation lies on the line tangent to the solution curve. To find this value, use the point-slope equation of a line.

$$y_1 - y_0 = m(x_1 - x_0)$$

The slope of the equation is given by the differential equation $f(x, y)$. Substituting in the differential equation and solving for y_1 gives the y value approximation.

$$y_1 = y_0 + f(x_0, y_0)\Delta x$$

You can continue in this way to approximate subsequent points on the solution curve.

EXAMPLE 7

Use Euler's method to approximate $y(1)$ given that $y(x)$ is the solution to the differential equation $y' = x + y$ passing through the point (0, 1). Use a step of $\Delta x = 0.1$.

The initial values are $x_0 = 0$ and $y_0 = 1$. The subsequent points can be found using the slope $y' = f(x, y) = x + y$ and the step size of 0.1.

$y_n = y_{n-1} + f(x_{n-1,}y_{n-1})\Delta x$

$y(0.1) \approx y_1 = 1 + f(0, 1)(0.1) = 1 + (0 + 1)(0.1) = 1.1$

$y(0.2) \approx y_2 = 1.1 + f(0.1, 1.1)(0.1) = 1.1 + (0.1 + 1.1)(0.1) = 1.22$

$y(0.3) \approx y_3 = 1.22 + f(0.2, 1.22)(0.1) = 1.22 + (0.2 + 1.22)(0.1) = 1.362$

$y(0.4) \approx y_4 = 1.362 + f(0.3, 1.362)(0.1) = 1.362 + (0.3 + 1.362)(0.1) = 1.5282$

$y(0.5) \approx y_5 = 1.5282 + f(0.4, 1.5282)(0.1) = 1.5282 + (0.4 + 1.5282)(0.1) = 1.72102$

$y(0.6) \approx y_6 = 1.72102 + f(0.5, 1.72102)(0.1) = 1.72102 + (0.5 + 1.72102)(0.1) = 1.943122$

$y(0.7) \approx y_7 = 1.943122 + f(0.6, 1.943122)(0.1) = 1.943122 + (0.6 + 1.943122)(0.1) = 2.1974342$

$y(0.8) \approx y_8 = 2.1974342 + f(0.7, 2.1974342)(0.1) = 2.1974342 + (0.7 + 2.1974342)(0.1) = 2.4871776$

$y(0.9) \approx y_9 = 2.4871776 + f(0.8, 2.4871776)(0.1) = 2.4871776 + (0.8 + 2.4871776)(0.1) = 2.8158953$

$y(1) \approx y_{10} = 2.8158953 + f(0.9, 2.8158953)(0.1) = 2.8158953 + (0.9 + 2.8158953)(0.1) = 3.18748483$

Therefore, $y(1)$ is approximately 3.187.

SEARCH

To see step-by-step videos of these problems, enter the page number into the SWadvantage.com Search Bar.

Euler's Method

Given a differential equation $y' = f(x, y)$ and an initial value (x_0, y_0) with step size Δx, subsequent (x_n, y_n) values may be found by:

$x_n = x_{n-1} + \Delta x$ and $y_n = y_{n-1} + f(x_{n-1,}y_{n-1})\Delta x$

Separation of Variables

Grouping Like Variables

Some differential equations include both x and y terms. To find the general solution to such equations, you can use the method of **separation of variables** in which you rearrange the equation by grouping x terms with dx and y terms with dy and then integrate.

EXAMPLE 1

Find the general solution to the equation $y' = \dfrac{2x}{2y}$. Check your solution.

Write the original equation.	$y' = \dfrac{2x}{2y}$
Multiply both sides by $2y$.	$2yy' = 2x$
Integrate both sides with respect to x.	$\int 2yy'\,dx = \int 2x\,dx$
Substitute the notation $\dfrac{dy}{dx}$ for y'.	$\int 2y\dfrac{dy}{dx}\,dx = \int 2x\,dx$
Cancel dx terms on the left.	$\int 2y\,dy = \int 2x\,dx$
Integrate.	$y^2 + C_1 = x^2 + C_2$
Combine the constants.	$y^2 = x^2 + C$

Therefore, the general solution is $y^2 = x^2 + C$.

CHECK Differentiate both sides of the equation.

$$\frac{d}{dx}(y^2) = \frac{d}{dx}(x^2 + C)$$

$$(2y)\left(\frac{dy}{dx}\right) = 2x + 0$$

$$\frac{dy}{dx} = \frac{2x}{2y} \checkmark$$

EXAMPLE 2

Find the general solution to the equation $y' = \dfrac{\cos x}{3y^2}$.

Write the original equation.	$y' = \dfrac{\cos x}{3y^2}$
Multiply both sides by $3y^2$.	$3y^2 y' = \cos x$
Integrate both sides with respect to x.	$\int 3y^2 y'\,dx = \int \cos x\,dx$
Substitute the notation $\dfrac{dy}{dx}$ for y'.	$\int 3y^2 \dfrac{dy}{dx}\,dx = \int \cos x\,dx$
Cancel dx terms.	$\int 3y^2\,dy = \int \cos x\,dx$
Integrate both sides.	$y^3 + C_1 = \sin x + C_2$
Combine the constants.	$y^3 = \sin x + C$

Therefore, the general solution is $y^3 = \sin x + C$.

EXAMPLE 3

Find the general solution of $3y^2y' = 3x^2$. Check your solution.

Write the original equation. $3y^2y' = 3x^2$

Substitute the notation $\frac{dy}{dx}$ for y'. $3y^2\frac{dy}{dx} = 3x^2$

Write the equation in differential form. $3y^2\,dy = 3x^2\,dx$

Integrate both sides. $\int 3y^2\,dy = \int 3x^2\,dx$

Integrate, combining the two constants of integration. $y^3 = x^3 + C$

Therefore the general solution is $y^3 = x^3 + C$.

CHECK Differentiate both sides with respect to x. $\frac{d}{dx}(y^3) = \frac{d}{dx}(x^3 + C)$

$3y^2\left(\frac{dy}{dx}\right) = 3x^2$

$3y^2y' = 3x^2$ ✔

SEARCH

To see step-by-step videos of these problems, enter the page number into the SWadvantage.com Search Bar.

Notice in Example 3 that a differential equation may be solved by writing it in differential form, with dy on one side and dx on the other, and then integrating both sides of the equation. The result is $\int dy$ on one side of the equation and $\int dx$ on the other side. This procedure does not mean you are doing different things to different sides of the equation. You are actually differentiating both sides with respect to dx and canceling: $\int \frac{dy}{dx}dx \rightarrow \int dy$.

EXAMPLE 4

Find the general solution of $\cos^2 x\,\frac{dy}{dx} = 1$. Check your solution.

Write the original equation. $\cos^2 x\,\frac{dy}{dx} = 1$

Combine the x term with dx. $dy = \frac{1}{\cos^2 x}\,dx$

Integrate both sides. $\int dy = \int \frac{1}{\cos^2 x}\,dx$

Rewrite to match a known integration rule. $\int dy = \int \sec^2 x\,dx$

Integrate, combining the two constants of integration. $y = \tan x + C$

Therefore the general solution is $y = \tan x + C$.

CHECK Differentiate both sides with respect to x. $\frac{d}{dx}(y) = \frac{d}{dx}(\tan x + C)$

$\frac{dy}{dx} = \sec^2 x = \frac{1}{\cos^2 x}$

$\cos^2 x\,\frac{dy}{dx} = 1$ ✔

Finding Particular Solutions

Once you have found the general solution to a differential equation by separating the variables, you can find the particular solution using an initial condition. When integrating, you can combine the constants of integration and write them as a single constant C.

SEARCH

To see step-by-step videos of these problems, enter the page number into the SWadvantage.com Search Bar.

EXAMPLE 5

Find the particular solution to the differential equation $y' = \frac{5x}{y}$ if $y(1) = 2$.

STEP 1 Use separation of variables to find the general solution.

Write the equation using $\frac{dy}{dx}$ notation.	$\frac{dy}{dx} = \frac{5x}{y}$
Cross multiply to group corresponding variables.	$y\,dy = 5x\,dx$
Integrate both sides of the equation.	$\int y\,dy = \int 5x\,dx$
Integrate, simplifying and combining the constants.	$y^2 = 5x^2 + C$

STEP 2 Use the initial condition to find the particular solution.

Substitute the initial condition into the general solution.	$2^2 = 5(1)^2 + C$
Solve for C.	$C = -1$

Therefore, the particular solution is $y^2 = 5x^2 - 1$.

EXAMPLE 6

Find the particular solution to the differential equation $y' = y^2\sqrt{x}$ if $y(0) = -1$.

STEP 1 Use separation of variables to find the general solution.

Write the equation using $\frac{dy}{dx}$ notation.	$\frac{dy}{dx} = y^2\sqrt{x}$
Group corresponding variables.	$\frac{dy}{y^2} = \sqrt{x}\,dx$
Rewrite with exponents and integrate.	$\int y^{-2}\,dy = \int x^{\frac{1}{2}}\,dx$
Integrate, combining the two constants of integration.	$-y^{-1} = \frac{2x^{\frac{3}{2}}}{3} + C$

STEP 2 Use the initial condition to find the particular solution.

Substitute $y(0) = -1$ into the general solution.	$-(-1)^{-1} = \frac{2(0)^{\frac{3}{2}}}{3} + C$
Solve for C.	$C = 1$

Therefore, the particular solution is $-y^{-1} = \frac{2x^{\frac{3}{2}}}{3} + 1$.

Notice that the solutions to the differential equations do not necessarily have to be written explicitly with y by itself on one side of the equation.

EXAMPLE 7

Find the particular solution to the differential equation $y' = y^2(1 + x)^2$ if $y(-1) = 3$.

STEP 1 Use separation of variables to find the general solution.

Write the equation using $\frac{dy}{dx}$ notation.

$$\frac{dy}{dx} = y^2(1 + x)^2$$

Group corresponding variables.

$$\frac{dy}{y^2} = (1 + x)^2\, dx$$

Integrate both sides.

$$\int \frac{dy}{y^2} = \int (1 + x)^2\, dx$$

Rewrite using exponents.

$$\int y^{-2}\, dy = \int (1 + x)^2\, dx$$

Integrate, combining the two constants of integration.

$$-y^{-1} = \frac{(1 + x)^3}{3} + C$$

STEP 2 Use the initial condition to find the particular solution.

Substitute $y(-1) = 3$ into the general solution.

$$-(3)^{-1} = \frac{(1 + (-1))^3}{3} + C$$

Solve for C.

$$C = -\frac{1}{3}$$

Therefore, the particular solution is $-y^{-1} = \frac{(1 + x)^3}{3} - \frac{1}{3}$.

EXAMPLE 8

Find the equation of the curve that passes through the point (0, 0) and has a slope of $\frac{3x^2}{4y + \sin y}$ at any point on the curve.

STEP 1 Use separation of variables to find the general solution.

Write the slope using $\frac{dy}{dx}$ notation.

$$\frac{dy}{dx} = \frac{3x^2}{4y + \sin y}$$

Group corresponding variables.

$$(4y + \sin y)\, dy = 3x^2\, dx$$

Integrate both sides.

$$\int (4y + \sin y)\, dy = \int 3x^2\, dx$$

Write the integral as the sum of two integrals.

$$\int 4y\, dy + \int \sin y\, dy = \int 3x^2\, dx$$

Integrate, combining the two constants of integration.

$$2y^2 - \cos y = x^3 + C$$

STEP 2 Use the initial condition to find the particular solution.

Substitute $y = 0$ and $x = 0$ into the general solution.

$$2(0)^2 - \cos 0 = (0)^3 + C$$

Simplify.

$$0 - 1 = 0 + C$$

Solve for C.

$$C = -1$$

Therefore, the particular solution is $2y^2 - \cos y = x^3 - 1$.

Need More HELP?

Remember: Slope is the instantaneous rate of change (derivative) of a function.

Growth and Decay

SOUTHWESTERN

Proportional Rates of Change

There are endless real world examples of differential equations involving functions of growth and decay. Many of these problems involve rates of change that are proportional to their functions. The rate of change is expressed by $\frac{dy}{dt} = ky$ for a constant of proportionality k. As shown in Example 1 below, the solution is $y = y_0 e^{kt}$, where y_0 is the value of y at time t. You can determine k if you know the value of y at any other time.

EXAMPLE 1

The rate of change of y with respect to t is $\frac{dy}{dt} = ky$.

a. Find the general solution to the differential equation.

Write the original equation.	$\frac{dy}{dt} = ky$
Separate the variables.	$\frac{1}{y}\, dy = k\, dt$
Write the integral for both sides.	$\int \frac{1}{y}\, dy = \int k\, dt$
Integrate.	$\ln y = kt + C_1$
Use the definition of a natural logarithm.	$y = e^{kt + C_1}$
Use the product of like bases rule.	$y = e^{kt} e^{C_1}$
Since e^{C_1} is a constant, write e^{C_1} as C.	$y = Ce^{kt}$

> **Need More HELP?**
> Remember the integral for a reciprocal.
> $\int \frac{1}{x}\, dx = \ln x$

b. Find the particular solution if $y(0) = y_0$.

Substitute $y = y_0$ and $t = 0$.	$y_0 = Ce^{k(0)}$
Apply $e^0 = 1$.	$y_0 = C(1)$
Solve for C.	$C = y_0$

Therefore, the particular solution to $\frac{dy}{dt} = ky$ is $y = y_0 e^{kt}$.

GOT TO KNOW!

Law of Exponential Growth and Decay

The equation for a rate of change of y that is proportional to y is $\frac{dy}{dt} = ky$, where t is time and k is the constant of proportionality.

If $y(0) = y_0$, then the solution is $y(t) = y_0 e^{kt}$,

where $k > 0$ indicates exponential growth

and $k < 0$ indicates exponential decay.

EXAMPLE 2

For a function y, $\dfrac{dy}{dt} = ky$. Find the value of y when $t = 2$ if $y(0) = 3$ and $y(1) = 9$.

STEP 1 Find the solution to the differential equation.

Write the general solution with $y_0 = 3$.	$y = 3e^{kt}$
Substitute $y(1) = 9$.	$9 = 3e^{k(1)}$
Simplify.	$3 = e^k$
Take the natural log of both sides.	$\ln 3 = k \approx 1.099$

Therefore, the solution to the differential equation is $y \approx 3e^{(1.099)t}$.

STEP 2 Find the value of $y(2)$.

Substitute $t = 2$ into the solution.	$y = 3e^{(1.099)(2)}$
Simplify.	≈ 27.021

Need More

HELP

For help with natural logarithms, see *Common Logs* and *Natural Logs* in *Advanced Algebra* (p. 1978).

EXAMPLE 3

A population of bacteria grows at a rate of $y' = ky$, where k is constant and t is measured in days. If the population doubles every 7 days, find the value of k.

Write the general solution.	$y = y_0 e^{kt}$
Substitute $\dfrac{y}{y_0} = 2$ when $t = 7$.	$2 = e^{7k}$
Take the natural log of both sides.	$\ln 2 = 7k$
Solve for k.	$k \approx 0.099$

SEARCH

To see step-by-step videos of these problems, enter the page number into the SWadvantage.com Search Bar.

EXAMPLE 4

A certain flu virus spreads at a rate proportional to the number of people infected at any time t in days. If 1,500 people are infected when the virus is first recorded, and 4,000 people are infected 10 days later, how many people would a projection show to be infected at $t = 14$ days?

STEP 1 Find the solution to the differential equation.

Write the general solution with $y_0 = 1500$.	$y = 1500e^{kt}$
Substitute $y(10) = 4000$.	$4000 = 1500e^{k(10)}$
Divide by 1500.	$\dfrac{4000}{1500} = e^{10k}$
Take the natural log of both sides.	$\ln\left(\dfrac{4000}{1500}\right) = 10k$
Solve for k.	$k \approx 0.09808$

Therefore, the solution to the differential equation is $y \approx 1500e^{(0.09808)t}$.

STEP 2 Find the value of $y(14)$.

Substitute $t = 14$ into the solution.	$y = 1500e^{(0.09808)(14)}$
Simplify.	$\approx 5{,}921$ people

Need More

HELP ?

For help with exponential decay, go to *Exponential Decay* in *Advanced Algebra* (p. 2000).

Half-Life

The **half-life** of a substance is the time it takes a substance to undergo radioactive decay to half of the original amount. You can model half-life using the equation for exponential decay, $\frac{dy}{dt} = ky$. The solution is then $y = y_0 e^{kt}$, where y_0 is the original amount of the substance.

EXAMPLE 5

A given substance has a half-life of 120 years. How many years would it take for 30 grams of the substance to decay to 1 gram?

STEP 1 Use the half-life to determine the value of k.

Write the solution with $\frac{y}{y_0} = \frac{1}{2}$ at $t = 120$.

$$\frac{1}{2} = e^{120k}$$

Take the natural log of both sides.

$$\ln\frac{1}{2} = 120k$$

Solve for k.

$$k \approx -0.006$$

Therefore, the half-life equation with $y_0 = 30$ is $y = 30e^{-(0.006)t}$.

STEP 2 Solve for t when $y = 1$ gram.

Substitute $y = 1$.

$$1 = 30e^{-(0.006)t}$$

Divide by 30.

$$\frac{1}{30} = e^{-(0.006)t}$$

Take the natural log of both sides.

$$\ln\frac{1}{30} = -0.006t$$

Solve for t.

$$t \approx 567 \text{ years}$$

EXAMPLE 6

The half-life of cobalt-60 is 5.27 years. How much of a 25-gram sample of cobalt-60 would be left after 2.25 years?

STEP 1 Use the half-life to determine the value of k.

Write the solution with $\frac{y}{y_0} = \frac{1}{2}$ at $t = 5.27$.

$$\frac{1}{2} = e^{(5.27)k}$$

Take the natural log of both sides.

$$\ln\frac{1}{2} = (5.27)k$$

Solve for k.

$$k \approx -0.1315$$

Therefore, the half-life equation with $y_0 = 25$ is $y = 25e^{-(0.1315)t}$.

STEP 2 Solve for y when $t = 2.25$ years.

Substitute $t = 2.25$.

$$y = 25e^{-(0.1315)(2.25)}$$

Solve for y.

$$y \approx 19 \text{ grams}$$

Newton's Law of Cooling

Newton's Law of Cooling states that the rate of change of the temperature of an object is proportional to the difference between the object's temperature and the temperature of the substance surrounding the object. You can describe the rate of cooling using the equation for exponential decay written in the form $\frac{dT}{dt} = k\Delta T$, where ΔT is the difference in temperature.

The solution to the differential equation is $\Delta T = Ce^{kt}$. For other exponential growth and decay equations, you can simply substitute the initial value of the function for C. For cooling problems, however, you must calculate C using the temperature of the substance surrounding the object, as shown in Example 7.

EXAMPLE 7

A cup of coffee with a temperature of 120°C is placed in an office whose thermostat is kept at 65°C. If the temperature of the coffee is 109°C after 15 minutes, find the temperature of the coffee after 22 minutes.

STEP 1 Use given information with Newton's Law of Cooling.

Write the differential equation using $\Delta T = T - 65$. $\qquad \frac{dT}{dt} = k(T - 65)$

Write the solution to the differential equation. $\qquad T - 65 = Ce^{kt}$

STEP 2 Determine the value of C.

Use the initial condition $T(0) = 120$. $\qquad 120 - 65 = Ce^{k(0)}$

Apply $e^0 = 1$. $\qquad 120 - 65 = C(1)$

Solve for C. $\qquad C = 55$

Therefore, the solution to the differential equation is $T - 65 = 55e^{kt}$.

STEP 3 Solve for k.

Substitute $T = 109$ and $t = 15$. $\qquad 109 - 65 = 55e^{15k}$

Simplify. $\qquad \frac{4}{5} = e^{15k}$

Take the natural log of both sides. $\qquad \ln\left(\frac{4}{5}\right) = 15k$

Solve for k. $\qquad k \approx -0.015$

Therefore, the solution to the differential equation is $T \approx 55e^{-(0.015)t} + 65$

STEP 4 Find the temperature after 22 minutes.

Substitute $t = 22$. $\qquad T \approx 55e^{-(0.015)(22)} + 65$

Simplify. $\qquad \approx 105°C$

Therefore, the coffee will be approximately 105°C after 22 minutes in the office.

SEARCH

To see step-by-step videos of these problems, enter the page number into the SWadvantage.com Search Bar.

Logarithmic, Exponential, and Transcendental Functions

What Came Before?
- Rules of differentiation
- Rules of integration

What's This About?
- Differentiation and integration rules for exponential functions
- Differentiation and integration rules for logarithmic functions
- Derivatives of inverse trigonometric functions

Practical Apps
- The intensity of sunlight under water at various depths can be estimated by using a differential equation.
- Differential equations can be used to model the reduction in cases of an infectious disease as it is being eradicated.

Just for FUN!

Q: What was the calculus expert hoping to get?

A: A Cauchy job.

CONTENTS | UPLOAD | DOWNLOAD | *Calculus*

You can find more practice problems online by visiting:
www.SWadvantage.com

Derivatives: Exponential Rule

Base *e*

The derivative of the exponential function e^x is the simplest derivative in calculus since the derivative is the same as the original function. Substitution and the Chain Rule make it possible to differentiate exponential functions with more complicated exponents.

Need More

HELP ?

For help with rules of differentiation, go to *Sum, Difference, and Constant Rules* (p. 2170); *Power, Product, and Quotient Rules* (p. 2172); and *Chain Rule* (p. 2176).

EXAMPLE 1

Find the derivative of $y = 4e^x$.

Write the original problem.	$y = 4e^x$
Use the Constant Multiple Rule.	$y' = 4\dfrac{d}{dx}(e^x)$
Differentiate.	$y' = 4e^x$

EXAMPLE 2

Find the derivative of $y = x^2 e^x$.

Write the original problem.	$y = x^2 e^x$
Use the Product Rule.	$y' = x^2 \dfrac{d}{dx}(e^x) + e^x \dfrac{d}{dx}(x^2)$
Differentiate.	$y' = x^2 e^x + 2xe^x$

EXAMPLE 3

Find: $\dfrac{d}{dx} e^{-\sqrt{x}}$

Let $u = -\sqrt{x}$.	$\dfrac{d}{dx}\left(e^{-\sqrt{x}}\right) = \dfrac{d}{dx}(e^u)$
Use the Chain Rule.	$= e^u \dfrac{du}{dx}$
Substitute back $u = -\sqrt{x}$.	$= e^{-\sqrt{x}} \dfrac{d}{dx}(-\sqrt{x})$
Differentiate.	$= e^{-\sqrt{x}}\left(-\dfrac{1}{2}x^{-\frac{1}{2}}\right)$
Simplify.	$= -\dfrac{e^{-\sqrt{x}}}{2\sqrt{x}}$
	$= -\dfrac{1}{2e^{\sqrt{x}}\sqrt{x}}$

GOT TO KNOW!

Derivative of e^x

$$\dfrac{d}{dx}e^x = e^x$$

$$\dfrac{d}{dx}e^u = e^u \dfrac{du}{dx}$$

SEARCH

To see step-by-step videos of these problems, enter the page number into the SWadvantage.com Search Bar.

EXAMPLE 4

Find the equation for the slope of the tangent line to the curve of $y = 3e^{2x}$.

The slope is the derivative of the function. $\dfrac{dy}{dx} = \dfrac{d}{dx}(3e^{2x})$

Let $u = 2x$. $= 3\dfrac{d}{dx}(e^u)$

Use the Chain Rule. $= 3\,e^u\dfrac{du}{dx}$

Substitute back $u = 2x$. $= 3e^u\dfrac{d}{dx}(2x)$

Differentiate. $= 3e^{2x}(2)$

Simplify. $= 6e^{2x}$

EXAMPLE 5

Find the equation of the tangent line to the curve $y = \dfrac{4\cos x}{e^x}$ when $x = 0$.

STEP 1 Find the slope of the tangent line, $\dfrac{dy}{dx}$, when $x = 0$.

Use the Quotient Rule. $\dfrac{dy}{dx} = \dfrac{e^x\frac{d}{dx}(4\cos x) - 4\cos x\frac{d}{dx}(e^x)}{(e^x)^2}$

Differentiate. $= \dfrac{-4e^x \sin x - 4e^x \cos x}{e^{2x}}$

Substitute $x = 0$. $= \dfrac{-4e^{(0)} \sin(0) - 4e^{(0)} \cos(0)}{e^{2(0)}}$

Evaluate. $= \dfrac{-4(1)(0) - 4(1)(1)}{1}$

Simplify. $= -4$

STEP 2 Find y when $x = 0$.

Use the original function. $y = \dfrac{4\cos x}{e^x}$

Substitute $x = 0$. $= \dfrac{4\cos(0)}{e^{(0)}}$

Simplify. $= \dfrac{4(1)}{1} = 4$

STEP 3 Find the equation of the tangent line.

Use the point-slope equation of a line. $(y - y_1) = \dfrac{dy}{dx}(x - x_1)$

Substitute $(0, 4)$ and $\dfrac{dy}{dx} = -4$. $(y - 4) = -4(x - 0)$

Simplify. $y = -4x + 4$

Bases Other Than *e*

You can find the derivative of exponential functions with constant bases using the derivative formula for exponential functions. This formula is useful for determining the rate of change of many real-world situations such as interest rate and population growth.

EXAMPLE 6

Find the derivative of $y = 4^x$.

Write the original problem. $\quad\quad\quad\quad\quad\quad\quad y = 4^x$

Use the formula for the derivative of a^x. $\quad y' = (\ln 4)(4^x)$

EXAMPLE 7

Find the derivative of $y = x^3(5^{\sqrt{x}})$.

Write the original problem. $\quad\quad y = x^3(5^{\sqrt{x}})$

Use the Product Rule. $\quad\quad y' = x^3 \frac{d}{dx}(5^{\sqrt{x}}) + 5^{\sqrt{x}} \frac{d}{dx}(x^3)$

Use the Chain Rule. $\quad\quad y' = x^3(\ln 5)(5^{\sqrt{x}})\frac{d}{dx}(\sqrt{x}) + 5^{\sqrt{x}}\frac{d}{dx}(x^3)$

Differentiate. $\quad\quad\quad y' = x^3(\ln 5)(5^{\sqrt{x}})\left(\frac{1}{2}x^{-\frac{1}{2}}\right) + 5^{\sqrt{x}}(3x^2)$

EXAMPLE 8

Find: $\frac{d}{dx}\left[(2^x)(\sin x)\right]$

Use the Product Rule. $\quad\quad \frac{d}{dx}\left[(2^x)(\sin x)\right] = 2^x\frac{d}{dx}(\sin x) + \sin x\frac{d}{dx}(2^x)$

Differentiate. $\quad\quad\quad\quad\quad\quad\quad\quad\quad\quad = 2^x(\cos x) + (\sin x)(\ln 2)(2^x)$

Watch Out !

Unlike the derivative of e^x, the derivative of a function like 4^x is not the same as the original function 4^x.

GOT TO KNOW !

Derivative of Exponential Functions With Base *a*

$$\frac{d}{dx}a^x = (\ln a)a^x$$

$$\frac{d}{dx}a^u = (\ln a)a^u\frac{du}{dx}$$

EXAMPLE 9

Find the equation for the slope of the tangent line to the curve of $y = \frac{6^x}{x+1}$.

Use the Quotient Rule.

$$\frac{dy}{dx} = \frac{(x+1)\frac{d}{dx}(6^x) - 6^x\frac{d}{dx}(x+1)}{(x+1)^2}$$

Differentiate.

$$= \frac{(x+1)(\ln 6)(6^x) - 6^x(1)}{(x+1)^2}$$

Simplify.

$$= \frac{(x+1)(\ln 6)(6^x) - 6^x}{(x+1)^2}$$

SEARCH

To see step-by-step videos of these problems, enter the page number into the SWadvantage.com Search Bar.

EXAMPLE 10

Find the rate of change of inflation for time $t > 0$ given the inflation equation $y = 500(1.03)^t$.

The rate of change is the derivative of the function.

Use the Constant Multiple Rule.

$$\frac{dy}{dt} = 500\frac{d}{dt}(1.03^t)$$

Differentiate.

$$= 500(\ln 1.03)(1.03^t)$$

EXAMPLE 11

Determine whether the rate of change is increasing or decreasing in Example 10. Explain the meaning of the your answer.

Find the second derivative.

$$\frac{d^2y}{dt^2} = \frac{d}{dt}[500(\ln 1.03)(1.03^t)]$$

Differentiate.

$$= 500(\ln 1.03)(\ln 1.03)(1.03^t)$$

Since the second derivative is positive for any $t > 0$, the rate of change is increasing. This means that the rate of inflation is increasing as time increases.

Need More HELP?

For help with increasing and decreasing functions, go to *Relationships Between f, f', f"* (p. 2190).

EXAMPLE 12

Find the rate of depreciation of the value of a $16,000 car when $t = 3$ years if the equation for its value is $y = 16,000(0.85)^t$.

The rate of change is the derivative of the function.

Use the Constant Multiple rule.

$$\frac{dy}{dt} = 16,000\frac{d}{dt}(0.85^t)$$

Differentiate.

$$= 16,000(\ln 0.85)(0.85^t)$$

Evaluate the rate of change when $t = 3$.

$$= 16,000(\ln 0.85)(0.85^{(3)})$$

Simplify.

$$= -1596.91$$

Therefore, when $t = 3$ years, the value of the car is depreciating at a rate of $1596.91 a year.

Derivatives: Logarithmic Rule

Natural Logarithms

The inverse function of e^x is the natural logarithm function $\ln x$. The derivative of the natural logarithm function is the reciprocal of the x-value of the point of differentiation.

EXAMPLE 1

Find the derivative of $y = \ln 3x$.

METHOD 1

Use the Product Property of Logarithms.	$y = \ln 3 + \ln x$
Differentiate.	$\dfrac{dy}{dx} = 0 + \dfrac{1}{x}$
Simplify.	$= \dfrac{1}{x}$

METHOD 2

Use the Chain Rule. Let $u = 3x$.	$\dfrac{dy}{dx} = \dfrac{du}{dx}\dfrac{d}{du}(\ln u)$
Differentiate $\ln u$.	$= \dfrac{1}{u}\dfrac{du}{dx}$
Substitute back $u = 3x$.	$= \dfrac{1}{3x}\dfrac{d}{dx}(3x)$
Differentiate $3x$.	$= \dfrac{1}{3x}(3) = \dfrac{1}{x}$

EXAMPLE 2

Find the derivative of $y = \ln x^3$.

METHOD 1

Use the Power Property of Logarithms.	$y = \ln x^3 = 3\ln x$
Differentiate.	$\dfrac{dy}{dx} = 3\left(\dfrac{1}{x}\right)$
Simplify.	$= \dfrac{3}{x}$

METHOD 2

Use the Chain Rule. Let $u = 3x^2$.	$\dfrac{dy}{dx} = \dfrac{du}{dx}\dfrac{d}{du}(\ln u)$
Differentiate $\ln u$.	$= \dfrac{1}{u}\dfrac{du}{dx}$
Substitute back $u = 3x^2$.	$= \dfrac{1}{x^3}\dfrac{d}{dx}(x^3)$
Differentiate $3x$.	$= \dfrac{1}{x^3}(3x^2) = \dfrac{3}{x}$

SEARCH 🔍

To see step-by-step videos of these problems, enter the page number into the SWadvantage.com Search Bar.

EXAMPLE 3

Find the instantaneous rate of change of $y = \ln(4x^2 + x + 1)$ when $x = 1$.

The instantaneous rate of change is the derivative of the function.

Use the Chain Rule. Let $u = 4x^2 + x + 1$. 　　$\dfrac{dy}{dx} = \dfrac{du}{dx}\dfrac{d}{du}(\ln u)$

Differentiate $\ln u$. 　　$= \dfrac{1}{u}\dfrac{du}{dx}$

Substitute back $u = 4x^2 + x + 1$. 　　$= \dfrac{1}{4x^2 + x + 1}\dfrac{d}{dx}(4x^2 + x + 1)$

Differentiate $4x^2 + x + 1$. 　　$= \dfrac{1}{4x^2 + x + 1}(8x + 1)$

Simplify. 　　$= \dfrac{8x + 1}{4x^2 + x + 1}$

Substitute $x = 1$. 　　$= \dfrac{8(1) + 1}{4(1)^2 + (1) + 1}$

Simplify. 　　$= \dfrac{3}{2}$

Therefore, the instantaneous rate of change when $x = 1$ is $\dfrac{3}{2}$.

EXAMPLE 4

Find the slope of the tangent line of $y = \ln(1 - x)^2$ when $x = 0$.

The slope of the tangent line is the derivative of the function.

Use the Power Property of Logarithms to rewrite the function. 　　$y = 2\ln(1 - x)$

Use the Chain Rule. Let $u = 1 - x$. 　　$\dfrac{dy}{dx} = 2\dfrac{du}{dx}\dfrac{d}{du}(\ln u)$

Differentiate $\ln u$. 　　$= 2\dfrac{1}{u}\dfrac{du}{dx}$

Substitute back $u = 1 - x$. 　　$= \dfrac{2}{1 - x}\dfrac{d}{dx}(1 - x)$

Differentiate $u = 1 - x$. 　　$= \dfrac{2}{1 - x}(-1)$

Simplify. 　　$= \dfrac{2}{x - 1}$

Substitute $x = 0$. 　　$= \dfrac{2}{0 - 1}$

Simplify. 　　$= -2$

Therefore, the slope of the tangent line when $x = 0$ is -2.

Logarithms with Base *a*

The function $\log_a x$ is the inverse of the exponential function a^x. The derivative of logarithmic functions with base *a* is the reciprocal of the logarithm's argument times one over the natural logarithm of the base.

EXAMPLE 5

Find the derivative of $y = \log_4 3x$.

METHOD 1

Use the Product Property of Logarithms.	$y = \log_4 3 + \log_4 x$
Differentiate.	$y' = 0 + \dfrac{1}{\ln 4}\left(\dfrac{1}{x}\right)$
Simplify.	$= \dfrac{1}{x \ln 4}$

METHOD 2

Use the Change of Base Formula to use natural logarithms.	$y = \log_4 3x = \dfrac{\ln 3x}{\ln 4}$
Write the derivative using the Constant Multiple Rule.	$y' = \dfrac{1}{\ln 4}\dfrac{d}{dx}(\ln 3x)$
Differentiate.	$y' = \dfrac{1}{\ln 4}\left(\dfrac{1}{3x}\right)(3) = \dfrac{1}{x \ln 4}$

METHOD 3

Use the Chain Rule. Let $u = 3x$.	$\dfrac{dy}{dx} = \dfrac{d}{dx}\log_4 u$
Differentiate $\log_4 u$.	$= \dfrac{1}{\ln 4}\left(\dfrac{1}{u}\right)\dfrac{du}{dx}$
Substitute back $u = 3x$.	$= \dfrac{1}{\ln 4}\left(\dfrac{1}{3x}\right)\dfrac{d}{dx}(3x)$
Differentiate $3x$.	$= \dfrac{1}{\ln 4}\left(\dfrac{1}{3x}\right)(3)$
Simplify.	$= \dfrac{1}{x \ln 4}$

GOT TO KNOW!

Derivative of $\log_a x$

$$\frac{d}{dx}\log_a x = \frac{1}{\ln a}\left(\frac{1}{x}\right)$$

$$\frac{d}{dx}\log_a u = \frac{1}{\ln a}\left(\frac{1}{u}\right)\frac{du}{dx}$$

EXAMPLE 6

Find the equation for the slope of the line tangent to $y = \log_{10}(\sin 2x)$.

The slope of the tangent line is the derivative of the function.

Write the original equation. $\qquad\qquad y = \log_{10}(\sin 2x)$

Write the derivative with respect to x. $\qquad \dfrac{dy}{dx} = \dfrac{d}{dx}\log_{10}(\sin 2x)$

Let $u = \sin 2x$. $\qquad\qquad\qquad = \dfrac{d}{dx}\log_{10} u$

Use the Chain Rule. $\qquad\qquad\qquad = \dfrac{1}{\ln 10}\left(\dfrac{1}{u}\right)\dfrac{du}{dx}$

Substitute back $u = \sin 2x$. $\qquad\qquad = \dfrac{1}{\ln 10}\left(\dfrac{1}{\sin 2x}\right)\dfrac{d}{dx}(\sin 2x)$

Differentiate $3x$. $\qquad\qquad\qquad = \dfrac{1}{\ln 10}\left(\dfrac{1}{\sin 2x}\right)(2\cos 2x)$

Simplify. $\qquad\qquad\qquad\qquad = \dfrac{2\cot 2x}{\ln 10}$

Therefore, the equation for the slope of the tangent line is $y' = \dfrac{2\cot 2x}{\ln 10}$.

SEARCH 🔍

To see step-by-step videos of these problems, enter the page number into the SWadvantage.com Search Bar.

EXAMPLE 7

Use logarithms to find the derivative of $y = x^x$.

Write the original equation. $\qquad\qquad\qquad y = x^x$

Take the log base 10 of both sides. $\qquad\quad \log y = \log x^x$

Use the Power Property of Logarithms. $\quad \log y = x \log x$

Differentiate both sides with respect to x. $\quad \dfrac{d}{dx}(\log y) = \dfrac{d}{dx}(x \log x)$

Use the Product Property of Differentiation. $\quad \dfrac{d}{dx}(\log y) = (x)\dfrac{d}{dx}(\log x) + (\log x)\dfrac{d}{dx}(x)$

Differentiate. $\qquad\qquad \left(\dfrac{1}{\ln 10}\right)\left(\dfrac{1}{y}\right)\dfrac{dy}{dx} = (x)\left(\dfrac{1}{\ln 10}\right)\left(\dfrac{1}{x}\right) + (\log x)(1)$

Simplify by canceling the x terms. $\quad \left(\dfrac{1}{\ln 10}\right)\left(\dfrac{1}{y}\right)\dfrac{dy}{dx} = \dfrac{1}{\ln 10} + \log x$

Solve for $\dfrac{dy}{dx}$. $\qquad\qquad\qquad \dfrac{dy}{dx} = (y \ln 10)\left(\dfrac{1}{\ln 10} + \log x\right)$

Simplify by distributing $\ln 10$. $\qquad\qquad = y(1 + \ln 10 \log x)$

Substitute the expression for y. $\qquad\qquad = x^x(1 + \ln 10 \log x)$

Need More

HELP ❓

Remember: Log x is called the common logarithm and has a base of 10.

Exponential Integrals

Integrating Base *e* Exponential Functions

The integral of the exponential function e^x is the function itself. If x is replaced by a function of x, you can solve the integral by u-substitution.

EXAMPLE 1

Find: $\int \dfrac{e^{\sqrt{x}}}{2\sqrt{x}} \, dx$

STEP 1 Determine u and du.   Let $u = \sqrt{x}$

   Differentiate. $\dfrac{du}{dx} = \dfrac{1}{2} x^{-\frac{1}{2}}$

   Write the equation in differential form. $du = \dfrac{1}{2\sqrt{x}} \, dx$

STEP 2 Solve the integral using u-substitution.

   Substitute u and du. $\int \dfrac{e^{\sqrt{x}}}{2\sqrt{x}} \, dx = \int e^u \, du$

   Integrate. $= e^u + C$
   Substitute back $u = \sqrt{x}$. $= e^{\sqrt{x}} + C$

EXAMPLE 2

Find: $\int \dfrac{4 + e^x}{e^{2x}} \, dx$

STEP 1 Simplify the integral.

   Separate the fraction. $\int \dfrac{4 + e^x}{e^{2x}} \, dx = \int \left(\dfrac{4}{e^{2x}} + \dfrac{e^x}{e^{2x}} \right) dx$

   Write with negative exponents. $= \int (4e^{-2x} + e^{-x}) \, dx$
   Use the Sum Property of Integration. $= \int 4e^{-2x} \, dx + \int e^{-x} \, dx$

STEP 2 Use u-substitution for each integral.

   Let $u = -2x$ Let $v = -x$

   $\dfrac{du}{dx} = -2$ $\dfrac{dv}{dx} = -1$

   $-2\,du = 4\,dx$ $-dv = dx$

STEP 3 Solve the integral.

   Substitute u, du, v, and dv. $\int \dfrac{4 + e^x}{e^{2x}} \, dx = -2\int e^u \, du - \int e^v \, dv$

   Integrate. $= -2e^u - e^v + C$

   Substitute back $u = -2x$ and $v = -x$. $= -2e^{-2x} - e^{-x} + C$

   Rewrite with positive exponents. $= \dfrac{-2}{e^{2x}} - \dfrac{1}{e^x} + C$

Integrating Base *a* Exponential Functions

The integral of the exponential function a^x is the function itself divided by ln *a*. As with base *e* exponentials, if *x* is replaced by a function of *x*, you can use *u*-substitution before integrating.

EXAMPLE 3

Find: $\int 3^x \, dx$

Use the formula. $\quad \int 3^x \, dx = \frac{1}{\ln 3} 3^x + C$

EXAMPLE 4

Find: $\int x(4^{x^2}) \, dx$

STEP 1 Determine *u* and *du*.

Differentiate.

Write the equation in differential form.

Let $u = x^2$

$\frac{du}{dx} = 2x$

$\frac{1}{2} du = x \, dx$

STEP 2 Solve the integral using *u*-substitution.

Substitute *u* and *du*.

Integrate.

Substitute back $u = x^2$.

$\int x(4^{x^2}) \, dx = \frac{1}{2} \int 4^u \, du$

$= \frac{1}{2} \left(\frac{1}{\ln 4}\right)(4^u) + C$

$= \frac{1}{2} \left(\frac{1}{\ln 4}\right)(4^{x^2}) + C$

EXAMPLE 5

Find: $\int 5^{\cos x} \sin x \, dx$

STEP 1 Determine *u* and *du*.

Differentiate.

Write the equation in differential form.

Let $u = \cos x$

$\frac{du}{dx} = -\sin x$

$-du = \sin x \, dx$

STEP 2 Solve the integral using *u*-substitution.

Substitute *u* and *du*.

Integrate.

Substitute back $u = \cos x$.

$\int 5^{\cos x} \sin x \, dx = -\int 5^u \, du$

$= -\left(\frac{1}{\ln 5}\right)(5^u) + C$

$= -\left(\frac{1}{\ln 5}\right)(5^{\cos x}) + C$

SEARCH

To see step-by-step videos of these problems, enter the page number into the SWadvantage.com Search Bar.

Logarithmic Integrals

Integrating $\frac{1}{x}$

According to the Power Rule for Integration, $\int x^n\, dx = \frac{x^{n+1}}{n+1} + C$, but this rule cannot be applied if $n = -1$. The result would be $\frac{x^0}{0}$, which is undefined. Instead, the integral of $\frac{1}{x}$ is the function whose derivative is $\frac{1}{x}$. The derivative of $\ln x$ is $\frac{1}{x}$, where $x > 0$. Therefore, the integral of $\frac{1}{x}$ is $|\ln x|$.

EXAMPLE 1

Find: $\int \frac{3}{x}\, dx$

Use the Constant Multiple Property.

$$\int \frac{3}{x}\, dx = 3\int \frac{1}{x}\, dx$$

Use the formula for the integral of $\frac{1}{x}$.

$$= 3 \ln |x| + C$$

EXAMPLE 2

SEARCH

To see step-by-step videos of these problems, enter the page number into the SWadvantage.com Search Bar.

Find: $\int \frac{1}{x+1}\, dx$

Use u-substitution. Let $u = x + 1$, $du = dx$.

$$\int \frac{1}{x+1}\, dx = \int \frac{1}{u}\, du$$

Use the formula for the integral of $\frac{1}{x}$.

$$= \ln |u| + C$$

Substitute back $u = x + 1$.

$$= \ln |x + 1| + C$$

EXAMPLE 3

Find: $\int \frac{x^2 + 2x + 1}{x^3}\, dx$

Separate the terms.

$$\int \frac{x^2 + 2x + 1}{x^3}\, dx = \int \left(\frac{1}{x} + \frac{2}{x^2} + \frac{1}{x^3} \right) dx$$

Use the Sum Property for Integrals.

$$= \int \frac{1}{x}\, dx + \int \frac{2}{x^2}\, dx + \int \frac{1}{x^3}\, dx$$

Use negative exponents.

$$= \int \frac{1}{x}\, dx + \int 2x^{-2}\, dx + \int x^{-3}\, dx$$

Integrate.

$$= \ln |x| - \frac{2}{x} - \frac{1}{2x^2} + C$$

EXAMPLE 4

Find: $\int_0^{\frac{\pi}{4}} \frac{\cos x}{\sin x + 1}\, dx$

STEP 1 Determine u and du for u-substitution.

Let $u = \sin x + 1$

Differentiate.

$\dfrac{du}{dx} = \cos x$

Write the equation in differential form.

$du = \cos x\, dx$

STEP 2 Solve the integral.

Rewrite in terms of u.

$\int_0^{\frac{\pi}{4}} \dfrac{\cos x}{\sin x + 1}\, dx = \int_{x=0}^{x=\frac{\pi}{4}} \dfrac{1}{u}\, du$

Integrate.

$= \left[\ln |u|\right]_{x=0}^{x=\frac{\pi}{4}}$

Substitute back $u = \sin x + 1$.

$= \left[\ln |\sin x + 1|\right]_0^{\frac{\pi}{4}}$

Evaluate at the endpoints.

$= \ln \left|\sin\!\left(\dfrac{\pi}{4}\right) + 1\right| - \ln |\sin 0 + 1|$

Simplify.

≈ 0.535

> **Watch Out !**
>
> When using u-substitution to evaluate a definite integral, remember that the limits of integration apply to x, not to u.

EXAMPLE 5

Find: $\int_1^2 \frac{1 + 6x \ln 3x}{x \ln 3x}\, dx$

STEP 1 Determine u and du for u-substitution.

Let $u = \ln 3x$

Differentiate.

$\dfrac{du}{dx} = \dfrac{1}{x}$

Write in differential form.

$du = \dfrac{1}{x}\, dx$

STEP 2 Solve the integral.

Separate the terms.

$\int_1^2 \dfrac{1 + 6x \ln 3x}{x \ln 3x}\, dx = \int_1^2 \dfrac{1}{x \ln 3x}\, dx + \int_1^2 6\, dx$

Rewrite the first integral in terms of u.

$= \int_{x=1}^{x=2} \dfrac{1}{u}\, du + \int_1^2 6\, dx$

Integrate.

$= \left[\ln |u|\right]_{x=1}^{x=2} + 6x|_1^2$

Substitute back $u = \ln 3x$.

$= \left[\left|\ln |\ln 3x|\right|\right]_1^2 + + 6x|_1^2$

Evaluate at the endpoints.

$= \left|\ln |(\ln 3)(2)|\right| - \left|\ln |(\ln 3)(1)|\right|$
$\quad + 6(2 - 1)$

Simplify.

≈ 6.693

Inverse Trigonometric Functions

Derivatives of Inverse Trigonometric Functions

The derivatives of inverse trigonometric functions are not trigonometric functions themselves but rational functions. Memorizing the formulas in the *Got To Know!* box below is the best way to prepare for differentiating problems involving inverse trigonometric functions.

Need More HELP?

For more help with inverse trigonometric functions, go to *Inverse Sine Function* in *Trigonometry* (Book 1, p. 1022).

EXAMPLE 1

Find y' if $y = 2\sin^{-1} x$.

STEP 1 Determine u and $\dfrac{dy}{dx}$.   Let $u = x$ $\dfrac{du}{dx} = 1$

STEP 2 Find the derivative. $\dfrac{dy}{dx} = 2\dfrac{d}{dx}(\sin^{-1} x)$

Substitute $u = x$. $= 2\dfrac{d}{dx}(\sin^{-1} u)$

Differentiate. $= (2)\dfrac{du/dx}{\sqrt{1 - u^2}}, |u| < 1$

Write in terms of x. $= \dfrac{2}{\sqrt{1 - x^2}}$

Ways to REMEMBER

Notice that the formulas for the co-functions (cosine, cosecant and cotangent) only differ by -1 from their corresponding co-functions.

EXAMPLE 2

Find y' if $y = \tan^{-1} x^2$.

STEP 1 Determine u and $\dfrac{du}{dx}$.   Let $u = x^2$ $\dfrac{du}{dx} = 2x$

STEP 2 Find the derivative. $\dfrac{dy}{dx} = \dfrac{d}{dx}(\tan^{-1} x^2)$

Substitute $u = x^2$. $= \dfrac{d}{dx}(\tan^{-1} u)$

Differentiate. $= \dfrac{du/dx}{1 + u^2}$

Write in terms of x. $= \dfrac{2x}{1 + (x^2)^2} = \dfrac{2x}{1 + x^4}$

GOT TO KNOW!

Derivatives of Inverse Trigonometric Functions

Let $u = f(x)$.

$$\frac{d}{dx}(\sin^{-1} u) = \frac{du/dx}{\sqrt{1 - u^2}}, |u| < 1 \qquad \frac{d}{dx}(\cos^{-1} u) = \frac{-du/dx}{\sqrt{1 - u^2}}, |u| < 1 \qquad \frac{d}{dx}(\tan^{-1} u) = \frac{du/dx}{1 + u^2}$$

$$\frac{d}{dx}(\csc^{-1} u) = \frac{-du/dx}{|u|\sqrt{u^2 - 1}}, |u| > 1 \qquad \frac{d}{dx}(\sec^{-1} u) = \frac{du/dx}{|u|\sqrt{u^2 - 1}}, |u| > 1 \qquad \frac{d}{dx}(\cot^{-1} u) = \frac{-du/dx}{1 + u^2}$$

EXAMPLE 3

Find $\dfrac{dy}{dx}$ if $y = x^2 \sin^{-1} x$.

Use the Product Rule.
$$\frac{dy}{dx} = x^2\left(\frac{d}{dx}(\sin^{-1} x)\right) + (\sin^{-1} x)\left(\frac{d}{dx}(x^2)\right)$$

Differentiate.
$$= x^2\left(\frac{1}{\sqrt{1 - x^2}}\right) + (\sin^{-1} x)(2x)$$

Simplify.
$$= \frac{x^2}{\sqrt{1 - x^2}} + 2x \sin^{-1} x$$

Need More

HELP ?

Remember—Another way to write the inverse trigonometric functions is to use the prefix *arc*. For example, the inverse of sin x can be written as either $\sin^{-1}x$ or arcsin x.

EXAMPLE 4

Find $\dfrac{dy}{dx}$ if $y = \text{arcsec } 3x$.

STEP 1 Determine u and $\dfrac{du}{dx}$.   Let $u = 3x$ $\dfrac{du}{dx} = 3$

STEP 2 Find the derivative.
$$\frac{dy}{dx} = \frac{d}{dx}(\sec^{-1} 3x)$$

Substitute $u = x^2$.
$$= \frac{d}{dx}(\sec^{-1} u)$$

Use the formula for the derivative of inverse secant.
$$= \frac{du/dx}{|u|\sqrt{u^2 - 1}}$$

Write in terms of x.
$$= \frac{3}{|3x|\sqrt{(3x)^2 - 1}} = \frac{1}{|x|\sqrt{9x^2 - 1}}$$

EXAMPLE 5

Find $\dfrac{dy}{dx}$ if $y = \cos^{-1} \sqrt{5x}$.

STEP 1 Determine u and $\dfrac{du}{dx}$.   Let $u = \sqrt{5x} = (5x)^{\frac{1}{2}}$ $\dfrac{du}{dx} = \frac{1}{2}(5x)^{-\frac{1}{2}}(5) = \dfrac{5}{2\sqrt{5x}}$

STEP 2 Find the derivative.
$$\frac{dy}{dx} = \frac{d}{dx}\left(\cos^{-1} \sqrt{5x}\right)$$

Substitute $u = \sqrt{5x}$.
$$= \frac{d}{dx}(\cos^{-1} u)$$

Use the formula for the derivative of inverse cosine.
$$= \frac{-du/dx}{\sqrt{1 - u^2}}$$

Write in terms of x.
$$= \frac{-\dfrac{5}{2\sqrt{5x}}}{\sqrt{1 - \left(\sqrt{5x}\right)^2}} = \frac{-\sqrt{5}}{2\sqrt{x}\sqrt{1 - 5x}}$$

SEARCH

To see step-by-step videos of these problems, enter the page number into the SWadvantage.com Search Bar.

Integrals with Inverse Trigonometric Function Solutions

When integrating rational functions, always check to see if the function fits one of the integral formulas for the inverse trigonometric functions. In some cases, you can use algebraic manipulation to make a given function match one of the formulas.

SEARCH

To see step-by-step videos of these problems, enter the page number into the SWadvantage.com Search Bar.

EXAMPLE 6

Find: $\int \dfrac{1}{\sqrt{4-x^2}}\,dx$

Rewrite the function to match the formula for $\sin^{-1} x$.

$$\int \frac{dx}{\sqrt{4-x^2}} = \int \frac{dx}{\sqrt{2^2-x^2}}$$

Differentiate.

$$= \sin^{-1}\frac{x}{2} + C$$

EXAMPLE 7

Find: $\int \dfrac{x^2}{16+x^6}\,dx$

STEP 1 Determine u and du. Let $u = x^3$ $\dfrac{1}{3}du = x^2\,dx$

STEP 2 Evaluate the integral.

Rewrite the function to match the formula for $\tan^{-1} x$.

$$\int \frac{x^2}{16+x^6}\,dx = \int \frac{x^2}{4^2+(x^3)^2}\,dx$$

Substitute u and du.

$$= \frac{1}{3}\int \frac{1}{2^2+u^2}\,du$$

Integrate.

$$= \left(\frac{1}{3}\right)\frac{1}{4}\tan^{-1}\frac{u}{4} + C$$

Write in terms of x and simplify.

$$= \frac{1}{12}\tan^{-1}\frac{x^3}{4} + C$$

GOT TO KNOW!

Integrals with Inverse Trigonometric Function Solutions

Let $u = f(x)$ and $a > 0$.

$$\int \frac{1}{\sqrt{a^2-u^2}}\,du = \sin^{-1}\frac{u}{a} + C$$

$$\int \frac{1}{u\sqrt{u^2-a^2}}\,du = \frac{1}{a}\sec^{-1}\frac{|u|}{a} + C$$

$$\int \frac{1}{a^2+u^2}\,du = \frac{1}{a}\tan^{-1}\frac{u}{a} + C$$

EXAMPLE 8

Find: $\int \frac{x+1}{\sqrt{1-x^2}}\, dx$

STEP 1 Use algebraic manipulation to match the integrand to the formula with a $\sin^{-1} x$ solution.

Separate the integrand into two fractions. $\int \frac{x+1}{\sqrt{1-x^2}}\, dx = \int \frac{x}{\sqrt{1-x^2}}\, dx + \int \frac{1}{\sqrt{1-x^2}}\, dx$

STEP 2 Use u-substitution for the first integral. Let $u = 1 - x^2 \qquad -\frac{1}{2}\, du = x\, du$

STEP 3 Evaluate the integral.

Rewrite the first integral in terms of u. $\int \frac{x+1}{\sqrt{1-x^2}}\, dx = -\frac{1}{2} \int u^{-\frac{1}{2}}\, du + \int \frac{1}{\sqrt{1-x^2}}\, dx$

Integrate. $= -\frac{1}{2}\left(\frac{u^{\frac{1}{2}}}{\frac{1}{2}}\right) + \sin^{-1} x + C$

Write in terms of x and simplify. $= -\sqrt{1-x^2} + \sin^{-1} x + C$

EXAMPLE 9

Find: $\int \frac{1}{x^2 + 2x + 5}\, dx$

STEP 1 Use algebraic manipulation to match the integrand to the formula with a $\tan^{-1} x$ solution.

Complete the square. $x^2 + 2x + 5 = (x^2 + 2x + 1^2) + 5 - 1^2 = (x+1)^2 + 4$

STEP 2 Evaluate the integral.

Rewrite the integrand. $\int \frac{1}{x^2 + 2x + 5}\, dx = \int \frac{1}{(x+1)^2 + 4}\, dx$

Integrate. $= \frac{1}{2} \tan^{-1} \frac{(x+1)}{2} + C$

Need More HELP?

For help with completing the square, go to *Completing the Square* in *Algebra* (p. 1706).

EXAMPLE 10

Find: $\int \frac{\sin x}{\cos^2 x + 1}\, dx$

STEP 1 Determine u and du. Let $u = \cos x \qquad du = -\sin x\, dx$

STEP 2 Evaluate the integral.

Rewrite the integral in terms of u. $\int \frac{\sin x}{\cos^2 x + 1}\, dx = \int \frac{1}{u^2 + 1}\, du$

Integrate. $= \frac{1}{1} \tan^{-1} \frac{u}{1} + C$

Write in terms of x and simplify. $= \tan^{-1}(\cos x) + C$

Calculus

Limit Rules

Constant Rule	$\lim\limits_{x \to c} k = k$
Constant Multiplier Rule	$\lim\limits_{x \to c} kf(x) = k \lim\limits_{x \to c} f(x)$
Sum Rule	$\lim\limits_{x \to c} [f(x) + g(x)] = \lim\limits_{x \to c} f(x) + \lim\limits_{x \to c} g(x)$
Difference Rule	$\lim\limits_{x \to c} [f(x) - g(x)] = \lim\limits_{x \to c} f(x) - \lim\limits_{x \to c} g(x)$
Product Rule	$\lim\limits_{x \to c} [f(x) \cdot g(x)] = \lim\limits_{x \to c} f(x) \cdot \lim\limits_{x \to c} g(x)$
Quotient Rule	$\lim\limits_{x \to c} \dfrac{f(x)}{g(x)} = \dfrac{\lim\limits_{x \to c} f(x)}{\lim\limits_{x \to c} g(x)}$, if $\lim\limits_{x \to c} g(x) \neq 0$
Power Rule	$\lim\limits_{x \to c} [f(x)]^n = \left[\lim\limits_{x \to c} f(x) \right]^n$
nth Root Rule	$\lim\limits_{x \to c} \sqrt[n]{f(x)} = \sqrt[n]{\lim\limits_{x \to c} f(x)}$, if $\lim\limits_{x \to c} f(x) > 0$
Limits of Radicals	$\lim\limits_{x \to c} \sqrt[n]{x} = \sqrt[n]{c}$, for all c when n is odd, and for $c > 0$ when n is even.
Limits of Composite Functions	If $\lim\limits_{x \to c} g(x) = L$ and $\lim\limits_{x \to c} f(x) = f(L)$, then $f(g(x)) = f\left(\lim\limits_{x \to c} g(x) \right) = f(L)$.

For Derivative Rules, see the table of Derivatives on the next page, or go to pages 2170 and 2172 for constant, sum, difference, power, product, and quotient rules.

For Integral Rules, see the table of Integrals on the next page, or go to page 2234 for constant, constant multiplier, sum, difference, and power rules.

Volume of a Solid of Revolution

Disk Method (x-axis)	$V = \pi \int_a^b [R(x)]^2\, dx$
Disk Method (y-axis)	$V = \pi \int_a^b [R(y)]^2\, dy$
Washer Method (x-axis)	$V = \pi \int_a^b (f(x))^2 - (g(x))^2\, dx$
Washer Method (y-axis)	$V = \pi \int_a^b (f(y))^2 - (g(y))^2\, dy$
Shell Method (x-axis)	$V = 2\pi \int_a^b yf(y)dx$
Shell Method (y-axis)	$V = 2\pi \int_a^b xf(x)dx$

Formulas, Theorems, and Definitions

Special Trigonometric Limits	$\lim\limits_{a \to 0} \dfrac{\sin a}{a} = 1$; $\lim\limits_{a \to 0} \dfrac{1 - \cos a}{a} = 0$
Definition of a Derivative	$f'(x) = \lim\limits_{\Delta x \to 0} \dfrac{f(x + \Delta x) - f(x)}{\Delta x}$
Chain Rule	$\dfrac{d}{dx}[f(g(x))] = f'(g(x)) \cdot g'(x)$
The Mean Value Theorem	$f'(c) = \dfrac{f(b) - f(a)}{b - a}$
Area Between Two Curves	$A = \int_a^b f(x)dx - \int_a^b g(x)dx = \int_a^b [f(x) - g(x)]dx$
Fundamental Theorem of Calculus	$\int_a^b f(x)dx = F(b) - F(a)$
Second Fundamental Theorem of Calculus	$\dfrac{d}{dx} \int_a^x f(t)dt = f(x)$
The Mean Value Theorem for Integrals	$\int_a^b f(x)dx = f(c)(b - a)$
Average Value of a Function	$f(c) = \dfrac{1}{b - a} \int_a^b f(x)dx$
Integration by Parts	$\int u\,dv = uv - \int v\,du$

Volumes of Solids with Known Cross Sections

Square	$V = \int (\text{base})^2\, dx$
Semicircle	$V = \dfrac{\pi}{8} \int (\text{base})^2\, dx$
Right Isosceles Triangle	$V = \dfrac{1}{2} \int (\text{base})^2\, dx$
Equilateral Triangle	$V = \dfrac{\sqrt{3}}{4} \int (\text{base})^2\, dx$

Derivatives

Function, f	Derivative, $\frac{df}{dx}$	Function, f	Derivative, $\frac{df}{dx}$	Function, f	Derivative, $\frac{df}{dx}$
c	0	$\frac{u}{v}$	$\frac{(vu' - uv')}{v^2}$	arc tan x	$\frac{1}{(1+x^2)}$
x	1	$f[u(x)]$	$\frac{df}{du} \cdot \frac{du}{dx}$	arc cot x	$-\frac{1}{(1+x^2)}$
kx	k	$\sin x$	$\cos x$	arc sec x	$\frac{1}{|x|\sqrt{x^2-1}}$
x^n	nx^{n-1}	$\cos x$	$-\sin x$	arc csc x	$-\frac{1}{|x|\sqrt{x^2-1}}$
$k[g(x)]$	$kg'(x)$	$\tan x$	$\sec^2 x$	e^x	e^x
$\frac{1}{x}$	$-\frac{1}{x^2}$	$\cot x$	$-\csc^2 x$	a^x	$a^x \ln a$
$\frac{1}{x^n}$	$-\frac{n}{x^{n+1}}$	$\sec x$	$\sec x \tan x$	$\ln x$	$\frac{1}{x}$
$\sqrt{x}$	$\frac{1}{2\sqrt{x}}$	$\csc x$	$\csc x \cot x$	$\log_a x$	$\frac{1}{x \ln a}$
$u + v$	$u' + v'$	arc sin x	$\frac{1}{\sqrt{1-x^2}}$	$f^{-1}(x)$	$\frac{1}{\frac{d}{dx}\left(f(f^{-1}(x))\right)}$
uv	$uv' + vu'$	arc cos x	$-\frac{1}{\sqrt{1-x^2}}$		

Integrals

Function, f	Integral, $\int f\, dx$	Function, f	Integral, $\int f\, dx$	Function, f	Integral, $\int f\, dx$
k	kx	e^x	e^x	$\sec^2 x$	$\tan x$
x	$\frac{1}{2}x^2$	$\ln x$	$x \ln x - x$	$\csc^2 x$	$-\cot x$
x^n	$\frac{x^{n+1}}{(n+1)}\ \ n \neq -1$	$\sin x$	$-\cos x$	$\sec x \tan x$	$\sec x$
$\frac{1}{x}$	$\ln x$	$\cos x$	$\sin x$	$\csc x \cot x$	$-\csc x$
$\frac{1}{x^n}$	$-\frac{1}{(n-1)x^{n-1}}\ \ n \neq 1$	$\tan x$	$\ln \sec x$	$\frac{1}{(ax+b)}$	$\left(\frac{1}{a}\right)\ln(ax+b)$
$\sqrt{x}$	$\frac{2}{3}x^{\frac{3}{2}}$	$\cot x$	$\ln \sin x$	$\frac{1}{(x^2+a^2)}$	$\left(\frac{1}{a}\right)\arctan\left(\frac{x}{a}\right)$
$\frac{1}{\sqrt{x}}$	$2\sqrt{x}$	$\sec x$	$\ln(\tan x + \sec x)$	$\frac{1}{(x^2-a^2)}$	$\left(\frac{1}{2a}\right)\ln\frac{(y-a)}{(x+a)}$
$x^{\frac{n}{r}}$	$\frac{rx^{\left(\frac{n}{r}\right)+1}}{r+n}$	$\csc x$	$\ln(\csc x - \cot x)$	$\frac{1}{\sqrt{(a^2-x^2)}}$	$\arcsin\left(\frac{x}{a}\right)$
$x^{-\frac{n}{r}}$	$\frac{r}{(r-n)x^{\left(\frac{n}{r}\right)-1}}$	$\sin^2 x$	$\frac{1}{2}x - \frac{1}{2}\sin x \cos x$	$\frac{1}{\sqrt{(x^2 \pm a^2)}}$	$\ln\left(x + \sqrt{(x^2 \pm a^2)}\right)$

Symbols

Foundations of Mathematics

>	is greater than	46
<	is less than	46
=	is equal to	46
°	degrees of an angle	50
+	addition	56
−	subtraction	62
×	multiplication	68
÷	division	74
$\overline{)}$	division	76
10^2	exponent; power of ten	94
3 · 4; 3(4)	multiplication	96
$\parallel$	is parallel to	129
$\perp$	is perpendicular to	130
$\overline{AB}$	line segment AB	132
AB	length of $\overline{AB}$	132
$\overleftrightarrow{AB}$	line AB	132
$\overrightarrow{AB}$	ray AB	133
$\angle A$	angle A	136
°	degrees	137
⌐	right angle symbol	156
|	tally mark	182
%	percent	196

Numbers and Operations

•	decimal point	216
>	greater than	222
<	less than	222
=	equal to	222
R	real numbers	268
Q	rational numbers	268
Z	integers numbers	268
W	whole numbers	268
N	natural numbers	268
$\sqrt{4}$	square root	268
$0.\overline{3}$	repeating decimal; 0.33 . . .	270
3^4	exponent	294
$\frac{1}{a}$	reciprocal	346
$a : b, \frac{a}{b}$	ratio	364
%	percent	380
. . .	and so on	434

Measurement

°F	degrees Fahrenheit	496
°C	degrees Celsius	518
π	pi; $\frac{22}{7}$, about 3.14	544
$\approx$	is approximately equal to	544

Geometry

$\rightarrow$	maps into	612, 834
$\sim p$	not p	614
$\leftrightarrow$	if and only if	616
$\cong$	is congruent to	621
$\angle$	angle	621
°	degrees	624
$m\angle C$	measure of angle C	629
$\parallel$	is parallel to	630
$\overleftrightarrow{AB}$	line AB	630
$\perp$	is perpendicular to	633
$\overline{AB}; AB$	line segment AB; length of $\overline{AB}$	639
$\overset{\frown}{AB}$	arc AB	728
$\odot A$	circle A	729
$\triangle ABC$	triangle ABC	734
$\sim$	is similar to	790
A'	image of A; A prime	834

Trigonometry

′ ″	minutes seconds	896
DMS	degrees/minutes/seconds	896
sin A	sine of $\angle A$	902
cos A	cosine of $\angle A$	902
tan A	tangent of $\angle A$	902
θ	theta (angle measure)	903
csc A	cosecant of $\angle A$	904
sec A	secant of $\angle A$	904
cot A	cotangent of $\angle A$	904
$\sin^{-1} x$	inverse sine	915
$\cos^{-1} x$	inverse cosine	915
$\tan^{-1} x$	inverse tangent	915
$\overrightarrow{AB}$ or $\mathbf{v}$	vector	1066
$\|\mathbf{a}\|$	magnitude of a vector	1066
$\langle x, y \rangle$	ordered pair vector	1070
$\mathbf{u} \cdot \mathbf{v}$	dot product of two vectors	1082
(r, θ)	polar coordinates	1093

Statistics and Probability

$P(\text{event})$	probability of the event	1232
$n!$	factorial	1245
$_nP_r$	permutations	1246
$_nC_r$	combinations	1249
|	tally mark	1260
$2\mid 6$	stem-and-leaf plot key	1276
$\in$	element of a set	1290
$\subset$	subset	1290
$\cap$	intersection of a set	1291
$\cup$	union of a set	1291
$\sim$	complement of a set	1291
$\bar{x}$	mean of a set	1324
Σ	sigma: summation	1324
σ	lowercase sigma	1324
μ	mu: mean	1340
$\ddot{p}$	sample proportion	1350
z_c	z-score	1350
$P(B\mid A)$	probability of event B given event A	1360

Algebra

$\lvert a \rvert$	absolute value of a	1387
$-x$	opposite of x	1387
a^b	a = base; b = exponent	1394
$\sqrt{a}$	principal square root	1400
$\pm$	plus or minus	1400
$\{1, 2, \ldots\}$	set notation	1402
$(\ ), [\ ]$	for grouping	1419
x	variable or input	1422
x_1, x_2, y_1, y_2	specific values of a variable	1429
(x, y)	ordered pair	1436
y	output variable	1437
$f(x)$	"f of x", function value at x	1450
$=$	is equal to	1458
$\neq$	is not equal to	1458
$\stackrel{?}{=}$	does it equal?	1459
$<$	is less than	1492
$>$	is greater than	1492
$\leq$	is less than or equal to	1492
$\geq$	is greater than or equal to	1492
m	slope	1542
b	y-intercept	1542
i	imaginary number, $\sqrt{-1}$	1641

Advanced Algebra

(x, y, z)	ordered triple	1754
$m \times n$	matrix, m rows, n columns	1772
$\begin{bmatrix} a & b \\ c & d \end{bmatrix}$	matrix	1772
$\det(M)$	determinant	1794
A^{-1}	inverse of matrix a	1798
a_n	general term of sequence	1862
S_n	partial sum of sequence	1863
$\sum_{n=1}^{3}$	summation	1864
i	imaginary unit, $\sqrt{-1}$	1894
$a + bi$	complex number	1896
e	eccentricity	1940
$\sqrt[n]{a}$	principal nth root	1954
a^n	nth power of a	1966
a^{-n}	$\frac{1}{a^n}$	1966
$a^{\frac{1}{n}}$	$\sqrt[n]{a}$	1967
$\log b$	common logarithm, base 10	1974
$\ln x$	natural logarithm, $\log_e x$	1975, 2004
e	base for natural log; ≈ 2.718	1975, 2004
$\log_b x$	logarithm of x, base b	2006
$(a, b], [a, b)$	interval notation	2014
$(f \circ g)(x)$	composition, $f(g(x))$	2063
$f^{-1}(x)$	inverse of a function	2090

Calculus

$\lim_{x \to c} f(x)$	limit	2110
δ, ε	Greek delta, Greek epsilon	2112
$[x]$	greatest integer function	2132
DNE	does not exist	2132
$\infty, -\infty$	infinity, negative infinity	2136
$\therefore$	therefore	2146
$[0, \pi)$	half open interval	2151
Δx	change in x	2158
$f'(x)$	derivative of f	2159
$\frac{dy}{dx}\big|_c$	derivative at point c	2177
$f''(x)$	second derivative of f	2184
$f^{(n)}(x)$	nth derivative of f	2184
$\int f(x)dx$	integral	2234
$\int_a^b f(x)dx$	definite interval	2246
$F(x)\big|_a^b$	endpoints of an interval	2246

Foundations of Mathematics

Basic Addition Facts

+	0	1	2	3	4	5	6	7	8	9	10
0	0	1	2	3	4	5	6	7	8	9	10
1	1	2	3	4	5	6	7	8	9	10	11
2	2	3	4	5	6	7	8	9	10	11	12
3	3	4	5	6	7	8	9	10	11	12	13
4	4	5	6	7	8	9	10	11	12	13	14
5	5	6	7	8	9	10	11	12	13	14	15
6	6	7	8	9	10	11	12	13	14	15	16
7	7	8	9	10	11	12	13	14	15	16	17
8	8	9	10	11	12	13	14	15	16	17	18
9	9	10	11	12	13	14	15	16	17	18	19
10	10	11	12	13	14	15	16	17	18	19	20

Basic Subtraction Facts

−	0	1	2	3	4	5	6	7	8	9	10
0	0										
1	1	0									
2	2	1	0								
3	3	2	1	0							
4	4	3	2	1	0						
5	5	4	3	2	1	0					
6	6	5	4	3	2	1	0				
7	7	6	5	4	3	2	1	0			
8	8	7	6	5	4	3	2	1	0		
9	9	8	7	6	5	4	3	2	1	0	
10	10	9	8	7	6	5	4	3	2	1	0

Basic Addition Facts

$0+0=0$	$1+0=1$	$2+0=2$	$3+0=3$	$4+0=4$	$5+0=5$	$6+0=6$	$7+0=7$	$8+0=8$	$9+0=0$	$10+0=10$
$0+1=1$	$1+1=2$	$2+1=3$	$3+1=4$	$4+1=5$	$5+1=6$	$6+1=7$	$7+1=8$	$8+1=9$	$9+1=10$	$10+1=11$
$0+2=2$	$1+2=3$	$2+2=4$	$3+2=5$	$4+2=6$	$5+2=7$	$6+2=8$	$7+2=9$	$8+2=10$	$9+2=11$	$10+2=12$
$0+3=3$	$1+3=4$	$2+3=5$	$3+3=6$	$4+3=7$	$5+3=8$	$6+3=9$	$7+3=10$	$8+3=11$	$9+3=12$	$10+3=13$
$0+4=4$	$1+4=5$	$2+4=6$	$3+4=7$	$4+4=8$	$5+4=9$	$6+4=10$	$7+4=11$	$8+4=12$	$9+4=13$	$10+4=14$
$0+5=5$	$1+5=6$	$2+5=7$	$3+5=8$	$4+5=9$	$5+5=10$	$6+5=11$	$7+5=12$	$8+5=13$	$9+5=14$	$10+5=15$
$0+6=6$	$1+6=7$	$2+6=8$	$3+6=9$	$4+6=10$	$5+6=11$	$6+6=12$	$7+6=13$	$8+6=14$	$9+6=15$	$10+6=16$
$0+7=7$	$1+7=8$	$2+7=9$	$3+7=10$	$4+7=11$	$5+7=12$	$6+7=13$	$7+7=14$	$8+7=15$	$9+7=16$	$10+7=17$
$0+8=8$	$1+8=9$	$2+8=10$	$3+8=11$	$4+8=12$	$5+8=13$	$6+8=14$	$7+8=15$	$8+8=16$	$9+8=17$	$10+8=18$
$0+9=9$	$1+9=10$	$2+9=11$	$3+9=12$	$4+9=13$	$5+9=14$	$6+9=15$	$7+9=16$	$8+9=17$	$9+9=18$	$10+9=19$
$0+10=10$	$1+10=11$	$2+10=12$	$3+10=13$	$4+10=14$	$5+10=15$	$6+10=16$	$7+10=17$	$8+10=18$	$9+10=19$	$10+10=20$

Basic Subtraction Facts

$0-0=0$										
$1-0=1$	$1-1=0$									
$2-0=2$	$2-1=1$	$2-2=0$								
$3-0=3$	$3-1=2$	$3-2=1$	$3-3=0$							
$4-0=4$	$4-1=3$	$4-2=2$	$4-3=1$	$4-4=0$						
$5-0=5$	$5-1=4$	$5-2=3$	$5-3=2$	$5-4=1$	$5-5=0$					
$6-0=6$	$6-1=5$	$6-2=4$	$6-3=3$	$6-4=2$	$6-5=1$	$6-6=0$				
$7-0=7$	$7-1=6$	$7-2=5$	$7-3=4$	$7-4=3$	$7-5=2$	$7-6=1$	$7-7=0$			
$8-0=8$	$8-1=7$	$8-2=6$	$8-3=5$	$8-4=4$	$8-5=3$	$8-6=2$	$8-7=1$	$8-8=0$		
$9-0=9$	$9-1=8$	$9-2=7$	$9-3=6$	$9-4=5$	$9-5=4$	$9-6=3$	$9-7=2$	$9-8=1$	$9-9=0$	
$10-0=10$	$10-1=9$	$10-2=8$	$10-3=7$	$10-4=6$	$10-5=5$	$10-6=4$	$10-7=3$	$10-8=2$	$10-9=1$	$10-10=0$

Basic Multiplication Facts

×	0	1	2	3	4	5	6	7	8	9	10
0	0	0	0	0	0	0	0	0	0	0	0
1	0	1	2	3	4	5	6	7	8	9	10
2	0	2	4	6	8	10	12	14	16	18	20
3	0	3	6	9	12	15	18	21	24	27	30
4	0	4	8	12	16	20	24	28	32	36	40
5	0	5	10	15	20	25	30	35	40	45	50
6	0	6	12	18	24	30	36	42	48	54	60
7	0	7	14	21	28	35	42	49	56	63	70
8	0	8	16	24	32	40	48	56	64	72	80
9	0	9	18	27	36	45	54	63	72	81	90
10	0	10	20	30	40	50	60	70	80	90	100

Basic Division Facts

÷	1	2	3	4	5	6	7	8	9	10
1	1	2	3	4	5	6	7	8	9	10
2	2	4	6	8	10	12	14	16	18	20
3	3	6	9	12	15	18	21	24	27	30
4	4	8	12	16	20	24	28	32	36	40
5	5	10	15	20	25	30	35	40	45	50
6	6	12	18	24	30	36	42	48	54	60
7	7	14	21	28	35	42	49	56	63	70
8	8	16	24	32	40	48	56	64	72	80
9	9	18	27	36	45	54	63	72	81	90
10	10	20	30	40	50	60	70	80	90	100

Basic Multiplication Facts

zeros	0×0=0	1×0=0	2×0=0	3×0=0	4×0=0	5×0=0	6×0=0	7×0=0	8×0=0	9×0=0	10×0=0
ones	0×1=0	1×1=1	2×1=2	3×1=3	4×1=4	5×1=5	6×1=6	7×1=7	8×1=8	9×1=9	10×1=10
twos	0×2=0	1×2=2	2×2=4	3×2=6	4×2=8	5×2=10	6×2=12	7×2=14	8×2=16	9×2=18	10×2=20
threes	0×3=0	1×3=3	2×3=6	3×3=9	4×3=12	5×3=15	6×3=18	7×3=21	8×3=24	9×3=27	10×3=30
fours	0×4=0	1×4=4	2×4=8	3×4=12	4×4=16	5×4=20	6×4=24	7×4=28	8×4=32	9×4=36	10×4=40
fives	0×5=0	1×5=5	2×5=10	3×5=15	4×5=20	5×5=25	6×5=30	7×5=35	8×5=40	9×5=45	10×5=50
sixes	0×6=0	1×6=6	2×6=12	3×6=18	4×6=24	5×6=30	6×6=36	7×6=42	8×6=48	9×6=54	10×6=60
sevens	0×7=0	1×7=7	2×7=14	3×7=21	4×7=28	5×7=35	6×7=42	7×7=49	8×7=56	9×7=63	10×7=70
eights	0×8=0	1×8=8	2×8=16	3×8=24	4×8=32	5×8=40	6×8=48	7×8=56	8×8=64	9×8=72	10×8=80
nines	0×9=0	1×9=9	2×9=18	3×9=27	4×9=36	5×9=45	6×9=54	7×9=63	8×9=72	9×9=81	10×9=90
tens	0×10=0	1×10=10	2×10=20	3×10=30	4×10=40	5×10=50	6×10=60	7×10=70	8×10=80	9×10=90	10×10=100

Basic Division Facts

ones	0÷1=0	1÷1=1	2÷1=2	3÷1=3	4÷1=4	5÷1=5	6÷1=6	7÷1=7	8÷1=8	9÷1=9	10÷1=10
twos	0÷2=0	2÷2=1	4÷2=2	6÷2=3	8÷2=4	10÷2=5	12÷2=6	14÷2=7	16÷2=8	18÷2=9	20÷2=10
threes	0÷3=0	3÷3=1	6÷3=2	9÷3=3	12÷3=4	15÷3=5	18÷3=6	21÷3=7	24÷3=8	27÷3=9	30÷3=10
fours	0÷4=0	4÷4=1	8÷4=2	12÷4=3	16÷4=4	20÷4=5	24÷4=6	28÷4=7	32÷4=8	36÷4=9	40÷4=10
fives	0÷5=0	5÷5=1	10÷5=2	15÷5=3	20÷5=4	25÷5=5	30÷5=6	35÷5=7	40÷5=8	45÷5=9	50÷5=10
sixes	0÷6=0	6÷6=1	12÷6=2	18÷6=3	24÷6=4	30÷6=5	36÷6=6	42÷6=7	48÷6=8	54÷6=9	60÷6=10
sevens	0÷7=0	7÷7=1	14÷7=2	21÷7=3	28÷7=4	35÷7=5	42÷7=6	49÷7=7	56÷7=8	63÷7=9	70÷7=10
eights	0÷8=0	8÷8=1	16÷8=2	24÷8=3	32÷8=4	40÷8=5	48÷8=6	56÷8=7	64÷8=8	72÷8=9	80÷8=10
nines	0÷9=0	9÷9=1	18÷9=2	27÷9=3	36÷9=4	45÷9=5	54÷9=6	63÷9=7	72÷9=8	81÷9=9	90÷9=10
tens	0÷10=0	10÷10=1	20÷10=2	30÷10=3	40÷10=4	50÷10=5	60÷10=6	70÷10=7	80÷10=8	90÷10=9	100÷10=10

Foundations of Mathematics

Place Value

	Billions			Millions			Thousands			Ones	
hundred billions	ten billions	billions	hundred millions	ten millions	millions	hundred thousands	ten thousands	thousands	hundreds	tens	ones
2	3	6,	9	1	7,	4	0	5,	3	8	9

Forms of a Number

Standard form	236,917,405,389
Expanded form	200,000,000,000 + 30,000,000,000 + 6,000,000,000 + 900,000,000 + 10,000,000 + 7,000,000 + 400,000 + 5,000 + 300 + 80 + 9
Word form	two hundred thirty-six billion, nine hundred seventeen million, four hundred five thousand, three hundred eighty-nine
Short word form	236 billion, 917 million, 405 thousand, 389

Hints on Memorizing Facts

1. Focus on the ways to memorize facts that are listed on the next page.

2. Memorize the facts by saying the facts aloud.
   - For $3 + 8$, say "Three plus eight equals eleven."
   - For $8 - 3$, say "Eight minus three equals five."
   - For 8×7, say "Eight times seven equals fifty-six."
   - For $56 \div 8$, say "Fifty-six divided by eight equals seven."

3. Memorize a few facts at a time. Work on 2 or 3 facts per day. Start with the easier facts.

4. Practice saying the facts in reverse order, so you don't have to memorize so many facts.
   $8 + 5 = 13, 5 + 8 = 13$ $9 - 4 = 5, 9 - 5 = 4$

5. Memorize one set of times tables at a time. Work on the set until you have mastered it. Then move to another set.

6. Use the relationship of multiplication to division. To remember $10 \div 2 = 5$, think $5 \cdot 2 = 10$.

7. Play fact games.
   - Toss two dice and add the dots that come up. Then have a friend toss two dice and add the dots. Then subtract the smaller sum from the larger sum.
   - Play multiplication facts bingo with some friends.
   - Play "Beat the Clock."

8. Make flash cards and use them on your own or with friends and family. Time how long it takes you to say a set of facts. Try this again the next day and see if you can beat your previous time.

9. Every day, review the facts you know or usually know. Then work on two new facts and play games to practice them.

10. Use a calculator. Enter the fact. Before you press ENTER, say the answer. Then press ENTER to see if you are correct.

Go
For It!

Addition Facts: Memorize Fewer Than 121 Facts

There are 121 basic facts, but here are some ways to cut down the task.
- 0 plus any number is that number.
- 1 plus any number is the next number when you count.
- 2 plus any even number is the next even number.
- 2 plus any odd number is the next odd number.
- 10 plus any one-digit number is a teen number with the 1 in the tens place and the one-digit number in the ones place.
- If you know 2 + 3, you know 3 + 2. This takes care of half of the 121 facts.
- Once you memorize the doubles, the near doubles are easy to remember.
- Any number plus 9 is one less than that number plus ten.

Subtraction Facts: Memorize Fewer Than 121 Facts

There are 121 basic facts, but here are some ways to cut down the task.
- Any number minus 0 is itself.
- Any number minus itself is 0.
- Any number minus 1 is the previous counting number.
- Any even number minus 2 is the previous even number.
- Any odd number minus 2 is the previous odd number.
- Any teen number minus 10 is the digit in the ones place of the teen number.
- If you know 8 − 3 = 5, you also know 8 − 5 = 3. This takes care of half of the subtraction facts.
- Nine minus any number is one less than 10 minus the same number.

Multiplication Facts: Memorize Fewer Than 121 Facts

There are 121 basic facts, but here are some ways to cut down the task.
- Any number times 0 is 0.
- Any number times 1 is itself.
- Any number times 10 is that number with a zero to its right.
- Any number times 2 is the double of that number. For example, $2 \cdot 3 = 3 + 3$, or 6.
- The product of any number times 5 will always have 0 or 5 in the ones place.
- Four times a number is its double times 2. For example, $4 \cdot 3 = 2(2 \cdot 3) = 2(6) = 12$.
- Flip the numbers. If you know $3 \cdot 7 = 21$, you also know that $7 \cdot 3 = 21$.
- Think "one group more" or "one group less." If you know that $3 \cdot 4 = 12$, you know that $4 \cdot 4 = 12 + 4 = 16$.

Division Facts: Memorize Fewer Than 100 Facts

There are 100 facts to remember. Here are some ways to reduce the number of facts you need to memorize.
- Any number divided by 1 is the number itself.
- Any number divided by itself is 1.
- When a number that ends in zero is divided by 10, the quotient is the number without the zero. For example, $50 \div 10 = 5$.
- Pairs of facts are related. If you know that $15 \div 3 = 5$, then you know that $15 \div 5 = 3$.

Foundations of Mathematics

Data Graphs

Pictographs

A *pictograph* uses pictures or symbols to represent data. You can use a pictograph to compare amounts.

Favorite Type of Music

Classical	●●
Country	●●●●
Rap	●●●
Rock	●●◖
Other	●

Key: ● = 2 votes

Bar Graphs

A *bar graph* is a type of data display that uses bars to organize information. You can compare the information on a bar graph by comparing the lengths of the bars.

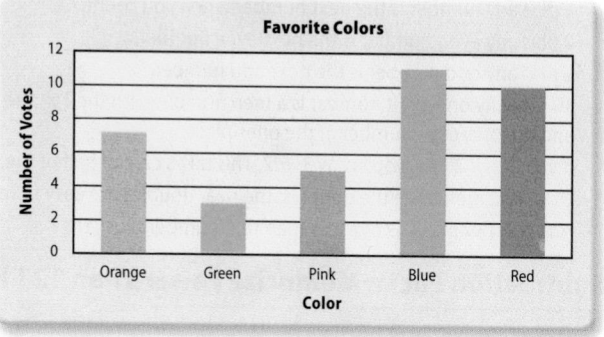

Line Graphs

A *line graph* is a data display that shows information as data points connected by line segments. A line graph usually shows change over time.

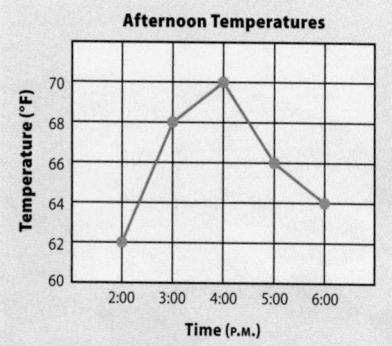

Circle Graphs

A *circle graph* uses sections of a circle to display a set of data as parts of a whole. The whole circle represents 100% of the data.

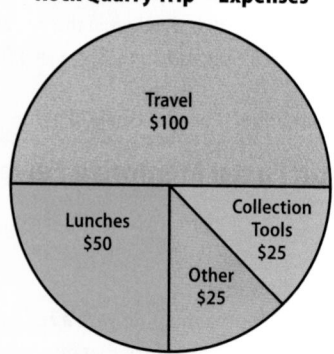

Lines

Points, Lines, Planes

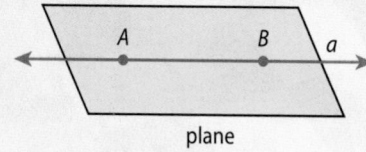

plane

Line Segment

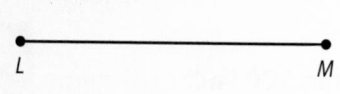

Ray

Intersecting Lines

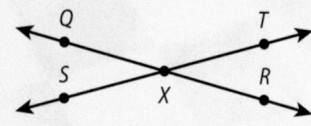

Parallel Lines

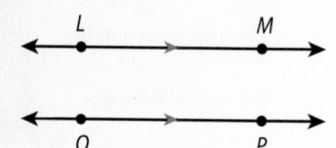

Perpendicular Lines

right angle symbol →

Angles

Angles Classified by Measure

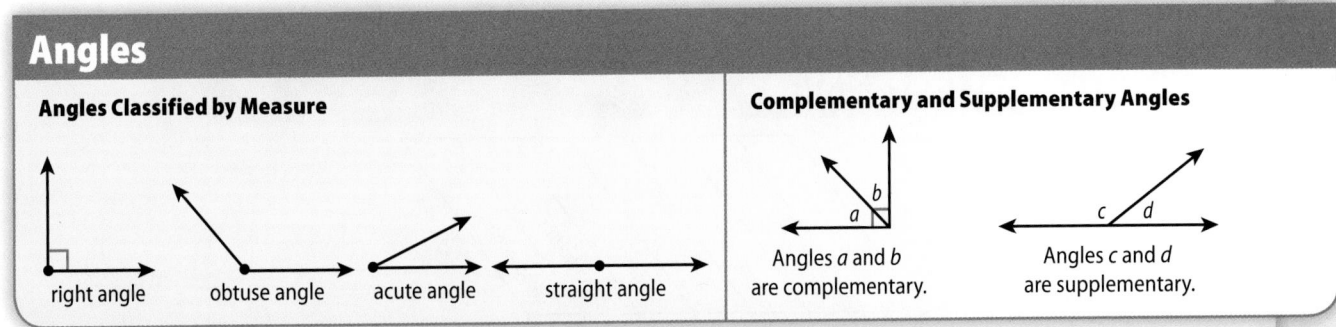

right angle   obtuse angle   acute angle   straight angle

Complementary and Supplementary Angles

Angles *a* and *b* are complementary.

Angles *c* and *d* are supplementary.

Polygons

Regular Polygons	Triangles	Quadrilaterals	Three-Dimensional Figures
Triangle 3 sides	**Equilateral** 3 equal sides	**Trapezoid** One pair of parallel sides	**Cube and Prism** Vertex, Face, Edge
Quadrilateral 4 sides	**Isosceles** 2 equal sides	**Parallelogram** Two pairs of parallel sides	**Cylinder** Base, Curved surface, Base
Pentagon 5 sides	**Scalene** no equal sides	**Rhombus** Parallelogram with 4 congruent sides	**Pyramid** Vertex, Face, Edge, Base
Hexagon 6 sides	**Right** 1 right angle	**Rectangle** Parallelogram with 4 right angles	**Cone** Vertex, Curved surface, Base
Octagon 8 sides	**Acute** 3 acute (<90°) angles	**Square** Rectangle with 4 congruent sides	**Sphere** Center, Radius
	Obtuse 1 obtuse (>90°) angle		

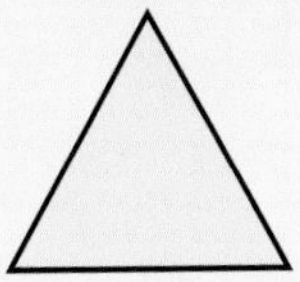

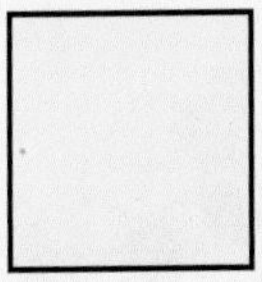

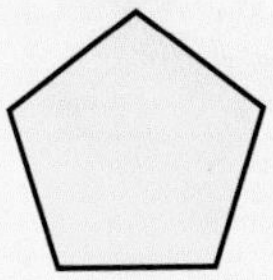

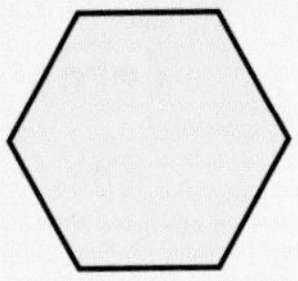

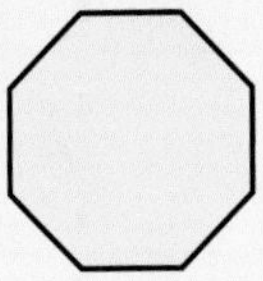

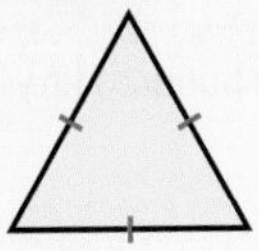

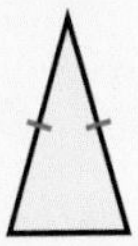

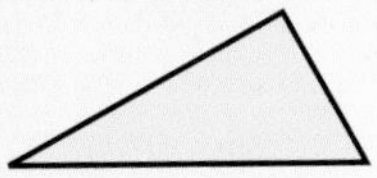

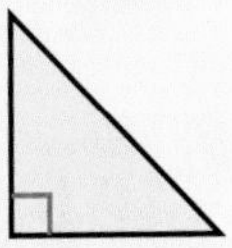

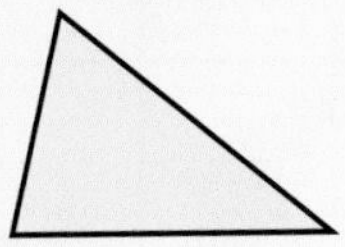

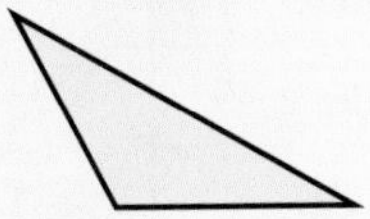

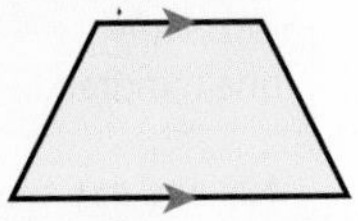

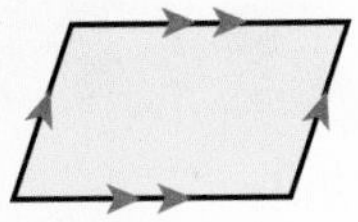

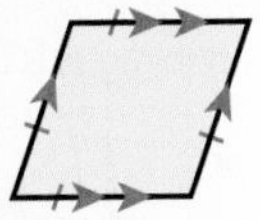

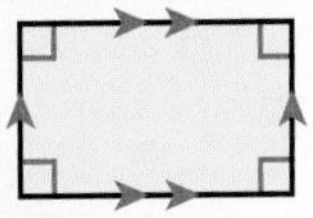

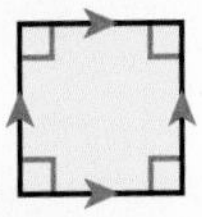

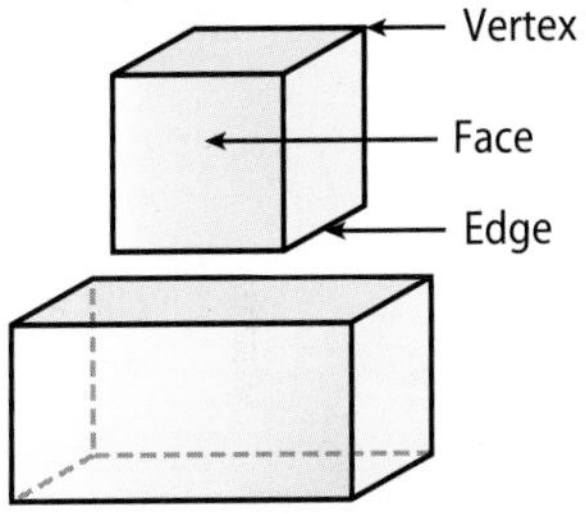

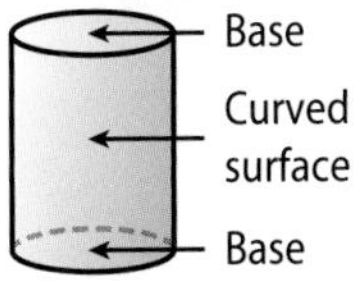

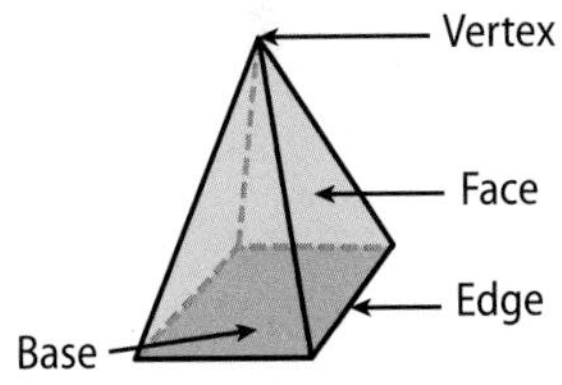

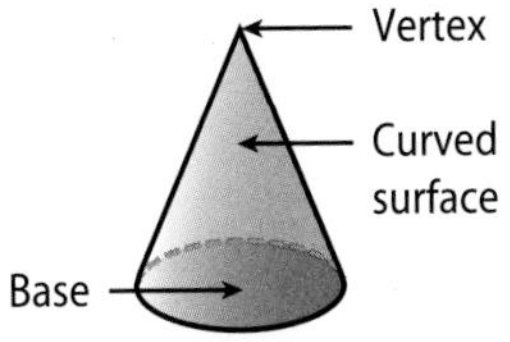

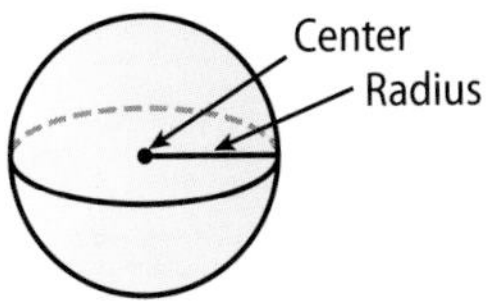

Numbers and Operations

Decimal Place Value

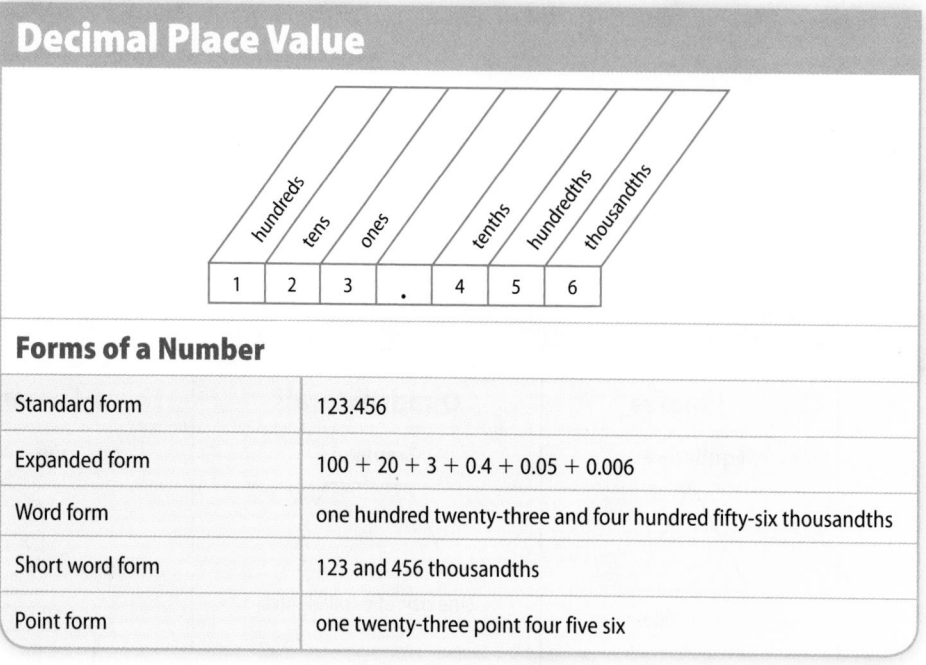

Forms of a Number

Standard form	123.456
Expanded form	$100 + 20 + 3 + 0.4 + 0.05 + 0.006$
Word form	one hundred twenty-three and four hundred fifty-six thousandths
Short word form	123 and 456 thousandths
Point form	one twenty-three point four five six

Tests for Divisibility

Divisible by	Rule
2	The digit in the ones place is an even digit: 0, 2, 4, 6, or 8.
3	The sum of the digits is divisible by 3.
4	The number formed by the last two digits is divisible by 4.
5	The digit in the ones place is 0 or 5.
6	The number is divisible by both 2 and 3.
8	The number formed by the last three digits is divisible by 8.
9	The sum of the digits is divisible by 9.
10	The digit in the ones place is 0.

Powers of 10

Power of 10	Value	Zeros
10^0	1	0
10^1	10	1
10^2	100	2
10^3	1,000	3
10^4	10,000	4
10^5	100,000	5
10^6	1,000,000	6
10^7	10,000,000	7

Four-Step Problem Solving Plan

Step 1	Read	• Read the problem carefully. You can restate the problem in your own words. • Determine what the problem is asking you to find. • Identify what you know. This is the information given in the problem. • Identify what you need to find out to solve the problem. This is the question asked. You can restate it in your own words.
Step 2	Plan	• Plan how to find the answer to the question. • Think about other similar problems you have solved. Think about how the information you know can help you find the answer. • Choose a problem solving strategy.
Step 3	Solve	• Solve the problem using your plan. As you work, you can revise your plan if you need to. • Make sure you write a sentence that states your answer.
Step 4	Check	• Check your work. • Make sure you have answered the question that was asked. • Make sure your answer makes sense by using another problem solving strategy to check your work.

Formulas, Properties, and Theorems

The Fundamental Theorem of Arithmetic	Every positive integer greater than 1 has exactly one set of prime factors (one prime factorization).
Cross Products Property	The cross products of two fractions are the products of the numerator of one fraction and the denominator of the other fraction. If the cross products of two ratios (fractions) are equal, then the ratios form a proportion.
Percent: Find What Number Is a Given Percent of Another Number	$n = p \times b$ number (n) is a given percent (p) of a given base number (b)
Percent: Find What Percent One Number Is of Another Number	$p = \frac{n}{b}$ percent (p) one number (n) is of another number (b)
Percent: Find a Number When Given a Certain Percent of the Number	$b = \frac{n}{p}$ base number (b) when given a number (n) and the percent (p) the number is of the base number
Percent of Increase	$p\% = \frac{\text{amount of increase}}{\text{original amount}}$ amount of increase = new amount − original amount
Percent of Decrease	$p\% = \frac{\text{amount of decrease}}{\text{original amount}}$ amount of decrease = larger amount − the smaller amount
Simple Interest	$I = prt$ where I is the interest earned or paid, p is the principal amount, r is the interest rate per year, t is the time in years

Ways to Check Answers

Addition

- Reverse the addition order. Add from the bottom of a column to the top of the column, if you had added from top to bottom to solve the problem.
- Use a calculator to enter the computation. Check the calculator result with your answer.
- Use an estimation strategy (*see list below*).

Subtraction

- Reverse the operation. Add the difference (answer) to the subtrahend (number being subtracted).
- Use a calculator to enter the computation. Check the calculator result with your answer.
- Use an estimation strategy (*see list below*).

Multiplication

- Reverse the order of the factors.
- Factor the multiplier, and use the factors to multiply.
- Use a calculator to enter the computation. Check the calculator result with your answer.
- Use an estimation strategy (*see list below*).

Division

- Reverse the operation. Multiply the quotient (answer) by the divisor.
- Factor the divisor and divide each factor separately.
- Use a calculator to enter the computation. Check the calculator result with your answer.
- Use an estimation strategy (*see list below*).

Methods for Estimating

Rounding	• Round numbers so that you can use mental math to perform the computation. • For whole numbers and decimals, add 1 if the digit in the place to the right of the one you're rounding to is greater than or equal to 5. Add 0 if it's less than 5.
Benchmarks	• Rounding to a benchmark instead of a place value sometimes gives you an estimate that is closer to the actual answer. • There are benchmarks for both fractions and decimals.
Compatible Numbers	• Compatible numbers are values that are close to the numbers given in a computation. Choose compatible numbers that make it easy to use mental math. • For division, choose the number for the divisor first. Then find a compatible number for the dividend.
Front-end Estimation	• Use only the whole number parts of decimals or mixed numbers to perform a computation. • You can use the decimal or fraction parts to get a closer estimate.

Benchmarks for Fractions

If the numerator is . . .	Round to . . .
Much less than one-fourth of the denominator	0
About one-fourth of the denominator	$\frac{1}{4}$
About one-half of the denominator	$\frac{1}{2}$
About three-fourths of the denominator	$\frac{3}{4}$
Much greater than three-fourths of the denominator	1

Benchmarks for Decimals

To make addition or subtraction easier, round to ...
0
0.25
0.5
0.75
1

Fraction-Decimal-Percent Equivalents

$\frac{1}{100}$	= 0.01	= 1%	$\frac{8}{16}, \frac{6}{12}, \frac{5}{10}, \frac{4}{8}, \frac{3}{6}, \frac{2}{4}, \frac{1}{2}$	= 0.5	= 50%	
$\frac{1}{16}$	= 0.0625	= $6\frac{1}{4}$%	$\frac{5}{9}$	= 0.5555...	= $55\frac{5}{9}$%	
$\frac{1}{12}$	= 0.0833...	= $8\frac{1}{3}$%	$\frac{9}{16}$	= 0.5625	= $56\frac{1}{4}$%	
$\frac{1}{10}$	= 0.1	= 10%	$\frac{4}{7}$	= 0.571428...	= $57\frac{1}{7}$%	
$\frac{1}{9}$	= 0.1111...	= $11\frac{1}{9}$%	$\frac{7}{12}$	= 0.5833...	= $58\frac{1}{3}$%	
$\frac{2}{16}, \frac{1}{8}$	= 0.125	= $12\frac{1}{2}$%	$\frac{10}{16}, \frac{5}{8}$	= 0.625	= $62\frac{1}{2}$%	
$\frac{1}{7}$	= 0.142857...	= $14\frac{2}{7}$%	$\frac{8}{12}, \frac{6}{9}, \frac{4}{6}, \frac{2}{3}$	= 0.6666...	= $66\frac{2}{3}$%	
$\frac{2}{12}, \frac{1}{6}$	= 0.1666...	= $16\frac{2}{3}$%	$\frac{11}{16}$	= 0.6875	= $68\frac{3}{4}$%	
$\frac{13}{16}$	= 0.1875	= $18\frac{3}{4}$%	$\frac{7}{10}$	= 0.7	= 70%	
$\frac{2}{10}, \frac{1}{5}$	= 0.2	= 20%	$\frac{5}{7}$	= 0.714285...	= $71\frac{3}{7}$%	
$\frac{2}{9}$	= 0.2222...	= $22\frac{2}{9}$%	$\frac{12}{16}, \frac{9}{12}, \frac{6}{8}, \frac{3}{4}$	= 0.75	= 75%	
$\frac{4}{16}, \frac{3}{12}, \frac{2}{8}, \frac{1}{4}$	= 0.25	= 25%	$\frac{7}{9}$	= 0.7777...	= $77\frac{7}{9}$%	
$\frac{2}{7}$	= 0.285714...	= $28\frac{4}{7}$%	$\frac{8}{10}, \frac{4}{5}$	= 0.8	= 80%	
$\frac{3}{10}$	= 0.3	= 30%	$\frac{13}{16}$	= 0.8125	= $81\frac{1}{4}$%	
$\frac{5}{16}$	= 0.3125	= $31\frac{1}{4}$%	$\frac{10}{12}, \frac{5}{6}$	= 0.8333...	= $83\frac{1}{3}$%	
$\frac{4}{12}, \frac{3}{9}, \frac{2}{6}, \frac{1}{3}$	= 0.3333...	= $33\frac{1}{3}$%	$\frac{6}{7}$	= 0.857142...	= $85\frac{5}{7}$%	
$\frac{6}{16}, \frac{3}{8}$	= 0.375	= $37\frac{1}{2}$%	$\frac{14}{16}, \frac{7}{8}$	= 0.875	= $87\frac{1}{2}$%	
$\frac{4}{10}, \frac{2}{5}$	= 0.4	= 40%	$\frac{8}{9}$	= 0.8888...	= $88\frac{8}{9}$%	
$\frac{5}{12}$	= 0.4166...	= $41\frac{2}{3}$%	$\frac{9}{10}$	= 0.9	= 90%	
$\frac{3}{7}$	= 0.428571...	= $42\frac{6}{7}$%	$\frac{11}{12}$	= 0.9166...	= $91\frac{2}{3}$%	
$\frac{7}{16}$	= 0.4375	= $43\frac{3}{4}$%	$\frac{15}{16}$	= 0.9375	= $93\frac{3}{4}$%	
$\frac{4}{9}$	= 0.4444...	= $44\frac{4}{9}$%	$\frac{16}{16}, \frac{12}{12}, \frac{10}{10}, \frac{8}{8}, \frac{6}{6}, \frac{4}{4}, \frac{2}{2}$	= 1.000	= 100%	

STAY
Focused

Measurement

U.S. Customary System	Metric System
Length	
1 mile (mi) = 1,760 yards = 5,280 feet **1 yard (yd)** = 3 feet = 36 inches **1 foot (ft)** = 12 inches $\frac{1}{36}$ yard = $\frac{1}{12}$ foot = **1 inch (in.)**	**1 kilometer (km)** = 1,000 m 0.001 km = **1 meter (m)** = 100 cm = 1,000 mm 0.01 m = **1 centimeter (cm)** = 10 mm 0.001 m = 0.1 cm = **1 millimeter (mm)**
Area	
1 square mile (mi²) = 640 acres **1 acre (a)** = 4,840 yd² **1 square yard (yd²)** = 9 ft² **1 square foot (ft²)** = 144 in.² $\frac{1}{144}$ ft² = **1 square inch (in.²)**	**1 square kilometer (km²)** = 1,000,000 m² **1 square meter (m²)** = 10,000 cm² **1 square centimeter (cm²)** = 100 mm² 0.01 cm² = **1 square millimeter (mm²)**
Volume	
1 cubic yard (yd³) = 27 ft³ **1 cubic foot (ft³)** = 1,728 in.³ $\frac{1}{1,728}$ ft³ = **1 cubic inch (in.³)**	**1 cubic meter (m³)** = 1,000,000 cm³ **1 cubic centimeter (cm³)** = 1,000 mm³ 0.001 cm³ = **1 cubic millimeter (mm³)**
Capacity (Liquid)	
1 gallon (gal) = 4 qt = 8 pt = 16 c = 128 fl oz **1 quart (qt)** = 2 pt = 4 c = 32 fl oz **1 pint (pt)** = 2 c = 16 fl oz **1 cup (c)** = 8 fl oz $\frac{1}{8}$ cup = **1 fluid ounce (fl oz)**	**1 kiloliter (kL)** = 1,000 L 0.001 kL = **1 liter (L)** = 100 cL = 1,000 mL 0.01 L = **1 centiliter (cL)** = 10 mL 0.001 L = 0.1 cL = **1 milliliter (mL)**
Weight	**Mass**
1 ton (t) = 2,000 pounds **1 pound (lb)** = 16 ounces $\frac{1}{16}$ pound = **1 ounce (oz)**	**1 metric ton (t)** = 1,000 kg 0.001 t = **1 kilogram (kg)** = 1,000 g 0.001 kg = **1 gram (g)** = 100 cg = 1,000 mg 0.01 g = **1 centigram (cg)** = 10 mg 0.001 g = 0.1 cg = **1 milligram (mg)**
Temperature	
32°F = freezing point of water 98.6°F = normal body temperature 212°F = boiling point of water $F = \frac{9}{5}C + 32$ or $F = 1.8C + 32$	0°C = freezing point of water 37°C = normal body temperature 100°C = boiling point of water $C = \frac{5}{9}(F - 32)$

Do Your BEST!

Time

60 seconds (s) = **1 minute (min)** 60 minutes = **1 hour (h)** 24 hours = **1 day (d)** 7 days = **1 week (wk)** 4 weeks (approx.) = **1 month (mo)**	365 days = **1 year (yr)** 52 weeks (approx.) = 1 year 12 months = 1 year 10 years = 1 decade 100 years = 1 century

Equivalents

1 acre = 43,560 square feet = 4,840 square yards

1 bushel (U.S.) = 2,150.42 cubic inches
= 32 quarts

1 cord = 128 cubic feet

1 cubic centimeter = 0.061 cubic inch

1 cubic foot = 7.481 gallons = 1,728 cubic inches

1 cubic inch = 0.554 fluid ounce
= 16.387 cubic centimeters

1 cubic meter = 1.308 cubic yards

1 cubic yard = 0.765 cubic meter = 27 cubic feet

1 cup = 8 fluid ounces = 0.5 liquid pint

1 gallon (U.S.) = 231 cubic inches
= 128 U.S. fluid ounces
= 4 liquid quarts

1 liter = 1.057 liquid quarts

1 meter = 39.37 inches = 1.094 yards

1 micron = 0.001 millimeter = 0.00003937 inch

1 mile, nautical = 1.852 kilometers
= 1.151 statute miles
= 6,076.1155 feet

1 milliliter = 0.061 cubic inch

1 pint, dry = 33.600 cubic inches = 0.551 liter

1 pint, liquid = 28.875 inches = 0.473 liter
= 2 cups = 16 fluid ounces

1 pound, avoirdupois = 7,000 grains = 16 ounces
= 453.59237 grams

1 quart, dry (U.S.) = 67.201 cubic inches
= 1.101 liters

1 quart, liquid (U.S.) = 57.75 cubic inches
= 0.946 liter
= 2 pints = 32 fluid ounces

1 square foot = 929 square centimeters
= 144 square inches

1 square inch = 6.45 square centimeters

1 square kilometer = 0.386 square miles
= 247.105 acres

1 square meter = 1.196 square yards
= 10.764 square feet

1 square mile = 640 acres

1 square yard = 0.836 square meter
= 9 square feet
= 1,296 square inches

1 tablespoon = 3 teaspoons = 0.5 fluid ounce

1 ton, metric = 2,204.623 pounds
= 1.102 net tons

1 ton, net or short = 2,000 pounds
= 0.907 metric ton

1 yard = 0.9144 meter = 3 feet = 36 inches

Conversions

To Convert	Into	Multiply By
angstroms	microns	0.0001
centimeters	feet	0.03281
centimeters	inches	0.3937
cubic cm	cubic inches	0.06102
cubic feet	cubic meters	0.02832
days	seconds	86,400.0
degrees (angle)	radians	0.01745
fathoms	feet	6.0
feet	centimeters	30.48
feet	meters	0.3048
feet/min.	cm/sec.	0.5080
feet/sec.	knots	0.5921
feet/sec.	statute mi./hr.	0.6818
furlongs/hr.	statute mi./hr.	0.125
furlongs	feet	660.0
gallons (liq.)	liters	3.785
gal. of water	pounds of water	8.3453
grams	oz. (avoirdupois)	0.03527
grams	pounds	0.002205
hours	days	0.04167
hours	weeks	0.005952
inches	centimeters	2.540
kilograms	pounds	2.205
kilometers	feet	3,280.8
kilometers	mi. (statute)	0.6214
knots	feet/hr.	6080.0
knots	nautical mi./hr.	1.0
knots	statute mi./hr.	1.151
liters	gallons (liq.)	0.2642
liters	pints (liq.)	2.113
meters	feet	3.281
meters	mi. (nautical)	0.0005396
meters	mi. (statute)	0.0006214
microns	meters	0.000001
mi. (nautical)	feet	6,076.115
mi. (statute)	feet	5,280.0
mi. (nautical)	kilometers	1.852
mi. (statute)	kilometers	1.609
mi. (nautical)	mi. (statute)	1.1508
mi. (statute)	mi. (nautical)	0.8684
mi. (statute)/hr.	feet/min.	88.0
millimeters	inches	0.03937
oz. (avoirdupois)	grams	28.3495
oz. (avoirdupois)	lb. (avoirdupois)	0.0625
pints (liq.)	gallons (liq.)	0.125
pints (liq.)	quarts (liq.)	0.5
lb. (avoirdupois)	kilograms	0.4536

Measurement

Length Formulas		Perimeter *P*, Circumference *C*
$P = s_1 + s_2 + s_3$	**Triangle** s_1, s_2, s_3 are lengths of sides	
$P = 2\ell + 2w$ or $P = 2(\ell + w)$	**Rectangle** ℓ is length w is width	
$P = 4s$	**Square** s is length of each side	
$P = 2\ell + 2w$ or $P = 2(\ell + w)$	**Parallelogram** ℓ is length w is width	
$P = ns$	**Regular Polygon** n is number of sides s is length of each side	
$C = \pi d$ or $C = 2\pi r$	**Circle** π is pi, a number about 3.14 or $\frac{22}{7}$ d is length of diameter r is length of radius	

Area Formulas		Area *A*, Surface Area *SA*
$A = \ell w$ or $A = bh$	**Rectangle** ℓ is length b is length of the base w is width h is height	
$A = s^2$	**Square** s is length of each side	
$A = bh$	**Parallelogram** b is length of the base h is height	
$A = \frac{1}{2}bh$	**Triangle** b is length of the base h is height	
$A = \frac{1}{2}ab$	**Right Triangle** a is length of one leg b is length of the other leg	
$A = \frac{s^2}{4}\sqrt{3}$	**Equilateral Triangle** s is length of each side	
$A = \frac{1}{2}h(b_1 + b_2)$	**Trapezoid** h is height b_1 is length of one parallel side b_2 is length of other parallel side	
$A = \frac{1}{2}ap$	**Regular Polygon** a is length of an apothem p is perimeter of polygon	

Table continued on next page

Measurement

Area Formulas		Area *A*, Surface Area *SA*
$A = \frac{1}{2}d_1 d_2$	**Kite** d_1 is length of one diagonal d_2 is length of other diagonal	
$A = \pi r^2$	**Circle** π is pi, a number about 3.14 or $\frac{22}{7}$ r is length of the radius	
$SA = 6e^2$	**Cube** e is length of each edge	
$SA = Ph + 2B$	**Rectangular Prism** P is perimeter of the base h is height B is area of the base	
$SA = 2\pi rh + 2\pi r^2$ or $SA = 2\pi r(h + r)$	**Right Cylinder** π is pi, a number about 3.14 or $\frac{22}{7}$ r is length of the radius of the base h is height	
$SA = \frac{1}{2}P\ell + B$	**Pyramid** P is perimeter of the base ℓ is slant height B is area of the base	
$SA = \pi r\ell + \pi r^2$ or $SA = \pi r(\ell + r)$	**Right Cone** π is pi, a number about 3.14 or $\frac{22}{7}$ r is length of the radius of the base ℓ is slant height	
$SA = 4\pi r^2$	**Sphere** π is pi, a number about 3.14 or $\frac{22}{7}$ r is length of the radius	

Volume Formulas		Volume *V*
$V = e^3$	**Cube** e is length of each edge	
$V = \ell wh$	**Rectangular Prism** ℓ is length w is width h is height	
$V = Bh$	**Prism** B is area of the base h is height	
$V = \pi r^2 h$	**Right Cylinder** π is pi, a number about 3.14 or $\frac{22}{7}$ r is length of the radius of the base h is height	
$V = \frac{1}{3} Bh$	**Pyramid** B is area of the base h is height	
$V = \frac{1}{3} \pi r^2 h$	**Right Cone** π is pi, a number about 3.14 or $\frac{22}{7}$ r is length of the radius of the base h is height	
$V = \frac{4}{3} \pi r^3$	**Sphere** π is pi, a number about 3.14 or $\frac{22}{7}$ r is length of the radius	

Statistics and Probability

Formulas

Probability (theoretical)	$P(\text{event}) = \dfrac{\text{number of favorable outcomes}}{\text{number of total outcomes}}$
Probability (experimental)	$P(\text{event}) = \dfrac{\text{number of times an event occurs}}{\text{number of trials}}$
Complement C of an Event E	$P(C) = P(\text{not } E)$ $P(C) = 1 - P(E)$ $P(\text{not } E) = 1 - P(E)$ $P(E) + P(\text{not } E) = 1$
Independent Events	$P(A \text{ and } B) = P(A) \cdot P(B)$ $P(A \text{ or } B) = P(A) + P(B) - P(A \text{ and } B)$
Dependent Events	$P(A \text{ and } B) = P(A) \cdot P(B \mid A)$
Odds for an Event	$\text{Odds in favor} = \dfrac{\text{number of favorable outcomes}}{\text{number of unfavorable outcomes}}$
Odds Against an Event	$\text{Odds against} = \dfrac{\text{number of unfavorable outcomes}}{\text{number of favorable outcomes}}$
Permutations	${}_nP_r = \dfrac{n!}{(n - r)!}$
Combinations	${}_nC_r = \dfrac{n!}{r!(n - r)!}$
Binomial Probability	$P(k \text{ successes in } n \text{ trials}) = {}_nC_r \cdot p^k(1 - p)^{n-k}$
Outlier	$n < Q1 - 1.5(IQR)$ or $n > Q3 + 1.5(IQR)$
Linear Interpolation and Extrapolation	$y = y_1 + \left(\dfrac{y_2 - y_1}{x_2 - x_1}\right)(x - x_1)$
Variance	$\sigma^2 = \dfrac{\Sigma(x_i - \bar{x})^2}{n}$
Standard Deviation	$\sigma = \sqrt{\dfrac{\Sigma(x_i - \bar{x})^2}{n}}$
Margin of Error	$ME = z_c\sqrt{\dfrac{\hat{p}(1 - \hat{p})}{n}} \qquad ME = z_c \cdot \dfrac{\sigma}{\sqrt{n}}$
Confidence Interval	$\hat{p} \pm ME \qquad\qquad \bar{x} \pm ME$

Theorems

Fundamental Counting Principle	If there are m ways to choose a first item and n ways to choose a second item after the first item has been chosen, then there are $m \times n$ ways to choose both items.
Binomial Theorem	$(a + b)^n = \left({}_nC_0\right)a^n + \left({}_nC_1\right)a^{n-1}b + \left({}_nC_2\right)a^{n-2}b^{2} + \ldots + \left({}_nC_{n-1}\right)ab^{n-1} + \left({}_nC_n\right)b^n$ $(a + b)^n = \displaystyle\sum_{k=0}^{n} {}_nC_k a^{n-k}b^k$

Data Graphs

Line Plots

A *line plot* displays data along a number line. Each number in the data set is represented by an X or another symbol.

Midterm Scores in Science

```
                        X
                        X     X
                        X     X     X
      X     X     X     X     X     X
      X     X     X     X     X     X
      X     X     X     X     X     X     X
    ─────────────────────────────────────────
     89    90    91    92    93    94    95
```

Scatter Plots

A *scatter plot* is a graph that shows data points on a coordinate grid. Each data point represents a pair of values.

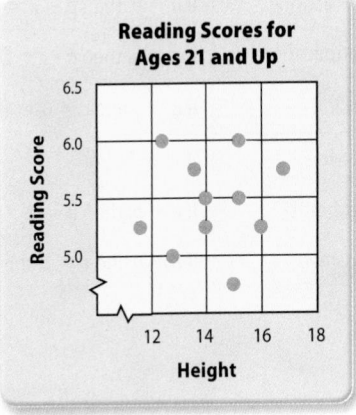

Histograms

A *histogram* displays the frequency of a set of data in equal-size intervals, or ranges, of data.

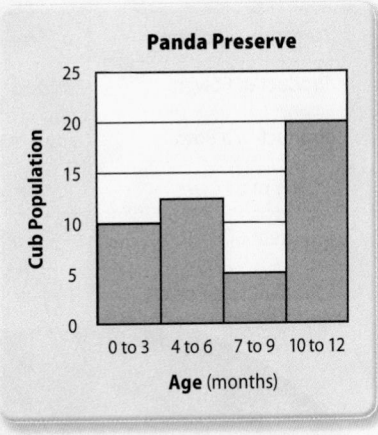

Stem-and-Leaf Plots

A *stem-and-leaf plot* is a data display that can be used to show how data are distributed. The data are in numerical order in two columns.

**Cars Parked
(Past 10 Days)**

Stem	Leaf
0	1 2 3 6
1	0 0 3 6
2	0 9

Key: 2 | 9 = 29

Box-and-Whisker Plots

A *box-and-whisker plot* is a data display that divides a set of data into four equal parts. It shows how the data are distributed among these parts.

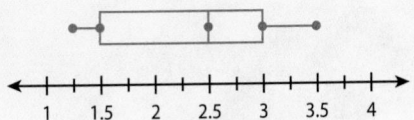

Venn Diagrams

A *Venn diagram* is a graphic display that uses overlapping circles (or squares) to show the relationship between sets and subsets of data.

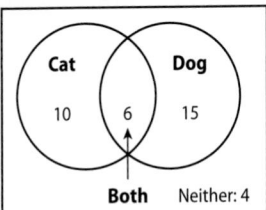

2349

Algebra

Properties of Equality

Addition	If $a = b$, then $a + c = b + c$.
Subtraction	If $a = b$, then $a - c = b - c$.
Multiplication	If $a = b$, then $a \cdot c = b \cdot c$.
Division	If $a = b$ and $c \neq 0$, then $\frac{a}{c} = \frac{b}{c}$.
Reflexive	$a = a$
Symmetric	If $a = b$, then $b = a$.
Transitive	If $a = b$ and $b = c$, then $a = c$.

Properties of Inequality

Addition	If $a < b$, then $a + c < b + c$.
Subtraction	If $a < b$, then $a - c < b - c$.
Multiplication	If $a < b$ and $c > 0$, then $a \cdot c < b \cdot c$.
	If $a < b$ and $c < 0$, then $a \cdot c > b \cdot c$.
Division	If $a < b$ and $c > 0$, then $\frac{a}{c} > \frac{b}{c}$.
	If $a < b$ and $c < 0$, then $\frac{a}{c} > \frac{b}{c}$.
Transitive	If $a < b$ and $b < c$, then $a < c$.

These properties are also true for $>$, $\leq$, and $\geq$.

Properties of Real Numbers

Commutative Property	$a + b = b + a$ $a \cdot b = b \cdot a$
Associative Property	$(a + b) + c = a + (b + c)$ $(a \cdot b) \cdot c = a \cdot (b \cdot c)$
Distributive Property	$a(b + c) = ab + ac$ $a(b - c) = ab - ac$
Closure for Addition	$a + b$ is a real number.
Closure for Multiplication	$a \cdot b$ is a real number.
Identity Property	$a + 0 = a$ $a \cdot 1 = a$
Inverse Property	$a + (-a) = 0$ $a \cdot \frac{1}{a} = 1$
Multiplication by 0	$a \cdot 0 = 0$
Multiplication by -1	$a \cdot (-1) = -a$
Zero Product	If $ab = 0$, then $a = 0$, $b = 0$ or both a and $b = 0$.

Properties of Exponents

Zero exponent	$a^0 = 1$
Negative exponent	$a^{-1} = \frac{1}{a}$
Product of Powers	$a^m \times a^n = a^{m+n}$
Product to a Power	$(ab)^n = a^n \times b^n$
Power of a Power	$(a^m)^n = a^{m \cdot n}$
Quotient of Powers	$\frac{a^m}{a^n} = a^{m-n}$
Quotient to a Power	$\left(\frac{a}{b}\right)^n = \frac{a^n}{b^n}$

Translating Word Problems into Algebra

1. Read the problem carefully, and determine what number or numbers need to be found.

2. Represent this unknown number with a variable, for example, *x*.

3. Identify key words that show what operations are used with the numbers and variables in the problem.

4. Words like *equals* or *is* tell you to write an equation rather than just an expression.

5. Use numbers, variables, operation symbols, and a relationship stated in the problem to write any expression needed.

6. To write an equation, write two expressions and connect them with an equals sign.

Solving Word Problems

Step 1 Read the problem carefully and determine what number or numbers you need to find.

Step 2 Represent one unknown number with a variable.

Step 3 Use a condition stated in the problem to write an expression for a second number.

Step 4 Use a second condition to find two expressions that are equal. Then write these two expressions algebraically and connect them with an equals sign.

Step 5 Solve the equation.

Step 6 Check to make sure the result matches the conditions stated in the problem.

Operations with Signed Numbers

Adding

If the numbers have the same signs, add the absolute values and use the sign of the numbers.	$5 + 11 = 16$	$-5 + (-11) = -16$
If the numbers have different signs, subtract their absolute values and use the sign of the number with the greater absolute value.	$-7 + 11 = 4$ $7 + (-11) = -4$	$-15 + 6 = -9$ $15 + (-6) = 9$

Subtracting

To subtract a number, add its opposite.	$8 - 6 = 8 + (-6)$	$-1 - 7 = -1 + (-7)$

Multiplying or Dividing

If two numbers have the same sign, their product or quotient is positive.	$(+)(+) = (+)$ $(-)(-) = (+)$	$(+) \div (+) = (+)$ $(-) \div (-) = (+)$
If two numbers have different signs, their product or quotient is negative.	$(+)(-) = (-)$ $(-)(+) = (-)$	$(+) \div (-) = (-)$ $(-) \div (+) = (-)$

Algebra

Graphing (x, y) on the Coordinate Plane

Value of x	Value of y	Location of Point
+	+	Quadrant I
−	+	Quadrant II
−	−	Quadrant III
+	−	Quadrant IV
0	+ or −	on the y-axis
+ or −	0	on the x-axis

Quadrant II (x negative, y positive)   Quadrant I (x positive, y positive)

Quadrant III (x negative, y negative)   Quadrant IV (x positive, y negative)

Formulas

Polynomials

Binomial squares	$(a + b)^2 = a^2 + 2ab + b^2$ $(a − b)^2 = a^2 − 2ab + b^2$
Difference of squares	$a^2 − b^2 = (a + b)(a − b)$
Difference of cubes	$a^3 − b^3 = (a − b)(a^2 + ab + b^2)$
Sum of cubes	$a^3 + b^3 = (a + b)(a^2 − ab + b^2)$

Linear Equations

Slope	$m = \dfrac{y_2 − y_1}{x_2 − x_1}$
Slope-Intercept Form	$y = mx + b$
Point-Slope Form	$y − y_1 = m(x − x_1)$
Standard Form	$Ax + By = C$

Quadratic Equations and Functions

Standard Form	$ax^2 + bx + c = 0$
Quadratic Formula	$x = \dfrac{−b \pm \sqrt{b^2 − 4ac}}{2a}$
Discriminant	$b^2 − 4ac$
Vertex Form of a Function	$f(x) = a(x − h)^2 + k$
Line of Symmetry	$x = −\dfrac{b}{2a}$

Distance

horizontal distance between two points (x_1, y_1) and (x_2, y_2) on the coordinate plane	$|x_2 − x_1|$
vertical distance between two points (x_1, y_1) and (x_2, y_2) on the coordinate plane	$|y_2 − y_1|$

Theorems

Rational Zeros Theorem	If the polynomial function has integer coefficients, then every rational zero has this form. $\frac{p}{q}$ ← a factor of the constant term ← a factor of the leading coefficient
Rational Roots Theorem	If a polynomial equation $P(x) = 0$ has integer coefficients, then every rational root has this form. $\frac{p}{q}$ ← a factor of the constant term ← a factor of the leading coefficient
The Fundamental Theorem of Algebra and Its Corollary	*Theorem:* If $P(x)$ is a polynomial of degree n, then the equation $P(x) = 0$ has at least one root, which is complex. *Corollary:* If $P(x)$ is a polynomial of degree n, then the equation $P(x) = 0$ has exactly n roots when multiplicities are taken into account.
The Remainder Theorem	If a polynomial function $P(x)$ is divided by $x - a$, then the remainder r is equal to $P(a)$.
Descartes' Rule of Signs for Negative Real Zeros	The number of negative real zeros of the polynomial function $P(x)$ is either: • equal to the number of sign changes in $P(-x)$ or • less than the number of sign changes in $P(-x)$ by an even number.
Irrational Zeros Theorem	If $P(x)$ has a zero of the form $a + b\sqrt{c}$, it also has a zero of the form $a - b\sqrt{c}$.

Systems of Two Linear Equations

One Solution	No Solution	Infinitely Many Solutions
consistent system independent system	inconsistent system	consistent system dependent system
intersecting lines	parallel lines	same line
different slopes	same slope different y-intercepts	same slope same y-intercept

Geometry

Formulas

Distance Formula	$d = \sqrt{(x_2 - x_1)^2 + (y_2 - y_1)^2}$	Lateral Area of a Regular Pyramid	$LA = \frac{1}{2}Ps$
Midpoint Formula	$\left(\frac{x_1 + x_2}{2}, \frac{y_1 + y_2}{2}\right)$	Lateral Area of a Regular Cone	$LA = \pi rs$
Slope m	$m = \frac{y_2 - y_1}{x_2 - x_1}$	Euler's Formula	$F + V = E + 2$
Slope-Intercept Form of an Equation for a Line	$y = mx + b$	Length of an Arc	$\ell = 2\pi r\left(\frac{x°}{360°}\right)$
Point-Slope Form of an Equation for a Line	$y - y_1 = m(x - x_1)$	Area of a Sector	$A = \pi r^2\left(\frac{x°}{360°}\right)$
Equation of a Circle	$(x - h)^2 + (y - k)^2 = r^2$ with center (h, k) and radius r		

Perimeter, Area, and Volume

Figure	Perimeter Formula	Area Formula
Regular Polygon	$P = ns$	$A = \frac{1}{2}ap$
Triangle	$P = s_1 + s_2 + s_3.$	$A = \frac{1}{2}bh$
Square	$P = 4s$	$A = s^2$
Rectangle	$P = 2\ell + 2w$ or $2(\ell + w)$	$A = \ell \cdot w$
Parallelogram	$P = 2(s_1 + s_2)$	$A = b \cdot h$
Trapezoid	$P = s_1 + s_2 + s_3 + s_4$	$A = \frac{1}{2}h(b_1 + b_2)$
Circle	circumference: $C = \pi d$ or $C = 2\pi r$	$A = \pi r^2$

Figure	Surface Area Formula	Volume Formula
Cube	$SA = 6s^2$	$V = s^3$
Rectangular Prism	$SA = Ph + 2B$	$V = Bh$
Pyramid	$SA = \frac{1}{2}P\ell + B$	$V = \frac{1}{3}Bh$
Cylinder	$SA = 2\pi rh + 2\pi r^2$	$V = \pi r^2 h$
Cone	$SA = \pi r\ell + \pi r^2$	$V = \frac{1}{3}\pi r^2 h$
Sphere	$SA = 4\pi r^2$	$V = \frac{4}{3}\pi r^3$

Congruence Properties

Property	Segments	Angles
Reflexive	$\overline{AB} \cong \overline{AB}$	$\angle X \cong \angle X$
Symmetric	If $\overline{AB} \cong \overline{CD}$, then $\overline{CD} \cong \overline{AB}$.	If $\angle X \cong \angle Y$, then $\angle Y \cong \angle X$.
Transitive	If $\overline{AB} \cong \overline{CD}$ and $\overline{CD} \cong \overline{EF}$, then $\overline{AB} \cong \overline{EF}$.	If $\angle X \cong \angle Y$ and $\angle Y \cong \angle Z$, then $\angle X \cong \angle Z$.

Logic Statements

Statement	In Words	In Symbols
Conditional	If p, then q.	$p \rightarrow q$
Inverse	If not p, then not q.	$\sim p \rightarrow \sim q$
Converse	If q, then p.	$q \rightarrow p$
Contrapositive	If not q, then not p.	$\sim q \rightarrow \sim p$
Biconditional	p if and only if q.	$p \leftrightarrow q$

Math SMART!

Truth Table for $p \rightarrow q$

Hypothesis p	Conclusion q	Conditional $p \rightarrow q$	Converse $q \rightarrow p$	Biconditional $p \leftrightarrow q$
T	T	T	T	T
T	F	F	T	F
F	T	T	F	F
F	F	T	T	T

Laws of Logic

The Law of Detachment

If $p \rightarrow q$ is true and p is true, then q is true.

Law of Syllogism

If $p \rightarrow q$ is true and $q \rightarrow r$ is true, then $p \rightarrow r$ must be true.

Types of Reasoning

Deductive Reasoning	• Uses properties, rules, definitions, theorems, given facts, and the laws of logic to arrive at a conclusion. • The conclusion must be true if the hypotheses are true.
Inductive Reasoning	• Uses observations and patterns. • The conclusion is not necessarily true.

Geometry

Angles

Angle Addition Postulate: If point *M* is in the interior of ∠*JKL*, then m∠*JKM* + m∠*MKL* = m∠*JKL*.

Linear Pair Theorem: If two angles form a linear pair, then they are supplementary.

Congruent Supplements Theorem: If two angles are supplementary to the same angle (or to congruent angles), then the angles are congruent.

Congruent Complements Theorem: If two angles are complementary to the same angle (or to congruent angles), then the angles are congruent.

Vertical Angles Theorem: Vertical angles are congruent.

Right Angle Congruence Theorem: All right angles are congruent.

Theorem (p. 628): If two angles are congruent and supplementary, then each angle is a right angle.

Corresponding Angles Postulate: If two parallel lines are cut by a transversal, then corresponding angles are congruent.

Converse of the Corresponding Angles Postulate: If two lines are cut by a transversal and corresponding angles are congruent, then the lines are parallel.

Alternate Interior Angles Theorem: If two parallel lines are cut by a transversal, then alternate interior angles are congruent.

Converse of the Alternate Interior Angles Theorem: If two lines are cut by a transversal and alternate interior angles are congruent, then the lines are parallel.

Alternate Exterior Angles Theorem: If two parallel lines are cut by a transversal, then alternate exterior angles are congruent.

Converse of the Alternate Exterior Angles Theorem: If two lines are cut by a transversal and alternate exterior angles are congruent, then the lines are parallel.

Same-Side Interior Angles Theorem: If two parallel lines are cut by a transversal, then same-side interior angles are supplementary.

Converse of the Same-Side Interior Angles Theorem: If two lines are cut by a transversal and same-side interior angles are supplementary, then the lines are parallel.

Polygons

Polygon Interior Angle-Sum Theorem: The sum of the measures of the interior angles of a polygon with *n* sides is $(n - 2)180°$.

Polygon Exterior Angle-Sum Theorem: The sum of the measures of the exterior angles of a polygon is 360°.

Parallel and Perpendicular Lines

Theorem (p. 633): In a plane, if two lines are perpendicular to the same line, then they are parallel.

Theorem (p. 814): If two non-vertical lines are parallel, then their slopes are equal.

Theorem (p. 814): If the slopes of two non-vertical lines are equal, then the lines are parallel.

Theorem (p. 816): If two non-vertical lines are perpendicular, then their slopes are negative reciprocals.

Theorem (p. 816): If the slopes of two non-vertical lines are negative reciprocals, then the lines are perpendicular.

Parallel Postulate: Given a line and a point not on the line, there is exactly one line through the point parallel to the line.

Circles

Arc Addition Postulate: The measure of an arc formed by two adjacent arcs is the sum of the measures of the two arcs. $m\widehat{AC} = m\widehat{AB} + m\widehat{BC}$	**Inscribed Angle Theorem:** The measure of an inscribed angle is half the measure of its intercepted arc.
Theorem (p. 728): In the same circle or in congruent circles, two minor arcs are congruent if and only if their central angles are congruent.	**Corollary:** If two inscribed angles intercept the same arc, then they are congruent.
Theorem (p. 734): In the same circle (or in congruent circles), congruent chords have congruent central angles.	**Corollary:** An angle inscribed in a semicircle is a right angle.
Converse of Theorem (p. 734): In the same circle (or in congruent circles), congruent central angles have congruent chords.	**Corollary:** If a quadrilateral is inscribed in a circle, then its opposite angles are supplementary.
Theorem (p. 736): In the same circle (or in congruent circles), congruent arcs have congruent chords.	**Tangent-Chord Angle Theorem:** The measure of an angle whose sides are a tangent and a chord equals half the measure of the intercepted arc.
Converse of Theorem (p. 736): In the same circle (or congruent circles), congruent chords have congruent arcs.	**Tangent-Tangent Angle Theorem:** The measure of the angle formed by two tangents drawn from a point outside a circle equals half the difference of the measures of the intercepted arcs.
Theorem (p. 738): If a diameter (or radius) is perpendicular to a chord, then it bisects the chord and its arc.	**Corollary:** The measure of the angle formed by two tangents drawn from a point outside a circle is 180° minus the measure of the intercepted minor arc.
Theorem (p. 738): If a radius bisects a chord that is not a diameter, then it is perpendicular to the chord.	**Chord-Chord Angle Theorem:** If two chords intersect in a circle, the measure of an angle formed is half the sum of the measures of arcs intercepted by the angle and its vertical angle.
Theorem (p. 738): The perpendicular bisector of a chord passes through the center of the circle.	**Secant-Secant Angle Theorem:** The measure of the angle formed by two secants drawn from a point outside a circle equals half the difference of the measures of the intercepted arcs.
Theorem (p. 739): If two chords of a circle are congruent, then they are equidistant from the center.	**Secant-Tangent Theorem:** The measure of the angle formed by a secant and a tangent drawn from a point in the exterior of a circle equals half the difference of the measures of the intercepted arcs.
Theorem (p. 739): If two chords of a circle are equidistant from the center, then they are congruent.	**Theorem (p. 758):** If two chords intersect inside a circle, then the product of the segment lengths of one chord is equal to the product of the segment lengths of the other.
Theorem (p. 740): If a line is tangent to a circle, then it is perpendicular to the radius drawn to the point of tangency.	**Theorem (p. 760):** If two secants intersect outside a circle, then the product of the lengths of one secant segment and its external segment is equal to the product of the other secant segment and its external segment.
Theorem (p. 740): If a line in the plane of a circle is perpendicular to the radius at a point on the circle, then the line is tangent to the circle.	**Theorem (p. 762):** If a secant and a tangent intersect outside a circle, then the product of the lengths of the secant segment and its external segment is equal to the length of the tangent segment squared.
Two-Tangent Theorem: Two tangent segments drawn from a point not on a circle are congruent.	

Geometry

Quadrilaterals

Theorem (p. 644): If both pairs of opposite sides of a quadrilateral are congruent, then the quadrilateral is a parallelogram.

Theorem (p. 645): If two sides of a quadrilateral are both congruent and parallel, then the quadrilateral is a parallelogram.

Theorem (p. 650): The diagonals of a rectangle are congruent.

Theorem (p. 651): If a parallelogram has one right angle, then it is a rectangle.

Theorem (p. 652): The diagonals of a rhombus are perpendicular.

Theorem (p. 652): The diagonals of a rhombus bisect the angles of the rhombus.

Trapezoid Midsegment Theorem: The midsegment of a trapezoid is parallel to each of the bases, and its length is half the sum of the lengths of the bases.

Theorem (p. 658): The base angles of an isosceles trapezoid are congruent.

Theorem (p. 659): The diagonals of an isosceles trapezoid are congruent.

Theorem (p. 660): If a quadrilateral is a kite, then exactly one pair of opposite angles is congruent.

Theorem (p. 661): The diagonals of a kite are perpendicular.

Triangles

Triangle Inequality Theorem: The sum of the lengths of any two sides of a triangle is always greater than the length of the third side.

Hinge Theorem: If two sides of one triangle are congruent to two sides of another triangle, but their included angles are not congruent, then the side opposite the larger included angle is longer than the side opposite the smaller included angle.

Converse of Hinge Theorem: If two sides of one triangle are congruent to two sides of another triangle, but the third sides are not congruent, then the angle opposite the longer side is larger than the angle opposite the shorter side.

Triangle Angle-Sum Theorem: The sum of the angle measures of a triangle is 180°.

Corollary: The acute angles of a right triangle are complementary.

Corollary: The measure of each angle of an equiangular triangle is 60°.

Exterior Angle Theorem: The measure of an exterior angle of a triangle equals the sum of the measures of its remote interior angles.

Pythagorean Inequality Theorem: Given: a, b, and c are the side lengths of a triangle with c the length of the longest side:

If $c^2 < a^2 + b^2$, then $\triangle ABC$ is acute.
If $c^2 > a^2 + b^2$, then $\triangle ABC$ is obtuse.

Side-Side-Side Congruence Postulate (SSS): If three sides of one triangle are congruent to the corresponding three sides of another triangle, then the triangles are congruent.

Side-Angle-Side Congruence Postulate (SAS): If two sides and the included angle of one triangle are congruent to the corresponding sides and included angle of another triangle, then the triangles are congruent.

Angle-Side-Angle Congruence Postulate (ASA): If two angles and the included side of one triangle are congruent to the corresponding angles and included side of another triangle, then the triangles are congruent.

Angle-Angle-Side Congruence Theorem (AAS): If two angles and a non-included side of one triangle are congruent to the corresponding angles and non-included side of another triangle, then the triangles are congruent.

Angle-Angle Similarity Postulate (AA): If two angles of one triangle are congruent to the corresponding angles of another triangle, then the triangles are similar.

Triangles (continued)

CPCTC: Corresponding Parts of Congruent Triangles are Congruent.

Theorem (p. 784): If two sides of a triangle are congruent, then the angles opposite those sides are congruent.

Theorem (p. 784): If two angles of a triangle are congruent, then the sides opposite those angles are congruent.

Theorem (p. 786): If a triangle is equilateral, it is also equiangular.

Theorem (p. 786): If a triangle is equiangular, it is also equilateral.

Side-Side-Side Similarity Theorem (SSS): If three sides of one triangle are proportional to the corresponding sides of another triangle, then the triangles are similar.

Side-Angle-Side Similarity Theorem (SAS): If two sides of one triangle are proportional to the corresponding sides of another triangle and the included angles are congruent, then the triangles are similar.

Theorem (p. 804): If a segment that is parallel to a side of a triangle intersects the other two sides, then it divides those two sides into proportional segments.

Theorem (p. 804): If a segment divides two sides of a triangle into proportional segments, then it is parallel to the third side.

Theorem (p. 805): An angle bisector of a triangle divides the opposite sides into two segments that are proportional to the other two sides of the triangle.

Theorem (p. 806): A midsegment of a triangle is parallel to one side of the triangle and is half as long as that side.

Theorem (p. 831): The lines that contain the altitudes of a triangle are concurrent.

Right Triangles

Pythagorean Theorem: The sum of the squares of the lengths of the legs of a right triangle equals the square of the length of the hypotenuse.

$$a^2 + b^2 = c^2$$

Converse of the Pythagorean Theorem: If the sum of the squares of the lengths of two sides of a triangle is equal to the square of the length of the third side, then the triangle is a right triangle.

45°–45°–90° Triangle Theorem: In a 45°–45°–90° triangle, the length of the hypotenuse is $\sqrt{2}$ times the length of a leg.

30°–60°–90° Triangle Theorem: In a 30°–60°–90° triangle, the hypotenuse is twice the length of the shorter leg, and the longer leg is $\sqrt{3}$ times the length of the shorter leg.

Leg-Leg Congruence (LL): If both legs of a right triangle are congruent to the corresponding legs of another right triangle, then the triangles are congruent.

Leg-Angle Congruence (LA): If one leg and an acute angle of a right triangle are congruent to the corresponding leg and acute angle of another right triangle, then the triangles are congruent.

Hypotenuse-Angle Congruence (HA): If the hypotenuse and an acute angle of a right triangle are congruent to the hypotenuse and corresponding acute angle of another right triangle, then the triangles are congruent.

Hypotenuse-Leg Congruence (HL): If the hypotenuse and one leg of a right triangle are congruent to the hypotenuse and corresponding leg of another right triangle, then the triangles are congruent.

Theorem (p. 796): If the altitude is drawn to the hypotenuse of a right triangle, then the two triangles formed are similar to the original triangle and to each other.

Corollary: The length of the altitude drawn to the hypotenuse of a right triangle is the geometric mean of the lengths of the segments into which it divides the hypotenuse.

Corollary: The length of a leg of a right triangle is the geometric mean of the lengths of the hypotenuse and the adjacent segment of the hypotenuse.

Challenge YOURSELF!

Advanced Algebra

Formulas

Conic Sections

Circles	$(x-h)^2 + (y-k)^2 = r^2$	$\dfrac{(x-h)^2}{r^2} + \dfrac{(y-k)^2}{r^2} = 1$
	Horizontal Axis	**Vertical Axis**
Ellipse	$\dfrac{(x-h)^2}{a^2} + \dfrac{(y-k)^2}{b^2} = 1$	$\dfrac{(x-h)^2}{b^2} + \dfrac{(y-k)^2}{a^2} = 1$
Hyperbola	$\dfrac{(x-h)^2}{a^2} - \dfrac{(y-k)^2}{b^2} = 1$	$\dfrac{(x-h)^2}{b^2} - \dfrac{(y-k)^2}{a^2} = 1$
Parabola	$x - h = \dfrac{1}{4p}(y-k)^2$	$y - k = \dfrac{1}{4p}(x-h)^2$

Variation

Inverse Variation	$y = \dfrac{k}{x}$ or $k = xy$
Direct Variation	$y = kx$, or $k = \dfrac{y}{x}$
Joint Variation	$y = kxz$ or $k = \dfrac{y}{xz}$
Power Function	$y = ax^b$

Interest

Simple Interest	$I = Prt$
Compound Interest	$A = P\left(1 + \dfrac{r}{n}\right)^{nt}$

Exponential Models

Growth	$A(t) = a(1+r)^t$
Decay	$A(t) = a(1-r)^t$

Sequences and Series

	Arithmetic	**Geometric**
First term	a or a_1	a or a_1
Number of terms	n	n
Constant	difference, d	ratio, r
Sequence, explicit	$a_n = a_1 + (n-1)d$	$a_n = a_1 r^{n-1}$, if $r \neq 0$
Sequence, recursive	$a_n = a_{n-1} + d$	$a_n = r \cdot a_{n-1}$
Partial Sum of Sequence (Sum of finite series)	$S_n = \dfrac{n(a_1 + a_n)}{2}$; $S_n = \dfrac{n[2a_1 + (n-1)d]}{2}$	$S_n = \dfrac{a_1(1 - r^n)}{1 - r}$, if $r \neq 1$
Sum of Infinite Series	None	$S = \dfrac{a_1}{1 - r}$, if $|r| < 1$
Fibonacci sequence	$a_n = \dfrac{\left(1 + \sqrt{5}\right)^n - \left(1 - \sqrt{5}\right)^n}{2^n \sqrt{5}}$	

Cramer's Rule

| 2 equations in 2 variables | $x = \dfrac{\det(M_x)}{\det(M_c)} = \dfrac{\begin{vmatrix} c & b \\ f & e \end{vmatrix}}{\begin{vmatrix} a & b \\ d & e \end{vmatrix}}$ and $y = \dfrac{\det(M_y)}{\det(M_c)} = \dfrac{\begin{vmatrix} a & c \\ d & f \end{vmatrix}}{\begin{vmatrix} a & b \\ d & e \end{vmatrix}}$ | 3 equations in 3 variables | $x = \dfrac{\det(M_x)}{\det(M_c)}, y = \dfrac{\det(M_y)}{\det(M_c)}, z = \dfrac{\det(M_z)}{\det(M_c)}$ |

Properties of Logarithms

	Exponential	For all b	Common logs	Natural logs
Zero	$b^0 = 1, b \neq 0$	$\log_b 1 = 0$	$\log 1 = 0$	$\ln 1 = 0$
One	$b^1 = b$	$\log_b b = 1$	$\log 10 = 1$	$\ln e = 1$
Product	$b^x \cdot b^y = b^{x+y}$	$\log_b(xy) = \log_b x + \log_b y$	$\log(xy) = \log x + \log y$	$\ln(xy) = \ln x + \ln y$
Quotient	$b^{\frac{x}{y}} = b^{x-y}, y \neq 0$	$\log_b\left(\dfrac{x}{y}\right) = \log_b x - \log_b y$	$\log\left(\dfrac{x}{y}\right) = \log x - \log y$	$\ln\left(\dfrac{x}{y}\right) = \ln x - \ln y$
Reciprocal	$b^{\frac{1}{y}} = b^{-y}, y \neq 0$	$\log_b\left(\dfrac{1}{y}\right) = -\log_b y$	$\log\left(\dfrac{1}{y}\right) = -\log y$	$\ln\left(\dfrac{1}{y}\right) = -\ln y$
Power	$(b^x)^y = b^{xy}$	$\log_b x^y = y \log_b x$	$\log x^y = y \log x$	$\ln x^y = y \ln x$
Change of Base		$\log_b x = \dfrac{\log x}{\log b} = \dfrac{\ln x}{\ln b}$		

Properties of Radicals

Exponents	$a^{\frac{1}{n}} = \sqrt[n]{a}, n \neq 0$	$a^{\frac{m}{n}} = \left(\sqrt[n]{a}\right)^m = \sqrt[n]{a^m}, n \neq 0$
Product Rule	$\sqrt{a \cdot b} = \sqrt{a} \cdot \sqrt{b}$	$\sqrt[n]{a} \cdot \sqrt[n]{b} = \sqrt[n]{ab}$
Quotient Rule	$\dfrac{\sqrt{a}}{\sqrt{b}} = \sqrt{\dfrac{a}{b}}, b \neq 0$	$\dfrac{\sqrt[n]{a}}{\sqrt[n]{b}} = \sqrt[n]{\dfrac{a}{b}}, b \neq 0$

Go For It!

Transformations of Functions

Reflections

$g(x) = -f(x)$	over x-axis
$g(x) = f(-x)$	over y-axis

Dilations

$g(x) = f(cx)$	horizontal $0 < c < 1$: stretch $c > 1$: shrink
$g(x) = c \cdot f(x)$	vertical $0 < c < 1$: shrink $c > 1$: stretch

Translations

$g(x) = f(x - h) + k$	$h > 0$: right h units
$g(x) = ab^{x-h} + k$	$h < 0$: left h units
$g(x) = \dfrac{a}{x - h} + k$	$k > 0$: up k units
$g(x) = \sqrt{x - h} + k$	$k < 0$: down k units

Advanced Algebra

Solving Word Problems

Step 1	Read the problem carefully. Determine what number or numbers need to be found.
Step 2	Represent one unknown number with a suitable variable.
Step 3	Use conditions stated in the problem to write expressions for other numbers.
Step 4	Use additional conditions to find the relationship between expressions. Write the expressions algebraically. Connect them with the appropriate sign ($=, <, >, \leq,$ or $\geq$.)
Step 5	Solve the equation or inequality.
Step 6	Check to see if the resulting solution matches the conditions stated in the problem.

Word Problem Formulas

Distance	$d = rt$	d = distance r = rate t = time
Consecutive Number	$A = n + (n + 1)$ $B = n(n + 2)$	n = the first of two consecutive numbers $n + 1$ = the next consecutive number $n + 2$ = the next consecutive odd or even number A = sum of two consecutive numbers B = product of two consecutive odd (or even) numbers
Digit	$A(u + t + h) = u + 10t + 100h$	A = number multiplied by the sum of the digits u = the ones digit of the given number t = the tens digit of the given number h = the hundreds digit of the given number
Coin	$0.25q + 0.1d + 0.05n + 0.01p = A$	q = number of quarters d = number of dimes n = number of nickels p = number of pennies A = total worth
Lever	$\ell_1 w_1 = \ell_2 w_2$	ℓ_1 = length from fulcrum to first weight w_1 = first weight ℓ_2 = length from fulcrum to second weight w_2 = second weight
Work	$\dfrac{1}{a} + \dfrac{1}{b} = \dfrac{1}{n}$	a = length of time it takes person A to complete a task b = length of time it takes person B to complete a task n = length of time it would take A and B to complete the task together

Word Problem Formulas (continued)

Mixture Use this table format.

Concentration	Volume	Percent Substance	Total Volume Substance
1	V	$a\%$	$0.01(a)(V)$
2	Total $- V$	$b\%$	$0.01(b)(\text{Total} - V)$
Final	Total	$c\%$	$0.01(c)(\text{Total})$

Parent Functions

Linear (Identity)
$y = x$

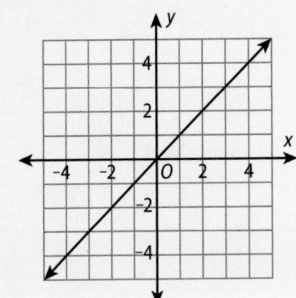

Quadratic (Squared)
$y = x^2$

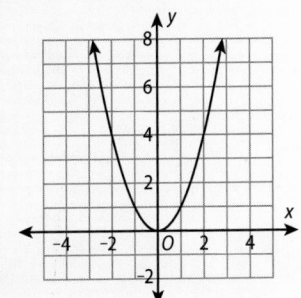

Cubic (Cubed)
$y = x^3$

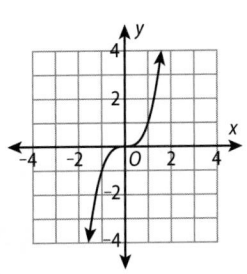

Rational (Reciprocal)
$y = \frac{1}{x}$

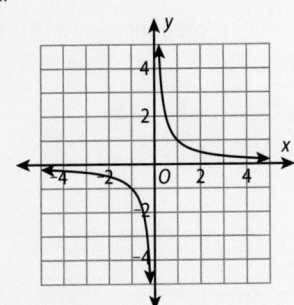

Radical (Square Root)
$y = \sqrt{x}$

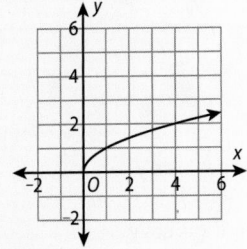

Cube Root
$y = \sqrt[3]{x}$

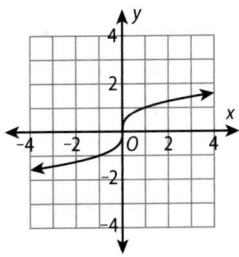

Absolute Value
$y = |x|$

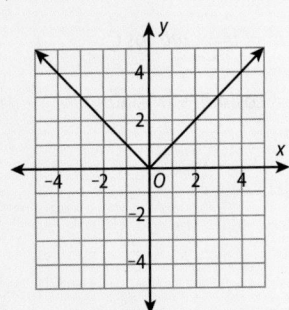

Exponential
$y = e^x$

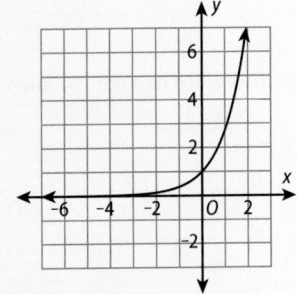

Natural Logarithm
$y = \ln x$

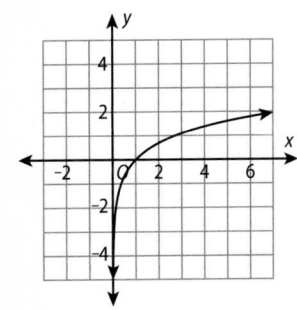

Trigonometry

Trigonometric Ratios

$$\sin A = \frac{\text{leg opposite } \angle A}{\text{hypotenuse}} \qquad \cos A = \frac{\text{leg adjacent } \angle A}{\text{hypotenuse}} \qquad \tan A = \frac{\text{leg opposite } \angle A}{\text{leg adjacent } \angle A}$$

$$\csc A = \frac{\text{hypotenuse}}{\text{leg opposite } \angle A} \qquad \sec A = \frac{\text{hypotenuse}}{\text{leg adjacent } \angle A} \qquad \cot A = \frac{\text{leg adjacent } \angle A}{\text{leg opposite } \angle A}$$

Trigonometric Values of the Special Angles

Degrees	Radians	$\sin \theta$	$\cos \theta$	$\tan \theta$	$\csc \theta$	$\sec \theta$	$\cot \theta$
0	0	0	1	0	undefined	1	undefined
30	$\frac{\pi}{6}$	$\frac{1}{2}$	$\frac{\sqrt{3}}{2}$	$\frac{\sqrt{3}}{3}$	2	$\frac{2\sqrt{3}}{3}$	$\sqrt{3}$
45	$\frac{\pi}{4}$	$\frac{\sqrt{2}}{2}$	$\frac{\sqrt{2}}{2}$	1	$\sqrt{2}$	$\sqrt{2}$	1
60	$\frac{\pi}{3}$	$\frac{\sqrt{3}}{2}$	$\frac{1}{2}$	$\sqrt{3}$	$\frac{2\sqrt{3}}{3}$	2	$\frac{\sqrt{3}}{3}$
90	$\frac{\pi}{2}$	1	0	undefined	1	undefined	0

Conversion Formulas

Degrees to Radians:	$y \text{ radians} = x° \cdot \frac{\pi \text{ radians}}{180°}$	Radians to Degrees:	$y° = x \text{ radians} \cdot \frac{180°}{\pi \text{ radians}}$
Rectangular coordinates to Polar coordinates:		Polar coordinates to Rectangular coordinates:	
$P(x, y)$	$r = \pm\sqrt{x^2 + y^2}$ and $\cos q = \frac{x}{r}$ and $\sin q = \frac{y}{r}$	$P(r, q)$	$x = r \cos q$ and $y = r \sin q$

Rules and Properties

Inverse sine	$y = \sin^{-1} x$ if and only if $x = \sin y$
Inverse cosine	$y = \cos^{-1} x$ if and only if $x = \cos y$
Inverse tangent	$y = \tan^{-1} x$ if and only if $x = \tan y$
Law of Sines	$\frac{\sin A}{a} = \frac{\sin B}{b} = \frac{\sin C}{c}$
Law of Cosines	$a^2 = b^2 + c^2 - 2bc \cos A \qquad b^2 = a^2 + c^2 - 2ac \cos B \qquad c^2 = a^2 + b^2 - 2ab \cos C$
DeMoivre's Theorem	Let $z = r \cos \theta + (r \sin \theta)i$ and n be a positive integer. $\qquad z^n = r^n \cos(n\theta) + (r^n \sin(n\theta))i$
Magnitude of a Vector in the Plane	$\left\| \overrightarrow{PQ} \right\| = \sqrt{(x_2 - x_1)^2 + (y_2 - y_1)^2}$
Angle Between Two Vectors	$\mathbf{u} \cdot \mathbf{v} = \|\mathbf{u}\| \|\mathbf{v}\| \cos \theta$
Dot Product of Two Vectors	$\mathbf{u} \cdot \mathbf{v} = x_1 x_2 + y_1 y_2$

Identities

Reciprocal Identities

$\sin\theta = \dfrac{1}{\csc\theta}$	$\cos\theta = \dfrac{1}{\sec\theta}$	$\tan\theta = \dfrac{1}{\cot\theta}$
$\csc\theta = \dfrac{1}{\sin\theta}$	$\sec\theta = \dfrac{1}{\cos\theta}$	$\cot\theta = \dfrac{1}{\tan\theta}$

Quotient Identities

$\tan\theta = \dfrac{\sin\theta}{\cos\theta}$	$\cot\theta = \dfrac{\cos\theta}{\sin\theta}$

Negative Identities

$\sin(-\theta) = -\sin\theta$	$\cos(-\theta) = \cos\theta$	$\tan(-\theta) = -\tan\theta$
$\csc(-\theta) = -\csc\theta$	$\sec(-\theta) = \sec\theta$	$\cot(-\theta) = -\cot\theta$

Pythagorean Identities

$\cos^2\theta + \sin^2\theta = 1$	$\tan^2\theta + 1 = \sec^2\theta$	$\cot^2\theta + 1 = \csc^2\theta$
$\sin\theta = \pm\sqrt{1 - \cos^2\theta}$	$\sec\theta = \pm\sqrt{1 + \tan^2\theta}$	$\csc\theta = \pm\sqrt{1 + \cot^2\theta}$

Cofunction Identities

$\sin\theta = \cos(90° - \theta)$	$\tan\theta = \cot(90° - \theta)$	$\sec\theta = \csc(90° - \theta)$
$\cos\theta = \sin(90° - \theta)$	$\cot\theta = \tan(90° - \theta)$	$\csc\theta = \sec(90° - \theta)$

Coterminal Identities

$\sin\theta = \sin(360° + \theta)$	$\cos\theta = \cos(360° + \theta)$	$\tan\theta = \tan(360° + \theta)$
$\csc\theta = \csc(360° + \theta)$	$\sec\theta = \sec(360° + \theta)$	$\cot\theta = \cot(360° + \theta)$

Sum and Difference Identities

$\sin(\alpha + \beta) = \sin\alpha\cos\beta + \cos\alpha\sin\beta$	$\sin(\alpha - \beta) = \sin\alpha\cos\beta - \cos\alpha\sin\beta$
$\cos(\alpha + \beta) = \cos\alpha\cos\beta - \sin\alpha\sin\beta$	$\cos(\alpha - \beta) = \cos\alpha\cos\beta + \sin\alpha\sin\beta$
$\tan(\alpha + \beta) = \dfrac{\tan\alpha + \tan\beta}{1 - \tan\alpha\tan\beta}$	$\tan(\alpha - \beta) = \dfrac{\tan\alpha - \tan\beta}{1 + \tan\alpha\tan\beta}$

Double-Angle Identities

$\sin 2\alpha = 2\sin\alpha\cos\alpha$	$\cos 2\alpha = \cos^2\alpha - \sin^2\alpha$
	$\cos 2\alpha = 1 - 2\sin^2\alpha$
$\tan 2\alpha = \dfrac{2\tan\alpha}{1 - \tan^2\alpha}$	$\cos 2\alpha = 2\cos^2\alpha - 1$

Identities (continued)

Half-Angle Identities

$$\sin\frac{\alpha}{2} = \pm\sqrt{\frac{1 - \cos\alpha}{2}}$$

$$\cos\frac{\alpha}{2} = \pm\sqrt{\frac{1 + \cos\alpha}{2}}$$

$$\tan\frac{\alpha}{2} = \pm\sqrt{\frac{1 - \cos\alpha}{1 + \cos\alpha}}, \cos\alpha \neq -1$$

$$\tan\frac{\alpha}{2} = \frac{1 - \cos\alpha}{\sin\alpha}, \sin\alpha \neq 0$$

$$\tan\frac{\alpha}{2} = \frac{\sin\alpha}{1 + \cos\alpha}, \cos\alpha \neq -1$$

Product-to-Sum Identities

$$\cos\alpha\cos\beta = \frac{1}{2}\left[\cos(\alpha - \beta) + \cos(\alpha + \beta)\right]$$

$$\sin\alpha\cos\beta = \frac{1}{2}\left[\sin(\alpha + \beta) + \sin(\alpha - \beta)\right]$$

$$\sin\alpha\sin\beta = \frac{1}{2}\left[\cos(\alpha - \beta) - \cos(\alpha + \beta)\right]$$

$$\cos\alpha\sin\beta = \frac{1}{2}\left[\sin(\alpha + \beta) - \sin(\alpha - \beta)\right]$$

Sum-to-Product Identities

$$\sin x + \sin y = 2\sin\left(\frac{x + y}{2}\right)\cos\left(\frac{x - y}{2}\right)$$

$$\cos x + \cos y = 2\cos\left(\frac{x + y}{2}\right)\cos\left(\frac{x - y}{2}\right)$$

$$\sin x - \sin y = 2\cos\left(\frac{x + y}{2}\right)\sin\left(\frac{x - y}{2}\right)$$

$$\cos x - \cos y = -2\sin\left(\frac{x + y}{2}\right)\sin\left(\frac{x - y}{2}\right)$$

Trigonometry

Trigonometric Functions

Angle	Radians	Sine	Cosine	Tangent	Cotangent	Secant	Cosecant		
0°	0.0000	0.0000	1.0000	0.0000	undefined	1.0000	undefined	1.5708	90°
1	0.0175	0.0175	0.9998	0.0175	57.2900	1.0002	57.2987	1.5533	89
2	0.0349	0.0349	0.9994	0.0349	28.6363	1.0006	28.6537	1.5359	88
3	0.0524	0.0523	0.9986	0.0524	19.0811	1.0014	19.1073	1.5184	87
4	0.0698	0.0698	0.9976	0.0699	14.3007	1.0024	14.3356	1.5010	86
5	0.0873	0.0872	0.9962	0.0875	11.4301	1.0038	11.4737	1.4835	85
6	0.1047	0.1045	0.9945	0.1051	9.5144	1.0055	9.5668	1.4661	84
7	0.1222	0.1219	0.9925	0.1228	8.1443	1.0075	8.2055	1.4486	83
8	0.1396	0.1392	0.9903	0.1405	7.1154	1.0098	7.1853	1.4312	82
9	0.1571	0.1564	0.9877	0.1584	6.3138	1.0125	6.3925	1.4137	81
10	0.1745	0.1736	0.9848	0.1763	5.6713	1.0154	5.7588	1.3963	80
11	0.1920	0.1908	0.9816	0.1944	5.1446	1.0187	5.2408	1.3788	79
12	0.2094	0.2079	0.9781	0.2126	4.7046	1.0223	4.8097	1.3614	78
13	0.2269	0.2250	0.9744	0.2309	4.3315	1.0263	4.4454	1.3439	77
14	0.2443	0.2419	0.9703	0.2493	4.0108	1.0306	4.1336	1.3265	76
15	0.2618	0.2588	0.9659	0.2679	3.7321	1.0353	3.8637	1.3090	75
16	0.2793	0.2756	0.9613	0.2867	3.4874	1.0403	3.6280	1.2915	74
17	0.2967	0.2924	0.9563	0.3057	3.2709	1.0457	3.4203	1.2714	73
18	0.3142	0.3090	0.9511	0.3249	3.0777	1.0515	3.2361	1.2566	72
19	0.3316	0.3256	0.9455	0.3443	2.9042	1.0576	3.0716	1.2392	71
20	0.3491	0.3420	0.9397	0.3640	2.7475	1.0642	2.9238	1.2217	70
21	0.3665	0.3584	0.9336	0.3839	2.6051	1.0711	2.7904	1.2043	69
22	0.3840	0.3746	0.9272	0.4040	2.4751	1.0785	2.6695	1.1868	68
23	0.4014	0.3907	0.9205	0.4245	2.3559	1.0864	2.5593	1.1694	67
24	0.4189	0.4067	0.9135	0.4452	2.2460	1.0946	2.4586	1.1519	66
25	0.4363	0.4226	0.9063	0.4663	2.1445	1.1034	2.3662	1.1345	65
26	0.4538	0.4384	0.8988	0.4877	2.0503	1.1126	2.2812	1.1170	64
27	0.4712	0.4540	0.8910	0.5095	1.9626	1.1223	2.2027	1.0996	63
28	0.4887	0.4695	0.8829	0.5317	1.8807	1.1326	2.1301	1.0821	62
29	0.5061	0.4848	0.8746	0.5543	1.8040	1.1434	2.0627	1.0647	61
30	0.5236	0.5000	0.8660	0.5774	1.7321	1.1547	2.0000	1.0472	60
31	0.5411	0.5150	0.8572	0.6009	1.6643	1.1666	1.9416	1.0297	59
32	0.5585	0.5299	0.8480	0.6249	1.6003	1.1792	1.8871	1.0123	58
33	0.5760	0.5446	0.8387	0.6494	1.5399	1.1924	1.8361	0.9948	57
34	0.5934	0.5592	0.8290	0.6745	1.4826	1.2062	1.7883	0.9774	56
35	0.6109	0.5736	0.8192	0.7002	1.4281	1.2208	1.7434	0.9599	55
36	0.6283	0.5878	0.8090	0.7265	1.3764	1.2361	1.7013	0.9425	54
37	0.6458	0.6018	0.7986	0.7536	1.3270	1.2521	1.6616	0.9250	53
38	0.6632	0.6157	0.7880	0.7813	1.2799	1.2690	1.6243	0.9076	52
39	0.6807	0.6293	0.7771	0.8098	1.2349	1.2868	1.5890	0.8901	51
40	0.6981	0.6428	0.7660	0.8391	1.1918	1.3054	1.5557	0.8727	50
41	0.7156	0.6561	0.7547	0.8693	1.1504	1.3250	1.5243	0.8552	49
42	0.7330	0.6691	0.7431	0.9004	1.1106	1.3456	1.4945	0.8378	48
43	0.7505	0.6820	0.7314	0.9325	1.0724	1.3673	1.4663	0.8203	47
44	0.7679	0.6947	0.7093	0.9657	1.0355	1.3902	1.4396	0.8029	46
45°	0.7854	0.7071	0.7071	1.0000	1.0000	1.4142	1.4142	0.7854	45°
		Cosine	Sine	Cotangent	Tangent	Cosecant	Secant	Radians	Angle

Parent Functions

Sine

$y = \sin x$

period = 2π; amplitude = 1

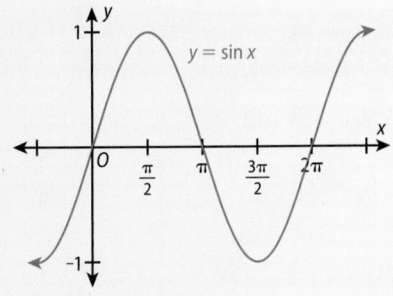

Cosine

$y = \cos x$

period = 2π; amplitude = 1

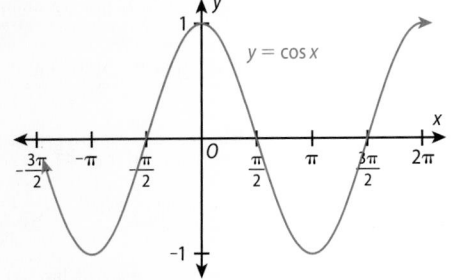

Tangent

$y = \tan x$

period = π; asymptotes: $x = \frac{\pi}{2} + k\pi$

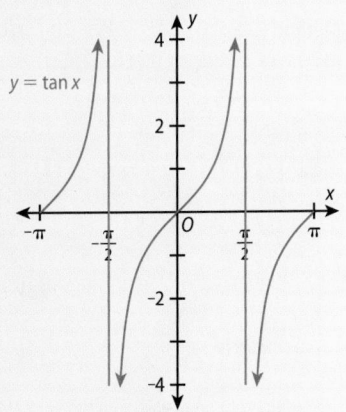

Cotangent

$y = \cot x$

period = π; asymptotes: $x = k\pi$

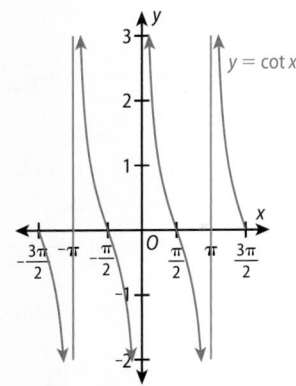

Secant

$y = \sec x$

period = π; asymptotes: $x = \frac{\pi}{2} + k\pi$

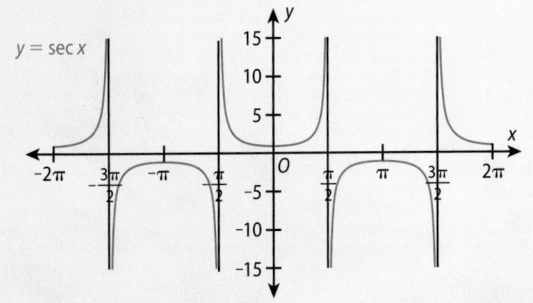

Cosecant

$y = \csc x$

period = π; asymptotes: $x = k\pi$

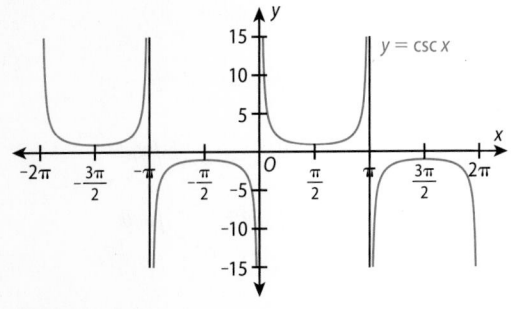

Calculus

Limit Rules

Constant Rule	$\lim\limits_{x \to c} k = k$
Constant Multiplier Rule	$\lim\limits_{x \to c} kf(x) = k \lim\limits_{x \to c} f(x)$
Sum Rule	$\lim\limits_{x \to c} [f(x) + g(x)] = \lim\limits_{x \to c} f(x) + \lim\limits_{x \to c} g(x)$
Difference Rule	$\lim\limits_{x \to c} [f(x) - g(x)] = \lim\limits_{x \to c} f(x) - \lim\limits_{x \to c} g(x)$
Product Rule	$\lim\limits_{x \to c} [f(x) \cdot g(x)] = \lim\limits_{x \to c} f(x) \cdot \lim\limits_{x \to c} g(x)$
Quotient Rule	$\lim\limits_{x \to c} \dfrac{f(x)}{g(x)} = \dfrac{\lim\limits_{x \to c} f(x)}{\lim\limits_{x \to c} g(x)}$, if $\lim\limits_{x \to c} g(x) \neq 0$
Power Rule	$\lim\limits_{x \to c} [f(x)]^n = \left[\lim\limits_{x \to c} f(x) \right]^n$
nth Root Rule	$\lim\limits_{x \to c} \sqrt[n]{f(x)} = \sqrt[n]{\lim\limits_{x \to c} f(x)}$, if $\lim\limits_{x \to c} f(x) > 0$
Limits of Radicals	$\lim\limits_{x \to c} \sqrt[n]{x} = \sqrt[n]{c}$, for all c when n is odd, and for $c > 0$ when n is even.
Limits of Composite Functions	If $\lim\limits_{x \to c} g(x) = L$ and $\lim\limits_{x \to c} f(x) = f(L)$, then $f(g(x)) = f\left(\lim\limits_{x \to c} g(x)\right) = f(L).$

For Derivative Rules, see the table of Derivatives on the next page, or go to pages 2170 and 2172 for constant, sum, difference, power, product, and quotient rules.

For Integral Rules, see the table of Integrals on the next page, or go to page 2234 for constant, constant multiplier, sum, difference, and power rules.

Volume of a Solid of Revolution

Disk Method (x-axis)	$V = \pi \int_a^b [R(x)]^2\, dx$
Disk Method (y-axis)	$V = \pi \int_a^b [R(y)]^2\, dy$
Washer Method (x-axis)	$V = \pi \int_a^b (f(x))^2 - (g(x))^2\, dx$
Washer Method (y-axis)	$V = \pi \int_a^b (f(y))^2 - (g(y))^2\, dy$
Shell Method (x-axis)	$V = 2\pi \int_a^b yf(y)dx$
Shell Method (y-axis)	$V = 2\pi \int_a^b xf(x)dx$

Formulas, Theorems, and Definitions

Special Trigonometric Limits	$\lim\limits_{a \to 0} \dfrac{\sin a}{a} = 1;\ \lim\limits_{a \to 0} \dfrac{1 - \cos a}{a} = 0$
Definition of a Derivative	$f'(x) = \lim\limits_{\Delta x \to 0} \dfrac{f(x + \Delta x) - f(x)}{\Delta x}$
Chain Rule	$\dfrac{d}{dx}[f(g(x))] = f'(g(x)) \cdot g'(x)$
The Mean Value Theorem	$f'(c) = \dfrac{f(b) - f(a)}{b - a}$
Area Between Two Curves	$A = \int_a^b f(x)dx - \int_a^b g(x)dx = \int_a^b [f(x) - g(x)]dx$
Fundamental Theorem of Calculus	$\int_a^b f(x)dx = F(b) - F(a)$
Second Fundamental Theorem of Calculus	$\dfrac{d}{dx} \int_a^x f(t)dt = f(x)$
The Mean Value Theorem for Integrals	$\int_a^b f(x)dx = f(c)(b - a)$
Average Value of a Function	$f(c) = \dfrac{1}{b - a} \int_a^b f(x)dx$
Integration by Parts	$\int u\, dv = uv - \int v\, du$

Volumes of Solids with Known Cross Sections

Square	$V = \int (\text{base})^2\, dx$
Semicircle	$V = \dfrac{\pi}{8} \int (\text{base})^2\, dx$
Right Isosceles Triangle	$V = \dfrac{1}{2} \int (\text{base})^2\, dx$
Equilateral Triangle	$V = \dfrac{\sqrt{3}}{4} \int (\text{base})^2\, dx$

Derivatives

Function, f	Derivative, $\frac{df}{dx}$	Function, f	Derivative, $\frac{df}{dx}$	Function, f	Derivative, $\frac{df}{dx}$
c	0	$\frac{u}{v}$	$\frac{(vu' - uv')}{v^2}$	arc tan x	$\frac{1}{(1+x^2)}$
x	1	$f[u(x)]$	$\frac{df}{du} \cdot \frac{du}{dx}$	arc cot x	$-\frac{1}{(1+x^2)}$
kx	k	$\sin x$	$\cos x$	arc sec x	$\frac{1}{|x|\sqrt{x^2-1}}$
x^n	nx^{n-1}	$\cos x$	$-\sin x$	arc csc x	$-\frac{1}{|x|\sqrt{x^2-1}}$
$k[g(x)]$	$kg'(x)$	$\tan x$	$\sec^2 x$	e^x	e^x
$\frac{1}{x}$	$-\frac{1}{x^2}$	$\cot x$	$-\csc^2 x$	a^x	$a^x \ln a$
$\frac{1}{x^n}$	$-\frac{n}{x^{n+1}}$	$\sec x$	$\sec x \tan x$	$\ln x$	$\frac{1}{x}$
$\sqrt{x}$	$\frac{1}{2\sqrt{x}}$	$\csc x$	$\csc x \cot x$	$\log_a x$	$\frac{1}{x \ln a}$
$u + v$	$u' + v'$	arc sin x	$\frac{1}{\sqrt{1-x^2}}$	$f^{-1}(x)$	$\frac{1}{\frac{d}{dx}(f(f^{-1}(x)))}$
uv	$uv' + vu'$	arc cos x	$-\frac{1}{\sqrt{1-x^2}}$		

Integrals

Function, f	Integral, $\int f\,dx$	Function, f	Integral, $\int f\,dx$	Function, f	Integral, $\int f\,dx$
k	kx	e^x	e^x	$\sec^2 x$	$\tan x$
x	$\frac{1}{2}x^2$	$\ln x$	$x \ln x - x$	$\csc^2 x$	$-\cot x$
x^n	$\frac{x^{n+1}}{(n+1)}\ n \neq -1$	$\sin x$	$-\cos x$	$\sec x \tan x$	$\sec x$
$\frac{1}{x}$	$\ln x$	$\cos x$	$\sin x$	$\csc x \cot x$	$-\csc x$
$\frac{1}{x^n}$	$-\frac{1}{(n-1)x^{n-1}}\ n \neq 1$	$\tan x$	$\ln \sec x$	$\frac{1}{(ax+b)}$	$\left(\frac{1}{a}\right)\ln(ax+b)$
$\sqrt{x}$	$\frac{2}{3}x^{\frac{3}{2}}$	$\cot x$	$\ln \sin x$	$\frac{1}{(x^2+a^2)}$	$\left(\frac{1}{a}\right)\text{arc tan}\left(\frac{x}{a}\right)$
$\frac{1}{\sqrt{x}}$	$2\sqrt{x}$	$\sec x$	$\ln(\tan x + \sec x)$	$\frac{1}{(x^2-a^2)}$	$\left(\frac{1}{2a}\right)\ln\frac{(y-a)}{(x+a)}$
$x^{\frac{n}{r}}$	$\frac{rx^{(\frac{n}{r})+1}}{r+n}$	$\csc x$	$\ln(\csc x - \cot x)$	$\frac{1}{\sqrt{(a^2-x^2)}}$	$\text{arc sin}\left(\frac{x}{a}\right)$
$x^{-\frac{n}{r}}$	$\frac{r}{(r-n)x^{(\frac{n}{r})-1}}$	$\sin^2 x$	$\frac{1}{2}x - \frac{1}{2}\sin x \cos x$	$\frac{1}{\sqrt{(x^2 \pm a^2)}}$	$\ln\left(x + \sqrt{(x^2 \pm a^2)}\right)$

Glossary

A

absolute maximum (p. 2202) The highest point on a closed interval.

absolute minimum (p. 2202) The lowest point on a closed interval.

absolute value (p. 1387) The distance of a number from zero on a number line.

absolute value of a complex number (p. 1114) The absolute value of a complex number $a + bi$ is $\sqrt{a^2 + b^2}$.

acre (p. 482) A unit of area equal to 43,560 square feet.

acute angle (pp. 140, 624, 894) An angle with measure greater than 0° and less than 90°.

acute triangle (p. 156) A triangle with three acute angles.

add or subtract from a known fact (p. 70) A way to find the product of two numbers.

addends (p. 82) The numbers that are added to form a sum.

addition (pp. 56, 82) Mathematical operation in which the values of two or more numbers are combined.

addition method (p. 1572) A method of solving a system of equations that involves adding the equations to eliminate a variable.

additive identity (p. 1414) The number zero; the sum of zero and any number is that number.

additive inverse (p. 1415) The opposite of a given number.

adjacent angles (pp. 146, 625) Coplanar angles that share only an endpoint and one side.

adjacent arcs (p. 728) Arcs of the same circle that share exactly one endpoint.

algebraic expression (p. 1422) A mathematical phrase that contains one or more numbers, one or more variables, and one or more arithmetic operations.

algebraic inequality (p. 1492) A mathematical phrase that contains an inequality with a variable.

alternate exterior angles (p. 150) Two non-adjacent exterior angles on opposite sides of a transversal.

alternate interior angles (pp. 150, 630) Two non-adjacent interior angles on opposite sides of a transversal.

altitude of a triangle (pp. 537, 872) The perpendicular distance from a vertex to the line containing the side opposite that vertex.

amplitude (p. 952) The absolute value of half the difference between the maximum and minimum values of a trigonometric function.

angle (pp. 136, 894) A figure formed by two rays with a common endpoint.

angle bisector (p. 868) A ray that divides an angle into two adjacent angles that are congruent.

angle of depression (p. 924) The angle between a horizontal line and the line of sight from an observer to an object at a lower level.

angle of elevation (p. 924) The angle between a horizontal line and the line of sight from an observer to an object at a higher level.

angle of rotation See *rotation*.

angular velocity (p. 942) The number of degrees (radians, or revolutions) per unit time through which a point travels along a circular path.

apothem (p. 690) The distance from the center to a side of a regular polygon.

arc (p. 728) Part of a circle between two points on a circle.

arc of a chord (p. 736) The minor arc cut off by a chord of a circle.

area (pp. 482, 504, 528) The size of the surface of a flat figure or shape.

arithmetic pattern (p. 438) A pattern that grows when the same number is added to each subsequent term.

arithmetic sequence (p. 1859) A sequence in which consecutive terms differ by a constant amount d.

arithmetic series (p. 1862) The sum of the terms of an arithmetic sequence.

array (pp. 69, 75) An arrangement of objects in rows and columns where each row has the same number of objects.

asymptote (pp. 968, 1932, 1996, 2020) A line that a graph gets closer and closer to, but never touches or crosses.

average value of a function (p. 2270) If f is a continuous function on $[a, b]$, then the average value $f(c)$ is $f(c) = \frac{1}{b-a}\int_a^b f(x)dx$.

axis of a cone (p. 713) The line segment whose endpoints are the vertex of the cone and the center of the base.

axis of revolution (p. 2278) The line about which a two-dimensional figure revolves that results in a three-dimensional figure, called a *solid of revolution*.

axis of symmetry (pp. 1688, 1910) The line that can be drawn through a parabola so that one side of the parabola is a reflection of the other. It is perpendicular to the directrix and passes through the focus.

B
---

bar graph (pp. 188, 1270) A graph that uses horizontal or vertical bars to display data in categories.

base angles of a trapezoid (p. 656) Each pair of angles that lie on the same base of a trapezoid.

base angles of an isosceles triangle (p. 784) The two angles adjacent to the base of an isosceles triangle.

base design (p. 706) A drawing that shows the base of a figure made of cubes and the number of cubes in each position.

base of a power (pp. 294, 1396) A number that is used as a factor a given number of times.

base of an isosceles triangle (p. 784) The side that is not a leg, or any side if the triangle is equilateral.

base(s) of a geometric figure See *cone, cylinder, prism, pyramid, trapezoid.*

benchmark (p. 316) A reference number such as $0, \frac{1}{2}$, and 1 to which other numbers are compared.

biased sample (p. 1222) A sample that overrepresents or underrepresents some part of the population.

biconditional statement (p. 616) A statement of the form p *if and only if* q. p is true if and only if q is true.

binomial (pp. 1348, 1600) A polynomial that has two terms.

binomial coefficient (p. 1349) The formula for n items taken k at a time, $_nC_k = \frac{n!}{k!(n-k)!}$.

binomial experiment (p. 1344) An experiment that has exactly two possible outcomes, one of which is called a success.

boundary line (p. 1558) The graph of the related equation in the graph of a linear inequality.

bounded (p. 1590) An area on a graph that is completely enclosed by line segments and forms a polygon.

box-and-whisker plot (p. 1280) A data display that divides a set of data into four equal parts and shows how the data is displayed among these parts.

capacity (pp. 484, 506) The measure of the maximum amount of a liquid (or some other substance) a container can hold.

Celsius scale (p. 518) A scale for measuring temperature in which the freezing point of water is 0° and the boiling point is 100°.

center of a circle (pp. 162, 728) The point in the plane of a circle that is the same distance from every point on the circle.

center of a dilation (p. 850) The point about which a figure is dilated.

center of a regular polygon (p. 690) The center of the circumscribed circle.

center of rotation (p. 842) The point about which a figure is rotated.

central angle of a circle (p. 728) An angle whose vertex is the center of a circle.

central angle of a regular polygon (p. 690) An angle formed by two radii of the circumscribed circle.

centroid (p. 866) The intersection of the three medians of a triangle.

chord (pp. 162, 734) A segment whose endpoints are points on a circle.

circle (pp. 162, 728, 1920) The set of points in a plane the same distance from a given point, called the *center*.

circle graph (pp. 194, 1272) A graph that uses a circle to display a set of data as parts of a whole.

circumcenter (p. 876) The point where the perpendicular bisectors of the sides of a triangle intersect.

circumcircle of a polygon (p. 877) A circle that passes through all of the vertices of a polygon.

circumference (p. 162) The distance around a circle.

circumscribed circle (p. 877) A circle that contains all the vertices of a polygon.

closed interval (p. 2151) A set of real numbers that contains its endpoints.

cluster sample (p. 1227) A sample that has a population that is separated into subgroups, which are selected at random.

coefficient (pp. 588, 1422, 1601) The number that is multiplied by the variables of a term.

cofunctions (p. 905) Sine and cosine, secant and cosecant, tangent and cotangent.

combination (p. 1248) An arrangement of items, events, or people from a set without regard to the order.

combinatorial identity (p. 1249) A combination that in general has a value of $_nC_n$ that is equal to 1.

common difference (p. 1859) The constant amount by which consecutive terms differ in an arithmetic sequence.

common factor (p. 287) A factor shared by two or more numbers.

common logarithm (p. 1974) A logarithm with base 10 in a logarithmic expression.

common multiple (p. 288) A multiple shared by two or more numbers.

common ratio (p. 1866) The nonzero constant that is the ratio of consecutive terms in a geometric sequence.

common tangent (p. 742) A line (or segment) that is tangent to two coplanar circles.

compatible numbers (pp. 111, 115, 119, 123) Numbers that are easy to add, subtract, multiply, or divide mentally.

complement of an event (pp. 1255, 1291) All of the outcomes different from the favorable outcomes. The sum of the probability of an event and the probability of its complement is 1.

complementary angles (pp. 148, 625, 894) Two angles whose measures total 90°.

complementary events (p. 1255) Two events that make up all the possible outcomes of an experiment.

completing the square (p. 1706) A method for finding real solutions to a quadratic equation by forming an equivalent equation with a perfect trinomial square on one side.

complex conjugate (pp. 1641, 1902) The complex conjugate of the number $a + bi$ is $a - bi$, and vice versa.

complex fraction (p. 1990) A fraction, $\frac{a}{b}$, in which either a or b, or both, are rational expressions.

complex number (pp. 1110, 1896) Any number of the form $a + bi$, where a and b are real numbers and i is the imaginary unit. The number a is called the *real part* and b is called the *imaginary part*. If $a = 0$, then bi is called an *imaginary number*.

composite figure (pp. 552, 582) A figure that is made up of two or more other figures.

composite number (p. 284) A whole number greater than 1 that has more than two factors.

composition (p. 852) A combination of two or more transformations.

compound event (p. 1358) An event made of two or more simple events.

compound inequality (p. 1512) When two simple inequalities are joined by *and* or *or*.

compound interest (pp. 400, 1839, 1999) The interest paid on both the principal and any previously earned interest.

compound locus (p. 721) The set of all points that satisfy several conditions.

compound statement (p. 1512) A statement formed by using the word *and* or *or* to combine two simple statements.

conclusion (p. 612) The part of a conditional statement that follows the word *then*.

concurrent lines (pp. 831, 866) Lines that intersect at the same point, called the *point of concurrency*.

conditional probability (p. 1360) The probability that event *B* occurs, given that event *A* has occurred.

conditional statement (p. 612) A statement of the form *if p, then q*.

cone (pp. 174, 568, 576, 713) A geometric solid with a circular base and one vertex, called the *vertex* of the cone. The *height* of a cone is the distance from the vertex to the plane containing the base. See also *right cone*.

confidence interval (p. 1350) An interval, with limits at either end, with a specified probability of including the parameter being estimated.

confidence level (p. 1350) The probability that a result will fall within a confidence interval.

congruent angles (pp. 146, 622) Angles that have equal measures.

congruent arcs (pp. 729, 736) Two arcs in the same circle or in congruent circles that have the same measure.

congruent figures (pp. 622, 766) Figures that have the same shape and size.

congruent segments (p. 622) Segments that have equal lengths.

conjecture (p. 620) A conclusion reached by using inductive reasoning.

conjugate of a real number (p. 1961) For a number written as the sum of two terms, the conjugate of the number is the difference of the terms, and vice versa. $a + b$ and $a - b$ are conjugates.

conjugate of a complex number (pp. 1119, 1641, 1902) The conjugate of $z = x + yi$ is $\bar{z} = x - yi$. See also *complex conjugate*.

conjunction (p. 1513) A compound statement with two statements separated by the word *and*. An inequality using *and* is a conjunction.

consistent system (p. 1580) A system of equations with at least one solution.

constant (p. 1422) A quantity that does not change.

constant differences (p. 2042) The differences in consecutive terms in a sequence are all equal.

constant of proportionality (p. 1842) A constant positive ratio by which two variable quantities are proportionally related.

constraints (p. 1588) In linear programming, the linear inequalities that restrict the solution.

construction (p. 860) A geometric drawing that is made using only a straightedge and a compass.

continuous (p. 2144) If $\lim_{x \to c} f(x) = f(c)$ then f is continuous at $x = c$.

contrapositive of a statement (p. 615) The contrapositive of "if p, then q" is "if not q, then not p."

convenience sample (p. 1228) A sample where the members of the population that are easiest to contact or survey are selected for the sample.

converse of a statement (p. 614) The converse of "if p, then q" is "if q, then p."

conversion factor (p. 492) A ratio of equal quantities measured in different units.

coordinate plane (p. 1442) A plane formed by two number lines that intersect at right angles.

coordinate proof (p. 828) A proof that involves figures in the coordinate plane.

corollary (p. 669) A statement whose proof follows directly from another theorem.

correlation (p. 1313) The strength of the relationship between two variables.

correlation coefficient (p. 1333) Measures the strength of the correlation between the two variables.

corresponding angles (p. 630) Angles that lie in corresponding positions on the same side of a transversal.

cosecant ratio See *trigonometric ratios*.

cosine ratio See *trigonometric ratios*.

cotangent ratio See *trigonometric ratios*.

coterminal angles (pp. 895, 930) Two angles in standard position that have the same terminal side.

count back (p. 64) A strategy for finding the difference of two numbers.

count on (p. 58) A strategy for finding a sum.

counterexample (p. 613) An example that proves a conditional false.

CPCTC (p. 776) An abbreviation for "corresponding parts of congruent triangles are congruent."

critical point (p. 2191) A point on a graph that indicates where the graphical behavior of a function changes.

critical value (p. 2191) When a function *f* is defined at a point *c*, and the first derivative of the function at that point is zero or does not exist, then *c* is a critical value.

cross products (p. 369) The product of the numerator of one fraction and the denominator of another fraction.

cross section (p. 718) The intersection of a three-dimensional figure and a plane.

cube (pp. 166, 178) A rectangular prism all of whose faces are congruent squares.

cumulative frequency (p. 1263) The sum of the frequencies of the data up to a given level.

cumulative frequency distribution (p. 1328) A distribution that shows how many values are less than or equal to any given value in a data set.

cumulative percent frequency table (p. 1328) A distribution that shows the percent of data values less than or equal to a given value.

cylinder (pp. 170, 572) A geometric solid with two congruent parallel circular bases.

data (p. 1218) A collection of numbers, measures, or other information.

deductive reasoning (p. 618) The process of using properties, rules, definitions, theorems, and given facts to arrive at a conclusion.

degree of a polynomial (p. 1601) The greatest degree of all the terms in the polynomial.

denominator of a fraction (pp. 302, 304) See *fraction*.

dependent events (p. 1360) The outcome of one event affects the outcome of the other event.

dependent system (p. 1580) A system of linear equations that has infinitely many solutions.

dependent variable (pp. 1438, 1531) The variable, *y*, when the value of *y* depends on the value of *x*.

derivative (p. 2160) The slope of a line tangent to a function at each point of the function.

determinant (p. 1794) In a 2 by 2 matrix, the product of elements in the main diagonal minus the product of the elements in the other diagonal.

deviation from the mean (p. 1324) The difference in value between a data element and the mean of its data set.

diameter (pp. 162, 734) A line segment that contains the center of a circle and whose endpoints are points on the circle, or the length of that segment.

difference (pp. 62, 88) The result of subtraction.

difference of two squares (p. 1616) The product when a binomial of the form $a + b$ is multiplied by a binomial of the form $a - b$.

differential equation (p. 2294) An equation relating a function and one or more of its derivatives.

differentiation (p. 2159) The process of finding a derivative.

dilation (p. 850) A transformation that produces an image similar to the original figure. Also called a *similarity transformation*. For a dilation with *scale factor r*:
If $|r| > 1$, the image is larger than the original. The dilation is an *enlargement*.
If $|r| < 1$, the image is smaller than the original. The dilation is a *reduction*.

dimensional analysis (p. 492) A method of converting from one unit to another within a system of measurement.

dimensions (p. 1772) The number of rows and columns in a matrix.

direct variation (p. 1842) Two variable quantities related proportionally by a constant positive ratio.

direction angles (p. 1072) The angles that a vector $\mathbf{v} = \langle x, y, z \rangle$ makes with the positive x-axis, the positive y-axis, and the positive z-axis, respectively.

directrix (p. 1910) A fixed line associated with a parabola, where each point of the parabola is equidistant from the directrix and the focus.

discontinuous (p. 2144) A function which for certain values or between certain values of the variable does not vary continuously as the variable increases.

discount (p. 397) The difference between the original price of an item and the sale price of the item.

discriminant (p. 1714) The value of $b^2 - 4ac$ in a quadratic equation $ax^2 + bx + c = 0$.

disjunction (p. 1514) A compound statement with two statements separated by the word *or*. An inequality using *or* is a disjunction.

disk (p. 2278) A slice of a solid figure, when the slice is perpendicular to the axis of revolution and is a right circular cylinder.

displacement (pp. 2198, 2272) The change in position over a time interval.

dividend (p. 100) In the quotient $a \div b$, the dividend is a.

divisible (p. 290) A whole number is *divisible* by another whole number if there is no remainder when the first number is divided by the second.

division (pp. 74, 100) Mathematical operation in which the number of equal groups in a total are found. Division is the inverse of *multiplication*.

divisor (p. 100) In the quotient $a \div b$, the divisor is b.

DMS notation (p. 896) Degrees/minutes/seconds notation.

dodecahedron (p. 178) A regular polyhedron with 12 faces that are congruent regular pentagons.

domain (pp. 1436, 1978) The set of all input values x in a relation.

dot product (p. 1082) The quantity $\mathbf{u} \cdot \mathbf{v} = x_1 x_2 + y_1 y_2$, where $\mathbf{u} = \langle x_1, y_1 \rangle$ and $\mathbf{v} = \langle x_2, y_2 \rangle$.

double stem-and-leaf plot (p. 1286) A plot used to compare two sets of data that shows how data are distributed.

double-bar graph (p. 1284) A graph that uses side-by-side bars to display related data.

double-line graph (p. 1285) A graph that displays the changes of two related sets of data over time.

doubles and near doubles (p. 59) A strategy for finding a sum.

draw a diagram (p. 452) A problem-solving strategy.

e (p. 2004) The base for natural logarithms.

eccentricity (p. 1940) A number, represented by *e*, that describes the "roundness" of a conic section.

edge of a prism (p. 166) The intersection of two faces of a prism.

element (p. 1772) Each number or value in a matrix.

element of a cone (p. 713) Any segment joining the vertex to a point on the circumference of the base.

elimination method (p. 1576) The process of adding equations, or their multiples, to eliminate a variable in a system of equations.

ellipse (pp. 1928, 1941) A type of conic section. For two given points, the *foci*, an ellipse is the set of all points in a plane such that the sum of the distance to each focus is constant.

empirical rule (p. 1340) Provides a quick estimate of the spread of data in a normal distribution given the mean and standard deviation.

enlargement See *dilation*.

equal matrices (p. 1774) Two matrices that have the same dimensions, and corresponding elements have the same value.

equally likely (p. 1232) Two outcomes that have equal probabilities.

equation (pp. 1422, 1458) Two algebraic expressions separated by an equal sign, indicating that the two sides have equal value.

equiangular triangle (pp. 669, 786) A triangle with three congruent angles.

equilateral polygon (p. 676) A polygon in which all the sides are congruent.

equilateral triangle (pp. 156, 538, 786) A triangle with three congruent sides.

equivalent expressions (p. 1406) Expressions that have the same value for any values of the variables.

equivalent fractions (p. 308) Fractions that have the same value.

equivalent ratios (p. 368) Ratios that have the same value.

equivalent vectors (p. 1066) Vectors with the same magnitude and direction.

estimate (pp. 110, 114, 118, 122) A reasonable answer that is close to the exact answer.

evaluate (p. 1422) Substitute a given value for each variable, and then simplify the expression.

even functions (p. 1625) Polynomial functions of degree 2, 4, 6, and so on.

even number (p. 54) A number that is divisible by two.

expanded form (p. 44) The form of a number that expresses the number as the sum of the values of it digits.

experiment (pp. 1236, 1354) An act, operation, or process that can be used to generate outcomes.

experimental probability (p. 1236) The ratio of the number of times a favorable outcome occurs to the total number of trials.

explicit (p. 2208) A relationship between variables in which one variable is solved in terms of the other.

explicit rule (p. 1884) Gives the value of the general term a_n in terms of n.

exponent (pp. 94, 294, 1396) A number that tells how many times a factor is used in a product.

exponential decay function (pp. 2000, 2053) Functions of the form $y = ab^x$ where $0 < b < 1$. If r is the rate of decay, a is the initial amount, and t is time, $y = a(1 - r)^t$.

exponential equations (p. 1978) Equations that contain a variable in an exponent.

exponential functions (p. 1996) Functions that contain a variable in an exponent.

exponential growth function (pp. 1996, 2052) Functions of the form $y = ab^x$, where $b > 1$. If r is the rate of growth, a is the initial amount, and t is time, $y = a(1 + r)^t$.

exponential notation (p. 1396) Expresses multiplication as a power.

exterior angle of a polygon (p. 670) An angle formed by extending one side of a polygon.

extraneous solution (pp. 2013, 2027, 2035, 2038) A solution of a transformed equation that is not in the domain of or a solution of the original equation.

extrapolation (p. 1318) An estimate outside a set of known points.

f(*x*) (p. 1450) The function rule applied to *x*.

face of a prism (p. 166) Any one of the flat surfaces that make up a prism.

fact family (p. 80) Sets of related facts that use the same numbers.

factor theorem (p. 1646) A polynomial $P(x)$ has a factor of $x - a$ if and only if $P(a) = 0$.

factor tree (p. 296) A diagram that shows how to break a number down into its prime factors.

factorial See n *factorial*.

factoring (p. 1660) Rewriting an expression as the product of its factors.

factors (pp. 96, 286) Numbers that are multiplied to find a product.

Fahrenheit scale (p. 496) A scale for measuring temperature in which the freezing point of water is 32° and the boiling point is 212°.

feasible region (p. 1590) The graph of the solution of the system of linear inequalities that form the constraints.

Fibonacci sequence (p. 1878) A sequence named for Italian mathematician Leonardo of Pisa, also known as Fibonacci. The first two terms of the sequence are 1, and each successive term is the sum of the previous two terms.

finite sequence (p. 1858) A sequence that has a specific number of terms.

finite series (p. 1862) The sum of a finite number of terms.

first quartile (p. 1331) The median of the data that are less than the overall median.

first-order differences (pp. 1690, 2042) The differences between values of *y* for consecutive values of *x*. In a linear function, first-order differences are constant for constant change in *x*.

foci (pp. 1928, 1932, 1941, 1942) Two fixed points used to define an ellipse or hyperbola.

focus (p. 1910) A fixed point used with the directrix to define a parabola.

FOIL (p. 1610) A method of multiplying binomials using the Distributive Property. Its name can help you remember the process: first-outside-inside-last.

formula (p. 527) An equation that shows a relationship between two or more quantities.

45°-45°-90° triangle (pp. 684, 898) An isosceles right triangle.

fractal (p. 809) A self-similar figure made by iteration.

fraction (pp. 302, 304) A number that names a part of a whole or a part of a set; any number written in the form $\frac{a}{b}$, where *a* and *b* are integers and $b \neq 0$. The numerator of the fraction is *a*, and the denominator is *b*.

frequency (p. 1260) The number of times an event, a number, or a range of events occurs.

frequency polygon (p. 1269) A graph of the data in a frequency table that show the midpoints of the intervals, which can be used to estimate the mean.

frequency table (p. 182) A tally chart or table that includes the frequency of each kind of data.

function (pp. 950, 1439) A relation, or a set of ordered pairs, such that for each element in the domain of the function, there is exactly one element in the range.

function notation (p. 1450) A notation in which a function is named with a letter and the input is shown in parentheses after the function name, such as *f*(*x*).

G

general term (p. 1858) The *n*th term of a sequence.

geometric mean (p. 797) The positive square root of the product of two positive numbers.

geometric pattern (p. 438) A pattern that grows when each subsequent term is multiplied by the same number.

geometric sequence (p. 1866) A sequence in which the ratio of consecutive terms is a non-zero constant.

geometric series (p. 1870) The sum of the terms of a geometric sequence.

glide reflection (p. 852) A composition of a translation (glide) and a reflection over a line that is parallel to the direction of the translation.

golden ratio (p. 1879) A special number approximately equal to 1.6180339887.

golden rectangle (p. 791) A rectangle that can be divided into a square and a rectangle that is similar to the original rectangle.

graph of an inequality (p. 1492) The graph of all solutions of the inequality on a number line.

great circle (p. 1052) The intersection of a sphere and a plane containing the center of the sphere.

greatest common factor (GCF) (p. 287) The greatest factor shared by two or more numbers.

growth factor (pp. 1998, 2003) The quantity $1 + r$ in the exponential growth equation $y = a(1 + r)^x$.

H

half-life (p. 2055) The time it takes a substance to undergo radioactive decay to half of the original amount.

half-open interval (p. 2151) A continuous set of real numbers that contains only one endpoint.

half-plane (pp. 1558, 1936) The region on one side of the line in the graph of an inequality, or on one side of a boundary curve.

half-turn (p. 844) A rotation of 180º or $-180°$.

hexagonal prism (p. 167) A prism whose base is a hexagon.

higher-order derivative (p. 2184) The derivative of a derivative function.

higher-order equations (p. 1720) Equations of degree 3 or greater.

histogram (p.1267) A graph that displays the frequency of a set of data in equal-size intervals, or ranges, of data.

horizontal component (p. 1070) The x-coordinate of a point representing a vector $\mathbf{v} = (x, y)$.

horizontal translation (p. 1695) Movement of a figure along a horizontal line; $f(x - h)$ translates $f(x)$ horizontally h units.

hyperbola (p. 1932) A type of conic section. The hyperbola is the set of all points in a plane such that the difference of the distances from two fixed points, called the *foci*, is a positive constant.

hypotenuse (p. 678) The side opposite the right angle in a right triangle. It is the longest side.

hypothesis (p. 612) The part of a conditional statement that follows the word *if*.

I

icosahedron (p. 178) A regular polyhedron with 20 faces that are congruent equilateral triangles.

identity matrix for multiplication (p. 1784) A matrix that acts like the number 1 in real-number multiplication.

image See *transformation*.

imaginary number See *complex number*.

imaginary unit i (pp. 1110, 1894) The square root of -1.

implicit (p. 2208) A relationship between variables in which one variable is not solved in terms of the other.

implicit differentiation (p. 2208) A method of finding the derivative of both sides of an equation with respect to x and then solving for $\frac{dy}{dx}$.

improper fraction (p. 306) A fraction in which the numerator is greater than the denominator.

incenter (p. 880) The point where the bisectors of the angles of a triangle intersect.

included angle (p. 770) An angle formed by two consecutive sides of a polygon.

included side (p. 772) A side that is shared by two consecutive angles of a polygon.

inconsistent system (p. 1580) A system of equations with no solution.

independent events (p. 1358) The outcome of one event does not influence the outcome of the other event.

independent system (p. 1580) A system of linear equations with exactly one solution.

independent variable (pp. 1438, 1531) A variable whose value determines the value of a dependent variable.

indeterminate form (p. 2124) A rational function in which the limit of the numerator and the denominator both equal zero as x approaches c.

index (p. 1954) The number n in the radical $\sqrt[n]{a}$.

index of summation (p. 1862) Used to indicate the lower and upper limit of the summation, for example $\displaystyle\sum_{k-1}^{3}$.

indirect measurement (p. 800) Using similar triangles to find a length that cannot be measured directly.

inductive reasoning (p. 620) The process of making a conclusion based on observations.

inequality (p. 1492) A mathematical statement that two quantities are not or may not be equal.

infinite geometric series (p. 1874) The sum of the terms of an infinite geometric sequence.

infinite sequence (p. 1858) A sequence that has an infinite number of terms.

infinite series (p. 1862) The sum of an infinite number of terms.

inflection point (pp. 2194, 2204) The point at which a function changes concavity.

initial side of an angle (p. 894) The side that lies on the x-axis. The other side of the angle is the *terminal side*.

initial value (pp. 1998, 2003) For the exponential growth or decay function $y = a(1 \pm r)^x$, a is the initial value.

initial value problem (p. 2295) A problem in which the identity of an unknown function of an independent variable is sought, given the derivative of the function and the value of the function at a specified point.

input (p. 1437) The first number in each ordered pair; the value substituted in an expression or function.

inscribed angle (p. 744) An angle whose vertex is on a circle and whose sides contain chords of the circle.

inscribed circle (p. 883) A circle that is tangent to each side of a polygon.

integers (pp. 268, 1386, 1402) The set of whole numbers and their opposites, $\{ \ldots -3, -2, -1, 0, 1, 2, 3, \ldots \}$.

integration (p. 2234) The process of identifying a function from its derivative.

integration by parts (p. 2258) A method to use if an integral includes the product of two functions but does not fit the *u*-substitution style.

interest (pp. 398, 1838) A fee paid for the use of borrowed money.

interior angle of a polygon (p. 670) An angle determined by two consecutive sides of a polygon.

interquartile range (pp. 1281,1299) The difference between the first quartile and the third quartile of the data.

intersecting lines (p. 129) Lines that share exactly one point.

intersection (p. 1291) The set of elements common to two or more sets.

inverse function (p. 2090) A function that has the range of the original function as its domain and the domain of the original function as its range.

inverse matrix (p. 1798) The matrix which when multiplied by the original matrix gives the identity matrix as the solution.

inverse of a statement (p. 614) The inverse of "if *p* then *q*" is "if not *p* then not *q*."

inverse operations (pp. 81, 1460) Operations that perform opposite tasks, or that "undo" each other; addition and subtraction are inverse operations; multiplication and division are inverse operations.

inverse variation (p. 1846) A relationship in which one variable quantity increases as the other variable quantity decreases and their product is constant.

irrational number (pp. 268, 1402) A real number that cannot be written as the quotient of two integers.

irregular polygon (p. 154) Any polygon that is not regular.

isometric drawing (p. 698) A drawing that shows three sides of a figure, using triangular isometric dot paper.

isometry (p. 834) A transformation that preserves congruence.

isosceles trapezoid (p. 658) A trapezoid with congruent legs.

isosceles triangle (pp. 156, 784) A triangle with at least two congruent sides.

iteration (p. 808) Repeatedly performing a rule.

joint variation (p. 1850) When a quantity varies directly with the product of two or more quantities.

kite (p. 660) A quadrilateral with exactly two pairs of congruent, consecutive sides.

lateral area of a cone (p. 714) The area of the curved surface.

lateral area of a pyramid (p. 711) The sum of the areas of the lateral faces.

lateral faces See *prism, pyramid*.

lateral surface of a cylinder (p. 562) The curved surface of a cylinder.

latus rectum (LR) (p. 1910) The segment that passes through the focus of a parabola and is parallel to the directrix.

Law of Detachment (p. 618) The law that states that if a conditional statement is true and its hypothesis is true, then the conclusion is true.

Law of Syllogism (p. 618) The law that states that if $p \rightarrow q$ is true and $q \rightarrow r$ is true, then $p \rightarrow r$ must be true.

leading coefficient (p. 1624) The coefficient of the term of a polynomial of greatest degree.

leading question (p. 1223) A biased survey question that makes people more or less likely to answer in a particular way.

leading term (p. 1624) The term of a polynomial with the greatest degree.

least common denominator (LCD) (pp. 289, 1986) The least common multiple of the denominators of two or more fractions.

least common multiple (LCM) (p. 288) The common multiple of two or more numbers that has the least value.

legs of a right triangle (p. 678) The two shorter sides that form the right angle in a right triangle.

legs of a trapezoid (p. 656) The sides of a trapezoid that are not the bases.

legs of an isosceles triangle (p. 784) The two congruent sides of an isosceles triangle.

length (pp. 478, 500) The distance between two points.

like fractions (p. 319) Fractions with the same denominator.

like radicals (p. 1958) Radicals that have the same index and the same radicand.

like terms (p. 1412) Terms that contain the same variables raised to the same powers.

limit (pp. 1874, 2010) The sum of an infinite geometric series. The value of a function as its variable approaches a particular value.

line (p. 128) A straight path in a plane that continues without end in two directions. A line has no width.

line graph (pp. 192, 1446) A data display that shows information as data points connected by line segments; often used to display data that change over time.

line of best fit (pp. 1332, 1556) A straight line that most closely follows the trend of data points in a scatter plot.

line of reflection See *reflection*.

line of symmetry (p. 846) A reflection line.

line plot (p. 1321) A graph that displays frequency data as stacks of marks along a number line.

line segment (p. 132) Part of a line consisting of two endpoints on the line and all points between the two endpoints.

line symmetry (p. 846) When there is a reflection over a line that maps a figure onto itself. Also called *reflection symmetry*. See also *line of symmetry*.

linear combination of vectors (p. 1080) Any expression of the form $a\mathbf{u} + b\mathbf{v}$, where a and b are scalars and $\mathbf{u}$ and $\mathbf{v}$ are vectors.

linear combinations (p. 1576) Sum of multiples of equations in a system of equations, used to eliminate a variable.

linear equation (p. 1529) An equation with a graph that is a straight line.

linear function (p. 1451) Any function with a graph that is a straight line.

linear pair (p. 625) Two adjacent angles whose exterior sides lie on a straight line.

linear programming (p. 1588) A useful branch of mathematics that maximizes or minimizes the value of a function, within the restrictions of a system of linear inequalities.

linear velocity (p. 942) The distance per unit time that a point travels along a circular path.

linear-quadratic system (p. 1728) A system of equations that includes a quadratic equation and a linear equation.

local linearity (p. 2169) The linear appearance of a function at a certain point.

local maximum (pp. 1654, 2202) The value of the function at a turning point; any high point on a graph of a function.

local minimum (pp. 1654, 2202) The value of the function at a turning point; any low point on a graph of a function.

location principle (p. 1630) A principle, useful in locating the roots of an equation, stating that if a continuous function has opposite signs for two values of the independent variable, then it is zero for some value of the variable between these two values.

locus (p. 720) The set of all points that satisfy a given condition.

logarithmic function (p. 2006) An equation written in the form $y = \log_b x$, where $b > 0$ and $b \neq 1$. The inverse of an exponential function.

logically equivalent statements (p. 615) Statements that always have the same truth value.

lower extreme (p. 1280) The least data value in a set.

lower quartile (p. 1280) The median of the lower half of the data.

magnitude of a vector (p. 1066) The length of a vector.

main diagonal (pp. 1784, 1792) The diagonal of a square matrix drawn from the upper left corner to the lower right corner.

major arc (p. 728) An arc larger than a semicircle.

major axis (p. 1928) The longer of the perpendicular segments through the center of an ellipse, which contains the foci.

make ten (p. 59) A strategy for finding a sum.

margin of error (p. 1350) An interval, or range, around a sample measure that is likely to contain the corresponding population measure.

markup (p. 395) The difference between the price a store pays for an item (wholesale price) and the price a buyer pays for an item (retail price).

mass (p. 510) The measure of the amount of matter in an object.

mathematical induction (p. 1888) The method of proving that a statement is true for all natural numbers.

matrix (p. 1772) A rectangular arrangement of numbers or values.

maximum value (p. 1691) The maximum value(s) of the function over its entire domain; the y-coordinate of the vertex of a quadratic function that opens downward.

mean (pp. 198, 1279, 1294) The sum of the data in a data set divided by the number of items in the set. Also called the *average*.

measure of an arc (p. 728) The measure of a minor arc equals the measure of its central angle. The measure of a major arc is 360° minus the measure of the minor arc with the same endpoints. The measure of a semicircle is 180°.

measures of central tendency (p. 202) Different ways to describe the "center" of a data set.

median (pp. 202, 1278, 1294) The middle number (or the mean of the two middle numbers) when a data set is arranged in order from least to greatest.

median of a triangle (pp. 822, 865) A segment whose endpoints are a vertex of the triangle and the midpoint of the opposite side.

midpoint of a segment (p. 820) A point that divides a segment into two congruent segments.

midsegment of a trapezoid (p. 656) The segment whose endpoints are the midpoints of the legs.

midsegment of a triangle (p. 806) The segment whose endpoints are the midpoints of two sides of a triangle.

midsegment triangle (p. 806) The triangle formed by the three midsegments of another triangle.

minimum value (p. 1691) The minimum value(s) of a function over its entire domain; the y-coordinate of the vertex of a quadratic function that opens upward.

minor (p. 1797) The new, smaller determinant formed after one element is identified in a determinant and then used to form a determinant by deleting the rest of the row and column for that element.

minor arc (p. 728) An arc shorter than a semicircle.

minor axis (p. 1928) The shorter of the perpendicular segments through the center of an ellipse.

minuend (p. 88) The number another number is subtracted from in a difference. In $a - b$, a is the minuend.

minute (p. 896) One-sixtieth of a degree.

mixed number (p. 306) Any number consisting of a whole number and a proper fraction.

mode (pp. 204, 1279, 1295) The number or element in a data set that appears most often in the set.

monomial (pp. 1600, 1982) An algebraic expression consisting of a number or a product of numbers and variables.

multiple (p. 288) The product of a counting number and a positive integer.

multiplicand (p. 96) The first of two numbers in a product.

multiplication (pp. 68, 96) Mathematical operation in which a number of sets of equal size are combined.

multiplicative identity (p. 1414) The number 1; multiplying 1 by any number gives that number.

multiplicative inverse (pp. 1416, 1983) The reciprocal of a number. The product of a number and its multiplicative inverse is 1.

multiplicity (p. 1642) The number of times that $x - r$ is a factor of an equation $P(x) = 0$.

multiplier (p. 96) The second of two numbers in a product.

mutually exclusive events (p. 1366) Two events that cannot happen at the same time.

n **factorial** (p. 1245) The product in which the factors are descending natural numbers starting with n. The factorial of zero is defined to be 1.

natural logarithm (p. 1975) The logarithm to the base e, where e is called the Euler number and is an irrational constant of about 2.71828.

natural numbers (pp. 268, 1402) The set of counting numbers, $\{1, 2, 3, \dots\}$.

negation of a statement (p. 614) A statement with the opposite truth value. The negation of p is $\sim p$.

negative angle (p. 895) An angle determined by a clockwise rotation.

negative reciprocals (p. 816) Two numbers whose product is -1.

net (pp. 558, 566, 694) A two-dimensional diagram that you can fold to form a three-dimensional figure.

non-removable discontinuity (p. 2144) A discontinuity that implies that you cannot make the function continuous by any value $f(c)$.

nonresponse (p. 1222) Occurs when some people selected for a sample do not respond to the survey.

normal distribution (p. 1340) A way to describe data that appears as a bell-shaped curve symmetrical around the mean.

normal line (p. 2213) A line that is perpendicular to the tangent line of a curve at the point of tangency.

number pattern (pp. 438, 440) A sequence of numbers that follow a rule.

numerator of a fraction (pp. 302, 304) See *fraction*.

objective function (p. 1592) The function to be maximized or minimized, subject to the constraints of a linear programming problem.

observation (p. 1354) A record or measure of events that occur with no intervention by the researcher.

obtuse angle (pp. 140, 624, 894) An angle with measure greater than 90° and less than 180°.

obtuse triangle (p. 156) A triangle with one obtuse angle.

octagonal prism (p. 167) A prism whose base is an octagon.

octahedron (p. 178) A regular polyhedron with eight faces that are congruent equilateral triangles.

odd functions (p. 1625) Polynomial functions of degree 1, 3, 5, and so on.

odd number (p. 54) A whole number that is not divisible by two.

odds (p. 1254) A comparison of the number of favorable outcomes with the number of unfavorable outcomes in an event.

odometer (p. 478) An instrument used to measure distances in miles.

open interval (p. 2150) A continuous set of real numbers that does not contain its endpoints.

opposites (p. 1386) Numbers that are the same distance from but on opposite sides of zero on a number line. The opposite of a is $-a$, and the sum of opposites is zero.

optimization function (p. 1588) The function that is maximized or minimized in linear programming; the objective function.

order of a differential equation (p. 2294) The power of the highest derivative of an equation.

order of symmetry (p. 847) The number of rotations of the smallest angle greater than 0° and less than or equal to 360° that produces an image that coincides with the original.

ordered pair (p. 1436) A pair of numbers (x, y) used to locate a point on a coordinate plane; the first number tells how far to move horizontally and the second number tells how far to move vertically.

ordered triple (p. 1754) A set of three numbers (x, y, z) that describe a point in a three-dimensional coordinate system.

origin (p. 1442) The point where the coordinate axes intersect.

orthocenter (p. 873) The point where the altitudes of a triangle intersect.

orthogonal vectors (p. 1084) Perpendicular vectors.

orthographic drawing (p. 702) A drawing that shows up to six views of a three-dimensional figure.

outcome (p. 1232) The result of an experiment.

outlier (pp. 1283, 1298) A very large or very small value that is not typical of its data set.

output (p. 1437) The second number in each ordered pair; the value of the expression or function.

overlapping events (p. 1366) Two events that can happen at the same time.

parabola (pp. 1910, 1916) A type of conic section. For a given point, called the *focus*, and a given line not through the focus, called the *directrix*, a parabola is the set of all points such that the distance to the focus equals the distance to the directrix.

paragraph proof (p. 626) A proof that uses complete sentences to explain and justify each step, eventually reaching the desired conclusion.

parallel lines (pp. 129, 630) Coplanar lines that do not intersect.

parallelogram (pp. 158, 532, 638) A quadrilateral with two pairs of parallel sides.

parametric equations (p. 1106) A set of equations that define x and y in terms of another variable, called a *parameter*.

parent functions (pp. 1625, 2098) The most basic form of a number of related graphs with similar features. The related forms are transformations of the parent function.

parent quadratic function (p. 1688) The function $y = x^2$.

partial product (p. 96) A product formed by multiplying the multiplicand by one digit of the multiplier when the multiplier has more than one digit.

partial sum (p. 1863) Sum of the first n terms of a sequence.

Pascal's triangle (p. 1347) An arithmetic triangle that is used to calculate the binomial coefficients of various numbers; used in algebra and probability with the binomial theorem. Each row starts and ends with 1 and each other number is the sum of the two numbers above it.

pattern (p. 432) A sequence that follows a rule.

percent (pp. 196, 277, 380) A ratio that compares a number to 100.

percent of change (increase or decrease) (pp. 394, 396) The ratio of the amount of change to the original quantity expressed as a percent.

percentile rank (p. 1329) The percent of the total number of values less than or equal to a value.

perfect square (pp. 1400, 1952) A number that is the square of a rational number.

perfect-square trinomial (p. 1614) A polynomial that is the result of squaring a binomial.

perimeter (p. 524) The distance around a closed plane figure.

period (p. 40) Each group of three places on a place-value chart.

period of a function (p. 950) The length of the repeating portion of a function.

periodic function (p. 950) A function f such that $f(x) = f(x + np)$, where x is any real number in the domain of f, n is an integer, and p is a positive real number. The smallest value of p is the *period* of the function.

permutation (p. 1244) An arrangement of a group, or set, of objects in a particular order.

perpendicular bisector of a segment (pp. 864, 876) A line, ray, or segment that is perpendicular to the given segment at its midpoint.

perpendicular lines (p. 130) Two lines that intersect to form right angles.

phase shift (p. 962) A horizontal translation of a periodic function.

pictograph (p. 186) A graph that uses symbols to display data.

piecewise function (p. 2076) A function that is defined by two or more equations.

plane (pp. 128, 144) A flat, two-dimensional surface that extends infinitely in all directions.

Platonic solids (p. 178) The five regular polyhedra: tetrahedron, cube, octahedron, dodecahedron, and icosahedron.

point (p. 128) A location in space. A point has no size.

point of concurrency See *concurrent lines*.

point of symmetry (p. 848) The point about which you can rotate a figure 180° so that its image coincides with the original figure.

point of tangency See *tangent to a circle*.

point symmetry (p. 848) 180° rotational symmetry.

polar coordinate system (p. 1092) The coordinate system in a plane determined by a point, called the *pole*, and the *polar axis*, a ray that has the pole as its endpoint.

polar coordinates of a point (p. 1092) The ordered pair (r, θ), where r is a real number and θ is an angle measure.

polygon (p. 154) A closed plane figure with three or more straight sides that intersect only at their endpoints.

polynomial (pp. 1600, 1982) An algebraic expression that is the sum of one or more monomials.

polynomial function (p. 1624) A function of degree n, where n is a nonnegative integer, and the degrees of the terms are decreasing from n to 0.

population (pp. 1218, 1222) The set of individuals or items that represent the data in a data set.

positive angle (p. 895) An angle determined by a counterclockwise rotation.

postulate (p. 624) A statement that is accepted as true without being proven.

power (pp. 294, 1396) A number written as a base with an exponent.

power function (p. 2056) A function in the form $y = ax^b$.

power of ten (pp. 94, 588) The product when 10 is multiplied by itself a given number of times.

pre-image See *transformation*.

prime factorization (p. 296) Writing a number as the product of it prime factors.

prime number (p. 284) A whole number greater than 1 that has exactly two factors, 1 and the number itself.

prime polynomial (p. 1670) A polynomial that cannot be factored.

principal (pp. 398, 1838) The amount of money deposited, invested, or borrowed.

principal square root (pp. 1400, 1952) The nonnegative square root of a number.

principal values of inverse trigonometric functions (pp. 1022, 1026, 1030) The values in the restricted domains of the corresponding trigonometric functions.

prism (pp. 166, 570) A geometric solid with two congruent parallel *bases* that are polygons. The *lateral faces* are parallelograms.

probability (p. 1232) A numerical measure of the likelihood that a given event will occur.

product (pp. 68, 96) The result of multiplication.

proper fraction (p. 306) A fraction in which the numerator is less than the denominator.

proportion (p. 369) An equation that states two ratios are equal.

protractor (p. 137) A tool used to measure angles.

pure imaginary number (p. 1896) Any complex number of the form $a + bi$ for which $a = 0$ and $b \neq 0$.

pyramid (pp. 172, 566, 574, 710) A geometric solid with one *base* that is a polygon and *lateral faces* that are triangles. The common vertex of the triangular faces is the *vertex* of the pyramid. The distance from the vertex to the plane containing the base is the *height* (altitude) of the pyramid. See also *regular pyramid*.

Pythagorean triple (p. 681) Three whole numbers a, b, and c, where $a^2 + b^2 = c^2$.

quadrantal angle (pp. 895, 929) An angle whose terminal side lies on the x-axis or the y-axis.

quadrants (p. 1524) The four regions into which the x- and y-axes divide the coordinate plane.

quadratic function (p. 1688) Any function that can be written in the standard form $y = ax^2 + bx + c$, where $a \neq 0$.

quadratic-quadratic system (p. 1732) A system of equations that consists of two quadratic equations.

quadrilateral (p. 158) A polygon with four sides.

quarter-turn (p. 844) A rotation of 90° or −90°.

quartiles (p. 1331) The four parts that a data set is divided into, each containing an equal number of data values.

quotient (pp. 74, 100) The result of dividing one number by another.

R

radian (p. 936) A measure of a central angle of a circle based on arc length, where 2π radians is equal to 360°.

radical function (p. 2032) A function that contains a variable under a radical symbol.

radical inequality (p. 2036) An inequality that contains a variable under a radical symbol.

radical sign (pp. 1400, 1952, 1954) The designated symbol for the principal square root of a mathematical quantity.

radicand (pp. 1400, 1952, 1954, 2032) The number or expression under the radical sign.

radius of a circle (pp. 162, 728, 1920) A segment whose endpoints are the center of a circle and a point on the circle, or the length of that segment.

radius of a regular polygon (p. 690) A segment whose endpoints are the center and a vertex of the polygon, or the length of that segment.

random sample (p. 1224) A sample for which each member of the identified population is equally likely to be selected.

randomized block design (p. 1354) In the statistical theory of the design of experiments, blocking is the arranging of experimental units in groups (blocks) that are similar to one another.

range (pp. 1436, 1978) The set of all output values y in a relation.

range of a data set (pp. 204, 1278) The difference between the greatest and the least value in a data set.

rate (p. 366) A ratio that compares quantities with different units of measure.

rate of change (p. 1536) A ratio that compares the change in the dependent variable with the change in the independent variable.

rate of decay (p. 2053) The growth rate b in the exponential equation $y = ab^x$, where $0 < b < 1$.

ratio (p. 364) A comparison of two quantities by division.

rational equation (p. 2026) An equation that contains fractional, or rational, expressions.

rational expression (pp. 1986, 1990) The quotient of two polynomials $\frac{a}{b}$, with $b \neq 0$.

rational function (p. 2020) A function of the form $y = \frac{p(x)}{q(x)}$, where $p(x)$ and $q(x)$ are polynomials and $q(x) \neq 0$.

rational number (pp. 268, 1402, 1970) A number that can be written in the form $\frac{p}{q}$ where p and q are integers, and $q \neq 0$.

rationalizing the denominator (p. 1964) The process by which a fraction containing radicals in the denominator is rewritten to have only rational numbers in the denominator.

raw score (p. 1341) An original data value in a normal distribution before conversion to a standard normal z-score.

ray (p. 133) Part of a line consisting of one endpoint and all points of the line on one side of the endpoint.

real numbers (pp. 268, 1402) The combined set of rational numbers and irrational numbers.

reciprocals (pp. 346, 1983) Two numbers whose product is 1.

rectangle (p. 158, 650) A parallelogram with four right angles.

rectangular prism (p. 166) A prism with a rectangular base.

recursive rule (p. 1880) The rule for each term of a sequence written in terms of one or more of the preceding terms.

reduction See *dilation*.

reference angle (pp. 931, 932) The smallest positive acute angle that the terminal side of an angle makes with the x-axis.

reflection (pp. 838, 2086) An isometry that *flips* a figure over a line, called the *line of reflection*.

reflection symmetry See *line symmetry*.

regression (pp. 1332, 1336) A statistical analysis analyzing the association between two variables. It is used to find the relationship between two variables.

regrouping (pp. 84, 90, 228, 233) Organizing a value in a different way in order to rename a number.

regular polygon (pp. 154, 525, 676) A polygon with congruent sides and congruent angles.

regular polyhedron (p. 178) A polyhedron in which all faces are congruent regular polygons and the same number of faces meet at each vertex.

regular pyramid (p. 711) A pyramid with a base that is a regular polygon. The lateral faces are congruent isosceles triangles. The height of each lateral face is the *slant height* of the regular pyramid.

regular tessellation (p. 854) A tessellation consisting of congruent copies of a regular polygon.

related rates (p. 2214) A class of problems in which rates of change are related by means of differentiation.

relation (p. 1436) A set of ordered pairs.

relative frequency (p. 1262) A ratio of the number of times the event occurs and the total number of events.

remainder (pp. 100, 290) The whole number that is left when the divisor does not divide evenly into the dividend.

remote interior angles (p. 670) For each exterior angle of a triangle, the two interior angles that are not adjacent to the exterior angle.

removable discontinuity (p. 2144) A discontinuity that implies that you can make a function continuous by defining or changing the function value $f(c)$.

renaming a measure (pp. 485, 489) Expressing the same quantity using a different unit of measure.

repeated addition (p. 70) A way to find the product of two numbers.

repeated solution (p. 1642) A solution that occurs more than once in a factored equation when using the Zero-Product Property.

repeating decimal (pp. 257, 270) A decimal in which one digit or a block of digits repeats indefinitely.

replication (p. 1355) Observations made under identical conditions.

resultant (p. 1067) The sum of two vectors.

rhombus (pp. 158, 650) A parallelogram with four congruent sides.

Riemann sum (p. 2242) A method of using the areas of rectangles to approximate the total area under a curve on a graph.

right angle (pp. 140, 624, 894) An angle with measure 90°.

right cone (p. 713) A cone whose axis is perpendicular to the base. The *slant height* is the length of a segment whose endpoints are the vertex of the cone and a point on the circumference of the base. An *oblique cone* is any cone that is not a right cone.

right triangle (p. 156) A triangle with one right angle.

rise (p. 1537) The vertical distance between two points on the graph; the change in y.

root of a polynomial (p. 1110) Any solution of a polynomial equation.

root of an equation (p. 1630) A solution to an equation of the form $f(x) = 0$. Roots may be real or complex.

roses (p. 1101) A family of graphs of the polar equations of the form $r = \sin(n\theta)$ and $r = \cos(n\theta)$, where $n \geq 2$.

rotation (p. 842) An isometry that turns a figure about a point, called the *center of rotation*. Rays from the center of rotation to corresponding points on the pre-image and image form the *angle of rotation*.

rotational symmetry (p. 847) If a figure can be rotated about a point by a rotation of less than 360° so that the figure coincides with itself, the figure has rotational symmetry. See also *center of rotation*.

rounding (p. 224) Expressing a number to a given place value.

run (p. 1537) The horizontal distance between two points on the graph; change in x.

same-side interior angles (p. 630) Interior angles on the same side of a transversal.

sample (pp. 1218, 1222) A subset of the population.

sample space (pp. 1232, 1358) The set of all possible outcomes of an experiment.

sampling with replacement (p. 1359) When a population element can be selected more than one time in an experiment.

sampling without replacement (p. 1360) When a population element can be selected only one time in an experiment.

scalar (p. 1066) A real number used as a multiplier.

scalar multiple of a vector (p. 1078) The vector with magnitude $|a| \cdot \|\mathbf{v}\|$ and the same direction as vector $\mathbf{v}$ if $a > 0$ and direction opposite to $\mathbf{v}$ if $a < 0$.

scalar multiplication (p. 1778) The operation of multiplying a real number by every element in a matrix.

scale (p. 372) A ratio between the measurements in a scale drawing and the measurements of a real object.

scale drawing (p. 372) An enlarged or reduced drawing of a real object.

scale factor of a dilation (p. 850) The number that describes the size change in a dilation. See also *dilation*.

scalene triangle (p. 156) A triangle with no congruent sides.

scatter plot (p. 1264) A graph that shows data points on a coordinate grid.

scientific notation (p. 588) A number written as the product of a power of 10 and a number greater than or equal to 1 and less than 10.

secant (p. 754) A line that intersects the circle in two points.

secant ratio See *trigonometric ratios*.

secant segment (p. 758) A segment of a secant that has one endpoint on a circle, one endpoint outside the circle, and intersects the circle in two points.

second (p. 896) One-sixtieth of a minute.

second quartile (p. 1331) The median of the data; the 50th percentile.

second-order differences (pp. 1690, 2042) The differences between the first-order differences in a function or sequence.

sector of a circle (or circle graph) (pp. 194, 732) A part of a circle that looks like a wedge, bounded by two radii and an arc of the circle.

segment (p. 132) Part of a line consisting of two endpoints on the line and all points between the two endpoints. Also called *line segment*.

self-similar figure (p. 808) A figure that can be divided into parts that are similar to the original figure.

semi-regular tessellation (p. 855) A tessellation consisting of more than one type of regular polygon where the arrangement of polygons is the same at each vertex.

semicircle (p. 728) Half a circle.

separation of variables (p. 2302) A technique where certain differential equations are rewritten in the form $f(x)dx = g(y)dy$, which is then solvable by integrating both sides of the equation.

sequence (p. 432) A set of numbers, objects, or shapes arranged in a specific order. See also *pattern*.

sequence (p. 1858) A function whose domain is a set of ordered numbers. See also *arithmetic sequence, geometric sequence, finite sequence, infinite sequence*.

series (p. 1862) Sum of the terms of a sequence.

set (pp. 268, 1290) A collection of items or objects.

set theory (p. 1290) The branch of mathematics that deals with the properties of sets.

similar figures (p. 790) Figures that have the same shape but not necessarily the same size.

similarity ratio (p. 790) The ratio of the lengths of corresponding sides of similar figures.

similarity transformation See *dilation*.

simple interest (pp. 398, 1838) Interest calculated only on the amount originally deposited, called the *principal*.

simple random sample (p. 1227) A sample in which every member of a population has an equal possibility of being selected.

simplest form of a fraction (p. 311) A fraction in which the numerator and denominator have no common factor other than 1.

sine ratio See *trigonometric ratios*.

skew lines (pp. 144, 630) Noncoplanar lines.

slant height See *right cone, regular pyramid*.

slope (pp. 814, 1537) The steepness of a line expressed as a ratio; the slope m of the line containing points (x_1, y_1) and (x_2, y_2) is given by the formula $m = \frac{y_2 - y_1}{x_2 - x_1}$.

slope field (p. 2298) A graph of the slopes determined by a differential equation at multiple points.

solid (p. 166) A three-dimensional geometric figure.

solid of revolution (pp. 716, 2278) The three-dimensional figure that results from revolving a two-dimensional shape about a line, called the *axis of revolution*.

solution of an inequality (p. 1492) The set of all numbers that make the inequality true.

solution set (p. 1492) The set of all solutions of an equation or inequality.

solve an equation (p. 1458) To find the missing value(s) that makes the equation true.

solving literal equations (p. 1840) Solving a formula or equation for one of the variables other than the one that is already isolated.

space (p. 722) The set of all points.

speed (p. 2201) Distance covered per unit of time; the absolute value of velocity.

sphere (pp. 176, 578, 1052) The set of all points in space at a given distance from a given point.

spherical angle (p. 1052) The angle between two intersecting arcs on a sphere.

square (pp. 158, 532, 654) A rectangle with four congruent sides.

square matrix (pp. 1784, 1792) A matrix with an equal number of rows and columns.

square pyramid (p. 172) A pyramid with a square base.

square root (p. 1400) A number that is multiplied by itself, or squared, to form a product.

standard deviation (p. 1325) A numerical value used to indicate how widely data values are spread; the square root of variance.

standard form of a complex number (p. 1896) The form $a + bi$, where both a and b are real numbers.

standard form of a linear equation (p. 1548) $Ax + By = C$, where $A > 0$ and A, B, and C are relatively prime integers.

standard form of a number (p. 44) The form of a number that uses digits.

standard position of an angle (p. 895) An angle with vertex at the origin and initial side on the positive x-axis.

stem-and-leaf plot (p. 1276) A data display that can be used to show how data are distributed.

straight angle (pp. 140, 624, 894) An angle with measure 180°.

stratified sample (p. 1227) A sampling method where the researcher divides the population into separate groups, called *strata*. Then, a sample (often a simple random sample) is drawn from each group.

subset (p. 1290) A set that consists of the items that are common to related sets.

substitution method (p. 1565) A method of solving systems of equations by solving an equation for one variable and then substituting the expression for that variable in the other equation(s).

subtrahend (p. 88) The subtracted number in a difference. In $a - b$, b is the subtrahend.

subtraction (pp. 62, 88) Mathematical operation in which the value of one number is taken away from the value of another number. Subtraction is the inverse of *addition*.

sum (pp. 56, 82) The result of adding two or more addends.

supplementary angles (pp. 148, 625, 894) Two angles whose measures total 180°.

surface area (p. 558) The sum of the areas of all the faces of a geometric solid. See also *cone*, *cylinder*, *prism*, *pyramid*, *sphere*.

survey (pp. 184, 1222) A way of collecting data from a group of people, called a *population*.

switch factors (p. 71) A way to find the product of two numbers.

switch the order (p. 58) A strategy for finding a sum.

symmetry (p. 846) A figure has symmetry when a transformation maps a figure onto itself.

synthetic division (p. 1678) A shorthand process used to divide a polynomial in standard form by a linear binomial in the form $x - a$ by using only coefficients.

system of linear equations (p. 1564) A set of two or more linear equations with two or more variables.

system of linear inequalities (p. 1582) A set of two or more linear inequalities with two or more variables.

system of trigonometric equations or inequalities (p. 1043) A set of two or more trigonometric equations or inequalities with two or more variables.

systematic sample (p. 1227) A sample where the first element is randomly selected from the first k elements on the population list. Thereafter, every kth element on the list is selected.

take apart (p. 71) A strategy to find the product of two numbers.

tally chart (p. 182) A chart that uses tally marks to record the frequency of data.

tangent circles (p. 742) Coplanar circles that intersect in exactly one point.

tangent line approximation (p. 2169) A tangent line is used to approximate a function's value at a point.

tangent ratio See *trigonometric ratios*.

tangent segment (pp. 741, 762) A segment whose endpoints are a point of tangency and another point on the tangent line.

tangent to a circle (p. 740) A line in the plane of a circle that intersects the circle in exactly one point. The point is the *point of tangency*.

term of a pattern (p. 433) Each number, object, or shape in a pattern.

term of a polynomial (pp. 1412, 1600) Each monomial that is added to form a polynomial.

term of a sequence (p. 1858) Each of the numbers in a sequence.

terminal side of an angle See *initial side of an angle*.

terminating decimal (p. 270) A decimal that has a finite number of decimal places.

tessellation (p. 854) An arrangement of shapes that cover the plane with no overlaps and no gaps.

tetrahedron (p. 178) A regular polyhedron with four faces that are congruent equilateral triangles.

theorem (p. 626) A statement that can be proven through deductive reasoning.

theoretical probability (p. 1232) A comparison of the number of favorable outcomes to the number of possible equally likely outcomes.

think addition (p. 64) A strategy for finding the difference of two numbers.

think multiplication (p. 75) A strategy for finding the quotient of two numbers.

third quartile (p. 1331) The median of the data that are greater than the overall median; the 75th percentile.

30°-60°-90° triangle (pp. 686, 900) A special right triangle.

transformation (pp. 834, 1694, 2078) A function that maps each point P in the plane onto a unique point in the plane P', called the *image* of P. The point P is the *pre-image* of P'. See also *translation, reflection, rotation, dilation*.

translation (p. 834) An isometry in which all the points in the plane are moved the same distance in the same direction. A translation can be described with a *vector*.

transversal (pp. 150, 630) A line that intersects two or more coplanar lines.

transverse axis (p. 1932) The segment of length $2a$ whose endpoints are the vertices of a hyperbola.

trapezium (p. 158) A quadrilateral with no parallel sides.

trapezoid (pp. 158, 540, 656) A quadrilateral with exactly one pair of parallel sides. The parallel sides are called the bases.

tree diagram (p. 1240) A diagram that shows all the possible outcomes of one or more events in an organized manner.

trend (p. 1285) A pattern of change in data.

trial (p. 1236) A single observation or one of the repetitions in an experiment.

triangular prism (p. 167) A prism with a triangular base.

triangular pyramid (p. 172) A pyramid with a triangular base.

trigonometric equation (p. 1032) An equation that involves at least one trigonometric function.

trigonometric identity (pp. 904, 996) A trigonometric equation that is true for all acceptable values of the variables in the equation.

trigonometric inequality (p. 1040) An inequality that involves at least one trigonometric function.

trigonometric ratios (pp. 902, 904) In a right triangle with acute angle A, the trigonometric ratios are defined as follows:

$$\textbf{sine } \text{of } \angle A = \frac{\text{leg opposite } \angle A}{\text{hypotenuse}}$$

$$\textbf{cosecant } \text{of } \angle A = \frac{\text{hypotenuse}}{\text{leg opposite } \angle A}$$

$$\textbf{cosine } \text{of } \angle A = \frac{\text{leg adjacent to } \angle A}{\text{hypotenuse}}$$

$$\textbf{secant } \text{of } \angle A = \frac{\text{hypotenuse}}{\text{leg adjacent to } \angle A}$$

$$\textbf{tangent } \text{of } \angle A = \frac{\text{leg opposite } \angle A}{\text{leg adjacent to } \angle A}$$

$$\textbf{cotangent } \text{of } \angle A = \frac{\text{leg adjacent to } \angle A}{\text{leg opposite } \angle A}$$

trigonometry (p. 902) The study of angles and their measures.

trinomial (p. 1600) A polynomial with three terms.

truth value (p. 613) Whether a conditional statement is true or false.

turning points (p. 1626) The places where the direction of a curve changes; also known as points of inflection.

two-column proof (p. 631) A proof organized in two columns—the steps of the proof and the corresponding reasons.

unbounded (p. 1590) A graph is unbounded if it extends infinitely in any direction.

undercoverage (p. 1222) Occurs when some portions of a population are left out of a sample.

union (p. 1291) The elements that are in one or both sets when two sets are combined.

unit circle (p. 944) A circle centered at the origin with the radius equal to one unit.

unit fraction (p. 302) A fraction whose numerator is 1.

unit price (p. 366) A unit rate that gives a cost per unit.

unit rate (p. 366) The rate for one unit of a given quantity.

unit vector (p. 1084) A vector with a magnitude of 1.

universal set (p. 1290) A set containing all elements of a problem under consideration.

unlike fractions (p. 322) Fractions with different denominators.

unlike terms (p. 1412) Terms that differ in either a variable or the power of a variable.

upper extreme (p. 1280) The greatest data value in a set.

upper quartile (p. 1280) The median of the upper half of the data.

use a model (p. 65) A strategy for finding the difference of two numbers.

use tens (p. 64) A strategy for finding the difference of two numbers.

variable (p. 1422) A letter or symbol that represents a quantity that can change.

variance (p. 1324) The sum of the squares of the deviations from the mean, divided by the number of elements in the data set.

vector (pp. 837, 1066) A quantity with magnitude and direction. See also *magnitude of a vector*, *transformation*.

Venn diagram (p. 1288) A graphic display that uses overlapping circles (or squares) to show the relationship between sets and subsets of data.

vertex angle of an isosceles triangle (p. 784) The angle opposite the base.

vertex of a cone See *cone*.

vertex of a parabola (pp. 1688, 1691, 1910) The point on a parabola where it intersects the axis of symmetry; the highest or lowest point on a parabola.

vertex of a polygon (p. 154) A point where two sides intersect.

vertex of a prism (p. 166) A point where two or more edges intersect.

vertex of a pyramid See *pyramid*.

vertex of an angle (pp. 136, 894) The endpoint of the two rays that form an angle.

vertical angles (p. 146) The two opposite angles formed where two lines intersect.

vertical component (p. 1070) The y-coordinate of a point representing a vector $\mathbf{v} = (x, y)$.

vertical translation (p. 1695) A movement of a figure along a vertical line; $f(x) + k$ translates $f(x)$ vertically k units.

vertices (p. 1590) In linear programming, the corner points of the feasible region, where the lines of the equations of two constraints intersect.

vertices (pp. 1930, 1932) In conic sections, the endpoints of the major axis of an ellipse and of the transverse axis of a hyperbola.

volume (p. 570) A measure of the space a three-dimensional figure occupies. See also *cone, cylinder, prism, pyramid, sphere.*

voluntary-response sample (p. 1228) A self-selected sample where members of the population volunteer to be in the sample.

weight (p. 488) The measure of how heavy an object is.

whole numbers (pp. 268, 1402) The set of the natural numbers and zero, {0, 1, 2, 3, . . . }.

word form (p. 42) The form of a number that uses words only.

write a number sentence (p. 450) A problem-solving strategy.

x-axis (p. 1442) The horizontal number line on a coordinate plane.

x-coordinate (p. 1436) The x-value in an ordered pair.

x-intercept (p. 1532) The value of x where a graph crosses the x-axis.

y-axis (p. 1442) The vertical number line on a coordinate plane.

y-coordinate (p. 1436) The y-value in an ordered pair.

y-intercept (p. 1532) The value of y where a graph crosses the y-axis.

zero matrix (p. 1778) A matrix where every element is zero.

zero of a function (p. 1626) An input value that has a corresponding output value equal to zero.

z-score (p. 1341) The number of standard deviations between a data value and the mean; the standard score.

Notes

Index

AA, 792–793
AAS, 774–775
Absolute maximum/minimum, 2202
  of area, 2224
  on closed interval, 2204, 2220–2227, 2230
  of discontinuous functions, 2231
  of distance, 2226–2227
  on open interval, 2230
  of volume of solids, 2223
Absolute value, 1095, 1387–1389
  adding integers and, 1391
  of complex numbers, 1906–1907
  solving equations with, 1480–1483
Absolute-value equations, 1480–1483
Absolute-value expressions, 1389
Absolute-value functions, 2098, 2132–2133
Absolute-value inequalities
  disjunctions, 1520–1521
  with expressions within absolute-value bars, 1518–1519
  with "greater than," 1519, 1520
  with "less than," 1516–1517, 1521
Acceleration, 2184, 2199–2201, 2274–2275
Accumulation of change, 2248–2249, 2276
Accuracy in measurement, 603
Acre, 482
Acute angles, 140–142, 624, 894
  in right triangles, 918
  trigonometric ratios of, 902–913
Acute triangle, 682, 683
  angles of, 1060
  area of, 537–538
  circumcenter of, 879
  orthocenter of, 873
Addend, 82, 229–231
Addition, 56–61
  of angles, 624–625, 897
  of Celsius degrees, 519
  column method, 18–19
  of complex numbers, 1896–1897
  of constant to data values, 1302–1303
  of decimals, 226–231
  estimating sums, 110–113, 422
  fact families of, 80, 81
  facts, 60–61
  finding perimeter, 524
  of fractions with like denominators, 318–321
  of fractions with unlike denominators, 322–323, 422
  of functions, 2066–2067
  with improper fractions, 324
  inequalities with, 1496–1497
  of integers, 1390–1391
  of matrices, 1774–1777

  memorizing the facts, 58–61
  of metric units, 502, 508, 512
  of mixed numbers, 321
  modeling, 57, 84–85
  of numbers greater than 10, 82–87
  opposite-change method, 19
  partial sums method, 16–17
  part-part-whole, 57
  with place-value chart, 86–89
  of polynomials, 1604–1605
  properties of, 1406–1413, 1926–1927
  of radical expressions, 1958–1959
  of rational expressions, 1986–1987, 1989
  regrouping, 84–87, 228
  relationship to multiplication, 68, 70, 336
  relationship to subtraction, 80
  of segments, 861
  significant digits and, 601
  of sine function, 520–521
  solving systems of linear equations with, 1572–1573
  standard algorithm, 14, 87
  strategies for, 58–61, 84–87
  of temperatures, 497, 519
  of trigonometric functions, 982–983
  of U.S. Customary units, 480–481, 486, 490
  of vectors, 1067–1069, 1074–1078
  word problems, 112
  See also Sum(s)
Addition method, 1572–1573
Addition Property of Equality, 1463, 1471
Addition Property of Inequality, 1497
Additive identity, 1414
Additive Identity Property, 1414, 1417
Additive inverse, 1415
Additive Inverse Property, 1415, 1417
Add or subtract from a known fact strategy, 70
Adjacent angles, 146–147, 625
Adjacent arcs, 728
Advanced algebra, 1750–2105
  tables, 1156–1159, 2101–2105, 2358–2361
Age problems, 1826–1827
Algebraic expressions, 1422–1425
  degree of, 1601
  terms of, 1600, 1602
  translating words into, 1821
  See also Binomials; Monomials; Polynomials
Algebraic identities, 1961
Algebraic inequalities, 1492
Algebraic properties of matrices, 1789
Algebra, 1382–1749
  tables, 1146–1149, 1746–1749, 2348–2351

Algebra tiles, 1604, 1608, 1661, 1706
Algorithms, standard
  for addition, 87
  for division, 101–102
  for multiplication, 99
  for subtraction, 93
  teaching methods using, 14, 15
Alternate exterior angles, 149–150, 631
Alternate Exterior Angles Theorem, 631
Alternate interior angles, 149–150, 630, 631
Alternate Interior Angles Theorem, 631
Altitude of a triangle, 537
  concurrence of, 831
  construction of, 872
  relationships in right triangles, 796–839
Ambiguous case, 1054–1057
Ambiguous digits, 600
Amplitude
  of cosine function, 955–957, 960–961, 972
  of cotangent function, 971
  of sine function, 952–955, 958, 959, 974
  of tangent function, 971
  of vertical translations, 966
Angle Addition Postulate, 624–625
Angle-Angle-Side Postulate (AAS), 774–775
Angle-Angle Similarity Theorem (AA), 792–793
Angle bisectors, 629, 805, 868–39
Angle of reflection, 801, 803
Angle of rotation, 842, 847
Angle pairs, 136–143
  adjacent, 146–147, 625
  alternate exterior, 149–150, 630, 631
  alternate interior, 149–150, 630, 631
  complementary, 148–149, 625, 626, 894, 904, 1000
  congruent, 146–147, 622, 624–629, 640, 641, 658, 745, 862–863
  consecutive, 640, 641
  corresponding, 622, 630, 766, 874
  coterminal, 895, 930–931
  formed by intersecting lines, 627–628
  formed by transversal, 149–151, 630–633, 874
  linear, 625, 626
  same-side interior angles, 630
  supplementary, 148–149, 625, 626, 640, 641, 894
  vertical, 146–147, 627–628
Angles, 625, 628
  acute, 140–142, 624, 894
  adding/subtracting, 624–625, 897
  bisector of, 629, 868
  central, 197, 728
  of circle, 748–751
  classification of, 140–142, 624, 894

G

O

of markup, 395, 404
modeling, 380–381, 390
solving equations with, 1478–1479
of a whole number, 384–385, 407
word problems with, 402–407
Perfect *n*th roots, 1954–1955
Perfect square, 1400, 1952
Perfect square trinomials, 1614, 1617, 1666, 1674–1675, 1706, 1735, 1985
Perimeter, 524–527, 530
of composite figures, 552, 554–555
of cross sections, 719
finding by adding, 524
finding using a formula, 526, 554–555
of a kite, 658
of parallelograms, 553
of rectangles, 553
of regular polygons, 525–526, 553
of trapezoids, 553
of triangles, 553
See also Circumference
Periodic functions, 947, 950. *See also* Trigonometric functions
Period of a function, 950–951, 953
of cosine, 955–957, 960–961, 972
of cotangent, 970, 971
of harmonic motion, 986
of sine, 952–955, 958, 959, 974
of tangent, 968–969, 971
Periods of numbers, 40, 42
Permutations, 1244–1247, 1252–1253
Perpendicular bisector of a triangle, 822, 876–879
Perpendicular lines, 130, 131, 144
construction of, 864, 870–873, 876–879
dot product of, 1082–1083
from incenter of a triangle, 881
parallel lines in a plane and, 633
slopes of, 816–817, 1082, 2213
Perspective drawing, 698–701, 723
Phase shift, 962–965
Pi (π)
as irrational number, 268, 271, 1405
relationship to circles, 544, 548–551
value of, 546, 548
Pictographs, 186–187, 1308
Piecewise functions, 2076–2077, 2117, 2134–2135
Pie chart, 194–197
Place value
in addition, 83
to billions, 40–41
comparing/ordering numbers with, 46–49, 283
reading whole numbers, 42–43
rounding whole numbers, 50–51
in subtraction, 89
to thousandths, 216–217
writing whole numbers, 44–45

Place-value chart
addition with, 86, 227–229
decimals, 216–219, 227–229, 233
multiplying using, 98
reading/comparing numbers using, 40–41
rounding numbers using, 51
subtraction with, 92, 233
Plane, 128, 144, 1758–1761
xy-plane, 1072–1073, 1084–1085, 1754–1759
xz-plane, 1754–1759
See also Coordinate plane
Platonic solids, 178–179
Point of concurrency, 866
centroid of a triangle, 866–867
circumcenter of a triangle, 876–879
incenter of a triangle, 880–883
orthocenter of a triangle, 873
Point of symmetry, 848
Point of tangency, 740
Points, 128, 2146–2147
continuity at, 2144–2149
derivative at, 2160
identification of, 130
integral solutions through, 2238–2239
modeling power functions using, 2056–2057
plotting in coordinate plane, 1114, 1443, 1445
plotting in three dimensions, 1754–1757
in polar planes, 1114
rotation of, 980–981
translations of, 834
writing linear equation given two, 1546–1547
zero vectors as, 1075
Point-slope form of linear equation, 817, 823, 1544–1547, 2212
converting to, 1552, 1553
equation for tangent line, 2177, 2182–2183
tangent line approximation, 2168
Points of inflection, 1626, 1654–1655
Point symmetry, 847, 848
Polar axis, 1093
Polar coordinates, 1092–1099
of complex numbers, 1114–1117
converting to/from rectangular coordinates, 1096–1097
Polar coordinate system, 1093
representing complex numbers in, 1114–1117
using multiple representations in, 1094–1095
using tests for symmetry, 1103
Polar equations, 1098–1099
of conic sections, 1104
graphs of, 1100–1105
parametric equations, 1106–1109

Polar form
of complex numbers, 1114–1117
converting to/from rectangular form, 1098–1099
dividing complex numbers in, 1119
multiplying complex numbers, 1118
powers of complex numbers in, 1120–1121
Polygon Exterior Angles-Sum Theorem, 674–675
Polygon Interior Angle-Sum Theorem, 672–673
Polygons, 154
angles of, 672–675
area of, 528–543, 690–691
classification of, 154–159
exterior angles of, 674–675
finding length of side, 527
inscribed in a circle, 746
interior angles of, 672–673
irregular, 154
perimeter of, 524–526
regular, 154, 676–677
similar, 790–791
tessellation of, 854–857
See also Specific polygon
Polyhedron, 178–179, 724–725. *See also* Geometric solids; Solids
Polynomial equations, 1630–1635
complex conjugates, 1633, 1640–1641
factoring, 1111
roots/zeros/solutions of, 1110–1113, 1630–1635, 1636, 1640–1641, 1682–1685, 1719
solving by factoring, 1633, 1634–1635, 1684–1685
solving higher-order, 1720–1721
solving with graphs, 1633
synthetic division, 1112–1113
Theorems concerning, 1642–1643, 1644–1645, 1683–1685
See also Quadratic equations
Polynomial functions, 1672, 2118–2119
adding/subtracting, 1607
behavior of, 1654–1657
complex roots of, 1641
continuity of, 2150
degree of, 1624, 1625
derivatives of, 2185
Descartes' Rule of Signs, 1651
end behavior of, 1625, 1656–1657
evaluating with division, 1644–1645
factor of, 1646–1647, 1654
graphing from intercepts, 1654
graphs of, 1625–1627
limits of, 2111, 2119
reflections of, 2086–2087
remainders and values of, 1644–1645
roots (zeros) of, 1628–1635, 1636–1641, 1648–1654, 1683–1685, 2155
rule of signs for real zeros, 1648–1649